SEVENTH EDITION

Ananthanarayan and Paniker's
Textbook
of
Microbiology

(Late) R Ananthanarayan
BA, MBBS (Madras), DB, PhD (London)
Formerly, Professor of Microbiology,
Medical Colleges Calicut, Kottayam, Trivandrum and Gulbarga
and Adviser to the DHS, Kerala, on Laboratory Services

CK Jayaram Paniker
MD
Formerly, Director-Professor of Microbiology and Principal,
Medical College, Calicut, Kerala

This edition edited by

CK Jayaram Paniker

THE
NATIONAL
BOOK DEPOT
OPP. WADIA CHILDREN'S HOSPITAL
PAREL, MUMBAI - 400 012
TEL. : 2413 1362 / 2413 2411 / 2416 5274
FAX : 022 - 2413 0877
E-mail : nationalbook55@rediffmail.com

Orient Longman

Dedicated

to

Dr. R. Ananthanarayan
17.8.1913–6.2.1998

ORIENT LONGMAN PRIVATE LIMITED

Registered Office
3-6-752 Himayatnagar, Hyderabad 500 029 (A.P), India
e-mail : cogeneral@orientlongman.com

Other Offices
Bangalore/Bhopal/Bhubaneshwar/Chennai/Ernakulam/Guwahati/
Hyderabad/Jaipur/Kolkata/Lucknow/Mumbai/New Delhi/Patna

© Orient Longman Private Limited 1978, 1981, 1986, 1990, 1996, 2000, 2005

First published 1978
Reprinted 1979, 1980
Second Edition 1981
Reprinted 1982, 1983, 1984, 1985
Third Edition 1986
Fourth Edition 1990
Reprinted 1991, 1992 (twice), 1994, 1995 (twice)
Fifth Edition 1996
Reprinted 1996, 1997 (thrice)
Reprint with revision 1998
Reprinted 1999
Sixth Edition 2000
Reprinted 2001 (twice), 2002 (twice), 2003 (twice), 2004 (thrice)
Seventh Edition 2005
Reprint 2005 (fifth), 2006 (twice), 2007

ISBN 13: 978- 81- 250- 2808- 6
ISBN 10: 81-250-2808-0

Typeset by
Ashwini Systems,
Chennai 600 014

Printed in India by
Multivista Global Ltd
Chennai 600 042

Published by
Orient Longman Private Ltd
160, Anna Salai
Chennai 600 002
e-mail : chegeneral@orientlongman.com

SEVENTH EDITION

Ananthanarayan and Paniker's

Textbook
of
Microbiology

Preface to the Seventh Edition

Only four years have passed since the sixth edition of *Textbook of Microbiology* was published, but rapid developments in the subject have made a new edition necessary. During this short period, new infectious diseases have emerged or re-emerged in new forms. For example, Severe Acute Respiratory Syndrome (SARS) virus appeared suddenly causing death and panic in many countries, and the Bird Flu virus posed repeated pandemic threats.

Microbiology has become an increasingly important discipline, set to face new challenges. Exciting advances in diagnostic microbiology using sophisticated techniques can help in the rapid identification of new pathogens and serve to contain them. This was shown by the identification of the new SARS virus within weeks by concerted multidisciplinary international efforts. While such scientific progress is a boon, some of it can be potentially dangerous, as for instance in the recent case of chemical synthesis of a complete pathogenic poliovirus in the laboratory.

In this edition, the seventh, relevant new information has been added and all chapters revised and updated, maintaining the general format of the book. The *Textbook of Microbiology* has been in use now for more than a quarter of a century. It has benefited greatly from the comments and suggestions from students, teachers and other readers.

Their help is gratefully acknowledged.

C.K. Jayaram Paniker
Shanthi, 1/3833, East Hill Road,
Calicut, Kerala 637 006.

Preface to the First Edition

Many of the health problems in developing countries like India are different from those of developed countries. Bacterial diseases still play a considerable role in diseases in our country. Topics such as cholera and enteric diseases are important to us though only of less or academic interest to the developed countries. The increasing importance of the newer knowledge in immunology to health and disease is not adequately stressed in most of the extant textbooks. Virus diseases which are responsible for nearly 60 per cent of human illness require wider coverage. The general approach to the teaching of microbiology in our country has also been rather static. All these factors called for a textbook of microbiology more suited to countries like India.

We therefore undertook this endeavour based on our experience of teaching undergraduates and postgraduates for over two decades. We omitted the discipline of parasitology from our book since we already have an excellent textbook on the subject published in India.

This book has taken us over three years to write and over a year in publication. Naturally we would be out of date to a certain and inevitable extent. We do not claim any perfection. On the contrary, we have requested medical students and teachers all over the country to write to us about any shortcomings and give us suggestions as to how to improve the book. We shall spare no pains in seeing that their valuable suggestions are given effect to in our second edition.

R. Ananthanarayan
C.K. Jayaram Paniker

Acknowledgements

For kind permission to use illustrations, supply of photographs, helpful suggestions and advice, the author is indebted to the following organisations and persons:
World Health Organization; Indian Council of Medical Research; National Institute of Virology, Pune; Dr. G. Balkrish Nair, Dr. A.N. Ghosh, Dr. T.N. Naik and Dr. Triveni Krishnan of National Institute of Cholera and Enteric diseases, Calcutta, Prof. M. Mathan and Prof. T. Jacob John of Christian Medical College, Vellore, Prof. Arun Chitale, Jaslok Hospital, Mumbai; Dr. S.M. Sirsat, Cancer Research Institute, Mumbai; Prof. M.D. Mathur, Maulana Azad Medical College, New Delhi, Prof. J. Shanmugham, SCT Medical Centre, Trivandrum; Dr. Girija G. Rao, Medical College, Calicut; Dr. G.M. Warke, HiMedia Laboratories, Mumbai.

Contents

Part IV

Historical Introduction

Medical microbiology is the study of microbes that infect humans, the diseases they cause, their diagnosis, prevention and treatment. It also deals with the response of the human host to microbial and other antigens.

Disease and death have always held the attention of the human mind. Ancient humans ascribed them to divine wrath and other supernatural forces. Later, other concepts such as the effect of the environment, of bodily constitution and of faulty diet were proposed. There have been, from very early times, occasional suggestions that diseases may result from invasion of the body by external contagion. Varo and Columella in the first century BC postulated that diseases were caused by invisible beings (Animalia minuta), inhaled or ingested. Fracastorius of Verona (1546) proposed a contagium vivum as a possible cause of infectious disease and von Plenciz (1762) suggested that each disease was caused by a separate agent. Kircher (1659) reported finding minute worms in the blood of plague victims, but with the equipment available to him it is more likely that what he observed were only blood cells.

As microbes are invisible to the unaided eye, definitive knowledge about them had to await the development of microscopes. The credit for having first observed and reported bacteria belongs to Antony van Leeuwenhoek, a draper in Delft, Holland, whose hobby was grinding lenses and observing diverse materials through them. In 1683 he made accurate descriptions of various types of bacteria and communicated them to the Royal Society of London. The significance of these observations was not realised then and to Leeuwenhoek the world of 'little animalcules' as he called them, represented only a curiosity of nature. It was only some two centuries later that their importance in medicine and biology as a whole came to be recognised.

The earliest discovery of a pathogenic microorganism was probably made by Augustino Bassi (1835), who showed that the muscardine disease of silkworms was caused by a fungus. Davaine and Pollender (1850) observed anthrax bacilli in the blood of animals dying of the disease. In fact, even before the microbial etiology of infections had been established, Oliver Wendell Holmes in the USA (1843) and Ignaz Semmelweis in Vienna (1846) had independently concluded that puerperal sepsis was contagious. Semmelweis also identified its mode of transmission by doctors and medical students attending on women in labour in the hospital and had prevented it by the simple measure of washing hands in an antiseptic solution, for which service to medicine and humanity, he was persecuted by medical orthodoxy and driven insane.

The development of microbiology as a scientific discipline dates from Louis Pasteur (1822–95). Though trained as a chemist, his studies on fermentation led him to take an interest in microorganisms. He established that fermentation was the result of microbial activity and that different types of fermentations were associated with different types of microorganisms (1857). The basic principles and techniques of microbiology were evolved by Pasteur during his enquiry into the origin of microbes. This was then the subject of much controversy. Needham, an Irish priest, had in 1745 published experiments purporting the spontaneous generation (abiogenesis) of microorganisms in putrescible fluids. This view was opposed by Spallanzani, an Italian abbot (1769). In a series of classic experiments, Pasteur proved conclusively that all forms of life, even microbes, arose only from their like and not *de novo*. In the course of these studies, he introduced techniques of sterilisation and developed the steam steriliser, hot-air oven and autoclave. He also established the differing growth needs of different bacteria. His work attracted such attention and he attained such eminence in the world of science that not only France but all Europe looked to him to solve major problems in various fields. Thus started his studies on pebrine, anthrax, chicken cholera and hydrophobia. An accidental observation that chicken cholera bacillus cultures left on the bench for several weeks lost their pathogenic property but retained their ability to protect the birds against subsequent infection by them, led to the discovery of the process of attenuation and the development of live vaccines. He attenuated cultures of the anthrax bacillus by incubation at high temperature (42–43 °C) and proved that inoculation of such cultures in animals induced specific protection against anthrax. The success of such immunisation was dramatically demonstrated by a public experiment on a farm at Pouilly-le-Fort (1881) during which vaccinated sheep, goats and cows were challenged with a virulent anthrax bacillus culture. All the vaccinated animals survived the challenge, while an equal number of unvaccinated control animals succumbed to it. It was Pasteur who coined the term *vaccine* for such prophylactic preparations to commemorate the first of such preparations, namely cowpox, employed by Jenner for protection against smallpox. The greatest impact in medicine was made by Pasteur's development of a vaccine for hydrophobia. This was acclaimed throughout the world. The Pasteur Institute, Paris was built by public

contributions and similar institutions were established soon in many other countries for the preparation of vaccines and for the investigation of infectious diseases.

An immediate application of Pasteur's work was the introduction of antiseptic techniques in surgery by Lister (1867) effecting a pronounced drop in mortality and morbidity due to surgical sepsis. Lister's antiseptic surgery involving the use of carbolic acid was cumbersome and hazardous but was a milestone in the evolution of surgical practice from the era of 'laudable pus' to modern aseptic techniques.

While Pasteur in France laid the foundations of microbiology, Robert Koch (1843–1910) in Germany perfected bacteriological techniques during his studies on the culture and life cycle of the anthrax bacillus (1876). He introduced staining techniques and methods of obtaining bacteria in pure culture using solid media. He discovered the bacillus of tuberculosis (1882) and the cholera vibrio (1883).

Pasteur and Koch attracted many gifted disciples who discovered the causative agents of several bacterial infections and enlarged the scope and content of microbiology by their labours. In 1874 Hansen described the leprosy bacillus; in 1879 Neisser described the gonococcus; in 1881 Ogston discovered the staphylococcus; in 1884 Loeffler isolated the diphtheria bacillus; in 1884 Nicolaier observed the tetanus bacillus in soil; in 1886 Fraenkel described the pneumococcus; in 1887 Bruce identified the causative agent of Malta fever; in 1905 Schaudinn and Hoffmann discovered the spirochete of syphilis.

Roux and Yersin (1888) identified a new mechanism of pathogenesis when they discovered the diphtheria toxin. Similar toxins were identified in tetanus and some other bacteria. The toxins were found to be specifically neutralised by their antitoxins. Ehrlich who studied toxins and antitoxins in quantitative terms laid the foundations of biological standardisation.

The causative agents of various infectious diseases were being reported by different investigators in such profusion that it was necessary to introduce criteria for proving the claims that a microorganism isolated from a disease was indeed causally related to it. These criteria, first indicated by Henle, were enunciated by Koch and are known as Koch's postulates. According to these, a microorganism can be accepted as the causative agent of an infectious disease only if the following conditions are satisfied:

1. The bacterium should be constantly associated with the lesions of the disease.
2. It should be possible to isolate the bacterium in pure culture from the lesions.
3. Inoculation of such pure culture into suitable laboratory animals should reproduce the lesions of the disease.
4. It should be possible to reisolate the bacterium in pure culture from the lesions produced in the experimental animals.

An additional criterion introduced subsequently requires that specific antibodies to the bacterium should be demonstrable in the serum of patients suffering from the disease. Though it may not always be possible to satisfy all the postulates in every case, they have proved extremely useful in sifting doubtful claims made regarding the causative agents of infectious diseases.

By the beginning of the twentieth century, many infectious diseases had been proved to be caused by bacteria. But there remained a large number of diseases such as smallpox, chickenpox, measles, influenza and the common cold for which no bacterial cause could be established. During his investigation of rabies in dogs, Pasteur had suspected that the disease could be caused by a microbe too small to be seen even under the microscope. The existence of such ultramicroscopic microbes was proved when Ivanovsky (1892) reproduced mosaic disease in the tobacco plant, by applying to healthy leaves juice from the diseased plants from which all bacteria had been removed by passage through fine filters. Beijerinck (1898) confirmed these findings and coined the term *virus* for such filterable infectious agents. Loeffler and Frosch (1898) observed that the foot and mouth disease of cattle was caused by a similar filter-passing virus. The first human disease proved to have a viral etiology was yellow fever. The US Army Commission under Walter Reed, investigating yellow fever in Cuba (1902) established not only that it was caused by a filterable virus but also that it was transmitted through the bite of infected mosquitoes. Landsteiner and Popper (1909) showed that poliomyelitis was caused by a filterable virus and transmitted the disease experimentally to monkeys. Investigation of viruses and the diseases caused by them was rendered difficult as viruses could not be visualised under the light microscope or grown in culture media. Though the larger viruses could be seen after appropriate staining under the light microscope, detailed study of their morphology had to wait till the introduction of the electron microscope by Ruska (1934) and subsequent refinements in electron microscopic techniques. Cultivation of viruses was possible only in animals or in human volunteers till the technique of growing them on chick embryos was developed by Goodpasture in the 1930s. The application of tissue culture in virology expanded the scope of virological techniques considerably.

The possibility that virus infection could lead to malignancy was first put forth by Ellerman and Bang (1908). Peyton Rous (1911) isolated a virus causing sarcoma in fowls. Several viruses have since been isolated which cause natural and experimental tumours in animals and birds. Viruses also cause malignant transformation of infected cells in tissue culture. The discovery of viral and cellular oncogenes has shed light on the possible mechanisms of viral oncogenesis. After many decades of futile search, positive proof of a virus causing human malignancy was established when the virus of human T-cell leukemia was isolated in 1980.

Twort (1915) and d'Herelle (1917) independently discovered a lytic phenomenon in bacterial cultures. The agents responsible were termed bacteriophages – viruses that attack bacteria. Early hopes that bacteriophages may have therapeutic applications had to be abandoned but these viruses have paid unexpected scientific dividends. The essential part of viruses is their core of nucleic acid which acts as the carrier of genetic information in the same manner as in higher organisms. The discipline of molecular biology owes its origin largely to studies on the genetics of bacteriophages and bacteria.

It had been noticed from very early days that persons surviving an attack of smallpox did not develop the disease when exposed to the infection subsequently. This observation had been applied for the prevention of the disease by producing a mild form of smallpox intentionally (variolation). This practice, prevalent in India, China and other ancient civilisations from time immemorial, was introduced in England by Lady Mary Wortley Montague (1718) who had observed the custom in Turkey. Variolation was effective but hazardous. Jenner, observing the immunity to smallpox in milkmaids who were exposed to occupational cowpox infection, introduced the technique of vaccination using cowpox material (1796). This was the first instance of scientific immunisation and, though introduced empirically, has stood the test of time. Jenner's vaccination paved the way for the ultimate eradication of smallpox.

The next major discovery in immunity was Pasteur's development of vaccines for chicken cholera, anthrax and rabies. While the techniques introduced by him were successful, the mechanism of protection afforded by them remained obscure. The explanation of the underlying mechanism came from two sources. Nuttall (1888) observed that defibrinated blood had a bactericidal effect, and Buchner (1889) noticed that this effect was abolished by heating the sera for one hour at 55 °C. The heat labile bactericidal factor was termed

'alexine'. A specific humoral factor or 'antibody' was described by von Behring and Kitasato (1890) in the serum of animals which had received sublethal doses of tetanus toxin. Pfeiffer (1893) demonstrated bactericidal effect in vivo by injecting live cholera vibrios intraperitoneally in guinea pigs previously injected with killed vibrios. The vibrios were shown to undergo lysis. The humoral nature of such lytic activity was proved by Bordet (1895), who defined the two components participating in the reaction, the first being heat stable and found in immune sera (antibody or substance sensibilicatrice) and the second being heat labile and identical with Buchner's alexine, subsequently named 'complement'. Soon a number of other ways were demonstrated in which antibodies react with antigens, such as agglutination, precipitation, complement fixation and neutralisation. Metchnikoff (1883) discovered the phenomenon of phagocytosis and proposed the phagocytic response as the prime defence against the microbial invasion of tissues. This led to the cellular concept of immunity. Polemics regarding the significance of the cellular and humoral mechanisms of immunity were largely put to rest with the discovery by Wright (1903) of opsonisation, in which antibodies and phagocytic cells act in conjunction.

Prior experience with a microorganism or other antigen did not always result in the beneficial effect of immunity or protection. At times it caused the opposite effect. Koch (1890) had noticed that when the tubercle bacillus or its protein was injected into a guinea pig already infected with the bacillus, an exaggerated response took place – a hypersensitivity reaction known as Koch's phenomenon. Portier and Richet (1902), studying the effect of the toxic extracts of sea anemones in dogs made the paradoxical observation that dogs which had prior contact with the toxin were abnormally sensitive to even minute quantities of it subsequently. This phenomenon was termed anaphylaxis. Later, many similar reactions were observed, both experimentally and in nature, of injury, disease or even death resulting from repeated contacts with antigens. The importance of this phenomenon, in the pathogenesis of many human diseases, led to the development of the discipline of allergy.

The characteristic feature of immunity, whether it is protective or destructive (as in allergy), is its specificity. As the mediators of humoral immunity (antibodies) are globulins, the explanation for the exquisite specificity of the immunological reaction had to await the advances in protein chemistry. The pioneering work of Landsteiner laid the foundations of immunochemistry. Chemists dominated the study of immunity for several decades, and theories of antibody synthesis were postulated by them, which sometimes ran counter to biological laws. In 1955, Jerne proposed the natural selection theory of antibody synthesis which attempted to explain the chemical specificity and biological basis of antibody synthesis, signifying a return to the original views of antibody formation proposed by Ehrlich (1898). Burnet (1957) modified this into the clonal selection theory, a concept which, with minor alterations, holds sway even now. The last few decades have witnessed an explosion of conceptual and technical advances in immunology. Immunological processes in health and disease are now better understood following the identification of the two components of immunity – the humoral or antibody mediated processes and the cellular or cell mediated processes – which develop and are manifest in separate pathways.

Till recently, a teleological view of immunity prevailed. It was considered a protective mechanism designed to defend the body against invasion by microorganisms. Based on the original suggestion of Thomas (1959), Burnet (1967) developed the concept of *immunological surveillance*, according to which the primary function of the immune system is to preserve the integrity of the body, seeking and destroying all 'foreign' antigens, whether autogenous or external in origin. Malignancy was visualised as a failure of this function, and the scope of immunity was enlarged

to include natural defence against cancer. Another aspect of this role of immunity is in the rejection of homografts. Understanding of the immunological basis of transplantation, largely due to the work of Medawar and Burnet, made successful transplants possible by elective immunosuppression and proper selection of donors based on histocompatibility. The history of transplantation thus runs parallel to the history of blood transfusion, which was unsuccessful and even fatal before the discovery of blood groups by Landsteiner (1900).

In the early twentieth century, attempts were made to exploit the immunological information available by the development of vaccines and sera for the prophylaxis and treatment of infectious diseases. Till Domagk (1935) initiated scientific chemotherapy with the discovery of prontosil, antisera were the only specific therapeutic agents available for the management of infectious diseases.

Fleming (1929) made the accidental discovery that the fungus Penicillium produces a substance which destroys staphylococci. Work on this at Oxford by Florey, Chain and their team during the Second World War led to the isolation of the active substance penicillin and its subsequent mass production. This was the beginning of the antibiotic era. Other similar antibiotics were discovered in rapid succession. With the sudden availability of a wide range of antibiotics with potent antibacterial activity, it was hoped that bacterial infections would be controlled within a short period. But soon the development of drug resistance in bacteria presented serious difficulties.

With the development of a wide variety of antibiotics active against the whole spectrum of pathogenic bacteria, and of effective vaccines against most viral diseases, expectations were raised about the eventual elimination of all infectious diseases. The global eradication of smallpox inspired visions of similar campaigns against other major pestilences. However, when new infectious diseases began to appear, caused by hitherto unknown micro-organisms, or by known microbes producing novel manifestations, it was realised that controlling microbes was a far more difficult task than was imagined. The climax came in 1981 when AIDS was identified in the USA and began its pandemic spread. Unceasing vigil appears essential to protect humans from microbes.

Apart from the obvious benefits such as specific methods of diagnosis, prevention and control of infectious diseases, medical microbiology has contributed to scientific knowledge and human welfare in many other ways. Microorganisms constitute the smallest forms of living beings and, therefore, have been employed as models of studies on genetics and biochemistry. As nature's laws are universal in application, information derived from the investigation of microbes holds true, in the main, for humans as well.

Studies on microorganisms have contributed, more than anything else, to unravelling the genetic code and other mysteries of biology at the molecular level. Bacteria and their plasmids, yeasts and viruses are routinely employed as vectors in recombinant DNA technology. They have made available precious information and powerful techniques for genetic manipulation and molecular engineering. They need to be used wisely and well for the benefit of all living beings.

The number of Nobel laureates in Medicine and Physiology awarded the prize for their work in microbiology, listed below, is evidence of the positive contribution made to human health by the science of microbiology.

1901	Emil A von Behring
1902	Ronald Ross
1905	Robert Koch
1907	CLA Laveran
1908	Paul Ehrlich and Elie Metchnikoff
1913	Charles Richet
1919	Jules Bordet
1926	Johannes Fibiger
1928	Charles Nicolle
1930	Karl Landsteiner
1939	Gerhardt Domagk
1945	Alexander Fleming, Howard Florey and EB Chain
1951	Max Theiler
1952	Selman A Waksman
1954	JF Enders, FC Robbins and TH Weller
1958	GW Beadle, Joshua Lederberg and EL Tatum
1960	Macfarlane Burnet and Peter Brian Medawar
1965	Francois Jacob, Andre Lwoff and Jacques Monod
1966	Peyton Rous
1969	Max Delbruck, AD Hershey and Salvador Luria
1972	Gerald Edelman and Rodney Porter
1975	David Baltimore, Renato Dulbecco and Howard M Temin
1976	S Baruch, Blumberg and Carleton Gajdusek
1978	W Arber, D Nathans and HO Smith
1980	Baruj Benacerraf, Jean Dausset and George Snell
1984	Niels Jerne, Cesar Milstein and Georges Kohler
1987	Susumu Tonegawa
1989	J. Michael Bishop and E Varmus
1996	Paul Doherty and Rolf Zinkernagel
1997	Stanley Prusiner

Further Reading

Benacerraf B et al. 1980. *A History of Bacteriology and Immunology*. London: William Heinemann.

Clark PF 1961. *Pioneer Microbiologists of America*. Madison: University of Wisconsin Press.

Collard P 1976. *The Development of Microbiology*. Cambridge University Press.

deKruif P 1958. *Microbe Hunters*. London: Hutchison.

Foster WD 1970. *A History of Medical Bacteriology and Immunology*. London: Cox and Wyman.

Lechevalier HA and M Solotorovsky 1974. *Three Centuries of Microbiology*. Dover Publications.

Marquardt M 1951. *Paul Ehrlich*. New York: Schuman.

Parish HJ 1968. *Victory with Vaccines – The Story of Immunisation*. London: Livingstone.

Vallery Radot R 1948. *The Life of Pasteur*. trans. by RL Devonshire. London: Constable.

Waterson AP and L Wilkinson 1978. *An Introduction to the History of Virology*. London: Cambridge University Press.

Williams G 1960. *Virus Hunters*. London: Hutchison.

Morphology and Physiology of Bacteria

Microorganisms are a heterogeneous group of several distinct classes of living beings. They were originally classified under the plant and animal kingdoms. As this proved unsatisfactory, they were classified under a third kingdom, the *protista*. Based on differences in cellular organisation and biochemistry, the kingdom protista has been divided into two groups prokaryotes and eukaryotes. Bacteria and blue green algae are prokaryotes, while fungi, other algae, slime moulds and protozoa are eukaryotes.

Bacteria are prokaryotic microorganisms that do not contain chlorophyll. They are unicellular and do not show true branching, except in the so-called 'higher bacteria' (Actinomycetales).

SIZE OF BACTERIA

The unit of measurement used in bacteriology is the micron (micrometre, μm)

1 micron (μ) or micrometre (μm) = one thousandth of a millimetre.

1 millimicron (mμ) or nanometre (nm) = one thousandth of a micron or one millionth of a millimetre.

1 Angstrom unit (Å) = one tenth of a nanometre.

The limit of resolution with the unaided eye is about 200 microns. Bacteria, being much smaller, can be visualised only under magnification. Bacteria of medical importance generally measure 0.2–1.5 μm in diameter and about 3–5 μm in length.

Table 2.1 Some differences between prokaryotic and eukaryotic cells

Character	Prokaryotes	Eukaryotes
Nucleus		
Nuclear membrane	Absent	Present
Nucleolus	Absent	Present
Deoxyribonucleoprotein	Absent	Present
Chromosome	One (circular)	More than one (linear)
Mitotic division	Absent	Present
Cytoplasm		
Cytoplasmic streaming	Absent	Present
Pinocytosis	Absent	Present
Mitochondria	Absent	Present
Lysosomes	Absent	Present
Golgi apparatus	Absent	Present
Endoplasmic reticulum	Absent	Present
Chemical composition		
Sterols	Absent	Present
Muramic acid	Present	Absent

MICROSCOPY

The morphological study of bacteria requires the use of microscopes. Microscopy has come a long way since Leeuwenhoek first observed bacteria over three hundred years ago using hand-ground lenses. The following types of microscopes are employed now.

Optical or light microscope: Bacteria may be examined under the compound microscope, either in the living state or after fixation and staining. Examination of wet films or 'hanging drops' indicates the shape, arrangement, motility and approximate size of the cells. But due to lack of contrast, details cannot be appreciated.

Phase contrast microscopy: improves the contrast and makes evident the structures within cells that differ in thickness or refractive index. Also, the differences in refractive index between bacterial cells and the surrounding medium make them clearly visible. Retardation, by a fraction of a wavelength, of the rays of light that pass through the object, compared to the rays passing through the surrounding medium, produces 'phase' differences between the two types of rays. In the phase contrast microscope, 'phase' differences are converted into differences in intensity of light, producing light and dark contrast in the image.

Dark field / Dark ground microscope: Another method of improving the contrast is the dark field (dark ground) microscope in which reflected light is used instead of the transmitted light used in the ordinary microscope. The essential part of the dark field microscope is the dark field condenser with a central circular stop, which illuminates the object with a cone of light, without letting any ray of light to fall directly on the objective lens. Light rays falling on the object are reflected or scattered on to the objective lens, with the result that the object appears self-luminous against a dark background. The contrast gives an illusion of increased resolution, so that very slender organisms such as spirochetes, not visible under ordinary illumination, can be clearly seen under the dark field microscope.

The resolving power of the light microscope is limited by the wavelength of light. In order to be seen and delineated (resolved), an object has to have a size of approximately half the wavelength of the light used. With visible light, using the best optical systems, the limit of resolution is about 300 nm. If light of shorter wavelength is employed, as in the ultraviolet microscope, the resolving power can be proportionately extended.

Two specialised types of microscopes are 1) the interference microscope which not only reveals cell organelles but also enables quantitative measurements of the chemical constituents of cells such as lipids, proteins and nucleic acids, and 2) the polarisation microscope which enables the study of intracellular structures using differences in birefringence.

Electron microscope: In the electron microscope, a beam of electrons is employed instead of the beam of light used in the optical microscope. The electron beam is focused by circular electromagnets, which are analogous to the lenses in the light microscope. The object which is held in the path of the beam scatters the electrons and produces an image which is focused on a fluorescent viewing screen. As the wavelength of electrons used is approximately 0.005 nm, as compared to 500 nm with visible light, the resolving power of the electron microscopes should be theoretically 100,000 times that of light microscopes but in practice, the resolving power is about 0.1 nm.

The technique of shadow-casting with vaporised heavy metals has made possible pictures with good contrast and three-dimensional effect. Another valuable technique in studying fine structure is negative staining with phosphotungstic acid.

Gas molecules scatter electrons, and it is therefore necessary to examine the object in a vacuum. Hence, only dead and dried objects can be examined in the electron microscope. This may lead to considerable distortion in cell morphology. A method introduced to overcome this disadvantage is freeze-etching, involving the deep-freezing of specimens in a liquid gas and the subsequent formation of carbon-platinum replicas of the material. Since such frozen cells may remain viable, it is claimed that freeze-etching enables the study of cellular ultrastructure as it appears in the living state. The recent development of very high voltage electron microscopes may render possible the eventual examination of live objects. The scanning electron microscope is a useful innovation which permits the study of cell surfaces with greater contrast and higher resolution than with the shadow-casting technique.

STAINED PREPARATIONS

Live bacteria do not show much structural detail under the light microscope due to lack of contrast. Hence it is customary to use staining techniques to produce colour contrast. Bacteria may be stained in the living state, but this type of staining is employed only for special purposes. Routine methods for staining of bacteria involve drying and fixing smears, procedures that kill them. Bacteria have an affinity for basic dyes due to the acidic nature of their protoplasm. The following are staining techniques commonly used in bacteriology.

Simple stains: Dyes such as methylene blue or basic fuchsin are used for simple staining. They provide colour contrast, but impart the same colour to all bacteria.

Negative staining: Here, bacteria are mixed with dyes such as Indian ink or nigrosin that provide a uniformly coloured background against which the unstained bacteria stand out in contrast. This is particularly useful in the demonstration of bacterial capsules which do not take simple stains. Very slender bacteria such as spirochetes that are not demonstrable by simple staining methods can be viewed by negative staining.

Impregnation methods: Cells and structures too thin to be seen under the ordinary microscope may be rendered visible if they are thickened by impregnation of silver on the surface. Such methods are used for the demonstration of spirochetes and bacterial flagella.

Differential stains: These stains impart different colours to different bacteria or bacterial structures. The two most widely used differential stains are the Gram stain and the acid fast stain.

The *Gram stain* was originally devised by the histologist Christian Gram (1884) as a method of staining bacteria in tissues. The staining technique consists of four steps:

1. primary staining with a pararosaniline dye such as crystal violet, methyl violet or gentian violet;
2. application of a dilute solution of iodine;
3. decolourisation with an organic solvent such as ethanol, acetone or aniline;
4. counterstaining with a dye of contrasting colour, such as carbol fuchsin, safranine or neutral red.

The Gram stain differentiates bacteria into two broad groups. Gram positive bacteria are those that resist decolourisation and retain the primary stain, appearing violet. Gram negative bacteria are decolourised by organic solvents and, therefore, take the counterstain, appearing red. The exact mechanism of the Gram reaction is not understood. The Gram positive cells have a more acidic protoplasm, which may account for their retaining the basic primary dye more strongly than the Gram negative bacteria. Decolourisation is not an all-or-none phenomenon. Even Gram positive cells may be decolourised by prolonged treatment with the organic solvent. Conversely, inadequate decolourisation may cause all cells to appear Gram positive. The Gram reaction may be related to the permeability of the bacterial cell wall and cytoplasmic membrane to the dye-iodine complex, the Gram negative, but not the Gram positive cells, permitting the outflow of the complex during decolorisation. The Gram positive bacteria become Gram negative when the cell wall is damaged.

Gram staining is an essential procedure used

in the identification of bacteria and frequently is the only method required for studying their morphology. Gram reactivity is of considerable importance as the Gram positive and negative bacteria differ not merely in staining characteristics and in structure but also in several other properties such as growth requirements, susceptibility to antibiotics and pathogenicity.

The *acid fast stain* was discovered by Ehrlich, who found that after staining with aniline dyes, tubercle bacilli resist decolourisation with acids. The method, as modified by Ziehl and Neelsen, is in common use now. The smear is stained by a strong solution of carbol fuchsin with the application of heat. It is then decolourised with 20 per cent sulphuric acid and counterstained with a contrasting dye such as methylene blue. The acid fast bacteria retain the fuchsin (red) colour, while the others take the counterstain. Acid fastness has been ascribed to the high content and variety of lipids, fatty acids and higher alcohols found in tubercle bacilli. A lipid peculiar to acid fast bacilli, a high molecular weight hydroxy acid wax containing carboxyl groups (mycolic acid) is acid fast in the free state. Acid fastness is not a property of lipids alone but depends also on the integrity of the cell wall.

SHAPE OF BACTERIA

Depending on their shape, bacteria are classified into several varieties (Fig. 2.1):

1. Cocci (from *kokkos* meaning berry) are spherical or oval cells.
2. Bacilli (from *baculus* meaning rod) are rod shaped cells.
3. Vibrios are comma shaped, curved rods and derive the name from their characteristic vibratory motility.
4. Spirilla are rigid spiral forms.
5. Spirochetes (from *speira* meaning coil and *chaite* meaning hair) are flexuous spiral forms.
6. Actinomycetes are branching filamentous bacteria, so called because of a fancied resemblance to the radiating rays of the sun when seen in tissue lesions (from *actis* meaning ray and *mykes* meaning fungus).
7. Mycoplasmas are bacteria that are cell wall deficient and hence do not possess a stable morphology. They occur as round or oval bodies and as interlacing filaments. When cell wall synthesis becomes defective, either spontaneously or as a result of drugs like penicillin, bacteria lose their distinctive shape. Such cells are called protoplasts, spheroplasts or L forms.

Bacteria sometimes show characteristic cellular arrangement or grouping (Fig. 2.2). Thus, cocci may be arranged in pairs (diplococci), chains (streptococci), groups of four (tetrads) or eight (sarcina), or as grape-like clusters (staphylococci).

Some bacilli too may be arranged in chains (streptobacilli). Others are arranged at angles to each other, presenting a cuneiform or Chinese letter pattern (corynebacteria). The type of cellular arrangement is determined by the plane through which binary fission takes place and by the tendency of the daughter cells to remain attached even after division.

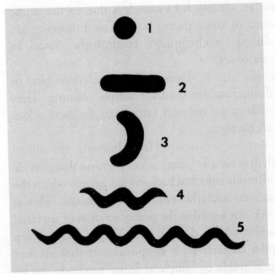

Fig. 2.1 Shapes of bacteria : 1. coccus 2. bacillus 3. vibrio 4. spirillum 5. spirochete

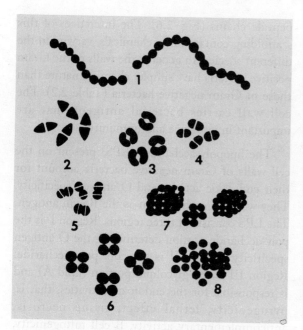

Fig. 2.2 Arrangement of cocci: 1. streptococci
2. pneumococci 3. gonococci 4. meningococci
5. *Neisseria catarrhalis* 6. *Gaffkya tetragena*
7. sarcina 8. staphylococci

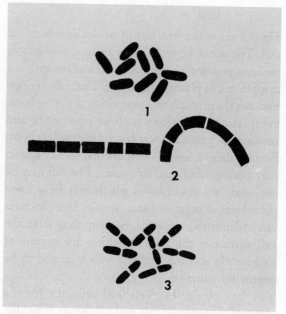

Fig. 2.3 Arrangement of bacilli : 1. bacilli in cluster
2. bacilli in chains (*B. anthrax*) 3. diplobacilli
(*K. pneumoniae*)

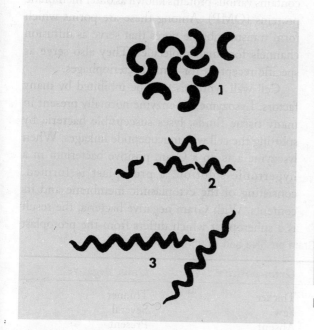

Fig. 2.4 Arrangements of curved bacteria : 1. vibrio
2. spirilla 3. spirochetes

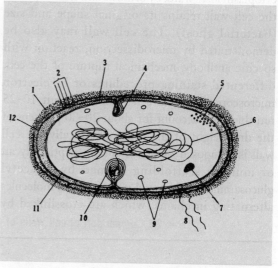

Fig. 2.5 Diagram of an *idealised* bacterial cell :
1. Capsule 2. Pili 3.Outer membrane 4. Division
septum 5. Ribosome 6. DNA 7. Granular inclusions 8. Flagella 9. Fat globules 10. Mesosome
11. Cytoplasmic membrane 12. Peptidoglycan

BACTERIAL ANATOMY

Fig. 2.5 shows the structure of an idealised bacterial cell. The outer layer or cell envelope consists of two components − a rigid cell wall and beneath it a cytoplasmic or plasma membrane. The cell envelope encloses the protoplasm, comprising the cytoplasm, cytoplasmic inclusions such as ribosomes and mesosomes, granules, vacuoles and the nuclear body. Besides these essential components, some bacteria may possess additional structures. The cell may be enclosed in a viscid layer, which may be a loose slime layer, or organised as a capsule. Some bacteria carry filamentous appendages protruding from the cell surface − the flagella which are organs of locomotion and the fimbriae which appear to be organs for adhesion.

The cell wall: The cell wall accounts for the shape of the bacterial cell and confers on it rigidity and ductility. The cell wall cannot be seen by direct light microscopy and does not stain with simple stains. It may be demonstrated by plasmolysis. When placed in a hypertonic solution, the cytoplasm loses water by osmosis and shrinks, while the cell wall retains its original shape and size (bacterial ghost). The cell wall may also be demonstrated by microdissection, reaction with specific antibody, mechanical rupture of the cell, differential staining procedures or by electron microscopy. Bacterial cell walls are about 10–25 nm thick and account for about 20–30 per cent of the dry weight of the cells. Chemically the cell wall is composed of mucopeptide (peptidoglycan or murein) scaffolding formed by N acetyl glucosamine and N acetyl muramic acid molecules alternating in chains, which are crosslinked by peptide chains (Fig. 2.6). The interstices of this scaffolding contain other chemicals, varying in the different species. In general, the walls of the Gram positive bacteria have simpler chemical nature than those of Gram negative bacteria (Table 2.2). The cell wall carries bacterial antigens that are important in virulence and immunity.

The lipopolysaccharides (LPS) present on the cell walls of Gram negative bacteria account for their endotoxic activity and O antigen specificity. They were formerly known as the Boivin antigen. The LPS consists of three regions. Region I is the polysaccharide portion determining the O antigen specificity. Region II is the core polysaccharide. Region III is the glycolipid portion (lipid A) and is responsible for the endotoxic activities, that is, pyrogenicity, lethal effect, tissue necrosis, anticomplementary activity, B cell mitogenicity, immunoadjuvant property and antitumour activity.

The outermost layer of Gram negative bacterial cell wall is called the outer membrane, which contains various proteins known as outer membrane proteins (OMP). Among these are porins which form transmembrane pores that serve as diffusion channels for small molecules. They also serve as specific receptors for some bacteriophages.

Cell wall synthesis may be inhibited by many factors. Lysozyme, an enzyme normally present in many tissue fluids, lyses susceptible bacteria by splitting the cell wall mucopeptide linkages. When lysozyme acts on a Gram positive bacterium in a hypertonic solution, a protoplast is formed, consisting of the cytoplasmic membrane and its contents. With Gram negative bacteria, the result is a spheroplast which differs from the protoplast

Table 2.2 Comparison of cell walls of Gram positive and Gram negative bacteria

	Gram positive	Gram negative
Thickness	Thicker	Thinner
Variety of aminoacids	Few	Several
Aromatic and sulphur containing aminoacids	Absent	Present
Lipids	Absent or scant	Present
Teichoic acid	Present	Absent

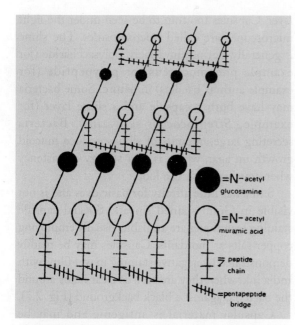

Fig. 2.6 Chemical structure of bacterial cell wall

Legend:
- ● = N-acetyl glucosamine
- ○ = N-acetyl muramic acid
- = peptide chain
- = pentapeptide bridge

in that some cell wall material is retained. Protoplasts and spheroplasts are spherical, regardless of the original shape of the bacterium. Cell wall deficient forms of bacteria may probably have a role in the persistence of certain chronic infections such as pyelonephritis.

Cytoplasmic membrane: The cytoplasmic (plasma) membrane is a thin (5–10 nm) layer lining the inner surface of the cell wall and separating it from the cytoplasm. It acts as a semipermeable membrane controlling the inflow and outflow of metabolites to and from the protoplasm. Passage through the membrane is not solely a function of the molecular size of the particles but depends, in many cases, on the presence in the membrane of specific enzymes (permeases). Electron microscopy shows the presence of three layers constituting a 'unit membrane' structure. Chemically, the membrane consists of lipoprotein with small amounts of carbohydrate. Sterols are absent, except in mycoplasma.

Cytoplasm: The bacterial cytoplasm is a colloidal system of a variety of organic and inorganic solutes in a viscous watery solution. It differs from eukaryotic cytoplasm in not exhibiting internal mobility (**protoplasmic streaming**) and in the absence of endoplasmic reticulum or mitochondria. The cytoplasm stains uniformly with basic dyes in young cultures but becomes increasingly granular with age. The cytoplasm contains ribosomes, mesosomes, inclusions and vacuoles.

Ribosomes are centres of protein synthesis. They are slightly smaller than the ribosomes of eukaryotic cells (sedimentation constant 70 S) and are seen integrated in linear strands of mRNA to form polysomes.

Mesosomes (chondroids) are vesicular, convoluted or multilaminated structures formed as invaginations of the plasma membrane into the cytoplasm. They are more prominent in Gram positive bacteria. They are the principal sites of respiratory enzymes in bacteria and are analogous to the mitochondria of eukaryotes. *Mesosomes* are often seen in relation to the nuclear body and the site of synthesis of cross wall septa, suggesting that they coordinate nuclear and cytoplasmic division during binary fission.

Intracytoplasmic inclusions may be of various types, the chief of which are volutin, polysaccharide, lipid and crystals. They are characteristic for different species and depend on the age and condition of the culture. **Volutin** granules (*metachromatic* or *Babes-Ernst granules*) are highly refractive, strongly basophilic bodies consisting of polymetaphosphate. They appear reddish when stained with polychrome methylene blue or toluidine blue (*metachromasia*). Special staining techniques such as Albert's or Neisser's demonstrate the granules more clearly. Volutin granules are characteristically present in diphtheria bacilli. Their function is uncertain. They have been considered to represent a reserve of energy and phosphate for cell metabolism but they are most frequent in cells grown under conditions of nutritional deficiency and tend to disappear when the deficient nutrients are supplied. Polysaccharide granules may be demonstrated by staining with iodine, and lipid inclusions with fat soluble dyes such as Sudan black. They appear to be storage products. Vacuoles are fluid-containing cavities separated from the cytoplasm by a membrane. Their function and significance are uncertain.

Nucleus: Bacterial nuclei can be demonstrated by acid or ribonuclease hydrolysis and subsequent staining for nuclear material. They may be seen by electron microscopy. They appear as oval or elongated bodies, generally one per cell. Some cells may possess two or more nuclear bodies due to asynchrony between nuclear and cytoplasmic division.

Bacterial nuclei have no nuclear membrane or nucleolus. The nuclear deoxyribonucleic acid (DNA) is not associated with basic protein. The genome consists of a single molecule of double-stranded DNA arranged in the form of a circle, which may open under certain conditions to form a long chain, about 1 mm in length. The bacterial chromosome is haploid and replicates by simple fission instead of by mitosis as in higher cells. The differences between the nuclei of bacteria and higher organisms form the main basis for classifying them as prokaryotes and eukaryotes.

Bacteria may possess extranuclear genetic elements consisting of DNA. These cytoplasmic carriers of genetic information are termed *plasmids* or *episomes* (see Chapter 8). Besides being transmitted to daughter cells during binary fission, they may be transferred from one bacterium to another either through conjugation or the agency of bacteriophages. They are not essential for the life of the cell they inhabit but may confer on it certain properties like toxigenicity and drug resistance which may constitute a survival advantage.

Slime layer and capsule: Many bacteria secrete a viscid material around the cell surface. When this is organised into a sharply defined structure, as in the pneumococcus, it is known as the *capsule*. When it is a loose undemarcated secretion, as in leuconostoc, it is called the *slime* layer. Capsules too thin to be seen under the light microscopes are called *microcapsules*. The slime is generally, but not invariably, polysaccharide (for example pneumococcus) or polypeptide (for example anthrax bacillus) in nature. Some bacteria may have both a capsule and a slime layer (for example, *Streptococcus salivarius*). Bacteria secreting large amounts of slime produce mucoid growth on agar, which is of a stringy consistency when touched with the loop.

Slime has little affinity for basic dyes and is not visible in Gram stained smears. Special capsule staining techniques are available, usually employing copper salts as mordants. Capsules may be readily demonstrated by negative staining in wet films with India ink, when they are seen as clear halos around the bacteria, against a black background (Fig. 2.7).

Capsular material is antigenic and may be demonstrated by serological methods. When a suspension of a capsulated bacterium is mixed with its specific anticapsular serum and examined under the microscope, the capsule becomes very prominent and appears 'swollen' due to an increase in its refractivity. This capsule swelling or *Quellung reaction*, described by Neufeld (1902) was widely employed for the typing of pneumococci in the pre-sulphonamide days when lobar pneumonia used to be treated with specific anticapsular sera. Capsules protect bacteria from deleterious agents such as lytic enzymes found in nature. They also contribute to the virulence of pathogenic bacteria by inhibiting phagocytosis. Loss of the capsule by mutation may render the bacterium avirulent. Repeated subcultures in vitro lead to the loss of capsule and also of virulence.

Flagella: Motile bacteria, except spirochetes, possess one or more unbranched, long, sinuous filaments called flagella, which are the organs of locomotion. Each flagellum consists of three distinct parts, the filament, the hook and the basal body. The filament is external to the cell and connected to the hook at the cell surface.

The hook-basal body portion is embedded in

the cell envelope. The hook and basal body are antigenically different. Mechanical detachment of the filament does not impair the viability of the cell. The flagella are 3–20 µm long and are of uniform diameter (0.01–0.013 µm) and terminate in a square tip. The wavelength and thickness of the filament are characteristic of each species but some bacteria exhibit biplicity, that is, they have flagella of two different wavelengths (Fig. 2.8). Flagella are made up of a protein (flagellin) similar to keratin or myosin. Though flagella of different genera of bacteria have the same chemical composition, they are antigenically different. Flagellar antigens induce specific antibodies in high titres. Flagellar antibodies are not protective but are useful in serodiagnosis.

The presence or absence of flagella and their number and arrangement are characteristic of different genera of bacteria (Fig. 2.9). Flagella may be arranged all round the cell (peritrichous) as in typhoid bacilli, or situated at one or both ends of the cell (polar). Polar flagella may be single (monotrichous) as in cholera vibrios, in tufts (lophotrichous) as in spirilla or with flagella at both poles (amphitrichous).

Flagella are less than 0.02 µm in thickness and hence beyond the limit of resolution of the light microscope. They may, in some instances, be seen under dark ground illumination. They can be visualised by special staining techniques in which their thickness is increased by mordanting, or by electron microscopy (Fig. 2.10). Due to the difficulty of demonstrating flagella directly, their presence is usually inferred from the motility of bacteria. Motility can be observed by noting the spreading type of growth on a semisolid agar medium. Under the microscope, active motility has to be differentiated from the passive movements of the cells, either due to air currents or due to Brownian movement. Bacterial motility may range from the slow 'stately' motion of peritrichate bacteria (for example, Bacillus) to the darting movement of polar flagellated vibrios. The cholera vibrio may move as fast as 200 µm per second.

Fimbriae: Some Gram negative bacilli carry very fine, hair-like surface appendages called fimbriae or pili. They are shorter and thinner than flagella (about 0.5 µm long and less than 10 nm thick) and project from the cell surface as straight filaments. At least eight morphological types of pili are known, classifiable as either common or sex pili on the basis of their function. Pili comprise self-aggregating monomers of pilin. They originate in the cell membrane. Fimbriae can be seen only under the electron microscope. They are unrelated to motility and are found on motile as well as nonmotile cells. They are best developed in freshly isolated strains and in liquid cultures. They tend to disappear following subcultures on solid media.

Fimbriae function as organs of adhesion, helping the cells to adhere firmly to particles of various kinds. This property may serve to anchor the bacteria in nutritionally favourable micro environments. Fimbriated bacteria form surface pellicles in liquid media. Many fimbriated cells (for example Escherichia, Klebsiella) agglutinate red

Fig. 2.7 Pneumococci negatively stained with India ink to show capsule

blood cells of guinea pigs, fowl, horses and pigs strongly, human and sheep cells weakly, and ox cells scarcely at all.

Hemagglutination provides a simple method for detecting the presence of such fimbriae. The hemagglutination is specifically inhibited by D-mannose (mannose sensitive).

Fimbriae are antigenic. As members of different genera may possess the same fimbrial antigen, it is necessary to ensure that the bacterial antigens employed for serological tests and preparation of antisera are devoid of fimbriae.

A special type of fimbria are the sex pili. These are longer and fewer in number than other fimbriae. They are found on 'male' bacteria and help in the attachment of those cells to 'female' bacteria,

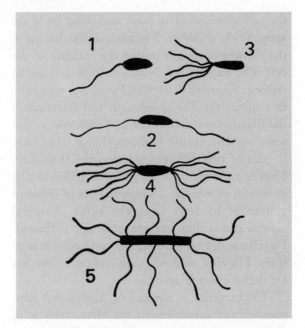

Fig. 2.9 Types of flagellar arrangement: 1. single flagellum 2. single flagellum at each pole 3. tuft of flagella at one pole 4. tufts of flagella at both poles 5. peritrichous flagella

forming hollow conjugation tubes through which, it is assumed, genetic material is transferred from the donor to the recipient cell. Pili are classified into different types (for example, F, I) based on susceptibility to specific bacteriophages.

Spore: Some bacteria, particularly members of the genera Bacillus and Clostridium have the ability to form highly resistant resting stages called spores. Each bacterium forms one spore, which on germination forms a single vegetative cell. Sporulation in bacteria, therefore, is not a method of reproduction. As bacterial spores are formed inside the parent cell, they are called endospores.

While the exact stimulus for sporulation is not known, it occurs after a period of vegetative growth and is presumed to be related to the depletion of exogenous nutrients. Sporulation is initiated by the appearance of a clear area, usually near one end of the cell, which gradually becomes more opaque to form the 'forespore'. The fully developed spore has

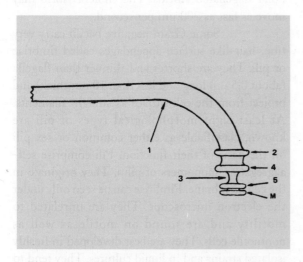

Fig. 2.8 Flagellum and its parts. 1. Arrow shows the junction of the hook and filament. 2, Ring for attachment to outer lipopolysaccharide O antigen-complex membrane of the cell wall. 3. Rod connecting top and bottom rings. 4.Ring for its association with the peptidoglycan layer of the cell wal. 5. Ring located just above cytoplasmic membrane M ring for attachment to the cytoplasmic membrane.

at its core the nuclear body, surrounded by the spore wall, a delicate membrane from which the cell wall of the future vegetative bacterium will develop. Outside this is the thick spore cortex, which in turn is enclosed by a multilayered tough spore coat. Some spores have an additional outer covering called exosporium, which may have distinctive ridges and grooves (Fig. 2.11). New antigens appear on sporulation.

Young spores are seen attached to the parent cell. The shape and position of the spore and its size relative to the parent cell are species characteristics. Spores may be central (equatorial), terminal or subterminal. They may be oval or spherical. They may or may not distend the bacillary body (Fig. 2.12).

Bacterial spores constitute some of the most resistant forms of life. They may remain viable for centuries. They are extremely resistant to desiccation and relatively so to chemicals and heat. Though some spores may resist boiling for prolonged periods, spores of all medically important species are destroyed by autoclaving at 120 °C for 15 minutes. Methods of sterilisation and disinfection should ensure that spores also are destroyed. Sporulation helps bacteria survive for long periods under unfavourable environments.

When transferred to conditions conducive for growth, spores germinate. The spore loses its refractility and swells. The spore wall is shed and the germ cell appears by rupturing the spore coat and elongates to form the vegetative bacterium.

Spores may be seen in unstained preparation as refractile bodies. The forespore stains intensely, but once the spore envelope is laid down, the spore does not stain readily. Spores appear as unstained areas in Gram stained preparations, but being more acid fast than the vegetative cells, they can be stained by a modification of the Ziehl-Neelsen technique.

Pleomorphism and involution forms: Some species of bacteria exhibit great variation in the shape and size of individual cells. This is known as pleomorphism. Certain species (for example, plague bacillus, gonococcus) show swollen and aberrant forms in ageing cultures, especially in the presence of high salt concentration. These are known as involution forms. Many of the cells may

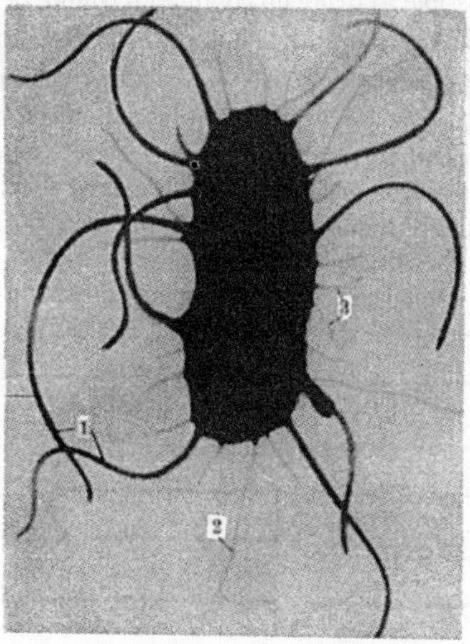

Fig. 2.10 Electron micrograph of *E. coli*. 1. Flagella 2. F. pili 3. ordinary pili or fimbriae

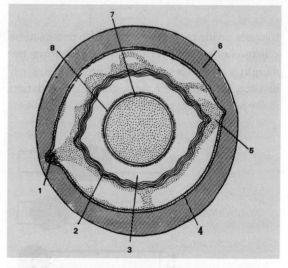

Fig. 2.11 Diagrammatic representation of a bacterial spore. 1. Germinal groove 2. Outer cortical layer 3. Cortex 4. Internal spore coat 5. Subcoat material 6. Outer spore coat 7. Cytoplasmic membrane 8. Cell wall primordium

be nonviable. Pleomorphism and involution forms are often due to defective cell wall synthesis. Involution forms may also develop due to the activity of autolytic enzymes.

L forms: Kleineberger-Nobel, studying cultures of *Streptobacillus moniliformis*, observed swollen cells and other aberrant morphological forms and named them L forms, after Lister Institute, London, where the observation was made. L forms are seen in several species of bacteria, developing either spontaneously or in the presence of penicillin or other agents that interfere with cell wall synthesis. L forms may be unstable in that the morphological abnormality is maintained only in the presence of penicillin or other inducing agents, or stable, when the aberrant form becomes the permanent feature of the strain and is retained in serial subcultures. L forms resemble mycoplasma in several ways, including morphology, type of growth on agar and filterability. It is possible that mycoplasmas represent stable L forms of as yet unidentified parent bacteria.

Growth and Multiplication of Bacteria

Bacteria divide by binary fission. When a bacterial cell reaches a certain size, it divides to form two daughter cells. Nuclear division precedes cell division and, therefore, in a growing population, many cells carrying two nuclear bodies can be seen.

The cell divides by a constrictive or pinching process, or by the ingrowth of a transverse septum across the cell. In some species, the daughter cells may remain partially attached after division.

The interval of time between two cell divisions, or the time required for a bacterium to give rise to two daughter cells under optimum conditions, is known as the generation time or population doubling time. In coliform bacilli and many other medically important bacteria, the generation time is about 20 minutes. Some bacteria are slow-growing; the generation time in tubercle bacilli is about 20 hours and in lepra bacilli as long as about 20 days. As bacteria reproduce so rapidly and by geometric progression, a single bacterial cell can theoretically give rise to 10^{21} progeny in 24 hours, with a mass of approximately 4,000 tonnes! In actual practice, when bacteria are grown in a vessel of liquid medium (batch culture), multiplication is arrested after a few cell divisions due to depletion of nutrients or accumulation of toxic products. By the use of special devices for replenishing nutrients and removing bacterial cells (chemostat or turbidistat), it is possible to maintain continuous culture of bacteria for industrial or research purposes. When pathogenic bacteria multiply in host tissues, the situation may be intermediate between a batch culture and a continuous culture; the source of nutrients may be inexhaustible but the parasite has to contend with the defence mechanisms of the body. Bacteria growing on solid

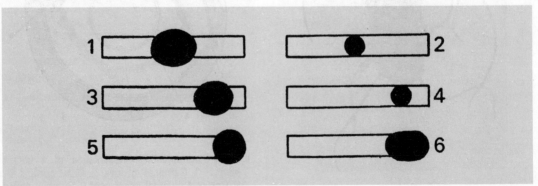

Fig. 2.12 Types of bacterial spores. 1. central, bulging, 2. central, not bulging, 3. subterminal, bulging, 4. subterminal, not bulging, 5. terminal, spherical, 6. terminal, oval.

media form colonies. Each colony represents a clone of cells derived from a single parent cell. In liquid media, growth is diffuse.

Bacterial growth may be considered at two levels, increase in the size of the individual cell and increase in the number of cells. The former is ordinarily limited and when the critical size is reached, the cell divides, except when cell division is inhibited by substances like penicillin or acriflavine or by growth in magnesium deficient media. Growth in numbers can be studied by bacterial counts. Two types of bacterial counts can be made—total count and viable count.

The **total count** gives the total number of cells in the sample, irrespective of whether they are living or not. It can be obtained by

1. direct counting under the microscope using counting chambers,
2. counting in an electronic device as in the Coulter counter,
3. direct counting using stained smears prepared by spreading a known volume of the culture over a measured area of a slide,
4. comparing relative numbers in smears of the culture mixed with known numbers of other cells,
5. by opacity measurements using an absorptio meter or nephalometer,
6. by separating the cells by centrifugation or filtration and measuring their wet or dry weight, and
7. chemical assay of cell components such as nitrogen.

The viable count measures the number of living cells, that is, cells capable of multiplication. Viable counts are obtained by dilution or plating methods. In the dilution method, the suspension is diluted to a point beyond which unit quantities do not yield growth when inoculated into suitable liquid media (extinction). Several tubes are inoculated with varying dilutions and the viable count calculated statistically from the number of tubes showing growth. The method does not give accurate values but is used widely in water bacteriology for estimation of the 'presumptive coliform count' in drinking water.

In the plating method, appropriate dilutions are inoculated on solid media, either on the surface of plates or as pour plates. The number of colonies that develop after incubation gives an estimate of the viable count. The method commonly employed is that described by Miles and Misra (1938) in which serial dilutions are dropped on the surface of dried plates and colony counts obtained.

Bacterial Growth Curve

When a bacterium is seeded into a suitable liquid medium and incubated, its growth follows a definite course. If bacterial counts are made at intervals after inoculation and plotted in relation to time, a growth curve is obtained (Fig. 2.13). The curve shows the following phases:

Lag phase: Immediately following the seeding of a culture medium, there is no appreciable increase in numbers, though there may be an increase in the size of the cells. This initial period is the time required for adaptation to the new environment, during which the necessary enzymes and metabolic intermediates are built up in adequate quantities for multiplication to proceed. The duration of the lag phase varies with the species, size of inoculum, nature of culture medium and environmental factors such as temperature.

Log (logarithmic) or exponential phase: Following the lag phase, the cells start dividing and their numbers increase exponentially or by geometric progression with time. If the logarithm of the viable count is plotted against time, a straight line will be obtained.

Stationary phase: After a varying period of exponential growth, cell division stops due to depletion of nutrients and accumulation of toxic products. The number of progeny cells formed is just enough to replace the number of cells that die. The viable count remains stationary as an equilibrium exists between the dying cells and the newly formed cells.

Phase of decline: This is the phase when the population decreases due to cell death. Besides

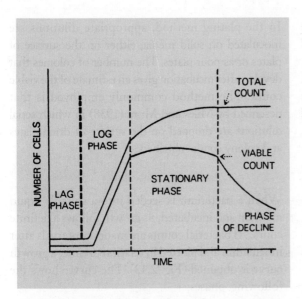

Fig. 2.13 Bacterial growth curve. The viable count shows lag, log, stationary and decline phases. In the total count, the phase of decline is not evident.

nutritional exhaustion and toxic accumulation, cell death may also be caused by autolytic enzymes.

When the total count is plotted, it parallels the viable count up to the stationary phase but it continues steadily without any phase of decline. With autolytic bacteria, even the total count shows a phase of decline.

The various stages of the growth curve are associated with morphological and physiological alterations of the cells. Bacteria have the maximum cell size towards the end of the lag phase. In the log phase, cells are smaller and stain uniformly. In the stationary phase, cells frequently are Gram variable and show irregular staining due to the presence of intracellular storage granules. Sporulation occurs at this stage. Also, many bacteria produce secondary metabolic products such as exotoxins and antibiotics. Involution forms are common in the phase of decline.

BACTERIAL NUTRITION

The bacterial cell has the same general chemical pattern as the cells of higher organisms. The principal constituent of bacterial cells is water,

which represents about 80 per cent of the total weight. Proteins, polysaccharides, lipids, nucleic acids, mucopeptides and low molecular weight compounds make up the rest. Bacterial metabolism also is closely similar to the metabolism of the higher organisms, exemplifying the 'unity of biochemistry'. There are, however, some differences which are exploited in selective toxicity and chemotherapy.

For growth and multiplication of bacteria, the minimum nutritional requirements are water, a source of carbon, a source of nitrogen and some inorganic salts. Water is the vehicle for the entry of all nutrients into the cells and for the elimination of all waste products. It participates in the metabolic reactions and also forms an integral part of the protoplasm.

Bacteria can be classified nutritionally, based on their energy requirements and on their ability to synthesise essential metabolites. Bacteria which derive their energy from sunlight are called *phototrophs* and those that obtain energy from chemical reactions are called *chemotrophs*. Bacteria that can synthesise all their organic compounds are called *autotrophs*. Those that are unable to synthesise their own metabolites and depend on preformed organic compounds are called *heterotrophs*. Autotrophs are able to utilise atmospheric carbon dioxide and nitrogen. They are capable of independent existence in water and soil and are of no medical importance, though they are of vital concern in agriculture and the maintenance of soil fertility. Heterotrophic bacteria are unable to grow with carbon dioxide as the sole source of carbon. The nutritional requirements of heterotrophs vary widely. Some may require only a single organic substance such as glucose, while others may need a large number of different compounds such as aminoacids, nucleotides, lipids, carbohydrates and coenzymes.

Bacteria require a supply of inorganic salts, particularly the anions phosphate and sulphate, and the cations sodium, potassium, magnesium, iron, manganese and calcium. These are normally present in the natural environments where bacteria live but will have to be supplied in culture media. Some ions such as cobalt may be needed in trace amounts.

Some bacteria require certain organic compounds in minute quantities. These are known as growth factors or bacterial vitamins. Growth factors are called *essential* when growth does not occur in their absence, or *accessory* when they enhance growth, without being absolutely necessary for it. In many cases, bacterial vitamins are identical with the vitamins necessary for mammalian nutrition, particularly those belonging to the B group, thiamine, riboflavine, nicotinic acid, pyridoxine, folic acid and vitamin B12.

If a microorganism requiring an essential growth factor is inoculated into a medium containing an excess of all other nutrients, its growth will be proportional to the amount of the limiting substance added. Within a certain range, the concentration of the growth factor will bear a linear relationship to the amount of growth of the organism. This is the principle of microbiological assays, which provide a very sensitive and specific method for estimation of many aminoacids and vitamins, as in the determination of vitamin B12 using *Lactobacillus leichmannii*.

OXYGEN REQUIREMENT AND METABOLISM

Depending on the influence of oxygen on growth and viability, bacteria are divided into aerobes and anaerobes. **Aerobic bacteria** require oxygen for growth. They may be obligate aerobes like the cholera vibrio, which will grow only in the presence of oxygen, or facultative anaerobes which are ordinarily aerobic but can also grow in the absence of oxygen, though less abundantly. Most bacteria of medical importance are facultative anaerobes. **Anaerobic bacteria**, such as clostridia, grow in the absence of oxygen and the obligate anaerobes may even die on exposure to oxygen. **Microaerophilic** bacteria are those that grow best in the presence of a low oxygen tension.

The reason for the apparent toxicity of oxygen for anaerobic bacteria is not well understood. It has been suggested that in the presence of oxygen, hydrogen peroxide and other toxic peroxides accumulate. The enzyme catalase which splits hydrogen peroxide is present in most aerobic bacteria but is absent in the anaerobes. Another reason might be that obligate anaerobes possess essential enzymes that are active only in the reduced state.

The influence of free oxygen is related to the metabolic character of the bacterium. Aerobic bacteria obtain their energy and intermediates only through oxidation involving oxygen as the ultimate hydrogen acceptor, while the anaerobes use hydrogen acceptors other than oxygen. Facultative anaerobes may act in both ways. In the case of aerobes, where the ultimate electron acceptor is atmospheric oxygen (aerobic respiration), the carbon and energy source may be completely oxidised to carbon dioxide and water. Energy is provided by the production of energy-rich phosphate bonds and the conversion of adenosine diphosphate (ADP) to adenosine triphosphate (ATP). This process is known as *oxidative phosphorylation*. Anaerobic bacteria use as electron acceptors compounds such as nitrates or sulphates instead of oxygen (anaerobic respiration). A more common process in anaerobic metabolism may be a series of oxidoreductions in which the carbon and energy source acts as both the electron donor and electron acceptor. This process is known as **fermentation** and leads to the formation of several organic end products such as acids and alcohols, as well as of gas (carbon dioxide and hydrogen). During the process of fermentation, energy-rich phosphate bonds are produced by the introduction of organic phosphate into intermediate metabolites. This process is known as *substrate-level phosphorylation*. The energy-rich phosphate groups so formed are used for conversion of ADP to ATP.

In determining the growth of aerobic and

anaerobic bacteria, what is more important than the presence or absence of oxygen is the state of oxidation of the environment. The oxidising or reducing condition of a system is indicated by the net readiness of all the components in that system to take up, or part with electrons. This is known as the *oxidation–reduction (redox) potential* of the system. The redox potential of a medium is best estimated by measuring the electrical potential difference set up between the medium and an unattackable electrode immersed in it. This electrode potential (Eh) can be measured in millivolts. The more oxidised the system, the higher the potential. A simpler, though less accurate, method of measuring the redox potential is the use of oxidation–reduction indicators such as methylene blue, and noting the change in colour.

CARBON DIOXIDE

All bacteria require small amounts of carbon dioxide for growth. This requirement is usually met by the carbon dioxide present in the atmosphere, or produced endogenously by cellular metabolism. Some bacteria like *Brucella abortus* require much higher levels of carbon dioxide (5–10 per cent) for growth, especially on fresh isolation (capnophilic).

TEMPERATURE

Bacteria vary in their requirements of temperature for growth. For each species, there is a 'temperature range', and growth does not occur above the maximum or below the minimum of the range. The temperature at which growth occurs best is known as the 'optimum temperature', which in the case of most pathogenic bacteria is 37 °C. Bacteria which grow best at temperatures of 25–40 °C are called *mesophilic*. All parasites of warm blooded animals are mesophilic. Within the group of mesophilic bacteria, some like *Pseudomonas aeruginosa* have a wider range (5–43 °C), while others like the gonococcus have a restricted range (30–39 °C).

Psychrophilic bacteria are those that grow best at temperatures below 20 °C, some of them even

growing at temperatures as low as –7 °C. They are soil and water saprophytes and though not of direct medical importance, may cause spoilage of refrigerated food. Another group of nonpathogenic bacteria, the *thermophiles*, grow best at high temperatures, 55–80 °C. They may cause spoilage of underprocessed canned food. Some thermophiles (like *Bacillus stearothermophilus*) form spores that are exceptionally thermoresistant. Extremely thermophilic bacteria have been identified which can grow at temperatures as high as 250 °C.

Bacteria also differ in the effect of temperature on viability. Heat is an important method for the destruction of microorganisms (sterilisation), moist heat causing coagulation and denaturation of proteins and dry heat causing oxidation and charring. Moist heat is more lethal than dry heat. The lowest temperature that kills a bacterium under standard conditions in a given time is known as the *thermal death point*. Under moist conditions most vegetative, mesophilic bacteria have a thermal death point between 50 and 65 °C and most spores between 100 and 120 °C.

At low temperatures some species die rapidly but most survive well. Storage in the refrigerator (3–5 °C) or the deep freeze cabinet (–30 to –70 °C) is used for preservation of cultures. Rapid freezing as with solid carbon dioxide or the use of a stabiliser such as glycerol, minimises the death of cells on freezing.

MOISTURE AND DRYING

Water is an essential ingredient of bacterial protoplasm and hence drying is lethal to cells. However, the effect of drying varies in different species. Some delicate bacteria like *Treponema pallidum* are highly sensitive, while others like staphylococci withstand drying for months. Spores are particularly resistant to desiccation and may survive in the dry state for several decades. Drying in vacuum in the cold (*freeze drying* or *lyophilisation*) is a method for the preservation of bacteria, viruses and many labile biological materials.

H-ION CONCENTRATION

Bacteria are sensitive to variations in pH. Each species has a pH range, above or below which it does not survive, and an optimum pH at which it grows best. The majority of pathogenic bacteria grow best at neutral or slightly alkaline reaction (pH 7.2–7.6). Some acidophilic bacteria such as lactobacilli grow under acidic conditions. Others, such as the cholera vibrio, are very sensitive to acid, but tolerate high degrees of alkalinity. Strong solutions of acid or alkali (5% hydrochloric acid or sodium hydroxide) readily kill most bacteria, though mycobacteria are exceptionally resistant to them.

LIGHT

Bacteria (except the phototrophic species) grow well in the dark. They are sensitive to ultraviolet light and other radiations. Cultures die if exposed to sunlight. Exposure to light may influence pigment production. Photochromogenic mycobacteria form a pigment only on exposure to light and not when incubated in the dark.

OSMOTIC EFFECT

Bacteria are more tolerant to osmotic variation than most other cells due to the mechanical strength of their cell walls. Sudden exposure to hypertonic solutions may cause osmotic withdrawal of water and shrinkage of protoplasm – *plasmolysis*. This occurs more readily in Gram negative than in Gram positive bacteria. Sudden transfer from a concentrated solution to distilled water may cause *plasmoptysis* (excessive osmotic imbibition leading to swelling and rupture of the cell).

MECHANICAL AND SONIC STRESS

Though bacteria have tough cell walls, they may be ruptured by mechanical stress such as grinding or vigorous shaking with glass beads. They may also be disintegrated by exposure to ultrasonic vibration.

Further Reading

Blair DF 1995. How bacteria sense and swim. *Annual Rev Microbiol* 49:489.
Dawes IW and W Sutherland 1991. *Microbial Physiology*, 2nd ed. Oxford: Blackwell.
Gould GW and A Hurst 1983. *The Bacterial Spore*. London: Academic Press.
Moat AG and JW Foster 1995. *Microbial Physiology*, 3rd edn. New York: Wiley-Liss.
Stanier RY et al 1986. *The Microbial World*, 5th edn. New Jersey: Prentice-Hall.

Sterilisation and Disinfection

Microorganisms are ubiquitous. Since they cause contamination, infection and decay, it becomes necessary to remove or destroy them from materials or from areas. This is the object of sterilisation. The process of sterilisation is used in microbiology for preventing contamination by extraneous organisms, in surgery for maintaining asepsis, in food and drug manufacture for ensuring safety from contaminating organisms, and in many other situations. The methods of sterilisation employed depend on the purpose for which it is carried out, the material which has to be sterilised and the nature of the microorganisms that are to be removed or destroyed.

Sterilisation is defined as the process by which an article, surface or medium is freed of all living microorganisms either in the vegetative or spore state. *Disinfection* means the destruction or removal of all pathogenic organisms, or organisms capable of giving rise to infection. The term *antisepsis* is used to indicate the prevention of infection, usually by inhibiting the growth of bacteria in wounds or tissues. Chemical disinfectants which can be safely applied to skin or mucous membrane and are used to prevent infection by inhibiting the growth of bacteria are called *antiseptics*. *Bactericidal* agents or *germicides* are those which are able to kill bacteria. *Bacteriostatic* agents only prevent the multiplication of bacteria which may, however, remain alive. A chemical which is bactericidal at a particular concentration, may only be bacteriostatic at a higher dilution.

Cleaning, though a routine nontechnical procedure, plays an important preparatory role before sterilisation or disinfection, by removing soil and other dirt and reducing the microbial burden, making sterilisation more effective. *Decontamination* refers to the process of rendering an article or area free of danger from contaminants, including microbial, chemical, radioactive and other hazards.

The various agents used in sterilisation can be classified as follows :

A. Physical agents

1. Sunlight.
2. Drying.
3. Dry heat: flaming, incineration, hot air.
4. Moist heat: pasteurisation, boiling, steam under normal pressure, steam under pressure.
5. Filtration: candles, asbestos pads, membranes.
6. Radiation.
7. Ultrasonic and sonic vibrations.

B. Chemicals

1. Alcohols: ethyl, isopropyl, trichlorobutanol.
2. Aldehydes: formaldehyde, glutaraldehyde.
3. Dyes.
4. Halogens.
5. Phenols.
6. Surface-active agents.
7. Metallic salts.
8. Gases: ethylene oxide, formaldehyde, beta propiolactone.

SUNLIGHT

Sunlight possesses appreciable bactericidal activity and plays an important role in the spontaneous sterilisation that occurs under natural conditions. The action is primarily due to its content of ultraviolet rays, most of which, however, are screened out by glass and the presence of ozone in the outer regions of the atmosphere. Under natural conditions, its sterilising power varies according to circumstances. Direct sunlight, as in tropical countryside where it is not filtered off by impurities in the atmosphere, has an active germicidal effect due to the combined effect of ultraviolet and heat rays. Semple and Grieg showed that in India, typhoid bacilli exposed to the sun on pieces of white drill cloth were killed in two hours, whereas controls kept in the dark were still alive after six days. Bacteria suspended in water are readily destroyed by exposure to sunlight.

DRYING

Moisture is essential for the growth of bacteria. Four-fifths of the weight of the bacterial cell is due to water. Drying in air has therefore, a deleterious effect on many bacteria. However, this method is unreliable and is only of theoretical interest. Spores are unaffected by drying.

HEAT

Heat is the most reliable method of sterilisation and should be the method of choice unless contraindicated. Materials that may be damaged by heat can be sterilised at lower temperatures, for longer periods or by repeated cycles. The factors influencing sterilisation by heat are:

1. nature of heat—dry heat or moist heat,
2. temperature and time,
3. number of microorganisms present,
4. characteristics of the organisms, such as, species, strain, sporing capacity, and
5. type of material from which the organisms have to be eradicated.

The killing effect of dry heat is due to protein denaturation, oxidative damage and the toxic effect of elevated levels of electrolytes. The lethal effect of moist heat is due to the denaturation and coagulation of protein. The advantage of steam lies in the latent heat liberated when it condenses on a cooler surface, raising the temperature of that surface. In the case of the spore, steam condenses on it, increasing its water content with ultimate hydrolysis and breakdown of the bacterial protein. In a completely moisture-free atmosphere, bacteria, like many proteins, are more resistant to heat. They are killed when oxidation of the cell constituents occurs and this requires much higher temperatures than that needed for coagulation of proteins.

The time required for sterilisation is inversely proportional to the temperature of exposure and can be expressed as 'thermal death time', which is the minimum time required to kill a suspension of organisms at a predetermined temperature in a specified environment. The sterilisation time is related to the number of organisms in the suspension, presence or absence of spores, and the strain and characteristics of organism. The recommended minimum sterilising times do not include the time taken to reach the specified temperature. The nature of the material in which the organisms are heated affects the rate of killing. The presence of organic substances, proteins, nucleic acids, starch, gelatin, sugar, fats and oils, increase the thermal death time. The presence of disinfectants and high acid or alkaline pH hasten bacterial killing.

DRY HEAT

Flaming: Inoculating loop or wire, the tip of forceps and searing spatulas are held in a bunsen flame till they become red hot. Inoculation loops carrying infective material may be dipped in a disinfectant before flaming to prevent spattering.

Incineration: This is an excellent method for safely destroying materials such as contaminated cloth, animal carcasses, and pathological materials. Plastics such as PVC and polythene can be dealt with similarly but polystyrene materials emit clouds of dense black smoke and hence should be autoclaved in appropriate containers.

Hot air oven: This is the most widely used method of sterilisation by dry heat. A holding period of 160 °C for one hour is used to sterilise glassware,

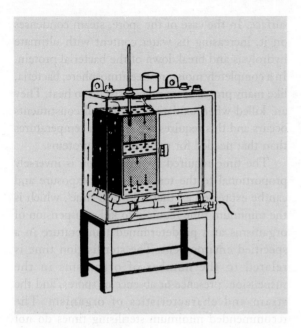

Fig. 3.1 Hot air oven

forceps, scissors, scalpels, all-glass syringes, swabs, some pharmaceutical products such as liquid paraffin, dusting powder, fats and grease. Hot air is a bad conductor of heat and its penetrating power is low. The oven is usually heated by electricity, with heating elements in the wall of the chamber. It must be fitted with a fan to ensure even distribution of air and elimination of air pockets (Fig. 3.1). It should not be overloaded. The material should be arranged so as to allow free circulation of air in between the objects. Glassware should be perfectly dry before being placed in the oven. Test tubes and flasks should be wrapped in paper. Rubber materials, except silicon rubber, will not withstand the temperature. At 180 °C cotton plugs may get charred. Cutting instruments such as those used in ophthalmic surgery, should ideally be sterilised for two hours at 150 °C. The British Pharmacopoeia recommends a holding time of one hour at 150 °C for oils, glycerol and dusting powder. The oven must be allowed to cool slowly for about two hours before the door is opened, since the glassware may crack due to sudden or uneven cooling.

Sterilisation control: The spores of a nontoxigenic strain of *Clostridium tetani* are used as a microbiological test of dry heat efficiency. Paper strips impregnated with 10^6 spores are placed in envelopes and inserted into suitable packs. After sterilisation, the strips are removed and inoculated into thioglycollate or cooked meat media and incubated for sterility test under strict anaerobic conditions for five days at 37 °C.

A Browne's tube (green spot) is available for dry heat and is convenient for routine use. After proper sterilisation a green colour is produced (after 60 minutes at 160 °C or 115 minutes at 150 °C). Thermocouples may also be used periodically.

MOIST HEAT

Temperatures below 100 °C

For pasteurisation of milk: The milk is heated at either 63 °C for 30 minutes (the holder method) or 72 °C for 15–20 seconds (the flash process) followed by cooling quickly to 13 °C or lower. By these processes all nonsporing pathogens such as mycobacteria, brucellae and salmonellae are destroyed. *Coxiella burnetii* is relatively heat resistant and may survive the holder method.

Vaccines of nonsporing bacteria are heat inactivated in special vaccine baths at 60 °C for one hour. Serum or body fluids containing coagulable proteins can be sterilized by heating for one hour at 56 °C in a water bath on several successive days.

Media such as Lowenstein—Jensen and Loeffler's serum are rendered sterile by heating at 80–85 °C for half an hour on three successive days in an *inspissator*.

Though practically all mesophilic nonsporing bacteria are killed by exposure to moist heat at 60 °C for 30 minutes, *Staphylococcus aureus* and *Streptococccus faecalis* require 60 minutes. A temperature of 80 °C for 5–10 minutes destroys the vegetative forms of all bacteria, yeasts and moulds. Among the most heat resistant cells are the spores of *Clostridium botulinum* which require

120 °C for four minutes, or 100 °C for 330 minutes for their destruction. Most viruses are inactivated very rapidly at 60 °C, but some are relatively resistant, for example, poliovirus and hepatitis B virus which may survive for 30 minutes and over 10 hours respectively, at this temperature.

Temperature at 100 °C

Boiling: Vegetative bacteria are killed almost immediately at 90–100 °C, but sporing bacteria require prolonged periods of boiling. Boiling is *not* recommended for sterilising of instruments used for surgical procedures and should be regarded only as a means of disinfection. Nothing short of autoclaving at high pressure can destroy spores and ensure sterilisation. Hard water should not be used. Sterilisation may be promoted by the addition of 2% sodium bicarbonate to the water.

In cases where boiling is considered adequate, the material should be immersed in the water and boiled for 10–30 minutes. The lid of the steriliser should not be opened during the period.

Steam at atmospheric pressure (100°C):

An atmosphere of free steam is used to sterilize culture media which may decompose if subjected to higher temperatures. A Koch or Arnold steamer is usually used. (Laboratory autoclaves can also be used for this purpose.) This is an inexpensive method. The container and medium are simultaneously sterilised, evaporation from the medium is prevented and the apparatus requires little or no attention.

The steamer consists of a tinned copper cabinet with the walls suitably lagged. The lid is conical, enabling drainage of condensed steam, and a perforated tray fitted above the water level ensures that the material placed on it is surrounded by steam (Fig. 3.2). A single exposure of ninety minutes usually ensures sterilisation but for media containing sugars or gelatin an exposure of 100 °C for 20 minutes on three successive days is used. This is known as *tyndallisation* or *intermittent sterilisation*. The principle is that the first exposure kills all vegetative bacteria, and the spores, since they are

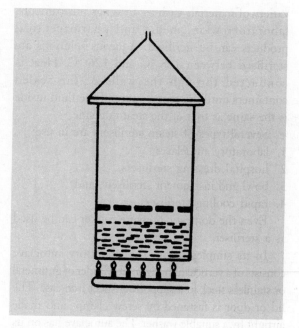

Fig. 3.2 Steamer

in a favourable medium, will germinate and be killed on the subsequent occasions. Though generally adequate, this method may fail with spores of certain anaerobes and thermophiles.

Steam under pressure: The principle of the autoclave or steam steriliser is that water boils when its vapour pressure equals that of the surrounding atmosphere. Hence when pressure inside a closed vessel increases, the temperature at which water boils also increases. Saturated steam has penetrative power. When steam comes into contact with a cooler surface it condenses to water and gives up its latent heat to that surface (1600 ml steam at 100 °C and at atmospheric pressure condenses into one ml of water at 100 °C and releases 518 calories of heat). The large reduction in volume sucks in more steam to the area and the process continues till the temperature of that surface is raised to that of the steam. The condensed water ensures moist conditions for killing the microbes present.

Sterilisation by steam under pressure is carried out at temperatures between 108 °C and 147 °C. By using the appropriate temperature and time, a variety of materials such as dressings, instruments, laboratory ware, media and pharmaceutical products can be sterilised. Aqueous solutions are sterilised between 108 °C and 126 °C. Heat is conducted through the walls of the sealed containers until the temperature of the fluid inside is the same as that of the steam outside.

Several types of steam sterilisers are in use:

1. laboratory autoclaves,
2. hospital dressing sterilisers,
3. bowl and instrument sterilisers, and
4. rapid cooling sterilisers.

Even the domestic pressure cooker can be used as a steriliser.

In its simplest form, the laboratory autoclave consists of a vertical or horizontal cylinder of gunmetal or stainless steel, in a supporting sheet iron case. The lid or door is fastened by screw clamps and made airtight by a suitable washer. The autoclave has on its lid or upper side a discharge tap for air and steam, a pressure gauge and a safety valve that can be set to blow off at any desired pressure. Heating is by gas or electricity (Fig. 3.3).

Sufficient water is put in the cylinder, the material to be sterilised is placed on the tray, and the autoclave is heated. The lid is screwed tight with the discharge tap open. The safety valve is adjusted to the required pressure. The steam-air mixture is allowed to escape freely till all the air has been displaced. This can be tested by leading the escaping steam into a pail of water through a rubber tubing. When no more air bubbles come out in the pail the discharge tap is closed. The steam pressure rises inside and when it reaches the desired set level, the safety valve opens and the excess steam escapes. From this point, the holding period is calculated. When the holding period is over, the heater is turned off and the autoclave allowed to cool till the pressure gauge indicates that the pressure inside is equal to the atmospheric pressure. The discharge tap is opened slowly and air is let into the autoclave. If the tap is opened when the pressure inside is high, liquid media will

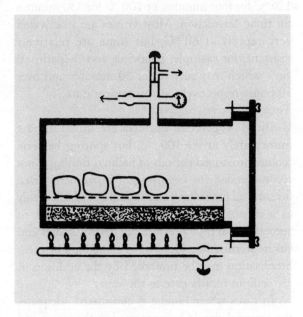

Fig. 3.3 A simple autoclave

tend to boil violently and spill from the container and sometimes an explosion may occur. If opened after the pressure inside has fallen below atmospheric pressure, an excessive amount of water would have evaporated and lost from the media.

The defects in this type of autoclave are:

1. The method of air discharge is inefficient, and it is difficult to decide when the discharge is complete. If the air is not completely removed, the desired temperature will not be attained.
2. There is no facility for drying the load after sterilisation and before taking it out.

The domestic pressure cooker serves as a miniature autoclave and may be used for sterilising small articles in clinics and similar establishments.

A wide variety of autoclaves have been manufactured incorporating various devices for overcoming these defects and other difficulties in working.

Sterilisation control: For determining the efficacy of moist heat sterilisation, spores of *Bacillus stearothermophilus* are used as the test organism. This is a thermophilic organism with an optimum growth temperature of 55–60 °C and its spores

Table 3.1 Recommended temperature and duration for heat sterilisation

Method	Temperature (°C)	Holding time (in minutes)
Autoclave	121	15
	126	10
	134	3
Hot air oven	160	45
	170	18
	180	7.5
	190	1.5

require an exposure of 12 minutes at 121 °C to be killed. Paper strips impregnated with 10^6 spores are dried at room temperature and placed in paper envelopes. These envelopes are inserted in different parts of the load. After sterilisation, the strips are inoculated into a suitable recovering medium and incubated for sterility test at 55 °C for five days.

Chemical indicators, autoclave tapes and thermocouples may also be used instead.

FILTRATION

Filtration helps to remove bacteria from heat labile liquids such as sera and solutions of sugars or antibiotics used for preparation of culture media. As viruses pass through ordinary filters, filtration can be used to obtain bacteria-free filtrates of clinical samples for virus isolation. Filter discs also help to concentrate bacteria from liquids as for example in testing water samples for cholera vibrios or typhoid bacilli. Bacterial toxins can be obtained by passing cultures through filters.

The following types of filters have been used.

Candle filters: These are manufactured in different grades of porosity and have been used widely for purification of water for industrial and drinking purposes. They are of two types: (a) Unglazed ceramic filters (for example, Chamberland and Doulton filter; (b) Diatomaceous earth filters (for example, Berkefeld and Mandler filters).

Asbestos filters are disposable, single-use discs. They have high adsorbing capacity and tend to alkalinise filtered liquids. The carcinogenic potential of asbestos has discouraged their use. Examples are Seitz and Sterimat filters.

Sintered glass filters are prepared by heat-fusing finely powdered glass particles of graded sizes. They have low absorptive property and can be cleaned easily but are brittle and expensive.

Membrane filters made of cellulose esters or other polymers have largely replaced other types of filters. They are routinely used in water purification and analysis, sterilisation and sterility testing, and for the preparation of solutions for parenteral use. They come in a wide range of average pore diameters (APD), the 0.22 mm size being most widely used for sterilisation.

RADIATION

Two types of radiation are used for sterilisation, nonionising and ionising. Infrared and ultraviolet rays are of the nonionising low energy type, while gamma rays and high energy electrons are the high energy ionising type.

Nonionising radiation: Here electromagnetic rays with wavelengths longer than those of visible light are used. These are to a large extent absorbed as heat. Hence infrared radiation can be considered as a form of hot air sterilisation. Infrared radiation is used for rapid mass sterilisation of prepacked items such as syringes and catheters. Ultraviolet radiation is used for disinfecting enclosed areas such as entryways, operation theatres and laboratories.

Ionising radiation: X-rays, gamma rays and cosmic rays are highly lethal to DNA and other vital constituents. They have very high penetrative power. Since there is no appreciable increase in temperature in this method, it is referred to as cold sterilisation. Commercial plants use gamma radiation for sterilising items like plastics, syringes, swabs, catheters, animal feeds, cardboard, oils, greases, fabrics and metal foils.

High energy electron radiation as a method of sterilisation is not widely used in medicine.

ULTRASONIC AND SONIC VIBRATION

Ultrasonic and sonic waves are credited with bactericidal powers but the results have been variable. Microorganisms vary in their sensitivity to them and survivors have been found after such treatment. Hence this method is of no practical value in sterilisation and disinfection.

CHEMICAL AGENTS

Several chemical agents are used as antiseptics and disinfectants. However little is known about the mechanism of action of many of these agents. An ideal antiseptic or disinfectant should :

- have a wide spectrum of activity and must be effective against all microorganisms, that is, bacteria including spores, viruses, protozoa and fungi;
- be active in the presence of organic matter;
- be effective in acid as well as alkaline media;
- have speedy action;
- have high penetrating power;
- be stable;
- be compatible with other antiseptics and disinfectants;
- not corrode metals;
- not cause local irritation or sensitisation;
- not interfere with healing;
- not be toxic if absorbed into circulation;
- be cheap and easily available; and be safe and easy to use.

Such an ideal chemical is yet to be found.

The factors that determine the potency of disinfectants are:

- concentration of the substance;
- time of action;
- pH of the medium;
- temperature;
- nature of the organisms; and
- presence of extraneous material;

Chemical agents act in various ways. The main modes of action are:

1. protein coagulation;
2. disruption of cell membrane resulting in exposure, damage or loss of the contents;
3. removal of free sulphydryl groups essential for the functioning of the enzymes; and
4. substrate competition: A compound resembling the essential substrate of the enzyme diverts or misleads the enzymes necessary for the metabolism of the cell and causes cell death.

ALCOHOLS

Ethyl alcohol (ethanol) and isopropyl alcohol are the most frequently used. They are used mainly as skin antiseptics and act by denaturing bacterial proteins. They have no action on spores. To be effective, they must be used at a concentration of 60–90 per cent in water. Protein slows its action whereas 1% mineral acid or alkali enhances the action. Isopropyl alcohol is preferred as it is a better fat solvent, more bactericidal and less volatile. It is used for the disinfection of clinical thermometers.

Methyl alcohol is effective against fungal spores and is used for treating cabinets and incubators affected by them. The insides of the chambers are wiped with liberal amounts of methanol. A pad moistened with methanol and a dish of water (to ensure high humidity) are kept inside, and the incubator is left at working temperature for several hours. Methyl alcohol vapour is toxic and inflammable.

ALDEHYDES

Formaldehyde is active against the amino group in the protein molecule. In aqueous solutions, it is markedly bactericidal and sporicidal and also has a lethal effect on viruses. It is used to preserve anatomical specimens, and for destroying anthrax spores in hair and wool; 10 % formalin containing 0.5% sodium tetraborate is used to sterilise clean metal instruments.

Formaldehyde gas is used for sterilising instruments and heat sensitive catheters and for fumigating wards, sick rooms and laboratories. Under properly controlled conditions, clothing, bedding, furniture and books can be satisfactorily disinfected.

The gas is irritant and toxic when inhaled. Surfaces which have been disinfected by this agent may give off an irritant vapour for some time after disinfection. This can be nullified by exposure to ammonia vapour after disinfection has been completed.

Glutaraldehyde: This has an action similar to formaldehyde. It is specially effective against tubercle bacilli, fungi and viruses. It is less toxic and irritant to the eyes and skin than formaldehyde. It has no deleterious effect on the cement or lenses of instruments such as cystoscopes and bronchoscopes. It can be safely used to treat corrugated rubber anesthetic tubes and face masks, plastic endotracheal tubes, metal instruments and polythene tubing.

DYES

Two groups of dyes, aniline dyes and acridine dyes are used extensively as skin and wound antiseptics. Both are bacteriostatic in high dilution but are of low bactericidal activity. The aniline dyes in use are brilliant green, malachite green and crystal violet. They are more active against Gram positive organisms than against Gram negative organisms. They have no activity against tubercle bacilli, and hence the use of malachite green in the Lowenstein–Jensen medium. Though they are nonirritant to the tissues and nontoxic, they are considerably inhibited by organic material such as pus. Their lethal effects on bacteria are believed to be due to their reaction with the acid groups in the cell. These dyes are used in the microbiology laboratory as selective agents in culture media.

The acridine dyes are more active against Gram positive organisms than against Gram negative but are not as selective as the aniline dyes. They are affected very little by the presence of organic matter. The more important dyes are proflavine, acriflavine, euflavine and aminacrine. They show no significant differences in potency. If impregnated in gauze, they are slowly released in a moist environment, and hence their advantage and use in clinical medicine. They impair the DNA complexes of the organisms and thus kill or destroy the reproductive capacity of the cell.

HALOGENS

Iodine in aqueous and alcoholic solution has been used widely as a skin disinfectant. It is actively bactericidal, with moderate action against spores. It is active against the tubercle bacteria and viruses. Compounds of iodine with nonionic wetting or surface active agents known as iodophores are claimed to be more active than the aqueous or alcoholic solutions of iodine.

Chlorine and its compounds have been used as disinfectants for many years. Water supplies, swimming pools, food and dairy industries use chlorine for disinfection. Chlorine is used commonly as hypochlorites. Chlorine and hypochlorites are markedly bactericidal. They have a wide spectrum of action against viruses. The organic chloramines are used as antiseptics for dressing wounds.

PHENOLS

These are obtained by distillation of coal tar between temperatures of 170 °C and 270 °C. Lister, the father of antiseptic surgery, first introduced their use in surgery (1865). Since then a wide range of phenolic compounds have been developed as disinfectants. The lethal effect of phenols is due to their capacity to cause cell membrane damage, releasing cell contents and causing lysis. Low concentrations of phenol precipitate proteins. Membrane-bound oxidases and dehydrogenases are inactivated by concentrations of phenol that are rapidly bactericidal for microbes.

Phenol (carbolic acid) is a powerful microbicidal substance. This and other phenolic disinfectants derived from coal tar are widely used as disinfectants for various purposes in hospitals. Lysol and cresol are active against a wide range of organisms. They are not readily inactivated by the presence of organic matter and are thus good general disinfectants. These are toxic to humans. Various proprietary preparations or formulations of phenol are in wide use. The related chlorophenols and chloroxyphenols, though less toxic and irritant, are less active and more readily inactivated by organic matter. Both these groups of substances are relatively inactive against Pseudomonas. Various combinations of these are used in the control of pyogenic cocci in surgical and neonatal units in hospitals. Hexachlorophene is potentially toxic and should be used with care. Chlorhexidine (Hibitane) is a relatively nontoxic skin antiseptic most active against Gram positive organisms and fairly effective against Gram negative ones. Aqueous solutions are used in the treatment of wounds.

GASES

Ethylene oxide: This is a colourless liquid with a boiling point of 10.7 °C, and at normal temperature and pressure is a highly penetrating gas with a sweet ethereal smell. It is highly inflammable and in concentrations in air greater than 3%, highly explosive. By mixing it with inert gases such as carbon dioxide or nitrogen, to a concentration of 10%, its explosive tendency is eliminated.

Its action is due to its alkylating the amino, carboxyl, hydroxyl and sulphydryl groups in protein molecules. In addition, it reacts with DNA and RNA. Its use as a disinfectant presents a potential toxicity to human beings, including mutagenicity and carcinogenicity. It is effective against all types of microorganisms including viruses and spores.

It diffuses through many types of porous materials and readily penetrates some plastics. It is specially used for sterilising heart—lung machines, respirators, sutures, dental equipment, books and clothing. It is unsuitable for fumigating rooms because of its explosive property. It has been successfully used to sterilise a wide range of materials such as glass, metal and paper surfaces, clothing, plastics, soil, some foods and tobacco. It is irritant, and personnel working with it have to take strict precautions.

Formaldehyde gas: This is widely employed for fumigation of operation theatres and other rooms. After sealing the windows and other outlets, formaldehyde gas is generated by adding 150 g of $KMnO_4$ to 280 ml formalin for every 1000 cu. ft (28.3 cu. m) of room volume. The reaction produces considerable heat, and so heat resistant vessels should be used. After starting generation of formaldehyde vapour, the doors should be sealed and left unopened for 48 hours.

Betapropiolactone (BPL): This is a condensation product of ketane and formaldehyde with a boiling point of 163 °C. Though as a gas it has low penetrating power, it is said to be more efficient for fumigating purposes than formaldehyde. It has a rapid biocidal action but unfortunately has carcinogenic activity. For sterilisation of biological products 0.2% BPL is used. It is capable of killing all microorganisms and is very active against viruses.

SURFACE ACTIVE AGENTS

Substances which alter energy relationship at interfaces, producing a reduction of surface or interfacial tension are referred to as surface active agents. They are widely used as wetting agents, detergents and emulsifiers. They are classified into four main groups, anionic, cationic, nonionic and amphoteric. The most important antibacterial agents are the cationic surface active agents. These act on the phosphate groups of the cell membrane and also enter the cell. The membrane loses its semipermeability and the cell proteins are denatured. The cationic compounds in the form of quaternary ammonium compounds are markedly bactericidal, being active against Gram positive organisms and to a lesser extent on Gram negative ones. They have no action on spores, tubercle bacilli and most viruses. The common compounds are acetyl trimethyl ammonium bromide (Cetavlon or cetrimide) and benzalkonium chloride. These are most active at alkaline pH. Acid inactivates them. Organic matter reduces their action and anionic surface active agents, like ordinary soaps, render them inactive. The anionic compounds, e.g., common soap, have moderate action. Soaps prepared from saturated fatty acids (such as coconut oil) are more effective against Gram negative bacilli while those prepared from unsaturated fatty acids (oleic acid) have greater action against Gram positive and Neisseria group of organisms. The amphoteric or ampholytic compounds, known as 'Tego' compounds, are active against a wide range of Gram positive and Gram negative organisms and some viruses. These, however, are not in general use.

METALLIC SALTS

Though all salts have a certain amount of germicidal action depending on their concentration, salts of heavy metals have a greater action. The salts of silver, copper and mercury are used as disinfectants. They are protein coagulants and have the capacity to combine with free sulphydryl groups of cell enzymes, when used at appropriate concentrations.

Mercuric chloride, once used as a disinfectant is highly toxic. The organic compounds, thiomersal, phenyl mercury nitrate and mercurochrome, are less toxic and are used as mild antiseptics and have a marked bacteriostatic, but a weak bactericidal and limited fungicidal action. Silver salts in aqueous solution have a limited use. Copper salts are used as fungicides.

TESTING OF DISINFECTANTS

There is no single reliable test available to determine efficiency of a disinfectant. This is due to the number of parameters which influence disinfectant activity. Traditionally in such tests phenol is taken as the standard. In the Rideal Walker test, suspensions containing equal numbers of typhoid bacilli are submitted to the action of varying concentrations of phenol and of the disinfectant to be tested. The dilution of the test disinfectant which sterilises the suspension in a given time, divided by the corresponding dilution of phenol is stated as the phenol coefficient (Phenol = 1) of the disinfectant. This test does not reflect natural conditions as the bacteria and the disinfectant react directly without any organic matter being present. Modifications have therefore been suggested. In the Chick Martin test, the disinfectant acts in the presence of organic matter (dried yeast or feces). Even this modification falls short of simulating natural conditions. Various other modifications have been introduced, but no test is entirely satisfactory.

Further Reading

Block SS (ed). 1991. *Chemical Disinfection in Hospitals*, 2ⁿᵈ edn. London, Public Health Laboratory Service.
Gardner JF. and MM. Peel 1991. *Introduction to Sterilization and Disinfection*, 2ⁿᵈ edn. Edinburgh: Churchill Livingstone.
Russell AD et al. 1992. *Principles and Practice of Disinfection, Sterilisation and Preservation*. 2ⁿᵈ edn. Oxford: Blackwell Scientific.

4   Culture Media

Bacteria have to be grown *(cultured)* for them to be identified, as only rarely can they be recognised by their morphology alone. The study of bacteria involves the study of bacterial populations rather than of single bacterial cells. In the human and animal bodies, as well as in other natural sources, bacteria occur as mixed populations. By appropriate procedures they have to be grown separately *(isolated)* on *culture media* and obtained as *pure cultures* for study.

Numerous culture media have been devised. The original media used by Louis Pasteur were liquids such as urine or meat broth. Liquid media have many disadvantages. Bacteria growing in liquid media may not exhibit specific characteristics for their identification. It is also difficult to isolate different types of bacteria from mixed populations, using liquid media. However, liquid media have their uses, for example, for obtaining bacterial growth from blood or water when large volumes have to be tested, and for preparing bulk cultures of antigens or vaccines.

While bacteria grow diffusely in liquids, they produce discrete visible growth on solid media. If inoculated in suitable dilutions, bacteria form *colonies*, which are clones of cells originating from a single bacterial cell. On solid media, bacteria have distinct colony morphology and exhibit many other characteristic features such as pigmentation or hemolysis, making identification easy. The earliest solid medium was cooked cut potato used by Robert Koch. Later he introduced *gelatin* to solidify liquid media but it was not satisfactory as gelatin is liquefied at 24 °C and also by many proteolytic bacteria. The use of agar to solidify culture media was suggested by Frau Hesse, the wife of one of the investigators in Koch's laboratory, who had seen her mother using agar for making jellies!

Agar (or agar-agar) is now universally used for preparing solid media. Agar is obtained from some types of seaweeds. Its chief constituent is a long chain polysaccharide. It also contains varying amounts of inorganic salts and small quantities of a protein-like substance. It has virtually no nutritive value and is not affected by the growth of bacteria. Agar is hydrolysed at high temperatures, at high acid or alkaline pH. Its unique property is that it melts at 98 °C and usually sets at 42 °C depending on agar concentration. Approximately 2% agar is employed for solid media. The jellifying property varies in different brands of agar; for example, New Zealand agar has more jellifying capacity than Japanese agar. Agar is manufactured either in long shreds or as powder. There may be variations between different batches of the same brand, apart from the differences due to a different source of agar.

Another almost universal ingredient of common media is *peptone*. It is a complex mixture of partially digested proteins. Its constituents are proteoses, polypeptides and aminoacids, a variety of inorganic salts including phosphates, potassium and magnesium and certain accessory growth factors such as riboflavin. Different brands of peptone show appreciable differences in composition and growth promoting properties. There may be variations between different batches of the same brand.

Special brands of peptone such as neopeptone

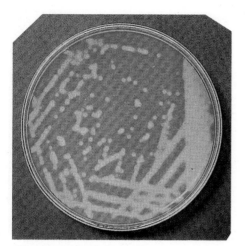

Blood agar: *Strep pyogenes*
showing beta hemolysis

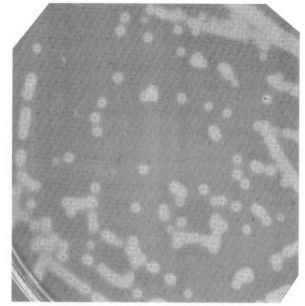

Blood agar: Strep pyogenes magnified to show
small colonies surrounded by zones of clear hemolysis

Blood agar with alpha hemolytic
viridans streptococci

Blood tellurite agar showing black colonies
of diphtheria bacilli

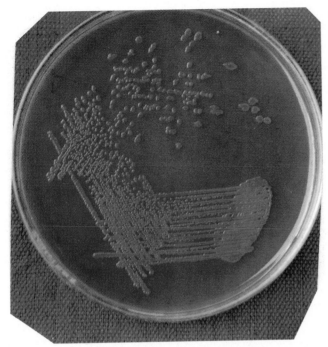

MacConkey agar with smooth, pink colonies
of *Escherichia coli*

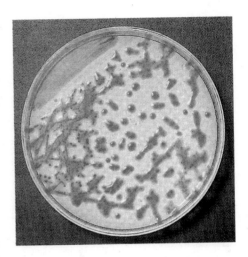

MacConkey agar with large, mucoid
Kleb.pneumoniae colonies

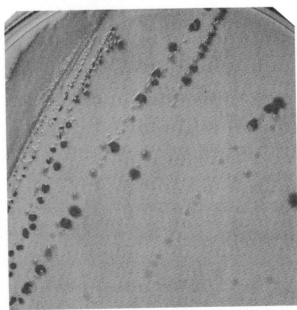

MacConkey agar with colonies
of *E coli* (pink) and *S typhi* (colourless)

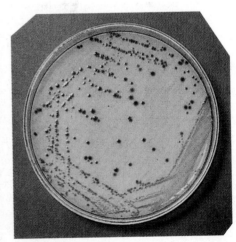

TCBS agar with green colonies
of V parahemolyticus

and proteose peptone are available for special uses. Commercially available peptones or digest broth can be used. Meat extract is also available commercially and is known as Lab-Lemco. Blood, serum and yeast extract are other common ingredients.

TYPES

Media have been classified in many ways:
1. Solid media, liquid media, semisolid media.
2. Simple media, complex media, synthetic or defined media, semidefined media, special media. Special media are further divisible into: enriched media, enrichment media, selective media, indicator or differential media, sugar media, and transport media.
3. Aerobic media, anaerobic media.

Simple media (basal media): An example is nutrient broth. It consists of peptone, meat extract, sodium chloride and water. Nutrient agar, made by adding 2% agar to nutrient broth is the simplest and most common medium in routine diagnostic laboratories. If the concentration of agar is reduced to 0.2–0.5%, semisolid or sloppy agar is obtained which enables motile organisms to spread. Increasing the concentration of agar to 6% prevents spreading or swarming by organisms such as Proteus.

Complex media: These have added ingredients for special purposes or for bringing out certain characteristics or providing special nutrients required for the growth of the bacterium under study.

Synthetic or defined media: These media are prepared from pure chemical substances and the exact composition of the medium is known. These are used for various special studies such as metabolic requirements. Simple peptone water medium, 1% peptone with 0.5% NaCl in water, may be considered a semidefined medium since its composition is approximately known.

Enriched media: In these media, substances such as blood, serum, or egg are added to a basal medium. They are used to grow bacteria which are more exacting in their nutritional needs. Examples are blood agar, chocolate agar and egg media.

Enrichment media: In mixed cultures or in materials containing more than one bacterium, the bacterium to be isolated is often overgrown by the unwanted bacteria. Usually the nonpathogenic or commensal bacteria tend to overgrow the pathogenic ones, for example *S. typhi* being overgrown by *E. coli* in cultures from feces. In such situations, substances which have a stimulating effect on the bacteria to be grown or an inhibitory effect on those to be suppressed are incorporated in the medium. If such substances are added to a liquid medium, the result is an absolute increase in the numbers of the wanted bacterium relative to the other bacteria. Such media are called enrichment media, for example tetrathionate broth where the tetrathionate inhibits coliforms while allowing typhoid-paratyphoid bacilli to grow freely, and Selenite F broth for dysentery bacilli.

Selective media: As in the above case, if the inhibiting substance is added to a solid medium, it enables a greater number of the required bacterium to form colonies than the other bacteria, for example, desoxycholate citrate medium for dysentery bacilli. Such solid media are known as selective media.

Indicator media: These media contain an indicator which changes colour when a bacterium grows in them, for example incorporation of sulphite in Wilson and Blair medium. *S. typhi* reduces sulphite to sulphide in the presence of glucose and the colonies of *S. typhi* have a black metallic sheen. Potassium tellurite in McLeod's medium is reduced to metallic tellurium by the diphtheria bacillus to produce black colonies.

Differential media: A medium which has substances incorporated in it, enabling it to bring out differing characteristics of bacteria and thus helping to distinguish between them, is called a differential medium. For example, MacConkey's medium which consists of peptone, lactose, agar, neutral red and taurocholate shows up lactose fermenters as pink colonies, while nonlactose fermenters are colourless or pale. This may also be termed indicator medium.

Some of these terms for media are interchangeable. For example, the blood agar medium is an enriched medium but bacteria lysing red cells show a clearing around their colonies. Thus, it is an indicator medium as well. There are many special media for demonstrating particular characteristics, like Nagler's medium which enables us to view lecithinase activity.

Sugar media: The term 'sugar' in microbiology denotes any fermentable substance. They may be:

1. Monosaccharides – a) pentoses, e.g., arabinose, xylose, b) hexoses, e.g., dextrose, mannose
2. Disaccharides, e.g., saccharose, lactose
3. Polysaccharides, e.g., starch, inulin
4. Trisaccharides, e.g., raffinose
5. Alcohols, e.g., glycerol, sorbitol
6. Glucosides, e.g., salicin, aesculin
7. Noncarbohydrate substances, e.g., inositol.

The usual sugar media consist of 1% of the sugar in peptone water along with an appropriate indicator. A small tube (Durham's tube) is kept inverted in the sugar tube to detect gas production. For organisms which are exacting in their growth requirements (for example pneumococci), Hiss' serum sugars are used. They contain 3% serum.

Transport media: In the case of delicate organisms (like gonococci) which may not survive the time taken for transporting the specimen to the laboratory or may be overgrown by nonpathogens (such as dysentery or cholera organisms in feces), special media are devised for transporting the specimens. These are termed transport media, for example, Stuart's medium—a non-nutrient soft agar gel containing a reducing agent to prevent oxidation, and charcoal to neutralise certain bacterial inhibitors—for gonococci, and buffered glycerol saline for enteric bacilli.

Anaerobic media: These media are used to grow anaerobic organisms, for example, Robertson's cooked meat medium.

Various media to test special properties like urease production, and composite media for simultaneous demonstration of different features have been devised. They are dealt with in the appropriate chapters.

For identifying prepared media, a colour code is usually adopted. This depends on the laboratory or group of laboratories. One colour or a mixture of colours is used on the cotton stopper, or colour paints are used on the caps.

Culture media used to be prepared in laboratories themselves, starting with basic ingredients. Not only was this laborious but it also led to considerable batch variation in the quality of media. With the ready availability of commercial dehydrated culture media, the process of media making has become simpler and its quality more uniform.

Further Reading

Atlas PM and LC Parks 1999. *Microbiological Media*. Maryland: CRC Press.

Cruickshank R et al. 1975. *Medical Microbilology* Vol. II, *The Practice of Medical Microbiology*, 12th edn. London: Churchill Livingstone.

Difco Manual of Dehydrated Culture Media and Reagents. 1977. 9th edn. Michigan: Difco Laboratories.

Oxoid Manual 1976. 3rd edn. Basingstoke: Oxoid Ltd.

Murray PR et al 1999. *Manual of Clinical Microbiology*. 7th edn. Washington DC: ASM Press.

Culture Methods

Culture methods employed depend on the purpose for which they are intended. In the clinical laboratory, the indications for culture are mainly to:

1. isolate bacteria in pure culture;
2. demonstrate their properties;
3. obtain sufficient growth for preparation of antigens and for other tests;
4. type isolates by methods such as bacteriophage and bacteriocin susceptibility;
5. determine sensitivity to antibiotics;
6. estimate viable counts; and
7. maintain stock cultures.

The methods of culture used ordinarily in the laboratory are the streak, lawn, stroke, stab, pour plate and liquid cultures. Special methods are employed for culturing anaerobic bacteria.

The *streak culture* (surface plating) method is routinely employed for the isolation of bacteria in pure culture from clinical specimens. A platinum loop is charged with the specimen to be cultured. Owing to the high cost of platinum, loops for routine work are made of Nichrome resistance wire (24 SWG size). One loopful of the specimen is transferred onto the surface of a well dried plate, on which it is spread over a small area at the periphery. The inoculum is then distributed thinly over the plate by streaking it with the loop in a series of parallel lines, in different segments of the plate. The loop should be flamed and cooled between the different sets of streaks. On incubation, growth may be confluent at the site of original inoculation, but becomes progressively thinner, and well separated colonies are obtained over the final series of streaks.

The *lawn* or *carpet culture* provides a uniform surface growth of the bacterium and is useful for bacteriophage typing and antibiotic sensitivity testing (disc method). It may also be employed when a large amount of growth is required on solid media as, for instance, in the preparation of bacterial antigens and vaccines. Lawn cultures are prepared by flooding the surface of the plate with a liquid culture or suspension of the bacterium, pipetting off the excess inoculum and incubating the plate. Alternatively, the surface of the plate may be inoculated by applying a swab soaked in the bacterial culture or suspension.

The *stroke culture* is made in tubes containing agar *slope (slant)* and is employed for providing a pure growth of the bacterium for slide agglutination and other diagnostic tests.

Stab cultures are prepared by puncturing a suitable medium such as nutrient gelatin or glucose agar with a long, straight, charged wire. The medium is allowed to set, with the tube in the upright position, providing a flat surface at the top of the medium. Stab cultures are employed mainly for demonstration of gelatin liquefaction and oxygen requirement of the bacterium under study. They are also used in the maintenance of stock cultures.

For preparing *pour plate culture*, tubes containing 15 ml of the agar medium are melted and left to cool in a water bath at 45–50 °C. Appropriate dilutions of the inoculum (of 1 ml) are added to the molten agar, mixed well and the contents of the tubes poured into sterile Petri dishes and allowed to set. After incubatioin, colonies will be seen well distributed throughout the depth of the medium and can be enumerated using colony counters. The pour plate method gives an estimate of the viable bacterial count in a suspension and is the recommended method for quantitative urine cultures.

In the *sweep plate* method, the edges of the Petri dishes containing the culture medium are rubbed over the fabric, with the medium facing it. The dust particles stirred up from the cloth settle on the culture medium, and colonies develop on incubation. They can be counted and estimates made.

Liquid cultures in tubes, bottles or flasks may be inoculated by touching with a charged loop or by adding the inoculum with pipettes or syringes. Large inocula can be employed in liquid cultures and hence this method is adopted for blood culture and for sterility tests, where the concentration of bacteria in the inocula is expected to be small. Liquid cultures are preferable for inocula containing antibiotics and other inhibitory substances, as these are rendered ineffective by dilution in the medium. Liquid cultures are also preferred when large yields are desired, the yield being enhanced by agitation, aeration, addition of nutrients and removal of toxic metabolites (continuous culture methods). The major disadvantage of liquid culture is that it does not provide a pure culture from mixed inocula.

ANAEROBIC CULTURE METHODS

Anaerobic bacteria differ in their requirement of and sensitivity to oxygen. Some, such as *Cl. histolyticum*, are aerotolerant and may produce some growth on the surface of aerobic plates, while others such as *Cl. tetani*, are strict anaerobes and form surface growth only if the oxygen tension is less than 2 mmHg. A number of methods have been described for achieving anaerobiosis, by exclusion of oxygen or production of a vacuum, displacement of oxygen with other gases, absorption of oxygen by chemical or biological means, and reduction of oxygen.

1. Cultivation in vacuum was attempted by incubating cultures in a vacuum desiccator, but the method is unsatisfactory as some oxygen is always left behind. Fluid cultures may boil over and the media may get detached from the plates in the vacuum produced. This method is not in use now.

2. Displacement of oxygen with gases such as hydrogen, nitrogen, helium or carbon dioxide is sometimes employed, but this method rarely produces complete anaerobiosis. A popular, but ineffective method is the candle jar. Here inoculated plates are placed inside a large airtight container and a lighted candle kept in it before the lid is sealed. The burning candle is expected to use up all the oxygen inside before it is extinguished, but some oxygen is always left behind. The candle jar provides a concentration of carbon dioxide which stimulates the growth of most bacteria.

3. In the chemical or biological method, alkaline pyrogallol absorbs oxygen. This method, first introduced by Buchner (1888), has been employed with different modifications for providing anaerobiosis. Pyrogallic acid added to a solution of sodium hydroxide in a large test tube placed inside an airtight jar provides anaerobiosis but a small amount of carbon monoxide, which is formed during the reaction, may be inhibitory to some bacteria. The method has been applied to single tube and plate cultures. The Spray anaerobic dish is a glass dish with its bottom partitioned into two halves, the top accommodating half of a Petri dish carrying the medium. Pyrogallic acid and sodium hydroxide are placed in the separate halves at the bottom of the dish. The inoculated culture plate is inverted on the top of the dish and is sealed completely. The dish is then rocked to mix the reagents, producing anaerobiosis. The anaerobic dish is not in use now.

A simple modification consists of a Petri dish, between the two halves of which is inserted a metal disc of slightly larger diameter, with a hole in the centre. The metal disc is attached to the bottom half of the Petri dish with plasticine. Through the central hole a few pellets of sodium hydroxide and 10 ml of a 10% solution of pyrogallic acid are added. The inoculated half of the Petri dish is then inverted on the metal disc and sealed tightly.

The method in common use employs a disc of filter paper having the same diameter as a Petri dish. It is placed on top of one half of the dish and a mixture of pyrogallol and sodium carbonate, in dry powder form, is spread on it. The inoculated plate is inverted over the filter paper and sealed tight with molten wax. The dry pyrogallol mixture is activated by the moisture within the closed system, and complete anaerobiosis develops within about two hours.

Instead of alkaline pyrogallol, anaerobiosis has been produced within jars with a mixture of chromium and sulphuric acid (Rosenthal method) or with yellow phosphorous.

Absorption of oxygen from small closed systems has been attempted by incubation along with aerobic bacteria, germinating seeds or

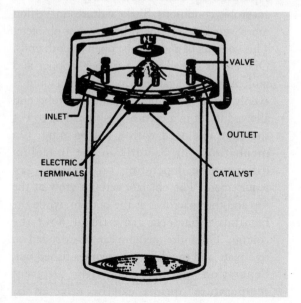

Fig. 5.1 McIntosh–Fildes jar

chopped vegetables. Anaerobiosis produced by such biological methods is slow and ineffective.

The most reliable and widely used anaerobic method is the *McIntosh–Fildes'* anaerobic jar (Fig. 5.1). It consists of a stout glass or metal jar with a metal lid which can be clamped air tight with a screw. The lid has two tubes with taps, one acting as the gas inlet and the other as the outlet. The lid also has two terminals which can be connected to an electrical supply. Leading from the terminals and suspended by stout wires on the underside of the lid is a small grooved porcelain spool around which is wrapped a layer of palladinised asbestos. Inoculated culture plates are placed inside the jar, with the medium in the bottom half of the plates, and the lid clamped tight. The outlet tube is connected to a vacuum pump and the air inside is evacuated. The outlet tap is then closed and the inlet tube connected to a hydrogen supply. After the jar is filled with hydrogen, the electric terminals are connected to a current supply so that the palladinised asbestos is heated. This acts as a catalyst for the combination of hydrogen with the residual oxygen present in the jar. This method ensures complete anaerobiosis but carries the risk of explosion, which may rarely occur. This risk can be eliminated by modification of the catalyst. Alumina pellets coated with palladium in a gauze sachet suspended from the lid of the jar act as a catalyst at room temperature, as long as the sachet is kept dry.

The *Gaspak* is now the method of choice for preparing anaerobic jars. The Gaspak is commercially available as a disposable envelope, containing chemicals which generate hydrogen and carbon dioxide on the addition of water. After the inoculated plates are kept in the jar, the Gaspak envelope, with water added, is placed inside and the lid screwed tight. Hydrogen and carbon dioxide are liberated and the presence of a cold catalyst in the envelope permits the combination of hydrogen and oxygen to produce an anaerobic environment. The Gaspak is simple and effective, eliminating the need for drawing a vacuum and adding hydrogen.

An indicator should be employed for verifying the anaerobic condition in the jars. Reduced methylene blue is generally used for this purpose. It remains colourless anaerobically but turns blue on exposure to oxygen.

4. Reduction of oxygen in the medium is achieved by the use of various reducing agents, including 1% glucose, 0.1% thioglycolate, 0.1% ascorbic acid and 0.05% cysteine. Broth is an easily prepared anaerobic medium into which pieces of red hot metallic iron are introduced. It is then layered over with sterile vaseline. Broth containing fresh animal tissue, such as rabbit kidney, spleen, testes or heart (Smith–Noguchi medium), supports the growth of many anaerobes.

Thioglycolate broth with hemin and vitamin K is an enriched liquid medium for culturing anaerobic and microaerophilic bacteria. Addition of a small quantity of agar enhances the anaerobic capacity of the medium by slowing the diffusion of oxygen in it.

Robertson's cooked meat medium is probably the most widely used fluid medium for the culture of anaerobes. It consists of fat-free minced cooked meat in broth, with a layer of sterile vaseline over it. It permits the growth of even strict anaerobes and indicates their saccharolytic or proteolytic activities, by the meat being turned red or black, respectively.

For fastidious anaerobes, particularly for quantitative cultures, pre-reduced media and an anaerobic chamber ('glove box') may be used. The anaerobic chamber is an airtight, glass-fronted cabinet filled with inert gas, with an entry lock for the introduction and removal of materials, and gloves for the hands.

METHODS OF ISOLATING PURE CULTURES

The following methods may be employed for isolating pure cultures of bacteria from mixtures:

1. Surface plating is the method routinely employed in clinical bacteriology and enables the isolation of distinct colonies which may be picked out, if necessary for further purification and study.

2. Enrichment, selective and indicator media are widely used for the isolation of pathogens from specimens such as feces, with varied flora.

3. Pure cultures may be obtained by pretreatment of specimens with appropriate bactericidal substances which destroy the unwanted bacteria. This method is the standard practice for the isolation of tubercle bacilli from sputum and other clinical specimens, by treatment with alkali, acid or other substances to which most commensals are susceptible but tubercle bacilli are resistant.

4. Obligate aerobes and anaerobes may be separated by cultivation under aerobic or anaerobic conditions. Shake cultures in Veillon tubes were in use formerly but are now obsolete. This consists of a glass tube open at both ends. One end is closed with a rubber stopper and molten glucose agar in which the inoculum is evenly dispersed is poured into the tube and allowed to set in a vertical position. The top of the tube is closed with a cotton plug. On incubation, the bacteria in the inoculum differentiate depending on their oxygen requirement. The obligate aerobes grow at the top and the anaerobes at the bottom, while the facultative bacteria grow throughout the column. The entire medium can be extruded on to a plate and the different colonies fished out.

5. Separation of bacteria with different temperature optima can be effected by incubation at different temperatures. Only

thermophilic bacteria grow at 60 °C. A mixture containing *N. meningitidis* and *N. catarrhalis* can be purified by incubation at 22 °C when only the latter grows.

6. By heating a mixture containing vegetative and spore forming bacteria, at 80 °C the former can be eliminated. This method is useful for the isolation of tetanus bacilli from dust and similar sources.

7. Separation of motile from nonmotile bacteria can be effected using *Craigie's tube*. This consists of a tube of semisolid agar, with a narrow tube open at both ends placed in the centre of the medium in such a way that it projects above the level of the medium. The mixture is inoculated into the central tube. On incubation, the motile bacteria alone traverse the agar and appear at the top of the medium outside the central tube.

A U-tube also serves the same purpose, inoculation being performed in one limb and the subculture taken from the other. This method can also be used to obtain phase variants in Salmonella species.

8. Pathogenic bacteria may be isolated from mixtures by inoculation into appropriate animals. Anthrax bacilli can be distinguished from other aerobic sporulating bacilli by inoculation into mice or guinea pigs. Anthrax bacilli produce a fatal septicemia and may be cultured pure from the heart blood.

9. Bacteria of differing sizes may be separated by the use of selective filters. Filters are widely used for separating viruses from bacteria.

Further Reading

Collee JG et al. 1996. *Practical Medical Microbiology*. 4th edn. Edinburgh: Churchill Livingstone.

Murray PR et al. 1999. *Manual of Clinical Microbiology*. 7th edn. Washington, DC: American Society of Microbiology.

Identification of Bacteria

Once a bacterium has been obtained in pure culture, it has to be identified. The following characteristics have to be studied in the process.

MORPHOLOGY

The morphology of the bacterium depends on a number of factors such as the strain studied, nature of the culture medium, temperature and time of incubation, age of the culture and the number of subcultures it has undergone. The characteristics noted are shape, size, arrangement, motility, flagella, spores and capsules. All these cannot be made out in a single medium. The shape may be spherical, filamentous, rod shaped, comma shaped or spiral. The axis of the organism may be straight or curved. The length and breadth may vary. The sides of the organism may be parallel, convex, concave or irregular. The ends may be cut straight, rounded or tapering. Considerable variations in shape and size leading to club, navicular and swollen or shadow or giant forms may be seen. They may be arranged singly, in pairs, in tetrads or in packets of eight, or in chains, short or long, in the case of cocci; bacilli may be arranged at random, in short or long chains, in Chinese letter patterns, as palisades or in bundles; vibrios may be single or in S or spiral forms. They may be nonmotile, sluggishly motile, actively motile or may exhibit darting motility. They may be without flagella, that is atrichate, or monotrichate, lophotrichate, amphitrichate or peritrichate. The spores, when present may be oval or spherical or ellipsoidal and may be of the same width or wider than that of the bacillary body. The spores may be equatorial, subterminal or terminal. Capsules may or may not be present. Hanging drop preparations, dark ground illumination, phase contrast or electron microscopy, all help in these studies.

STAINING REACTIONS

The age of the culture is important. In older cultures, staining characteristics either vary or are not brought out well. Simple stains bring out the morphology best. Differential and special stains are necessary to bring out characteristics like flagella, capsules, spores and metachromatic granules. The Gram stain divides bacteria into Gram positive and Gram negative; the Ziehl–Neelsen stain into acid fast and non–acid fast. The fluorescent antibody technique enables one to identify them according to their surface antigens.

The study of morphology and staining characteristics helps in preliminary identification of the isolate.

CULTURAL CHARACTERISTICS

These provide additional information for the identification of the bacterium. The characteristics revealed in different types of media are noted. While studying colonies on solid media, the following features are noted:

1. shape—circular, irregular, or rhizoid;
2. size in millimetres;
3. elevation—effuse, elevated, convex, concave, umbonate or umbilicate;
4. margins—bevelled or otherwise;
5. surface—smooth, wavy, rough, granular, papillate or glistening;

6. edges—entire, undulate, crenated, fimbriate or curled;
7. colour;
8. structure—opaque, translucent or transparent;
9. consistency—membranous, friable, butyrous or viscid;
10. emulsifiability; and
11. whether they are differentiated into a central and a peripheral portion.

In a stroke culture, note

1. the degree of growth—scanty, moderate, or profuse;
2. their nature—discrete or confluent, filiform, spreading or rhizoid;
3. their elevation, surface, edges, colour, structure, odour, emulsifiability, consistency and changes in the medium.

In a fluid medium, the degree of growth, presence of turbidity and its nature, presence of deposit and its character, nature of surface growth such as pellicle and its quality and ease of disintegration, and odour are noted.

RESISTANCE

The resistance of the organism to heat and to disinfectants is tested, both for vegetative and spore forms. The resistance of *S. faecalis* heat at 60 °C for half an hour and of clostridial spores to boiling for various periods are examples. Resistance to antibiotic and chemotherapeutic agents and bacteriocins would also help in differentiation and identification.

METABOLISM

The requirements of oxygen, the need for carbon dioxide, the capacity to form pigments, and the production of hemolysis help in classification.

FERMENTATION AND OTHER BIOCHEMICAL PROPERTIES

The more important and widely used tests are described below:

1. **Sugar fermentation:** This is tested in sugar media. Acid production is shown by change in the colour of the medium to pink or red, and the gas produced collects in Durham's tube.

2. **Litmus milk:** There may be no change in the medium, or acid or alkali may be produced; clotting of milk, peptonisation or saponification may occur. The clot may be disrupted by the gas produced (stormy fermentation).

3. **Indole production:** This is tested in a peptone water culture after 48 or 96 hours incubation at 37 °C. This test demonstrates the production of indole from tryptophane. Add 0.5 ml Kovac's reagent and shake gently. Red colour indicates a positive reaction. Kovac's reagent consists of

Paradimethylaminobenzaldehyde	10 g
Amyl or isoamyl alcohol	150 ml
Concentrated HCl	50 ml

This is prepared in small quantities and stored in the refrigerator.

4. **Methyl red test (MR):** This test is employed to detect the production of acid during the fermentation of glucose and the maintenance of a pH below 4.5 in an old culture. Five drops of 0.04% solution of methyl red are added to the culture in glucose phosphate medium which had been incubated at 30 °C for five days, mixed well and read at once. Red colour is positive while yellow signifies a negative test.

5. **Voges–Proskauer test (VP):** This test depends on the production of acetyl methylcarbinol from pyruvic acid, as an intermediate stage in its conversion to 2:3 butylene glycol. In the presence of alkali and atmospheric oxygen, the small amount of acetyl methyl carbinol present in the medium is oxidised to diacetyl which reacts with the peptone of the broth to give a red colour.

The test is performed by adding 0.6 ml of a 5% solution of α-naphthol in ethanol and 0.2 ml of 40% KOH to one ml of a glucose phosphate medium culture of the organism incubated at 30 °C for five days or 37 °C for 48 hours. In a positive reaction, a pink colour appears in 2–5 minutes, deepening to magenta or crimson in half an hour. In a negative reaction, it remains colourless for half an hour. Traces of pink colouration should be ignored.

6. Citrate utilisation: Koser's citrate medium has citrate as the sole source of carbon. Ability to use this substance is indicated by the production of turbidity in the medium.

Indole, MR, VP and citrate tests are very useful in the identification and classification of enteric Gram negative bacteria. These tests are commonly referred to by the sigla 'IMViC' tests.

7. Nitrate reduction: This is tested after growing the bacterium for five days at 37 °C in a broth containing 1% KNO_3. The test reagent consists of a mixture of equal volumes of solutions of sulphanilic acid and α-naphthylamine in 5 Nα acetic acid mixed just before use. 0.1 ml of the test reagent is added to the culture. A red colour developing within a few minutes siginifies a positive reaction, while absence of colour indicates a negative reaction. This is a test for the presence of the enzyme nitrate reductase which reduces nitrate to nitrite.

8. Production of ammonia: To a peptone water culture grown for five days at 37 °C, Nessler's reagent is added. Brown colour is positive and faint yellow colour negative.

9. Urease test: This test is done in Christensen's urease medium. Inoculate the slope heavily and incubate at 37 °C. Examine after four hours and after overnight incubation. The test should not be considered negative till after four days of incubation. Urease positive cultures produce a purple pink colour. Urease producing bacteria reduce urea to ammonia which is responsible for the colour.

10. Hydrogen sulphide production: Some organisms decompose sulphur-containing aminoacids producing H_2S among the products. When cultured in media containing lead acetate, they turn them black or brown. Instead of lead acetate, ferric ammonium citrate or ferrous acetate can be used. The organisms can be grown in culture tubes. Between the cotton plug and the tube insert a filter paper strip soaked in 10% lead acetate solution and dried. Browning of the paper indicates H_2S production.

11. Methylene blue reduction: One drop of 1% aqueous methylene blue is added to the broth culture, and incubated at 37 °C. Complete decolourisation is strongly positive, while green colour is weakly positive.

12. Catalase production: Place a loopful H_2O_2 on colonies on nutrient agar. Prompt effervescence indicates catalase production. Culture media containing blood are unsuitable for the test as blood contains catalase.

13. Oxidase reaction: This reaction is due to a cytochrome oxidase which catalyses oxidation of reduced cytochrome by oxygen. A 1.0–1.5% solution of tetramethyl p-phenylene diamine hydrochloride is poured over the colonies. Oxidase positive colonies become maroon, purple and black in 10–30 minutes. The test can also be done by Kovac's method. A strip of filter paper, soaked in the oxidase reagent is placed in a Petri dish and the colony to be tested is smeared on the paper in a line about 5 mm long. In a reaction the smeared area turns dark in 10 seconds. The solution should be freshly prepared.

14. Egg yolk reaction: Organisms producing lecithinase (for example, *Cl. perfringens*) when grown on a solid egg yolk medium, form colonies surrounded by a zone of clearing.

15. Growth in presence of KCN: Buffered liquid medium containing KCN in a final concentration of about 1/13,000 is used to identify some KCN tolerant enteric bacilli.

16. Composite media are being used increasingly for the identification of isolates. These are convenient and economical, as a single composite medium indicates different properties of the bacterium which otherwise would have required the use of many separate media. A popular composite medium is the Triple Sugar Iron (TSI) medium which indicates whether a bacterium ferments glucose only, or lactose and sucrose also, with or without gas formation, besides indicating H_2S production as well. The medium is distributed in tubes, with a butt and slant. After inoculation, if the slant remains red and the butt becomes yellow, all the sugars – glucose, lactose and sucrose – are fermented. Bubbles in the butt indicate gas production and blackening of the medium shows formation of H_2S. The TSI medium facilitates preliminary identification of Gram negative bacilli.

Other tests such as fermentation of organic acids, oxidation of gluconate, aminoacid decarboxylation, and hydrolysis of sodium hippurate are sometimes employed. With increasing knowledge of the metabolic processes in the growth of various bacteria, the number of tests too is on the increase. Special manuals have to be consulted for the details and utility of these tests.

Antigenic Structure: By using specific sera we can identify organisms by agglutination or other suitable serological reactions. Immunofluorescence test is useful in some cases.

Bacteriophage and bacteriocin typing: These enable intraspecies typing of some bacteria. Pathogenicity: Pathogenicity tests by inoculation of the test organism into laboratory animals like the guinea pig, rabbit, rat and mouse by intradermal, subcutaneous, intramuscular, intraperitoneal, intracerebral or intravenous, or by oral or nasal spray were common procedures for identification of isolates in the past. They are rarely used now because simpler in vitro tests are available.

RAPID IDENTIFICATION METHODS

While classical phenotypic characterisation of isolates takes days, automated methods are now available which only take hours. Identification is simplified by the detection of specific enzymes, toxins, antigens or metabolic end products of the isolates. For example, many obligate anaerobes can be identified rapidly by gas liquid chromatography of the short chain fatty acids produced by them during glucose fermentation. Molecular methods such as polymerase chain reaction and other amplification procedures coupled with nucleic acid probes carrying specific DNA or RNA base sequences are now widely used for identifying microbes.

Further Reading

Cowan ST ed. 1978. *Dictionary of Medical Taxonomy.* London: Oxford University Press.
Cowan ST and KJ Steel 1965. *Manual for the Identification of Medical Bacteria.* London: Cambridge University Press.
Finegold SM and EJ Baron 1986. *Bailey and Scott's Diagnostic Bacteriology.* 7th edn St.Louis: CV Mosby.
Goodfellow M and RG Board ed. 1980. *Microbiological Classification and Identification.* London: Academic Press.
Murray P et al. eds. 1999. *Manual of Clinical Microbiology.* 7th edn. Washington: American Society for Microbiology.

Bacterial Taxonomy

Bacterial taxonomy or systematics comprises three components:

1. Classification, or the orderly arrangement of units. A group of units is called a *taxon* (pl. *taxa*), irrespective of its hierarchic level.
2. Identification of an unknown with a defined and named unit, and
3. Nomenclature, or the naming of units.

For purposes of classification, it is necessary to determine as many characteristics of bacteria as possible. Such characteristics may be weighted, greater importance being given to some than to others, or they may be assigned equal importance, depending on the method of classification. On the contrary, for purposes of identifying bacterial isolates, it is important to devise a key using the minimum number of important characteristics which can be easily tested.

Bacterial classification: The first attempts at bacterial classification (Mueller 1786; Ehrenberg 1838) were made when little was known about bacteria. Haeckel (1866) classified all unicellular organisms as Protista. Cohn (1872–75) made a morphological classification, integrating bacteria with the blue-green algae in the class Schizophyta. A detailed system of classification was proposed by Migula (1894). As more information became available on the physiological and biochemical properties of bacteria, these were employed in proposing new systems of bacterial classification by Knight (1936), Kluyver and van Niel (1936) and others.

Bacterial classification presents special problems. Linnaeus (1735) divided all living beings into two kingdoms, plant and animal. Bacteria had been placed in the plant kingdom and designated as *Schizomycetes* (fission fungi). But as bacteria present features common to both plants and animals, it has been proposed that a new kingdom, Monera, be created to accommodate all microorganisms without true nuclei, plastids and sexual reproduction (Stanier and van Niel 1941). This proposal has not met with universal acceptance.

Kingdoms are divided successively into division, class, order, family, tribe, genus and species. For example, the full taxonomical position of the typhoid bacillus is as follows:

Division	*Protophyta*
Class	*Schizomycetes*
Order	*Eubacteriales*
Family	*Enterobacteriaceae*
Tribe	*Salmonellae*
Genus	*Salmonella*
Species	*Salmonella typhi*

The species concept in bacteria: Species is the standard taxonomical unit in biology. With higher forms of life, a species unit constitutes a stage of evolution, with a characteristic morphology, and is delimited by the failure of interbreeding outside the unit. But in bacteria, the species concept is vague and ill defined. Due to the absence of fossil remains in bacteria, the evolutionary status of species cannot be established. Morphological differences are insufficient for the definition of bacterial species. The general absence of sexual reproduction in bacteria prevents the use of inbreeding as a test for differentiation between species.

In spite of these difficulties, the concept of species provides a convenient unit in bacterial taxonomy. Besides morphological features, criteria useful for the definition of bacterial species are physiological, biochemical, antigenic and pathogenic properties. As 'species' is a genetic concept, definitive information can be obtained by comparison of the nucleotide base ratios, which are constant for any one species but may be different in different species. Genetic homology can be demonstrated by DNA hybridization between different individuals of the same species. Comparison of rRNA sequences helps to arrange bacterial species into a phylogenetic tree. 16SrRNA sequencing has emerged as useful tool for identifying many new unculturable pathogens (e.g. *Bartonella henselae*).

An important difference between the classification of bacteria and that of higher organisms is that in the former, the properties of a population are studied, and not of an individual. A population derived by binary fission from a single cell is called a **clone**. A single bacterial colony represents a clone. Though all the cells in a clone are expected to be identical in all respects, a few of them may show differences due to mutation. A population of bacteria derived from a particular source, such as a patient, is called a **strain**.

The general absence of sexual reproduction in bacteria serves to maintain their character constant. But bacteria possess several features that contribute to some degree of heterogeneity in their populations. Their short generation time and high rate of mutation lead to the presence, in any population, of cells with altered characters. Methods of genetic exchange such as transformation, transduction and conjugation cause differences in character. Prophage and plasmid DNA can induce new properties.

Phylogenetic classification: There are two approaches to bacterial classification. The hierarchical classification represents a branching tree like arrangement, one characteristic being employed for division at each branch or level. This system is called phylogenetic because it implies an evolutionary arrangement of species. Here some characteristics are arbitrarily given special weightage. Depending on the characteristic so chosen, the classification would give different patterns. For example, the intestinal Gram negative bacilli have been traditionally classified depending on whether they ferment lactose or not. While this provides a useful distinction between the pathogenic and nonpathogenic groups of these bacilli, a different but useful classification could be obtained using fermentation of sucrose as the criterion. While classification based on weighted characteristic is a convenient method, it has the serious drawback that the characters used may not be valid. Fermentation of lactose, in the example cited, is not an essential and permanent characteristic. It may be acquired or lost, upsetting the system of arrangement.

Adansonian classification: The Adansonian classification, so called after Michael Adanson who introduced it in the eightenth century, avoids the use of weighted characteristics. It makes no phylogenetic assumption but merely takes into account all the characteristics expressed at the time of study. Hence it is called a *phenetic system*. It gives equal weight to all measurable features, and groups organisms on the basis of similarities of several characteristics. The availability of computers has extended the scope of phenetic classification by permitting comparisons of very large numbers of properties of several organisms at the same time. This is known as *numerical taxonomy*.

Molecular or genetic classification: This is based on the degree of genetic relatedness of different organisms. Since all properties are ultimately based on the genes present, this classification is said to be the most natural or fundamental method. DNA relatedness can be tested by studying the nucleotide sequences of DNA and by DNA hybridisation or recombination methods. The nucleotide base composition and base ratio (Adenine–Thymine:Guanine–Cytosine ratio) varies widely among different groups of microorganisms, though it is constant for members of the same species. Molecular classification has been employed more with viruses than with bacteria.

No method of bacterial classification is universally accepted. The method most widely adopted is presented in successive editions of *Bergey's Manual of Determinative Bacteriology*.

Intraspecies classification: For diagnostic or epidemiological purposes, it is often necessary to subclassify bacterial species. This may be based on biochemical properties (biotypes), antigenic features (serotypes), bacteriophage susceptibility (phage types) or production of bacteriocins (colicin types). A species may be divided first into groups and then into types, as for example, in streptococci.

Much greater discrimination in intraspecies typing has been achieved by the application of newer techniques from immunology, biochemistry and genetics. Investigations of epidemiology and pathogenesis using these techniques have been collectively referred to as *molecular epidemiology*. The methods used are of two types: phenotypic (study of expressed characteristics) and genotypic (direct analysis of genes, chromosomal and extrachromosomal DNA). Molecular phenotypic methods include electrophoretic typing of bacterial proteins and immunoblotting. Genotypic methods include plasmid profile analysis, restriction endonuclease analysis of chromosomal DNA with Southern blotting, PCR and nucleotide sequence analysis. Some of these techniques are considered in the chapter *Bacterial Genetics*.

NOMENCLATURE

The need for applying generally accepted names for bacterial species is self-evident. Chaos will result if the same bacterium is referred to by different names by different workers. International agreement on bacterial nomenclature is ensured by the Code of Nomenclature which has the authority of the International Association of Microbiological Societies.

Two kinds of names are given to bacteria. The first is the *casual* or common name which varies from country to country and is in the local language. Names such as 'typhoid bacillus' and 'gonococcus' are casual names. Such names are useful for communication at the local level. The second is the scientific or international name which is the same throughout the world. The scientific name consists usually of two words, the first being the name of the genus and the second the specific epithet (for example *Bacillus subtilis*). The generic name is usually a Latin noun. The specific epithet is an adjective or noun and indicates some property of the species (for example *albus*, meaning white), the animal in which it is found (for example *suis*, means pig), the disease it causes (*tetani*, of tetanus), the person who discovered it (*welchii*, after Welch) or the place of its isolation (*london*). The generic name always begins with a capital letter and the specific epithet with a small letter, even if it refers to a person or place (for example *Salmonella london*).

TYPE CULTURES

As a point of reference, type cultures of bacteria are maintained in international reference laboratories. The type cultures contain representatives of all established species. The original cultures of any new species described are deposited in type collections. They are made available by the reference laboratories to other workers for study and comparison.

Further Reading

Cowan ST. ed. 1978. *Dictionary of Medical Taxonomy*. London: Oxford University Press.
Cowan ST and KJ Steel 1965. *Manual for the Identification of Medical Bacteria*. London: Cambridge University Press.
Finegold SM and EJ Baron 1986. *Bailey and Scott's Diagnostic Bacteriology*. 7th edn. St. Louis: CV. Mosby.
Goodfellow M and RG Board ed. 1980. *Microbiological Classification and Identification*. London: Academic Press.
Murray P et al, eds. 1999. *Manual of Clinical Microbiology*. 7th edn. Washington: American Society for Microbiology.

Bacterial Genetics

Genetics, a name coined by the British biologist William Bateson in 1906, is the study of heredity and variation, seeking to understand the causes of the resemblances and differences between parents and their progeny. Like other organisms, bacteria also breed true and maintain their characteristics from generation to generation, yet at the same time, exhibit variations in particular properties in a small proportion of their progeny. Though heritability and variation in bacteria had been noticed from the early days of bacteriology, it was not realised then that bacteria too obey the laws of genetics.

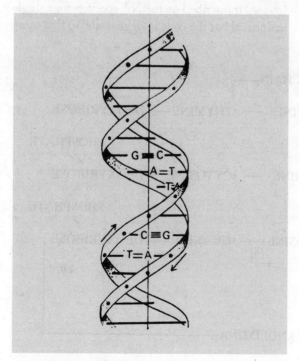

Fig. 8.1 DNA double helix

Even the existence of a bacterial nucleus was a subject of controversy. The differences in morphology and other properties were attributed by Nageli (1877) to bacterial *pleomorphism*, which postulated the existence of a single, or perhaps a few species of bacteria, which possessed a protean capacity for variation. With the development and application of precise methods of pure culture, it became apparent that different types of bacteria retained constant form and function through successive generations. This led to the concept of *monomorphism*, proposed by Cohn and Koch, which admitted of little potential for variation and separated bacteria into species based upon single character differences.

It was only since the 1940s that principles of genetics were applied to bacteria and their viruses. This has led not merely to a better understanding of the genetic processes but also to fundamental advances in biology and biochemistry and to the birth of a new branch of science, molecular biology.

BASIC PRINCIPLES OF MOLECULAR BIOLOGY

The 'central dogma' of molecular biology is that deoxyribonucleic acid (DNA) carries genetic information, which is transcribed onto ribonucleic acid (RNA) and then translated as the particular polypeptide (DNA $\rightarrow$ RNA $\rightarrow$ polypeptide). As the nature and functions of a cell are basically determined by the specific polypeptides that constitute its proteins and enzymes, it is evident that the essential material of heredity is DNA which is the storehouse of all information for protein synthesis. (An exception exists in the case of some viruses in which the genetic material is RNA instead of DNA.)

The DNA molecule is composed of two chains of nucleotides wound together in the form of a 'double helix' (Fig. 8.1). Each chain has a backbone of deoxyribose and phosphate residues arranged alternately. Attached to each deoxyribose is one of four nitrogenous bases, the purines, adenine (A) and guanine (G), and the pyrimidines, thymine (T) and cytosine (C). The double-stranded nature of the molecule is stabilised by hydrogen bonding between the bases on the opposite strands in such a manner that adenine is always linked to thymine, and guanine to cytosine (Fig. 8.2).

Adenine and thymine thus form a complementary base pair, and guanine and cytosine form another. A molecule of DNA will, therefore, contain as many units of adenine as thymine, and of guanine as cytosine but the ratio of each pair of bases $(A + T)/(G + C)$, though constant for each species, varies widely from one bacterial species to another. The DNA molecule replicates by first unwinding at one end to form a fork, each strand of the fork acting as a template for the synthesis of a complementary strand, with which it then forms a double helix.

Basically, RNA is structurally similar to DNA, except for two major differences. It contains the sugar ribose (instead of deoxyribose which is present in DNA) and the base uracil (instead of thymine which is present in DNA). Three distinct types of RNA can be distinguished on the basis of structure and function: messenger RNA (mRNA), ribosomal RNA (rRNA) and transfer RNA (tRNA). DNA acts as the template for the synthesis of mRNA and, therefore, the bases in the two will be complementary to each other. Adenine, guanine, cytosine and uracil in mRNA will be complementary to thymine, cytosine, guanine and adenine, respectively, in the DNA.

Genetic information is stored in the DNA as a code, the unit of the code consisting of a sequence of three bases, that is, the code is triplet. Each triplet (codon) transcribed on mRNA specifies for a single aminoacid but the code is 'degenerate' so that more

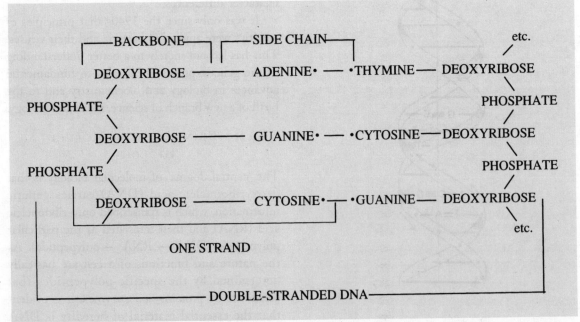

Fig. 8.2 A segment of double stranded DNA illustrating its chemical structure

than one codon may exist for the same aminoacid. Thus, the triplet AGA codes for arginine but the triplets AGG, CGU, CGC, CGA and CGG also code for the same aminoacid. The code is non-overlapping, each triplet being a distinct entity, and no base in one codon is employed as part of the message of an adjacent codon. Three codons (UAA, UAG and UGA) do not code for any aminoacid and are called 'nonsense codons'. They act as punctuation marks (stop codons) terminating the message for the synthesis of a polypeptide.

A segment of DNA carrying codons specifying for a particular polypeptide is called a *gene*. A DNA molecule consists of a large number of genes, each of which contains hundreds of thousands of nucleotides. The bacterial chromosome consists of a double-stranded molecule of DNA arranged in a circular form. When straightened, it is about 1,000 μm in length. The length of DNA is usually expressed as kilobases (1 kb = 1,000 base pairs). Bacterial DNA is about 4,000 kb and the human genome about 3 million kb long.

In higher forms of life, several stretches of DNA that do not appear to function as codons occur between the coding sequences of genes. These apparently useless noncoding intrusions are called *introns*, while the stretches of coded genes are called *exons*. During transcription, the genome is copied in its entirety, both introns and exons. The introns are then excised from the RNA copy before being translated by the ribosomes into proteins.

EXTRACHROMOSOMAL GENETIC ELEMENTS

In addition to chromosomal DNA, most bacteria possess extrachromosomal genetic elements. These are not essential for the normal life and functioning of the host bacterium but may confer on it properties such as drug resistance and toxigenicity leading to survival advantage under appropriate conditions. *Plasmids* are circular DNA molecules present in the cytoplasm of bacteria, capable of autonomous replication (*independent replicons*). By

their ability to transfer genes from one cell to another, plasmids have become important vectors in genetic engineering. Plasmids may also be seen in yeasts, which are eukaryotes. Plasmid DNA sometimes may be integrated with chromosomal DNA. The name *episome* was employed for such integrated forms, though this distinction is not usually made now.

Plasmids have been classified in many ways, depending on whether they are self-transmissible or nontransmissible (nonconjugating), on the property encoded (sex, drug resistance, etc.), by restriction endonuclease fingerprinting or other criteria. An important method of plasmid classification is by *incompatibility typing*. Closely related plasmids do not coexist stably in the same bacterial cell, while unrelated plasmids can. On this basis, plasmids have been classified into different *incompatibility groups*. They have also been classified based on the types of conjugation tube induced, which determine the susceptibility of the host bacterium to lysis by some virulent bacteriophages.

GENOTYPIC AND PHENOTYPIC VARIATIONS

The sum total of the genes that make up the genetic apparatus of a cell (genome) establishes its genotype, which is the hereditary constitution of the cell that is transmitted to its progeny. The genotype includes the complete genetic potential of the cell, all of which may or may not be expressed in a given environmental situation.

The phenotype (*phaeno* meaning display) is the physical expression of the genotype in a given environment. It follows, therefore, that a cell may exhibit different phenotypic appearances in different situations; for example, the typhoid bacillus is normally flagellated but when grown in phenol agar, the flagella are not synthesised. This is only a phenotypic variation determined by the environment and is reversed when subcultured from phenol agar into broth. Another example of environmental influence is the synthesis by *E. coli* of the enzyme beta-galactosidase, necessary for lactose fermentation. The bacillus possesses the genetic information for the synthesis of the enzyme but the actual synthesis takes place only when it is grown in a medium containing lactose. When grown in a medium containing glucose only, the enzyme is not synthesised. Such enzymes which are synthesised only when induced by the substrate are called *induced enzymes*, as opposed to *constitutive enzymes*, which are synthesised irrespective of the presence or absence of the substrate.

Phenotypic variations are influenced by the environment, limited in range by the genotype, temporary and not heritable. Variations are said to be genotypic when they are due to alterations in the genome. Genotypic variations are stable, heritable and not influenced by the environment. They may occur by mutation or by one of the mechanisms of genetic transfer or exchange, such as transformation, transduction, lysogenic conversion and conjugation.

MUTATION

Mutation is a random, undirected, heritable variation caused by an alteration in the nucleotide sequence at some point of the DNA of the cell. It may be due to addition, deletion or substitution of one or more bases (point mutation). Multiple mutations cause extensive chromosomal rearrangements. A *missense mutation* is one in which the triplet code is altered so as to specify an aminoacid different from that normally located at a particular position in the protein. Deletion of a nucleotide within a gene may cause premature polypeptide chain termination by generating a nonsense codon, i.e., *nonsense mutation*. *Transversion* is substitution of a purine for a pyramidine and vice versa in base pairing. *Suppressor mutation* is reversal of a mutant phenotype by another mutation at a position on the DNA distinct from that of the original mutation. All genes are susceptible to mutational events but

not all mutations are expressed. Some mutations involve vital functions, and such mutants are nonviable (*lethal mutation*). A type of lethal mutation which is of great interest is 'conditional mutation'. A *conditional lethal mutant* may be able to live under certain conditions (permissive conditions). The commonest type of conditional mutant is the temperature sensitive (*ts*) mutant, which is able to live at the permissive temperature (say, 35 °C), but not at the restrictive temperature (say, 39 °C).

Each gene undergoes mutation with a fixed frequency. Mutation rates of individual genes in bacteria range from 10^{-4} to 10^{-10} per bacterium per division. The molecular mechanism of mutation is that during DNA replication, some 'error' creeps in while the progeny strands are copied. For instance, instead of thymine bonding with adenine, it may, due to tautomerism, sometimes bond with guanine. Though mutation occurs spontaneously, its frequency can be increased by several agents (*mutagens*) such as UV rays, alkylating agents, acridine dyes, 5-bromouracil and 2-aminopurine.

Mutation is a natural event, taking place all the time at its particular frequency in all the dividing forms of life. Most mutants, however, go unrecognised as the mutation may be lethal or may affect some minor function that may not be expressed. Mutation is best appreciated when it involves a function which can be readily observed. For example, an *E. coli* mutant that loses its ability to ferment lactose can be readily detected on MacConkey agar but is unrecognisable on nutrient agar. Mutation is of vital importance when it confers a survival advantage. If a streptomycin resistant mutant of the tubercle bacillus develops in a patient under treatment with the drug, it multiplies selectively and ultimately replaces the original drug sensitive population of bacteria. But in a patient who is not on treatment, the mutation confers no survival advantage and, therefore, preferential multiplication of the mutant does not occur. Such changes in the character of bacterial populations, observed in the presence of a selective environment, were formerly considered to be 'adaptations'. By a *post hoc, ergo propter hoc* reasoning, the environment and the variation were believed to have a cause-and-effect relationship. Such induced variations were considered heritable in the Lamarckian sense. It was the demolition of this concept of adaptation in the 1940s that established bacterial genetics on a firm scientific basis.

The proof that bacteria undergo spontaneous mutation independent of the environment was first provided by Luria and Delbruck (1943) by the 'fluctuation test'. They found that very wide fluctuations occurred in the numbers of bacteriophage resistant *E. coli* colonies when samples were plated from several separate small volume cultures, as compared to samples tested from a single large volume culture. Statistically, this indicated that mutations occurred randomly in the separate small volume cultures, some early and some late, resulting in the wide fluctuation. In the large volume cultures, fluctuations were within limits of sampling error. However, the logic of this experiment was not widely appreciated by microbiologists, probably due to the complicated statistical interpretation. It was the simple but elegant 'replica-plating' technique of Lederberg and Lederberg (1952) that proved the point beyond doubt. Using a velvet template, they were able to transfer inocula from colonies on a master plate, onto a number of other plates, retaining the relative positions of the colonies in all the plates. By such replica-plating on culture plates with and without bacteriophages, they were able to show that bacteriophage resistant mutants appeared without the bacteria ever having had contact with a selective agent.

Mutation may affect any gene and hence may modify any characteristic of the bacterium. Mutants may vary in properties such as nutritional requirements, biochemical reaction, antigenic structure, morphological features, colony form, drug susceptibility, virulence and host range. The practical importance of bacterial mutation lies mainly in the field of drug resistance and the development of live vaccines.

TRANSMISSION OF GENETIC MATERIAL (GENE TRANSFER)

Transformation: Transformation is the transfer of genetic information through the agency of free DNA. It was the first example of genetic exchange in bacteria to have been discovered. Griffith in 1928 found that mice died when injected with a mixture of live noncapsulated (R) pneumococci and heat killed capsulated (S) pneumococci, neither of which separately proved fatal. If in the experiment, the live (R) pneumococci were derived from capsular type II and the killed (S) strain from type III, from blood cultures of the mice that had died, live type III capsulated pneumococcus could be isolated, showing that some factor in the heat killed type III pneumococcus had transferred the information for capsule synthesis to the live rough strain. Such transformation was subsequently demonstrated in vitro also. The nature of the transforming principle was identified as DNA by Avery, Macleod and McCarty in 1944.

Transduction: The transfer of a portion of the DNA from one bacterium to another by a bacteriophage is known as transduction. Bacteriophages are viruses that parasitise bacteria and consist of a nucleic acid core and a protein coat. During the assembly of bacteriophage progeny inside infected bacteria, 'packaging errors' may occur occasionally. A phage particle may have at its core, besides its own nucleic acid, a segment of the host DNA. When this particle infects another bacterium, DNA transfer is effected and the recipient cell acquires new characteristics coded by the donor DNA. Transduction may be 'generalised', when it involves any segment of the donor DNA at random, or it may be 'restricted', when a specific bacteriophage transduces only a particular genetic trait. Restricted transduction has been studied intensively in the 'lambda' phage of *E. coli*. The prophage lambda is inserted in the bacterial chromosome only between the genes determining galactose utilisation (*gal*) and biotin synthesis (*bio*) and therefore it transduces only either of these.

Transduction is not confined to transfer of chromosomal DNA. Episomes and plasmids may also be transduced. The plasmids determining penicillin resistance in staphylococci are transferred from cell to cell by transduction.

Transduction appears to be the most widespread mechanism of gene transfer among prokaryotes and provides an excellent tool for the genetic mapping of bacteria. Any group of bacteria for which bacteriophages exist can be subject to transduction. It has been reported that transduction may occasionally be effected in eukaryotic cells also. Transduction has been proposed as a method of genetic engineering in the treatment of some inborn errors of metabolism.

Lysogenic conversion: Bacteriophages exhibit two types of lifecycle. In the *virulent* or *lytic* cycle, large numbers of progeny phages are built up inside the host bacterium, which ruptures to release them. In the *temperate* or *nonlytic* cycle, the host bacterium is unharmed. The phage DNA becomes integrated with the bacterial chromosome as the *prophage*, which multiplies synchronously with the host DNA and is transferred to the daughter cells. This process is called lysogeny and bacteria harbouring prophages are called *lysogenic* bacteria. Lysogeny is extremely frequent in nature.

In lysogenic bacteria, the prophage behaves as an additional segment of the bacterial chromosome, coding for new characteristics. This process by which the prophage DNA confers genetic information to a bacterium is called *lysogenic* or *phage conversion*. In transduction, the phage acts only as a vehicle carrying bacterial genes from one cell to another but in lysogenic conversion the phage DNA itself is the new genetic element. Lysogenic conversion influences susceptibility to bacteriophages (immunity to superinfection with the same or related phages) and antigenic characteristics. Of great medical importance is the lysogenic conversion in diphtheria bacilli, which acquire toxigenicity (and therefore virulence) by lysogenisation with the phage beta. Elimination of the phage from a toxigenic strain renders it nontoxigenic.

Conjugation: Conjugation is the process whereby a 'male' or 'donor' bacterium 'mates' or makes physical contact with a 'female' or 'recipient' bacterium and transfers genetic elements into it. This has been considered to be the bacterial equivalent of sexual mating in higher organisms but the analogy is irrelevant as, following conjugation, the female bacterium is in turn converted into a male cell! Bacterial conjugation was first described by Lederberg and Tatum (1946) in a strain of *E. coli* called K12 and has been most extensively studied in this strain.

Conjugation takes place between a male cell and a female cell. The maleness or donor status of a cell is determined by the presence in it of a plasmid which codes for specialised fimbria (*sex pilus*) which projects from the surface of the cell. The plasmid DNA replicates and a copy of it passes from the donor to the recipient cell, probably along the sex pilus (*conjugation tube*). As a result, the recipient attains donor status and can in turn conjugate with other female cells. The maleness in bacteria is thus a transmissible or 'infectious' characteristic. Along with the plasmid DNA, portions of the host DNA also are sometimes transferred to the recipient. The donor DNA then combines with the DNA of the recipient, effecting genetic recombination. It was in *E. coli* K12 that the role of plasmids in conjugation was first recognised. The plasmid responsible was termed the 'sex factor' or 'fertility (F) factor'. When other similar plasmids were also discovered, the term 'transfer factor' came to be used for all such plasmids which conferred on their host cells the ability to act as donors in conjugation.

The F factor: The F factor is a transfer factor that contains the genetic information necessary for the synthesis of the sex pilus and for self-transfer but is devoid of other identifiable genetic markers such as drug resistance. Cells carrying the F factor (F$^+$ cells) have no distinguishing features other than their ability to mate with F$^-$ cells and render them F$^+$. The F factor is actually an episome and has the ability to exist in some cells in the 'integrated state' or inserted into the host chromosome. Such cells are able to transfer chromosomal genes to recipient cells with high frequency and are known as Hfr cells. Following conjugation with an Hfr cell, an F$^-$ only rarely becomes F$^+$, though it receives chromosomal genes from the donor.

This conversion of an F$^+$ cell into the Hfr state is reversible. When the F factor reverts from the integrated state to the free state, it may sometimes carry with it some chromosomal genes from near its site of attachment. Such an F factor incorporating some chromosomal genes is called an F prime (F$'$) factor. When an F$'$ cell mates with a recipient, it transfers, along with the F factor, the host genes incorporated with it. This process of transfer of host genes through the F$'$ factor resembles transduction and has therefore been called *sexduction* (Fig. 8.3).

Colicinogenic (Col) factor: Several strains of coliform bacteria produce colicins — antibiotic-like substances which are specifically and selectively lethal to other enterobacteria. As similar substances are produced by bacteria other than coliforms also (pyocin by *Pseudomonas pyocyanea*, diphthericin by *Corynebacterium diphtheriae*), the name *bacteriocin* has been given to this group of substances. The specificity of action of bacteriocins enables intraspecies classification of certain bacteria (for example, *Shigella sonnei, Ps. aeruginosa*).

Colicin production is determined by a plasmid called the Col factor, which resembles the F factor in promoting conjugation, leading to self-transfer and, at times, transfer of chromosomal segments.

Resistance transfer factor (RTF): This plasmid is of great medical importance as it leads to the spread of multiple drug resistance among bacteria.

This extrachromosomal mechanism of drug resistance was first reported by Japanese workers (1959) investigating the sudden increase in infections caused by the Shigella strains, resistant simultaneously to sulphonamides, streptomycin, chloramphenicol and tetracycline. They observed that patients excreting such Shigella strains also shed in their feces *E. coli* strains resistant to the same drugs. Transfer of multiple drug resistance was demonstrated between *E. coli* and Shigella strains both in vitro and in vivo. The resistance is plasmid mediated and is transferred by conjugation. This mechanism of drug resistance is known as *transferable, episomal* or *infectious drug resistance.*

This plasmid consists of two components – the transfer factor called the *resistance transfer factor* (RTF) which is responsible for conjugational transfer, and a *resistance determinant (r)* for each of the several drugs. The whole plasmid (RTF + r determinants) is known as the R factor. An R factor can have several r determinants, and resistance to as many as eight or more drugs can be transferred simultaneously (Fig. 8.4). Sometimes the RTF may dissociate from the r determinants, the two components existing as separate plasmids. In such cases, though the host cell remains drug resistant, the resistance is not transferable. The RTF can have attached to it determinants other than those for drug resistance. Enterotoxin and hemolysin production in some enteropathogenic *E. coli* are transmitted by this transfer factor.

Transferable drug resistance is seen widely in various pathogenic and commensal bacteria of man and animals, such as *Enterobacteriaceae, Vibrio, Pseudomonas, Pasteurella.* The transfer can be effected readily in vitro but in the normal gut, it is inhibited by several factors such as anaerobic conditions, bile salts, alkaline pH and the abundance of anaerobic Gram positive bacteria minimising the

BACTERIAL GENETICS

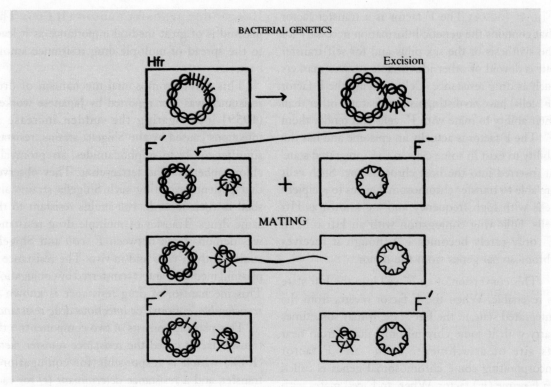

Fig. 8.3 Sexduction. The integrated *F* factor of a *Hfr* cell may revert to the cytoplasmic state. During excision some host genes may be incorporated in the *F'* factor (*F*). When an *F'* cell mates with an *F⁻* cell, the host gene is transferred to the recipient.

chances of contact between donor cells and suitable recipient cells. But in the intestines of persons on oral antibiotic therapy, transfer occurs readily due to the destruction of the sensitive normal flora and the selection pressure produced by the drug.

Transferable drug resistance is now universal in distribution and involves all antibiotics in common use. Its incidence is directly proportional to the frequency of use of antibiotics in the area. Bacteria carrying R factors can be transmitted from animals to man. Hence indiscriminate use of antibiotics in veterinary practice or in animal feeds can also lead to an increase of multiple drug resistance in the community. The addition of antibiotics in animal feeds has for this reason been prohibited by legislation in some countries. Widespread resistance has considerably diminished the clinical efficacy of most antibiotics.

GENETIC MECHANISMS OF DRUG RESISTANCE IN BACTERIA

Bacteria may acquire drug resistance by mutation or by one of the methods of genetic transfer. The biochemical mechanisms of resistance may be several, including decreased permeability to the drug, development of alternative metabolic pathways, and production of enzymes inactivating the drugs.

Mutational resistance is mainly of two types: (1) the stepwise mutation, as seen with penicillin, where high levels of resistance are achieved only by a series of small-step mutations; and (2) the 'one-step' mutation, as seen with streptomycin, where the mutants differ widely in the degree of resistance, some exhibiting low resistance, while others may be highly resistant, and some even streptomycin dependent.

In clinical practice, mutational resistance is of great importance in tuberculosis. If a patient is treated with streptomycin alone, initially the bacilli die in large numbers but soon resistant mutants appear and multiply unchecked. If two or more antituberculous drugs are used for combined treatment, repopulation by resistant mutants does not occur, as a mutant resistant to one drug will be destroyed by the other drug. The possibility of a mutant exhibiting resistance to multiple drugs simultaneously is so remote as to be virtually nonexistent. This is the rationale behind combined treatment in tuberculosis. However, inspite of this knowledge, inadequate or inappropriate treatment over the years has caused extensive resistance in tubercle bacilli, leading to a pandemic of multidrug resistant tuberculosis (MDR TB) across the world.

Resistance transfer by transformation can be demonstrated experimentally but its significance in nature is not known. Acquisition of resistance by transduction is common in staphylococci. The penicillinase plasmids, which are transmitted by transduction, may also carry determinants for resistance to mercuric chloride and erythromycin.

Transferable drug resistance mediated by the R factor is the most important method of drug resistance. Acquisition of an R factor simultaneously confers resistance to several drugs and therefore treatment with a combination of drugs is not useful. The resistance is due to the production of degrading enzymes, and the level of resistance is usually high. Resistance may be transferred between bacteria of different taxonomic groups. While resistant mutants usually have a lower growth rate and reduced virulence as compared to the wild strains, bacteria carrying R factors are apparently normal in other respects. R factors in some cases may even lead to enhanced virulence. Multiple drug resistance was initially seen in bacteria causing diarrhea and such other mild infections that did not call for antibiotic treatment as a routine. But subsequently it has spread to virtually all pathogenic bacteria affecting

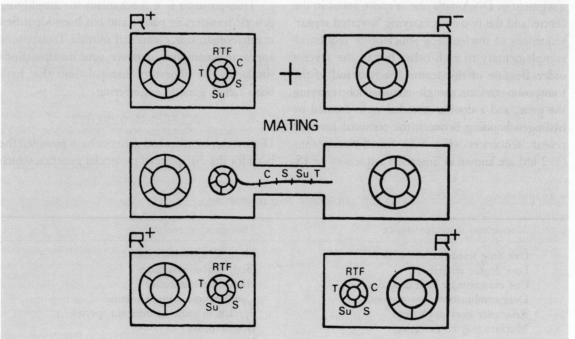

Fig. 8.4 **Transferable drug resistance. The R⁺ cell carries the R factor, consisting of RTF and r determinants. Its transfer to a sensitive R⁻ bacterium converts the recipients into a resistant R⁺ cell.**

humans and animals, making antibiotic therapy of infections ineffective.

In the laboratory, R factors may sometimes be eliminated by treating bacteria with acridine dyes or ethidium bromide. But in the community, the only way to prevent widespread dissemination of multiple resistance is to restrict the use of antibiotics to the essential minimum.

TRANSPOSABLE GENETIC ELEMENTS

Certain structurally and genetically discrete segments of DNA have been identified that have the ability to move around in a `cut-and-paste' manner between chromosomal and extrachromosomal DNA molecules within cells. These DNA molecules are called *transposons* ('jumping genes') and this mode of genetic transfer, *transposition*. The earliest of such mobile genes was discovered by Barbara McClintock in plants during work in the 1940s and 50s, for which she was awarded the Nobel Prize for Medicine in 1983. A transposon is a segment of DNA with one or more genes in the centre, and the two ends carrying 'inverted repeat' sequences of nucleotides—nucleotide sequences complementary to each other but in the reverse order. Because of this feature, each strand of the transposon can form a single-stranded loop carrying the gene, and a double-stranded stem formed by hydrogen bonding between the terminal inverted repeat sequences (Fig. 8.5). Small transposons (1–2 kb) are known as 'insertion sequences' or IS.

Transposons attach at certain regions of chromosomal, plasmid or phage DNA. Insertion of a transposon leads to the acquisition of new characteristics by the recipient DNA molecule. Unlike plasmids, transposons are not self replicating and depend on chromosomal or plasmid DNA for replication.

By transposition, a segment of the DNA can be transferred from a molecule to another molecule that has no genetic homology with either the transposable element or with the donor DNA. In this it differs from recombination. As sizeable chunks of DNA are added by transposition, the recipient molecule becomes heavier.

Characteristics transferred by transposons may sometimes confer survival advantage under appropriate environmental conditions. It has been suggested that the resistance-determinant segments of the R factors may have evolved as collections of transposons, each carrying a gene that confers resistance to one or several antibiotics.

Transposition is a mechanism for amplifying genetic transfers in nature and has been identified in microorganisms, plants and animals. Transposons appear to accomplish in nature, gene manipulations similar to the laboratory manipulations that have been called 'genetic engineering'.

MOLECULAR GENETICS

Discoveries in microbial genetics have provided the basis for the discipline of molecular genetics, which

Table 8.1 Comparison of mutational and transferable drug resistance

Mutational drug resistance	Transferable resistance
One drug resistance at a time	Multiple drug resistance
Low degree resistance	High degree resistance
Can overcome by high drug dose	High dose ineffective
Drug combinations can prevent	Combinations cannot prevent
Resistance does not spread	Spreads to same or different species
Mutants may be defective	Not defective
Virulence may be low	Virulence not decreased

is concerned with the analysis and manipulation of DNA using biochemical and microbiological techniques. It has been stated that these techniques have revolutionised the study of biology and medicine, probably more than any technique since the development of the light microscopes. Some techniques and applications of molecular genetics are discussed below.

Genetic engineering: The most important application of molecular genetics in biotechnology is genetic engineering or recombinant DNA (rDNA) technology. This consists of isolation of the genes coding for any desired protein from microorganisms or from cells of higher forms of life including human beings, and their introduction into suitable microorganisms, in which the genes would be functional, directing the production of the specific protein. Such cloning of genes in microorganisms enables the preparation of the desired protein in pure form, in large quantities and at a reasonable cost.

Different strategies have been employed for obtaining the desired genes. For very small proteins, such as the pituitary hormone somatostatin whose complete aminoacid sequences are known, the genes can be synthesised in the laboratory. With larger proteins, this is not possible. The DNA can be cleaved by specific enzymes called restriction endonucleases and the fragments containing the desired genes isolated. This does not work with DNA of higher organisms as they contain introns. In such cases, the messenger RNA concerned can be isolated from cells producing the desired protein. A DNA copy is made from the mRNA using the enzyme reverse transcriptase. The double-stranded DNA gene is then prepared using DNA polymerase. This is incorporated into suitable vectors or carriers, such as plasmids or temperate bacteriophages, for

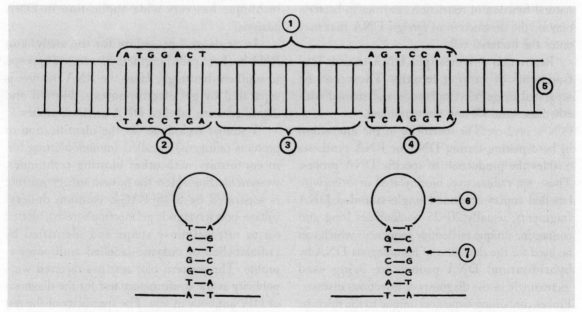

Fig. 8.5 Diagrammatic representation. The figure above shows a transposon along the course of a DNA molecule, consisting of a gene in the middle and inverted repeat sequences of nucleotides at either end. The figures below represent the stem and loop structure formed by each strand of the transposon. The loop consists of the gene and the stem is formed by hydrogen bonding between the terminal repeat sequences. The stem and loop form can attach to insertion sites on recipient DNA. 1. Transposon. 2. Inverted repeat sequences. 3. Gene. 4. Inverted repeat sequences. 5. Double-stranded DNA. 6. Single-stranded loop consisting of gene. 7. Double-stranded stem formed by bonding of terminal inverted sequences.

insertion into microorganisms. The microorganism commonly employed is *E. coli* K12, though many other bacteria and yeasts have also been used.

Genetic engineering has become an established branch of biotechnology with great scope for commercial exploitation. Cloned human insulin, interferons, somatostatin, growth hormones and many other biologicals have already been marketed. Safer vaccines can be produced by cloning the protective antigens of pathogens, as has already been done, as in the case of foot and mouth disease, and hepatitis B and rabies viruses. This versatile technique has many extramedical applications also.

Restriction endonucleases: (restriction enzymes) are microbial enzymes which cleave double-stranded DNA at specific oligonucleotide sequences. Many such enzymes which act at different nucleotide sequences (for example, *Eco* RI, *Hind* III, *Taq* I) have been recognised. The natural function of restriction enzymes in bacteria may be the destruction of foreign DNA that may enter the bacterial cell.

Restriction enzymes split DNA strands into fragments of varying lengths. These can be separated by gel electrophoresis and stained with ethydium bromide and photographed.

DNA probes: The specificity of the interaction in base pairing during DNA or RNA synthesis enables the production of specific DNA *probes*. These are radioactive, biotinylated or otherwise labelled copies of cloned single-stranded DNA fragments, usually 20–25 nucleotides long and containing unique nucleotide sequences which can be used for the detection of homologous DNA by hybridisation. DNA probes are being used increasingly in the diagnosis of infectious diseases. Probes containing sequences unique to the microbe (strain, species or group) to be detected can be added to microbial cultures, body fluids, tissues or other materials suspected to contain the microbe or its DNA. The DNA probe hybridises with the complementary specific sequences on the microbe's DNA. The advantages of DNA probes for diagnosis are their high degree of specificity, ability to detect minute quantities of complementary DNA even in the presence of other microbes, and the capacity to recognise microbes that are either difficult or impossible to culture. DNA probes for the detection of many pathogens are now commercially available.

Blotting techniques: DNA fragments obtained by restriction enzyme digestion and separation on gel can be transferred from the gel by blotting to nitrocellulose or nylon membranes that bind the DNA. The DNA bound to the membrane is denatured (converted to the single-stranded form) and treated with radioactive single-stranded DNA probes. These will hybridise with homologous DNA to form radioactive double-stranded segments, which can be detected on X-ray film. This highly sensitive technique for identifying DNA fragments by DNA : DNA hybridisation is called *Southern blotting*, after EM Southern who devised it. This technique has very wide application in DNA analysis.

An analogous procedure for the analysis of RNA has been called *northern blotting* (as opposed to southern blotting!). Here the RNA mixture is separated by gel electrophoresis, blotted and identified using labelled DNA or RNA probes.

A similar technique for the identification of proteins (antigens) is called *immunoblotting* (or, in conformity with other blotting techniques, *western blotting*). Here the protein antigen mixture is separated by SDS–PAGE (sodium dodecyl sulfate–polyacrylamide gel electrophoresis), blotted on to nitrocellulose strips and identified by radiolabelled or enzyme-labelled antibodies as probes. The western blot test has received wide publicity as the confirmatory test for the diagnosis of HIV antibody in sera. The specificity of the test depends on its ability to separately identify antibodies directed against different antigens of the pathogen (for example, against the surface, core and reverse transcriptase antigens of HIV).

Polymerase chain reaction (PCR): This is a rapid automated method for the amplification of specific DNA sequences (or genes), invented by Kary B Mullis in 1983, for which he won the Nobel Prize in Chemistry in 1993. PCR consists of several cycles of sequential DNA replication where the products of the first cycle become the template for the next cycle. It makes available abundant quantities of specific DNA sequences starting from sources containing minimal quantities of the same.

The technique is as follows: two oligonucleotide primers complementary to the flanking region of the DNA sequence to be amplified are incubated with the target DNA, nucleotides and DNA polymerase. The reaction consists of three essential steps:

1. heat denaturation of the sample DNA to single strand;
2. annealing of sequence-specific oligonucleotide primers to the boundaries of the DNA segment; and
3. extension of the primers by DNA polymerase to form new double-stranded DNA across the segment by sequential addition of deoxynucleotides.

These three steps constitute one cycle of the reaction. These cycles are repeated several times, usually for 20–50 cycles in the thermocycler, at the end of which hundreds of thousands of copies of the original target sequences are available. As the reaction steps take place at high temperature (50–95 °C), a heat-stable polymerase, such as Taq I has to be employed.

With its enormous capacity to amplify DNA, PCR is a versatile tool useful in diverse areas such as diagnosis of infectious, genetic or neoplastic diseases, in forensic investigations, in archeobiological studies of ancient specimens and in the examination of phylogenetic relationships in evolution.

Based on the principle of PCR, other target amplification systems have been developed. One such, Transcription mediated amplification (TMA) which amplifies ribosomal RNA instead of DNA has been applied as a rapid diagnostic technique for infections such as tuberculosis where cultures are difficult or delayed.

Molecular epidemiology: One offshoot of molecular genetics is molecular epidemiology. Here molecular methods such as plasmid profile analysis, genomic fingerprinting and PCR are used for the identification and matching of microbial isolates for epidemiological purposes.

Genetic mapping: As a result of the remarkable advances in molecular genetics, it has been possible to delineate the complete genomic sequences of bacteriophages and other viruses, bacteria and their plasmids, and even of some eukaryotes including mammals. Quite apart from the useful information it has provided in microbiology, its success emboldened the international scientific community to venture on the 'human genome project', the most expensive and ambitious scientific project so far undertaken in biology. The results of this mammoth study became available by the dawn of the twenty-first century and have opened vistas in human biology and medicine, as well as controversies and dilemmas that transcend medicine.

Further Reading

Hardy K. 1986. *Bacterial Plasmids*. 2nd edn. Reinhold.

Innis MA et al. 1990. *PCR Protocols*, San Diego: Academic Press.

Mullis KB. 1993. 'The polymerase chain reaction.' Nobel Lecture, Stockholm.

Sambrook J et al. 1989. *Molecular Cloning*. Cold Spring Harbour Laboratory.

Tompkins LS. 1992. The use of molecular methods in infectious diseases, *New Engl J Med*. 327:1290.

Towner KJ and A Cockayne 1993. *Molecular Methods for Microbial Identification and Typing*. London: Chapman-Hall.

Watson JD et al. 1983. *Recombinant DNA*. New York: Scientific American Books.

Infection

Infection and immunity involve interaction between the animal body (host) and the infecting microorganism. Based on their relationship to their hosts, microorganisms can be classified as *saprophytes* (from Greek sapros decayed; and *phyton* plant) and parasites. Saprophytes are free-living microbes that subsist on dead or decaying organic matter. They are found in soil and water and play an important role in the degradation of organic materials in nature. They are generally incapable of multiplying on living tissues and therefore are of little relevance in infectious disease. Exceptionally, however, some saprophytes like *B. subtilis* may infect devitalised hosts whose natural resistance is greatly reduced (opportunistic infection). Parasites are microbes that can establish themselves and multiply in hosts. Parasitic microbes may be either pathogens (from Greek *pathos* suffering, and *gen* produce, that is, disease-producing) or *commensals* (from Latin *com* with; and *mensa*, table, i.e., living together). Pathogens are microorganisms that are capable of producing disease in the host. Commensal microbes live in complete harmony with the host without causing any damage to it. The normal bacterial flora of the body consist largely of commensals. Many commensals behave as facultative pathogens in that they can produce disease when the host resistance is lowered.

It is necessary to distinguish between the term 'infection' and 'infectious disease'. The lodgement and multiplication of a parasite in or on the tissues of a host constitute infection. It does not invariably result in disease. In fact, disease is but a rare consequence of infection, which is a common natural event.

Infections may be classified in various ways. Initial infection with a parasite in a host is termed *primary infection*. Subsequent infections by the same parasite in the host are termed *reinfections*. When a new parasite sets up an infection in a host whose resistance is lowered by a preexisting infectious disease, this is termed *secondary infection*. The term *focal infection* (more appropriately *focal sepsis*) indicates a condition where, due to infection or sepsis at localised sites such as appendix or tonsils, generalised effects are produced. When in a patient already suffering from a disease a new infection is set up from another host or another external source, it is termed cross-infection. Cross-infections occurring in hospitals are called *nosocomial infections* (from Greek *nosocomion* hospital). The term *iatrogenic infection* refers to physician-induced infections resulting from investigative, therapeutic or other procedures. Depending on whether the source of infection is from the host's own body or from external sources, infections are classified as *endogenous* or *exogenous*, respectively. Based on the clinical effects of infections, they may be classified into different varieties. *Inapparent infection* is one where clinical effects are not apparent. The term *subclinical infection* is often used as a synonym. *Atypical infection* is one in which the typical or characteristic clinical manifestations of the particular infectious disease are not present. Some parasites, following infection, may remain in the tissues in a latent or hidden form proliferating and producing clinical disease when the host resistance is lowered. This is termed *latent infection*.

SOURCES OF INFECTION

Humans: The commonest source of infection for humans are humans themselves. The parasite may originate from a patient or a carrier. A *carrier* is a person who harbours the pathogenic microorganism without suffering from any ill-effect because of it. Several types of carriers have been identified. A *healthy carrier* is one who harbours the pathogen but has never suffered from the disease caused by the pathogen, while a *convalescent carrier* is one who has recovered from the disease and continues to harbour the pathogen in his body. Depending on the duration of carriage, carriers are classified as *temporary* and *chronic*. The *temporary carrier* state lasts less than six months, while *chronic carriage* may last for several years and sometimes even for the rest of one's life. The term *contact carrier* is applied to a person who acquires the pathogen from a patient, while the term *paradoxical carrier* refers to a carrier who acquires the pathogen from another carrier.

Animals: Many pathogens are able to infect both human beings and animals. Animals may, therefore, act as sources of human infection. In some instances, the infection in animals may be asymptomatic. Such animals serve to maintain the parasite in nature and act as the reservoir of human infections. They are, therefore, called *reservoir hosts*. Infectious diseases transmitted from animals to human beings are called *zoonoses*. Zoonotic diseases may be bacterial (plague from rats), viral (rabies from dogs), protozoal (toxoplasmosis from cats), helminthic (hydatid disease from dogs) or fungal (zoophilic dermatophytes from cats and dogs).

Insects: Blood sucking insects may transmit pathogens to human beings. The diseases so caused are called *arthropod-borne diseases*. Insects such as mosquitoes, ticks, mites, flies, fleas and lice that transmit infections are called **vectors**. Transmission may be mechanical (for example, transmission of dysentery or typhoid bacilli by the domestic fly). Such vectors are called *mechanical vectors*. In other instances, the pathogen multiplies in the body of the vector, often undergoing part of its developmental cycle in it. Such vectors are termed *biological vectors* (for example, *Aedes aegypti* mosquito in yellow fever, Anopheles mosquito in malaria). Biological vectors transmit infection only after the pathogen has multiplied in them sufficiently or has undergone a developmental cycle. The interval between the time of entry of the pathogen into the vector and the vector becoming infective is called the *extrinsic incubation period*.

Besides acting as vectors, some insects may also act as reservoir hosts (for example, ticks in relapsing fever and spotted fever). Infection is maintained in such insects by transovarial or transstadial passage.

Soil and water: Some pathogens can survive in the soil for very long periods. Spores of tetanus bacilli may remain viable in the soil for several decades and serve as the source of infection. Fungi (*Histoplasma capsulatum, Nocardia asteroides*) and also parasites such as roundworm and hookworm survive in the soil and cause human infection.

Water may act as the source of infection either due to contamination with pathogenic microorganisms (cholera vibrio, infective hepatitis virus) or due to the presence of aquatic vectors (cyclops in guineaworm infection).

Food: Contaminated food may act as a source of infection. The presence of pathogens in food may be due to external contamination (food poisoning by staphylococcus) or due to pre-existent infection in meat or other animal products (salmonellosis).

METHODS OF TRANSMISSION OF INFECTION

Contact: Infection may be acquired by contact, which may be direct or indirect. Sexually transmitted diseases such as syphilis and gonorrhea illustrate spread by direct contact. The term *contagious* disease had been used for diseases transmitted by direct contact, distinct from *infectious disease* signifying all other modes of transmission. This distinction is now not generally employed. Indirect contact may be through the agency of *fomites*, which are inanimate objects such as clothing, pencils or toys which may be contaminated by a pathogen from one person and act as a vehicle for its transmission to another. Pencils shared by school children may act as fomites in the transmission of diphtheria, and face towels in trachoma.

Inhalation: Respiratory infections such as influenza and tuberculosis are transmitted by inhalation of the pathogen. Such microbes are shed by the patients into the environment, in secretions from the nose or throat during sneezing, speaking or coughing. Large drops of such secretions fall to the ground and dry there. Pathogens resistant to drying may remain viable in the dust and act as sources of infection. Small droplets, under 0.1 mm in diameter, evaporate immediately to become minute particles or *droplet nuclei* (usually 1–10 μm in diameter) which remain suspended in the air for long periods, acting as sources of infection.

Ingestion: Intestinal infections are generally acquired by the ingestion of food or drink contaminated by pathogens. Infection transmitted by ingestion may be waterborne (cholera), foodborne (food poisoning) or handborne (dysentery). The importance of fingerborne transmission is being increasingly recognised, not only in the case of pathogens entering through the mouth, but also those that enter through the nose and eyes.

Inoculation: Pathogens, in some instances, may be inoculated directly into the tissues of the host. Tetanus spores implanted in deep wounds, rabies virus deposited subcutaneously by dog bite and arboviruses injected by insect vectors are examples. Infection by inoculation may be iatrogenic when unsterile syringes and surgical equipment are employed. Hepatitis B and the Human Immunodeficiency Virus (HIV) may be transmitted through transfusion of infected blood, or the use of contaminated syringes and needles, particularly among addicts of injectable drugs.

Insects: Insects may act as mechanical or biological vectors of infectious diseases.

Congenital: Some pathogens are able to cross the placental barrier and infect the fetus in utero. This is known as *vertical transmission*. This may result in abortion, miscarriage or stillbirth. Live infants may be born with manifestations of a disease, as in congenital syphilis. Intrauterine infection with the rubella virus, especially in the first trimester of pregnancy, may interfere with organogenesis and lead to congenital malformation. Such infections are known as *teratogenic infections*.

Iatrogenic and laboratory infections: Infection may sometimes be transmitted during administration of injections, lumbar puncture and catheterisation, if meticulous care in asepsis is lacking. Modern methods of treatment such as exchange transfusion, dialysis, and organ transplant surgery have increased the possibilities for iatrogenic infections. Laboratory personnel handling infectious material are at risk and special care should be taken to prevent laboratory infection.

The outcome of an infection will depend on the interaction between microbial factors which predispose to pathogenicity and host factors which contribute to resistance.

FACTORS PREDISPOSING TO MICROBIAL PATHOGENICITY

The terms 'pathogenicity' and 'virulence' refer to

the ability of a microbe to produce disease or tissue injury but it is convenient to make a fine distinction between them. 'Pathogenicity' is generally employed to refer to the ability of a microbial *species* to produce disease, while the term 'virulence' is applied to the same property in a strain of microorganism. Thus the species *M. tuberculosis* or the polio virus is referred to as being pathogenic. The pathogenic species *M. tuberculosis* and the polio virus contain strains of varying degrees of virulence including those which are avirulent, such as the vaccine strains. The virulence of a strain is not constant and may undergo spontaneous or induced variation. Enhancement of virulence is known as *exaltation* and can be demonstrated experimentally by serial passage in susceptible hosts. Reduction of virulence is known as *attenuation* and can be achieved by passage through unfavourable hosts, repeated cultures in artificial media, growth under high temperature or in the presence of weak antiseptics, desiccation, or prolonged storage in culture.

Virulence is the sum total of several determinants, as detailed below.

Adhesion: The initial event in the pathogenesis of many infections is the attachment of the bacteria to body surfaces. This attachment is not a chance event but a specific reaction between surface *receptors* on host cells and adhesive structures *(ligands)* on the surface of bacteria. These adhesive structures are called *adhesins*. Adhesins may occur as organised structures, such as fimbriae or fibrillae and pili, or as colonisation factors. This specific adhesin may account for the tissue tropisms and host specificity exhibited by many pathogens. Adhesins serve as virulence factors, and loss of adhesins often renders the strain avirulent. Adhesins are usually made of protein and are antigenic in nature. Specific immunisation with adhesins has been attempted as a method of prophylaxis in some infections, as for instance against *E. coli* diarrhea in calves and piglets, and gonorrhea in human beings.

Invasiveness: This refers to the ability of a pathogen to spread in the host tissues after establishing infection. Highly invasive pathogens characteristically produce spreading or generalised lesions (e.g., streptococcal septicemia following wound infection), while less invasive pathogens cause more localised lesions (e.g., staphylococcal abscess). Some pathogens, though capable of

Table 9.1 Distinguishing features of exotoxins and endotoxins

Exotoxins	*Endotoxins*
1. Proteins	Lipopolysaccharides
2. Heat labile	Heat stable
3. Actively secreted by cells; diffuse into surrounding medium	Form part of cell wall; do not diffuse into surrounding medium
4. Readily separable from cultures by physical means such as filtration	Obtained only by cell lysis
5. Action often enzymic	No enzymic action
6. Specific pharmacological effect for each exotoxin	Effect nonspecific; action common to all endotoxins
7. Specific tissue affinities	No specific tissue affinity
8. Active in very minute doses	Active only in very large doses
9. Highly antigenic	Weakly antigenic
10. Action specifically neutralised by antibody	Neutralisation by antibody ineffective

causing serious or even fatal diseases, lack invasiveness altogether (e.g., the tetanus bacillus which remains confined to the site of entry and produces the disease by elaborating a potent toxin).

Toxigenicity: Bacteria produce two types of toxins—exotoxins and endotoxins.

Exotoxins are heat labile proteins which are secreted by certain species of bacteria and diffuse readily into the surrounding medium. They are highly potent in minute amounts and constitute some of the most poisonous substances known. One mg of tetanus or botulinum toxin is sufficient to kill more than one million guinea pigs and it has been estimated that 3 kg of botulinum toxin can kill all the inhabitants of the world. Treatment of exotoxins with formaldehyde yields toxoids which are nontoxic but retain the ability to induce antibodies (antitoxins). They exhibit specific tissue affinities and pharmacological activities, each toxin producing a typical effect which can be made out by characteristic clinical manifestations or autopsy appearances. Exotoxins are generally formed by Gram positive bacteria but may also be produced by some Gram negative organisms such as Shiga's dysentery bacillus, vibrio cholera and enterotoxigenic *E. coli.*

Endotoxins are heat stable lipopolysaccharides (LPS) which form an integral part of the cell wall of Gram negative bacteria. Their toxicity depends on the lipid component (lipid A). They are not secreted outside the bacterial cell and are released only by the disintegration of the cell wall. They cannot be toxoided. They are poor antigens and their toxicity is not completely neutralised by the homologous antibodies. They are active only in relatively large doses. They do not exhibit specific pharmacological activities. All endotoxins, whether isolated from pathogenic or nonpathogenic bacteria, produce similar effects. Administration of small quantities of endotoxin in susceptible animals causes an elevation of body temperature manifested within 15 minutes and lasting for several hours. The pyrogenic effect of fluids used for intravenous administration is usually due to the presence of endotoxins from contaminant bacteria. Intravenous injections of large doses of endotoxin and massive Gram negative septicemias cause endotoxic shock marked by fever, leucopenia, thrombocytopenia, significant fall in blood pressure, circulatory collapse and bloody diarrhea leading to death (Tables 9.1, 9.2).

Plasmids: Genes coding for some virulence characteristics may be plasmid borne. Examples of plasmid-borne virulence factors are surface antigens responsible for the colonisation of intestinal mucosa by *E. coli* and enterotoxin production by *E. coli* and *Staph. aureus.* Multiple drug resistance (R) plasmids increase the severity of clinical disease by their resistance to antibiotic therapy.

Bacteriophages: The classical example of phage directed virulence is seen in diphtheria. In diphtheria bacilli, the gene for toxin production is present in beta or other tox+ corynephages.

Communicability: The ability of a parasite to spread from one host to another is known as communicability. This property does not influence the production of disease in an individual host but determines the survival and distribution of a parasite in a community. A correlation need not exist between virulence and communicability. In fact, a highly virulent parasite may not exhibit a high degree of communicability due to its rapidly lethal effect on the host. In general, infections in which the pathogen is shed in secretions, as in respiratory or intestinal diseases, are highly communicable. In some instances, as in hydrophobia, human infection represents a dead end, there being an interruption in the spread of the pathogen to other hosts.

Development of epidemic and pandemic diseases requires the strain of pathogen to possess high degrees of virulence and communicability. **Other bacterial products:** Some bacterial products other than toxins, though devoid of intrinsic toxicity, may contribute to virulence by inhibiting the mechanisms of host resistance. Pathogenic staphylococci produce a thrombin-like enzyme coagulase which prevents phagocytosis by forming a fibrin barrier around the bacteria and walling off the lesion. Fibrinolysins promote the spread of infections by breaking down the fibrin barrier in tissues. Hyaluronidases split hyaluronic acid which is a component of intercellular connective tissue and thus facilitate the spread of infection along tissue spaces. Leucocidins damage polymorphonuclear leucocytes. Many pathogens produce hemolysins capable of destroying erythrocytes but their significance in pathogenicity is not clearly understood.

Bacterial appendages: Capsulated bacteria such as pneumococci, *K. pneumoniae* and *H. influenzae* are not readily phagocytosed. Some bacterial surface antigens such as the Vi antigen of *S. typhi*, *K antigens* of *E. coli* also help the bacteria to withstand phagocytosis and the lytic activity of complement.

Infecting dose: Successful infections require that an adequate number of bacteria should gain entry into the host. The dosage may be estimated as the minimum infecting dose (MID) or minimum lethal dose (MLD) which are, respectively, the minimum number of bacteria required to produce clinical evidence of infection or death, respectively, in a susceptible animal under standard conditions. As animals exhibit considerable individual variation in susceptibility, these doses are more correctly estimated as statistical expressions, ID 50 and LD 50, as the dose required to infect or kill 50 per cent of the animals tested under standard conditions.

Route of infection: Some bacteria, such as streptococci, can initiate infection whatever be the mode of entry. Others can survive and multiply only when introduced by the optimal routes. Cholera vibrios are infective orally but are unable to cause infection when introduced subcutaneously. This difference is probably related to modes by which different bacteria are able to initiate tissue damage and establish themselves. Bacteria also differ in their sites of election in the host body after introduction into tissues. They also differ in the ability to produce damage of different organs in different species of animals. Tubercle bacilli injected into rabbits cause lesions mainly in the kidney and infrequently in the liver and spleen, but in guinea pigs the lesions are mainly in the liver and spleen, the kidneys being spared. The reasons for such selective multiplication in tissues are largely obscure, though they may be related to the presence in tissues of substances that may selectively hinder or favour their multiplication.

TYPES OF INFECTIOUS DISEASES

Infectious diseases may be localised or generalised.

Table 9.2 Biological activities of endotoxins

Pyrogenicity	Lethal action	Depression of blood pressure
Activation of complement	Intravascular coagulation	Leucopenia
Leucocytosis	Inhibition of glucose and glycogen synthesis in the liver	Stimulation of B lymphocytes
Macrophage inhibition	Interferon release	Induction of prostaglandin synthesis

(Clotting of limulus lysate (lysate of amebocytes from horse-shoe crab, Limulus polyphemus, used as a test for detection of endotoxins).)

Localised infections may be superficial or deep-seated. Generalised infection involves the spread of the infecting agent from the site of entry by contiguity, through tissue spaces or channels, along the lymphatics or through the bloodstream. Circulation of bacteria in the blood is known as *bacteremia*. Transient bacteremia is a frequent event even in healthy individuals and may occur during chewing, brushing of teeth or straining at stools. The bacteria are immediately mopped up by phagocytic cells and are unable to initiate infection. *Bacteremia* of greater severity and longer duration is seen during generalised infections as in typhoid fever. *Septicemia* is the condition where bacteria circulate and multiply in the blood, form toxic products and cause high, swinging type of fever. Pyemia is a condition where pyogenic bacteria produce septicemia with multiple abscesses in the internal organs such as the spleen, liver and kidney.

Depending on their spread in the community, infectious diseases may be classified into different types. *Endemic diseases* are those which are constantly present in a particular area. Typhoid fever is endemic in most parts of India. An *epidemic* disease is one that spreads rapidly, involving many persons in an area at the same time. Influenza causes annual winter epidemics in the cold countries. A *pandemic* is an epidemic that spreads through many areas of the world involving very large numbers of people within a short period. Influenza, cholera, plague and enteroviral conjunctivitis are pandemic diseases. Epidemics vary in the rapidity of spread. Waterborne diseases such as cholera and hepatitis may cause explosive outbreaks, while diseases which spread by person-to-person contact evolve more slowly. Such creeping or smouldering epidemics, as that of cerebrospinal fever, are termed *prosodemic diseases*.

Further Reading

Mims CA. 1987. *The Pathogenesis of Infectious Disease.* 3rd edn. London: Academic Press.

Patrick S and MJ Larkin 1995. *Immunological and Molecular aspects of Bacterial Virulence.* Chichester: Wiley.

Poxton IR and JP Arbuthnot 1990. Determinants of bacterial virulence. In: *Topley and Wilson's Principles of Bacteriology, Virology and Immunity.* 8th edn. Vol.I. London: Edward Arnold.

Roth JA et al, eds 1988. *Virulence Mechanisms of Bacterial Pathogens.* Washington DC: American Society for Microbiology.

Immunity

The term 'immunity' traditionally refers to the resistance exhibited by the host towards injury caused by microorganisms and their products. However protection against infectious diseases is only one of the consequences of the immune response, which in its entirety is concerned with the reaction of the body against any foreign antigen.

Immunity against infectious diseases is of different types:

I Innate (Native) Immunity

(a) Nonspecific
- Species
- Racial
- Individual

(b) Specific
- Species
- Racial
- Individual

II Acquired (Adaptive) Immunity

(a) Active
- Natural
- Artificial

(b) Passive
- Natural
- Artificial

Innate or *native immunity* is the resistance to infections which an individual possesses by virtue of his genetic and constitutional make-up. It is not affected by prior contact with microorganisms or immunisation. It may be nonspecific, when it indicates a degree of resistance to infections in general, or specific where resistance to a particular pathogen is concerned.

Innate immunity may be considered at the level of the species, race or individual. Species immunity refers to the total or relative refractoriness to a pathogen, shown by all members of a species. For instance, all human beings are totally unsusceptible to plant pathogens and to many animal pathogens such as rinderpest or distemper. This immunity is something a person obtains by virtue of being a part of the human species. The mechanisms of species immunity are not clearly understood but may be due to physiological and biochemical differences between the tissues of the different host species, which determine whether or not a pathogen can multiply in them. An early insight into the basis of species immunity was gained by Pasteur's experiments on anthrax in frogs, which are naturally resistant to the disease but become susceptible when their body temperature is raised from 25 °C to 35 °C.

Within a species, different races may show differences in susceptibility to infections. This is known as *racial immunity*, the classic example of which is the high resistance of Algerian sheep to anthrax. Such racial differences are known to be genetic in origin, and by selection and inbreeding, it is possible to develop, at will, races that possess high degrees of resistance or susceptibility to various pathogens. It is difficult to demonstrate marked differences in immunity in human races, as controlled breeding is not possible in the human species. It has been reported that the people of Negroid origin in the USA are more susceptible than the Caucasians to tuberculosis. But such comparisons are vitiated by external influences such as differences in socioeconomic levels. An interesting instance of genetic resistance to *Plasmodium falciparum* malaria is seen in some parts of Africa and the Mediterranean coast. A hereditary abnormality of red cells (sickling), prevalent in the area, confers immunity to infection by the malarial parasite and may have evolved from the survival advantage conferred by it in a malarial environment.

The differences in innate immunity exhibited by different individuals in a race is known as *individual immunity*. The genetic basis of individual immunity is evident from studies on the incidence of infectious diseases in twins. It is well documented that homozygous twins exhibit similar degrees of resistance or susceptibility to lepromatous leprosy and tuberculosis. Such correlation is not seen in heterozygous twins.

Several factors influence the level of innate immunity in an individual:

Age: The two extremes of life carry higher susceptibility to infectious diseases as compared with adults. The fetus in utero is normally protected from maternal infection by the placental barrier. But some pathogens cross this barrier causing overwhelming infections resulting in fetal death. Some, such as rubella, herpes, cytomegaloviruses and *Toxoplasma gondii*, lead to congenital malformations. The heightened susceptibility of the fetus to infection is related to the immaturity of its immune apparatus. Newborn animals are more susceptible to experimental infections than older ones. Coxsackie viruses cause fatal infection in suckling mice but not in adults.

Increased susceptibility in the young may, in some instances, be due to hormonal influence. Tinea capitis caused by *Microsporum audouinii* frequently undergoes spontaneous cure with the onset of puberty. The susceptibility of the vaginal epithelium in prepubertal girls to gonococcal infection is another instance of the effect of sex hormones on resistance.

Some infections like poliomyelitis and chickenpox tend to be more severe in adults than in young children, due to hypersensitivity that causes greater tissue damage. Conversely, hepatitis B virus infections in the newborn are usually asymptomatic because clinical disease requires adequate immune response which is lacking at that age. However, the virus multiplies unrestrained and such neonates end up as chronic viral carriers, often developing late hepatic complications. Old persons are highly susceptible to infections due to the waning of their immune responses and other infirmities like enlarged prostate leading to urinary stasis.

Hormonal influences: Endocrine disorders such as diabetes mellitus, hypothyroidism and adrenal dysfunction are associated with an enhanced susceptibility to infections. The high incidence of staphylococcal sepsis in diabetes may be related to the increased level of carbohydrates in tissues. Corticosteroids exert an important influence on the response to infection. They depress the host's resistance by their antiinflammatory and antiphagocytic effects and by the suppression of antibody formation and hypersensitivity. They also have a beneficial effect in that they neutralise the harmful effect of bacterial products such as endotoxins. The elevated steroid level during pregnancy may be related to the heightened susceptibility of pregnant women to many infections. The reported effect of stress in increasing susceptibility to infections, may in some measure be due to the release of steroids.

Nutrition: The interaction between malnutrition and immunity is complex but, in general, both humoral and cell mediated immune processes are reduced when there is malnutrition. Cell mediated immune responses such as the Mantoux test become negative in severe protein deficiency, as in kwashiorkor. Because of its wide prevalence, malnutrition may well be the commonest cause of immunodeficiency.

Paradoxically, there is some evidence that certain

infections may not become clinically apparent in the severely malnourished. Malarial infection in the famine stricken may not induce fever but once their nutrition is improved, clinical malaria develops. It has also been reported that some viruses may not multiply in the tissues of severely malnourished individuals.

MECHANISMS OF INNATE IMMUNITY

Epithelial surfaces: The intact skin and mucous membrane covering the body protect it considerably against invasion by microorganisms. They provide much more than a mechanical barrier. Healthy skin possesses bactericidal activity to which the presence of high concentration of salt in the drying sweat, the sebaceous secretions and the long chain fatty acids and soaps contribute. When cultures of typhoid bacilli placed on healthy skin and on a glass surface are sampled at intervals, the bacteria on the skin are seen to be killed within minutes, while those on glass survive for several hours. The bactericidal activity of skin secretions is illustrated by the frequent mycotic and pyogenic infections seen in persons who immerse their hands in soapy water for long periods occupationally.

Though the skin frees itself readily of bacteria deposited on it (transients), its reactions are different to the bacterial flora normally resident on it. Resident flora are not easily removed even by washing and application of disinfectants.

The mucosa of the respiratory tract has several innate mechanisms of defence. The very architecture of the nose prevents entry of microorganisms to a large extent, the inhaled particles being arrested at or near the nasal orifices. Those that pass beyond are held by the mucus lining the epithelium, and are swept back to the pharynx where they tend to be swallowed or coughed out. The cough reflex is an important defence mechanism of the respiratory tract. The cilia on the respiratory epithelial cells propel particles upwards. Nasal and respiratory secretions contain mucopolysaccharides capable of combining with influenza and certain other viruses.

Particles that manage to reach the pulmonary alveoli are ingested by the phagocytic cells present there.

The mouth is constantly bathed in saliva which has an inhibitory effect on many microorganisms. Particles deposited in the mouth are swallowed and subjected to the action of the digestive juices. The high acidity of the stomach destroys most microorganisms. The pH becomes progressively alkaline from the duodenum to the ileum. The ileum contains a rich and varied flora and in the large intestine, the bulk of the contents is composed of bacteria.

The intestinal mucosa is covered by a lacelike network of mucus. Particles get enmeshed in the mucus and form small masses which are propelled by peristalsis.

The conjunctiva is freed of foreign particles by the flushing action of lachrymal secretions. The eyes become susceptible to infection when lachrymal secretions are absent. Tears contain the antibacterial substance lysozyme, first described by Fleming (1922). This is a thermolabile low molecular weight basic protein which acts as a muraminidase. Lysozyme is present in tissue fluids and in nearly all secretions except cerebrospinal fluid, sweat and urine. It acts by splitting certain polysaccharide components of the cell walls of susceptible bacteria. In the concentrations seen in tears and other secretions, lysozyme is active only against some nonpathogenic Gram positive bacteria. However, it occurs in phagocytic cells in concentrations high enough to be lethal to many pathogens.

The flushing action of urine eliminates bacteria from the urethra. Spermine and zinc present in the semen carry out antibacterial activity. The acidity of the adult vagina, due to the fermentation of glycogen in the epithelial cells by the resident aciduric bacilli, makes it inhospitable to many pathogens.

Antibacterial substances in blood and tissues: The complement system possesses bactericidal activity and plays an important role in the destruction of pathogenic bacteria that invade the blood and tissues (see chapter 14).

Several substances possessing antibacterial properties have been described in blood and tissues. These include (1) beta lysin, a relatively thermostable substance active against anthrax and related bacilli; (2) basic polypeptides such as leukins extracted from leucocytes and plakins from platelets; (3) acidic substances, such as lactic acid found in muscle tissue and in the inflammatory zones; and (4) lactoperoxidase in milk. While these substances possess antibacterial properties demonstrable experimentally, their relevance in the natural context is not clearly understood.

A method of defence against viral infections is the production of interferon by cells stimulated by live or killed viruses and certain other inducers. Interferon has been shown to be more important than specific antibodies in protection against and recovery from certain acute viral infections. Tissues and body secretions contain other antiviral substances.

Microbial antagonisms: The skin and mucous surfaces have resident bacterial flora which prevent colonisation by pathogens. Alteration of normal resident flora may lead to invasion by extraneous microbes, causing serious diseases such as staphylococcal or clostridial enterocolitis following oral antibiotics. The importance of normal bacterial flora in native immunity is exemplified by the extreme susceptibility of germ free animals to all types of infections.

Cellular factors in innate immunity: Natural defence against the invasion of blood and tissues by microorganisms and other foreign particles is mediated to a large extent by phagocytic cells which ingest and destroy them. Phagocytic cells, originally discovered by Metchnikoff (1883), were classified by him into microphages and macrophages. Microphages are polymorpho-nuclear leucocytes. Macrophages consist of histiocytes which are the wandering ameboid cells seen in tissues, the fixed reticuloendothelial cells and the monocytes in the blood. A major function of the reticuloendothelial system is the removal of foreign particles that enter the body. Phagocytic cells reach the sites of inflammation in large numbers, attracted by chemotactic substances, and ingest particulate materials. Capsulated bacteria, such as pneumococci, are not readily phagocytosed except in the presence of opsonins. They are more readily phagocytosed when trapped against a firm surface such as the alveolar wall than when they are free in tissue fluids. Bacteria are phagocytosed into a vacuole (phagosome), which fuses with the lysosomes found in the cell to form the phagolysosome. The bacteria are subjected to the action of the lytic enzymes in the phagolysosome and are destroyed. Some bacteria, such as brucella and lepra bacilli, resist intracellular digestion and may actively multiply inside the phagocytic cells. Phagocytosis in such instances may actually help to disseminate infection to different parts of the body. The importance of phagocytosis in protection against infection is evidenced by the enhanced susceptibility to infection seen either when the phagocytic cells are depleted, as in agranulocytosis, or when they are functionally deficient, as in chronic granulomatous disease. A class of lymphocytes called natural killer (NK) cells are important in nonspecific defence against viral infections and tumours. They selectively kill virus infected cells and tumour cells. NK cells are activated by interferons.

Inflammation: Tissue injury or irritation, initiated by the entry of pathogens or other irritants, leads to inflammation, which is an important, nonspecific defence mechanism. The arterioles at the site constrict initially and then dilate leading to an increased blood flow. There is a slowing of blood flow and margination of the leucocytes, which escape into the tissues by diapedesis and accumulate in large numbers, attracted by the chemotactic substances released at the site of injury. Microorganisms are phagocytosed and destroyed. There is an outpouring of plasma, which helps to dilute the toxic products present. A fibrin barrier is laid, serving to wall off the site of infection.

Fever: A rise of temperature following infection is a natural defence mechanism. It not merely helps to accelerate the physiological processes but may, in some cases, actually destroy the infecting pathogens. Therapeutic induction of fever was employed for the destruction of *Treponema pallidum* in the tissues of syphilitic patients before penicillin became available. Fever stimulates the production of interferon and aids recovery from viral infections.

Acute phase proteins: Infection or injury leads to a sudden increase in plasma concentrations of certain proteins, collectively called acute phase proteins. These include C reactive protein (CRP), mannose binding protein, alpha-1-acid glycoprotein, serum amyloid P component and many others. CRP and some other acute phase proteins activate the alternative pathway of complement. They are believed to enhance host resistance, prevent tissue injury and promote repair of inflammatory lesions.

ACQUIRED IMMUNITY

The resistance that an individual acquires during life is known as acquired immunity as distinct from inborn innate immunity. Acquired immunity is of two types, active and passive. *Active immunity* is the resistance developed by an individual as a result of an antigenic stimulus. It is also known as *adaptive immunity* as it represents an adaptive response of the host to a specific pathogen or other antigen. This involves the active functioning of the host's immune apparatus leading to the synthesis of antibodies and the production of immunologically active cells. Active immunity sets in only after a latent period which is required for the immunological machinery to be set in motion. During the development of active immunity, there is often a negative phase during which the level of measurable immunity may actually be lower than it was before the antigenic stimulus. This is because

the antigen combines with any pre-existing antibody and lowers its level in circulation. Once developed, the active immunity is long-lasting. If an individual who has been actively immunised against an antigen experiences the same antigen subsequently, the immune response occurs more quickly and abundantly than during the first encounter. This is known as *secondary response*. Besides the development of humoral and cellular immunity, active immunity is associated with immunological memory. This implies that the immune system is able to retain for long periods the memory of a prior antigenic exposure and to produce a secondary type of response when it encounters the same antigen again. Active immunisation is more effective and confers better protection than passive immunisation.

The resistance that is transmitted passively to a recipient in a 'readymade' form is known as *passive immunity*. Here the recipient's immune system plays no active role. There is no antigenic stimulus; instead, preformed antibodies are administered. There is no latent period in passive immunity, protection being effective immediately after passive immunisation. There is no negative phase. The immunity is transient, usually lasting for days or weeks, only till the passively transmitted antibodies are metabolised and eliminated. No secondary type response occurs in passive immunity. In fact, passive immunity diminishes in effect with repetition. When a foreign antibody is administered a second time, it is eliminated more rapidly than initially. Following the first injection of an antibody such as immune horse serum, the elimination is only by metabolic breakdown but during subsequent injections of horse serum, elimination is much quicker as it combines with antibodies to horse serum that would have been produced following its initial injection. This factor of *immune elimination* limits the usefulness of repeated passive immunisation. Passive immunisation is less effective and provides an immunity inferior to that provided by active immunisation. The main advantage of passive immunisation is that it acts immediately and, therefore, can be employed when 'instant' immunity is desired (Table 10.1).

Active immunity may be natural or artificial. **Natural active immunity** results from either a clinical or an inapparent infection by a microbe. A person who has recovered from an attack of measles develops natural active immunity. The large majority of adults in the developing countries possess natural active immunity to poliomyelitis due to repeated inapparent infections with polioviruses during childhood. Such immunity is usually long-lasting but the duration varies with the type of pathogen. The immunity is lifelong following many viral diseases such as chicken pox or measles. In some viral diseases, such as influenza or common cold, the immunity appears to be shortlived. Influenza can recur in an individual after a few months or a year but this is not so much due to lack of the immunising capacity of the virus as to its ability to undergo antigenic variation so that immunity following the first infection is not effective against the second infection caused by an antigenically novel virus. In common cold, the apparent lack of immunity is because the same clinical picture can be caused by infection with a large number of different viruses. The immunity following bacterial infection is generally less permanent than that following viral infections. Some, such as typhoid fever, induce durable protection. In syphilis, a special type of immunity known as 'premunition' is seen. Here, the immunity to reinfection lasts only as long as the original infection remains active. Once the disease is cured, the patient becomes susceptible to the spirochete again. In chancroid, another venereal disease, caused by *Haemophilus ducreyi*, there does not appear to be any effective immunity as the patient may develop lesions following reinfection even while the original infection is active.

Artificial active immunity is the resistance induced by vaccines. Vaccines are preparations of live or killed microorganisms or their products used for immunisation.

Examples of vaccines are as follows:
1. Bacterial vaccines
   a. Live (BCG vaccine for tuberculosis)
   b. Killed (Cholera vaccine)
   c. Subunit (Typhoid Vi antigen)
   d. Bacterial products (Tetanus toxoid)
2. Viral vaccines
   a. Live (Oral polio vaccine–Sabin)
   b. Killed (Injectable polio vaccine–Salk)
   c. Subunit (Hepatitis B vaccine)

Live vaccines initiate an infection without causing any injury or disease. The immunity following live vaccine administration therefore parallels that following natural infection though it may be of a lower order. The immunity lasts for several years but booster doses may be necessary. *Live vaccines* may be administered orally (as with the Sabin vaccine for poliomyelitis) or parenterally (as with the measles vaccine). *Killed vaccines* are generally less immunogenic than live vaccines, and protection lasts only for a short period. They have, therefore, to be administered repeatedly, generally at least two doses being required for the production of immunity. The first is known as the **primary dose** and the subsequent doses as booster doses. Killed vaccines may be given orally but this route is generally not effective. Parenteral administration provides humoral antibody response, which may be improved by the addition of 'adjuvants' (for example, aluminium phosphate).

Natural passive immunity is the resistance passively transferred from mother to baby. In human infants, maternal antibodies are transmitted predominantly through the placenta, while in animals such as pigs, transfer of antibodies occurs mainly orally through the colostrum. The human colostrum, which is also rich in IgA antibodies resistant to intestinal digestion, gives protection to the neonate. The human fetus acquires some ability to synthesise antibodies (IgM) from about the twentieth week of life but its immunological capacity is still inadequate at birth. It is only by about the age of three months that the infant

Table 10.1 Comparison of active and passive immunity

Active immunity	*Passive immunity*
Produced actively by host's immune system	Received passively. No active host participation
Induced by infection or by immunogens	Readymade antibody transferred
Durable effective protection	Transient, less effective
Immunity effective only after lag period	Immediate immunity
Immunological memory present	No memory
Booster effect on subsequent dose	Subsequent dose less effective
'Negative phase' may occur	No negative phase
Not applicable in the immunodeficient	Applicable in immunodeficient

acquires some measure of immunological independence. Until then, maternal antibodies give passive protection against infectious diseases to the infant. Transport of antibodies across the placenta is an active process and therefore the concentration of antibody in the fetal blood may sometimes be higher than that seen in the mother. Protection so afforded will ordinarily be adequate against all the common infectious diseases in the locality. It is for this reason that most pediatric infections are more common after the age of three months than in younger infants. By active immunisation of mothers during pregnancy, it is possible to improve the quality of passive immunity in the infants. Immunisation of pregnant women with tetanus toxoid is recommended for this purpose in communities in which neonatal tetanus is common.

Artificial passive immunity is the resistance passively transferred to a recipient by the administration of antibodies. The agents used for this purpose are hyperimmune sera of animal or human origin, convalescent sera and pooled human gamma globulin. These are used for prophylaxis and therapy. Equine hyperimmune sera such as antitetanus serum and ATS prepared from hyperimmunised horses used to be extensively employed. They gave temporary protection but carried the disadvantages of hypersensitivity and immune elimination. Human hyperimmune globulin (for example, tetanus immune globulin, TIG) is free from those complications and also gives more lasting protection. Antisera of animal

origin are now recommended only where human preparations are not available (anti gas gangrene and anti botulinum sera; antivenoms).

Convalescent sera (sera of patients recovering from infectious diseases) contain high levels of specific antibody. *Pooled human gammaglobulin* (gammaglobulin from pooled sera of healthy adults) contains antibodies against all common pathogens prevalent in the region. Convalescent sera and pooled human gammaglobulin were used for passive immunisation against some virus infections (like viral hepatitis A). Human gammaglobulin is also used in the treatment of patients with some immunodeficiencies. Gammaglobulin tends to aggregate and when injected intravenously may cause anaphylactic reaction due to complement activation. They are therefore to be given only intramuscularly. It has to be ensured that all preparations from human sera are free from the risk of infection with hepatitis B, hepatitis C, HIV and other infective agents.

Passive immunisation is indicated for immediate and temporary protection in a nonimmune host faced with the threat of an infection, when there is insufficient time for active immunisation to take effect. It is also indicated for the treatment of some infections. Passive immunisation may also be employed for the suppression of active immunity, when the latter may be injurious. An example is the use of Rh immune globulin during delivery to prevent immune response to the Rhesus factor in Rh negative women with Rh positive babies.

Sometimes a combination of active and passive methods of immunisation is employed. This is known as *combined immunisation*. Ideally, whenever passive immunisation is employed for immediate protection, combined immunisation is to be preferred, as in the protection of a nonimmune individual with a tetanus-prone wound. The method is to inject TIG in one arm and the first dose of tetanus toxoid in the other. This is followed by the full course of phased tetanus toxoid injections. TIG provides the protection necessary till the active immunity is able to take effect.

A special type of immunisation is the injection of immunologically competent lymphocytes. This is known as *adoptive immunity* and does not have general application. Instead of whole lymphocytes, an extract of immunologically competent lymphocytes, known as the 'transfer factor', can be used. This has been attempted in the treatment of certain types of diseases (for example lepromatous leprosy).

MEASUREMENT OF IMMUNITY

The truly valid measurement of immunity is to test the resistance of an individual to a challenge by the pathogen. This is, however, not applicable since the challenge itself alters the state of immunity. It is, therefore, not possible to measure accurately the level of immunity in an individual. Estimates of immunity are generally made by statistical methods using large numbers of individuals.

A simple method of testing immunity is to relate its level to some convenient indicator, such as demonstration of the specific antibody. This is not always reliable as the immune response to a pathogen consists of the formation of antibodies to several antigens present in it, as also to the production of cellular immunity. The antibodies may be demonstrated by a variety of techniques such as agglutination, precipitation, complement fixation, hemagglutination inhibition, neutralisation, ELISA and others. In the absence of exact information as to which antigen of the pathogen constitutes the

protective antigen, serological attempts to measure immunity are at best only approximations. In some instances, as in diphtheria where pathogenesis is due to a well-defined antigen (the toxin), the level of immunity can be assayed by in vitro or in vivo (Schick test) methods. Where protection is associated with cell-mediated immunity, skin tests for delayed hypersensitivity and in vitro tests for CMI afford an indication of immunity.

LOCAL IMMUNITY

The concept of local immunity, proposed by Besredka (1919–24), has gained importance in the treatment of infections which are localised or where it is operative in combating infection at the site of primary entry of the pathogen. In poliomyelitis, for instance, systemic immunity provided by active immunisation with the killed vaccine neutralises the virus when it enters the bloodstream, but it does not prevent multiplication of the virus at the site of entry (the gut mucosa) and its fecal shedding. This is achieved by the local intestinal immunity acquired either as a result of natural infection or immunisation with the live oral vaccine. In influenza, immunisation with the killed vaccine elicits a humoral antibody response. But the antibody titre in respiratory secretions is often not high enough to prevent infection. Natural infection or the live virus vaccine administered intranasally provides local immunity. A special class of immunoglobulins (IgA) forms the major component of local immunity.

One type of IgA antibody called *secretory IgA* is produced locally by plasma cells present on mucosal surfaces or in secretory glands. There appears to be a selective transport of such antibodies between the various mucosal surfaces and secretory glands. Thus, following intestinal exposure to an antigen, the specific IgA antibody and the plasma cells forming such an antibody can be demonstrated in breast milk. This indicates the existence of a common *mucosal* or *secretory immune system*. Besides providing local defence against microorganisms, the mucosal immune system may also be involved in handling various antigens that may come into contact with mucosal surfaces from the external environment or through food.

HERD IMMUNITY

This refers to the overall level of immunity in a community and is relevant in the control of epidemic diseases. When a large proportion of individuals in a community (herd) are immune to a pathogen, the herd immunity to the pathogen is satisfactory. When herd immunity is low, epidemics are likely to occur on the introduction of a suitable pathogen, due to the presence of large numbers of susceptible individuals in the community. Eradication of communicable diseases depends on the development of a high level of herd immunity rather than on the development of a high level of immunity in individuals.

Further Reading

Janeway CA and P Travers 1994. *Immunobiology*. London: Current Biology.
Gabay C and I Kushner 1999. Acute phase proteins. *N Engl J Med* 340:448.
Kwaitkowsky D. 2000. Susceptibility to infection. *Br Med J* 321:1061.
Roitt IM. 1994. *Essential Immunology*. 8th edn. London: Blackwell Scientific.
Weir DM and J Stewart 1997. *Immunology*. 8th edn. Edinburgh: Churchill Livingstone.

Antigens

An antigen has been defined as any substance which, when introduced parenterally into the body, stimulates the production of an antibody with which it reacts specifically and in an observable manner. This traditional description of an antigen is no longer comprehensive enough in the light of current concepts about the immune response. Some antigens may not induce antibodies but may sensitise specific lymphocytes leading to cell mediated immunity or may cause immunological tolerance.

The word 'parenteral' (meaning, outside the intestinal tract) is used in the definition because orally administered antigens are usually denatured by digestive enzymes and their antigenicity destroyed, so that no antibody formation takes place. When given parenterally, antigens do not undergo any such inactivation and can induce antibody production. However, there are exceptions and some antigens can be immunogenic when given orally, such as oral vaccines.

The word 'specifically' in the definition is important as specificity is the hallmark of all immunological reactions. An antigen introduced into the body reacts only with those particular immunocytes (B or T lymphocytes) which carry the specific marker for that antigen and which produce an antibody or cells complementary to that antigen only. The antibody so produced will react only with that particular antigen and with no other, though, immunological cross reaction may occur between closely related antigens.

The two attributes of antigenicity are (1) induction of an immune response (immunogenicity), and (2) specific reaction with antibodies or sensitised cells (immunological reactivity). Based on the ability to carry out these two functions, antigens may be classified into different types. A *complete antigen* is able to induce antibody formation and produce a specific and observable reaction with the antibody so produced. *Haptens* are substances which are incapable of inducing antibody formation by themselves but can react specifically with antibodies. (The term hapten is derived from the Greek *haptein* which means 'to fasten'.) Haptens become immunogenic (capable of inducing antibodies) on combining with a larger molecule carrier. Haptens may be complex or simple; while *complex haptens* can precipitate with specific antibodies, *simple haptens* are nonprecipitating. They can inhibit precipitation of specific antibodies by the corresponding antigen or complex hapten. Complex and simple haptens have been described as polyvalent and univalent, respectively, since it is assumed that precipitation requires the antigen to have two or more antibody combining sites.

The smallest unit of antigenicity is known as the *antigenic determinant* or *epitope*. The epitope is that small area on the antigen, usually consisting of four or five aminoacid or monosaccharide residues, possessing a specific chemical structure, electrical charge and steric (spatial) configuration, capable of sensitising an immunocyte and of reacting with its complementary site on the specific antibody or T-cell receptor. Epitopes may be present as a single linear segment of the primary sequence (sequential or linear epitope) or formed by bringing together on the surface residues from different sites of the peptide chain during its folding into the tertiary structure (conformational epitope). T cells recognise sequential epitopes, while B cells identify the tertiary configuration of the conformational epitopes. The combining area on the antibody molecule, corresponding to the epitope, is called the *paratope*. Epitopes and paratopes determine the specificity of immunological reactions. Antigens such as bacteria or viruses carry many different types of epitopes, presenting an antigenic mosaic. The presence of the same or similar epitopes on different antigens accounts for one type of antigenic cross- reaction.

DETERMINANTS OF ANTIGENICITY

A number of properties have been identified which make a substance antigenic but the exact basis of antigenicity is still not clear.

Size: Antigenicity is related to molecular size. Very large molecules, such as hemocyanins (MW 6.75 million), are highly antigenic and particles with low molecular weight (less than 5000) are nonantigenic or feebly so. Low molecular weight substances may be rendered antigenic by adsorbing them on large inert particles such as bentonite or kaolin. Some low molecular weight substances (such as picryl chloride, formaldehyde and penicillin) may be antigenic when applied on the skin, probably by combining with tissue proteins. They are haptens of low immunogenicity, effective in some persons only and related to hypersensitivity.

Chemical nature: Most naturally occurring antigens are proteins and polysaccharides. Lipids and nucleic acids are less antigenic. Their antigenicity is enhanced by combination with proteins. A certain degree of structural diversity is required for antigenicity. That probably explains why proteins which are composed of about 20 different aminoacids are better antigens than polysaccharides which have only four or five monosaccharide units. However, not all proteins are antigenic. A well-known exception is gelatin, which is nonimmunogenic because of its structural unstability.

Susceptibility to tissue enzymes: Only substances which are metabolised and are susceptible to the action of tissue enzymes behave as antigens. Antigens introduced into the body are degraded by the host into fragments of appropriate size containing the antigenic determinants. Phagocytosis and intracellular enzymes appear to play an essential role in breaking down antigens into immunogenic fragments. Substances unsusceptible to tissue enzymes such as polystyrene latex are not antigenic. Substances very rapidly broken down by tissue enzymes are also not antigenic. Synthetic polypeptides, composed of D-aminoacids which are not metabolised in the body, are not antigenic, while polypeptides consisting of L-aminoacids are antigenic.

Foreignness: Only antigens which are 'foreign' to the individual (nonself) induce an immune response. The animal body contains numerous antigens which induce an immune response when introduced into another individual or species. An individual does not normally mount an immune response against his own normal constituent antigens. This was first recognised by Ehrlich who proposed the concept of 'horror autotoxicus' (which means fear of self-poisoning). Tolerance of self antigens is conditioned by contact with them during the development of the immune apparatus. Breakdown of this homeostatic mechanism results in autoimmunisation and autoimmune disease.

In general, the antigenicity of a substance is related to the degree of its foreignness. Antigens from other individuals of the same species are less antigenic than those from other species. Antigens from related species are less antigenic than those from distant species.

Antigenic specificity: The basis of antigenic specificity is stereochemical, as was first demonstrated by Obermayer and Pick and confirmed by Landsteiner. Using haptens such as atoxyl coupled with protein, it was shown that antigenic specificity is determined by single chemical groupings and even by a single acid radical. The importance of the position of the antigenic determinant group in the antigen molecule was evidenced by the differences in specificity in compounds with the group attached at the *ortho, meta* or *para* positions. The influence of spatial configuration of the determinant group was shown by differences in antigenic specificity of the *dextro, levo* and *meso* isomers of substances such as tartaric acid.

Antigenic specificity is not absolute. Cross reactions can occur between antigens which bear stereochemical similarities. In some instances, apparent cross reactions may actually be due to the sharing of identical antigenic determinants by different antigens.

The specificity of natural tissue antigens of animals may be considered under different categories as species, iso-, auto- and organ specificities.

Species specificity: Tissues of all individuals in a species contain species-specific antigens. There exists some degree of cross-reaction between antigens from related species. This immunological relationship parallels phylogenetic relationships. It has been used in tracing evolutionary relationships between species. It also has forensic applications in the identification of the species of blood and of seminal stains. Phylogenetic relationships are reflected in the extent of cross reaction between antigens from different species that cause hypersensitivity. An individual sensitised to horse serum will react with serum from other equines but may not do so with bovine serum.

Isospecificity: Isoantigens are antigens found in some but not all members of a species. A species may be grouped depending on the presence of different isoantigens in its members. The best examples of isoantigens are the human erythrocyte antigens based on which individuals can be classified into different blood groups. These are genetically determined. They are of clinical importance in blood transfusion and in isoimmunisation during pregnancy. They were of help in determining disputed paternity cases, but have been supplanted by the more discriminatory DNA fingerprinting tests. Blood groups find application in anthropology.

Histocompatibility antigens are those cellular determinants specific to each individual of a species. They are recognised by genetically different individuals of the same species when attempts are made to transfer or transplant cellular material from one individual to another (described in Chapter 15).

Autospecificity: Autologous or self antigens are ordinarily nonantigenic but there are exceptions. Sequestrated antigens that are not normally found free in circulation or tissue fluids (such as eye lens protein normally confined within its capsule) are not recognised as self antigens. Similarly, antigens that are absent during embryonic life and develop later (such as sperm) are also not recognised as self antigens.

Organ specificity: Some organs, such as the brain, kidney and lens protein of different species, share the same antigen. Such antigens, characteristic of an organ or tissue and found in different species, are called organ specific antigens. The neuroparalytic complications following antirabic vaccination using sheep brain vaccines are a consequence of brain specific antigens shared by sheep and human beings. The sheep brain antigens induce immunological response in the vaccinees, damaging their nervous tissue.

Heterogenetic (heterophile) specificity: The same or closely related antigens may sometimes occur in different biological species, classes and kingdoms. These are known as heterogenetic or heterophile antigens, best exemplified by the Forssman antigen which is a lipid carbohydrate complex widely distributed in many animals, birds, plants and bacteria. It is absent in rabbits, so anti-Forssman antibody can be prepared in these animals. Other heterophile antigens are responsible for some diagnostic serological reactions in which antigens unrelated to etiological agents are employed (heterophile reaction). The Weil–Felix reaction in typhus fever, the Paul Bunnel test in infectious mononucleosis and the cold agglutinin test in primary atypical pneumonia are examples.

BIOLOGICAL CLASSES OF ANTIGENS

Depending on their ability to induce antibody formation, antigens are classified as T cell dependent (TD) and T cell independent (TI) antigens. Antibody production is the property of B lymphocytes. For the full expression of this function, however, the cooperation of T lymphocytes is necessary. Some antigens can directly stimulate antibody production by B cells, without the apparent participation of T cells. Such antigens are called TI antigens. Others that require T cell participation to generate an immune response are called TD antigens.

Several important differences exist between TI and TD antigens. TI antigens are structurally simple, being composed of a limited number of repeating epitopes, as in the case of the pneumococcal capsular polysaccharide, bacterial lipopolysaccharides and the flagellar protein flagellin. Their immune response is critically dose dependent. Too little is nonimmunogenic, while too much results in immunological tolerance rather than immunity. Their antibody response is usually limited to IgM and IgG3. They do not show immunological memory. TI antigens do not appear to require preliminary processing by macrophages. They are metabolised very slowly and remain in the body for long periods.

TD antigens, on the other hand, are structurally more complex, such as erythrocytes, serum proteins and a variety of protein–hapten complexes. They are immunogenic over a wide dose range and do not cause tolerance readily. They induce the full gamut of immunoglobulin isotypes—IgM, IgG, IgA and IgE. They show immunological memory, require preliminary processing, and are rapidly metabolised in the body.

Further Reading

Weir DM and J Stewart 1997. *Immunology*. 8th edn. Edinburgh: Churchill Livingstone.

Antibodies—Immunoglobulins

Towards the close of the nineteenth century, the humoral basis of immunity was established by the demonstration that following the introduction of an antigen into an animal, certain substances called antibodies appeared in the serum and tissue fluids, and reacted with the antigen specifically and in some observable manner. Depending on the observable reaction produced on mixing with antigens, the antibodies were designated variously as agglutinins, precipitins and so on. Sera having high antibody levels following infection or immunisation were called 'immune sera' (Fig. 12.1).

Fractionation of immune sera by half saturation with ammonium sulphate separated serum proteins into soluble albumins and insoluble globulins. Globulins could be separated into water soluble pseudoglobulins and insoluble euglobulins. Most

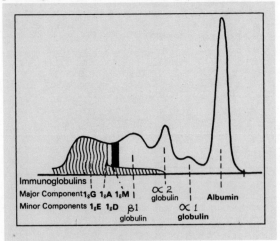

Fig. 12.1 Electrophoretic pattern of human serum showing the main components.

antibodies were found to be euglobulins. Tiselius (1937) separated serum proteins into albumin, alpha, beta and gammaglobulins based on their electrophoretic mobilities. Tiselius and Kabat (1938) showed that antibody activity was associated with the gammaglobulin fraction. The term gammaglobulin thereafter became synonymous with 'antibody'. Later, many antibodies, such as equine antitoxins, were found to migrate as beta or even alphaglobulins.

Sedimentation studies using the ultracentrifuge also disclosed the diversity of antibody molecules. Most antibody molecules sedimented at 7S* (mol. wt 150,000). Some were heavier – 19S globulins (mol. wt about 900,000), designated M or macroglobulins. The indiscriminate use of various terms (for example, the terms beta$_2$ M globulin, 19Sgamma globulin, gamma M globulin) to refer to the same fractions led to confusion. This was resolved when, in 1964, endorsed by the WHO, the generic term 'immunoglobulin' was internationally accepted for 'proteins of animal origin endowed with known antibody activity and for certain other proteins related to them by chemical structure'. The definition includes, besides antibody globulins, the abnormal proteins found in myeloma, macroglobulinemia, cryoglobulinemia and the naturally occurring subunits of immunoglobulins. Immunoglobulins are synthesised by plasma cells and to some extent by lymphocytes. Immunoglobulins provide a structural and chemical concept, while the term 'antibody' is a biological and functional concept. All antibodies are

*S = Svedberg Unit = A sedimentation constant of 1×10^{-13} seconds

immunoglobulins, but all immunoglobulins may not be antibodies.

Immunoglobulins constitute 20–25 per cent of the total serum proteins. Based on physicochemical and antigenic differences, five classes of immunoglobulins have been recognised—IgG, IgA, IgM, IgD and IgE. (Both Ig and γ are accepted abbreviations for immunoglobulins).

STRUCTURE

Studies involving the cleavage of the immunoglobulin molecule, poineered by Porter, Edelman, Nisonoff and their colleagues, have led to a detailed picture of its structure. Rabbit IgG antibody to egg albumin, digested by papain in the presence of cysteine, was split into two fractions— an insoluble fraction which crystallised in the cold (called *Fc* for *crystallisable*), and a soluble fragment which, while unable to precipitate with egg albumin, could still bind with it. This fragment is called the Fab (*antigen binding*) fragment. Each molecule of immunoglobulin is split by papain into three parts, one *Fc* and two *Fab* pieces, having a sedimentation coefficient of 3.5 S. When treated with pepsin, a 5 S fragment is obtained, which is composed essentially of two Fab fragments held together in position. It is bivalent and precipitates with the antigen. This fragment is called *F(ab')2*. The *Fc* portion is digested by pepsin into smaller fragments (Fig. 12.2).

Immunoglobulins are glycoproteins, each molecule consisting of two pairs of polypeptide chains of different sizes. The smaller chains are called 'light' (L) chains and the larger ones 'heavy' (H) chains. The L chain has a molecular weight of approximately 25,000 and the H chain of 50,000. The L chain is attached to the H chain by a disulphide bond. The two H chains are joined together by 1–5 S-S bonds, depending on the class of immunoglobulins (Fig. 12.3).

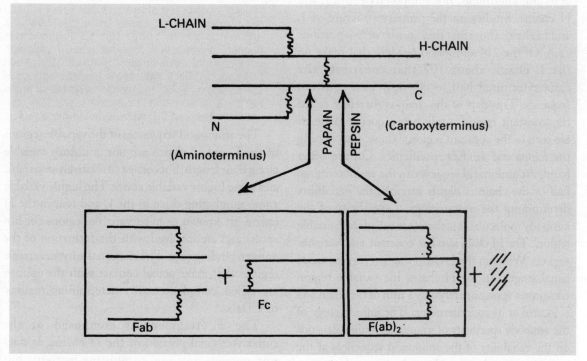

Fig. 12.2 **Basic structure of an immunoglobulin molecule and the fragments obtained by the cleavage by papain and pepsin**

The H chains are structurally and antigenically distinct for each class and are designated by the Greek letter corresponding to the immunoglobulin class as shown below:

Immunoglobulin class	H chain
IgG	γ (gamma)
IgA	α (alpha)
IgM	μ (mu)
IgD	δ (delta)
IgE	ε (epsilon)

The L chains are similar in all classes of immunoglobulins. They occur in two varieties, kappa (κ) and lambda (λ). A molecule of immunoglobulin may have either kappa or lambda chains, but never both together. *Kappa* and *lambda* are named after Korngold and Lapari who originally described them. The *kappa* and *lambda* chains occur in a ratio of about 2:1 in human sera.

The antigen combining site of the molecule is at its aminoterminus. It is composed of both L and H chains. Studies on the primary structure of L and H chains show that they consist of two portions each. Of the 214 aminoacid residues that make up the L chain, about 107 that constitute the carboxyterminal half, occur only in a constant sequence. This part of the chain is therefore called the 'constant region'. Only two sequence patterns are seen in the constant region – those determining the *kappa* and *lambda* specificities. On the other hand, the aminoacid sequence in the aminoterminal half of the chain is highly variable, the variability determining the immunological specificity of the antibody molecule. It is therefore called the 'variable region'. The H chain also has 'constant' and 'variable' regions. While in the L chain the two regions are of equal length, in the H chains the variable region constitutes approximately only a fifth of the chain and is located at its aminoterminus. The infinite range of the antibody specificity of immunoglobulins depends on the variability of the aminoacid sequences at the 'variable regions' of the H and L chains which form the antigen combining sites.

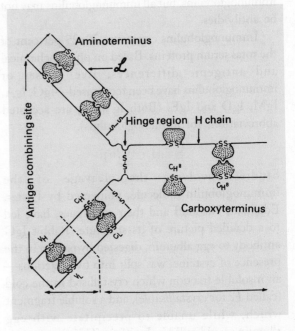

Fig.12.3 The four-peptide chain structure of the IgG molecule composed of two identical heavy (H) and two identical light (L) chains linked by interchains disulphide bonds. Loops formed by intrachain disulphide bonds are domains (shown stippled). Each chain has one domain in the variable region (VH and VL). Each light chain has one domain in the constant region (CL) while each heavy chain has three domains in the constant region (CH¹, CH² and CH³). Between CH¹ and CH² is the hinge region.

The aminoacid sequences of the variable regions of the L and H chains are not uniformly variable along their length, but consist of relatively invariable and some highly variable zones. The highly variable zones numbering three in the L and four in the H chains are known as hypervariable regions (or hot spots) and are involved with the formation of the antigen binding sites. The sites on the hypervariable regions that make actual contact with the epitope are called 'complementarity determining regions' or CDRs.

The *Fc* fragment is composed of the carboxyterminal portion of the H chains. It does not possess antigen combining activity but determines the biological properties of the immunoglobulin molecule such as complement fixation, placental transfer, skin fixation and catabolic rate. The portion of the H chain present in the *Fab* fragment is called the *Fd* piece. The H chain carries a carbohydrate moiety which is distinct for each class of immunoglobulins.

Each immunoglobulin peptide chain has internal disulphide links in addition to interchain disulphide bonds which bridge the H and L chains. These intrachain disulphide bonds form loops in the peptide chain, and each of the loops is compactly folded to form a globular domain, each domain having a separate function. The variable region domains, VL and VH, are responsible for the formation of a specific antigen binding site. The CH^2 region in IgG binds C1q in the classical complement sequence, and the CH^3 domain mediates adherence to the monocyte surface. The areas of the H chain in the C region between the first and second C region domains (CH^1 and CH^2) is the hinge region. It is more flexible and is more exposed to enzymes and chemicals. Papain acts here to produce one Fc and two Fab fragments (Fig. 12.3).

IMMUNOGLOBULIN CLASSES

Human sera contain IgG, IgA, IgM, IgD and IgE in the descending order of concentration. Table 12.1 shows their characteristics.

IgG: This is the major serum immunoglobulin, constituting about 80 per cent of the total. It has a molecular weight of 150,000 (7S). IgG may occasionally exist in a polymerised form. It is distributed approximately equally between the intravascular and extravascular compartments. It contains less carbohydrate than other immunoglobulins. It has a half–life of approximately 23 days. The catabolism of IgG is unique in that it varies with its serum concentration. When its level is raised, as in chronic malaria, kala azar or myeloma, the IgG synthesised against a particular antigen will be catabolised rapidly and may result in the particular antibody deficiency. Conversely, in hypogammaglobulinemia, the IgG given for treatment will be catabolised only slowly. The normal serum concentration of IgG is about 8–16 mg per ml.

IgG is the only maternal immunoglobulin that

Table 12.1 Some properties of immunoglobulin classes

	IgG	IgA*	IgM	IgD	IgE
Sedimentation coefficient (S)	7	7	19	7	8
Molecular weight	150,000	160,000	900,000	180,000	190,000
Serum concentration (mg/ml)	12	2	1.2	0.03	0.00004
Half life (days)	23	6	5	2–8	1–5
Daily production (mg/kg)	34	24	3.3	0.4	0.0023
Intravascular distribution (per cent)	45	42	80	75	50
Carbohydrate (per cent)	3	8	12	13	12
Complement fixation					
Classical	++	–	+++	–	–
Alternative	–	+	–	–	–
Placental transport	+	–	–	–	–
Present in milk	+	+	–	–	–
Selective secretion by seromucus glands	–	+	–	–	–
Heat stability (56 °C)	+	+	+	+	–

* IgA may occur in 7S, 9S and 11S forms.

is normally transported across the placenta and provides natural passive immunity in the newborn. It is not synthesised by the fetus in any significant amount. IgG binds to microorganisms and enhances their phagocytosis. Extracellular killing of target cells coated with IgG antibody is mediated through recognition of the surface Fc fragment by K cells bearing the appropriate receptors. Interaction of IgG complexes with platelet Fc receptors probably leads to aggregation and vasoactive amine release. IgG alone, among human immunoglobulins, can fix itself to guinea pig skin, but the significance of this property is not known. IgG participates in most immunological reactions such as complement fixation, precipitation, and neutralisation of toxins and viruses. It may be considered a general purpose antibody, protective against those infectious agents which are active in the blood and tissues. Passively administered IgG suppresses the homologous antibody synthesis by a feedback process. This property is utilised in the isoimmunisation of women by the administration of anti-Rh(D) IgG during delivery. With most antigens, IgG is a late antibody and makes its appearance after the initial immune response which is IgM in nature.

Four subclasses of IgG have been recognised (IgG1, IgG2, IgG3, IgG4), each possessing a distinct type of gamma chain, identifiable with specific antisera. The four IgG subclasses are distributed in human serum in the approximate proportions of 65 per cent, 23 per cent, 8 per cent and 4 per cent, respectively.

IgA: IgA is the second most abundant class, constituting about 10–13 per cent of serum immunoglobulins. The normal serum level is 0.6–4.2 mg per ml. It has a half life of 6–8 days. It is the major immunoglobulin in the colostrum, saliva and tears.

IgA occurs in two forms. **Serum IgA** is principally a monomeric 7S molecule (MW about 160,000). IgA found on mucosal surfaces and in secretions is a dimer formed by two monomer units joined together at their carboxyterminals by a glycopeptide termed the **J chain** (J for joining). This is called the **secretory IgA** (SIgA). Dimeric SIgA is synthesised by plasma cells situated near the mucosal or glandular epithelium. The J chain is also produced in the same cells. J chains are present also in other polymeric immunoglobulins such as IgM (Fig. 12.4).

SIgA contains another glycine rich polypeptide called the **secretory component** or **secretory piece**. This is not produced by lymphoid cells but by mucosal or glandular epithelial cells. Dimeric IgA binds to a receptor on the surface of the epithelial cells and is endocytosed and transported across the cells to the luminal surface. During this process, a part of the receptor remains attached to the IgA dimer. This part is known as the secretory component. The secretory piece is believed to protect IgA from denaturation by bacterial proteases in sites such as the intestinal mucosa which have a rich and varied bacterial flora. SIgA is a much larger molecule than serum IgA (11S; MW about 400,000).

SIgA is selectively concentrated in secretions

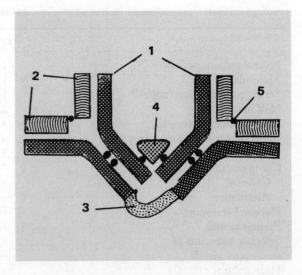

Fig. 12.4 Secretory IgA. 1. Heavy chain. 2. Light chain. 3. J chain. 4. Secretory component. 5. Disulphide bond

and on mucus surfaces forming an 'antibody paste' and is believed to play an important role in local immunity against respiratory and intestinal pathogens. Secretory IgA is relatively resistant to the digestive enzymes and reducing agents. IgA antibodies may function by inhibiting the adherence of microorganisms to the surface of mucosal cells by covering the organisms and thereby preventing their entry into body tissues. IgA does not fix complement but can activate the alternative complement pathway. It promotes phagocytosis and intracellular killing of microorganisms.

Two IgA subclasses have been described, IgA_1 and IgA_2. IgA_2 lacks interchain disulphide bonds between the heavy and light chains. Though IgA_2 is a minor component of serum IgA, it is the dominant form in the secretions.

IgM: IgM constitutes 5–8 per cent of serum immunoglobulins, with a normal level of 0.5–2 mg per ml. It has a half-life of about five days. It is a heavy molecule (19S; mol. wt 900,000 to 1,000,000, hence called 'the millionaire molecule'). IgM molecules are polymers of five four-peptide subunits, each bearing an extra CH domain (Fig. 12.5). As with IgA, polymerisation of the subunits depends upon the presence of the J chain. Though the theoretical valency is ten, this is observed only with small haptens. With larger antigens, the effective valency falls to five, probably due to steric hindrance. Most of IgM (80 per cent) is intravascular in distribution. Phylogenetically, IgM is the oldest immunoglobulin class. It is also the earliest immunoglobulin to be synthesised by the fetus, beginning by about 20 weeks of age. As it is not transported across the placenta, the presence of IgM in the fetus or newborn indicates intrauterine infection and its detection is useful in the diagnosis of congenital infections such as syphilis, rubella, HIV infection and toxoplasmosis. IgM antibodies are relatively short lived, disappearing earlier than IgG. Hence, their demonstration in serum indicates recent infection. Treatment of serum with 0.12M 2-mercaptoethanol selectively destroys IgM

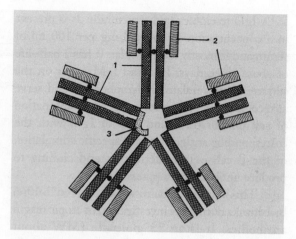

Fig. 12.5. IgM molecule. 1. Heavy chain. 2. Light. 3. J chain.

without affecting IgG antibodies. This is a simple method for the differential estimation of IgG and IgM antibodies.

The isohemagglutinins (anti-A, anti-B) and many other natural antibodies to microorganisms are usually IgM, as also antibodies to typhoid 'O' antigen (endotoxin) and reagin antibodies in syphilis.

The unique structural features of IgM appear particularly suited to the biological role of providing protection against microorganisms and other large antigens that have repeating antigenic determinants on their surface. A single molecule of IgM can bring about immune hemolysis, whereas 1000 IgG molecules are required for the same effect. IgM is also 500–1000 times more effective than IgG in opsonisation, 100 times more effective in bactericidal action and about 20 times in bacterial agglutination. In the neutralisation of toxins and viruses, however, it is less active than IgG. Being largely confined to the intravascular space, IgM is believed to be responsible for protection against blood invasion by microorganisms. IgM deficiency is often associated with septicemias.

Monomeric IgM is the major antibody receptor on the surface of B lymphocytes for antigen recognition.

IgD: IgD resembles IgG structurally. It is present in a concentration of about 3 mg per 100 ml of serum and is mostly intravascular. It has a half–life of about three days. IgD and IgM occur on the surface of unstimulated B lymphocytes and serve as recognition receptors for antigens. Combination of cell membrane bound IgD or IgM with the corresponding antigen leads to specific stimulation of the B cell—either activation and cloning to produce antibody, or suppression.

IgE: This immunoglobulin was discovered in 1966 by Ishizaka during the investigation of atopic reagin antibodies. It is an 8S molecule (MW about 190,000), with a half life of about two days. It resembles IgG structurally. It exhibits unique properties such as heat lability (inactivated at 56 °C in one hour) and affinity for the surface of tissue cells (particularly mast cells) of the same species (homocytotropism). It mediates the Prausnitz–Kustner reaction. It is susceptible to mercaptoethanol. It does not pass the placental barrier or fix complement. It is mostly extravascular in distribution. Normal serum contains only traces (a few nanograms per ml) but greatly elevated levels are seen in atopic (type 1 allergic) conditions such as asthma, hay fever and eczema. Children living in insanitary conditions, with a high load of intestinal parasites, have high serum levels of IgE.

IgE is chiefly produced in the linings of the respiratory and intestinal tracts. IgE deficiency has been associated with IgA deficiency in individuals with impaired immunity who present undue susceptibility to infection.

IgE is responsible for the anaphylactic type of hypersensitivity. The physiological role of IgE appears to be protection against pathogens by mast cell degranulation and release of inflammatory mediators. It is also believed to have a special role in defence against helminthic infections.

In general, IgG protects the body fluids, IgA the body surfaces and IgM the bloodstream, while IgE mediates reaginic hypersensitivity. IgD is a recognition molecule on the surface of B lymphocytes.

ABNORMAL IMMUNOGLOBULINS

Apart from antibodies, other structurally similar proteins are seen in serum in many pathological processes, and sometimes even in healthy persons. The earliest description of an abnormal immunoglobulin was the discovery by Bence Jones (1847) of the protein that bears his name. Bence Jones protein is found typically in multiple myeloma. It can be identified in urine by its characteristic property of coagulation when heated to 50 °C but redissolving at 70 °C. Bence Jones proteins are the light chains of immunoglobulins and so may occur as the *kappa* or *lambda* forms. But in any one patient, the chain is either *kappa* or *lambda* only, and never both, being uniform in all other respects also. This is because myeloma is a plasma cell dyscrasia in which there is unchecked proliferation of one clone of plasma cells, resulting in the excessive production of the particular immunoglobulin synthesised by the clone. Such immunoglobulins are, therefore, called monoclonal.

Multiple myeloma may affect plasma cells synthesising IgG, IgA, IgD or IgE. Similar involvement of IgM producing cells is known as *Waldenstrom's macroglobulinemia*. In this condition, there occurs excessive production of the respective myeloma proteins (M proteins) and of their light chains (Bence Jones proteins). A different disorder is found in 'heavy chain disease', which is a lymphoid neoplasia characterised by the overproduction of the Fc parts of the immuno-globulin heavy chains.

Cryoglobulinemia is a condition in which there is the formation of a gel or a precipitate on cooling the serum, which redissolves on warming. It may not always be associated with disease but is often found in myelomas, macroglobulinemias and autoimmune conditions such as systemic lupus erythematosus. Most cryoglobulins consist of either IgG, IgM or their mixed precipitates.

Because of the monoclonal nature of Bence Jones and other M proteins, they have been valuable models for the understanding of immunoglobulin structure and function.

IMMUNOGLOBULIN SPECIFICITIES

The immunoglobulin specificity of the greatest biological importance is idiotypic specificity pertaining to the nature of the antigen binding sites (paratopes). The specific antigenic determinants on the paratope are called **idiotopes**. The sum total of idiotopes on an Ig molecule constitutes its idiotype.

By immunisation with Fab fragments, antiidiotypic antibodies can be produced. These resemble the epitopes of the original antigen. Used as a vaccine, these show protection against the original antigen (pathogen or tumour) in experimental animals. Sequential antiidiotypic antibody formation is the basis of Jerne's network hypothesis of immune regulation.

Immunoglobulins exhibit other genetically determined specificities based on their antigenic structure. The antigenic specificities which distinguish between the different classes and subclasses of immunoglobulins present in all normal individuals of a given species are termed isotypic specificities. Antigenic specificities which distinguish immunoglobulins of the same class, between different groups of individuals in the same species, are called allotypic specificities.

Immunoglobulin allotypes have been studied in detail in the rabbit and guinea pig by using type-specific immune sera. Such deliberate immunisation is not possible in human beings, but antiallotype-specific antibodies may develop following blood tranfusion or passage of maternal IgG into the fetus. Antiallotype antibodies are also found in sera containing 'rheumatoid arthritis factor'.

Two allotypic systems are known in humans – the Gm system (for gamma marker) and the InV system (abbreviation of patient's name). The Gm is associated with the Fc portion of the IgG heavy chain. More than 25 Gm types have been identified so far. The InV system is associated with the kappa light chain and so has been renamed Km. Three Km allotypes have been identified.

Genetic markers associated with IgA are called 'Am'. To date, in the human system no allotypic markers have been found for lambda light chains or μ, δ or $\in$ heavy chains.

Further Reading

Goodman JW. 1991. Immunoglobulin structure and function. 7th edn. In *Basic and Clinical Immunology.*
Roitt IM and O Delves ed. 1992. *Encyclopedia of Immunology.* London: Academic Press.

Antigen—Antibody Reactions

Antigens and antibodies, by definition, combine with each other specifically and in an observable manner. The reactions between antigens and antibodies serve several purposes. In the body, they form the basis of antibody mediated immunity in infectious diseases, or of tissue injury in some types of hypersensitivity and autoimmune diseases. In the laboratory, they help in the diagnosis of infections, in epidemiological surveys, in the identification of infectious agents and of noninfectious antigens such as enzymes. In general, these reactions can be used for the detection and quantitation of either antigens or antibodies. Antigen–antibody reactions in vitro are known as *serological reactions.*

The reactions between antigens and antibodies occur in three stages. The primary stage is the initial interaction between the two, without any visible effects. This reaction is rapid, occurs even at low temperatures and obeys the general laws of physical chemistry and thermodynamics. The reaction is reversible, the combination between antigen and antibody molecules being effected by the weaker intermolecular forces such as Van der Waal's forces, ionic bonds and hydrogen bonding, rather than by the firmer covalent bonding. The primary reaction can be detected by estimating free and bound antigen or antibody separately in the reaction mixture by a number of physical and chemical methods, including the use of markers such as radioactive isotopes, fluorescent dyes or ferritin.

In most instances, but not all, the primary stage is followed by the secondary stage, leading to demonstrable events such as precipitation, agglutination, lysis of cells, killing of live antigens,

neutralisation of toxins and other biologically active antigens, fixation of complement, immobilisation of motile organisms and enhancement of phagocytosis. When such reactions were discovered one by one, it was believed that a different type of antibody was responsible for each type of reaction and the antibodies came to be designated by the reactions they were thought to produce. Thus, the antibody causing agglutination was called *agglutinin*, that causing precipitation *precipitin*, and so on, and the corresponding antigen, *agglutinogen, precipitinogen*, and so on. By the 1920s, this view was replaced by Zinsser's unitarian hypothesis which held that an antigen gave rise to only one antibody, which was capable of producing all the different reactions depending on the nature of the antigen and the conditions of the reaction. Both these extreme views are fallacious. While it is true that a single antibody can cause precipitation, agglutination and most of the other serological reactions, it is also true that an antigen can stimulate the production of different classes of immunoglobulins which differ in their reaction capacities as well as in other properties (Table 13.1).

Some antigen–antibody reactions occurring in vivo initiate chain reactions that lead to neutralisation or destruction of injurious antigens, or to tissue damage. These are tertiary reactions and include humonal immunity against infectious diseaseas as well as clinical allergy and other immunological diseases.

GENERAL FEATURES OF ANTIGEN–ANTIBODY REACTIONS

Antigen–antibody reactions have the following general characteristics:

Table 13.1 Comparative efficiency of the immunoglobulin classes in different serological reactions

Reaction	IgG	IgM	IgA
Precipitation	Strong	Weak	Variable
Agglutination	Weak	Strong	Moderate
Complement fixation	Strong	Weak	Negative

1. The reaction is specific, an antigen combining only with its homologous antibody and vice versa. The specificity, however, is not absolute and 'cross-reactions' may occur due to antigenic similarity or relatedness.
2. Entire molecules react and not fragments. When an antigenic determinant present in a large molecule or on a 'carrier' particle reacts with its antibody, whole molecules or particles are agglutinated.
3. There is no denaturation of the antigen or the antibody during the reaction.
4. The combination occurs at the surface. Therefore, it is the surface antigens that are immunologically relevant. Antibodies to the surface antigens of infectious agents are generally protective.
5. The combination is firm but reversible. The firmness of the union is influenced by the affinity and avidity of the reaction. Affinity refers to the intensity of attraction between the antigen and antibody molecules. It is a function of the closeness of fit between an epitope and the antigen combining region of its antibody. Avidity is the strength of the bond after the formation of the antigen–antibody complexes. It reflects the overall combining property of the various antibody molecules in an antiserum, possessing different affinity constants with the multiple epitopes of the antigen.
6. Both antigens and antibodies participate in the formation of agglutinates or precipitates.
7. Antigens and antibodies can combine in varying proportions, unlike chemicals with fixed valencies. Both antigens and antibodies are multivalent. Antibodies are generally bivalent, though IgM molecules may have five or ten combining sites. Antigens may have valencies upto hundreds.

MEASUREMENT OF ANTIGEN AND ANTIBODY

Many methods are available for the measurement of antigens and antibodies participating in the primary, secondary or tertiary reactions. Measurement may be in terms of mass (for example, mg nitrogen) or more commonly as units or titre. The antibody titre of a serum is the highest dilution of the serum which shows an observable reaction with the antigen in the particular test. The titre of a serum is influenced by the nature and quantity of the antigen and the type and conditions of the test. Antigens may also be titrated against sera.

Two important parameters of serological tests are sensitivity and specificity. Sensitivity refers to the ability of the test to detect even very minute quantities of antigen or antibody. When a test is highly sensitive, false negative results will be absent or minimal. Specificity refers to the ability of the test to detect reactions between homologous antigens and antibodies only, and with no other. In a highly specific test, false positive reactions are absent or minimal. In general, sensitivity and specificity of a test are in inverse proportion.

Originally, reagents for serological tests were prepared by individual laboratories, leading to batch variation, and lack of reproducibility and comparability. The commercial availability of ready-made standardised test kits has simplified test procedures, improved quality and greatly enlarged their scope and use.

SEROLOGICAL REACTIONS

PRECIPITATION REACTION

When a soluble antigen combines with its antibody in the presence of electrolytes (NaCl) at a suitable temperature and pH, the antigen–antibody complex forms an insoluble precipitate. When, instead of sedimenting, the precipitate remains suspended as floccules, the reaction is known as *flocculation*. Precipitation can take place in liquid media or in gels such as agar, agarose or polyacrylamide.

The amount of precipitate formed is greatly influenced by the relative proportions of antigens and antibodies. If increasing quantities of antigens are added to the same amount of antiserum in different tubes, precipitation will be found to occur most rapidly and abundantly in one of the middle tubes in which the antigen and antibody are present in optimal or equivalent proportions. In the preceding tubes in which the antibody is in excess, and in the later tubes in which the antigen is in excess the precipitation will be weak or even absent.

For a given antigen–antibody system, the optimal or equivalent ratio will be constant, irrespective of the quantity of the reactants. If the amounts of precipitate in the different tubes are plotted on a graph, the resulting curve will have three phases: an ascending part (prozone or zone of antibody excess), a peak (zone of equivalence) and a descending part (postzone or zone of antigen excess) (Fig. 13.1). This is called the zone phenomenon. Zoning occurs in agglutination and some other serological reactions. The prozone is of importance in clinical serology, as sera rich in antibody may sometimes give a false negative precipitation or agglutination result, unless several dilutions are tested.

MECHANISM OF PRECIPITATION

Marrack (1934) proposed the lattice hypothesis to explain the mechanism of precipitation. According to this concept, which is supported by considerable experimental evidence and is now widely accepted, multivalent antigens combine with bivalent

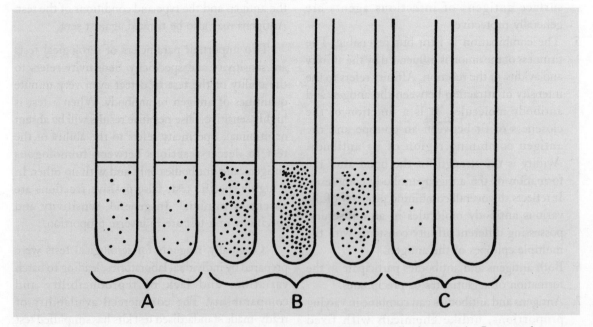

Fig. 13.1 A quantitative precipitation test showing: A. prozone (zone of antibody excess), B. zone of equivalence, C. zone of antigen excess

antibodies in varying proportions, depending on the antigen–antibody ratio in the reacting mixture. Precipitation results when a large lattice is formed consisting of alternating antigen and antibody molecules. This is possible only in the zone of equivalence. In the zones of antigen or antibody excess, the lattice does not enlarge, as the valencies of the antibody and the antigen, respectively, are fully satisfied (Fig. 13.2) The lattice hypothesis holds good for agglutination also.

APPLICATIONS OF PRECIPITATION REACTION

The precipitation test may be carried out as either a qualitative or quantitative test. It is very sensitive in the detection of antigens and as little as 1 µg of protein can be detected by precipitation tests. It therefore finds forensic application in the identification of blood and seminal stains, and in testing for food adulterants. Precipitation is relatively less sensitive for the detection of antibodies.

The following types of precipitation and flocculation tests are in common use:

Ring test: This, the simplest type of precipitation test, consists of layering the antigen solution over a column of antiserum in a narrow tube. A precipitate forms at the junction of the two liquids. Ring tests have only a few clinical applications now. Examples are Ascoli's thermoprecipitin test and the grouping of streptococci by the Lancefield technique.

Slide test: When a drop each of the antigen and antiserum are placed on a slide and mixed by shaking, floccules appear. The VDRL test for syphilis is an example of slide flocculation.

Tube test: The Kahn test for syphilis is an example of a tube flocculation test. A quantitative tube flocculation test is employed for the standardisation of toxins and toxoids. Serial dilutions of the toxin/toxoid are added to the tubes containing a fixed quantity of the antitoxin. The amount of toxin or toxoid that flocculates optimally with one unit of the antitoxin is defined as an Lf dose.

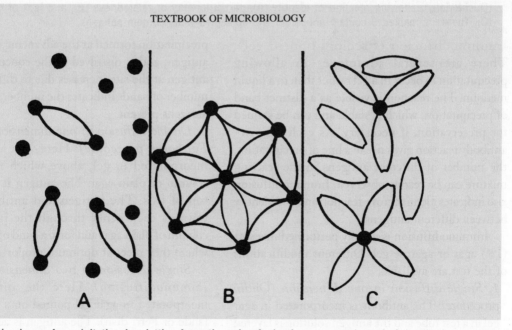

TEXTBOOK OF MICROBIOLOGY

A   B   C

Fig. 13.2 Mechanism of precipitation by lattice formation. In A (antigen excess) and C (antibody excess), lattice formation does not occur. In B (zone of equivalence), lattice formation and precipitation occur optimally. The dark spheres indicate antigen and the spindles bivalent antibody molecules.

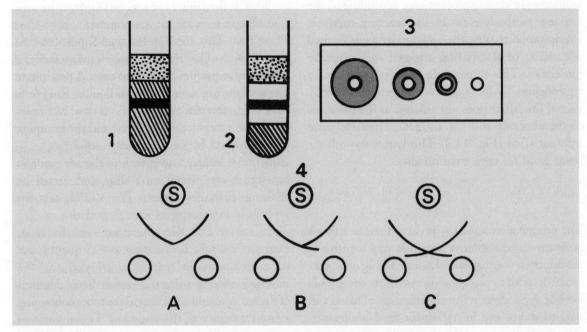

Fig. 13.3 Different types of immunodiffusion: 1. Single diffusion in one dimension (Oudin) 2. Double diffusion in one dimension (Oakley–Fulthorpe) 3. Radial immunodiffusion 4. Double diffusion in two dimensions (Ouchterlony), showing reaction of identity (A), partial identity or relatedness (B), and lack of relatedness (C). The wells marked S contain antiserum and unmarked wells contain antigens.

Immunodiffusion (Precipitation in gel): There are several advantages in allowing precipitation to occur in a gel rather than in a liquid medium. The reaction is visible as a distinct band of precipitation, which is stable and can be stained for preservation, if necessary. As each antigen–antibody reaction gives rise to a line of precipitation, the number of different antigens in the reacting mixture can be readily observed. Immunodiffusion also indicates identity, cross-reaction and nonidentity between different antigens.

Immunodiffusion is usually performed in a soft (1%) agar or agarose gel. Different modifications of the test are available:

1. Single diffusion in one dimension (Oudin procedure): The antibody is incorporated in agar gel in a test tube and the antigen solution is layered over it. The antigen diffuses downward through the agar gel, forming a line of precipitation that appears to move downwards. This is due to the precipitation formed at the advancing front of the antigen, and is dissolved as the concentration of antigen at the site increases due to diffusion. The number of bands indicates the number of different antigens present.

2. Double diffusion in one dimension (Oakley–Fulthorpe procedure): Here, the antibody is incorporated in gel, above which is placed a column of plain agar. The antigen is layered on top of this. The antigen and antibody move towards each other through the intervening column of plain agar and form a band of precipitate where they meet at optimum proportion.

3. Single diffusion in two dimensions (Radial immunodiffusion): Here the antiserum is incorporated in agar gel poured on a flat surface (slide or Petri dish). The antigen is added to the wells cut on the surface of the gel. It diffuses radially from the well and forms ring-shaped bands of precipitation (halos) concentrically around the well. The diameter of the halo gives an estimate of the concentration of the antigen. This method has been employed for the estimation of the immunoglobulin classes in sera and for screening sera for antibodies to influenza viruses, among others.

4. Double diffusion in two dimensions (Ouchterlony procedure): This is the immunodiffusion method most widely employed and helps to compare different antigens and antisera directly. Agar gel is poured on a slide and wells are cut using a template. The antiserum is placed in the central well and different antigens in the surrounding wells. If two adjacent antigens are identical, the lines of precipitate formed by them will fuse. If they are unrelated, the lines will cross each other. Cross-reaction or partial identity is indicated by spur formation (Fig. 13.3). A special variety of double diffusion in two dimensions is the Elek test for toxigenicity in diphtheria bacilli. When diphtheria bacilli are streaked at right angles to a filter paper strip carrying the antitoxin implanted on a plate of suitable medium, arrowhead shaped lines of precipitation appear on incubation, if the bacillus is toxigenic.

5. Immunoelectrophoresis: The resolving power of immunodiffusion was greatly enhanced when Grabar and Williams devised the technique of immunoelectrophoresis. This involves the electrophoretic separation of a composite antigen (such as serum) into its constituent proteins, followed by immunodiffusion against its antiserum, resulting in separate precipitin lines, indicating reaction between each individual protein with its antibody. This enables identification and approximate quantitation of the various proteins present in the serum. The technique is performed on agar or agarose gel on a slide, with an antigen well and an antibody trough cut on it. The test serum is placed in the antigen well and electrophoresed for about an hour. Antibody against human serum is then placed in the trough

and diffusion allowed to proceed for 18–24 hours. The resulting precipitin lines can be photographed and the slides dried, stained and preserved for record. Over 30 different proteins can be identified by this method in human serum. This is useful for testing for normal and abnormal proteins in serum and urine (Fig. 13.4).

Electroimmunodiffusion: The development of precipitin lines can be speeded up by electrically driving the antigen and antibody. Various methods have been described combining electrophoresis with diffusion. Of these, one-dimensional double electroimmunodiffusion (counterimmuno-electrophoresis) and one-dimensional single electroimmunodiffusion (rocket electrophoresis) are used frequently in the clinical laboratory.

1. Counterimmunoelectrophoresis (CIE, counter-current immunoelectrophoresis): This involves simultaneous electrophoresis of the antigen and antibody in gel in opposite directions resulting in precipitation at a point between them (Fig. 13.5). This method produces visible precipitation lines within thirty minutes and is ten times more sensitive than the standard double diffusion techniques. The clinical applications are for detecting various antigens such as alphafetoprotein in serum and specific antigens of cryptococcus and meningococcus in the cerebrospinal fluid.

2. One dimensional single electroimmunodiffusion (rocket electrophoresis): The main application of this technique is for quantitative estimation of antigens. The antiserum to the antigen to be quantitated is incorporated in agarose and gelled on the glass slide. The antigen, in increasing concentrations, is placed in wells punched in the set gel. The antigen is then electrophoresed into the antibody containing agarose (Fig. 13.6). The pattern of immunoprecipitation resembles a rocket and hence the name.

A variant of this is Laurell's two-dimensional electrophoresis. In this technique, the antigen mixture is first electrophoretically separated in a direction perpendicular to that of the final rocket

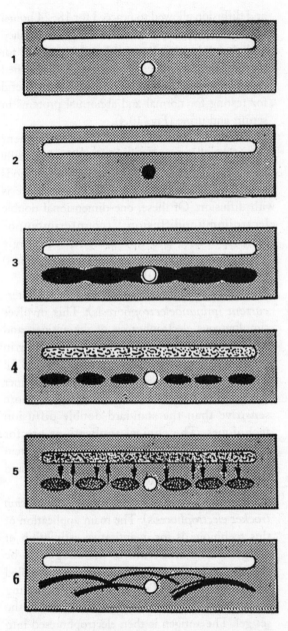

Fig. 13.4 Immunoelectrophoresis. 1. Semisolid agar layered on the glass slide. A well for antigen and a trough for antiserum cut out of agar. 2. Antigen well filled with human serum. 3. Serum separated by electrophoresis. 4. Antiserum trough filled with antiserum to whole human serum. 5. Serum and antiserum allowed to diffuse into agar. 6. Precipitin lines form for individual serum proteins.

stage. By this method one can quantitate each of several antigens in a mixture (Fig. 13.7).

AGGLUTINATION REACTION

When a particulate antigen is mixed with its antibody in the presence of electrolytes at a suitable temperature and pH, the particles are clumped or agglutinated. Agglutination is more sensitive than precipitation for the detection of antibodies. The same principles govern agglutination and precipitation. Agglutination occurs optimally when antigens and antibodies react in equivalent proportions. The zone phenomenon may be seen when either an antibody or an antigen is in excess. 'Incomplete' or 'monovalent' antibodies do not cause agglutination, though they combine with the antigen. They may act as 'blocking' antibodies, inhibiting agglutination by the complete antibody added subsequently.

APPLICATIONS OF AGGLUTINATION REACTION

Slide agglutination: When a drop of the appropriate antiserum is added to a smooth, uniform suspension of a particulate antigen in a drop of saline on a slide or tile, agglutination takes place. A positive result is indicated by the clumping together of the particles and the clearing of the drop. The reaction is facilitated by mixing the antigen and the antiserum with a loop or by gently rocking the slide. Depending on the titre of the serum, agglutination may occur instantly or within seconds. Clumping occurring after a minute may be due to drying of the fluid and should be disregarded. It is essential to have on the same slide a control consisting of the antigen suspension in saline, without the antiserum, to ensure that the antigen is not autoagglutinable. Agglutination is usually visible to the naked eye but may sometimes require confirmation under the microscope. Slide agglutination is a routine procedure for the identification of many bacterial isolates from clinical specimens. It is also the method used for blood grouping and cross-matching.

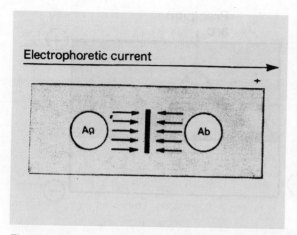

Fig. 13.5 Counterimmunoelectrophoresis (CIE). Antigen and antibody are driven together by an electric current and a precipitin line forms.

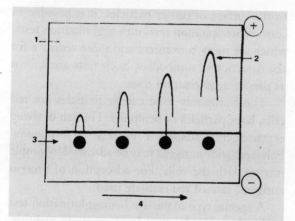

Fig. 13.6 Rocket electrophoresis. Antigen is driven into gel containing antibody. 1. Antibody in agarose gel. 2. Precipitinares 3. Antigen wells 4. Increasing antigen concentration.

Tube agglutination: This is a standard quantitative method for the measurement of antibodies. When a fixed volume of a particulate antigen suspension is added to an equal volume of serial dilutions of an antiserum in test tubes, the agglutination titre of the serum can be estimated. Tube agglutination is routinely employed for the serological diagnosis of typhoid, brucellosis and typhus fever.

In the Widal test used in typhoid, two types of antigens are used. The 'H' or the flagellar antigen on combining with its antibody forms large, loose, fluffy clumps resembling wisps of cottonwool. The O or somatic antigen forms tight, compact deposits resembling chalk powder. Agglutinated bacilli spread out in a disclike pattern at the bottom of the tubes.

The tube agglutination test for brucellosis may be complicated by the prozone phenomenon and the presence of 'blocking' antibodies. Several dilutions of the serum should be tested to prevent false negative results due to prozone. Incomplete or blocking antibodies may be detected by doing the test in hypertonic (5%) saline or albumin saline, or more reliably by the antiglobulin (Coombs) test.

The Weil–Felix reaction for serodiagnosis of typhus fevers is a heterophile agglutination test and is based on the sharing of a common antigen between typhus rickettsiae and some strains of proteus bacilli. Another example of the heterophile agglutination test is the *Streptococcus* MG agglutination test for the diagnosis of primary atypical pneumonia.

Examples of agglutination tests using red cells as antigens are the Paul Bunnel test and the cold agglutination test. The former is based on the presence of sheep cell agglutinins in the sera of infectious mononucleosis patients, which are adsorbed by ox red cells but not by guinea pig kidney extract. The cold agglutination test is positive in mycoplasmal (primary atypical) pneumonia. The patient's sera agglutinate human O group erythrocytes at 4°C, the agglutination being reversible at 37 °C.

The antiglobulin (Coombs) test: The antiglobulin test was devised by Coombs, Mourant and Race (1945) for the detection of anti-Rh antibodies that do not agglutinate Rh positive erythrocytes in saline. When sera containing incomplete anti-Rh antibodies are mixed with Rh positive red cells, the antibody globulin coats the surface of the erythrocytes, though they are not agglutinated. When such erythrocytes coated with

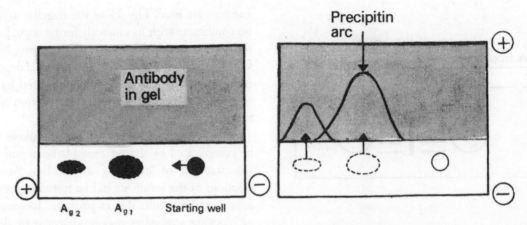

Fig.13.7 Laurell's variant of rocket electrophoresis (two-dimensional immunoelectrophoresis). First run: antigens are separated on the basis of electrophoretic mobility. The second run at right angles to the first drives the antigens into the antiserum containing gel to form precipitation peaks. The area of the peak is proportional to the concentration of the antigen.

the antibody globulin are washed free of all unattached protein and treated with a rabbit antiserum against human gammaglobulin (antiglobulin or Coombs serum), the cells are agglutinated. This is the principle of the antiglobulin test (Fig. 13.8).

The Coombs test may be direct or indirect. In the direct Coombs test, the sensitisation of the erythrocytes with incomplete antibodies takes place in vivo, as in the hemolytic disease of the newborn due to Rh incompatibility. When the red cells of erythroblastotic infants are washed free of unattached protein and then mixed with a drop of Coombs serum, agglutination results. The direct Coombs test is often negative in hemolytic disease due to ABO incompatibility.

In the indirect Coombs test, sensitisation of red cells with the antibody globulin is performed in vitro. Originally employed for detection of anti-Rh antibodies, the Coombs test is useful for demonstrating any type of incomplete or nonagglutinating antibody, as, for example, in brucellosis.

Passive agglutination test: The only difference between the requirements for the precipitation and agglutination tests is the physical nature of the antigen. By attaching soluble antigens to the surface of carrier particles, it is possible to convert precipitation tests into agglutination tests, which are more convenient and more sensitive for the detection of antibodies. Such tests are known as *passive agglutination tests.*

The commonly used carrier particles are red cells, latex particles or bentonite. Human or sheep erythrocytes adsorb a variety of antigens. Polysaccharide antigens may be adsorbed by simple mixing with the cells. For adsorption of protein antigens, tanned red cells are used.

A special type of passive hemagglutination test is the Rose–Waaler test. In rheumatoid arthritis, an autoantibody (RA factor) appears in the serum, which acts as an antibody to gammaglobulin. The RA factor is able to agglutinate red cells coated with globulins. The antigen used for the test is a suspension of sheep erythrocytes sensitised with a subagglutinating dose of rabbit antisheep erythrocyte antibody (amboceptor).

Polystyrene latex, which can be manufactured as uniform spherical particles, 0.8–1 m in diameter, can adsorb several types of antigens. Latex agglutination tests (latex fixation tests) are widely employed in the clinical laboratory for the detection of ASO, CRP, RA factor, HCG and many other antigens.

Passive agglutination tests are very sensitive and yield high titres, but may give false positive results. When instead of the antigen, the antibody is adsorbed to carrier particles in tests for estimation of antigens, the technique is known as reversed passive agglutination.

COMPLEMENT FIXATION TEST (CFT)

Complement takes part in many immunological reactions and is absorbed during the combination of antigens with their antibodies. In the presence of the appropriate antibodies, complement lyses erythrocytes, kills and, in some cases, lyses bacteria, immobilises motile organisms, promotes phagocytosis and immune adherence and contributes to tissue damage in certain types of hypersensitivity.

The ability of antigen antibody complexes to 'fix' complement is made use of in the complement fixation test (CFT). This is a very versatile and sensitive test, applicable with various types of antigens and antibodies and capable of detecting as little as 0.04 mg of antibody nitrogen and 0.1 mg of antigen. CFT is a complex procedure consisting of two steps and five reagents—antigen, antibody, complement, sheep erythrocytes and amboceptor (rabbit antibody to sheep red cells). Each of these reagents has to be separately standardised.

The antigen may be soluble or particulate. The antiserum should be heated at 56 °C (inactivated) for half an hour before the test to destroy any complement activity the serum may have and also to remove some nonspecific inhibitors of complement present in some sera (anticomplementary activity). The source of

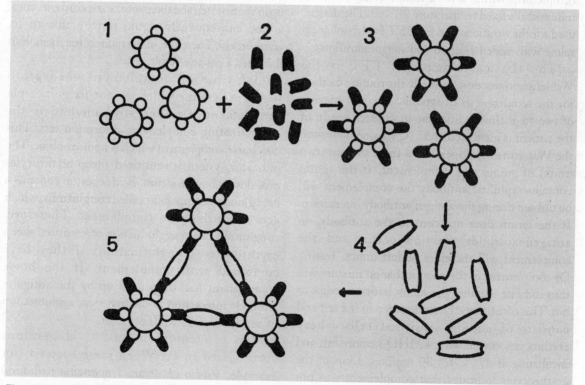

Fig. 13.8 Antiglobulin (Coombs) test. Rh positive erythrocytes (1) are mixed with incomplete antibody (2) The antibody coats the cells (3) but, being incomplete, cannot produce agglutination. On addition of antiglobulin serum (4) which is complete antibody to immunoglobulin, agglutination takes place.

complement is guinea pig serum. As complement activity is heat labile, the serum should be freshly drawn, or preserved either in the lyophilised or frozen state or with special preservatives, as in Richardson's method. The guinea pig serum should be titrated for complement activity. One unit or minimum hemolytic dose (MHD) of complement is defined as the highest dilution of the guinea pig serum that lyses one unit volume of washed sheep erythrocytes in the presence of excess hemolysin (amboceptor) within a fixed time (usually 30 or 60 minutes) at a fixed temperature (37 °C). The amboceptor should be titrated for hemolytic activity. One MHD of amboceptor is defined as the least amount (or highest dilution) of the inactivated amboceptor that lyses one unit volume of washed sheep erythrocytes in the presence of excess complement within a fixed time (usually 30 or 60 minutes) at a fixed temperature (37 °C). The diluent used for the titrations and for CFT is physiological saline with added calcium and magnesium ions.

The classical example of CFT is the Wassermann reaction, formerly the routine method for the serodiagnosis of syphilis. The test consists of two steps. In the first, the inactivated serum of the patient is incubated at 37 °C for one hour with the Wassermann antigen and a fixed amount (two units) of guinea pig complement. If the serum contains syphilitic antibody the complement will be utilised during the antigen antibody interaction. If the serum does not contain the antibody, no antigen–antibody reaction occurs and the complement will therefore be left intact. Testing for complement in the postincubation mixture will thus indicate whether the serum had antibodies or not. This constitutes the second step in the test and consists of adding sensitised cells (sheep erythrocytes coated with 4 MHD hemolysin), and incubating at 37 °C for 30 minutes. Lysis of the erythrocytes indicates that complement was not fixed in the first step and, therefore, the serum did not have the antibody (negative CFT). Absence of erythrocyte lysis indicates that the complement was

used up in the first step and, therefore, the serum contained the antibody (positive CFT) (Fig. 13.9).

Appropriate controls should be used, including the following: antigen and serum controls to ensure that they are not anticomplementary, complement control to ensure that the desired amount of complement is added, and cell control to see that sensitised erythrocytes do not undergo lysis in the absence of complement.

Indirect complement fixation test: Certain avian (for example, duck, turkey, parrot) and mammalian (for example, horse, cat) sera do not fix guinea pig complement. When such sera are to be tested, the indirect complement fixation test may be employed. Here the test is set up in duplicate and after the first step, the standard antiserum known to fix complement is added to one set. If the test serum contained antibody, the antigen would have been used up in the first step and therefore the standard antiserum added subsequently would not be able to fix complement. Therefore, in the indirect test, hemolysis indicates a positive result.

Conglutinating complement absorption test: For systems which do not fix guinea pig complement, an alternative method is the conglutinating complement absorption test. This uses horse complement which is nonhemolytic. The indicator system is sensitised sheep erythrocytes mixed with bovine serum. Bovine serum contains a beta globulin component called **conglutinin**, which acts as antibody to complement. Therefore, conglutinin causes agglutination of sensitised sheep erythrocytes (conglutination) if they have combined with complement. If the horse complement had been used up by the antigen–antibody interaction in the first step, agglutination of sensitised cells will not occur.

Other complement dependent serological tests: When some bacteria (for example, *Vibrio cholerae, Treponema pallidum*) react with the specific antibody in the presence of complement and particulate materials such as erythrocytes or platelets, the bacteria are aggregated and adhere to the cells. This is known as *immune adherence*. The *immobilisation test* is another complement dependent reaction. In the *Treponema pallidum immobilisation test*, a highly specific test formerly considered the 'gold standard' for the serodiagnosis of syphilis, the test serum is mixed with a live motile suspension of *T. pallidum* in the presence of complement. On incubation, the specific antibody inhibits the motility of treponemes. *Cytolytic* or *cytocidal tests* are also complement dependent. When a suitable live bacterium, such as the cholera vibrio, is mixed with its antibody in the presence of complement, the bacterium is killed and lysed. This forms the basis of the vibriocidal antibody test for the measurement of anticholera antibodies.

NEUTRALISATION TESTS

Virus neutralisation tests: Neutralisation of viruses by their antibodies can be demonstrated in various systems. Neutralisation of bacteriophages can be demonstrated by the plaque inhibition test. When bacteriophages are seeded in appropriate dilution on lawn cultures of susceptible bacteria, plaques of lysis are produced. Specific antiphage serum inhibits plaque formation. Neutralisation of animal viruses can be demonstrated in three systems – animals, eggs and tissue culture.

Toxin neutralisation: Bacterial exotoxins are good antigens and induce the formation of neutralising antibodies (antitoxins) which are important clinically, in protection against and recovery from diseases such as diphtheria and tetanus. The toxicity of endotoxins is not neutralised by antisera.

Toxin neutralisation can be tested in vivo or in vitro. Neutralisation tests in animals consist of injecting toxin–antitoxin mixtures and estimating the least amount of antitoxin that prevents death or disease in the animals. With the diphtheria toxin, which in small doses causes a cutaneous reaction, neutralisation tests can be done on rabbit skin. The Schick test is based on the ability of circulating antitoxin to neutralise the diphtheria toxin given intradermally, and indicates immunity or susceptibility to the disease. Toxin neutralisation in vitro depends on the inhibition of some demonstrable toxic effect. An example is the antistreptolysin O test, in which antitoxin present in patient sera neutralises the hemolytic activity of the streptococcal O hemolysin.

OPSONISATION

The name 'opsonin' was originally given by Wright (1903) to a heat labile substance present in fresh

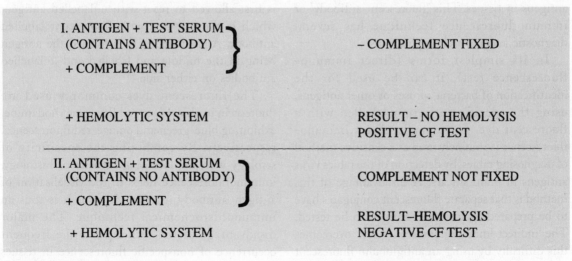

Fig. 13.9 Complement fixation test

normal sera, which facilitated phagocytosis. This factor was subsequently identified as complement. A heat stable serum factor with similar activity was called 'bacteriotropin'. This appears to be a specific antibody. The term opsonin is now generally used to refer to both these factors. Wright used the 'opsonic index' to study the progress of resistance during the course of diseases. The opsonic index was defined as the ratio of the phagocytic activity of the patient's blood for a given bacterium, to the phagocytic activity of blood from a normal individual. It was measured by incubating fresh citrated blood with the bacterial suspension at 37 °C for 15 minutes and estimating the average number of phagocytosed bacteria per polymorpho nuclear leucocyte (phagocytic index) from stained blood films.

IMMUNOFLUORESCENCE

Fluorescence is the property of absorbing light rays of one particular wavelength and emitting rays with a different wavelength. Fluorescent dyes show up brightly under ultraviolet light as they convert ultraviolet into visible light. Coons and his colleagues (1942) showed that fluorescent dyes can be conjugated to antibodies and that such 'labelled' antibodies can be used to locate and identify antigens in tissues. This 'fluorescent antibody' or immunofluorescence technique has several diagnostic and research applications.

In its simplest forms (direct immuno-fluorescence test), it can be used for the identification of bacteria, viruses or other antigens, using the specific antiserum labelled with a fluorescent dye. For example, direct immuno-fluorescence is routinely used as a sensitive method of diagnosing rabies, by detection of the rabies virus antigens in brain smears. A disadvantage of this method is that separate fluorescent conjugates have to be prepared against each antigen to be tested. The 'indirect immunofluorescence test' overcomes this difficulty by using an antiglobulin fluorescent conjugate. An example is the fluorescent treponemal

antibody test for the diagnosis of syphilis. Here, a drop of the test serum is placed on a smear of *T. pallidum* on a slide and after incubation, the slide is washed well to remove all free serum, leaving behind only antibody globulin, if present, coated on the surface of the treponemes. The smear is then treated with a fluorescent labelled antiserum to human gammaglobulin. The fluorescent conjugate reacts with antibody globulin bound to the treponemes. After washing away all the unbound fluorescent conjugate, when the slide is examined under ultraviolet illumination, if the test is positive the treponemes will be seen as bright objects against a dark background. If the serum does not have antitreponemal antibody, there will be no globulin coating on the treponemes and therefore they will not take on the fluorescent conjugates. A single antihuman globulin fluorescent conjugate can be employed for detecting human antibody to any antigen (Fig. 13.10).

Fluorescent dyes may also be conjugated with complement. Labelled complement is a versatile tool and can be employed for the detection of antigen or antibody. Antigens also take fluorescent labelling but not as well as antibodies do. For detection of antibodies by immunofluorescence, the *sandwich* technique can be employed. The antibody is first allowed to react with unlabelled antigen, which is then treated with fluorescent labelled antibody. A sandwich is thus formed the antigen being in the middle and labelled and unlabelled antibodies on either side.

The fluorescent dyes commonly used are fluorescein isothiocynate and lissamine rhodamine, exhibiting blue-green and orange-red fluorescence, respectively. By combining the specificity of serology with the localising capacity of histology, immunofluorescence helps in the visualisation of antigen–antibody reactions in situ. It is thus an immunohistochemical technique. The major disadvantage of the technique is the frequent occurrence of nonspecific fluorescence in tissues and other materials.

RADIOIMMUNOASSAY (RIA)

Besides fluorescent dyes, many other distinctive 'labels' also can be conjugated to antigens and antibodies. The most commonly used labels are radioisotopes and enzymes. A variety of tests have been devised for the measurement of antigens and antibodies using such labelled reactants. The term *binder-ligand-assay* has been used for these reactions. The substance (antigen) whose concentration is to be determined is termed the *analyte* or *ligand*. The binding protein (ordinarily, the antibody) which binds to the ligand is called the binder. The first reaction of this type was radioimmunoassay (RIA) described by Berson and Yallow in 1959. RIA permits the measurement of analytes upto picogram (10^{-12} g) quantities. RIA and its modifications have versatile applications in various areas of biology and medicine, including the quantitation of hormones, drugs, tumour markers, IgE and viral antigens. The importance of RIA was acknowledged when the Nobel Prize was awarded to Yallow for its discovery in 1977.

RIA is a competitive binding assay in which fixed amounts of antibody and radiolabelled antigen

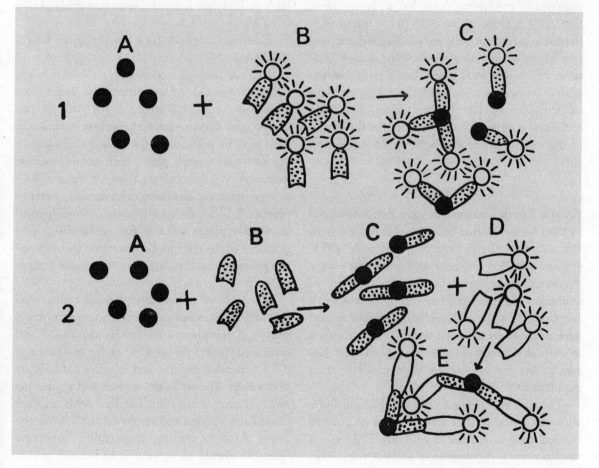

Fig 13.10 Immunofluorescence. 1. Direct test: Antigen (A) is mixed with fluorescent-conjugated antibody (B). The antigen–antibody complex is fluorescent. (C). **2 Indirect test:** Antigen (A) is mixed with antibody (B).The antigen–antibody complex (C) is treated with fluorescent conjugated antiglobulin serum (D). The final product is fluorescent (E).

react in the presence of unlabelled antigen. The labelled and unlabelled antigens compete for the limited binding sites on the antibody. This competition is determined by the level of the unlabelled (test) antigen present in the reacting system. After the reaction, the antigen is separated into 'free' and 'bound' fractions and their radioactive counts measured. The concentration of the test antigen can be calculated from the ratio of the bound and total antigen labels, using a standard dose response curve.

For any reacting system, the *standard dose response* or *calibrating curve* has to be prepared first. This is done by running the reaction with fixed amounts of antibody and labelled antigen, and varying known amounts of unlabelled antigen. The ratios of bound : total labels (B : T ratio) plotted against the analyte concentrations give the standard calibration curve. The concentration of antigen in the test sample is computed from the B : T ratio of the test by interpolation from the calibration curve.

ENZYME IMMUNOASSAYS (EIA)

Enzyme labelled conjugates were first introduced in 1966 for localisation of antigens in tissues, as an alternative to fluorescent conjugates. In 1971, enzyme labelled antigens and antibodies were developed as serological reagents for the assay of antibodies and antigens. Their versatility, sensitivity, simplicity, economy and absence of radiation hazard have made EIAs the most widely used procedure in clinical serology. The availability of test kits and facility for automation have added to their popularity.

The term *enzyme immunoassay* (EIA) includes all assays based on the measurement of enzyme labelled antigen, hapten or antibody. EIAs are of two basic types – homogeneous and heterogeneous. In homogeneous EIA, there is no need to separate the bound and free fractions so that the test can be completed in one step, with all reagents added simultaneously. This type of EIA can be used only

for assay of haptens such as drugs and not for microbial antigens and antibodies. An example of homogeneous EIA is *enzyme multiplied immunoassay technique* (EMIT), which is a simple assay method for small molecule drugs such as opiates, cocaine, barbiturates or amphetamine in serum.

Heterogeneous EIA requires the separation of the free and bound fractions either by centrifugation or by absorption on solid surfaces and washing. It is therefore a multistep procedure, with reagents added sequentially. The major type of heterogeneous EIA is Enzyme Linked Immunosorbent Assay (ELISA).

Enzyme Linked Immunosorbent Assays (ELISA).

ELISA is so named because the technique involves the use of an *immunosorbent* – an absorbing material specific for one of the components of the reaction, the antigen or antibody. This may be particulate, for example cellulose or agarose – or a solid phase such as polystyrene, polyvinyl or polycarbonate tubes or microwells – or membranes or discs of polyacrylamide, paper or plastic. ELISA is usually done using 96-well microtitre plates suitable for automation. The principle of the test can be illustrated by outlining its application for the detection of rotavirus antigen in feces.

The wells of a microtitre plate are coated with goat antirotavirus antibody. After thorough washing, the fecal samples to be tested are added and incubated overnight at 4 °C or for two hours at 37 °C. Suitable positive and negative controls are also set up. The wells are washed and guinea pig antirotavirus antiserum, labelled with alkaline phosphatase, added and incubated at 37 °C for one hour. After washing, a suitable substrate (paranitrophenyl phosphate) is added and held at room temperature till the positive controls show the development of a yellow colour. The phosphatase enzyme splits the substrate to yield a yellow compound.

If the test sample contains rotavirus, it is fixed to the antibody coating the wells. When the enzyme labelled antibody is added subsequently, it is in turn fixed. The presence of residual enzyme activity, indicated by the development of yellow colour, therefore denotes a positive test (Fig. 13.11). If the sample is negative, there is no significant colour change. An ELISA reader provides quantitative colour recordings.

The detection of antibody by ELISA can be illustrated by the anti-HIV antibody test. Purified inactivated HIV antigen is adsorbed onto microassay plate wells. Test serum diluted in buffer is added to the well and incubated at 37 °C for 30 minutes. The well is then thoroughly washed. If the serum

contains anti-HIV antibody, it will form a stable complex with the HIV antigen on the plate. A goat antihuman immunoglobulin antibody conjugated with horse radish peroxidase enzyme is added and incubated for 30 minutes. After thorough washing, the substrate O-phenylene diamine dihydrochloride is added and after 30 minutes, the colour that develops is read using a microassay plate reader. Positive and negative controls should invariably be used with test sera (Fig. 13.12).

The examples described above are of simple *noncompetitive sandwich* ELISA. The test can be made more specific by making serum antibody and enzyme labelled antibody compete for the binding sites on the antigen (*competitive* ELISA). Tests

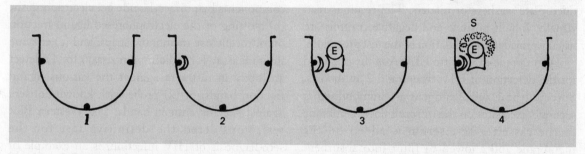

Fig. 13.11 ELISA for detection of rotavirus in feces. 1. Microassay plate coated with goat antibody to rotavirus. 2. When fecal suspension is added and incubated, rotavirus if present, will absorb to the coated antibody. 3. After thorough washings add guinea pig antirotavirus antibody conjugated with alkaline phosphatase enzyme. If rotavirus is present the conjugate will complex with it. 4. After washing add the substrate, paranitrophenyl phosphate. 5. If the enzyme conjugate is present, the substrate will be split to form yellow coloured product. This indicates a positive test. In a negative test there will be no significant colour formation.

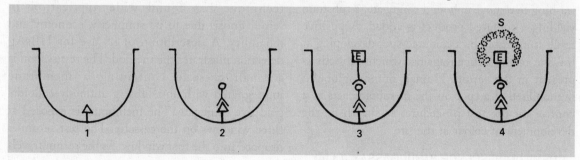

Fig. 13.12 ELISA for HIV antibody in serum. 1. Microassay plate coated with HIV antigen. 2. Test serum is added and incubated. Anti-HIV antibody. If present in the serum will attach to HIV antigen. 3. After washing, add goat antihuman immunoglobulin antibody conjugated with horse serum peroxidase enzyme. The conjugate will attach to anti-HIV antibody in a positive test. 4. After washing, add substrate OPD. 5. A colour develops in the positive test, while there will be no colour in a negative test.

for specific immunoglobulin classes (for example, IgM specific ELISA) are also available. *Capture ELISA* and *immunometric* tests are even more specific.

Several variations of the ELISA technique have been developed to provide simple diagnostic tests, including the card and dipstick methods suitable for clinical laboratory and bedside applications.

A simple modification of ELISA which has found wide application for testing one or a few samples of sera at a time is the *cylinder* or *cassette* ELISA. Here each specimen is tested in a separate disposable cassette. The test is rapid, taking only about 10 minutes as compared with the 2–4 hours taken for microplate ELISA. There is no need for microplate washers or readers. The result is read visually. Inbuilt positive and negative controls are usually provided for validation of the test procedure.

An example of cassette ELISA is the one used for the detection of HIV type 1 and 2 antibodies. Specific type 1 and 2 antigens are immobilised at separate fixed sites on the nitrocellulose membrane in the cassette. Test serum is added on the membrane and allowed to filter into absorbent material placed below it in the cassette base. Antibody, if present in the serum will bind to the appropriate antigen. After washing to remove unbound antibody, enzyme labelled antihuman immunoglobulin antibody is added. After additional washing to remove unbound conjugate, a substrate yielding a coloured product is added. A positive result is indicated by a coloured spot developing at the site of the antigen against which antibody is present in the serum. Human immunoglobulin immobilised at a spot on the membrane acts as a control for the test procedure, as shown by the development of colour at the site.

CHEMILUMINESCENCE IMMUNOASSAY (CLIA)

Chemiluminescence refers to a chemical reaction emitting energy in the form of light. Just as radioactive conjugates are employed in RIA fluorescent cojugates in IFA and enzymes in ELISA, chemiluminescent compounds (such as luminol or acridinium esters) are used in CLIA as the label to provide the signal during the antigenantibody reaction. The signal (light) can be amplified, measured and the concentration of the analyte calculated. The method has been fully automated and is being increasingly used in laboratories where the volume of work is large

IMMUNOELECTROBLOT TECHNIQUES

Immunoelectroblot or (electroimmunoblot) techniques combine the sensitivity of enzyme immunoassay with much greater specificity. The technique is a combination of three separate procedures: (a) separation of ligand–antigen components by polyacrylamide gel electrophoresis; (b) blotting of the electrophoresed ligand fraction on nitrocellulose membrane strips; and (c) enzyme immunoassay (or radioimmunoassay) to (1) detect antibody in test sera against the various ligand fraction bands; or (2) probe with known antisera against specific antigen bands. The Western Blot test, considered the definitive test for the serodiagnosis of HIV infection, is an example of the immunoelectroblot technique (see chapter 62 for details).

IMMUNOCHROMATOGRAPHIC TESTS

A one-step qualitative immunochromatographic technique has found wide application in serodiagnosis due to its simplicity, economy and reliability. A description of its use for HBsAg detection illustrates the method. The test system is a small cassette containing a membrane impregnated with anti-HbsAg antibody-colloidal gold dye conjugate. The membrane is exposed at three windows on the cassette. The test serum is dropped into the first window. As the serum travels upstream by capillary action, a coloured band appears at the second window (test site) if the serum contains HbsAg, due to the formation of a HbsAg-antibody conjugate complex. This is the positive reaction. Absence of a coloured band at the test site indicates a negative reaction. Simultaneously a coloured band should appear in every case at the third window, which forms an inbuilt control, in the absence of which the test is invalid. The test is claimed to be nearly as sensitive and specific as EIA tests.

IMMUNOELECTRONMICROSCOPIC TESTS

Immunoelectronmicroscopy: When viral particles mixed with specific antisera are observed under the electron microscope, they are seen to be clumped. This finds application in the study of some viruses such as the hepatitis A virus and the viruses causing diarrhea.

Immunoferritin test: Ferritin (an electron-dense substance from horse spleen) can be conjugated with antibody, and such labelled antibody reacting with an antigen can be visualised under the electron microscope.

Immunoenzyme test: Some stable enzymes, such as peroxidase, can be conjugated with antibodies. Tissue sections carrying the corresponding antigens are treated with peroxidase labelled antisera. The peroxidase bound to the antigen can be visualised under the electron microscope, by microhistochemical methods. Some other enzymes, such as glucose oxidase, phosphatases and tyrosinase, may also be included in immunoenzyme tests.

Further Reading

Balows A et al. 1991. *Manual of Clinical Microbiology.*Washington DC: American Society of Microbiology.
Hudson L and FC Hay 1989. *Practical Immunology*, 3rd edn. Oxford: Blackwell.
Kennedy DM and SJ Challacombe 1988. *ELISA and Other Solid Phase Immunoassays.* New York: John Wiley.
Rose NR et al. 1986. *Manual of Clinical Immunology.* 3rd edn. Washington DC: American Society for Microbiology.
Stites DP and AI Terr 1991. *Basic and Clinical Immunology*, 7th edn. Norwalk: Appleton–Lange.

The Complement System

The term 'complement' (C) refers to a system of factors which occur in normal serum and are activated characteristically by antigen–antibody interaction and subsequently mediate a number of biologically significant consequences.

Towards the end of the nineteenth century, it was noticed that bactericidal, bacteriolytic and hemolytic actions of the appropriate antibodies required the participation of a heat labile component present in the normal sera of human beings and animals. Buchner (1889) was the first to observe that the bactericidal effect of serum was destroyed by heating at 55 °C for one hour. Pfieffer (1894) discovered that cholera vibrios were lysed when injected intraperitoneally into specifically immunised guinea pigs (bacteriolysis in vivo or *Pfieffer's phenomenon*). Bordet (1895) extended these observations and established that immune bacteriolysis and hemolysis required two factors— the heat stable antibody and a heat labile factor, which was called alexine. This term has been replaced by the present name *complement* which was coined by Ehrlich, because this factor complemented the action of antibody.

Bordet and Gengou (1901) described the complement fixation test, using the hemolytic indicator system, as a sensitive serological reaction. This found wide application, and the Wassermann complement fixation test for syphilis became one of the most popular serological tests. For the next half century, interest in complement remained confined to its use as a tool in serological reactions. Since then the structural and functional complexities of the complement system have been defined and

its role as a mediator and amplifier of many immune and inflammatory reactions recognised. The complement system belongs to the group of biological effector mechanisms (called *triggered enzyme cascades*) which also includes coagulation, fibrinolytic and kinin systems. Such biological cascades have distinct advantages. For example, each enzyme in the cascade is able to activate many molecules of the succeeding component providing for amplification of the response at each step. Every step has its own control mechanisms so that the cascade can be regulated with precision.

GENERAL PROPERTIES

Complement is present in the sera of all mammals and also in that of most lower animals, including birds, amphibians and fishes. It is a nonspecific serological reagent in that complement from one species can react with antibodies from other species, though the efficiency of reaction is influenced by the taxonomic distance between the species. Complement constitutes about five per cent of normal serum proteins and is not increased as a result of immunisation.

Though some of its components are heat stable, complement as a whole is heat labile, its cytolytic activity undergoing spontaneous denaturation slowly at room temperature and being destroyed in 30 minutes at 56 °C. A serum, deprived of its complement activity by heating at 56 °C for 30 minutes, is then said to be 'inactivated'.

Complement (C) ordinarily does not bind to free antigen or antibody but only to antibody which has combined with its antigen. Various terms such as *fixation*, *binding* or *consumption* have been used to refer to the combination of C with bound immunoglobulin, leading to the activation of the classical C pathway. All classes of Ig do not fix C. Only IgM, IgG3, 1 and 2 (in that order) fix C, but not IgG4, IgA, IgD or IgE. The site of C binding is located on the Fc piece of the Ig molecule (CH^2 domain on IgG, CH^4 on IgM), and is expressed only when Ig is combined with its antigen. The fixation of C is not influenced by the nature of antigens, but only by the class of immunoglobulins.

COMPONENTS

The complement system consists of at least twenty chemically and immunologically distinct serum proteins comprising the complement components, the properdin system and the control proteins.

Complement is a complex of nine different fractions called C1 to C9. The fraction C1 occurs in serum as a calcium ion dependent complex, which on chelation with EDTA yields three protein subunits called C1q, r, and s. Thus C is made up of a total of 11 different proteins. C fractions are named C1 to C9 in the sequence of the cascading reaction, except that C4 comes after C1, before C2.

The model traditionally used to explain C activity in immune cytolysis is the lysis of erythrocyte sensitised by its antibody. The erythrocyte (E) antibody (A) complex is called EA, and when C components are attached to EA, the product is called EAC, followed by the components that have reacted (for example, EAC 14235 or EAC 1–5). When a C component acquires enzymatic or other demonstrable biological activity, it is indicated by a bar over the component number, for example, the enzymatically activated C1 is shown as $\overline{C1}$. Fragments cleaved from C components during the cascade are indicated by small letters (C3a, C3b). Inactivated forms of C components are indicated by the prefix 'i' (iC3b).

COMPLEMENT ACTIVATION

Complement is normally present in the body in an inactive form but when its activity is induced by antigen–antibody combination or other stimuli, C components react in a specific sequence as a cascade. Basically, the C cascade is a series of reactions in which the preceding components act as enzymes on the succeeding components, cleaving them into dissimilar fragments. The larger fragments usually join the cascade. The smaller fragments which are released often possess biological effects which contribute to defence mechanisms by amplifying the inflammatory process, increasing vascular permeability, inducing smooth muscle contraction, causing chemotaxis of leucocytes, promoting virus neutralisation, detoxifying endotoxins and effecting the release of histamine from mast cells.

The C cascade can be triggered off by two parallel but independent mechanisms or pathways which differ only in the initial steps. Once C3 activation occurs, the subsequent steps are common in both pathways, which have been called the classical C pathway and the alternative or properdin pathway.

The classical pathway is so called because it was the first one identified. But actually it is a more recently evolved mechanism of specific active immunity, while the alternative pathway represents a more primitive system of nonspecific innate immunity.

CLASSICAL PATHWAY

The chain of events in which C components react in a specific sequence following activation of C1 and typically culminate in immune cytolysis is known as the classical pathway (Fig. 14.1). It consists of the following steps:

1. The first step is the binding of C1 to the antigen–antibody complex (traditionally represented as EA). The recognition unit of C1 is C1q, which reacts with the Fc piece of bound IgM or IgG. C1q has six combining sites. Effective activation occurs only when C1q is attached to immunoglobulins by at least two of

its binding sites. One molecule of IgM or two molecules of IgG can therefore initiate the process. C1q binding in the presence of calcium ions leads to sequential activation of C1r and s.

2. Activated $\overline{C}$1s is an esterase (C1s esterase), one molecule of which can cleave several molecules of C4 – an instance of amplification. C4 is split into C4a, which is an anaphylatoxin, and C4b which binds to cell membranes along with C1.

3. $\overline{C14b}$ in the presence of magnesium ions cleaves C2 into C2a, which remains linked to cell-bound C4b, and C2b which is released into fluid phase. $\overline{C4b2a}$ has enzymatic activity and is referred to as the classical pathway C3 *convertase.*

4. C3 convertase splits C3 into two fragments : C3a which is an anaphylatoxin, and C3b which remains cell-bound along with $\overline{C4b2a}$ to form a trimolecular complex $\overline{C4b2a3b}$ which has enzymatic activity and is called C5 convertase.

5. The *membrane attack* phase of complement activity begins at this stage with C5 convertase cleaving C5 into C5a, an anaphylatoxin which is released into the medium, and C5b which continues with the cascade. C6 and C7 then join together. A heat stable trimolecular complex $\overline{C567}$ is formed, part of which binds to the cell membrane and prepares it for lysis by C8 and C9 which join the reaction subsequently. Most of $\overline{C567}$ escape and serve to amplify the reaction by adsorbing onto unsensitised 'bystander cells' and rendering them susceptible to lysis by C8 and C9. The unbound $\overline{C567}$ has chemotactic activity, though the effect is transient due to its rapid inactivation. The mechanism of complement mediated cytolysis is the production of 'holes', approximately 100 Å in diameter on the cell membrane. This disrupts the osmotic integrity of the membrane, leading to the release of the cell contents.

Although the classical pathway is generally activated by the antigen–antibody complexes or aggregated immunoglobulin, activation may also be due to other stimuli, such as DNA, C-reactive protein, trypsin-like enzymes or some retroviruses.

ALTERNATIVE C PATHWAY

The central process in the complement cascade is the activation of C3, which is the major component of C. In the classical pathway, activation of C3 is achieved by $\overline{C42}$ (classical C3 convertase). The activation of C3 without prior participation of C142 is known as the 'alternative pathway'.

The first example of the alternative pathway was the demonstration by Pillemer (1954) of the 'properdin system' as a group of serum proteins contributing to antimicrobial defence without requiring specific antibodies. The activator in this system was zymosan, a polysaccharide from the yeast cell wall, but many other substances can also activate the pathway. These activators include bacterial endotoxins, IgA and D, the cobra venom factor and the nephritic factor (a protein present in the serum of glomerulonephritis patients).

The first step in the alternative pathway is the binding of C3b to an activator. C3b is continuously generated in small quantities in the circulation but in the free state it is rapidly inactivated by the serum protein factors H and I. Bound C3b which is protected from such inactivation interacts with a serum protein called Factor B (also known as 'C3 proactivator') to form a magnesium-dependent complex 'C3b,B'. This complex is cleaved by another serum protein Factor D (also called 'C3 proactivator convertase') into two fragments – Ba and Bb. Fragment Ba is released into the medium. Fragment Bb remains bound to C3b, forming the esterase $\overline{C3b,Bb}$ complex, which is the alternative pathway C3 convertase. This enzyme $\overline{C3b,Bb}$ is extremely labile. The function of properdin (also called Factor P) is to stabilise the C3 convertase, which hydrolyses C3, leading to further steps in the cascade, as in the classical pathway (Fig. 14.2).

REGULATION OF C ACTIVATION

Unchecked complement activity can cause not only

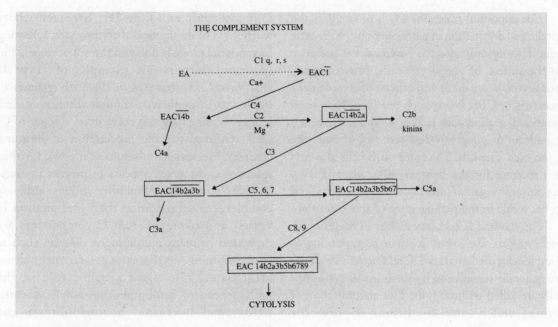

Fig. 14.1 Complement cascade—the classical pathway

exhaustion of the complement system but also serious damage to tissues. Several inbuilt control mechanisms regulate the complement cascade at different steps. These are mainly of two kinds: inhibitors which bind to complement components and halt their further function, and inactivators which are enzymes that destroy complement proteins.

A. INHIBITORS

1. Normal serum contains an inhibitor of C1 esterase (C1sINH). This heat labile alpha neuraminoglycoprotein also inhibits many other esterases found in blood, such as plasmin, kininogen and the Hageman factor. This does not prevent the normal progress of the complement cascade but checks its autocatalytic prolongation.
2. The S *protein* present in normal serum binds to $\overline{C567}$ and modulates the cytolytic action of the membrane attack complex.

B. INACTIVATORS

1. A serum betaglobulin, called *Factor I* (formerly known as C3b, C4b INAC, conglutinogen

activating factor or KAF), provides homeostatic control of C3 activation, particularly by the alternative pathway.
2. Another beta globulin *Factor H* acts in concert with Factor I modulating C3 activation.
3. *Anaphylatoxin inactivator* is an alphaglobulin that enzymatically degrades C3a, C4a and C5a which are anaphylatoxins released during the C cascade.
4. C4 *binding protein* controls the activity of cell-bound C4b.

Many other regulators of C activity have also been reported.

BIOLOGICAL EFFECTS OF C

Complement mediates immunological membrane damage (cytolysis, bacteriolysis), amplifies the inflammatory response and participates in the pathogenesis of certain hypersensitivity reactions. It exhibits antiviral activity and promotes phagocytosis and immune adherence. It also interacts with the coagulation, fibrinolytic and kininogenic systems of blood.

An important function of C is to facilitate the uptake and destruction of pathogens by phagocytic cells. This opsonic effect is based on the presence on the surface of phagocytic cells, (macrophages, monocytes, neutrophils and others) of complement receptors or CRs. Many such receptors have been identified, such as CR 1, 2, 3, 4 and C1q, which stimulate phagocytosis and removal of immune complexes. The CR 2 receptor on B cells also acts as a receptor for the Epstein—Barr virus (EBV), the causative agent of infectious mononucleosis, and so has a role in the pathogenesis of this condition.

The classical C pathway results in bacteriolysis and cytolysis. Cells vary in their susceptibility to complement mediated lysis. Gram negative bacteria are generally sensitive to lysis, while Gram positive cells are killed without lysis. The neutralisation of viruses under some conditions requires the participation of C.

C fragments released during the cascade reaction help in amplifying the inflammatory response. C2 kinins are vasoactive amines and increase capillary permeability. C3a and C5a are anaphylatoxic (histamine releasing) and chemotactic. $\overline{C567}$ is chemotactic and also brings about reactive lysis.

C participates in the cytotoxic (Type II) and immune complex (Type III) hypersensitivity reactions. The destruction of erythrocytes, following incompatible transfusion and thrombocytopenia in sedormid purpura, are examples of Type II reactions. C contributes to the pathogenesis of nephrotoxic nephritis, though immunological kidney damage may also occur in its absence of C. C is required for the production of immune complex diseases such as serum sickness and Arthus reaction. C, however, appears to prevent immune complex disease by solubilising antigen–antibody complexes and preventing their precipitation in vessels and tissues. Serum C components are decreased in many autoimmune diseases such as systemic lupus erythematosus and rheumatoid arthritis. C also plays a major role in the pathogenesis of autoimmune hemolytic anemia, paroxysmal nocturnal hemoglobinuria and hereditary angioneurotic edema.

Endotoxin is an efficient activator of the alternative C pathway. In endotoxic shock there is massive C3 fixation and platelet adherence. Large scale platelet lysis and release of large amounts of platelet factor lead to disseminated intravascular coagulation and thrombocytopenia. Gram negative septicemias and the dengue hemorrhagic syndrome

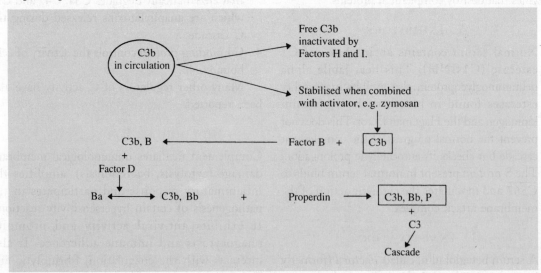

Fig. 14.2 Complement cascade—the alternative pathway

Table 14.1 Clinical syndromes associated with genetic deficiencies of complement components

Group	Deficiency	Syndrome
I	Cl inhibitor	Hereditary angioneurotic edema
II	Early components of classical pathway C1, C2, C4	SLE and other collagen vascular diseases
III	C3 and its regulatory protein C3b inactivator	Severe recurrent pyogenic infections
IV	C5 to C8	Bacteremia, mainly with Gram negative diplococci, toxoplasmosis
V	C9	No particular disease

may have a similar pathogenesis. Depletion of C protects against the Schwartzman reaction.

C bound to antigen–antibody complexes adheres to erythrocytes or to nonprimate platelets. This reaction, called *immune adherence*, contributes to defence against pathogenic microorganisms since such adherent particles are rapidly phagocytosed. C3 and C4 are necessary for immune adherence.

Bovine serum contains an unusual protein called conglutinin (K) which causes clumping of particles or cells coated with C, a process known as conglutination. Conglutinin reacts exclusively with bound C3. Though conglutinin behaves as an antibody to C, it is not an immunoglobulin and requires Ca^{++} for its activity. Antibodies with conglutinin-like activity (immunoconglutinin, IK) can be produced by immunisation with complement coated materials. They may also occur frequently in human beings and other mammals as autoantibodies to fixed C. The titres of serum IK rise in conditions such as infections and autoimmune diseases associated with increased fixation of C in vivo. High IK levels have been noticed in the saliva and jejunal secretions. They are IgA antibodies whose significance is not known.

QUANTITATION OF C AND ITS COMPONENTS

Complement activity of serum is measured by estimating the highest dilution of serum lysing sheep erythrocytes sensitised by antierythrocytic antibody. Estimation of individual complement components also uses hemolytic activity in a system containing an excess of all complement components except the one to be measured. C components can be quantitated also by radial immunodiffusion in agar but this method does not differentiate between active and inactive fractions.

BIOSYNTHESIS OF C

Complement components are synthesised in various sites in the body, such as the intestinal epithelium (C1), macrophages (C2, C4), spleen (C5, C8) and liver (C3, C6, C9). C is, to some extent, an 'acute phase substance' and rise in C levels (particularly C4, C3, C5 and C6) is observed during the acute phase of inflammation.

DEFICIENCIES OF THE COMPLEMENT SYSTEM

Complete or partial deficiencies of all the classical complement components and several of the C inhibitors have been described in humans or animals. Some are associated with severe diseases, while in others clinical manifestations are sporadic. C deficiencies result in the host being unable to efficiently eliminate the microbial antigens or circulating immune complexes. Recurrent bacterial and fungal infections and collagen diseases also occur (Table 14.1).

Deficiency of the C1 inhibitor is associated with

hereditary angioneurotic edema, a condition characterised by episodic angioedema of the subcutaneous tissues or of the mucosa of the respiratory or alimentary tracts. It may be fatal when the larynx and trachea are affected. The attack is precipitated by the local exhaustion of the reduced amount of the C1 inhibitor present, leading to the autocatalytic activation of C1 and the unrestrained

breakdown of C4 and C2. The main mediator of the edema appears to be the C2 kinin released. The attack may be treated by infusion of fresh plasma as a source of the inhibitor. Prophylactic administration of epsilon aminocaproic acid (or its analogues) is useful. They are believed to inhibit the activation of plasma enzymes, thus sparing the small amounts of the C1 inhibitor present.

Further Reading

Janeway CA and P Travers 1996. *Immunobiology*, 2nd edn. London: Current Biology.
Tomlinson S. 1993. *Complement defense mechanisms, Curr Opin Immunol*. 5, 83.
Weir DM and J Stewart 1997. *Immunology*. 8th edn. Edinburgh: Churchill Livingstone.

Structure and Functions of the Immune System

The lymphoreticular system is a complex organisation of cells of diverse morphology distributed widely in different organs and tissues of the body responsible for immunity. Lymphoreticular cells consist of lymphoid and reticuloendothelial components, with clearly demarcated functions. The lymphoid cells – lymphocytes and plasma cells – are primarily concerned with the specific immune response. The phagocytic cells, forming part of the reticuloendothelial system, are primarily concerned with the 'scavenger' functions of eliminating effete cells and foreign particles. They contribute to nonspecific immunity by removing microorganisms from blood and tissues. They also play a role in specific immunity, both in the afferent and efferent limbs of the immune response.

The functional anatomy of the lymphoid system can be appreciated only against the background of the 'two component concept' of immunity. The immune response to an antigen, whatever its nature, can be of two broad types—the humoral or antibody mediated immunity (AMI) and the cellular or cell mediated immunity (CMI). Humoral immunity is mediated by antibodies produced by plasma cells and present in blood and other body fluids (hence the name 'humoral' from 'humor' the old term for body fluids). Cellular immunity is mediated directly by sensitised lymphocytes. Cells for each of these components develop through separate channels and remain independent, though they may also interact in some instances (Fig. 15.1).

The lymphoid system consists of the lymphoid cells (lymphocytes and plasma cells) and lymphoid organs. Based on the different roles they perform, lymphoid organs can be classified into the central (primary) and the peripheral (secondary) lymphoid organs. The central lymphoid organs are lymphoepithelial structures in which the precursor lymphocytes proliferate, develop and acquire immunological capability. The thymus and the bursa of Fabricius in birds are primary lymphoid organs, being responsible for the cellular and humoral immune responses, respectively. The equivalent of the avian bursa in mammals is bone marrow. After acquiring immunocompetence, the lymphocytes migrate along blood and lymph streams, accumulate in the peripheral lymphoid organs and, following antigenic stimulus, effect the appropriate immune response. The spleen, lymph nodes and mucosa-associated lymphoid tissue (MALT) constitute the major peripheral lymphoid organs. Lymphoid tissue in the gut, lungs, liver and bone marrow and lymphoid collections in the adventitious tissue of all organs also form part of the peripheral lymphoid system.

CENTRAL (PRIMARY) LYMPHOID ORGANS

Thymus: The thymus anlage develops from the epithelium of the third and fourth pharyngeal pouches at about the sixth week of gestation. By the eighth week, mesenchymal stem cells (precursors of lymphocytes) from the yolk sac, fetal liver and bone marrow reach the thymus and differentiate into the thymic lymphoid cells (thymocytes). It is thus the first organ in all animal species to become predominantly lymphoid. In human beings, the thymus reaches its maximal relative size just before birth. It continues to grow till about the twelfth year. After puberty, it undergoes

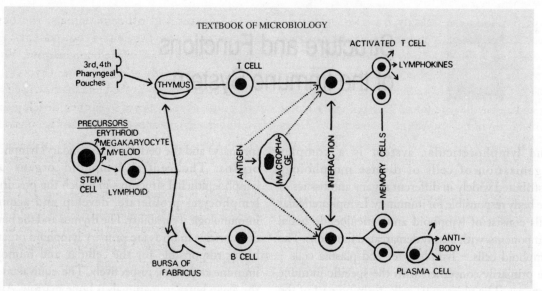

Fig. 15.1 Development of T and B cell systems

spontaneous progressive involution, indicating that it functions best in early life.

The thymus is located behind the upper part of the sternum. Aberrant thymic tissues are often found in neighbouring sites. The thymus has two lobes surrounded by a fibrous capsule. Septa arising from the capsule divide the gland into lobules which are differentiated into an outer cortex and an inner medulla. The cortex is crowded with actively proliferating small lymphocytes. The medulla consists mainly of epithelial cells and mature lymphocytes in the middle of which are the Hassall's corpuscles, which are whorl-like aggregations of epithelial cells.

Till the 1960s, the thymus was an organ without any recognised function. The fortuitous observations by Good (1954) of thymoma and impaired immunity in a patient, and by Miller (1961) of immunodeficiency·in neonatally thymectomised mice, paved the way for the understanding of the pivotal role of the organ in the development of cell mediated immunity. The primary function of the thymus is the production of thymic lymphocytes. It is the major site for lymphocyte proliferation in the body. However, of the lymphocytes produced,

only about one per cent leave the thymus. The rest are destroyed locally. The reason for this apparently wasteful process is not known. In the thymus, the lymphocytes acquire new surface antigens ('Thy' antigens). Lymphocytes conditioned in the thymus are called 'thymus (T) dependent lymphocytes' or 'T cells'. Unlike in the peripheral organs, lymphocyte proliferation in the thymus is not dependent on antigenic stimulation. In fact, peripheral antigenic stimuli do not lead to any immune response in the thymus. Antigen introduced directly into the thymus may lead to a local immune response.

The thymus confers immunological competence on the lymphocytes during their stay in the organ. Prethymic lymphocytes are not immunocompetent. In the thymus they are 'educated' so that they become capable of mounting cell mediated immune response against appropriate antigens. The importance of thymus in lymphocyte proliferation and development of CMI is evident from the lymphopenia, deficient graft rejection and the so called 'runt disease' seen in neonatally thymectomised mice. Deficient CMI is also seen in congenital aplasia of the thymus in human beings (DiGeorge syndrome), and in mice ('nude mice').

T lymphocytes are selectively seeded into certain sites in the peripheral lymphatic tissues, being found in the white pulp of the spleen, around the central arterioles, and in the paracortical areas of lymph nodes. These regions have been termed 'thymus dependent' as they are found grossly depleted after neonatal thymectomy. While thymectomy affects CMI primarily, it also diminishes antibody response to many types of antigens (thymus dependent antigens) such as sheep erythrocytes and bovine serum albumin. Humoral response to other antigens is unaffected.

Bursa of Fabricius: This is a lymphoepithelial organ arising as a pouch from the dorsal part of the cloaca in birds. It becomes a lymphoid organ by about the day 15 of embryonation, develops full functional ability near hatching and starts involuting by 7–13 weeks of age, corresponding to the age of puberty. The bursa is also a site of lymphocytic proliferation and differentiation. Stem cells from the yolk sac, fetal liver and bone marrow enter the bursa, proliferate and develop into immuno-competent 'bursal lymphocytes' or B cells (B for bursa or bone marrow). These migrate and seed selective areas in the peripheral lymphoid organs—the mantle, germinal follicles and perifollicular regions of the spleen, and the far cortical areas and medullary cords of lymph nodes. These are known as 'bursa dependent' or 'thymus independent areas'. Following appropriate antigenic stimulation, B lymphocytes transform into plasma cells and secrete antibodies.

The vital role of the bursa in humoral immunity was discovered accidentally by Glick and Chang (1956) who found that chickens bursectomised at hatching failed to form antibodies when challenged with a bacterial antigen. Immunocompetence is conferred on the lymphocytes by the bursa in stages. Competence for IgM production is acquired early (about day 14 of embryonation) and for IgG late (about day 21). Birds bursectomised on 18 to 20 days synthesise IgM, but not IgG.

In humans and other mammals, the bone marrow acts as the bursa equivalent. All lymphocytes originate in the bone marrow. While T lymphocytes develop in the thymus, B lymphocytes develop in the bone marrow itself. In the human fetus, Peyer's patches develop and lymphoid cells appear in the spleen and lymph nodes by the 20th week of gestation. From then on the fetus is able to produce IgM and IgD. It receives maternal IgG, but IgA and IgE are not present. At birth IgM production is enhanced, but IgG level falls steadily, to reach miminum levels by the 3rd month. IgG production then picks up and becomes adequate by 2–3 years. Full immunocompetence is attained only after the first decade of life.

PERIPHERAL (SECONDARY) LYMPHOID ORGANS

Lymph nodes: Lymph nodes are placed along the course of lymphatic vessels. They are surrounded by a fibrous capsule from which trabeculae penetrate into the nodes. The node can be differentiated into an outer cortex and an inner medulla. In the cortex are accumulations of lymphocytes (primary lymphoid follicles) within which germinal centres (secondary follicles) develop during antigenic stimulation. The follicles contain, besides proliferating lymphocytes, dendritic macrophages which capture and process the antigen. In the medulla, the lymphocytes, plasma cells and macrophages are arranged as elongated branching bands (medullary cords). The cortical follicles and medullary cords contain B lymphocytes and constitute the bursa dependent areas. Between the cortical follicles and medullary cords, there is a broad, ill-defined intermediate zone (paracortical area) which contains T lymphocytes and interdigitating cells. This constitutes the thymus dependent area (Fig. 15.2).

Lymph nodes act as a filter for lymph, each group of nodes draining a specific part of the body. They phagocytose foreign materials including microorganisms. They help in the proliferation and circulation of T and B cells. They enlarge following local antigenic stimulation.

Spleen: The spleen is the largest of the lymphoid organs. It has a capsule from which trabeculae descend, dividing the organ into several interconnected compartments. The branches of the splenic artery travel along the trabeculae, and on leaving them branch again to form the central arterioles, which are surrounded by a sheath of lymphoid tissues. This part is known as the white pulp of the spleen and may constitute about half to three quarters of the organ, following antigenic stimulation. The central arterioles proceed onto the red pulp, so called because of the abundance of red blood cells in it.

The periarterial lymphoid collections in the white pulp of the spleen are called the Malpighian corpuscles or follicles. Germinal centres develop following antigenic stimulation. Surrounding the germinal centre is a 'mantle layer' of lymphocytes. Immediately outside the periarterial lymphatic sheath and separating it from the red pulp lies the marginal zone. The lymphatic sheath immediately surrounding the central arteriole is the thymus dependent area of the spleen. The perifollicular region, germinal centre and mantle layer form the bursa dependent (thymus independent) areas (Fig. 15.3).

The spleen serves as the graveyard for effete blood cells, as a reserve tank and settling bed for blood and as a systemic filter for trapping circulating bloodborne foreign particles. The immunological function of the spleen is primarily directed against bloodborne antigens.

Mucosa associated lymphoid tissue (MALT): The mucosa lining the alimentary, respiratory, genitourinary and other lumina and surfaces are constantly exposed to numerous antigens. These areas are endowed with a rich collection of lymphoid cells, either specialised aggregates like the Peyer's patches or scattered isolated lymphoid follicles—collectively called the mucosa associated lymphoid tissue (MALT). Such lymphoid tissues in the gut, from the adenoids and tonsils to the follicles in the colon, are called the gut associated lymphoid tissue (GALT) and those in the respiratory tract, the bronchus associated lymphoid tissue (BALT).

MALT contains lymphoid as well as phagocytic cells. Both B and T cells are present. While the predominant immunoglobulin produced in the mucosa is secretory IgA, other immunoglobulin classes, IgG, IgM and IgE are also formed locally.

There appears to be a free traffic of antigen-specific effector lymphocytes between the various mucosal and secretory areas, so that an antigenic exposure at one site may cause production of the specific antibody at the other mucosal and secretory sites also. This indicates the existence of a common *mucosal* or *secretory* immune system and explains the superiority of oral or nasal immunisation over the parenteral route for many enteric and respiratory infections.

CELLS OF THE LYMPHORETICULAR SYSTEM

Lymphocytes: Lymphocytes are small, round cells found in peripheral blood, lymph, lymphoid organs and in many other tissues. In peripheral blood, they constitute 20–45 per cent of the leucocyte population, while in lymph and lymphoid organs they form the predominant cell type. The human body contains about 10^{12} lymphocytes, approximately 10^9 of them being renewed daily. Only about one per cent of the total body lymphocytes are present in the blood. Ehrlich (1879) who introduced a staining technique for blood cells described lymphocytes as nonmotile end cells with no recognisable function! Lymphocytes are now recognised as the major cellular elements responsible for immunological responses.

According to their size, lymphocytes can be classified into small (5–8 μm), medium (8–12 μm) and large (12–15 μm) lymphocytes. Small lymphocytes are the most numerous. They consist of a spherical nucleus with prominent nuclear chromatin and a thin rim of cytoplasm, containing scattered ribosomes but virtually devoid of endoplasmic reticulum or other organelles. They are capable of slow motility and during movement assume a 'hand mirror' form, with the nucleus in front and the cytoplasm as a tail behind.

Depending on their lifespan, they can be classified as short-lived and long-lived lymphocytes. In human beings, the short lived lymphocytes have a lifespan of about two weeks, while the long lived cells may last for three years or more, or even for life. Short lived lymphocytes are the effector cells in immune response, while the long lived cells act as the storehouse for immunological memory. Long lived cells are mainly thymus derived.

Lymphopoiesis takes place mainly in the central lymphoid organs where they differentiate and mature before entering the circulation and then the peripheral lymphoid organs and tissues like a policeman on beat patrol. These populations of lymphocytes do not remain distinct but mix together in a process known as 'lymphocyte recirculation'. There is a constant traffic of lymphocytes through the blood, lymph, lymphatic organs and tissues. This recirculation ensures that following introduction of antigen into any part of the body, lymphocytes of appropriate specificity would reach the site during their ceaseless wandering and mount an immune response. A lymphocyte completes one cycle of recirculation in about one or two days. Recirculating lymphocytes can be recruited by the lymphoid tissues whenever necessary. Recirculating lymphocytes are mainly T cells. B cells tend to be more sessile. Chronic thoracic duct drainage will therefore result in selective T cell depletion.

A lymphocyte that has been 'educated' by the central lymphoid organs becomes an 'immunologically competent cell' (ICC). Mature T and B cells, before they encounter antigens are called naïve cells. Such cells, though not actually engaged in an immunological response, are nevertheless fully qualified to undertake such a

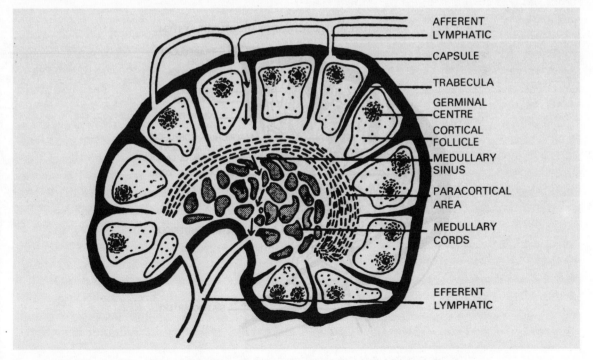

AFFERENT LYMPHATIC
CAPSULE
TRABECULA
GERMINAL CENTRE
CORTICAL FOLLICLE
MEDULLARY SINUS
PARACORTICAL AREA
MEDULLARY CORDS
EFFERENT LYMPHATIC

Fig. 15.2 Diagrammatic section of lymph node (arrows indicate the path of lymph flow).

responsibility when appropriately stimulated by an antigen. They subserve the following functions— recognition of antigens, storage of immunological memory, and immune response to specific antigens. Lymphocytes have antigen recognition mechanisms on their surface, enabling each cell to recognise only one antigen. The reaction of an immunocompetent cell to its specific antigen may be induction of either 'tolerance' or the immune response. The nature of immune response depends on whether the lymphocyte is a B or T cell. Stimulated T cells produce certain activation products (lymphokines) and induce CMI, while stimulated B cells divide and transform into plasma cells which synthesise immunoglobulins.

A number of surface antigens or markers have been identified on lymphocytes and other leucocytes by means of monoclonal antibodies. These markers reflect the stage of differentiation and functional properties of the cells. As they were given different designations by the investigators who prepared the antibodies, the same marker came to be known by different names (T4, Leu3, and so on). Order was introduced at the 'International Workshops for Leucocyte Differentiation Antigens' by comparing the specificities of different antisera. When a cluster of monoclonal antibodies was found to react with a particular antigen, it was defined as a separate marker and given a CD (cluster of differentiation) number. Over 150 CD markers have been identified so far. Table 15.1 lists a few CD markers, with their cell association and previous designations. (In spite of the CD nomenclature, some popular old names continue to be in use, for example, T4 and T8 are still in use for CD4 (helper/inducer) and CD8 (suppressor/ cytotoxic) cells).

The most clearcut differentiation between T and B cells is by their surface markers, for example, by demonstration of CD3 on T cells and Ig on B cells. Many other tests help in their differentiation (Table 15.2). These include:

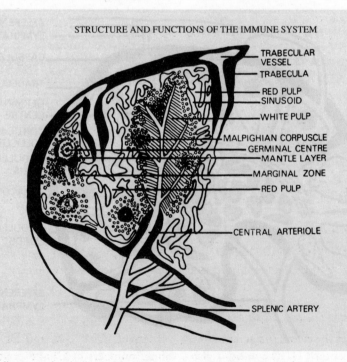

STRUCTURE AND FUNCTIONS OF THE IMMUNE SYSTEM

Fig. 15.3 Schematic diagram of splenic architecture

1. T cells bind to sheep erythrocytes forming rosettes (SRBC or E rosette) by CD2 antigen. B cells do not.
2. B cells bind to sheep erythrocytes coated with antibody and complement, forming EAC rosettes, due to the presence of a C3 receptor (CR2) on the B cell surface. This receptor (CR2) also acts as a receptor for the Epstein–Barr virus. T cells do not possess this.
3. B cells have immunoglobulin on their surface. Each B cell carries about 10^5 identical Ig molecules on its surface. The first Ig class to appear on the B cell surface is monomeric IgM. Subsequently other classes (either IgG, IgA or IgE) may be present, along with IgD. The surface Ig on a B cell will have only a single antigen specificity. It therefore serves as the antigen recognition unit. T cells do not have surface Ig. Instead they have T cell receptors (TCR) composed of two chains of polypeptides, linked to CD3.
4. T cells have thymus-specific antigens, which are absent on B cells.
5. T cells undergo blast transformation on treatment with mitogens such as phytohemagglutinin (PHA) or Concanavalin A (Con A), while B cells undergo similar transformation with bacterial endotoxins, Staphylococcus aureus (Cowan 1 strain) or EB virus.
6. Viewed under the scanning microscope, T cells are generally free of cytoplasmic surface projections, while B cells have an extensively filamentous surface, with numerous microvilli.

T Cell Maturation

T cell precursors from the yolk sac, fetal liver and bone marrow migrate to the thymus during the embryonic and postnatal stages. The earliest identifiable cells of T lineage are the CD7⁺ pro-T cells, which acquire CD2 on entering the thymus. They synthesise CD3 in the cytoplasm and become pre-T cells. T cell receptor (TCR) synthesis also takes place.

TCR is a heterodimer of glycoprotein chains expressed on the T cell surface, which in association with CD3 acts as the antigen recognition unit, analogous to the Ig on the surface of B cells. TCR occurs as two pairs of glycoprotein chains, either αβ or γδ. Pre-T cells differentiate into two lineages, expressing either αβ or γδ TCR chains. The large majority of T cells carry αβ TCR. TCR chains contain four separately encoded regions—V or variable, D or diversity, J or joining and C or constant, as in the case of immunoglobulins and hence belong to the *immunoglobulin gene superfamily*. By reassortment of these regions a very wide repertoire of antigen specificities can be formed on the T cell surface (Fig. 15.4).

Contact with self antigens within the thymus leads to the destruction of immature T cells carrying the corresponding TCR. Thus, self tolerance or elimination of T cells capable of reacting with self antigens takes place in the thymus. But cells capable of reacting with autoantigens continue to arise throughout life. These potentially harmful 'forbidden clones' are deleted by antigen specific suppresor cells. Immunocompetence against foreign antigens is also developed in the thymus.

T cells also develop MHC restriction so that CD8⁺ cells respond only to foreign antigens presented along with HLA Class I, and CD4⁺ cells to those presented with HLA Class II molecules.

Immature T cells in the thymus exhibit CD7, 2, 3, 1, 4 and 8, besides TCR. On functional maturity, they lose CD1 and differentiate into the two major subsets CD8⁻4⁺ or CD4⁻8⁺. Mature CD8⁻4⁺ TCR αβ cells are helper/inducer cells, inducing B cell differentiation, stimulating proliferation of CD8⁺ cytotoxic cells, producing lymphokines and regulating certain stages of erythropoiesis. CD4⁻8⁺ TCR αβ cells are suppressor/cytotoxic cells, inhibiting B cell antibody synthesis and acting as cytotoxic effector cells. Minor subsets of CD4⁺ cells and CD8⁺ cells also exist. Small numbers of CD4⁺8⁺ and CD4⁻8⁻ cells are also present in circulation.

The function of TCR γδ cells is not well understood, but they are believed to be immune surveillance cells on epithelial surfaces and a form of defense against intracellular bacteria.

Sequential antigenic changes characterising T cell maturation enable their easy identification. This has application in defining T cell malignancies. Acute T cell malignancies such as lymphoblastic leukemia and lymphomas involve early T cells, pro-T cells and other immature forms. Chronic T cell malignancies like mycosis fungoides, peripheral T cell lymphomas and HTLV-1 associated adult T cell leukemias involve mature T cells, mainly CD4+ cells.

T cells are broadly classified as *regulatory* and *effector* cells. Based on their surface markes, target cells and functions the following T cell category have been identified:

1. Helper/inducer cell (TH), with CD4 surface marker, MHC class II restriction; generally stimulating and promoting the growth of T cells and macrophages. Based on the different profiles of cytokines produced, two subsets are identified. TH1 and TH2.

   TH1 cells produce mainly the cytokines interferon gamma (IFN-γ) and interleukin-2 (IL2) which activate macrophages and T cells promoting CMI, destruction of target cells and killing of intracellular microbes, such as tubercle and lepra bacilli.

   TH2 cells produce mainly the cytokines IL4, 5 and 6 which stimulate B cells to form antibodies.

2. Suppressor T cell (Ts): these have CD8 surface marker and MHC class I restriction. They down regulate immune responses and check over stimulation.

3. Cytotoxic/cytolytic T cell (T$_c$) with CD8 surface marker and MHC class I restriction. These can kill and lyse target cells carrying new or foreign antigens, including tumour, allograft and virus infected cells.

4. Memory cells Tm both CD4 and CD8 cells provide memory and anamnestic immune responses.

B Cell Maturation

B lymphocyte precursors, pro-B cells, develop in the fetal liver during embryonic life and in the bone marrow afterwards continuously throughout life. Rearrangement of immunoglobulin genes takes place on their becoming pre-B cells, which synthesise cytoplasmic IgM. In the next stage – immature B cells – IgM is expressed on the cell surface. These cells migrate to the periphery and undergo immunoglobulin isotype switching so that instead of IgM alone, the cell expresses on its surface IgD, as well as one of the other Ig classes— IgM, IgG, IgA or IgE. By reassortment of Ig genes, B cells develop the capacity to produce Ig molecules which can react with all the possible epitopes. By a process of allelic exclusion, each B cell becomes programmed to form only one class of Ig, with either *kappa* and *lambda* light chain, possessing specificity to a single epitope alone, and to express it on the cell surface. By contact with self antigens during

Table 15.1 Leucocyte differentiation antigens (a few examples)

CD number	Cell type association	Former designations
CD 1	Thymocytes, Langerhans cells	T6, Leu 6
CD 2	T cell SRBC receptor	T11, Leu 5
CD 3	T cell antigen receptor complex	T3, Leu 4
CD 4	Helper T cell (receptor for HIV)	T4, Leu 3
CD 8	Suppressor/cytotoxic T cells	T8, Leu 2
CD 19	B cells	B4, Leu 12

Table 15.2 Some distinguishing characteristics of T cells, B cells and macrophages

Property	T cell	B cell	Macrophage
CD 3 receptor	+	−	−
Surface immunoglobulins	−	+	−
Receptor for Fc piece of IgG	−	+	+
EAC rosette (C3 receptor; CR2; EBV receptor)	−	+	−
SRBC rosette (CD2; measles receptor)	+	−	−
Thymus-specific antigens	+	−	−
Numerous microvilli, on surface	−	+	−
Blast transformation with:			
a. anti-CD 3	+	−	−
b. anti-Ig	−	+	−
c. PHA	+	−	−
d. Concanavalin A	+	−	−
e. Endotoxins	−	+	−
Phagocytic action	−	−	+
Adherence to glass surface	−	−	+

development, self tolerance is developed by clonal deletion or anergy.

On contact with its appropriate antigen, the mature B cell undergoes clonal proliferation. Some activated B cells become long-lived memory cells responsible for the recall phenomenon seen on subsequent contact with the same antigen. The majority of activated B cells are transformed into plasma cells.

Plasma cell is the antibody secreting cell. It is oval, about twice the size of a small lymphocyte, with an eccentrically placed oval nucleus containing large blocks of chromatin located peripherally (cartwheel appearance). The cytoplasm is large and contains abundant endoplasmic reticulum and a well-developed Golgi apparatus. It is structurally designed to be an immunoglobulin producing factory. Plasma cells are end cells and have a short lifespan of two or three days. A plasma cell makes an antibody of a single specificity, of a single immunoglobulin class and allotype, and of a single light chain type only. An exception is seen in the primary antibody response, when a plasma cell producing IgM initially, may later be switched to IgG production. While plasma cell is the best antibody producing cell, lymphocytes, lymphoblasts and transitional cells may also synthesise Ig to some extent.

A separate lineage of B cells, which are predominant in fetal and early neonatal life, express the T cell marker CD5 on their surface and have been named as B1 cells. Their progenitor cells move from the fetal liver to the peritoneal cavity where they multiply. They secrete low affinity polyreactive IgM antibodies, many of them autoantibodies. They are responsible for the T-independent 'natural' IgM antibacterial antibodies which appear in neonates seemingly without antigenic stimulus. CD5+ B cells may be relevant in the causation of autoimmune conditions.

NULL CELLS

When circulating lymphocytes are classified by their surface markers into T and B cells, about 5–10 per cent of the cells are found to lack features of either type. They were called *null cells*. Because of their morphology, they are also known as *large granular lymphocytes* (LGL). They are nearly double the size of the small lymphocytes, with indented nuclei and abundant cytoplasm containing several azurophilic granules, composed of mitochondria, ribosomes, endoplasmic reticulum and Golgi apparatus. LGL are a heterogeneous group of cells with differences in their functional and surface marker features. The most important member of this group is the *natural killer* (NK) cell. Others are the *antigen dependent cytotoxic cells* (ADCC) and the *lymphokine activated killer* (LAK) cells. The term NK cell is sometimes used as a common name for all null cells.

Natural killer cells possess spontaneous cytotoxicity towards various target cells, mainly malignant and virus infected cells. Their cytotoxicity is not antibody dependent or MHC restricted. NK activity is 'natural' or 'nonimmune' as it does not require sensitisation by prior antigenic contact. NK cells therefore form part of the innate immune set-up. They belong to a different lineage from T and B cells and are therefore normally active in 'severe combined immunodeficiency diseases', in which mature T and B cells are absent. They have CD16 and CD56 on their surface. They bind to the glycoprotein receptors on the surface of autologous as well as allogeneic target cells and release several cytolytic factors. One of these, *perforin*, which resembles complement component C9, causes trans-membrane pores through which cytotoxic factors, such as the tumour necrosis factor beta, enter the cell and destroy it by *apoptosis* (programmed cell death). NK cell activity is augmented by interferon. They are considered to be important in immune surveillance and natural defence against virus infected and malignant mutant cells.

A subpopulation of LGLs possesses surface receptors for the Fc part of Ig. They are capable of lysing or killing target cells sensitised with IgG antibodies. This antibody dependent cellular cytotoxicity is distinct from the action of cytotoxic T cells, which is independent of antibody. ADCC cells were formerly called killer (K) cells but are now classified with NK cells.

Lymphokine activated killer (LAK) cells are NK lymphocytes treated with interleukin-2 (IL2), which are cytotoxic to a wide range of tumour cells without affecting normal cells. LAK cells have shown promise in the treatment of some tumours such as renal cell carcinoma. IL2 also acts as a growth factor for NK cells.

Phagocytic cells: Phagocytosis is phylo-genetically the oldest defence mechanism in animals. Originating in protozoa as a combined mechanism for nutrition and defence, along the course of evolution, the phagocyte lost its trophic functions with the development of digestive enzymes. In higher organisms it specialised in the removal of foreign and autochthonous particles. Phagocytic cells are the mononuclear macrophages (of blood and tissues) and the polymorphonuclear microphages.

The blood macrophages (monocytes) are the largest of the lymphoid cells found in peripheral blood (12–15 µm). The tissue macrophages (histiocytes) are larger (15–20 µm). Mononuclear macrophage cells originate in the bone marrow from precursor cells and become monocytes in about six days. Monocytes in circulation have an approximate half-life of three days. They leave the circulation and reach various tissues to become transformed into macrophages, with morphological and functional features characteristic of the tissues, such as alveolar macrophages in the lungs and Kupffer cells in the liver. Tissue macrophages survive for months. Multinucleated cells and epithelioid cells seen in granulomatous inflammatory lesions such as tuberculosis originate from mononuclear macrophage cells.

The primary function of macrophages is phagocytosis. These cells move slowly in a ponderous and purposeful manner, their abundant cytoplasm thrusting out restless pseudopodia that glide harmlessly past normal body cells but engulf effete cells and foreign particles. They accumulate in areas of inflammation or tissue damage by chemotaxis. Particles sensitised by antibodies are phagocytosed more readily. The phagocytosed particle is held inside a vacuole (phagosome), the membrane of which fuses with a lysosome, forming a 'phagolysosome'. Lysosomal enzymes digest the particle, the remnants being extruded from the cells. While phagocytosis is an effective defence against most microorganisms, some (such as the bacilli of typhoid, brucellosis and tuberculosis) resist digestion and may multiply in the cells and be transported in them to other locations.

Macrophages express many surface receptors including Ia proteins, those for the Fc part of IgG, activated complement components and various lymphokines. *Mac 1* is a protein antigen found on mouse macrophages. A similar protein on human macrophages has been named *M1 marker*. This appears closely related to CR3, a cell receptor for C3 components.

Macrophages may participate in several ways in the induction and execution of the specific immune response. They trap the antigen and provide it, in optimal concentration, to the lymphocytes. Too high a concentration of antigen may be tolerogenic, and too low a concentration may not be immunogenic. It has also been shown that with some antigens, prior processing by macrophages is an essential prerequisite for induction of antibodies.

The processing and presentation of antigen by the macrophage to T cells require that both the cells possess surface determinants coded for by the same major histocompatibility complex (MHC) genes. The T cell can accept the processed antigen only if it is presented by a macrophage carrying on its surface the self-MHC antigens. When the macrophage bears a different MHC antigen, it cannot cooperate with the T cells. This is *MHC restriction*.

The functional efficiency of macrophages can be increased in many ways. They may be 'activated' by lymphokines, complement components or interferon. Activated macrophages are not antigen-specific. For example, activated macrophages from animals infected with one microorganism are cytotoxic to tumour cells as well as to many.other microorganisms. Activated macrophages show

morphological and functional changes as compared with unstimulated quiescent macrophages. They are larger, adhere better, spread faster on glass and are more phagocytic. They secrete a number of biologically active substances, including hydrolytic enzymes, binding proteins (fibronectin, transferrin), tumour necrosis factor (cachectin), colony stimulating factor (CSF) and interleukin 1 (formerly called the leukocyte activating factor). Interleukin 1 acts as an endogenous pyrogen and also induces synthesis of interleukin 2 by T cells. Interleukin 2 facilitates the activation of T cells. When stimulated by cytophilic antibodies and certain lymphokines, macrophages become 'armed'. Such armed macrophages are capable of antigen-specific cytotoxicity, which is important in antitumour activity and graft rejection.

Microphages are the polymorphonuclear leucocytes of the blood—neutrophils, eosinophils and basophils. Neutrophils are actively phagocytic and form the predominant cell type in acute inflammation. The phagocytic property of neutrophils is nonspecific, except for its augmentation by opsonins. They do not appear to have any role in specific immune processes. Eosinophilic leucocytes are found in large numbers in allergic inflammation, parasitic infections and around antigen–antibody complexes. They primarily inhabit tissues rather than the bloodstream. Their distinctive feature is the presence of two types of granules—the small, round, homogeneous ones and the large ovoid ones. The granules contain a variety of hydrolytic enzymes which bring about extracellular killing of large parasites. Eosinophils possess phagocytic activity but only to a limited degree.

Basophil leucocytes are found in the blood and tissues (mast cells). Their cytoplasm has large numbers of prominent basophilic granules containing heparin, histamine, serotonin and other hydrolytic enzymes. Degranulation of mast cells, with release of pharmacologically active agents, constitutes the effector mechanism in anaphylactic and atopic allergy.

STRUCTURE AND FUNCTIONS OF THE IMMUNE SYSTEM

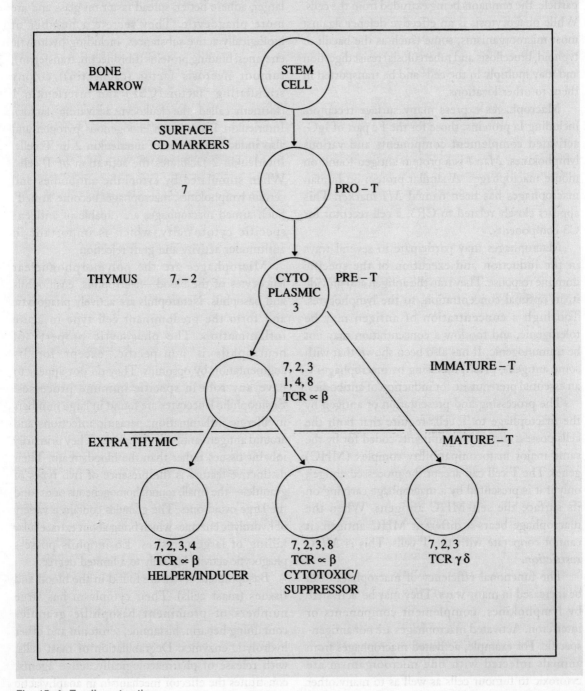

BONE
MARROW

STEM
CELL

SURFACE
CD MARKERS

7   PRO – T

THYMUS   7, – 2

CYTO
PLASMIC
3   PRE – T

7, 2, 3
1, 4, 8
TCR ∝ β

IMMATURE – T

EXTRA THYMIC   MATURE – T

7, 2, 3, 4
TCR ∝ β
HELPER/INDUCER

7, 2, 3, 8
TCR ∝ β
CYTOTOXIC/
SUPPRESSOR

7, 2, 3
TCR γ δ

Fig. 15. 4 T cell maturation

Dendritic cells: While macrophages are the major **antigen presenting cells**, another type of cell known as the dendritic cell also performs this function. **Dendritic cells** are bone marrow derived cells of a lineage different from the macrophages and T or B lymphocytes. They possess MHC class II antigens but not Fc or sheep RBC receptors or surface immunoglobulins. They have little or no phagocytic activity. They are highly pleomorphic, with a small central body and many long needle-like processes, and are present in the peripheral blood and in the peripheral lymphoid organs, particularly in the germinal areas of the spleen and lymph nodes. Dendritic cells are specially involved in the presentation of antigens to T cells during the primary immune response.

The B cell is another antigen presenting cell, particularly during the secondary immune response.

Langerhans cells in the skin possess features of macrophages and dendritic cells. They process and present antigens that reach the dermis.

MAJOR HISTOCOMPATIBILITY COMPLEX (MHC)

The primary function of the immune system is the recognition and elimination of foreign cells and antigens that enter the body. Tissues and organs grafted from one individual to another member of the same species ('allografts') are recognised as foreign and rejected. It was the early work of Gorer in the 1930s on the antigens responsible for allograft rejection in inbred mice that led to the discovery of the major histocompatibility complex (MHC).

Gorer identified two blood group antigen systems in mice, one of which (antigen 1) was common to all the strains. Antigen 2 was found only in some strains and appeared to be responsible for allograft rejection. This was called the H-2 antigen (H for histocompatibility; Chapter 20). The histocompatibility antigens are cell surface antigens that induce an immune response leading to rejection of allografts. (H-2 antigen system was found to be the major histocompatibility antigen

for mice and to be coded for by a closely linked multiallelic cluster of genes, which was called the **major histocompatibility complex**.

The development of congenic and recombinant strains of mice by Snell enabled the detailed analysis of the various loci of this complex. (The term 'congenic' means animals which differ only at a single genetic locus). Dausset pioneered studies on human leucocyte antigens, which were later found to be the major histocompatibility antigens in human beings.

The genetic basis of immune response, which had been suggested by many early observations, was proved by Benacerraf and colleagues, who established that the ability to respond immunologically to an antigen was conditioned by specific genes called the immune response (Ir) genes. For their work on MHC and the genetic control of immune response, Snell, Dausset and Benacerraf were awarded the Nobel Prize for Medicine in 1980.

Early studies on MHC were carried out in mice. However, all species of animals (including human beings) examined subsequently were found to possess a similar complex of genes on a segment of one chromosome pair, coding for three different classes of proteins:

1. Class I proteins that determine histocompatibility, and the acceptance or rejection of allografts (tissues or organs from different individuals within the same species);
2. Class II proteins that regulate the immune response; and,
3. Class III proteins that include some components of the complement system and a few others.

The name 'histocompatibility complex' arose because its discovery was based on transplantation experiments, and only later were the other two components of the complex identified. The major antigens determining histocompatibility in human beings are alloantigens, characteristically found on the surface of leucocytes. Human MHC antigens are therefore synonymous with human leucocyte antigens (HLA), and the MHC complex of genes with the HLA complex.

HLA complex: The HLA complex of genes is located on the short arm of chromosome 6 (Fig. 15.5). It consists of three separate clusters of genes:
1) HLA class I comprising A, B and C loci;
2) Class II or the D region consisting of DR, DQ and DP loci; and
3) Class III or the complement region containing genes for complement components C2 and C4 of the classical pathway, as well as properdin factor B of the alternative pathway, heat shock proteins and tumour necrosis factors α and β.

HLA loci are multiallelic, that is, the gene occupying the locus can be any one of several alternative forms (alleles). As each allele determines a distinct product (antigen), the HLA system is very pleomorphic. For example, at least 24 distinct alleles have been identified at HLA locus A and 50 at B.

HLA molecules: HLA antigens are two-chain glycoprotein molecules anchored on the surface membrane of cells (Fig. 15.6).

Class I molecules consist of a heavy peptide chain (alpha chain) noncovalently linked to a much smaller peptide called beta 2-microglobulin (beta chain). The beta chain has a constant aminoacid sequence and is coded for by a gene on chromosome 15. The alpha chain consists of three globoid domains (alpha 1, alpha 2, alpha 3) which protrude from the cell membrane and a small length of transmembrane C terminus reaching into the cytoplasm. The distal domains (alpha 1 and alpha 2) have highly variable aminoacid sequences and are folded to form a cavity or groove between them. Protein antigens processed by macrophages or dendritic cells to form small peptides are bound to this groove for presentation to CD8 T cells. The T cell will recognise the antigen only when presented as a complex with the MHC class I molecule and not otherwise (MHC restriction). When so presented, the CD8 cytotoxic killer cell destroys the target cell (for example, a virus infected cell).

HLA class I antigens (A, B and C) are found on the surface of virtually all nucleated cells. They are the principal antigens involved in graft rejection and cell mediated cytolysis. Class I molecules may function as components of hormone receptors.

HLA class II antigens are more restricted in distribution, being found only on cells of the immune system—macrophages, dendritic cells, activated T cells, and particularly on B cells.

Class II antigens are heterodimers, consisting of an alpha and a beta chain (Fig. 15.7). Each chain has two domains, the proximal domain being the constant region and the distal the variable. The two distal domains (alpha 1, beta 1) constitute the antigen-binding site, for recognition by CD4 lymphocytes, in a fashion similar to the recognition of the Class I antigen peptide complex by CD8 T cells. HLA class II molecules are primarily responsible for the graft-versus-host response and the mixed leucocyte reaction (MLR).

Both class I and II molecules are members of the immunoglobulin gene superfamily. The immune response (Ir) genes which control immunological responses to specific antigens are believed to be situated in the HLA Class II region, probably associated with the DR locus. Ir genes have been studied extensively in mice and located in the I region of mouse MHC. They code for Ia (I region associated) antigens consisting of 1A and 1E proteins. However, the relevance of Ir genes in humans is not clear.

HLA class III molecules are heterogeneous. They include complement components linked to the formation of C3 convertases, heat shock proteins and tumour necrosis factors. They also display polymorphism.

The MHC system was originally identified in the context of transplantation, which is an artificial event. In the natural state, besides serving as cell surface markers that help infected cells to signal cytotoxic and helper T cells, the enormous polymorphism of the MHC helps maximise protection against microbial infections. By increasing

STRUCTURE AND FUNCTIONS OF THE IMMUNE SYSTEM

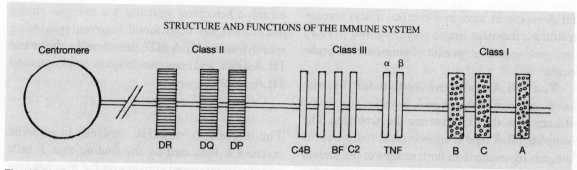

Fig. 15.5 **HLA complex loci on chromosome**

the specificity of self antigens, the MHC prevents microbes with related antigenic make up sneaking past host immune defences by molecular mimicry. The primary aim of the MHC may be defence against microbes and not against the graft.

MHC has been implicated in a number of nonimmunological phenomena such as individual odour, body weight in mice and egg laying in chickens.

HLA typing: Antisera for HLA typing were obtained principally from multiparous women as

they tend to have antibodies to the HLA antigens of their husbands, due to sensitisation during pregnancy. Monoclonal antibodies to HLA antigens have been developed. Typing is done serologically by microcytotoxicity, which tests for complement mediated lysis of peripheral blood lymphocytes with a standard set of typing sera. However, serological typing is not possible for HLA-DR antigens, which are detected by the mixed leucocyte reaction (MLR) and primed lymphocyte typing (PLT), respectively. Genetic methods are being used increasingly for

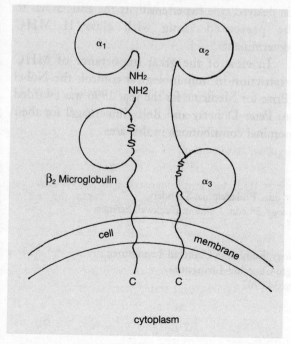

Fig. 15.6 HLA Class I molecule

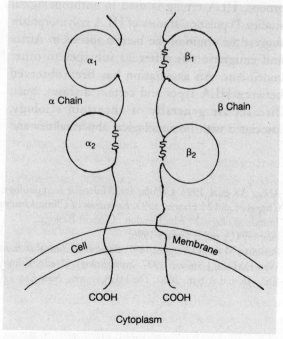

Fig. 15.7 HLA Class II molecule

HLA-typing in advanced centres. These employ restriction fragment length polymorphism (RFLP) and gene sequence specific oligonucleotide probe typing

The HLA antigens coded for by the combination of alleles at each locus on one strand of a chromosome pair represent the haplotype. The complete HLA type of an individual comprises the antigens represented on both strands of the diploid chromosome and so will consist of two haplotypes (for example, HLA-A1, -A2; -B7, -B12; -Cw3, -Dw8; Dw4; -Dw7; -DR1; -DR7; DQw1; -Qw3; -DPw4; -DPw6).

Due to the extreme pleomorphism of the HLA system, delineation of the HLA type provides a method of typing of individuals, that is far more discriminating than blood grouping. HLA typing is used primarily for testing compatibility between recipients and potential donors before tissue transplantation. It also has applications in disputed paternity. As the prevalence of HLA types varies widely between different human races and ethnic groups, HLA typing is used in anthropological studies. Population studies of HLA polymorphism suggest the origin of the human species in Africa and emigration as different subtypes to other continents. An association has been observed between HLA types and certain diseases. Such diseases are generally of uncertain etiology, associated with immunological abnormalities and exhibit a hereditary tendency. For example, strong association has been found between ankylosing spondylitis and HLA-B27, rheumatoid arthritis and HLA-DR4, and many autoimmune conditions and HLA-DR3.

MHC RESTRICTION

The importance of MHC antigens in immune reaction is indicated by the finding that T cells respond to processed antigens on the macrophages and other accessory cells only when they are presented along with the self-MHC antigen. This is known as MHC restriction. Both class I and class II antigens operate in this phenomenon. Cytotoxic T lymphocytes from immunised mice are able to kill and lyse virus infected target cells only when the T cells and target cells are of the same MHC type, so that the T cells can recognise class I MHC antigens on the target cells. Helper T cells can accept antigen presented by macrophages only when the macrophages bear the same class II MHC molecules on the surface. For T cells participating in delayed type hypersensitivity the antigen has to be presented along with class II MHC determinants.

In view of the great importance of MHC restriction in immunological control, the Nobel Prize for Medicine for the year 1996 was awarded to Peter Doherty and Rolf Zinkernagel for their seminal contributions in this area.

Further Reading

Abbas AK et al. 1994. *Cellular and Molecular Immunology.* 2nd edn. Philadelphia: Saunders.

Chapel H and M Haeney 1993. *Essentials of Clinical Immunology.* 5th edn. London: Blackwell Science.

Immunobiology, 2nd edn. London : Current Biology.

Janeway CA and P Travers 1996.

Peakman M and D Vergani 1997. *Basic and Clinical Immunology.* Edinburgh Churchill-Livingstone.

Weir DM and J Stewart 1997. *Immunology.* 8th edn. Edinburgh: Churchill-Livingstone.

Klein JK and A Sato 2000. The HLA system. *New Eng J Med* 343:702

Immune Response

The specific reactivity induced in a host by an antigenic stimulus is known as the immune response. In infectious disease it is generally equated with protection against invading microorganisms. But the immune response has a much wider scope and includes reactions against any antigen, living or nonliving. It may lead to consequences that are beneficial, indifferent or injurious to the host. It also includes the state of specific nonreactivity (tolerance) induced by certain types of antigenic stimuli. The immune response can be of two types — the humoral (antibody mediated) and the cellular (cell mediated) types. The two are usually developed together, though at times one or the other may be predominant or exclusive. They usually act in conjunction but may sometimes act in opposition.

Antibody mediated immunity (AMI) provides primary defence against most extracellular bacterial pathogens, helps in defence against viruses that infect through the respiratory or intestinal tracts, prevents recurrence of virus infections and participates in the pathogenesis of immediate (types 1, 2 and 3) hypersensitivity and certain autoimmune diseases. Cell mediated immunity (CMI) protects against fungi, viruses and facultative intracellular bacterial pathogens, participates in the rejection of homografts and graft-versus-host reaction, provides immunological surveillance and immunity against cancer, and mediates the pathogenesis of delayed (type 4) hypersensitivity and certain autoimmune diseases.

HUMORAL IMMUNE RESPONSE

The production of antibodies consists of three steps:

1. The entry of the antigen, its distribution and fate in the tissues and its contact with appropriate immunocompetent cells (*the afferent limb*).
2. The processing of antigen by cells and the control of the antibody forming process (*central functions*).
3. The secretion of antibody, its distribution in tissues and body fluids and the manifestations of its effects (*efferent limb*).

Antibody production follows a characteristic pattern consisting of:

a. A lag phase, the immediate stage following antigenic stimulus during which no antibody is detectable in circulation.
b. A log phase in which there is steady rise in the titre of antibodies.
c. A plateau or steady state when there is an equilibrium between antibody synthesis and catabolism.
d. The phase of decline during which the catabolism exceeds the production and the titre falls (Fig. 16.1).

PRIMARY AND SECONDARY RESPONSES

The antibody response to an initial antigenic stimulus differs qualitatively and quantitatively from the response to subsequent stimuli with the same antigen. The former is called the *primary response* and the latter the *secondary response* (Fig. 16.2). The primary response is slow, sluggish and short-lived, with a long lag phase and low titre of antibodies that does not persist for long. In contrast, the secondary response is prompt, powerful and prolonged, with a short or negligible lag phase and a much higher level of antibodies that lasts for long periods. The antibody formed in the primary response is predominantly IgM and in the secondary response IgG. The early antibody is more specific but less avid than the late antibody. The duration of the lag phase and the persistence of the antibody vary with the nature of the antigen. With some antigens such as diphtheria toxoid, the lag phase in the primary response may be as long as 2–3 weeks, while with pneumococcal polysaccharide, antibodies can be detected as early as within a few hours.

A single injection of an antigen helps more in sensitising or priming the immunocompetent cells producing the particular antibody than in the actual elaboration of high levels of antibody. Effective levels of antibody are usually induced only by subsequent injections of the antigen. It is for this reason that nonliving vaccines are given in multiple doses for active immunisation. The first injection is known as the *priming* dose and subsequent injections as *booster* doses. With live vaccines, a single dose is sufficient as multiplication of the organism in the body provides a continuing antigenic stimulus that acts as both the priming and booster dose.

When an antigen is injected into an animal already carrying the specific antibody in circulation,

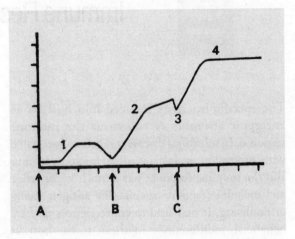

Fig. 16.2 Effect of repeated antigenic stimulus. A, B, C antigenic stimuli. 1. primary immune response. 2. secondary immune response. 3. negative phase. 4. high level of antibody following booster injection.

a temporary fall in the level of circulating antibody occurs due to the combination of the antigen with the antibody. This has been called the **negative phase**. It is followed by an increase in the titre of the antibody exceeding the initial level.

FATE OF ANTIGEN IN TISSUES

The manner in which an antigen is dealt with in the body depends on factors such as the physical and chemical nature of the antigen, its dose and route of entry, and whether the antigenic stimulus is primary or secondary. Antigens introduced intravenously are rapidly localised in the spleen, liver, bone marrow, kidneys and lungs. They are broken down by the reticuloendothelial cells and excreted in the urine, about 70–80 per cent being thus eliminated within one or two days. In contrast, antigens introduced subcutaneously are mainly localised in the draining lymph nodes, only small amounts being found in the spleen.

Particulate antigens are removed from circulation in two phases. The first is the

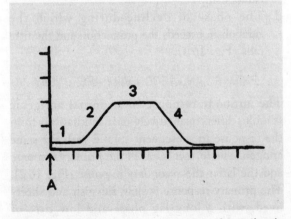

Fig. 16.1 Primary immune response. An antigenic stimulus 1. latent period. 2. rise in titre of serum antibody. 3. Steady state of antibody titre. 4. decline of antibody titre.

nonimmune phase during which the antigen is engulfed by the phagocytic cells, broken down and eliminated. With the appearance of the specific antibody, the phase of immune elimination begins, during which antigen—antibody complexes are formed and are rapidly phagocytosed, resulting in an accelerated disappearance of the antigen from circulation. With soluble antigens, three phases can be recognised—equilibration, metabolism and immune elimination. The phase of equilibration consists of diffusion of the antigen to the extravascular spaces. During the metabolic phase, the level of the antigen falls due to catabolic decay. During the phase of immune elimination, there is rapid elimination of the antigen with the formation of antigen—antibody complexes. Such complexes can cause tissue damage and may be responsible for 'immune complex diseases' such as serum sickness.

The speed of elimination of an antigen is related to the speed at which it is metabolised. Protein antigens are generally eliminated within days or weeks, whereas polysaccharides which are metabolised slowly, persist for months or years. Pneumococcal polysaccharide, for instance, may persist upto 20 years in human beings, following a single injection.

PRODUCTION OF ANTIBODIES

Immune response to an antigen is brought about by three types of cells: antigen processing cells (APC—principally macrophages and dendritic cells), T cells and B cells. The first step is the capture and processing of the antigens by APC and their presentation, in association with the appropriate MHC molecule, to T cells. While this step is essential for most antigens (T cell dependent antigens such as proteins and erythrocytes), in the case of T cell independent antigens, such as polysaccharides and other structurally simple molecules with repeating epitopes, antibody production does not require T cell participation.

Only when the processed antigen is presented on the surface of APC, in association with MHC molecules, to the T cell carrying the receptor (TCR) for the epitope is the T cell able to recognise it. In the case of CD4 (helper T/T_H) cells, the antigen has to be presented complexed with MHC Class II and for CD8 (cytotoxic T/T_C) cells with MHC class I molecules. B cells, which possess surface Ig and MHC class II molecules, can also present antigens to T cells, particularly during the secondary response.

The TH cell requires two signals for activation. The first signal is a combination of the T cell receptor (TCR) with the MHC class II-complexed antigen. The second signal is interleukin-1 (IL1) which is produced by the APC. The activated TH cell forms interleukin-2 and other cytokines required for B cell stimulation. These include IL4, IL5 and IL6 which act as B cell growth factor (BCGF) and the B cell differentiation factor (BCDF) that activate B cells which have combined with their respective antigens to clonally proliferate and differentiate into antibody-secreting plasma cells. A small proportion of activated B cells, instead of being transformed into plasma cells, become long lived memory cells producing a secondary type of response to subsequent contact with the antigen.

Cytotoxic T (CD8/TC) cells are activated when they contact antigens presented along with MHC class I molecules. They also need a second signal IL2, which is secreted by activated T_H cells. On contact with a target cell carrying the antigen on its surface, the activated T_C cells release cytotoxins that destroy the target, which may be virus infected or tumour cells. Some T_C cells also become memory cells (Fig. 16.3).

MONOCLONAL ANTIBODIES

A single antibody forming cell or clone produces antibodies specifically directed against a single antigen or antigenic determinant only. However, antibodies produced ordinarily by infection or antigens have multiple epitopes or antigenic determinants, each of which generates separate clones of lymphocytes. This results in antisera

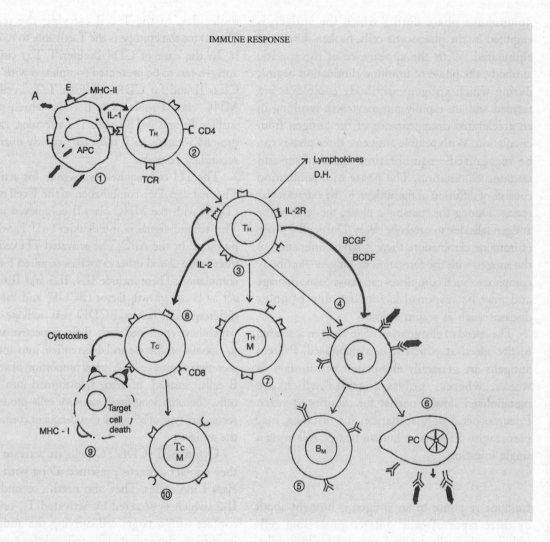

IMMUNE RESPONSE

Fig. 16.3 : Outline scheme of immune response against T cell dependent antigen
1. Antigen presenting cells (APC) process phagocytosed antigens (A) in their cytoplasm and present on the cell surface immunogenic epitopes (E) complexed with MHC Class II molecules.
2. Signals for the activation of CD4 (T_H) cells are a combination of the T Cell antigen receptor (TCR) with the MHC Class II antigen complex on APC, and stimulation by IL-1 released by APC.
3. The activated T_H cell sprouts IL-2 receptors and secretes cytokines which act on B cells carrying surface Ig for the epitope, causing cell growth and differentiation (4).
5. Some of the activated B cells become memory cells (B_M), while others are transformed into plasma cells (PC) secreting antibody against the antigen (6).
7. Some T_H cells remain as memory cells (THM).
8. Cytotoxic T cells are stimulated by IL-2 released by the activated T_H cell. On contract with the epitope complexed with MHC Class I molecules on the surface of target cells, the T_C cell releases cytotoxins which destroy the target cells (9).
10. Some T_C cells become memory cells (T_{CM}).

containing immunoglobulins of different classes with specificities against different epitopes of the antigen. On the other hand, when a clone of lymphocytes or plasma cells undergoes selective proliferation, as in multiple myeloma, antibodies with a single antigenic specificity accumulate. Such antibodies produced by a single clone and directed against a single antigenic determinant are called monoclonal antibodies. *Monoclonal antibodies* are very useful tools for diagnostic and research techniques.

An ingenious method for the large scale production of monoclonal antibodies against any desired antigen was developed by Kohler and Milstein in 1975. In recognition of the great importance of this hybridoma technology, the Nobel Prize for Medicine was awarded to them in 1984. Hybridomas are somatic cell hybrids produced by fusing antibody forming spleen cells with myeloma cells. The resultant hybrid retains the antibody producing capacity of the spleen cell and the ability of the myeloma cells to multiply indefinitely (Fig. 16.4).

Lymphocytes from the spleen of mice immunised with the desired antigen are fused with mouse myeloma cells grown in culture which do not form immunoglobulins and are deficient in the enzyme hypoxanthine phosphoribosyl transferase (HPRT). The fused cells are placed in basal culture medium (HAT medium containing hypoxanthine, aminopterin and thymidine) which does not permit the growth of the enzyme deficient myeloma cells. As normal lymphocytes cannot replicate indefinitely, only hybrid cells possessing properties of both the splenic lymphocytes and myeloma cells can grow in culture. These hybrid cells, called hybridomas, are cloned and examined for the production of antibodies. Clones producing antibodies against the desired antigen are selected for continuous cultivation. Such hybridomas can be maintained indefinitely in culture and will continue to form monoclonal antibodies. They may be also injected intraperitoneally in mice and monoclonal antibodies may be obtained by harvesting the ascitic fluid

produced. Hybridomas may be frozen for prolonged storage. The discovery of the hybridoma technology for the production of unlimited quantities of identical monoclonal antibodies of the same Ig class, possessing uniform specificity, affinity and other properties, created a revolution in immunology by opening up numerous diagnostic, therapeutic and research applications. Monoclonal antibodies against several antigens are now available commercially.

Murine monoclonal antibodies, however, proved unsuitable for human therapeutic use because they induced strong antimouse immune response. Moreover, the Fc piece of mouse Ig could not initiate effector defence mechanisms in human beings. Various modifications were introduced to improve efficiency. Cleaved Fab fragments could be coupled to various active substances like toxins, enzymes, radionuclides or cytotoxic drugs. Mouse monoclonals have been humanised by genetic manipulation to make chimeric antibodies consisting of murine variable regions and human constant regions. Grafting of murine monoclonal CDR loops on a human Ig framework provides a virtually human molecule. (The antigen binding surface of an antibody is composed of six hypervariable loops of aminoacids. These are called *complementarity determining regions* or CDRs).

Human monoclonal antibodies have subsequently been developed. Genes for particular antibody fragments have been fused to bacteriophage genes. Whole libraries of such antibodies have been built using bacteriophages. Large quantities of the desired antibody can be prepared by infecting bacteria with the appropriate bacteriophage. Such antibody engineering holds great promise for immunotherapy.

FACTORS INFLUENCING ANTIBODY PRODUCTION

Genetic factors: The immune response is under genetic control. The differences in immune response to the same antigen shown by different individuals in a species is determined by genetic differences. The terms 'responder' and

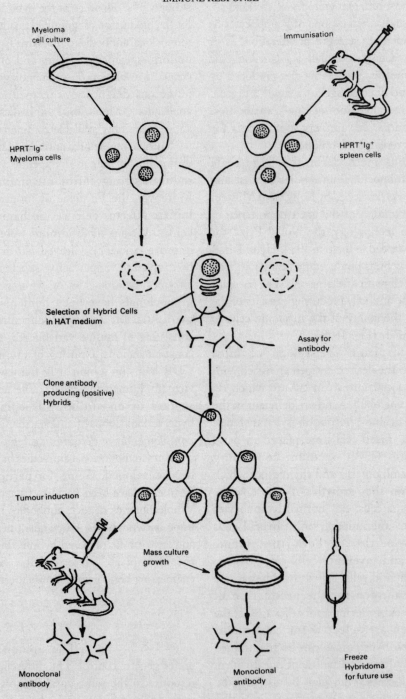

Fig. 16.4 : Monoclonal antibody production by hybridoma

'nonresponder' are used to describe the individual's capacity to respond to a particular antigen. The Ir (immune response) genes control this property.

Age: The embryo is immunologically immature. The capacity to produce antibodies starts only with the development and differentiation of lymphoid organs. The age at which embryos acquire immunological competence varies with different species. When the potential immunocompetent cell comes into contact with its specific antigen during embryonic life, the response is elimination of the cell or induction of tolerance. This is believed to be the basis for the nonantigenicity of self antigens. During embryonic life, the developing lymphoid cells come into contact with all the tissue antigens of the body released by cellular breakdown, so that all the clones of cells that have specificity towards self antigens are eliminated.

Immunocompetence is not complete at birth, but continues to develop as the infant grows. The infant has to depend on itself for antibody production from 3–6 months of age, by which time the maternal antibodies disappear. However, full competence is acquired only by about 5–7 years for IgG and 10–15 years for IgA. The ontogeny of antibody response also depends on the antigens concerned. B cell responses to most proteins and other T cell dependent antigens develop early, while responses to polysaccharides and other T cell independent antigens develop only later, usually by two years. Most IgG antibodies to polysaccharides are of the IgG2 type, and IgG2 producing B cells are the last to mature during infancy.

Nutritional status: Malnutrition affects the immune response adversely, though serum components necessary for immunity are conserved selectively till the nutritional deficiency becomes marked. Protein calorie malnutrition suppresses both humoral and cellular immune responses, the latter more severely. Deficiences of aminoacids (tryptophan, phenyl alanine, methionine, glycine, isoleucine) and vitamins (vitamin A, and B group factors riboflavine, pyridoxine, pantothenic acid,

folic acid) have been shown to cause a decrease in antibody synthesis.

Route of administration: The humoral immune response is better following parenteral administration of antigen than through oral or nasal routes. Large particulate antigens, such as bacteria or erythrocytes, are more effective when injected into tissues. The route of administration may also influence the type of antibody produced. For production of IgA antibodies, the oral or nasal route is most suitable. Inhalation of pollen antigens induces IgE synthesis, whereas the same antigens given parenterally lead to IgG antibodies. With some antigens the route of administration determines whether tolerance or antibody response results. Injection of protein antigens into the mesenteric vein or intrathymically usually induces tolerance. Sulzberger (1929) and Chase (1959) showed that guinea pigs can be rendered specifically tolerant if certain antigens are fed before a parenteral challenge (Sulzberger–Chase phenomenon). Application of simple chemicals to the skin usually leads to cellular immune response (delayed hypersensitivity) rather than antibody formation.

With some antigens the site of injection seems relevant. Hepatitis B vaccine is less immunogenic following gluteal injection than following injection into the deltoid. This may be due to the paucity of antigen presenting cells in the gluteal fat, delaying presentation of antigen to T and B cells.

Size and number of doses: Antibody response is, to an extent, dose dependent. An antigen is effective only above a minimum critical dose. Further increase in dose enhances the intensity of the antibody response. But beyond a certain level, increase in the dose of antigen does not improve the antibody response but may even inhibit it and induce tolerance. Mice injected with 0.5 µg of pneumococcal capsular polysaccharide produce specific antibodies but those injected with 50 µg of the antigen not only fail to form antibodies but may not respond even to subsequent doses of the same antigen. The massive antigenic stimulus appears to swamp the antibody producing system and paralyse it. This phenomenon was designated 'immunological paralysis' by Felton (1949).

The increased antibody response to a secondary antigenic stimulus has already been noticed. With repeated antigen injections, the antibody response increases progressively but after a certain stage, no further increase occurs.

The term 'anamnestic reaction' was originally applied to the production, in response to an antigenic stimulus, of a heterologous but related antibody that the host had earlier produced. For instance, a person who had been immunised earlier against typhoid bacilli may sometimes produce antityphoid antibodies in response to infection with some other bacterium. This may cause confusion in the serological diagnosis of typhoid fever but anamnestic reaction can be differentiated from a true secondary response as it is transient. The term 'anamnestic reaction' has been employed by some to refer to the secondary response as well, so there is some confusion in the use of this term.

Multiple antigens: When two or more antigens are administered simultaneously, the effects may vary. Antibodies may be produced against the different antigens just as though they had been given separately, or antibody response to one or the other of the antigens may be enhanced, or the response to one or more of them may be diminished (antigenic competition). When two bacterial vaccines (for example, typhoid and cholera vaccines) are given in a mixed form, the antibody response to each is not influenced by the other. When toxoids are given along with bacterial vaccines (for example, triple vaccine containing diphtheria and tetanus toxoids along with Bord pertussis vaccine) the response to the toxoid is potentiated. When diphtheria and tetanus toxoids are given together, with one in excess, the response to the other is inhibited. When triple antigen is given to a person who had earlier received a primary dose of diphtheria toxoid, the response to the tetanus and pertussis antigens will be diminished. Such antigenic competition is important, from a practical point of view, in immunisation with polyvalent antigens. For optimal effect, the nature and relative proportions of the different antigens in a mixture should be carefully adjusted.

Adjuvants: The term adjuvant refers to any substance that enhances the immunogenicity of an antigen. Adjuvants may confer immunogenicity on nonantigenic substances, increase the concentration and persistence of the circulating antibody, induce or enhance the degree of cellular immunity and lead to the production of 'adjuvant diseases' such as allergic disseminated encephalomyelitis. A variety of substances exhibit adjuvant activity.

Repository adjuvants such as aluminium hydroxide or phosphate and incorporation of protein antigens in the water phase of a water-in-oil emulsion (Freund's incomplete adjuvant), delay the release of antigen from the site of injection and prolong the antigenic stimulus. Others such as silica particles, beryllium sulphate and endotoxins activate macrophages. The most potent adjuvant is Freund's complete adjuvant, which is the incomplete adjuvant along with a suspension of killed tubercle bacilli. Besides increasing the humoral immune response, it induces a high degree of cellular immunity (delayed hypersensitivity) as well. As it produces a local granuloma, it is unsuitable for human use. The adjuvant effect of tubercle bacilli is due to a water soluble peptide MDP (muramyl dipeptide) which induces good antibody response without causing granuloma. Given in mineral oil or as liposomes, it also stimulates cell mediated immunity. Derivatives of MDP are being developed for human use. Gram negative bacilli show an adjuvant effect due to their lipopolysaccharide fraction. Bordetella pertussis, which has, in addition, a lymphocytosis-promoting factor acting on both T and B cells, acts as a good adjuvant for diphtheria and tetanus toxoids in triple vaccine. Other adjuvants commonly used with human vaccines are aluminium hydroxide or phosphate.

Immunosuppressive agents: These inhibit the immune response. They are useful in certain situations like transplantation, when it becomes necessary to prevent graft rejection. Examples of immunosuppressive agents are X-irradiation, radiomimetic drugs, corticosteroids, antimetabolites and other cytotoxic chemicals, and antilymphocytic serum.

Sublethal whole body irradiation suppresses antibody response. When antigenic stimulus follows 24 hours after irradiation, antibody production does not occur, whereas if the antigen is administered 2–3 days before irradiation, the antibody response is actually enhanced. The primary response is more radiosensitive than the secondary response.

Radiomimetic drugs are agents with an action resembling that of X-rays. They belong in general to the class of alkylating agents (for example, cyclophosphamide, nitrogen mustard). In human beings, cyclophosphamide given for three days after the antigen, completely suppresses the antibody response. It is much less effective when given before the antigen.

Corticosteroids cause depletion of lymphocytes from the blood and lymphoid organs. They also stabilise the membranes of cells and lysosomes, inhibiting histamine release and the inflammatory response. They suppress antibody formation in the rat, mouse and rabbit but are much less effective in guinea pigs, monkeys and human beings. Therapeutic doses have little effect on the antibody formation in human beings. They inhibit the induction and manifestations of delayed hypersensitivity in human beings.

Antimetabolites are substances that interfere with the synthesis of DNA, RNA or both and thus inhibit cell division and differentiation necessary for humoral and cellular immune responses. They include folic acid antagonists (methotrexate), alkylating agents (cyclophosphamide) and analogues of purine (6-mercaptopurine, azathioprine), cytosine (cytosine arabinoside) and uracil (5-fluorouracil). Many antimetabolites find clinical application in the prevention of graft rejection.

The drug most widely used now for immunosuppression is cyclosporine, a cyclic polypeptide derived from the soil fungus *Tolypocladium inflatum*. It is not cytotoxic for lymphocytes and has no antimitotic activity. It selectively inhibits helper T cell activity. A related drug is rapamycin.

Antilymphocyte serum (ALS) is a heterologous antiserum raised against lymphocytes. Antibody prepared against thymus cells is called antithymocyte serum (ATS). The corresponding globulin preparations are called ALG and ATG. They were used to prevent graft rejection. While all other immunosuppressive agents have undesirable side effects, ALS is devoid of any action other than that on lymphocytes. ALS acts primarily against T lymphocytes and therefore specifically on cell mediated immunity. Humoral antibody response to thymus independent antigens is unaffected and may even be enhanced. ALS acts only against lymphocytes in circulation and not cells in lymphoid organs. As ALS is a foreign protein, its effect is decreased on repeated administration, which may also lead to serum sickness and other hypersensitivity reactions. Monoclonal antibodies against specific lymphocyte membrane antigens have been prepared.

Effect of antibody: The humoral immune response to an antigen can be suppressed specifically by passive administration of the homologous antibody. The action appears to be by a feedback mechanism. The primary response is more susceptible to inhibition than the secondary response. The antibody may also combine with the antigen and prevent its availability for the immunocompetent cells. The inhibitory effect of a passively administered antibody on the humoral immune response has been applied in the prevention of Rh sensitisation in Rh negative women carrying Rh positive fetuses. This is achieved by the administration of anti-Rh globulin immediately following delivery (within 72 hours).

This effect is also relevant in the practice of combined immunisation as in diphtheria and tetanus. In such cases, the toxoid and antitoxin should be given at separate sites. Adsorbed toxoid should be used as the inhibitory effect is much less than with fluid toxoid.

Intravenous administration of immune globulin has been shown to have immunomodulatory effects. It has been used in the treatment of many diseases of presumed immunopathologic etiology, such as thrombocytopenias and autoimmune hemolytic anemias.

SUPERANTIGENS

Superantigens are certain protein molecules, such as staphylococcal enterotoxins that activate very large numbers of T cells irrespective of their antigenic specificities. While conventional antigen fragments bind to the αβ heterodimer groove of the MHC molecules through the V regions of TCR α and β chains, superantigens bind directly to the lateral aspect of the TCR β chain. Upto 20 per cent of the circulating T cells may be so activated, compared to conventional antigenic stimuli which involve only about 0.001 per cent of them. This exaggerated T cell activation leads to massive outpouring of T cell cytokines, causing multisystem dysfunctions, such as seen in staphylococcal toxic shock syndrome.

MITOGENS

Mitogens are certain substances that induce division of lymphocytes and other cells. Some of these, like the lectin glycoproteins bind to sugars on the surface of responsive cells and activate them, causing a polyclonal reaction. At low concentrations, they stimulate B cells without polyclonal activation. Lipopolysaccharide is such a B cell mitogen.

Some large molecules with repeating epitopes, such as pneumococcal polysaccharide directly interact with B cell surface immunoglobulins, leading to an IgM immune response. Such T-independent immune response with IgM antibody, is not associated either with Ig class switching or memory.

CELLULAR IMMUNE RESPONSE

The term 'cell mediated immunity' (CMI) refers to the specific immune responses that do not involve antibodies. For long the only demonstrable facet of CMI was the phenomenon of delayed hypersensitivity (DH) which resulted in injury rather than protection. The first description of a CMI response was the observation by Jenner (1798) that inoculation of vaccinia virus in an immune individual led to a local erythematous papule in 24–72 hours. He called this the 'reaction of immunity'. Koch (1890) described the exaggerated cutaneous reaction of tuberculous guinea pigs to the intradermal injection of tubercle bacillus or a protein extract of the bacillus (tuberculin). Thereafter, the tuberculin test became the paradigm for DH. The term 'delayed hypersensitivity' refers to the appearance of a skin lesion 48–72 hours after administration of the antigen. The lesion is an indurated nodule with infiltration by mononuclear cells. DH was found to be immunologically specific but it did not have any relation to antibodies and could not be transferred passively by serum. The cellular basis of DH was shown by Landsteiner and Chase (1942) by its passive transfer in guinea pigs through the injection of leucocytes from sensitised donors. With the recognition of the two component concept of immunity, DH and other types of CMI were found to be mediated by T lymphocytes. A variety of techniques are now available for the detection of CMI, though they lack the sensitivity and precision of antibody assays for humoral immunity.

SCOPE OF CMI

CMI participates in the following immunological functions:

1. Delayed hypersensitivity.
2. Immunity in infectious diseases caused by obligate and facultative intracellular parasites. These include infections with bacteria (for example, tuberculosis, leprosy, listeriosis, brucellosis), fungi (for example, histoplasmosis, coccidioidomycosis, blastomycosis), protozoa (for example, leishmaniasis, trypanosomiasis) and viruses (for example, measles, mumps).

3. Transplantation immunity and graft-versus-host reaction.
4. Immunological surveillance and immunity against cancer.
5. Pathogenesis of certain autoimmune diseases (for example, thyroiditis, encephalomyelitis).

INDUCTION OF CMI

The nature of the antigenic stimulus is important in the induction of CMI. It is best developed following infections with intracellular parasites. Killed vaccines and other nonliving antigens do not induce CMI unless administered with the Freund type of adjuvants. Only T cell dependent antigens lead to CMI. The application of certain chemicals on the skin induces DH.

Each T cell bears on its surface a specific receptor (TCR) for one epitope and combines only with antigens carrying that epitope. On contact with the appropriate antigen, T cells undergo blast transformation, clonal proliferation and differentiation into memory cells and effector cells providing CMI. T cells recognise antigens only when presented with MHC molecules. Helper T cells react with antigens presented on the surface of macrophages or other cells, complexed with MHC class II molecules. They then release biological mediators (lymphokines) which activate macrophages, enabling them to kill intracellular parasites. Cytotoxic T cells recognise antigen on the surface of cells (such as virus infected, tumour or allograft cells), in association with MCH class I molecules, secrete lymphokines and destroy the target cells.

CYTOKINES

Biologically active substances released by activated T lymphocytes were called lymphokines. Similar substances produced by monocytes or macrophages were called monokines. Initially they were given names based on their demonstrated biological effects (Table 16.1). As most lymphokines exhibit multiple biological effects and the same effect may be caused

Table 16.1 Examples of lymphokines

I. Affecting macrophages
  a. Migration inhibiting factor (MIF)
  b. Macrophage activation/aggregation factor (MAF)
  c. Macrophage chemotactic factor (MCF)

II. Affecting lymphocytes
  a. Blastogenic/mitogenic factor (BF/MF)
  b. T cell growth factor (TGF)
  c. B cell growth factor (BGF)

III. Affecting granulocytes
  a. Chemotactic factor (CF)
  b. Colony stimulating factor (CSF)

IV. Affecting cultured cells
  a. Lymphotoxin (LT)
  b. Interferon (IFN)
  c. Tumour necrosis factor (TNF)

V. Others
  a. Skin reactive factor (SRF)
  b. Transfer factor (TF)

by different lymphokines, their names lack precision. The term interleukin was therefore introduced for those products of leucocytes which exert a regulatory influence on other cells. Interferons, growth factors and others were found to have similar effects. Therefore all of them have been grouped under the term cytokines.

Cytokines are peptide mediators or intercellular messengers which regulate immunological, inflammatory and reparative host responses. They are highly potent hormone-like substances, active even at femtomolar (10^{-15}M) concentrations. They differ from endocrine hormones in being produced not by specialised glands but by widely distributed cells (such as lymphocytes, macrophages, platelets and fibroblasts), and acting not systemically but locally near the producing cells (paracrine effect) or directly on the producing cells themselves (autocrine effect). They are, in general, pleiotropic, having multiple effects on the growth and differentiation of various cell types. There is considerable overlap in the effects produced by different cytokines. Cloning of cytokines and the availability of monoclonal antibodies against them have helped to characterise them better (Table 16.2).

Table 16.2: Cytokines

Cytokine	Main sources	Major functions
A. INTERLEUKINS:		
IL-1 (α and β)	Macrophages and other cell types	Proliferation and differentiation of T, B and other cells; pyrogenic; induce acute phase proteins; bone marrow cell proliferation.
IL-2	T cells	Promote growth and differentiation of T and B cells, cytotoxicity of T and NK cells, secretion of other lymphokines.
IL-3	T cells	Multi-CSF
IL-4	T_H cells	Proliferation of B and cytotoxic T cells; increase IgGI and IgE production; enhance MHC class II and IgE receptors.
IL-5	T_H cells	Proliferation of eosinophils, stimulate IgA and IgM production.
IL-6	TH, macrophages, fibroblasts	Promote B cell differentiation; IgG production, acute phase proteins.
IL-7	Spleen, bone marrow stromal cells	B and T cell growth factor.
IL-8	Macrophages, others	Neutrophil chemotactic factor.
IL-9	T cell	T cell growth and proliferation
IL-10	T, B cells, macrophages	Inhibit IFN production and mononuclear cell functions.
IL-11	Bone marrow stromal cells	Induce acute phase proteins.
IL-12	T cells	Activate NK cells.
IL-13	T cells	Inhibit mononuclear cell functions.
B. COLONY-STIMULATING FACTORS:		
GM-CSF	T cells, macrophages, fibroblasts	T cell and macrophage growth stimulation
G-CSF	Fibroblasts, endothelium	Granulocyte growth stimulation.
M-CSF	Fibroblasts, endothelium	Macrophage growth stimulation.
C. TUMOUR NECROSIS FACTORS:		
TNF-a	Macrophages, monocytes	Tumour cytotoxicity, lipolysis, wasting, acute phase proteins, phagocytic cell activation, antiviral and antiparasitic effects, endotoxic shock.
TNF-b	T cells	Induce other cytokines.
D INTERFERONS:		
IFN a	Leucocytes	
IFN b	Fibroblasts	Antiviral activity
IFN g	T cells	Antiviral, macrophage activation; MHC Class I and II expression on cells.
E. OTHERS:		
TGF b	T and B cells	Inhibit T and B cell proliferation and hematopoiesis; promote wound healing.
LIF	T cells	Proliferation of stem cells; eosinophil chemotaxis.

The features of some important cytokines are presented below:

Interleukin-1: Originally described as the leucocyte activating factor (LAF) in 1972 and as the B cell activating factor (BAF) in 1974, this cytokine was renamed interleukin-1 (IL1) in 1979. IL1 is a stable polypeptide retaining its activity up to 56 °C and between pH 3–11. IL1 occurs in two molecular forms, IL1 alpha and beta. IL1 is principally secreted by macrophages and monocytes but can be produced by most other nucleated cells also. Its production is stimulated by antigens, toxins, injury and inflammatory processes and inhibited by cyclosporin A, corticosteroids and prostaglandins.

The immunological effects of IL1 include stimulation of T cells for the production of IL2 and other lymphokines, B cell proliferation and antibody synthesis, neutrophil chemotaxis and phagocytosis. It mediates a wide range of metabolic, physiological, inflammatory and hematological effects by acting on bone marrow, epithelial and synovial cells, fibroblasts, osteoclasts, hepatocytes, vascular endothelium and other targets. IL1 is an important endogenous pyrogen. Together with the tumour necrosis factor (TNF), it is responsible for many of the hematological changes in septic shock and also enhances the initial meningeal inflammation in bacterial meningitis. Cytokine inhibitors such as dexamethasone have been found to protect against the sequelae of such excessive meningeal inflammation. On the other hand, IL1 has a beneficial effect in severe infections in immunocompromised hosts.

Interleukin-2: The discovery in 1976 of a T cell growth factor (TCGF) produced by activated T cells, which induced T cell proliferation and enabled their maintenance in continuous culture, contributed greatly to the understanding of T cell functions. This cytokine, renamed IL2, is a powerful modulator of the immune response. It is the major activator of T and B cells and stimulates cytotoxic T cells and NK cells. It converts some null cells (LGL) into lymphokine activated killer (LAK) cells which can destroy NK resistant tumour cells. This property has been used in the treatment of certain types of cancer.

Interleukin-3: IL3 is a growth factor for bone marrow stem cells. It stimulates multilineage hematopoiesis and is therefore known also as the multicolony stimulating factor (multi-CSF).

Interleukin-4: Formerly known as the B cell growth factor-1 (BCGF-1), IL4 activates resting B cells and acts as a B cell differentiating factor. It also acts as a growth factor for T cells and mast cells. It enhances the action of cytotoxic T cells. It may have a role in atopic hypersensitivity as it augments IgE synthesis.

Interleukin-5: Formerly known as the B cell growth factor-II, IL5 causes proliferation of activated B cells. It also induces maturation of eosinophils.

Interleukin-6: IL6 is produced by stimulated T and B cells, macrophages and fibroblasts. It induces immunoglobulin synthesis by activated B cells and formation of IL2 receptors on T cells. It has a stimulatory effect on hepatocytes, nerve cells and hematopoietic cells. It acts as an inflammatory response mediator in host defence against infections.

Colony stimulating factors (CSF): These cytokines stimulate the growth and differentiation of pluripotent stem cells in the bone marrow. They have been named after the types of cell colonies they induce in soft agar culture—for example, granulocyte (G), or mononuclear (M) CSF. IL3 which induces growth of all types of hematopoietic cells is known as multi-CSF. In the body they cause other effects also, presumably by inducing cascades of other cytokines. They are responsible for adjusting the rate of production of blood cells according to requirements, for example, the massive granulocyte response seen in pyogenic infections. Colony stimulating factors have clinical applications for treating hematopoietic dysfunctions in infections and malignancies.

Tumour necrosis factors (TNF): The tumour necrosis factor occurs as two types, alpha and beta. A serum factor found to induce hemorrhagic necrosis in certain tumours was named the tumour necrosis factor. The same substance was independently described as Cachectin, a serum factor causing the wasting syndrome (cachexia) during chronic infections. This has been renamed TNFα. It is formed principally by activated macrophages and monocytes. It resembles IL1 in possessing a very wide spectrum of biological activities such as participation in the manifestations of endotoxic other cytokines. TNFβ, formerly known as lymphotoxin, is produced principally by T helper cells. Its effects are similar to those of TNFα.

Interferons (IFN): Originally identified as antiviral agents (see chapter 49), interferons are now classified as cytokines. There are three classes of IFNs, alpha produced by leucocytes, beta produced by fibroblasts and gamma by T cells activated by antigens, mitogens or exposure to IL2. IFNγ causes many immunological effects, such as macrophage activation, augmentation of neutrophil and monocyte functions, and antitumour activity.

Other cytokines: The transforming growth factor beta (TGFβ) was so named because of its ability to transform fibroblasts. Besides acting as a growth factor for fibroblasts and promoting wound healing, it also acts as a down regulator of some immunological and hematological processes.

The leukemia inhibitory factor (LIF), produced by T cells, helps stem cell proliferation and eosinophil chemotaxis.

Cytokine production is regulated by exogenous stimuli such as antigens and mitogens, as well as by endogenous factors such as neuroendocrine hormonal peptides (corticosteroids, endorphins) and products of lipoxygenase and cyclooxygenase pathways. They also regulate each other by positive and negative feedbacks. A number of cytokines (for example, IL1, 2, 3, colony stimulating factors, interferons) have already found therapeutic application. With better understanding of their properties, it is possible that many cytokines, their agonists and antagonists could eventually be used in the management of inflammatory, infectious, autoimmune and neoplastic conditions.

DETECTION OF CMI

The original method for detecting CMI was the skin test for delayed hypersensitivity (for example, the tuberculin test). A number of in vitro correlates of CMI have now become available. These include the lymphocyte transformation test (transformation of cultured sensitised T lymphocytes on contact with the antigen), target cell destruction (killing of cultured cells by T lymphocytes sensitised against them), and the migration inhibiting factor test which is commonly employed. As originally described, this consisted of incubating in a culture chamber, packed peritoneal macrophages in a capillary tube. The macrophages migrate to form a lacy, fan-like pattern. If the macrophages are from a guinea pig sensitised to tuberculoprotein, addition of tuberculin to the culture chamber will inhibit the migration (Fig. 16.5). This has been adapted

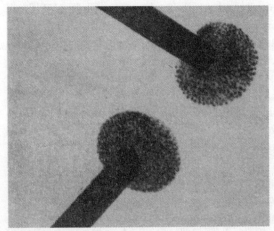

Fig. 16.5 Inhibition of migration of macrophage cells. *Left*: Exposure to antigen of cells from sensitised guinea pigs. Migration inhibited. *Right*: Control. Exposure to antigen of cells from normal guinea pigs. Shows foam—like migration of macrophages.

for clinical use by incubating human peripheral leucocytes in capillary tubes in culture chambers. When an antigen to which the individual has CMI is introduced into the culture medium, the leucocytes are prevented from migrating. By comparison with the control, it is possible to make a semiquantitative assessment of the migration inhibition.

TRANSFER FACTOR

Passive transfer of CMI was first achieved by the injection of viable leucocytes from sensitised donors. Lawrence (1954) reported transfer of CMI in human beings by the injection of extracts from leucocytes. This extract is known as the 'transfer factor' (TF). The transferred immunity is specific in that CMI can be transferred only to those antigens to which the donor is sensitive.

TF is a dialysable, low molecular weight substance (MW 2000 to 4000), resistant to trypsin, DNAase, RNAase and freeze thawing. It is stable for several years at $-20\ °C$ and in the lyophilised form at $4\ °C$. It is inactivated at $56\ °C$ in 30 minutes. It is not antigenic. Chemically, it appears to be a polypeptide–polynucleotide.

TF is highly potent, an extract from 0.1 ml of packed leucocytes being sufficient for transfer. The transferred CMI is systemic and not local at the injected site alone. Following TF injection, DH and various in vitro correlates of CMI can be demonstrated in the recipient. Humoral immunity is not transmitted by TF; TF transfers CMI to all the antigens to which the donor is sensitive, en bloc. It is possible to transfer CMI from the recipient to another in a serial fashion.

The mechanism of action of the TF is not known. TF could be an informational molecule or a specific gene derepressor capable of inducing antigenically uncommitted lymphocytes to produce antigen-specific receptors. TF activity was till recently demonstrable only in human beings but it has now been reported in monkeys, guinea pigs and mice.

TF has several applications. It has been used to restore immune capacity in patients with T cell deficiency (Wiskott–Aldrich syndrome). It has also been used in the treatment of disseminated infections associated with deficient CMI (lepromatous leprosy, tuberculosis, mucocutaneous candidiasis). It has been employed in the treatment of malignant melanoma and may be beneficial in other types of cancer as well. Its use has been suggested in some autoimmune diseases (systemic lupus erythematosus, rheumatoid arthritis) and diseases of unknown etiology (sarcoidosis, multiple sclerosis).

IMMUNOLOGICAL TOLERANCE

Immunological tolerance or immunological unresponsiveness is the condition in which contact with an antigen specifically abolishes the capacity to mount an immune response against that particular antigen when it is administered subsequently. This nonreactivity is specific to the particular antigen, immune reactivity to other antigens being unaffected.

The first example of immunological tolerance was the observation by Owen (1945) of erythrocyte chimerism in dizygotic cattle twins, each of the twins having erythrocytes of its own and the other's blood groups. As dizygotic twins are genetically dissimilar, they do not ordinarily accept transplants from each other but such transplants survive in cattle twins. The reason for this tolerance was shown to be the sharing of the same placental blood supply by the twins during intrauterine life. Based on this observation, Burnet and Fenner (1949) suggested that the unresponsiveness of individuals to self antigens was due to the contact of the immature immunological system with self antigens during embryonic life. Any antigen that comes into contact with the immunological system during embryonic life would be recognised as a self antigen and would not induce any immune response. They postulated that tolerance could be induced against foreign antigens if they were administered during embryonic life. This was proved experimentally by Medawar and his colleagues (1953) using two strains of syngeneic mice. When a skin graft from one inbred strain of mice (CBA) is applied on a mouse of another strain (A), it is rejected. If CBA cells are injected into fetal or newborn strain A mice, however, the latter when they grow up will freely accept skin grafts from CBA mice. The content of the self antigen appears to have been enlarged by contact with a foreign antigen during embryonic life. This phenomenon is called 'specific immunological tolerance'.

Development of tolerance is not confined to the embryo or newborn but can occur in adults also. Tolerance may be total or partial, short-lived or long-lasting. The induction, degree and duration of tolerance depend on the species and immunocompetence of the host, nature and dose of the antigen and the route of administration. Rabbits and mice can be rendered tolerant more rapidly than guinea pigs and chickens. Strain differences in tolerance induction are seen within species. The higher the degree of immuno-competence of the host, the more difficult it is to induce tolerance. It is for this reason that embryos and newborns are particularly susceptible to induction of tolerance. Tolerance can be induced in adults in whom immunocompetence is temporarily interrupted by immunosuppressive agents. Induction of tolerance is very difficult in adults already immunised against the antigen.

The physical state of the antigen is important. Soluble antigens and haptens are more tolerogenic than particulate antigens. The tolerogenicity of an antigen can be modified by certain procedures. When human gammaglobulin is heat aggregated, it is highly immunogenic in mice but is tolerogenic when deaggregated. Solutions of serum proteins centrifuged at high speed separate into tolerogenic supernatant and immunogenic sediment fractions. The induction of tolerance is dose dependent. There is a threshold dose, below which tolerance is not induced. Further increase in dose increases the duration of tolerance. With certain antigens, tolerance can be induced by two types of doses, one high and the other low, with intermediate doses producing immunity instead of tolerance. These are

known as 'high zone' and 'low zone' tolerance respectively. A special type of high zone tolerance is Felton's immunological paralysis. The duration of tolerance is variable. Tolerance can be prolonged by repeated tolerogenic stimuli. The route of administration that best induces tolerance is that whereby the antigen equilibrates throughout the extra- and intravascular compartments. With antigens that do not equilibrate readily or are rapidly eliminated, the route of choice is intravenous. Certain haptens that are immunogenic in guinea pigs by the intradermal route are tolerogenic orally or intravenously.

Tolerance can be overcome spontaneously or by an injection of cross-reacting immunogens. For example, tolerance to bovine serum albumin in rabbits can be abolished by immunisation with cross reacting human serum albumin. In general, tolerance to living agents is more lasting than that to nonliving substances. Naturally occurring tolerance is found in certain viral infections such as congenital rubella and cytomegalovirus infections in which there is persistent viremia with a decreased ability for the production of neutralising antibodies (persistent tolerant infection). In lymphocytic choriomeningitis infection in carrier mice, the virus may persist in virtually all the cells and tissues and be transmitted vertically to the offspring without any demonstrable immune response or pathogenic effect. When the tolerance is interrupted by an induction of antibody or an injection of sensitised lymphocytes, disease results. The mechanism of tolerance is not clear. In specific immunological tolerance in embryonic life, the clones of cells responding to the particular antigen were believed to be annihilated by contact with the antigen. This may not be entirely true, as self-reactive B cells can be found in adults. The more likely mechanism may be elimination of TH cells, effectively preventing B cell activation. This is the 'central mechanism' of tolerance induction. In other instances, the mechanism may be an 'afferent block' in which access of the antigen to immunocompetent cells is interfered with, or an 'efferent block' in which the antibody synthesised is neutralised or destroyed. T and B lymphocytes appear to possess differing sensitivity to tolerance induction, the former being more susceptible. In general, high doses of antigen induce B cell tolerance and repeated minute doses of antigen induce T cell tolerance.

Tolerance to humoral and cellular types of immunity is usually induced simultaneously. 'Split tolerance' can also occur where unresponsiveness is established for one parameter of the immune response and not to the other. In guinea pigs, DH to tuberculin can be inhibited, without affecting the production of a circulating antibody, by the injection of tuberculoprotein prior to immunisation with BCG.

THEORIES OF IMMUNE RESPONSE

A succession of theories have been put forward from time to time in order to explain the versatility, specificity, memory and other features of the immune response. Theories of immunity fall into two categories: instructive and selective. The instructive theories postulate that an immunocompetent cell is capable of synthesising antibodies of any specificity. The antigen encounters an immunocompetent cell and instructs it to produce the complementary antibody. Instructive theories were proposed by chemists who were more concerned with explaining the physicochemical aspects of specificity than with the biological principles of immune processes. Selective theories, on the contrary, shift the emphasis from the antigen to the immuno competent cell. They postulate that immunocompetent cells have only a restricted immunological range. The antigen exerts only a selective influence by stimulating the appropriate immuno-competent cell to synthesise an antibody. Side chain theory: The first plausible theory of immune response was the 'side chain' theory proposed by Ehrlich (1900). Cells were considered to have surface 'receptors' capable of reacting with substances having complementary 'side chains'. The

physiological significance of such receptors was in anchoring nutrients to cells before assimilation. When foreign antigens are introduced into the body, they combine with those cell receptors which have a complementary fit. This inactivates the receptors and interferes with the absorption of nutrients. As a compensatory mechanism, there is an overproduction of the same type of receptors, which spill over into the blood and circulate as antibodies. This was the first of the selection theories. It explained elegantly the specificity of the antibody response. However, when Landsteiner demonstrated that antibodies could be formed not only against natural antigens but also against various synthetic chemicals, this theory was abandoned. It was believed that an impossibly large number of receptors would be needed to account for the seemingly endless scope of antibody specificity. It is, however, remarkable how closely Ehrlich anticipated modern views on the immune response. Direct template theories: Instructive theories were proposed by Breinl and Haurowitz (1930), Alexander (1931) and Mudd (1932). According to these, the antigen (or the antigenic determinant) enters antibody forming cells and serves as a 'template' against which antibody molecules are synthesised so that they have combining sites complementary to the antigenic determinant. These are therefore known as 'direct template' theories. Pauling (1940) presented a more detailed model suggesting that specificity was determined by the folding of the antibody polypeptide chains to form a tertiary structure fitting the antigenic determinant.

Indirect template theory: Burnet and Fenner (1949) proposed this instructive theory to explain the synthesis of antibody as an adaptive protein. They postulated that the entry of the antigenic determinant into the antibody producing cell induced in it a heritable change. A 'genocopy' of the antigenic determinant was thus incorporated in its genome and transmitted to the progeny cells (indirect template). This theory explained specificity and the secondary response but became untenable with advances in the molecular biology of protein synthesis. Burnet and Fenner were the first to explain the nonantigenicity of self antigens by postulating the embryonic recognition of 'self markers'.

Natural selection theory: Jerne (1955) reintroduced the concept of the selective function of antigens in his natural selection theory. This postulated that about a million globulin (antibody) molecules were formed in embryonic life, which covered the full range of antigenic specificities. These globulins were the 'natural antibodies'. When an antigen was introduced, it combined selectively with the globulin that had the nearest complementary 'fit'. The globulin, with the combined antigen, homed in on the antibody forming cells and stimulated them to synthesise the same kind of antibody. Here, selection was postulated at the level of the antibody molecule. It did not explain the fact that immunological memory resides in the cells, and not in serum.

Clonal selection theory: Burnet (1957) proposed this theory which shifted immunological specificity to the cellular level.

According to the clonal selection hypothesis, during immunological development, cells capable of reacting with different antigens were formed by a process of somatic mutation. Clones of cells that had immunological reactivity with self antigens were eliminated during embryonic life. Such clones are called **forbidden clones**. Their persistence or development in later life by somatic mutation could lead to autoimmune processes. Each immunocompetent cell was capable of reacting with one antigen (or a small number of antigens) which could recognise and combine with antigens introduced into the body. The result of the contact with the specific antigen was cellular proliferation to form clones synthesising the antibody.

The clonal selection theory is more widely accepted than the other theories, though it is unable to account for all the features of the immune response.

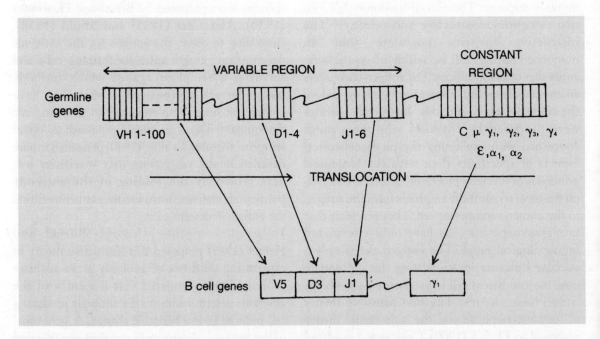

Fig. 16.6 Illustration of gene shuffling to form a B cell encoding for IgG-1 heavy chain with V_5, D_3, J variable region sequence (similar shuffling also occurs for light chains— not shown)

A variety of modifications and alternative theories have been proposed in recent times but none has succeeded in explaining all that is known of immunity.

As an explanation for the mechanism of regulation of antibody response, Jerne has postulated the network hypothesis. The variable region of an immunoglobulin molecule carrying the antigen-combining site is different in different antibodies. The distinct aminoacid sequences at the antigen-combining site and the adjacent parts of the variable region are termed idiotypes. The idiotype can, in turn, act as an antigenic determinant and induce antiidiotypic antibodies. These in turn can induce antibodies to them and so on, forming an idiotype network which is postulated to regulate the amount of antibodies produced and the number of antibody-forming cells in action. For his theoretical contribution to antibody formation and regulation of the immune system, Niels K. Jerne was awarded the Nobel Prize for Medicine in 1984.

The genetic basis of antibody diversity has been clarified recently. An individual has the capacity to produce an estimated 10^8 different antibody molecules. To have each such antibody molecule coded for by a separate gene would require millions of genes to be set apart for antibody production alone. This would obviously be impossible. The phenomenon of split genes explains this. The genetic information for the synthesis of an immunoglobulin molecule is not present in a continuous array of codons. Instead, this information occurs in several discontinuous stretches of DNA ('gene segments'), each coding for separate regions of the antibody molecule. As the constant regions are identical for immunoglobulins of any one type, there need be only one gene or a few genes for each constant region, as against a very large number of genes for the variable regions. For example, the kappa L chain genes are composed of three separate segments V, J and C. There are about a hundred different types of V (variable) domain sequences and only one C (constant) segment, with some five J (joining) segments in-between. By combining different V and J sequences with the C domain, it is possible to provide for antibodies with at least 500 different specificities. By palindromic arrangement (sequences that can be attached by either end), it is possible to generate many times more different specificities. The lambda chain has additional C sequences. The H chain gene has also a D (diversity) segment. By the shuffling of these different segments of the C and H chains, it is possible to have antibodies with far more than 10^8 types of specificity, a total repertoire that can react with any conceivable antigen. The split gene shuffling takes place during cell development and a mature B cell DNA will have only one combination of the different segments of the immunoglobulin gene and can therefore produce only one type of antibody (Fig. 16.6).

The discovery of split genes for immunoglobulins demolished the long standing dogma of 'one gene–one protein' and has important implications in biology, beyond immunology. For this discovery, Susumu Tonegawa was awarded the Nobel Prize for Medicine in 1987.

Further Reading

Engelhard VH. 1994. How cells process antigens. *Scient American* 44.

Janeway CA. 1993. How the immune system recognises invaders. *Scient American* 41.

Jerne NK. 1985. The generative grammar of the immune system. *Science*, 29,1057.

Llewellyn MB et al. 1992. Monoclonal antibodies, *BMJ* 305: 1269, 1348, 1424.

Remick DG and JS Friedland 1997. *Cytokines in health and disease.* 2nd edn. Basel: Marcel-Dekker.

Tonegawa S. 1983. Somatic generation of antibody diversity, *Nature* 302 : 575.

Weir DM and J Stewart 1997. *Immunology.* 8th edn. Edinburgh: Churchill-Livingstone.

Schwartz RS 2003. Diversity of the immune response. *New Eng J Med* 348:1017.

Immunodeficiency Diseases

Immunodeficiency diseases are conditions where the defence mechanisms of the body are impaired, leading to repeated microbial infections of varying severity and sometimes enhanced susceptibility to malignancies. Deficiencies of defence mechanisms may involve specific immune functions – humoral immunity, cell mediated immunity or both – or nonspecific mechanisms such as phagocytosis and complement, which augment and act in conjunction with specific immune processes. Immuno deficiencies may be classified as primary or secondary. *Primary immunodeficiencies* result from abnormalities in the development of the immune mechanisms. *Secondary immunodeficiencies* are consequences of disease, drugs, nutritional inadequacies and other processes that interfere with the proper functioning of the mature immune system.

PRIMARY IMMUNODEFICIENCIES

The established types of primary immunodeficiency syndromes are listed in Table 17.1. Though primary deficiencies of specific immunity can be conveniently classified as those affecting B cell responses, T cell responses, or both, it must be realised that there is considerable overlapping due to the intimate interaction between the B cell and the T cell systems. For instance, T cell deficiencies involving helper or suppressor T cells will have a profound effect on antibody response.

HUMORAL IMMUNODEFICIENCIES

X-linked agammaglobulinemia: This syndrome described by Bruton (1952) is the first immunodeficiency disease to have been recognised. It is seen only in male infants. Manifestations are not apparent till about six months of age due to the passive protection afforded by maternal antibodies. The disease presents as recurrent serious infections with pyogenic bacteria, particularly with pneumococci, streptococci, meningococci, *Pseudomonas and H. influenzae.* Patients respond normally to viral infections such as measles and chickenpox, though there have been reports of paralytic poliomyelitis and progressive encephalitis following immunisation with live virus vaccines or exposure to wild virus. As a general rule, live microbial vaccines should not be given to children with any type of primary immunodeficiency.

All classes of immunoglobulins are grossly depleted in the serum, the IgG level being less than a tenth, and IgA and IgM less than a hundredth of the normal level. Tonsils and adenoids are atrophic. Lymph node biopsy reveals a depletion of cells of the bursa-dependent areas. Plasma cells and germinal centres are absent even after antigenic stimulation. There is a marked decrease in the proportion of B cells in circulation. Antibody formation does not occur even after injections of antigens.

Cell mediated immunity is not affected. Delayed hypersensitivity of tuberculin and contact dermatitis types can be demonstrated. Allograft rejection is normal. Arthritis, hemolytic anemia and atopic manifestations are frequently observed. However, the wheal-and-flare response of atopic hypersensitivity cannot be demonstrated.

The incidence of this condition has been

Table 17.1 Classification of primary immunodeficiency syndromes

A. Disorders of specific immunity

   I. Humoral immunodeficiencies (B cell defects)
     a. X-linked agammaglobulinemia
     b. Transient hypogammaglobulinemia of infancy
     c. Common variable immunodeficiency (late onset hypogammaglobulinemia)
     d. Selective immunoglobulin deficiencies (IgA, IgM or IgG subclasses)
     e. Immunodeficiencies with hyper-IgM
     f. Transcobalamin II deficiency

   II. Cellular immunodeficiencies (T cell defects)
     a. Thymic hypoplasia (Digeorge's syndrome)
     b. Chronic mucocutaneous candidiasis
     c. Purine nucleoside phosphorylase (PNP) deficiency.

   III. Combined immunodeficiencies (B and T cell defects)
     a. Cellular immunodeficiency with abnormal immunoglobulin synthesis
       (Nezelof syndrome)
     b. Ataxia telangiectasia
     c. Wiskott–Aldrich syndrome
     d. Immunodeficiency with thymoma
     e. Immunodeficiency with short-limbed dwarfism
     f. Episodic lymphopenia with lymphocytotoxin
     g. Severe combined immunodeficiencies
       1. 'Swiss type' agammaglobulinemia
       2. Reticular dysgenesis of de Vaal
       3. Adenosine deaminase (ADA) deficiency

B. Disorders of complement
     a. Complement component deficiencies
     b. Complement inhibitor deficiencies

C. Disorders of phagocytosis
     a. Chronic granulomatous disease
     b. Myeloperoxidase deficiency
     c. Chediak–Higashi syndrome
     d. Leucocyte G6PD deficiency
     e. Job's syndrome
     f. Tuftsin deficiency
     g. Lazy leucocyte syndrome
     h. Hyper-IgE syndrome
     i. Actin-binding protein deficiency
     j. Shwachman's disease

reported as one in a hundred thousand population in the United Kingdom. Its management consists of the maintenance of an adequate level of immunoglobulins. This can be achieved with an initial administration of 300 mg of gammaglobulin per kg of body weight in three doses followed by monthly injections of 100 mg per kg. The slow fractional catabolic rate of IgG in this condition enables the maintenance of effective levels with this dosage. Commercial preparations of gammaglobulin contain only traces of IgA and IgM. To provide these, whole plasma infusions have been employed, the donors being tested for hepatitis and other transmissible infections.

TRANSIENT HYPOGAMMAGLOBULINEMIA OF INFANCY

This is due to an abnormal delay in the initiation of IgG synthesis in some infants. Maternal IgG is slowly catabolised in the newborn and reaches a level of 200 mg per 100 ml by the second month. Ordinarily, the infant begins synthesising its own IgG by this age. When there is a delay, immunodeficiency occurs. Recurrent otitis media and respiratory infections are the common diseases found in this condition. Spontaneous recovery occurs between 18 and 30 months of age. It may be found in infants of both sexes. Treatment with gammaglobulin may be required in some cases but it is not recommended prophylactically, as it may contribute to prolongation of immunodeficiency by a negative feedback inhibition of IgG synthesis.

COMMON VARIABLE IMMUNODEFICIENCY

This common form of immunodeficiency is also known as late onset hypogammaglobulinemia because it usually manifests only by 15–35 years of age. It is characterised by recurrent pyogenic infections and an increased incidence of autoimmune disease. Malabsorption and giardiasis are common. The total immunoglobulin level is usually less than 300 mg per 100 ml, with IgG less than 250 mg per 100 ml. B cells may be present in circulation in normal numbers, but they appear defective in their inability to differentiate into plasma cells and secrete immunoglobulins. Increased suppressor T cell and diminished helper T cell activity have been proposed as a cause of this disorder. Treatment is by administration of gammaglobulin preparations intramuscularly or intravenously.

SELECTIVE IMMUNOGLOBULIN DEFICIENCIES

In these conditions, there is selective deficiency of one or more immunoglobulin classes, while the others remain normal or elevated. These 'dysgammaglobulinemias' are common and have been reported in about one per cent of all patients with recurrent infections. Isolated IgA deficiency is the most common condition in this group, with a reported incidence of about 0.2 per cent in normal populations. These patients exhibit increased susceptibility to respiratory infection and steatorrhea. IgA deficiency is often accompanied by atopic disorders. Anti-IgA antibodies are present in many of these patients.

Selective IgM deficiency has been found to be associated with septicemia. Deficiencies of IgG subclasses have been observed in relation with chronic progressive bronchiectasis.

Immunodeficiencies with hyper-IgM: In this group of immunodeficiencies, some of which are X-linked and some inherited as autosomal recessive, low IgA and IgG levels are seen with elevated IgM. The IgM molecules appear to have normal structure and possess antibody activity. Patients show enhanced susceptibility to infections and autoimmune processes such as thrombocytopenia, neutropenia, hemolytic anemia and renal lesions. Some patients develop malignant infiltration with IgM-producing cells. Elevated IgM level with immunodeficiency is sometimes seen in congenital rubella.

Transcobalamin II deficiency: In this disorder, inherited as autosomal recessive, patients show metabolic effects of vitamin B12 deficiency including megaloblastic anemia and intestinal villous atrophy. The associated immunological defects are depleted plasma cells, diminished immunoglobulin levels and impaired phagocytosis. Treatment with vitamin B12 has been reported to restore hematopoietic, gastrointestinal and B cell functions but not phagocytic activity.

CELLULAR IMMUNODEFICIENCIES

Thymic hypoplasia (Digeorge's syndrome): This is a developmental defect involving the endodermal derivatives of the third and fourth pharyngeal pouches. It leads to aplasia or hypoplasia of the thymus and parathyroid glands. It does not appear to be hereditary and does not show a familial incidence. It is probably due to some intrauterine infection or other complications. It is usually associated with Fallot's tetrology and other anomalies of the heart and the great vessels, and a characteristic facial appearance. Neonatal tetany is present. Patients who survive the neonatal period show enhanced susceptibility to viral, fungal and bacterial infections, which ultimately prove fatal.

The immunodeficiency primarily involves cell mediated immunity. The thymus dependent areas of lymph nodes and spleen are depleted of lymphocytes. Circulating T cells are reduced in number. Delayed hypersensitivity and graft rejection are depressed. The humoral immune mechanism is largely unaffected. Antibody response to primary antigenic stimuli is normal but secondary response to many antigens is impaired. Transplantation of fetal thymus tissue has been reported to restore the immunological function.

Chronic mucocutaneous candidiasis: This constitutes an abnormal immunological response to Candida albicans. Patients develop severe chronic candidiasis of the mucosa, skin and nails. They do not show increased susceptibility to other infections but often have endocrinopathies. Cell mediated immunity to candida is deficient. In some cases there is a total failure of T cell response to any test antigen. Delayed hypersensitivity to candida antigens is absent but circulating antibodies to them are found in high titres. Intracellular killing of candida is defective. Transfer factor therapy, along with amphotericin B, has been reported effective.

Purine nucleoside phosphorylase (PNP) deficiency: The enzyme purine nucleoside phosphorylase is involved in the sequential degradation of purines to hypoxanthine and finally to uric acid. Patients who have PNP deficiency as an autosomal recessive inherited trait show decreased cell mediated immunity and recurrent or chronic infections. They usually present with hypoplastic anemia and recurrent pneumonia, diarrhea and candidiasis. A low serum uric acid may point to the diagnosis.

COMBINED IMMUNODEFICIENCIES

Cellular immunodeficiency with abnormal immunoglobulin synthesis (Nezelof syndrome): The term Nezelof syndrome has been rather loosely applied to a group of disorders, probably of varied etiology, where depressed cell mediated immunity is associated with selectively elevated, decreased or normal levels of immunoglobulin. The consistent features are a marked deficiency of T cell immunity and varying degrees of deficiency of B cell immunity. Patients are susceptible to recurrent fungal, bacterial, viral and protozoal diseases. Abundant plasma cells are seen in the spleen, lymph nodes, intestines and elsewhere in the body. Thymic dysplasia occurs with lymphoid depletion. Autoimmune processes such as hemolytic anemia are common. In spite of normal levels of immunoglobulins, antigenic stimuli do not induce antibody formation.

Histocompatible bone marrow transplantation, transfer factor and thymus transplantation have been used for treatment, with success in some cases. Adequate antimicrobial therapy is essential.

Ataxia telangiectasia: This is a hereditary condition transmitted in the autosomal recessive mode, where combined immunodeficiency is associated with cerebellar ataxia, telangiectasia, ovarian dysgenesis and chromosomal abnormalities. The earliest signs are ataxia and chorioathetoid movements which are usually noticed in infancy. Telangiectasia involving the conjunctiva, face and other parts of the body usually appears at five or six years of age. Death occurs due to sinopulmonary infection early in life, or malignancy in the second or third decade. The majority of patients lack serum and secretory IgA and some possess antibody to IgA. IgE deficiency is also frequent. Cell mediated immunity is also defective, resulting in an impairment of delayed hypersensitivity and graft rejection. The disease is progressive, with both neurological defects and immunodeficiency becoming more severe with time. Transfer factor therapy and fetal thymus transplants have been tried with some benefit.

Wiskott–Aldrich syndrome: This is an X-linked disease characterised by eczema, thrombocytopenic purpura and recurrent infections. Affected boys rarely survive the first decade of life, death being due to infection, hemorrhage or lymphoreticular malignancy. Cell mediated immunity undergoes progressive deterioration associated with cellular depletion of the thymus and the paracortical areas of lymph nodes. Serum IgM level is low but IgG and IgA levels are normal or elevated. Isohemagglutinins are absent in the serum. The humoral defect appears to be a specific inability to respond to polysaccharide antigens. Bone marrow transplantation and transfer factor therapy have been found beneficial.

Immunodeficiency with thymoma: This syndrome, occurring usually in adults, consists of a benign thymic tumour, impaired cell mediated immunity and agammaglobulinemia. It is frequently accompanied by aplastic anemia. This is of historical importance as one of the experiments of nature which suggested the immunological function of the thymus.

Immunodeficiency with short-limbed dwarfism: The features of this condition are a distinctive form of short-limbed dwarfism, ectodermal dysplasia, thymic defects and enhanced susceptibility to infection. These defects are apparently inherited as autosomal recessives.

Episodic lymphopenia with lympho-cytotoxin: In this syndrome there occurs an episodic but profound depression of T cell function by the action of a circulating complement dependent lymphocytotoxin. The toxin appears to be an antilymphocyte antibody. The patients lack 'immunological memory' so the secondary antibody response is abolished. The disease is familial.

Severe combined immunodeficiencies: These include many syndromes with severe deficiency of both humoral and cell mediated immune responses. They are inherited in the autosomal recessive mode and the primary defects are at the level of the early precursors of immunocompetent cells in the fetal liver and bone marrow. Many distinct patterns of severe combined immunodeficiency have been described.

In 1958, Swiss workers reported agammaglobulinemia with lymphocytopenia and severe defect in cell mediated immunity. This has been referred to as *Swiss type agamma-globulinemia*. The basic defect is presumed to be at the level of the lymphoid stem cell.

The most serious form of combined immunodeficiency is the *reticular dysgenesis of de Vaal*. Here the defect is at the level of the multipotent hemopoietic stem cell, as a result of which there is a total failure of myelopoiesis leading to lymphopenia, neutropenia, thrombocytopenia, anemia and bone marrow aplasia. The condition is invariably fatal in the first week of life.

Adenosine deaminase (ADA) *deficiency* is the first immunodeficiency disease associated with an enzyme deficiency. ADA catalyses the conversion of adenosine to inosine, an important step in the purine metabolic pathway. How this deficiency causes immunological impairment is not clear. The range of immunodeficiency varies from complete absence to mild abnormalities of B and T cell functions. The condition is associated with chondrocyte abnormalities which can be discerned radiologically.

DISORDERS OF COMPLEMENT

Complement component deficiencies: Genetic deficiencies have been detected for almost all the complement components in human beings. The defects are transmitted as autosomal recessive traits. Hemolytic and other functional activities are completely restored by supplying the deficient factor. Complement component deficiencies have been frequently associated with systemic lupus erythematosus. Recurrent pyogenic infections were found associated with C3 deficiency and neisserial infections with deficiency of C6, C7 and C8.

Complement inhibitor deficiencies: Hereditary angioneurotic edema is due to a genetic deficiency of C1 inhibitor. This relatively common defect is transmitted as an autosomal dominant. Androgens, aminocaproic acid and its analogue tranexamic acid have been found useful in the management of this condition. Plasma infusions, once recommended for treatment, have been given up as they were found to worsen the condition in some cases.

The rare deficiency of C3b inactivator has been associated with chronic recurrent pyogenic lesions.

DISORDERS OF PHAGOCYTOSIS

Phagocytosis may be impaired by either intrinsic or extrinsic defects. Intrinsic disorders may be due to defects within the phagocytic cell, such as enzyme deficiencies. Extrinsic disorders may be due to a deficiency of opsonic antibody, complement or other factors promoting phagocytosis, or to the effects of drugs or antineutrophil autoantibodies. Phagocytic dysfunction leads to increased susceptibility to infection, ranging from mild recurrent skin infections to overwhelming systemic infection.

Chronic granulomatous disease: This familial disease manifests itself as recurrent infection with low grade pathogens, starting early in life. The progress is chronic and the outcome fatal. Chronic suppurative granulomatous lesions develop in the skin and lymph nodes, along with hepatosplenomegaly, progressive infiltration of lungs and granulomatous septic osteomyelitis. Humoral and cellular immune responses are normal.

The bacteria involved in the recurrent infections are catalase positive pyogenic pathogens such as staphylococci and coliforms. Catalase negative pathogens such as streptococci and pneumococci are handled normally. Leucocytes from the patients are unable to kill catalase positive bacteria following phagocytosis. The bacteria multiply in the cells and, being protected from antibodies and antibiotics by their intracellular position, set up chronic suppurative infection. The diminished bactericidal capacity of the phagocytic cells is associated with a decrease of some metabolic processes like oxygen consumption, hexose monophosphate pathway activity and production of hydrogen peroxide. The diminished H_2O_2 production appears to be the major reason for the bactericidal defect. The leucocytes do not undergo degranulation following phagocytosis. The delayed granule rupture and defective release of myeloperoxidase also contribute to inefficient bactericidal activity. Leucocytes from the patients fail to reduce nitroblue tetrazolium (NBT) during phagocytosis. This property has been used as a screening method (NBT test) for the diagnosis of chronic granulomatous disease.

The disease shows two types of inheritance— the more common X-linked type seen in boys and the rare autosomal recessive type seen in girls.

Myeloperoxidase deficiency: In this rare disease, leucocytes have reduced myeloperoxidase. Patients are particularly liable to *Candida albicans* infection.

Chediak–Higashi syndrome: This is a genetic disorder characterised by decreased pigmentation of the skin, eyes and hair, photophobia, nystagmus and giant peroxidase positive inclusions in the cytoplasm of leucocytes. The inclusions may be the result of autophagocytic activity. The leucocytes possess diminished phagocytic activity. Patients suffer from frequent and severe pyogenic infections.

Leucocyte G6PD deficiency: In this rare disease, leucocytes are deficient in glucose 6 phosphate dehydrogenase and show diminished bactericidal activity after phagocytosis. The condition resembles chronic granulomatous disease in reduced myeloperoxidase activity and susceptibility to microbial agents, but the NBT test may be normal.

Job's syndrome: This is characterised by multiple large 'cold' staphylococcal abscesses containing large quantities of pus, occurring repeatedly on the skin and in various organs, with little inflammatory response. Atopic eczema, chronic nasal discharge and otitis media are common features. The serum immunoglobulins are normal, except for elevated IgE. The pathogenesis of the syndrome is not clear but it is probably a primary defect in phagocytic function.

Tuftsin deficiency: A leucokinin capable of stimulating phagocytosis, discovered at Tufts University, Boston, has been designated 'tuftsin'. Chemically, it is a small tetrapeptide (Thr-Lys-Pro-Arg). Patients with tuftsin deficiency have been reported to be prone to local and systemic bacterial infections.

Lazy leucocyte syndrome: The basic defect here is in chemotaxis and neutrophil mobility. The bone marrow has a normal number of neutrophils but there is a peripheral neutropenia, with poor leucocyte response to chemical and inflammatory stimulation. Patients show an increased susceptibility to bacterial infection, with recurrent stomatitis, gingivitis and otitis.

Hyper-IgE syndrome: These patients, of both sexes, have an early onset of eczema and recurrent bacterial infections such as abscesses, pneumonia and secondary infection of eczema. The organisms responsible include *Staphylococcus aureus and Streptococcus pyogenes.* Cellular and humoral immune mechanisms are normal but serum IgE levels are usually more than ten times the normal level.

Actin-binding protein deficiency: Frequent infection and slow mobility of leucocytes result from the defective actin-binding protein in these patients.

Shwachman's disease: In this condition, frequent infections are found together with decreased neutrophil mobility, pancreatic malfunction and bone abnormalities.

SECONDARY IMMUNODEFICIENCIES

A variety of factors such as malnutrition, malignancy, infections, metabolic disorders and cytotoxic drugs may lead to deficits in specific and nonspecific immunity. AIDS is a secondary immunodeficiency. Secondary immunodeficiencies are therefore very much more common than primary deficiencies.

Deficiencies of humoral and cellular immune response may occur secondarily during the course of many disease processes. Humoral deficiency results when B cells are depleted as in lymphoid malignancy, particularly in chronic lymphatic leukemia; when immunoglobulin catabolism is increased as in the nephrotic syndrome; when excessive loss of serum protein occurs as in exfoliative skin disease and in protein-losing enteropathies; and when excessive production of abnormal immunoglobulins occurs as in multiple myeloma. Cell mediated immunity is depressed in lymphoreticular malignancies, as in Hodgkin's disease; obstruction to lymph circulation or lymphorrheas; when the thymus dependent areas of lymph nodes are infiltrated with nonlymphoid cells as in lepromatous leprosy; and, transiently, following certain viral infections such as measles.

Nutritional deprivation affects both types of immune responses adversely. Ageing also causes waning in the efficiency of acquired immunity. Immunodeficiency follows the intentional or unintentional administration of immunosuppressive agents.

Further Reading

Rosen FS et al. 1984. The primary immunodeficiencies. *New Engl J Med* 311:235, 300.
Fischer A and A Arnaiz-Villena 1995. Immunodeficiencies of genetic origin. *Immunol Today* 16:510.
Stites DP and AI Terr 1991. *Basic and Clinical Immunology.* 7th edn. Connecticut: Appleton-Lange.
Wizgel H. 1993. Immunodeficiency. *Curr Opin Immunol* 5:567.

Hypersensitivity

Immunity was originally considered a protective process, helping the body to overcome infectious agents and their toxins. This however is only one aspect of the broad phenomenon of immunity which includes all manner of specific responses to antigens. Immune response may sometimes be injurious to the host. Sensitised individuals respond to subsequent antigenic stimuli in an inappropriate or exaggerated manner, leading to tissue damage, disease or even death. The term hypersensitivity refers to the injurious consequences in the sensitised host, following contact with specific antigens. In the protective processes of immunity, the focus of attention is the antigen and what happens to it—for example, killing of a bacterium or neutralisation of a toxin. In hypersensitivity, on the other hand, antigens are of little concern and often, they are innocuous or bland substances such as serum proteins or pollen. Hypersensitivity is concerned with what happens to the host as a result of the immune reaction.

Considerable confusion is attached to the use of the term 'allergy'. As originally used by von Pirquet, allergy meant an altered state of reactivity to an antigen, and included both types of immune responses, protective as well as injurious. It is still used in this broad sense by some. Others use the term 'allergy' to mean all immune processes harmful to the host, such as hypersensitivity and autoimmunity. Allergy is probably most commonly used as a synonym for hypersensitivity. It is sometimes employed in a narrow sense to refer to only one type of hypersensitivity, namely 'atopy'.

For induction of hypersensitivity reactions, the host should have had contact with the antigen (allergen). The initial contact sensitises the immune system, leading to the priming of the appropriate B or T lymphocytes. This is known as the 'sensitising' or 'priming' dose. Subsequent contact with the allergen causes manifestations of hypersensitivity. This is known as the 'shocking' dose.

CLASSIFICATION OF HYPERSENSITIVITY REACTIONS

Hypersensitivity reactions have been classified traditionally into 'immediate' and 'delayed' types, based on the time required for a sensitised host to develop clinical reactions on re-exposure to the antigen. The major differences between the immediate and delayed types of hypersensitivity reactions are shown in Table 18.1.

The immediate and delayed reactions are subdivided into several distinct clinical types:

I. **Immediate hypersensitivity** (B cell or antibody mediated)
　Anaphylaxis
　Atopy
　Antibody mediated cell damage
　Arthus phenomenon
　Serum sickness

II. **Delayed hypersensitivity** (T cell mediated)
　Infection (tuberculin) type
　Contact dermatitis type

Coombs and Gell (1963) classified hypersensitivity reactions into four types based on the different mechanisms of pathogenesis. Their classification, now widely used, is outlined below:

Table 18.1 Distinguishing features of immediate and delayed types of hypersensitivity

Immediate hypersensitivity	Delayed hypersensitivity
1. Appears and recedes rapidly.	1. Appears slowly, lasts longer.
2. Induced by antigens or haptens by any route.	2. Antigen or hapten intradermally or with Freund's adjuvant or by skin contact
3. Circulating antibodies present and responsible for reaction; 'antibody mediated' reaction.	3. Circulating antibodies may be absent and not responsible for reaction; 'cell mediated' reaction.
4. Passive transfer possible with serum.	4. Cannnot be transferred with serum; but possible with T cells or transfer factor.
5. Desensitisation easy, but short-lived.	5. Difficult, but long-lasting.

1. Type I (Anaphylactic, IgE or reagin dependent): Antibodies ('cytotropic' IgE antibodies) are fixed on the surface of tissue cells (mast cells and basophils) in sensitised individuals. The antigen combines with the cell-fixed antibody, leading to release of pharmacologically active substances (vasoactive amines) which produce the clinical reaction.

2. Type II (Cytotoxic or cell stimulating): This type of reaction is initiated by IgG (or rarely IgM) antibodies that react either with cell surface or tissue antigens. Cell or tissue damage occurs in the presence of complement or mononuclear cells. Type II reactions are intermediate between hypersensitivity and autoimmunity. Combination with antibody may, in some instances, cause stimulation instead of damage. An example is the 'long acting thyroid stimulator' (LATS), an antibody against some determinant on thyroid cells, which stimulates excessive secretion of thyroid hormone. (Such antibody mediated cell stimulation has also been called type V hypersensitivity.)

3. Type III (Immune complex or toxic complex disease): Here the damage is caused by antigen antibody complexes. These may precipitate in and around small blood vessels, causing damage to cells secondarily, or on membranes, interfering with their function.

4. Type IV (Delayed or cell mediated hypersensitivity): This is a cell mediated response. The antigen activates specifically sensitised CD4 and CD8 T cells, leading to the secretion of lymphokines, with fluid and phagocyte accumulation.

The classification and some of the features of hypersensitivity reactions are shown in Table 18.2. The four types of immunopathogenic mechanisms described are not mutually exclusive. Any given hypersensitive reaction may comprise the components of more than one, or all of these mechanisms. The pathology and clinical features of such immunological diseases would also be influenced by the contributions of many nonimmune body mechanisms such as inflammation, complement, coagulation, fibrinolytic and kininogenic systems, collectively called the *humoral amplification systems*.

TYPE I REACTIONS (IgE DEPENDENT)

These occur in two forms – the acute, potentially fatal, systemic form called anaphylaxis and the chronic or recurrent, nonfatal, typically localised form called atopy.

ANAPHYLAXIS

This is the classical immediate hypersensitivity reaction. The term anaphylaxis (*ana* = without, *phylaxis* = protection) was coined by Richet (1902) to describe his observation that dogs which had

Table 18.2 Types of hypersensitivity reaction and their features

Type of reaction	Clinical syndrome	Time required for manifestation	Mediators
Type 1: IgE type	1. Anaphylaxis 2. Atopy	Minutes	IgE: histamine and other pharmacological agents
Type II: Cytolytic and cytotoxic	Antibody mediated damage–thrombocytopenia–agranulocytosis, hemolytic anemia, etc.	Variable: hours to days	IgG: IgM, C
Type III: Immune complex	1. Arthus reaction 2. Serum sickness	Variable: hours to days	IgG: IgM, C, leucocytes
Type IV: Delayed hypersensitivity	1. Tuberculin 2. Contact dermatitis	Hours to days	T cells; lymphokines; macrophages

survived a sublethal injection of a toxic extract of sea anemones were rendered highly susceptible to minute doses of the toxin given days or weeks later, instead of becoming immune to it. Theobald Smith (1902) had noticed a similar phenomenon in guinea pigs, following widely spaced injections of toxin—antitoxin mixtures. Ehrlich named this the 'Theobald Smith phenomenon' and showed that it was independent of the toxin and antitoxin used, since the phenomenon could be induced with normal serum also.

Sensitisation is most effective when the antigen is introduced parenterally but may occur by any route, including ingestion or inhalation. In susceptible species, very minute doses can sensitise the host. Antigens as well as haptens can induce anaphylaxis. There should be an interval of at least 2–3 weeks between the sensitising dose and the shocking dose. Once sensitised, the individual remains so for long periods. The shocking dose is most effective when injected intravenously, less effective intraperitoneally or subcutaneously and least effective intradermally. The shocking antigen must be identical or immunologically closely related to the sensitising antigen. The clinical features of anaphylaxis are the same with any antigen but vary between species. The clinical effects are due to smooth muscle contraction and increased vascular permeability. The organs affected vary with the species. Tissues or organs predominantly involved in the anaphylactic reaction are known as 'target tissues' or 'shock organs'. Other changes seen in anaphylaxis are edema, decreased coagulability of blood, fall in blood pressure and temperature, leucopenia and thrombocytopenia.

There is considerable species variation in susceptibility to anaphylaxis. Guinea pigs are highly susceptible and rats very resistant. Rabbits, dogs and human beings are of intermediate susceptibility. Anaphylaxis can be readily induced in guinea pigs. If a small dose of egg albumin is injected intraperitoneally, followed 2–3 weeks later by a slightly larger dose of the same antigen intravenously, the guinea pig will exhibit a dramatic sequence of events. Within minutes the animal becomes irritable, sneezes, coughs, experiences respiratory distress, develops convulsions and dies. The heart continues to beat for some time after the respiration has stopped. At autopsy, the lungs are markedly emphysematous and do not collapse when the thorax is opened or even when they are cut into pieces. The shock organ is the lung. Death is due to the constriction of the smooth muscles of the bronchioles causing respiratory standstill.

In rabbits, death in anaphylactic shock is due to constriction of the pulmonary artery and its branches, leading to extreme dilatation of the right side of the heart. Respiratory movements continue after the cessation of the heartbeat. In dogs, the reaction is slower and takes 1–2 hours. There is constriction of the hepatic venous system with gross engorgement of the liver and profound fall of blood pressure. In human beings, fatal anaphylaxis is fortunately rare. Symptoms and signs of anaphylactic shock begin with itching of the scalp and tongue, flushing of the skin over the whole body and difficulty in breathing due to bronchial spasm. There may be nausea, vomiting, abdominal pain and diarrhea, sometimes with blood in the stool. Acute hypotension, loss of consciousness and death follow. Human anaphylaxis, once commonly associated with heterologous serum therapy, is now seen mostly following injections of antibiotics or other drugs. Insect stings can also cause anaphylaxis in human beings. Prompt treatment with adrenaline can be life-saving. Adrenaline is to be administered, 0.5 ml of a 1 in 1000 solution, subcutaneously or intramuscularly, the dose being repeated upto a total of 2 ml over 15 minutes, if necessary.

Cutaneous anaphylaxis: When a small shocking dose of an antigen is administered intradermally to a sensitised host, there will be a local wheal-and-flare response (local anaphylaxis). The wheal is a pale, central area of puffiness due to edema, which is surrounded by a flare caused by hyperemia and subsequent erythema. Cutaneous anaphylaxis (skin test for Type I hypersensitivity) is useful in testing for hypersensitivity and in identifying the allergen responsible in atopic diseases. In highly sensitised individuals, even the skin test may lead to serious and even fatal reactions. Hence a syringe loaded with adrenaline should always be kept ready whenever a skin test is performed to detect anaphylactic hypersensitivity.

Passive cutaneous anaphylaxis (PCA): This test developed by Ovary (1952) is an extremely sensitive in vivo method for detection of antibodies. A small volume of the antibody is injected intradermally into a normal animal. If the antigen, along with a dye such as Evans blue, is injected intravenously 4–24 hours afterwards, there will be an immediate blueing at the site of intradermal injection due to vasodilatation and increased capillary permeability (wheal-and-flare reaction). PCA can be used to detect human IgG antibody which is heterocytotropic (capable of fixing to cells of other species) but not IgE which is homocytotropic (capable of fixing to cells of homologous species only).

Anaphylaxis in vitro: Isolated tissues, such as intestinal or uterine muscle strips from sensitised guinea pigs, held in a bath of Ringer's solution will contract vigorously on addition of the specific antigen to the bath. This is known as the Schultz–Dale phenomenon. The reaction is specific and will be elicited only by the antigen to which the animal is sensitive. Tissues from normal animals can be passively sensitised by treatment with serum from sensitised animals.

Mechanism of anaphylaxis: The immunologic basis for hypersensitivity is cytotropic IgE antibody. Free IgE antibody in circulation is not relevant in anaphylaxis. Thus, an animal with a high titre of circulating antibody may be refractory to shock, while anaphylaxis may be caused by cell fixed antibody, even in the absence of detectable circulating antibody. While in human beings, IgE is the cytophilic antibody, in the guinea pig and mouse the analogous cytophilic antibody is IgG1.

IgE molecules are bound to surface receptors on mast cells and basophils. These cells carry large numbers of such receptors called Fc ER receptors, analogous to TCR receptors on T cell surface. IgE molecules attach to these receptors by their Fc end. Following exposure to the shocking dose, the antigen molecules combine with the cell bound IgE, bridging the gap between adjacent antibody molecules. This cross-linking increases the permeability of the cells to calcium ions and leads to degranulation, with release of biologically active substances contained in the granules. The manifestations of anaphylaxis are due to pharmacological mediators, which are of two kinds —primary mediators which are the preformed contents of mast cell and basophil granules (histamine, serotonin, eosinophil chemotactic factor of anaphylaxis, neutrophil chemotactic factor, heparin and various proteolytic enzymes) and secondary mediators which are newly formed upon stimulation by mast cells, basophils and other leucocytes (slow reacting substance of anaphylaxis, prostaglandins and platelet activating factor, and cytokines such as IL3, IL4, IL5, IL6; GM-CSF).

Primary mediators of anaphylaxis: *Histamine*: This is the most important vasoactive amine in human anaphylaxis. Histamine is formed by the decarboxylation of histidine found in the granules of mast cells, basophils and in platelets. Released into the skin, histamine stimulates sensory nerves, producing burning and itching sensations. It causes vasodilatation and hyperemia by an axon reflex (flare effect) and edema by increasing capillary permeability (wheal effect). Histamine induces smooth muscle contraction in diverse tissues and organs, including vasculature, intestines, uterus and especially the bronchioles. It also stimulates secretions (secretogogue effect).

1. **Serotonin (5-hydroxy tryptamine):** This is a base derived by decarboxylation of tryptophan. It is found in the intestinal mucosa, brain tissue and platelets. It causes smooth muscle contraction, increased capillary permeability and vasoconstriction. It is important in anaphylaxis in rats and mice but its role in human beings is uncertain.

2. **Chemotactic factors:** The eosinophil chemotactic factors of anaphylaxis (ECF-A) are acidic tetrapeptides released from mast cell granules which are strongly chemotactic for eosinophils. These probably contribute to the eosinophilia accompanying many hyper-sensitivity states. A high molecular weight chemotactic factor has been identified, which attracts neutrophils (NCF).

Heparin is an acidic mucopolysaccharide. It

contributes to anaphylaxis in dogs, but apparently not in human beings.

Enzymatic mediators such as proteases and hydrolases are also released from mast cell granules.

Secondary mediators of anaphylaxis

1. **Prostaglandins and leukotrienes:** They are derived by two different pathways from arachidonic acid, which is formed from disrupted cell membranes of mast cells and other leucocytes. The lipoxygenase pathway leads to the formation of leukotrienes, while the cyclo-oxygenase pathway leads to prostaglandins and thromboxane. A substance originally demonstrated in lungs, producing slow, sustained contraction of smooth muscles, and therefore termed slow reacting substance of anaphylaxis (SRS-A) has since been identified as a family of leukotrienes (LTB4, C4, D4, E4). Prostaglandin F2α and thromboxane A2 are powerful, but transient, bronchoconstrictors. Prostaglandins also affect secretion by mucous glands, platelet adhesion, permeability and dilatation of capillaries and the pain threshold.

2. **Platelet activating factor (PAF):** PAF is a low molecular weight lipid released from basophils which causes aggregation of platelets and release of their vasoactive amines.

Other mediators of anaphylaxis: Besides the products of mast cells and other leucocytes, several other biologically active substances have been implicated in anaphylaxis. These include the anaphylatoxins released by complement activation and bradykinin and other kinins formed from plasma kininogens.

Anaphylactoid reaction: Intravenous injection of peptone, typsin and certain other substances provokes a clinical reaction resembling anaphylactic shock. This is termed 'anaphylactoid reaction'. The clinical resemblance is due to the same chemical mediators participating in both reactions. The only difference is that anaphylactoid shock has no immunological basis and is a nonspecific mechanism involving the activation of complement and the release of anaphylatoxins.

Atopy: The term 'atopy' (literally meaning out of place or strangeness) was introduced by Coca (1923) to refer to naturally occurring familial hypersensitivities of human beings, typified by hay fever and asthma. The antigens commonly involved in atopy are characteristically inhalants (for example, pollen, house dust) or ingestants (for example, eggs, milk). Some of them are contact allergens, to which the skin and conjunctiva may be exposed. These atopens are generally not good antigens when injected parenterally but induce IgE antibodies, formerly termed as 'reagin' antibodies. Atopic sensitisation is developed spontaneously following natural contact with atopens. It is difficult to induce atopy artificially.

Predisposition to atopy is genetically determined, probably linked to MHC genotypes. Atopy therefore runs in families. What is inherited is not sensitivity to a particular antigen, or a particular atopic syndrome but the tendency to produce IgE antibodies in unusually large quantities. All individuals are capable of forming IgE antibodies in small amounts but in atopics IgE response is preponderant. About 10 per cent of persons have this tendency to overproduce IgE. It has been reported that bottlefed infants tend to develop atopy in later life more often than breastfed babies.

IgE differs from other immunoglobulins in the following respects:

1. It cannot be demonstrated by the conventional serological reactions such as precipitation or complement fixation. The first in vitro method for IgE detection was the radioallergosorbent test (RAST). Simpler techniques such as ELISA and passive agglutination have since been introduced.
2. While atopy occurs commonly in human beings, it is not easy to induce it experimentally in animals.
3. IgE is homocytotropic, that is, species specific. Only human IgE can fix to the surface of human cells. This is the basis of the Prausnitz–Kustner (PK) reaction, which was the original method for detecting atopic antibody. Prausnitz and Kustner (1921) reported that if serum collected from Kustner, who had atopic hypersensitivity to certain species of cooked fish, was injected intracutaneously into Prausnitz, followed 24 hours later by an intracutaneous injection of a small quantity of the cooked fish antigen into the same site, a wheal-and-flare reaction occurred within a few minutes. As reaginic IgE is homo-cytotropic, the test has to be carried out on human skin. It carries the risk of transmission of infection and so is no longer used.
4. Unlike other antibodies, IgE is heat sensitive and is inactivated at 56 °C in 2–4 hours. Heating appears to damage the Fc part of the IgE molecule, which is necessary for fixation to cells.
5. Atopic antibody does not pass through the placenta.

Atopic sensitivity is due to an overproduction of IgE antibodies. This is often associated with a deficiency of IgA. This association has led to the suggestion that IgA deficiency may predispose to atopy. The distribution of lymphocytes capable of synthesising IgA and IgE is closely parallel, especially in the submucosa. In normal individuals, the inhalant and ingestant antigens are dealt with by IgA lining the respiratory and intestinal mucosa and therefore they do not come into contact with the potential IgE producing cells. When IgA is deficient, the antigens cause massive stimulation of IgE forming cells, leading to overproduction of IgE.

The symptoms of atopy are caused by the release of pharmacologically active substances following the combination of the antigen and the cell fixed IgE. The clinical expression of atopic reactions is usually determined by the portal of entry of the antigen—conjunctivitis, rhinitis, gastrointestinal symptoms and dermatitis following exposure through the eyes, respiratory tract, intestine or skin, respectively. Sometimes the effects may be at sites remote from the portal of entry, for example, urticaria following ingestion of the allergen. Specific desensitisation (hyposensitisation) is often practised in the treatment of atopy.

TYPE II REACTION: CYTOLYTIC AND CYTOTOXIC

These reactions involve a combination of IgG (or rarely IgM) antibodies with the antigenic determinants on the surface of cells leading to cytotoxic or cytolytic effects. Examples are lysis of red cells caused by antierythrocyte antibodies in autoimmune anemias and hemolytic disease of the newborn. Alternatively, a free antigen or hapten may be absorbed on cell surfaces. Subsequent reaction of the combined antigen or hapten with its corresponding antibody leads to cell damage. Many drugs may act in this manner, leading to complement mediated lysis of red cells, leucocytes and platelets, causing hemolytic anemia, agranulocytosis and thrombocytopenic purpura.

In some Type II reactions, the antibody combines with cell surface receptors and disrupts normal function, either by uncontrolled activation (agonist effect as caused by the antibody 'long-acting thyroid stimulator' in Graves' disease) or by blocking (antagonist effect as in myasthenia gravis).

TYPE III REACTIONS: IMMUNE COMPLEX DISEASES

Arthus reaction: Arthus (1903) observed that when rabbits were repeatedly injected subcutaneously with normal horse serum, the initial injections had no local effect but with later injections, there occurred intense local reaction consisting of edema, induration and hemorrhagic necrosis. This is known as the Arthus reaction and is a local manifestation of generalised hypersensitivity. The tissue damage is due to formation of antigen–antibody precipitates causing complement activation and release of inflammatory

molecules. This leads to increased vascular permeability and infiltration of the site with neutrophils. Leucocyte–platelet thrombi are formed that reduce the blood supply and lead to tissue necrosis. The Arthus reaction can be passively transferred with sera containing precipitating antibodies (IgG, IgM) in high titres.

Arthus reaction forms a pathogenic component of many clinical syndromes. For example, intrapulmonary Arthus-like reaction to inhaled antigens, such as thermophilic actinomycetes from mouldy hay or grain causes Farmer's lung and other types of hypersensitivity pneumonitis.

Serum sickness: This is a systemic form of Type III hypersensitivity. As originally described by von Pirquet and Schick (1905), this appeared 7–12 days following a single injection of a high concentration of foreign serum such as the diphtheria antitoxin. The clinical syndrome consists of fever, lymphadenopathy, splenomegaly, arthritis, glomerulonephritis, endocarditis, vasculitis, urticarial rashes, abdominal pain, nausea and vomiting. The pathogenesis is the formation of immune complexes (consisting of the foreign serum and antibody to it that reaches high enough titres by 7–12 days), which get deposited on the endothelial lining of blood vessels in various parts of the body, causing inflammatory infiltration.

The plasma concentration of complement falls due to massive complement activation and fixation by the antigen antibody complexes. The disease is self limited. With continued rise in antibody production, the immune complexes become larger and more susceptible to phagocytosis and immune elimination. When all foreign antigen is thus eliminated and free antibody appears, the symptoms clear without any sequelae. The latent period of 7–12 days is required only for serum sickness following a single injection. With subsequent injections, the disease manifests earlier. Serum sickness differs from other types of hypersensitivity reaction in that a single injection can serve both as the sensitising dose and the shocking dose. As heterologous serum injections are not used often now, the syndrome is currently more commonly seen following injections of penicillin or other antibiotics.

Immune complexes occur in many diseases, including bacterial, viral and parasitic infections (for example, poststreptococcal glomerulonephritis, hepatitis type B, malaria), disseminated malignancies and autoimmune conditions. The nephritis and arthritis seen in these conditions may be caused by deposition of immune complexes.

TYPE IV REACTIONS: DELAYED HYPERSENSITIVITY

Type IV hypersensitivity reactions (delayed hypersensitivity) constitute one aspect of cell mediated immune response. These are typically provoked by intracellular microbial infections or haptens like simple chemicals applied on the skin, evolve slowly and consist of a mixed cellular reaction involving lymphocytes and macrophages in particular. The reaction is not induced by circulating antibodies but by sensitised T cells (Tdth, Th1, Th2, Tc) which, on contact with the specific antigen, release cytokines that cause biological effects on leucocytes, macrophages and tissue cells. Delayed hypersensitivity cannot be passively transferred by serum but can be transferred by lymphocytes or the transfer factor. Two types of delayed hypersensitivity are recognised – the tuberculin (infection) type and the contact dermatitis type.

Tuberculin (infection) type: The archetype of delayed hypersensitivity is the tuberculin reaction. When a small dose of tuberculin is injected intradermally in an individual sensitised to tuberculoprotein by prior infection or immunisation, an indurated inflammatory reaction develops at the site within 48–72 hours. In unsensitised individuals, the tuberculin injection provokes no response. The tuberculin test therefore provides useful indication of the state of delayed hypersensitivity (cell mediated immunity) to the bacilli. The tuberculin test differs from the skin test for Type I

hypersensitivity not only in the longer interval for appearance but also in its morphology and histology.

Tuberculin type hypersensitivity develops in many infections with bacteria, fungi, viruses and parasites, especially when the infection is subacute or chronic and the pathogen intracellular. A similar hypersensitivity is developed in allograft reaction and in many autoimmune diseases.

Cutaneous basophil hypersensitivity: A local reaction resembling the tuberculin response may be produced by intradermal injection of some protein antigens. This is not a delayed hypersensitivity reaction as it can be passively transferred by serum. Its histology is different from the tuberculin response, being characterised by prominent basophil infiltration. This was formerly known as the Jones–Mote reaction but is now termed cutaneous basophil hypersensitivity. Its significance is not known.

Contact dermatitis type: Delayed hypersensitivity sometimes results from skin contact with a variety of chemicals—metals such as nickel and chromium, simple chemicals like dyes, picryl chloride, dinitrochlorobenzene, drugs such as penicillin, and toiletries. Sensitisation is particularly liable when contact is with an inflamed area of skin and when the chemical is applied in an oily base. Antibiotic ointments applied on patches of dermatitis frequently provoke sensitisation. The substances involved are in themselves not antigenic but may acquire antigenicity on combination with skin proteins. Sensitisation requires percutaneous absorption. As most of the substances involved are fat soluble, passage along sebaceous glands may be the method of entry of the allergens.

Langerhans' cells of the skin capture locally applied hapten, along with the modified tissue proteins, and migrate to the draining lymph nodes where they present the processed antigen along with MHC molecules to T cells. The sensitised T cells travel to the skin site, where on contacting the antigen they realease various lymphokines. Th1 cells secrete IFNγ and IL2 which activate macrophages and other lymphocytes. Th2 cells release IL4, IL5, GM-CSF and other factors that lead to an influx of eosinophils and tissue damage. Activated Tc cells mediate killing of target cells.

Contact with the allergen in a sensitised individual leads to 'contact dermatitis', the lesions varying from macules and papules to vesicles that break down, leaving behind raw weeping areas typical of acute eczematous dermatitis. Hypersensitivity is detected by the 'patch test'. The allergen is applied to the skin under an adherent dressing. Sensitivity is indicated by itching appearing in 4–5 hours, and local reaction which may vary from erythema to vesicle or blister formation, after 24–28 hours.

SHWARTZMAN REACTION

This is not an immune reaction but rather a perturbation in factors affecting intravascular coagulation. It is traditionally described along with hypersensitivity reactions because of a superficial resemblance.

Shwartzman (1928) observed that if a culture filtrate of *S. typhi* is injected intradermally in a rabbit, followed 24 hours later by the same filtrate intravenously, a hemorrhagic necrotic lesion develops at the site of the intradermal injection. The intradermal and intravenous injections need not be of the same or even related endotoxins. Culture suspensions or filtrates of a variety of bacteria will sensitise the skin to intravenous injection by an equally wide variety of cultures or filtrates. This absence of specificity and the short interval between the two doses preclude any immunological basis for the reaction.

The initial (preparatory) dose is characteristically an endotoxin. The intravenous (provocative) injection can be a variety of substances —bacterial endotoxins, antigen–antibody complexes, starch, serum, kaolin and others. The preparatory injection causes accumulation of leucocytes which condition the site by release of lysosomal enzymes damaging capillary walls. Following the provocative dose, there occurs intravascular clotting, the thrombi leading to necrosis of vessel walls and hemorrhage.

If both the injections are given intravenously, the animal dies 12–24 hours after the second dose. Autopsy shows bilateral cortical necrosis of the kidneys and patchy hemorrhagic necrosis in the liver, spleen and other organs. An essentially similar phenomenon was described by Sanarelli (1924) in experimental cholera. The reaction is therefore called the Sanarelli–Shwartzman reaction or the generalised Shwartzman reaction.

It has been suggested that mechanisms similar to the Shwartzman reaction may operate in some clinical conditions such as the purpuric rashes of meningococcal septicemia and the acute hemorrhagic adrenal necrosis found in overwhelming infections (Waterhouse–Friderichsen syndrome).

Many infections, particularly Gram negative septicemias can lead to a septic shock syndrome with profound hypotension, hypoxia and oliguria. This may sometimes be accompanied by the adult respiratory distress syndrome (ARDS) with overwhelming neutrophil invasion of lungs.

Massive activation of complement by the alternative pathway, associated with release of thromboxane A2 and prostaglandins from platelets may lead to disseminated intravascular coagulation. The mechanism may be the excessive release of cytokines such as the tumour necrosis factor and interleukins 1 and 6 by macrophages and endothelial cells in response to contact with large quantities of lipopolysaccharide endotoxin. Some Gram positive infections may also cause similar effects. Staphylococcus aureus can induce TNF secretion by macrophages and peptidoglycan mediated platelet aggregation, leading to disseminated intravascular coagulation. Staphylococcal enterotoxin can act as a super antigen, activating whole families of T cells irrespective of their antigen specificities and causing massive release of cytokines, leading to the toxic shock syndrome. These conditions are not of immune origin but their pathogenic mechanisms resemble those in immune inflammation.

Further Reading

Chapel H. and M Haency 1993. *Essentials of Clinical Immunology*. 3rd edn. Oxford: Blackwell.

Evan PW. 1998. Anaphylaxis, *BMJ* 316:1442.

Frank M et al (eds). 1995. *Immunological Diseases*. Boston: Little Brown.

Holgate ST and MK Church 1993. *Allergy*. London: Gower.

Howarth PH. 1998. Allergy : Pathogenic mechanism. *New Eng J Med* 343:712.

Lachmann P et al. 1993. *Clinical Aspects of Immunology*. Oxford: Blackwell.

Roitt IM. 1994. *Essential Immunology*. 8th edn. Oxford: Blackwell.

Autoimmunity

Self-antigens are not ordinarily immunogenic. Ehrlich (1901) observed that goats produced antibodies against erythrocytes from other goats but not against their own, and postulated the concept of 'horror autotoxicus'. But he did not regard autoimmunisation as an impossibility and even envisaged its pathogenic possibility.

Autoimmunity is a condition in which structural or functional damage is produced by the action of immunologically competent cells or antibodies against the normal components of the body. Autoimmunity literally means 'protection against self' but it actually implies 'injury to self' and therefore it has been criticised as a contradiction in terms. 'Autoallergy' has been suggested as an acceptable alternative but the term autoimmunity has the sanction of wide usage.

The earliest example of autoimmunity was the observation by Metalnikoff (1900) that guinea pigs injected with their own spermatozoa produced sperm immobilising antibodies. Donath and Landsteiner (1904) identified circulating autoantibodies in paroxysmal cold hemoglobinuria —a hemolysin which binds with the patient's erythrocytes at low temperatures and produces complement dependent hemolysis on warming. This was the first description of an autoimmune disease in human beings. Dameshek and Schwartz (1938) established the autoimmune basis of acute hemolytic anemia. With the discovery of Coombs test for incomplete antibodies it became possible to demonstrate globulins bound to the surface of erythrocytes in this condition. Autoimmunisation could be induced in experimental animals by injection of self-antigens along with the complete Freund's adjuvant. The use of sensitive serological techniques led to the demonstration of autoantibodies in several diseases and even in a proportion of healthy individuals. Some autoantibodies, such as the antiidiotypic antibody may even be essential for the normal functioning of the immune system.

When the concept of autoimmunity came to be accepted as a pathogenic mechanism, a large number of diseases were suggested to have an autoimmune etiology, based on the finding of autoantibodies in the patients. This was soon recognised to be untenable as autoantibodies could be often incidental or the result, and not the cause of disease.

Criteria were proposed for proving the authenticity of putative autoimmune diseases, similar to Koch's postulates in infectious diseases. These were found to be not applicable in the case of such spontaneous and multifactorial conditions as autoimmune diseases. It may be proper to restrict the term 'autoimmune diseases' to those where autoimmune processes, humoral or cellular, are shown to be responsible for the pathogenesis, rather than merely associated. This is not strictly adhered to. Moreover, the border between autoimmunity and hypersensitivity is largely ill-defined or even nonexistent.

Diseases of autoimmune origin usually exhibit the following features:

1. An elevated level of immunoglobulins.
2. Demonstrable autoantibodies.
3. Deposition of immunoglobulins or their derivatives at sites of election, such as renal

glomeruli.

4. Accumulation of lymphocytes and plasma cells at the sites of lesion.

5. Benefit from corticosteroid or other immunosuppressive therapy.

6. The occurrence of more than one type of autoimmune lesion in an individual.

7. A genetic predisposition towards autoimmunity.

8. Incidence higher among females.

9. Chronicity. Usually nonreversible.

MECHANISMS OF AUTOIMMUNISATION

Cells or tissues may undergo antigenic alteration as a result of physical, chemical or biological influences. Such altered or 'neoantigens' may elicit an immune response. Neoantigens can arise in a variety of ways. Physical agents such as irradiation can cause antigenic alteration. Photosensitivity and cold allergy may represent sensitisation to self-antigens, altered by light and cold, respectively. Several chemicals, including drugs, can combine with cells and tissues and alter their antigenic nature. Contact dermatitis, which is traditionally considered a type of delayed hypersensitivity, can also be taken to be an autoimmune response to skin antigens altered by their combination with chemical allergens. Drug induced anemias, leucopenias and thrombocytopenias often have an autoimmune basis. Infectious microorganisms, particularly viruses and other intracellular pathogens, may induce alteration of cell antigens. Viral infections, such as infectious mononucleosis, are known to often precede autoimmune diseases. Bacterial enzymes also induce alteration of cell antigens. Neuraminidases formed by myxoviruses and many bacteria act on erythrocytes releasing the T antigen. The almost universal occurrence of T agglutinins in human sera is believed to represent a harmless autoimmune response following infections. Neoantigens may also arise by mutation. Such mutant cells may be immunogenic.

Immunological damage may result from immune responses induced by cross-reacting foreign antigens. The fortuitous similarity between some foreign and self-antigens is the basis of the 'cross reacting antigen' theory of autoimmunity. Organ specific antigens are present in several species. Injection of heterologous organ specific antigens may induce an immune response damaging the particular organ or tissue in the host. An example is the neurological injury that used to be a complication of antirabic immunisation in human beings with the neural vaccine of infected sheep brain tissue partially denatured by treatment with phenol. Its injection elicits an immune response against sheep brain antigens. This may cause damage to the individual's nerve tissue due to the cross-reaction between human and sheep brain antigens. Immunological injury due to cross-reacting antigens can also follow infections. Streptococcal M proteins and the heart muscle share antigenic characteristics. The immune response induced by repeated streptococcal infection can therefore damage the heart. Nephritogenic strains of streptococci possess antigens found in the renal glomeruli. Infection with such strains may lead to glomerulonephritis due to the antigenic sharing.

A related type of autoimmunisation is 'molecular mimicry' which is due to the presence in some infecting microorganisms and self-antigens, of epitopes with identical peptide sequences (instead of similarities in 'cross-reactions'). Examples of such homologous sequences are seen in arthritogenic Shigella flexneri and HLA-B27, Mycobacterium tuberculosis and joint membranes, Coxsackie B and myocardium.

Another hypothesis is polyclonal B cell activation. While an antigen generally activates only its corresponding B cell, certain stimuli nonspecifically turn on multiple B cell clones. Such stimuli include chemicals (for example, 2-mercaptoethanol), bacterial products (PPD, lipopolysaccharide), enzymes (trypsin), antibiotics (nystatin) and infections with some bacteria (mycoplasma), viruses (EB virus) and parasites (malaria). Multiple nonspecific antibodies form during some infectious diseases, such as antihuman erythrocyte cold antibodies in mycoplasma pneumonia and antisheep erythrocyte antibody in infectious mononucleosis. These polyclonal antibodies are IgM in nature, similar to the 'natural antibodies' produced by CD5+ B cells.

Breakdown of immunological homeostasis may lead to cessation of tolerance and the emergence of forbidden clones of immunocompetent cells capable of mounting immune response against self-antigens. Autoimmunisation may result when tolerance to a self-antigen is abrogated, as for instance by the injection of the self-antigen with Freund's adjuvant.

Enhanced helper T cell and decreased suppressor T cell functions have been suggested as causes of autoimmunity. Defects in the thymus, in stem cell development and macrophage function have also been postulated as causes.

Certain self-antigens are present in closed systems and are not accessible to the immune apparatus. These are known as sequestered antigens. An example is the lens antigen of the eye. The lens protein is enclosed in its capsule and does not circulate in the blood. Hence immunological tolerance against this antigen is not established during fetal life. When the antigen leaks out, following penetrating injury, it may induce an immune response causing damage to the lens of the other eye. An example of 'sequestration in time' is seen with sperm antigens. As spermatozoa develop only with puberty, the antigen cannot induce tolerance during fetal life. The sperm antigen is therefore not recognised as self and when it enters the circulation, it is immunogenic. This is believed to be the pathogenesis of orchitis following mumps. The virus damages the basement membrane of seminiferous tubules leading to the leakage of sperms and initiation of an immune response resulting in orchitis.

Defects in the idiotype–antiidiotype network have also been said to lead to autoimmunity. Genetic factors such as defective *Ir* or immunoglobulin genes have also been postulated.

In human autoimmune diseases and in animal models, genetic factors appear to influence the development and fate of autoimmune states. In spite of so many different possible mechanisms proposed, their actual role in autoimmunity, if any, has not been established.

Many animal models of spontaneous and induced autoimmunity have contributed to an understanding of this condition. Examples of spontaneous autoimmune diseases in animals are autoimmune hemolytic anemia in the New Zealand Black (NZB) mouse strain, systemic lupus erythematosus in NZB X NZW cross, insulin dependent diabetes mellitus in the nonobese diabetic (NOD) mouse, and thyroiditis in the obese strain (OS) chicken. Experimentally, autoimmunity can be induced in many animal species by injecting tissue extracts in the complete Freund's adjuvant—for example, experimental allergic encephalomyelitis with brain or spinal cord extracts, and thyroiditis with thyroid gland extract.

CLASSIFICATION OF AUTOIMMUNE DISEASES

Based on the site of involvement and nature of lesions, autoimmune diseases may be classified as hemocytolytic, localised (or organ specific), systemic (or nonorgan specific), and transitory diseases.

HEMOCYTOLYTIC AUTOIMMUNE DISEASES

Autoimmune hemolytic anemias: Autoantibodies against erythrocytes are demonstrable in this condition. Serologically, two groups of autoimmune anemias can be distinguished, characterised by 'cold' and 'warm' antibodies, respectively.

The cold autoantibodies are, generally, complete agglutinating antibodies belonging to the IgM class and agglutinate erythrocytes at 4 °C but not at 37 °C. Cold agglutinins were first detected by Donath and Landsteiner in paroxysmal cold hemoglobinuria. This condition, which used to frequently accompany syphilitic infection, is seldom seen nowadays. Cold agglutinins are also seen in primary atypical pneumonia, trypanosomiasis and blackwater fever.

Warm autoantibodies are generally incomplete, nonagglutinating antibodies usually belonging to the IgG class. They can be shown coating the erythrocytes in the direct Coombs test. Warm antierythrocyte antibodies are frequently seen in patients taking certain drugs such as sulphonamides, antibiotics, and alpha methyl dopa.

In autoimmune anemias, the red cells coated with antibodies are prematurely destroyed in the spleen and liver. Complement dependent intravascular hemolysis appears to be a rare event. **Autoimmune thrombocytopenia:** Autoantibodies directed against platelets occur in idiopathic thrombocytopenic purpura. Sedormid purpura is an instance of immune response against drug induced neoantigens on platelets. This condition is traditionally considered an antibody mediated hypersensitivity.

Autoimmune leucopenia: Nonagglutinating antileucocyte antibodies can be demonstrated in the serum of patients with systemic lupus erythematosus and rheumatoid arthritis.

Localised (Organ Specific) Autoimmune Diseases

Autoimmune diseases of the thyroid gland

1. Hashimoto's disease (Lymphadenoid goitre): This is the most typical and best studied of organ-specific autoimmune diseases. In 1956, Roitt and Doniach in England demonstrated antithyroglobulin antibodies in the sera of patients by precipitation in gel, and Witebsky and Rose in the USA by the more sensitive passive hemagglutination test. The latter workers also reproduced the disease in rabbits by immunisation with autologous thyroid tissue obtained by hemithyroidectomy.

Hashimoto's disease occurs more frequently in females and is associated with an enlargement of the thyroid gland and symptoms of hypothyroidism or frank myxedema. Histologically, the glandular structure is replaced by lymphoid tissue consisting of lymphocytes, histiocytes and plasma cells. Antibodies with different specificities have been found in this condition. They include antibodies that react with thyroglobulin, a second acinar colloid, microsomal antigen and a thyroid cell surface component.

2. Thyrotoxicosis (Graves' disease): The majority of patients with thyrotoxicosis possess antibody to thyroglobulin. Lymphocytic infiltration is common in thyrotoxic glands. The immunological basis of thyrotoxicosis is supported by the identification of the 'long acting thyroid stimulator' (LATS) which is an IgG antibody to the thyroid membrane antigen. Combination of LATS with the surface membrane of thyroid cells seems to stimulate excessive hormone secretion.

Addison's disease: The immunological basis of Addison's disease is suggested by lymphocytic infiltration of the adrenal glands and the presence of circulating antibodies directed against the cells of the zona glomerulosa. Similar lesions can be produced in experimental animals by immunisation with adrenal tissue in Freund's adjuvant.

Autoimmune orchitis: Experimental allergic orchitis with progressive damage to germinal epithelium and aspermatogenesis can be induced in guinea pigs by the injection of autogenous or allogeneic testes with Freund's adjuvant. A similar condition sometimes follows mumps orchitis. Lymphocytic infiltration of the testes and circulating antibodies to the sperms and germinal cells can be demonstrated in this condition.

Myasthenia gravis: In this disease, there is an abnormal fatiguability of muscles due to malfunction of the myoneural junction. An antibody against acetyl choline receptor on myoneural junctions of striated muscles is present in these patients. This prevents acetyl choline from combining with its receptor, and impairs muscular contraction. The thymus shows lymphoid hyperplasia and numerous germinal centres. Infants born to affected mothers show symptoms of the disease but recover spontaneously by the age of two months, coinciding with the disappearance of maternal antibodies. This suggests that the pathogenic factor in neonatal myasthenia may be the autoantibody passively acquired from the mother.

Autoimmune diseases of the eye: Two types of autoimmune diseases are seen in the eye. Cataract surgery sometimes leads to intraocular inflammation caused by the autoimmune response to the lens protein. This is known as *phacoanaphylaxis.*

Perforating injuries of the eye, particularly those involving the iris or ciliary bodies are often followed by *sympathetic ophthalmia* in the opposite eye. The disease can be produced in experimental animals by immunisation with uveal or retinal tissue in Freund's adjuvant and can be passively transferred with the spleen or lymph node cells but not with serum.

Pernicious anemia: Two types of autoantibodies are present in this condition. The first is directed against the parietal cells of the gastric mucosa. This is believed to cause achlorhydria and atrophic gastritis. The second type of antibody is directed against the intrinsic factor and prevents absorption of vitamin B_{12} either by blocking its attachment to the gastric intrinsic factor or by binding to the B_{12} intrinsic factor complex and interfering with its uptake by the intestinal mucosa.

Autoimmune diseases of the nervous system: The 'neuroparalytic accidents' following rabies vaccination represent injury to the nervous system by the immune response against the sheep nervous tissue in the vaccine, which cross reacts with human nerve tissue. An essentially similar condition, experimental allergic encephalomyelitis (EAE), can be produced in animals by immunisation with nervous tissue in Freund's adjuvant. The encephalogenic protein has been identified as the myelin basic protein (MBP) which shows no species specificity.

Idiopathic polyneuritis (Guillain–Barre syndrome) is considered an autoimmune response against the peripheral nervous tissue. It can be reproduced in experimental animals by immunisation with peripheral nervous tissue in an adjuvant.

Autoimmune diseases of the skin: Three serious diseases of the skin are considered to have an autoimmune basis. Pemphigus vulgaris may be caused by an antibody to the intercellular cement substance. In bullous pemphigoid, antibodies directed against the dermal epithelial junction have been demonstrated. Specific antibodies in dermatitis herpetiformis have not been identified.

SYSTEMIC (NONORGAN SPECIFIC) AUTOIMMUNE DISEASES

This group includes conditions characterised by immune response against a variety of self-antigens and damage to several organs and tissue systems. Klemperer (1942) classified a number of diseases of unknown origin with the common feature of connective tissue lesions as 'collagen diseases'. Included in this category are systemic lupus erythematosus (SLE), rheumatoid arthritis, polyarteritis nodosa, Sjogren's syndrome, dermatomyositis and scleroderma. All these conditions are associated with generalised autoimmune processes.

Systemic lupus erythematosus: This is a chronic, multisystem disease with remissions and exacerbations, terminating fatally. Patients have a variety of autoantibodies directed against cell nuclei, intracytoplasmic cell constituents, immuno globulins, thyroid and other organ specific antigens. Biological false positive reaction is seen in standard tests for syphilis. The abundance and variety of autoantibodies suggest a breakdown in the central control of immunological homeostasis.

The first immunological feature identified in SLE was the *LE cell phenomenon* described in 1948. The LE cell is a neutrophil containing a large, pale, homogeneous body (*LE body*) almost filling the cytoplasm. The LE body is the immunologically damaged nucleus of a leucocyte. Sometimes, instead of being intracellular, the LE body can be seen free, surrounded by a rosette of neutrophils. The fact that LE cell formation is due to an antibody (*LE factor*) present in SLE can be demonstrated by incubating normal blood with serum from an SLE patient. The nuclei of some leucocytes can be seen to swell and become pale and spherical. Neutrophils can be observed to surround these damaged cells, strip away the cytoplasm and engulf the free nucleus to form LE cells. Giemsa stained smears of blood or bone marrow can demonstrate LE cells, but its sensitivity is so low that this test has been replaced by other antibody tests for diagnosis.

Immunofluorescent tests for antinuclear antibody (ANA) show up different patterns of staining, such as homogeneous (diffuse), peripheral (outline), speckled and nucleolar staining patterns. ANA tests are sensitive but not specific for SLE, as they may be positive in many other autoimmune conditions, viral infections, chronic inflammatory processes, as well as in persons using certain medicines and in the aged.

Anti-DNA antibodies are tested by RIA or ELISA. Three major types of these antibodies are seen—those reacting with single stranded (ss), double stranded (ds) and both ss and ds DNA. Of these, high titre anti-ds DNA antibody is relatively specific for SLE. Another SLE specific antibody is anti-sm antibody.

Rheumatoid arthritis: This is a symmetric polyarthritis with muscle wasting and subcutaneous nodules, commonly associated with serositis, myocarditis, vasculitis and other disseminated lesions. It is found more commonly in women. The synovial membranes of the affected joints are swollen and edematous, with dense infiltration of lymphocytes and plasma cells. A striking feature is the presence of a circulating autoantibody called the 'Rheumatoid factor' (RF). This is usually a 19s IgM, though IgG, and IgA RF have also been demonstrated. RF acts as an antibody against the Fc fragment of immunoglobulins. They combine usually with IgG though some types of RF are directed towards other immunoglobulin classes. RF reacts with autologous, isologous or heterologous immunoglobulins. RF is generally considered to be an immunoglobulin behaving as antibody to determinants present in the patient's own IgG molecules, though some configurational alteration of IgG may be required before its reactivity with RF becomes demonstrable.

RF is detected by agglutination tests using, as antigens, particles coated with globulins. In the Rose–Waaler test, the original technique for detection of RF, sheep erythrocytes coated with a subagglutinating dose of antierythrocyte antibody (amboceptor) are used as the antigen in an agglutination test. In modifications of the test, latex and bentonite are used as the carrier particles for IgG. Antinuclear antibodies are frequently found in rheumatoid arthritis.

Polyarteritis nodosa: This is a necrotising angiitis involving medium sized arteries, ending fatally due to coronary thrombosis, cerebral hemorrhage or gastrointestinal bleeding. Polyarteritis is seen as a component of serum sickness and other toxic complex diseases. Immune complexes of hepatitis B virus antigen (Hbs Ag) in affected tissues, including the kidneys, have been demonstrated in 30–40 per cent of patients. Though it has been suggested that polyarteritis nodosa may be an autoimmune disease, the autoantibody responsible has not been identified.

Sjogren syndrome: This is a triad of conjunctivitis sicca, dryness of the mouth, with or without salivary gland enlargement, and rheumatoid arthritis. The syndrome may occur in association with other collagen diseases. Antinuclear antibodies and rheumatoid factor commonly occur in sera.

TRANSITORY AUTOIMMUNE PROCESSES

These include conditions such as anemia, thrombocytopenia or nephritis that follow certain infections or drug therapy. The infecting agent or drug induces antigenic alteration in some self-antigens. The immune response set up causes tissue damage. The disease is transient and undergoes spontaneous cure when the infection is controlled or the drug withdrawn.

PATHOGENESIS OF AUTOIMMUNE DISEASE

Many diseases are considered to be of autoimmune origin, based on their association with cellular or humoral immune responses against self-antigens. Autoantibodies are more easily detected than cellular autosensitisation. However, the mere presence of autoantibodies during the course of a disease does not prove their etiological role. Autoantibody formation may be a result of tissue injury and the antibody may help in promoting immune elimination of the damaged cell or tissue elements. A typical example is lepromatous leprosy in which

large amounts of autoantibodies are regularly found. It has been said that but for the lepra bacillus, lepromatous leprosy may have been proposed as an autoimmune disease.

The relative importance of humoral and cellular immune processes in the etiology of autoimmune diseases is not known. Antibodies may cause damage by the cytolytic or cytotoxic (type 2) and toxic complex (type 3) reactions. They are obviously important in hemocytolytic autoimmune diseases. Another mechanism of autoimmune tissue damage is by sensitised T lymphocytes (type 4 reaction). It is likely that humoral and cellular immune responses may act synergistically in the production of some autoimmune diseases. For example, experimental orchitis can be induced only when both types of immune responses are operative.

Once initiated, most autoimmune responses tend to be self perpetuating. Their progress can be arrested by immunosuppressive therapy, though the degree of response to such therapy varies in different diseases.

Further Reading

Weir DM and J Stewart 1997. *Immunology*. 8th edn. Edinburgh: Churchill Livingstone.
Peakman M and D Vergani 1997. *Basic and Clinical Immunology*. Edinburgh: Churchill Livingstone.
Roitt I et al. 1998. *Immunology*. 5th edn. London: Mosby.

Immunology of Transplantation and Malignancy

IMMUNOLOGY OF TRANSPLANTATION

When, as a result of disease or injury, an organ or tissue becomes irreparably damaged, or when an organ is congenitally defective or absent, transplantation or grafting becomes necessary for the restoration of function. The tissue or organ transplanted is known as the transplant or graft. The individual from whom the transplant is obtained is known as the *donor* and the individual to whom it is applied, the *recipient*.

Transplantation is one of mankind's ancient dreams. Chimeras, fanciful creatures composed of parts from different species, figure in the mythology and pantheon of all ancient nations. Such transplantations across the species barrier, however, do not succeed. It was recognised very early that transplants survive only when the tissue or organ is taken from the recipient himself, while grafts from another individual of the same species or from a different species would be rejected. The earliest application of transplantation appears to have been skin grafting for reconstruction of the severed nose, using the patient's own skin flaps – a technique described in the *Sushruta Samhita* (circa 800 BC).

The reasons for the rejection of exogenous grafts were for long suspected to be due to active immunity but it was only in the 1940s that the work of Medawar and his colleagues conclusively proved its immunological basis.

Classification of Transplants

Transplants may be classified in various ways:
1. Based on the organ or tissue transplanted, they are classified as kidney, heart, skin transplant,

and so on.
2. Based on the anatomical site of origin of the transplant and the site of its placement, grafts are classified as 'orthotopic' and 'heterotopic'. Orthotopic grafts are applied in anatomically 'normal' sites, as in skin grafts. Heterotopic grafts are placed in anatomically 'abnormal' sites, as when thyroid tissue is transplanted in a subcutaneous pocket.
3. Transplants may be of fresh tissues and organs or of stored ones.
4. Transplants may be of living or dead materials. Live grafts, such as kidney or heart, are expected to survive and function physiologically in the recipient and are called 'vital grafts'. Nonliving transplants like bone or artery merely provide a scaffolding on which new tissue is laid by the recipient. They are called 'static' or 'structural' grafts.
5. Transplants may be classified based on the genetic (and antigenic) relationship between the donor and the recipient (Table 20.1). An organ or tissue taken from an individual and grafted on himself is an autograft. A graft taken from an individual and placed on another individual of the same genetic constitution is called an isograft. Grafts made between identical twins or between syngeneic members of highly inbred strains of animals are examples of isografts. Grafts between two genetically nonidentical members of the same species are called allografts (formerly called homografts). Grafts between members of different species are called **xenografts** (formerly called heterografts).

THE ALLOGRAFT REACTION

When a skin graft from an animal (such as a rabbit) is applied on a genetically unrelated animal of the same species, the graft appears to be accepted initially. The graft is vascularised and seems morphologically and functionally healthy during the first two or three days. However, by about the fourth day, inflammation becomes evident and the graft is invaded by lymphocytes and macrophages. The blood vessels within the graft are occluded by thrombi, the vascularity diminishes and the graft undergoes ischemic necrosis. With extending necrosis, the graft assumes a scab-like appearance and sloughs off by the tenth day. This sequence of events resulting in the rejection of the allograft is known as the *first set response* (also known as the 'first set rejection or reaction').

If, in an animal which has rejected a graft by the first set response, another graft from the same donor is applied, it will be rejected in an accelerated fashion. Vascularisation commences but is soon interrupted by the inflammatory response. Necrosis sets in early and the graft sloughs off by the sixth day. The accelerated allograft rejection is known as the *second set response*.

Mechanism of allograft rejection: The immunological basis of graft rejection is evident from the specificity of the second set response. Accelerated rejection is seen only if the second graft is from the same donor as the first. Application of a skin graft from another donor will evoke only the first set response.

An allograft will be accepted if the animal is rendered immunologically tolerant. If suitable living cells (such as splenic cells) from one pure line strain of animal are injected into fetal or neonatal animals of another inbred strain, the latter, when they grow up, will accept grafts from the former animal. This is due to the induction of specific immunological tolerance against the donor tissues as a result of contact with them during embryonic life. The tolerance can be abolished by injecting lymphocytes from a nontolerant syngeneic animal, or more effectively, from a syngeneic animal sensitised against the donor tissues by a prior allotransplantation. This method of transferring immunity by means of lymphoid cells is known as *adoptive immunisation.*

Transplantation immunity is predominantly cell mediated. The first set response is brought about almost exclusively by T lymphocytes. Humoral antibodies are also produced during allograft rejection. They can be detected by a variety of methods including hemagglutination, lymphocytotoxicity, complement fixation and immunofluorescence. Antibodies are formed more rapidly and abundantly during a second set response than during primary rejection. Antibodies are believed to participate in the second set response along with cell mediated immunity. When a graft is applied to an animal possessing the specific antibodies in high titres, hyperacute rejection takes place. The graft remains pale and is rejected within hours without even an attempt at vascularisation.

Table 20.1 Terminology of grafts

Donor	Name	Synonyms
Self	Autograft	Autogenous or autogenic graft.
Different individual, genetically identical with recipient. Identical twin or member of same inbred strain	Isograft	Isologous or syngeneic graft or syngraft
Genetically unrelated member of same species	Allograft	Allogeneic graft. Formerly called homograft
Different species	Xenograft	Xenogeneic. Formerly called heterograft

This is known as the 'white graft response'. This type of hyperacute rejection is sometimes seen in human recipients of kidney transplants, who may possess preexisting antibody as a result of prior transplantation, transfusion or pregnancy. The glomeruli in such cases are choked by platelet and leucocyte agglomerates. Donor specific blood transfusions to recipients before kidney transplants have been found to favour graft survival. This may be due to the enhancing effect of antibodies to mismatched donor antigens, induced by the transfusion.

Humoral antibodies may sometimes act in opposition to cell mediated immunity, by inhibiting graft rejection. This phenomenon, called *immunological enhancement* was originally described by Kaliss in tumour transplants. If the recipient is pretreated with one or more injections of killed donor tissue and the transplant applied subsequently, it survives much longer than in control animals. The enhancing effect can be passively transferred to normal animals by an injection of serum from immunised animals, showing that the effect is due to humoral antibodies. The antibodies may bring about the enhancing effect in various ways. They may combine with the antigens released from the graft so that they are unable to initiate an immune response (afferent inhibition). The antibodies may combine with the lymphoid cells of appropriate specificity and, by a negative feedback influence, render them incapable of responding to the antigens of the graft (central inhibition). They may also cause 'efferent inhibition' by coating the surface of cells in the graft so that sensitised lymphocytes are kept out of contact with them.

Allograft immunity is a generalised response directed against all the antigens of the donor. A recipient sensitised by a skin graft will reject by the second set response not only another skin graft but also any other organ or tissue graft from the same donor.

HISTOCOMPATIBILITY ANTIGENS

Immune response against transplants depends on the presence in the grafted tissue of antigens that are absent in the recipient and hence recognised as foreign. It follows, therefore, that if the recipient possesses all the antigens present in the graft, there will be no immune response, and consequently no graft rejection, even when the donor and recipient are not syngeneic. The first generation (F1) hybrids between two inbred strains possess antigens representative of both the parent strains and will therefore accept grafts from either of the parental strains. If the two parental strains have genotypes AA and BB, respectively, the F1 hybrid will be of genotype AB. It can therefore accept tissues with genotype AA as well as BB, as it possesses both alleles. Transplantation in the reverse direction (from F1 to parent) will not succeed as strain AA will react against antigen B and strain BB against antigen A.

While transplants between members of a highly inbred strain of animals are successful, an exception is seen when the donor is a male and the recipient a female. Such grafts are rejected as the grafted male tissue (XY) will have antigens determined by the Y chromosome which will be absent in the female (XX) recipient. Grafts from the female to the male will succeed. This unilateral sex linked histoincompatibility is known as the *Eichwald–Silmser effect*.

Antigens that participate in graft rejection are called transplantation or histocompatibility antigens. The blood group antigens are important in transplantation. The term 'major histocompatibility system' refers to a system of cell antigens that exert a decisive influence on the fate of allografts. Major histocompatibility systems have been identified in different species – H2 in mice, AgB in rats, B in chickens, H1 in rabbits and DLA in dogs. The major histocompatibility system in human beings is the human leucocyte antigen (HLA) system. A description of the HLA system is presented in Chapter 15.

FACTORS FAVOURING ALLOGRAFT SURVIVAL

1. Next to ABO blood group compatibility, the most important factor in allograft survival is *HLA compatibility*. This is tested by HLA typing and tissue matching. HLA typing identifies the HLA antigens expressed on the surface of leucocytes.

   The standard typing method is the microcyto toxicity test. Lymphocyte suspensions are added to microwells of tissue typing trays predispensed with a panel of HLA typing sera, each containing alloantibodies to a specific HLA antigen, and incubated with complement. Cells carrying antigens corresponding to the HLA antiserum are killed by complement mediated membrane damage. These can be detected by the addition of eosin or trypan blue which stains only dead cells. The lymphocyte is presumed to have HLA antigens corresponding to the specificities of all the antisera that have caused cell death, as indicated by the staining.

   Antisera for HLA typing were originally obtained from multigravidae, placental fluid and from multiple blood transfusion recipients, who have antibodies against mismatched paternal or donor HLA antigens. These are now being replaced by monoclonal antibodies.

   More discriminating molecular methods have been developed for tissue typing. These include restriction fragment length polymorphism (RFLP) with southern blotting, and polymerase chain reaction (PCR) amplification using sequence specific primers.

   Once a set of HLA compatible donors is available (commonly, siblings of the patient), the best donors among them can be chosen by tissue matching. This is done by the mixed lymphocyte reaction or culture (MLR, MLC). It depends on the fact that T lymphocytes in culture, when exposed to HLA incompatible antigens, will undergo blast transformation, the intensity of the reaction being a measure of the antigenic disparity between the donor and recipient lymphocytes. The test, as performed, is a one-way test in which the donor lymphocytes are killed and only the recipient lymphocytes are permitted to be transformed in response to the incompatible antigens on the donor cells.

2. As allograft rejection is an immunological process, *immunosuppression* will inhibit it. This can be achieved in experimental animals by neonatal thymectomy, chronic lymphatic drainage or administration of ALS—procedures that will inhibit cell mediated immunity.

   Clinical transplantation employs a combination of immunosuppressive drugs, including steroids, azathioprene and the fungal metabolite cyclosporin A, which is currently the most effective agent.

3. There appear to be certain **privileged sites** where allografts are permitted to survive, safe from immunological attack. The fetus can be considered an intrauterine allograft as it contains antigens which are foreign to the mother. The reason why the fetus is exempt from rejection is not clear, though many explanations have been offered. The placenta acts as an immunological barrier by generating a hormone which is locally immunosuppressive. Major histocompatibility complex (MHC) antigens are present only in low density on trophoblastic cells and the cell membranes are relatively resistant to attack by T or K cells. Antigen shedding by the fetus blocks the aggressive T cells or antibodies by an enhancement effect. An incomplete mucopolysaccharide barrier rich in sialic acid surrounds the trophoblastic cells, protecting them from cytotoxic lymphocytes. The high concentration of alphafetoprotein in fetal blood also may be a factor, as it has immunosuppressive properties, which may protect the fetus against immunological damage from any maternal leucocytes entering fetal circulation.

Any site that is impenetrable to immunocompetent cells (for example, cartilage) is an immunologically privileged site. Areas where a lymphatic drainage system is absent such as brain, hamster cheek pouch or ineffective such as testes can accept allografts without rejection. Lack of vascularity at the site also prevents graft rejection. This is the reason for the success of corneal transplants.

GRAFT-VERSUS-HOST REACTION

Graft rejection is due to the reaction of the host to the grafted tissue (host-versus-graft response). The contrary situation, in which the graft mounts an immune response against the antigens of the host, is known as the graft-versus-host (GVH) reaction.

The GVH reaction occurs when the following conditions are present:

1. The graft contains immunocompetent T cells.
2. The recipient possesses transplantation antigens that are absent in the graft.
3. The recipient must not reject the graft.

Examples of situations leading to the GVH reaction are:

a. Allograft in a recipient in whom specific immunological tolerance has been induced.
b. Adult lymphocytes injected into an immunologically deficient recipient. The immunological deficiency may be due to immaturity (newborn) or immunosuppression.
c. F₁ hybrid receiving a transplant from any one parental strain.

The major clinical features of the GVH reaction in animals are retardation of growth, emaciation, diarrhea, hepatosplenomegaly, lymphoid atrophy and anemia, terminating fatally. The syndrome has been called *runt disease*.

IMMUNOLOGY OF MALIGNANCY

When a cell undergoes malignant transformation, it acquires new surface antigens. It may also lose some normal antigens. This makes a tumour antigenically different from the normal tissues of the host. A tumour

can, therefore, be considered an allograft and be expected to induce an immune response.

CLINICAL EVIDENCE OF IMMUNE RESPONSE IN MALIGNANCY

Several clinical observations indicate the presence of an immune response that prevents, arrests and occasionally cures malignancies.

1. Instances of spontaneous regression of established tumours have been reported, especially with neuroblastoma and malignant melanoma. On the analogy of the role played by the immune response in recovery from infections, it is believed that recovery from malignancy also may represent an immune process.

2. Dramatic cures sometimes follow chemotherapy of choriocarcinoma and Burkitt's lymphoma. Even a single dose of cytotoxic drug may, on occasion, result in a complete cure. Again, in some types of tumours, such as hypernephroma with pulmonary metastases, removal of the primary tumour often leads to a regression of the metastases. These observations suggest that once a large mass of tumour has been removed, mopping up operations can be effected by the immune process. The immune response appears to be effective only when the tumour is below a 'critical mass'.

3. There is a higher prevalence of certain types of cancers observed unexpectedly at autopsy, than their clinical incidence would suggest. This indicates that the immune system is able to deal with malignant cells as they arise and that only some of them are able to overcome the defence mechanisms and develop into clinical cancer.

4. Histological evidence of immune response against malignancy is provided by the presence of lymphocytes, plasma cells and macrophages infiltrating tumours. The cellular response resembles that seen in the allograft reaction. Tumours showing such cellular infiltration have a better prognosis than those that do not.

5. If the immune system plays a natural role in

preventing tumour development, a high incidence of malignancy should be expected in immune deficiency states. This is indeed so. An increased incidence of cancer, particularly lymphoreticular malignancies, is found in congenital immunodeficiency states, in AIDS and in patients undergoing chronic immunosuppressive therapy.

TUMOUR ANTIGENS

Tumour antigens are antigens that are present in malignant cells but absent in the corresponding normal cells of the host.

Tumour specific antigens are present on the membranes of malignant cells and induce an immune response when the tumour is transplanted in syngeneic animals. Such tumour specific antigens which induce rejection of tumour transplants in immunised hosts are termed tumour specific transplantation antigens (TSTA) or tumour associated transplantation antigens (TATA).

In chemically induced tumours, the TSTA is tumour specific. Different tumours possess different TSTA, even though induced by the same carcinogen. In contrast, the TSTA of virus induced tumours is virus specific in that all tumours produced by one virus will possess the same antigen, even if the tumours occur in different animal strains or species.

A second type of antigen is found in some tumours. These are the fetal antigens which are found in embryonic and malignant cells but not in normal adult cells. The best known examples are alphafetoprotein in hepatomas and the carcinoembryonic antigen found in colonic cancers. Their synthesis represents a dedifferentiation of malignant cells into more primitive forms.

The carcinoembryonic antigen is a glycoprotein which can be detected in the serum of many patients with carcinoma of the colon, particularly in the presence of metastases. However, it also appears in some other conditions such as alcoholic cirrhosis, and hence its diagnostic value is limited.

Alphafetoprotein is an alphaglobulin secreted by normal embryonic hepatocytes. Its serum level drops sharply after birth and is hardly detectable in adults. High levels are present in hepatic carcinoma, in which condition it is of diagnostic value. Prostate-specific antigen (PSA) has been used as a dignostic indicator for prostate cancer.

IMMUNE RESPONSE IN MALIGNANCY

Both humoral and cellular responses can be demonstrated in malignancy. Anti-TSTA antibodies can be demonstrated by indirect membrane immunofluorescence. Delayed hypersensitivity to tumour antigens can be detected by skin testing with tumour cell extracts. Cell mediated immunity can be demonstrated by the stimulation of DNA synthesis and lymphokine production by the patient's leucocytes on exposure to the tumour antigens. The lymphocytes from the patients are cytotoxic to the cultured tumour cells.

Cell mediated immunity is believed to be the mechanism of host defence against malignancy. The humoral response may not be relevant, or may even be detrimental due to its facilitating tumour growth by the process of enhancement.

IMMUNOLOGICAL SURVEILLANCE

The concept of immunological surveillance had its beginning in the observations of Ehrlich (1906). It was revived by Lewis Thomas in the 1950s and developed by Burnet. It postulates that the primary function of cell mediated immunity is to 'seek and destroy' malignant cells that arise by somatic mutation. Such malignant mutations are believed to occur frequently and would develop into tumours but for the constant vigilance of the immune system. Inefficiency of the surveillance mechanism, either as a result of ageing or in congenital or acquired immunodeficiencies, leads to an increased incidence of cancer. While this hypothesis is attractive, it may perhaps represent an oversimplification of a complex situation.

If immunological surveillance is effective, cancer

should not occur. The development of tumours represents a lapse in surveillance. The mechanisms of such lapses are not clear but several possibilities have been suggested. Due to the very fast rate of proliferation of malignant cells, they may be able to 'sneak through' before the development of an effective immune response and once they reach a certain mass may be beyond the power of immunological attack. Circulating tumour antigens may act as a 'smokescreen', coating the lymphoid cells and preventing them from acting on the tumour cells. The tumour antigens on malignant cells may be inaccessible to sensitised cells, being covered by some antigenically neutral substance. Humoral antibodies may cause immunological enhancement. 'Blocking' activity has been demonstrated in humoral factors. This may be due to the circulating antigen, antibody or antigen–antibody complexes. Some tumours may be of low immunogenicity or may form cytokines like transforming growth factor β (TGF-β) which suppresses cell mediated immunity.

IMMUNOTHERAPY OF CANCER

Different approaches have been attempted in the immunotherapy of cancer—passive, active and adoptive immunotherapy, specific and nonspecific.

Passive immunotherapy was the earliest method of cancer immunotherapy. Antisera prepared by immunising animals with tumour biopsy specimens were used for the treatment of human cancer as early as in 1895. This method was found to be of no use and therefore abandoned. A special type of serotherapy has recently been found beneficial in experimental tumours. Appropriate antisera that possess 'deblocking' activity in vitro have been found to cause regression of tumours, apparently by neutralising the circulating tumour antigens and permitting the sensitised lymphocytes to act on tumour cells. Monoclonal antibodies to tumour antigens may play a role as carriers in transporting cytotoxic or radioactive drugs specifically to the tumour cells.

Specific active immunotherapy by the injection of tumour cell 'vaccines' was tried early in last century but was given up as unprofitable. The method has been modified recently by using purified tumour cell membrane antigens and tumour cells treated with neuraminidase to increase their immunogenic potential.

Nonspecific active immunotherapy employs BCG and nonliving *Corynebacterium parvum*. Mathe, the leading proponent of cancer immunotherapy, has reported very good results in acute leukemia, following combined treatment with BCG and allogeneic or autochthonous leukemia blast cells. Intralesional BCG in malignant melanoma has been reported to induce complete remission in a high percentage of patients. It has also been used against intradermal recurrence of breast cancer following mastectomy. Dinitrochlorobenzene has been tried in the treatment of squamous and basal cell carcinoma of the skin. Glucan, a pyran copolymer derived from microorganisms, and levamisole, originally introduced as an anthelmintic, have been tried for stimulating cell mediated immunity and macrophage functions. Interferons have been employed in the treatment of leukemias.

Specific adoptive immunotherapy has been attempted with lymphocytes, transfer factor and 'immune RNA'. The donors have been persons who have been cured of their neoplasms or specifically immunised against the patient's tumour. Lymphokine activated killer (LAK) cells obtained by treatment of the natural killer cells with interleukin-2 have been found useful in the treatment of certain malignancies, such as renal carcinomas.

Immunotherapy is ineffective in the presence of a large mass of tumour cells. Its role appears to be more in getting rid of the residual malignant cells after the gross tumour has been removed. The best results in the treatment of cancer apparently follow an integrated approach to therapy, employing surgery, radiotherapy, chemotherapy and immunotherapy.

Further Reading

Barrett AJ. 1987. Graft-versus-host reaction – a review. *J Royal Soc Med* 80:368.

Bishop JM. 1987. The molecular genetics of cancer. *Science*, 235:305.

Lachmann PJ et al. 1993. *Clinical Aspects of Immunology*. 5ᵗʰ edn. Oxford: Blackwell.

Roitt I et al. 1998. *Immunology*. 5ᵗʰ edn. London: Mosby.

Rosenberg SA et al. 1988. New approaches to immunotherapy of cancer. *Annals Int Med* 108: 853.

Armstrong A. 2001. Cellular immunotherapy for cancer. *BMJ*, 323:1289.

Immunohematology

Blood has held a mysterious fascination for us from the dawn of time. It was considered the essence of life and was believed to cure diverse diseases and restore youth and vitality to the aged. Blood transfusion has been attempted from very early times but such attempts were fruitless and often fraught with disastrous consequences. Blood transfusion became scientifically feasible only after the discovery of blood groups by Landsteiner.

In his original experiment, Landsteiner (1900) cross tested serum from himself and five of his colleagues against their red blood cells. Three distinct patterns of agglutination were observed. Cells which failed to agglutinate with any of the serum samples were designated group O, while cells agglutinating in the two different patterns were called groups A and B, respectively. The fourth group AB was described later by his pupils von Decastallo and Sturli (1902). In 1930, Landsteiner was awarded the Nobel Prize for his discovery of human blood groups.

The ABO system is the most important of all the blood group systems and its discovery made blood transfusion possible. No other blood group antigens were discovered for the next 25 years. Using rabbit antisera to different samples of human red cells, Landsteiner and Levine (1926) discovered the MN and P antigens. Landsteiner and Wiener (1940) raised rabbit and guinea pig antisera against Rhesus monkey erythrocytes and tested them against human red cells. This led to the discovery of the 'Rhesus (Rh) factor'. Many more blood group antigens have been identified subsequently, mostly by studying antibodies in patients who had received multiple

blood transfusions or mothers of infants with hemolytic disease. The main blood group systems with the dates of their discovery are shown below.

ABO	1900	Duffy	1950
MN	1926	Kidd	1951
P	1926	Diego	1955
Rh	1940	Yt	1956
Lutheran	1945	Kg	1962
Lewis	1946	Dombrock	1965
Kell	1946	Colton	1967

Some antigens have been identified that occur very rarely, being limited to certain individuals or families. These have been termed 'private antigens'.

ABO BLOOD GROUP SYSTEM

The ABO system contains four blood groups and is determined by the presence or absence of two distinct antigens, A and B, on the surface of erythrocytes. Red cells of group A carry antigen A, cells of group B antigen B and cells of group AB have both A and B antigens, while group O cells have neither A nor B antigen. The four groups are also distinguished by the presence or absence of two distinct isoantibodies in the serum. The serum contains the isoantibodies specific for the antigen that is absent on the red cell. The serum of a group A individual has anti-B antibody, group B has anti-A and group O both anti-A and anti-B, while in group AB both anti-A and anti-B are absent (Table 21.1).

Group A is subdivided into A1 and A2. Antiserum of group A agglutinates group A1 cells powerfully but A2 cells only weakly. About 80 per cent of group A blood is A1 and 20 per cent A2. The subgroups of A antigen are represented in group AB also. The recognition of group A subgroups increases the number of ABO phenotypes from four to six: A1, A2, B, A2B, A1B and O. Other A subgroups (A3, A4, A5) have also been described but they are not clinically relevant.

Blood group antigens are inherited according to simple Mendelian laws. Their synthesis is determined by allelomorphic genes A, B and O. Genes A and B give rise to the corresponding antigens, but O is an amorph and does not produce any antigen. The frequency of ABO distribution differs in different peoples. Group O is the most common group and AB the rarest. The ABO distribution in Britain is approximately 0–47 per cent, A – 42 per cent, B – 8 per cent and AB – 3 per cent. In India, the distribution is approximately 0–40 per cent, A – 22 per cent, B – 33 per cent and AB – 5 per cent.

Anti-A and anti-B isoantibodies appear in the serum of infants by about the age of six months and persist thereafter. These are called 'natural' antibodies because they seem to arise under genetic control without any apparent antigenic stimulation. However, it is likely that they develop as a result of unidentified environmental stimuli with the blood group-like antigens present in bacteria or other sources. Natural anti-A and anti-B antibodies are IgM saline agglutinating antibodies reacting optimally between 4 °C and 18 °C but less active at 37 °C. Immune isoantibodies may develop following ABO incompatible pregnancy or transfusion. More commonly they result from the injection of substances containing blood group-like antigens, such as horse serum or bacterial vaccines made from media containing horse or hog extracts. Immune isoantibodies are 'albumin agglutinating' IgG antibodies reacting optimally at 37 °C and acting as hemolysins in the presence of complement. They are clinically more important than natural IgM antibodies and may cause more severe transfusion reactions.

H antigen: Red cells of all ABO groups possess a common antigen, the H antigen or H substance which is a precursor for the formation of A and B antigens. The amount of the H antigen is related to the ABO group of the cell, group O cells having the most and AB the least amount. Due to its universal distribution, the H antigen is not ordinarily important in grouping or blood transfusion. Bhende et al (1952) from Bombay reported the very rare instance in which A and B antigens as well as the H antigens are absent from red cells. This is known as 'Bombay' or OH blood. Such individuals have anti-A, anti-B and anti-H antibodies and their sera are incompatible with all red cells except of those with the same rare blood group.

A, B and H antigens are glycoproteins. They are not confined to erythrocytes but can be detected in almost all tissues and fluids of the body. While these antigens are always present in tissues, they are found in secretions (saliva, gastric juice, sweat) of only about 75 per cent of all persons. Such persons are called 'secretors' and those who lack blood group antigens in secretions are called

Table 21.1 Distribution of ABO antigens and antibodies in red cells and serum

	Red cells		Serum	
Group	Antigen present	Agglutinated by serum of group	Antibody present	Agglutinates cells of group
A	A	B, O	anti-B	B, AB
B	B	A, O	anti-A	A, AB
AB	A and B	A,B,O	None	None
O	None	None	Anti-A and anti-B	A, B, AB

'nonsecretors'. The secretion of ABH antigens is controlled by two allelic genes Se and se. Individuals who are homozygous or heterozygous for Se are secretors, while those who are se-se are nonsecretors.

A and B antigens are also found in certain animals and plants. They have been extracted and purified commercially from the stomach of horses and hogs. Blood group antibodies are also found in some animals. Substances specifically agglutinating A or B antigens have been detected in some plants. A potent anti-A1 agglutinin has been extracted from *Dolichos biflorus* and anti-*H* from *Ulex europaeus*. Blood group agglutinins of plant origin are known as 'lectins'.

RH BLOOD GROUP SYSTEM

Levine and Stetson (1939) demonstrated a new type of antibody in the serum of a woman who developed severe reactions following transfusion of her husband's ABO compatible blood. She had recently delivered a stillborn infant with hemolytic disease. They suggested that the woman may have been sensitised by some antigen inherited by the fetus from its father. Landsteiner and Wiener (1940) identified in the red cells of the majority of persons tested, an antigen that reacted with rabbit antiserum to Rhesus monkey erythrocytes. This antigen was called the 'Rhesus' or Rh factor. The 'new type' of antibody described by Levine and Stetson was identified as the anti-Rh factor antibody. Wiener and Peters (1940) demonstrated anti-Rh antibody in some persons who had received ABO compatible transfusion. Levine and colleagues (1941) proved that Rh sensitisation was the cause of hemolytic disease of the newborn.

The Rh system is complex and its study is complicated by the existence of two different theories and nomenclatures for the genes and antigens. Wiener proposed that Rh antigens are determined by any one of several allelic genes which may appear at a single locus and govern the production of the appropriate agglutinogen on the surface of erythrocytes. Each agglutinogen is in turn made up of one or more antigens. Fisher, on the other hand, postulated that Rh antigens are determined by three pairs of closely linked allelomorphic genes, Cc, Dd and Ee. Every individual possesses one member of each pair of these genes derived from each parent. Each gene would be responsible for the production of a specific antigen, which could be detected by its specific antibody.

The designations employed by the two systems for the different Rh types are as follows:

	Fisher	Wiener
Rh positive	CDe	Rh1
	cDE	Rh2
	cDe	Rho
	CDE	Rhz
Rh negative	Cde	rh/
	cdE	rh//
	cde	rh
	CdE	rhy

For routine purposes, the typing of persons as Rh positive or negative depends on the presence or absence of antigen D (Rho) on red cells and hence can be accomplished by testing with anti-D (anti-Rh) serum. This is because D is the most powerful Rh antigen and accounts for the vast majority of Rh incompatibility reactions. The distribution of Rh positives differs in different races. Among people of European descent, about 85 per cent are Rh positive and 15 per cent negative. Among Indians, approximately 93 per cent are Rh positive and 7 per cent negative.

A variant of D is known as Du. Red cells of Du subtype react with some but not all anti-D sera. Though Du cells may not be agglutinated by anti-D sera, they absorb the antibody on their surface. The Du subtype can therefore be detected by reacting red cell with anti-D serum and then doing a direct Coombs test. For the purpose of blood donation, Du cells are considered Rh positive. But when a Du individual requires transfusion, it is advisable to use Rh negative blood because he is capable of being immunised by standard Rh positive blood.

There are no natural anti-Rh antibodies in the serum. They arise only as a result of Rh incompatible pregnancy or transfusion.

OTHER BLOOD GROUP SYSTEMS

The Lewis blood group system consists of two antigens Le^a and Le^b. It differs from other blood group systems in that the antigens are present primarily in the plasma and saliva. Red cells acquire the antigen by adsorbing them from plasma. The Lewis phenotypes are closely related to the ABO group and to the secretor status of an individual. Naturally occurring Lewis antibodies are frequently found in the sera of persons lacking the corresponding antigen.

In the MN system, using rabbit antisera, persons were originally classified into three groups—M, N and MN. An antigen, S, was later added to this system. This system has expanded to include at least 28 antigens.

Blood group systems other than ABO and Rh are of little clinical importance as they do not usually cause transfusion reactions or hemolytic disease. They have applications in genetics, anthropology, tissue typing and forensic medicine. As blood group antigens are inherited from the parents, they are often useful in settling cases of disputed paternity.

MEDICAL APPLICATIONS OF BLOOD GROUPS

BLOOD TRANSFUSION

The existence of several different blood group antigens makes it almost impossible to obtain perfectly matched blood for transfusion. But in routine transfusion practice, only the ABO and Rh antigens are relevant. The other antigens are too weak to be of importance. Safety in blood transfusion requires that the following conditions be satisfied in choosing a donor.

1. The recipient's plasma should not contain any antibody that will damage the donor's erythrocytes.

2. The donor plasma should not have any antibody that will damage the recipient's red cells.

3. The donor red cells should not have any antigen that is lacking in the recipient. If the transfused cells possess a 'foreign antigen', it will stimulate an immune response in the recipient.

Ideally, the donor and recipient should belong to the same ABO group. It used to be held that O group cells could be transfused to recipients of any group as they possessed neither A nor B antigen. Hence the O group was designated as the 'universal donor'. The anti-A and anti-B antibodies in the transfused O blood group do not ordinarily cause any damage to the red cells of the A or B group recipients because they will be rendered ineffective by dilution in the recipient's plasma. But some O group plasma may contain isoantibodies in high titres (1:200 or above) so that damage to recipient cells may result. This is known as the 'dangerous O group'. The anti-A antibody in the O group blood is generally more potent than the anti-B antibody. Hence the O blood group is more likely to cause an adverse reaction when given to the A group recipients than to those of the B group. While the O group blood with low titre antibodies may be transfused to a patient of any other group in dire emergency, this practice should never be employed as a routine. Transfusion of large quantities of the O group blood to persons of any other group may cause adverse reactions.

Due to the absence of isoantibodies in plasma, the AB group persons were designated 'universal recipients'. AB group donors may not always be available due to their rarity and it may, on occasion, be necessary to use donors of other groups. In such cases, group A blood is safer than group B, because the anti-A antibody is usually more potent than the anti-B antibody.

Rh compatibility is important only when the recipient is Rh negative. An Rh positive person may safely receive either Rh positive or negative blood. But an Rh negative individual receiving Rh positive blood may form antibodies against the Rh antigen. A subsequent transfusion with Rh positive blood may then cause an adverse reaction. An additional risk in women is Rh sensitisation leading to hemolytic disease of the newborn. Therefore it is particularly important that Rh negative women who are not past childbearing age receive only Rh negative blood.

Besides ABO grouping and Rh typing of the donor and recipient, it is invariably necessary before transfusion to perform a 'cross matching' to ensure that the donor's blood is compatible with the recipient' blood. The routine procedure used in most blood banks is a rapid cross match by the tile or slide method. This is done in two parts – the major cross match where the donor red cells are tested against the recipient's serum, and the minor cross match where the recipient's cells are tested against the donor serum. One drop of a 5% suspension of donor red cells in saline is added to a drop of the recipient's serum on a porcelain tile or a glass slide, mixed and observed for agglutination. Though in most cases agglutination occurs early, it may sometimes be delayed. The result is to be read, macroscopically and under low power microscope, after incubation in a moist chamber for 10–15 minutes at room temperature. In the minor cross match, the same is repeated using recipient cells and donor serum. Only the major cross match is done ordinarily.

The saline slide test does not detect Rh and other minor incompatibilities. The most discriminating method is the Coombs cross match where washed donor cells and recipient serum are incubated in a water bath at 37 °C for two hours and a direct Coombs test done. This detects all incompatibilities, including incomplete antibodies.

Following an incompatible blood transfusion, the red cells may undergo clumping and intravascular hemolysis or they may be coated by antibodies, engulfed by phagocytes, removed from circulation and subjected to extravascular lysis. Incompatible transfusion may be accompanied by symptoms such as shivering, tingling sensation, excruciating headache, constricting precordial discomfort and severe lumbar pain. Hypotension, cold clammy skin, cyanosis, feeble pulse and other signs of collapse may be seen. Jaundice, hematuria, oliguria and anuria may follow.

Some transfusion reactions may be due to immunological processes other than blood group incompatibility. Rigor, urticaria and other manifestations often occur due to the recipient being hypersensitive to some allergen present in the donor blood. Serious reactions follow when hemolysed or contaminated blood is transfused.

Whenever any reaction occurs, the transfusion should be stopped immediately. The remainder of the donor blood should be sent to the blood bank for investigation.

The most common complications following blood transfusion are of infectious origin. Transfusion of blood contaminated by bacteria may lead to endotoxic shock or septicemia. Gross contamination can be recognised in most cases by inspection of the blood before transfusion, as hemolysis is usually apparent. Such contamination can be eliminated by proper techniques of blood collection and storage.

The most important infections transmitted at present by blood transfusion are the HIV and hepatitis viruses. Several cases of transfusion-induced AIDS have occurred before HIV screening of donors became mandatory. However, screening may not detect HIV infected donors during the window period when they are infectious. Hepatitis B, C, D and possibly others can be transmitted by transfusion. Screening for the hepatitis B surface antigen can exclude most HBV carriers but the available serological tests against other hepatitis viruses are not quite satisfactory.

Despite diligent screening, there exists a small risk (about 1 in 300,000) risk of transfusion associated HIV, HBV and HCV infections. The variant CJD prion is another risk in endemic areas like the UK where it is mandatory to screen donors for the prion and to remove leucocytes from blood before transfusion, as a precautionary measure.

Cytomegalovirus transmitted by transfusion may cause an infectious mononucleosis-like syndrome. Syphilis may be transmitted by transfusion of fresh blood from an infectious donor but not if the blood has been stored for three days or more before transfusion. Malaria is another disease transmissible by transfusion.

Whole blood transfusion is being replaced increasingly by blood component therapy, which causes fewer complications and results in more optimal utilisation of human blood which is a scarce commodity. For example, in anemia, packed red cell transfusion is more beneficial than whole blood as it provides greater oxygen carrying capacity with less circulatory overload and minimal electrolyte disturbance. Frozen red cells are available for transfusion in patients with rare blood groups. Similarly, leucocyte and platelet concentrates are available for specific needs. Plasma cryoprecipitates and Factor VIII are routinely used in treating hemophilia. Other coagulation factors are also available for different coagulation disorders. Such plasma products are manufactured from pooled human blood and may transmit HIV, hepatitis type B or C virus and other infectious agents unless great care is taken in the selection of donors and in manufacturing processes. An illustration of the enormity of the risk was the tragedy in France in the mid-1980s, when tainted blood caused HIV infection in over 4000 persons, of whom hundreds died of AIDS in the next few years. Charges of criminal negligence were framed against the persons considered responsible, from the Prime Minister downwards. Though the Prime Minister was acquitted, the Health Minister, the Head of the National Blood Transfusion Service and many other top officials were convicted.

Almost all adverse reactions of transfusion can be eliminated by autologous blood transfusion which is rapidly becoming popular. Here, blood is collected from the individual himself and stored for use during elective surgery. Blood collection may be started a month before the expected date of transfusion. Autologous transfusion eliminates not only infectious complications but also those due to minor blood group incompatibilities and hypersensitivity.

HEMOLYTIC DISEASE OF THE NEWBORN

When an Rh negative woman carries an Rh positive fetus, she may be sensitized against the Rh antigen by the passage of fetal red cells into the maternal circulation. Minor transplacental leaks may occur any time during pregnancy but it is during delivery that fetal cells enter the maternal circulation in large numbers. The mother is usually sensitized only at the first delivery and, consequently, the first child escapes damage (except where the woman has been sensitised already by prior Rh incompatible transfusion). During a subsequent pregnancy, Rh antibodies of the IgG class pass from the mother to the fetus and damage its erythrocytes. This is the pathogenesis of the hemolytic disease of the newborn. The clinical features may vary from a mere accentuation of the physiological jaundice in the newborn to erythroblastosis fetalis or intrauterine death due to hydrops fetalis.

Hemolytic disease does not affect all the offspring of Rh incompatible marriages. Its incidence is much less than the expected figures. The following factors influence the incidence of hemolytic disease due to Rh incompatibility:

Immunological unresponsiveness to the Rh antigen: Not every Rh negative individual forms Rh antibodies following antigenic stimulation. Some fail to do so even after repeated injection of Rh positive cells. They are called **nonresponders**. The reason for this immunological unresponsiveness is not known.

Fetomaternal ABO incompatibility: Rh immunisation is more likely to result when the mother and fetus possess the same ABO group. When Rh and ABO incompatibility coexist, Rh sensitisation in the mother is rare. In this situation the fetal cells entering the maternal circulation are believed to be destroyed rapidly by the ABO antibodies before they can induce Rh antibodies.

Number of pregnancies: The first child usually escapes disease because sensitisation occurs only during its delivery. The risk to the infant increases with each successive pregnancy.

Zygosity of the father: An individual may be homozygous or heterozygous with respect to D antigen. When the father is homozygous all his children will be Rh positive. When he is heterozygous, half his children will be Rh positive.

DETECTION OF Rh ANTIBODIES

Most Rh antibodies are of the IgG class, and being 'incomplete antibodies', they do not agglutinate Rh positive cells in saline. A minority are complete (saline agglutinating) antibodies of the IgM class. These are not relevant in the pathogenesis of hemolytic disease as they do not traverse the placenta.

IgG anti-D antibodies may be detected by the following techniques: (1) using a colloid medium such as 20 per cent bovine serum albumin; (2) using red cells treated with enzymes such as trypsin, pepsin, ficin or bromelin; and (3) by the indirect Coombs test. The last is the most sensitive method.

IDENTIFICATION OF Rh INCOMPATIBILITY

Rh typing should form a part of routine antenatal examination. When the woman is Rh negative, and her husband Rh positive, fetal complications should be expected. Women with Rh incompatible pregnancies should be screened for Rh antibodies by the indirect Coombs test at 32–34 weeks of pregnancy and at monthly intervals thereafter. The appearance of Rh antibodies during pregnancy or their increase in titre, if they were present already, would prove that the fetus is Rh positive. If amniocentesis is indicated, demonstration of Rh antigen in the amniotic fluid would also prove that

the fetus is Rh positive. In the case of hemolytic disease of the newborn, the maternal serum will show Rh antibodies in the indirect Coombs test and the infant's red cells will give a positive in the direct Coombs test.

When hemolytic disease is diagnosed antepartum, an intrauterine transfusion with Rh negative blood may be indicated. Red cells introduced into the fetal peritoneal cavity will find their way into the circulation and will survive normally. Premature delivery followed by transfusion may be necessary in some cases. When a baby is born with hemolytic disease, exchange transfusion with Rh negative ABO compatible blood is the treatment of choice.

PREVENTION OF Rh ISOIMMUNISATION

Remarkable success has been achieved in the prevention of Rh isoimmunisation by the administration of anti-Rh IgG antibody at the time when the antigenic stimulation is expected to take place. The passively administered antibody may prevent isoimmunisation by a negative feedback mechanism or by afferent inhibition. The recommended practice is to inject 100–300 μg of Rh immune IgG to an Rh negative woman immediately after delivery. To be effective, this should be employed from the first delivery onwards. The Rh immune globulin for the purpose is prepared from human volunteers.

ABO HEMOLYTIC DISEASE

Maternofetal ABO incompatibility is very common and in a proportion of these, hemolytic disease occurs in the newborn. In persons of blood group A or B, natural antibodies are IgM in nature and so do not cross the placenta to harm the fetus. However, in persons of blood group O, the isoantibodies are predominantly IgG in nature. Hence ABO hemolytic disease is seen largely in O group mothers, bearing A or B group fetus. As ABO hemolytic disease is due to naturally occurring maternal isoantibodies, it may occur even in the firstborn, without prior immunisation. ABO hemolytic disease is much milder than Rh disease, probably because erythrocytes of the newborn have fewer A or B antigenic sites as compared to adult erythrocytes. The direct Coombs test is therefore often negative in this condition, while the indirect Coombs test (neonatal serum with type-specific adult erythrocytes) is more commonly positive. Peripheral blood smear characteristically shows spherocytosis.

BLOOD GROUP AND DISEASES

It has been shown that some diseases may influence blood group antigens. Blood group antigens have been reported to become weak in leukemia. The reason for this is not known. The acquisition of B antigens by Group A persons has been observed following some infections. The antigen is believed to come from the infecting microorganism.

Red cell suspensions contaminated with certain bacteria, such as *Pseudomonas aeruginosa*, become agglutinable by all blood group sera and even by normal human sera. This phenomenon, known as the *Thomsen–Freidenreich phenomenon*, is due to the unmasking of a hidden antigen normally present on all human erythrocytes. This is called the **T antigen**. Anti-T agglutinins are normally present in human sera. Such panagglutinability of red cells has occasionally been observed in persons suffering from systemic bacterial infections.

Several investigators have attempted to correlate blood group and susceptibility to certain diseases. It has been shown that duodenal ulcer is more frequent in persons of blood group O than in others. An association has also been established between group A and cancer of the stomach.

Further Reading

Anderson KC and PM Ness eds. 1994. *Scientific Basis of Transfusion Medicine*. Philadelphia: Saunders.
Schraber GB et al. 1996. The risk of transfusion-transmitted viral infections. *New Engl J Med* 334:1685.

Staphylococcus

Staphylococci are Gram positive cocci that occur in grape-like clusters. They are ubiquitous and form the most common cause of localised suppurative lesions in human beings. Their ability to develop resistance to penicillin and other antibiotics enhances their importance as a human pathogen, especially in the hospital environment.

Staphylococci were first observed in human pyogenic lesions by von Recklinghausen in 1871. Pasteur (1880) obtained liquid cultures of the cocci from pus and produced abscesses by inoculating them into rabbits. It was Sir Alexander Ogston, a Scottish surgeon, who established conclusively the causative role of the coccus in abscesses and other suppurative lesions (1880). He also gave it the name Staphylococcus (Staphyle, in Greek, meaning 'bunch of grapes': kokkos, meaning a berry) due to the typical occurrence of the cocci in grape-like clusters in pus and in cultures. Ogston noticed that nonvirulent staphylococci were also often present on skin surfaces.

Most staphylococcal strains from pyogenic lesions were found to produce golden yellow colonies, and the strains from normal skin, white colonies on solid media. Rosenbach (1884) named them *Staph. aureus* and *Staph. albus* respectively. Passet (1885) described a third variety, *Staph. citreus*, producing lemon yellow colonies. However, the association between virulence and pigment production was not found to be constant.

Many other properties were proposed as indicators of virulence. These included hemolysis, gelatin liquefaction, lipolytic activity, production of urease, phosphatase and others, but none of these was found reliable. The most constant association was between virulence and production of the enzyme coagulase, and to a lesser extent fermentation of mannitol. Staphylococci were therefore classified into two groups: *Staph. aureus* (formerly also called *Staph pyogenes*) containing strains giving a positive coagulase test, fermenting mannitol and usually being pathogenic, and *Staph. epidermidis* (formerly also called *Staph. albus*) containing coagulase negative, mannitol nonfermenting and usually nonpathogenic strains. The *genus Staphylococcus* is now classified into 32 species and 15 subspecies based on the chemical composition of their cell wall components and other properties. Besides *Staph. aureus*, two coagulase negative species – *Staph. epidermidis, Staph. haemolyticus* and *Staph. saprophyticus* – can also cause human disease. Some other coagulase negative species such as *Staph. hominis* and *Staph. capitus* are part of the commensal flora of the human skin. Other species are parasitic on animals.

STAPHYLOCOCCUS AUREUS

Morphology: They are spherical cocci, approximately 1 μm in diameter, arranged characteristically in grape-like clusters (Fig. 22.1). Cluster formation is due to cell division occurring in three planes, with daughter cells tending to remain in close proximity. They may also be found singly, in pairs and in short chains of three or four cells, especially when examined from liquid culture. Long chains never occur. They are nonmotile and nonsporing. A few strains possess microscopically visible capsules, particularly in young cultures. Many apparently noncapsulated strains have small amounts of capsular material on the surface. They stain readily with aniline dyes and are uniformly Gram positive. Under the influence of penicillin and certain chemicals, they may change to L forms.

Cultural characteristics: They grow readily on ordinary media within a temperature range of 10–42 °C, the optimum being 37 °C and pH 7.4–7.6. They are aerobes and facultative anaerobes.

On nutrient agar, after incubation for 24 hours, the colonies are large (2–4 mm diameter), circular, convex, smooth, shiny, opaque and easily emulsifiable. Most strains produce golden yellow pigment, though some may be white, orange or yellow. The pigment does not diffuse into the medium. Pigment production occurs optimally at 22 °C and only in aerobic cultures. Pigment production is enhanced when 1% glycerol monoacetate or milk is incorporated in the medium. The pigment is believed to be a lipoprotein allied to carotene.

On nutrient agar slope, the confluent growth presents a characteristic `oil-paint' appearance. The colonies on blood agar are similar to those on nutrient agar. Most strains are hemolytic, especially when incubated under 20–25% carbon dioxide. Hemolysis is marked on rabbit or sheep blood and weak on horse blood agar.

They grow on MacConkey's medium, producing smaller colonies that are pink due to lactose fermentation.

In liquid media, uniform turbidity is produced. Several selective media have been devised for isolating Staph. aureus from specimens such as feces containing other bacteria. These include media containing 8–10 per cent NaCl (salt-milk agar, salt broth), lithium chloride and tellurite (Ludlam's medium), and polymyxin. For primary isolation, sheep blood agar is recommended. Human blood should not be used as it may contain antibodies or other inhibitors.

Biochemical reactions: They ferment a number of sugars, producing acid but no gas. Sugar fermentation is of no diagnostic value except for mannitol, which is usually fermented by Staph.

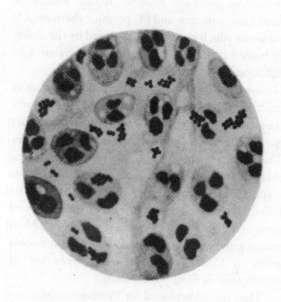

Fig. 22.1 Staphylococcus in a smear of pus

MR - methyl red   VP - voges Proskauer

aureus but not by other species. They are catalase positive (unlike streptococci) and usually hydrolyse urea, reduce nitrates to nitrites, liquefy gelatin and are MR and VP positive but indole negative. Most strains are lipolytic and when grown on media containing egg yolk, produce a dense opacity. Production of phosphatase can be demonstrated by culturing on nutrient agar containing phenolphthalein diphosphate. When such a culture is exposed to ammonia vapour, colonies assume a bright pink colour due to the presence of free phenolphthalein. This is a useful screening procedure for differentiating Staph. aureus from Staph. epidermidis in mixed cultures, as the former gives prompt phosphatase reaction, while the latter is usually negative or only weakly positive.

Staph. aureus strains usually exhibit the following characteristics: (1) coagulase positive; (2) greater biochemical activity, ferment mannite; (3) produce clear hemolysis on blood agar; (4) produce a golden yellow pigment; (5) liquefy gelatin;

(6) produce phosphatase; (7) in a medium containing potassium tellurite, reduce tellurite to form black colonies; and (8) produce thermostable nucleases which can be demonstrated by the ability of boiled cultures to degrade DNA in an agar diffusion test.

Resistance: Staphylococci are among the more resistant of nonsporing bacteria. Dried on threads, they retain their viability for 3–6 months. They have been isolated from dried pus after 2–3 months. They may withstand 60 °C for 30 minutes. Their thermal death point is 62 °C for 30 minutes. Some staphylococci require 80 °C for one hour to be killed. Heat resistant strains have the ability to grow at a higher temperature, even at 45 °C. Most strains grow in the presence of 10% NaCl and some even in 15% NaCl. These features are of significance in food preservation.

They resist 1% phenol for 15 minutes. Mercury perchloride 1% solution kills them in 10 minutes. Many aniline dyes are strongly bactericidal, crystal violet being lethal at a concentration of one in five hundred thousand and brilliant green, one in ten million.

Fatty acids inhibit the growth of staphylococci, the highly unsaturated acids having a more powerful action on coagulase positive than on coagulase negative strains. Staphylococci are uniformly resistant to lysozyme but some micrococci are sensitive to it. Staphylococci are generally sensitive to lysostaphin—a mixture of enzymes produced by a particular strain of *Staph. epidermidis.*

Staphylococci were uniformly sensitive to penicillin originally, though occasional strains from the preantibiotic era have been found retrospectively to be capable of producing penicillinase. Soon after penicillin came to be used clinically, resistant strains began to emerge, first in hospitals and then in the community at large.

Penicillin resistance is of three types

1. production of beta lactamase (penicillinase) which inactivates penicillin by splitting the beta lactam ring. Staphylococci produce four types of penicillinases, A to D. Hospital strains usually form type A penicillinase. Penicillinase is an inducible enzyme and its production is usually controlled by plasmids which are transmitted by transduction or conjugation. The same plasmid may carry genes for resistance to a range of other antibiotics and heavy metals.

2. Changes in bacterial surface receptors, reducing binding of beta-lactam antibiotics to cells. This change is normally chromosomal in nature and is expressed more at 30 °C than at 37 °C. This resistance also extends to cover beta lactamase resistant penicillins such as methicillin and cloxacillins. Some of these strains may show resistance to other antibiotics and heavy metals also and cause outbreaks of hospital infection. These strains have been called 'epidemic methicillin resistant *Staphylococcus aureus*' or EMRSA (as methicillin is an unstable drug, cloxacillin is used for sensitivity testing instead).

3. Development of tolerance to penicillin, by which the bacterium is only inhibited but not killed.

Staphylococci also exhibit plasmid-borne resistance to erythromycins, tetracyclines, aminoglycosides and almost all clinically useful antibiotics except vancomycin.

Pathogenicity and virulence: Staphylococci produce two types of diseases—infections and intoxications. In the former the cocci gain access to damaged skin, mucosal or tissue sites, colonise by adhering to cells or extracellular matrix, evade host defence mechanisms, multiply and cause tissue damage. In intoxications, the disease is caused by the bacterial toxins produced either in the infected host or preformed in vitro. A number of staphylococcal factors, both cell associated and extracellular, have been identified, which may influence virulence. However, apart from the exotoxins which cause specific clinical syndromes, no other factor has a decisive role in pathogenesis.

The virulence factors described include the following:

CELL ASSOCIATED POLYMERS

1. The cell wall polysaccharide peptidoglycan confers rigidity and structural integrity to the bacterial cell. It activates complement and induces release of inflammatory cytokines.
2. Teichoic acid, an antigenic component of the cell wall facilitates adhesion of the cocci to the host cell surface and protects them from complement-mediated opsonisation.
3. Capsular polysaccharide surrounding the cell wall inhibits opsonisation.

CELL SURFACE PROTEINS

1. Protein A present on most *Staph. aureus* strains has many biological properties, including chemotactic, antiphagocytic and anti-complementary effects. It also induces platelet damage and hypersensitivity. Protein A binds to the Fc terminal of IgG molecules (except IgG3), leaving the Fab region free to combine with its specific antigen. Protein A-bearing staphylococci coated with any IgG antiserum will be agglutinated if mixed with its corresponding antigen. This procedure known as coagglutination has many aplications, as for streptococcal grouping and gonococcal typing. Protein A is a B cell mitogen. It has also been used as a ligand for isolation of IgG.
2. Clumping factor, another surface protein is the 'bound coagulase' which is responsible for the 'slide coagulase' test. When a saline suspension of *Staph. aureus* is mixed on a slide with a drop of human plasma the cocci are clumped. The slide coagulase test is routinely used for the identification of *Staph. aureus* isolates. Capsulated strains may sometimes show a negative test because the clumping factor may be enveloped by the capsular polysaccharide.

EXTRACELLULAR ENZYMES

1. Coagulase is an enzyme which brings about clotting of human or rabbit plasma. It acts along with a 'coagulase reacting factor' (CRF) present in plasma, binding to prothrombin and converting fibrinogen to fibrin. Coagulase does not clot plasma of guinea pigs and some other species because they lack CRF. Calcium or other clotting factors are not required for coagulase action. Eight types of coagulase have been identified. Most human strains form coagulase type A. Coagulase and clumping factor (the so called 'bound coagulase') differ in many respects. Coagulase is an enzyme secreted into the medium. It requires the cooperation of CRF for its action. Bound coagulase is a heat stable constituent of the cell surface and its action is independent of CRF. Only one type of clumping factor has been identified. *Staph. aureus* strains usually form both coagulase and clumping factor. Coagulase test is the standard criterion for the identification of *Staph. aureus* isolates.
2. Lipases. Staphylococci produce a number of lipid hydrolases which help them in infecting the skin and subcutaneous tissues.
3. Hyaluronidase breaks down the connective tissue. Staphylokinase (fibrinolysin), fatty acid modifying enzymes and proteases help in initiation and spread of infection.
4. Nuclease. A heat stable nuclease is a characteristic feature of *Staph. aureus*.
5. Protein receptors. Staphylococci possess receptors for many mammalian proteins such as fibronectin, fibrinogen, IgG and C1q. These facilitate staphylococcal adhesion to host cell and tissues.

TOXINS

Cytolytic toxins: Cytolytic toxins are membrane-active substances, consisting of four hemolysins and a leucocidin.

Alpha hemolysin (Alpha toxin, lysin) is the most important among them. It is a protein inactivated at 70 °C, but reactivated paradoxically at 100 °C. This is because at 60–70 °C, the toxin combines with a heat labile inhibitor which is denatured at 100 °C, leaving the toxin free.

Alpha toxin lyses rabbit erythrocytes, but is less active against sheep and human red cells. It is also leucocidal, cytotoxic, dermonecrotic (on intradermal inoculation in rabbits), neurotoxic and lethal (on intravenous inoculation in rabbits). It is toxic to macrophages, lysosomes, muscle tissues, renal cortex and the circulatory system.

Beta hemolysin is a sphingomyelinase, hemolytic for sheep cells, but not for human or rabbit cells. It exhibits a 'hot–cold phenomenon', the hemolysis being initiated at 37 °C, but becoming evident only after chilling.

Gamma hemolysin is composed of two separate proteins, both of which are necessary for hemolytic activity.

Delta hemolysin has a detergent-like effect on cell membranes of erythrocytes, leucocytes, macrophages and platelets.

Leucocidin (called the Panton–Valentine toxin after its discoverers) is also a two component toxin, like the gamma lysin, being composed of two components (S and F). Such bicomponent membrane-active toxins as the staphylococcal leucocidin and gamma lysin have been grouped as *synergohymenotropic toxins.*

Enterotoxin: This toxin is responsible for the manifestations of staphylococcal food poisoning – nausea, vomiting and diarrhea 2–6 hours after consuming contaminated food containing preformed toxin. The toxin is relatively heat stable, resisting 100 °C for 10 to 40 minutes depending on the concentration of the toxin and nature of the medium. About two-thirds of *Staph. aureus* strains, growing in carbohydrate and protein foods secrete the toxin. Meat and fish or milk and milk products cooked and left at room temperature after contamination with staphylococci, for enough time for the toxin to accumulate, are the common items responsible. The source of infection is usually a food handler who is a carrier. The illness is usually self limited, with recovery in a day or so.

Eight antigenic types of enterotoxin are currently known, named A, B, C$_{1-3}$, D, E and H. They are formed by toxigenic strains, singly or in combination. The toxin is believed to act directly on the autonomic nervous system to cause the illness, rather than on the gastrointestinal mucosa. The toxin is antigenic and neutralised by the specific antitoxin. Type A toxin is responsible for most cases. Sensitive serological tests such as latex agglutination and ELISA are available for detection of the toxin.

The toxin is potent, microgram amounts being capable of causing the illness. Some cases of post antibiotic diarrhea are caused by enterotoxin-forming staphylococci. The toxin also exhibits pyrogenic, mitogenic, hypotensive, thrombo-cytopenic and cytotoxic effects.

Toxic shock syndrome toxin (TSST): Toxic shock syndrome (TSS) is a potentially fatal multisystem disease presenting with fever, hypotension, myalgia, vomiting, diarrhea, mucosal hyperemia and an erythematous rash which desquamates subsequently. This is associated with infection of mucosal or sequestered sites by TSST-producing *Staph. aureus* strains usually belonging to bacteriophage group I. TSST type-1 (formerly also known as enterotoxin type F or pyrogenic exotoxin C) is most often responsible, though enterotoxins B or C may also cause the syndrome.

TSS was first identified in 1978 in children and adolescents, but became widely known only in 1980 following outbreaks in the USA in menstruating women using highly absorbent vaginal tampons. Their vaginal swabs showed heavy growth of *Staph. aureus*, though blood cultures were invariably negative. TSST-1 antibody is seen in convalescents. This is protective and absence of TSST-1 antibody is a factor in the pathogenesis of the condition.

Though tampon-related TSS is now rare, the syndrome occurs in other infections of the skin, mucosa and other sites and also in some surgical wounds.

Staphylococcal enterotoxins and TSST-1 are

superantigens which are potent activators of T lymphocytes. Being Vβ restricted T cell mitogens, such superantigens stimulate very large numbers of T cells, without relation to their epitope specificity. This leads to an excessive and dysregulated immune response with release of cytokines interleukins 1, 2, tumour necrosis factor and interferon gamma. This explains the multisystem involvement and florid manifestations in staphylococcal food poisoning and TSS.

Exfoliative (epidermolytic) toxin: This toxin, also known as ET or 'exfoliatin' is responsible for the 'staphylococcal scalded skin syndrome' (SSSS), exfoliative skin diseases in which the outer layer of epidermis gets separated from the underlying tissues. The severe form of SSSS is known as Ritter's disease in the newborn and toxic epidermal necrolysis in older patients. Milder forms are pemphigus neonatorum and bullous impetigo.

STAPHYLOCOCCAL DISEASES

Staphylococcal infections are among the most common of bacterial infections and range from the trivial to the fatal. Staphylococcal infections are characteristically localised pyogenic lesions, in contrast to the spreading nature of streptococcal infections. Common staphylococcal infections are the following:

Skin and soft tissue: Folliculitis, furuncle (boil), abscess (particularly breast abscess), wound infection, carbuncle, impetigo, paronychia, less often cellulitis.

Musculoskeletal: Osteomyelitis, arthritis, bursitis, pyomyositis.

Respiratory: Tonsillitis, pharyngitis, sinusitis, otitis, bronchopneumonia, lung abscess, empyema, rarely pneumonia.

Central nervous system: Abscess, meningitis, intracranial thrombophlebitis.

Endovascular: Bacteremia, septicemia, pyemia, endocarditis

Urinary: Staphylococci are uncommon in routine urinary tract infections, though they do cause

infection in association with local instrumentation, implants or diabetes. Urinary isolates of staphylococci are to be considered significant even with low colony counts, as they may be related to bacteremia.

BACTERIOPHAGE TYPING

Staphylococci may be typed, based on their susceptibility to bacteriophages. An internationally accepted set of phages is used for typing. Staphylococcal phage typing is done by a pattern method. The strain to be typed is inoculated on a plate of nutrient agar to form a lawn culture. After drying, the phages are applied over marked squares in a fixed dose (routine test dose). After overnight incubation, the culture will be observed to be lysed by some phages but not by others. The phage type of the strain is expressed by the designations of all the phages that lyse it. Thus, if a strain is lysed only by phages 52, 79 and 80, it is called phage type 52/79/80. Phage typing is of great importance in epidemiological studies of staphylococcal infections.

International basic set of phages for typing
Staph. aureus *of human origin*

Group I	29, 52, 52A, 79, 80
Group II	3A, 3C, 55, 71
Group III	6, 42E, 47, 53, 54, 75, 77, 83A, 84, 85
Group IV	–
Group V	94, 96
Not allocated	81, 95

Not all cultures are typable by this procedure, and the susceptibility patterns of circulating strains vary in time and locality. Hence phages in the reference set require periodic revision.

Epidemiology: Staphylococci are primary parasites of human beings and animals, colonising the skin, skin glands and mucous membranes. The most common sources of infection are human patients and carriers; animals and inanimate objects being less important. Patients with superficial infections and respiratory infections disseminate large numbers of staphylococci into the environment. About 10–30 per cent of healthy persons carry staphylococci in the nose and about 10 per cent in the perineum and also on the hair. Vaginal carriage is about 5–10 per cent, which rises greatly during menses, a factor relevant in the pathogenesis of TSS related to menstruation.

Staphylococcal carriage starts early in life, colonisation of the umbilical stump being very common in babies born in hospitals. Some carriers, called 'shedders', disseminate very large numbers of cocci for prolonged periods. The cocci shed by patients and carriers contaminate fomites such as handkerchiefs, bed linen and blankets and may persist on them for days or weeks. Staphylococci may also come from infected domestic animals such as cows.

Staphylococcal disease may follow endogenous or exogenous infection. The modes of transmission may be by contact, direct or through fomites, by dust or by airborne droplets.

Hospital infections by staphylococci deserve special attention because of their frequency and because they are caused by strains resistant to various antibiotics. Staphylococci are a common cause of postoperative wound infection and other hospital cross infections. Most of these are due to certain strains of staphylococci that are present in the hospital environment, the so-called 'hospital strains'. They belong to a limited number of phage types and are commonly resistant to penicillin and other antibiotics routinely used in hospitals. Some of them, the 'epidemic strains', cause epidemics of hospital cross infections. The first of these to be recognised was phage type 80/81, which accounted for most of staphylococcal infections in hospitals throughout the world. They have since been replaced by other strains of staphylococci and by Gram negative bacilli.

Measures for the control of staphylococcal infection in hospitals include:

1. isolation of patients with open staphylococcal lesions;

2. detection of staphylococcal lesions among surgeons, nurses and other hospital staff and keeping them away from work till the lesions are healed;

3. strict aseptic techniques in theatres;

4. the oldest, simplest and the most effective method of checking hospital cross infection is hand washing, which unfortunately is often neglected.

If an outbreak of staphylococcal sepsis occurs, a search may be made for carriers among the hospital staff. Those detected should be treated with local applications of neomycin and chlorhexidine. In some institutions in America, eradication of the virulent resident strain has been attempted by the deliberate dissemination of a strain of low virulence. The latter may oust the former by interference. Antimicrobial prophylaxis by topical applications of antiseptics such as hexachlorophene has also been found useful.

Laboratory diagnosis: The specimens to be collected depend on the type of lesion (for example, pus from suppurative lesions, sputum from respiratory infections). In cases of food poisoning, feces and the remains of suspected food should be collected. For the detection of carriers, the usual specimen is the nasal swab. Swabs from the perineum, pieces of hair and umbilical stump may be necessary in special situations.

Direct microscopy with Gram stained smears is useful in the case of pus, where cocci in clusters may be seen. This is of no value for specimens like sputum where mixed bacterial flora are normally present.

Diagnosis may readily be made by culture. The specimens are plated on blood agar. Staphylococcal colonies appear after overnight incubation. Specimens where staphylococci are expected to be scanty and outnumbered by other bacteria (for example, swabs from carriers, feces in food poisoning cases) are inoculated on selective media like Ludlam's or salt-milk agar or Robertson's cooked meat medium containing 10 per cent sodium chloride. Smears are examined from the cultures and the coagulase test done when staphylococci are isolated.

Coagulase test is done by two methods – tube and slide coagulase tests. The tube coagulase test detects free coagulase. About 0.1 ml of a young broth culture or agar culture suspension of the isolate is added to about 0.5 ml of human or rabbit plasma in a narrow test tube. EDTA, oxalate or heparin may be used as the anticoagulant for preparing the plasma. Citrate is not recommended because it may be utilised by some contaminant bacteria, causing false positive results. Positive and negative controls are also set up. The tubes are incubated in a water bath at 37 °C for 3–6 hours. If positive, the plasma clots and does not flow when the tube is tilted. Continued incubation is not recommended as the clot may get lysed by the fibrinogen formed by some strains.

The slide test detecting bound coagulase is much simpler and usually gives results parallel with the tube test. When there is divergence, the tube test will be the deciding factor. For the slide test, the isolate is emulsified in a drop of saline on a slide. After checking for absence of autoagglutination, a drop of human or rabbit plama is added to the emulsion and mixed. Prompt clumping of the cocci indicates a positive test. Positive and negative controls also are set up.

Antibiotic sensitivity tests should be performed as a guide to treatment. This is important as staphylococci readily develop resistance to drugs.

Bacteriophage typing may be done if the information is desired for epidemiological purposes. Other typing methods include antibiogram pattern, plasmid profile, DNA fingerprinting, ribotyping and PCR-based analysis for genetic pleomorphism.

Serological tests may sometimes be of help in the diagnosis of hidden deep infections. Antistaphylolysin (antialphalysin) titres of more than two units per ml, especially when the titre is rising, may be of value in the diagnosis of deep seated infections such as bone abscesses.

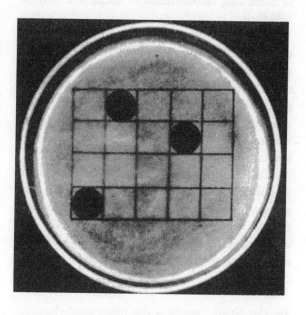

Fig. 22.2 Bacteriophage typing of staphylococci

Treatment

As drug resistance is so common among staphylococci, the appropriate antibiotic should be chosen based on antibiotic sensitivity tests. Benzyl penicillin is the most effective antibiotic, if the strain is sensitive. Methicillin was the first compound developed to combat resistance due to penicillinase (beta lactamase) production by staphylococci. Due to the limitations in clinical use of methicillin, cloxacillins are used instead against penicillinase-producing strains. But methicillin resistant strains of Staph. aureus (MRSA) became common, which were resistant not merely to penicillin, but also to all other beta lactam antibiotics and many others besides. For life threatening staphylococcal infections, vancomycin is the drug of choice. Strains resistant to vancomycin and teicoplanin have appeared in hospitals where antibiotic use is indiscriminate. For mild superficial lesions, systemic antibiotics may not be necessary. Topical applications of drugs not used systemically, as bacitracin, chlorhexidine or mupirocin may be sufficient.

Some strains show the phenomenon of drug tolerance. These strains will be found to be susceptible in the disc sensitivity test but their minimum bactericidal concentration will be very much higher than their minimum inhibitory concentration. They are not killed by antibiotics in the usual doses and persist, leading to failure in eradicating the infection.

The treatment of carriers is by local application of suitable antibiotics such as bacitracin and antiseptics such as chlorhexidine. In resistant cases posing major problems, rifampicin along with another oral antibiotic may be effective in long term suppression or elimination of the carrier state.

OTHER COAGULASE POSITIVE STAPHYLOCOCCI

Besides *Staph. aureus*, a few other staphylococcal species are coagulase positive, e.g. *Staph. intermedius* and *Staph. hyicus*. These are animal parasites and do not infect humans.

COAGULASE NEGATIVE STAPHYLOCOCCI

Coagulase negative staphylococci constitute a major component of the normal flora of the human body. Some species of coagulase negative staphylococci can produce human infections – *Staph. epidermidis*, *Staph. haemolyticus* and *Staph. saprophyticus*.

Staph. epidermidis is invariably present on normal human skin. It is nonpathogenic ordinarily but can cause disease when the host defences are breached. It is a common cause of stitch abscesses. It has a predilection for growth on implanted foreign bodies such as artificial heart valves, shunts, intravascular catheters and prosthetic appliances, leading to bacteremia. Hospital strains of *Staph. epidermidis* are usually multiple drug resistant. It can cause cystitis. Endocarditis may be caused, particularly in drug addicts.

Staph. saprophyticus may be present on normal human skin and the periurethral area and can cause urinary tract infection, particularly in sexually active young women. The infection is symptomatic and may involve the upper urinary tract also. Men are infected much less often, though it is sometimes seen in older persons. The infecting strains are usually sensitive to most common antibiotics, except nalidixic acid. *Staph. saprophyticus* is novobiocin resistant.

Table 22.1 lists the features useful for distinguishing the major species of staphylococci.

MICROCOCCI

These are Gram positive cocci which occur mostly in pairs, tetrads or irregular clusters. They are catalase and oxidase positive. They are aerobic with a strictly respiratory metabolism. They are parasitic on mammalian skin and are ordinarily nonpathogenic. They resemble staphylococci but in stained smears the cells are generally larger and more Gram variable than staphylococci. In cultures they form smaller colonies. The common laboratory test used to differentiate between micrococci and

Table 22.1 Features for distinguishing the major species of staphylococci

Characteristic	Staph. aureus	Staph. epidermidis	Staph. saprophyticus
Coagulase	+	-	-
Novobiocin sensitivity	S	S	R
Acid from mannitol anaerobically	+	-	-
Phosphatase	+	+	-

staphylococci is the Hugh and Leifson's oxidation–fermentation test in which micrococci show oxidative and staphylococci show fermentative patterns.

Further Reading

Cronley KB and GC Archer. 1997. *Staphylococcal human disease.* New York. Churchill-Livingstone.

Easmon, CSF and C Adlam 1983. *Staphylococci and Staphylococcal Infections* : London: Academic Press.

Kloos WE and TL Bannerman 1994. Clinical significance of coagulase negative staphylococci. *Clin. Microbiol Rev 7* : 117.

Marrack P and J Kapple 1990. Staphylococcal enterotoxins and their relatives. *Science* 248 : 705.

Rupp ME and GL Archer 1994. Coagulase negative staphylococci, *Am J Med* 94 : 313.

Sheagren JN. 1984. Staphylococcus aureus – the persistent pathogen, *New Engl J Med*, 310, 1368, 1437.

23

Streptococcus

Streptococci are Gram positive cocci arranged in chains or pairs (Fig. 23.1). They are part of the normal flora of humans and animals. Some of them are human pathogens. The most important of them is *Streptococcus pyogenes* causing pyogenic infections, with a characteristic tendency to spread, as opposed to staphylococcal lesions which are typically localised. It is also responsible for the nonsuppurative lesions, acute rheumatic fever and glomerulonephritis which occur as sequelae to infection.

Cocci in chains were first seen in erysipelas and wound infections by Billroth (1874), who called them streptococci (*streptos*, meaning twisted or coiled). Ogston (1881) isolated them from acute abscesses, distinguished them from staphylococci and established their pathogenicity by animal inoculation. Rosenbach (1884) isolated the cocci from human suppurative lesions and gave them the name *Streptococcus pyogenes*.

CLASSIFICATION

Several systems of classification have been employed but in medical bacteriology the following method is useful (Fig. 23.2).

Streptococci are first divided into obligate anaerobes and facultative anaerobes. The former are designated peptostreptococci and are considered in a later chapter. The aerobic and facultative anaerobic streptococci are classified on the basis of their hemolytic properties. Brown (1919) categorised them into three varieties based on their growth in 5% horse blood agar pour plate cultures.

Alpha (α) hemolytic streptococci produce a greenish discolouration with partial hemolysis around the colonies. The zone of lysis is small (1 or 2 mm wide) with indefinite margins, and unlysed erythrocytes can be made out microscopically within this zone. These are known as 'viridans streptococci' or *Streptococcus viridans* (from 'viridis' meaning green). The alpha streptococci are normal commensals in the throat, but may cause opportunist infections rarely. Pnemococcus *(Str. pneumoniae)* is also an alpha hemolytic streptococcus.

Beta (β) hemolytic streptococci produce a sharply defined, clear, colourless zone of hemolysis, 2–4 mm wide, within which red cells are

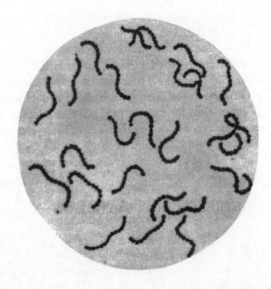

Fig. 23.1 Streptococci

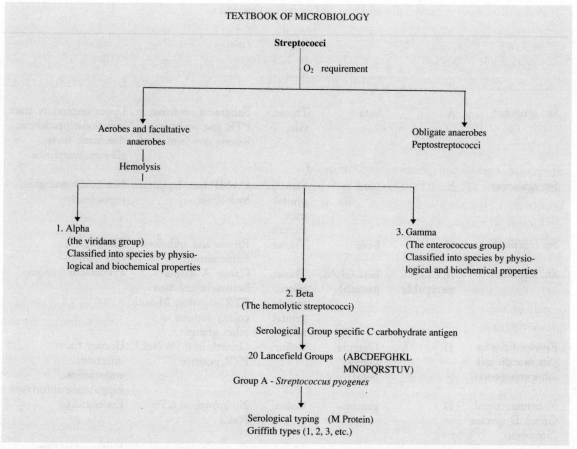

TEXTBOOK OF MICROBIOLOGY

Streptococci

O₂ requirement

Aerobes and facultative anaerobes

Hemolysis

Obligate anaerobes
Peptostreptococci

1. Alpha
(the viridans group)
Classified into species by physiological and biochemical properties

3. Gamma
(The enterococcus group)
Classified into species by physio-
logical and biochemical properties

2. Beta
(The hemolytic streptococci)

Serological | Group specific C carbohydrate antigen

20 Lancefield Groups   (ABCDEFGHKL
                         MNOPQRSTUV)

Group A - *Streptococcus pyogenes*

Serological typing   (M Protein)
Griffith types (1, 2, 3, etc.)

Fig. 23.2 Classification of streptococci

completely lysed. The term 'hemolytic streptococci' strictly applies only to beta lytic strains. Most pathogenic streptococci belong to this group.

Gamma (γ) or nonhemolytic streptococci produce no change in the medium and so are sometimes referred to as *'indifferent streptococci'*. They include the fecal streptococci (*enterococci*, *Str. faecalis*) and related species. They are called the 'enterococcus group'.

Hemolytic streptococci were classified by Lancefield (1933) serologically into groups based on the nature of a carbohydrate (C) antigen on the cell wall. These are known as *Lancefield groups*, twenty of which have been identified so far and named A–V (without I and J). The great majority of hemolytic streptococci that produce human

infections belong to group A. Hemolytic streptococci of group A are known as *Str. pyogenes*. These may be further subdivided into types based on the protein (M, T and R) antigens present on the cell surface (Griffith typing). About eighty types of *Str. pyogenes* have been recognised so far (types 1, 2, 3 and so on).

Table 23.1 shows the medically important streptococci and their characteristics.

STREPTOCOCCUS PYOGENES

Morphology: The individual cocci are spherical or oval 0.5–1.0 μm in diameter. Size variations result from cultural conditions, for example, when grown anaerobically, they are somewhat smaller. They are arranged in chains, the length of which

Table 23.1 Medically important streptococci and their characteristics

Species or common name	Lancefield group	Hemolysis	Habitat in human hosts	Laboratory tests	Common diseases caused
Str. pyogenes	A	beta	Throat, skin	Bacitracin sensitive; PYR test positive; Ribose not fermented	Upper respiratory tract infections; pyoderma; rheumatic fever; glomerulonephritis
Str. agalactiae	B	beta	Female genital tract, rectum	CAMP test, hippurate hydrolysis	Neonatal meningitis, septicemia
Str. equisimilis	C	beta	Throat	Ribose and trehalose fermentation	Pharyngitis, endocarditis
Str. anginosus	A, C, F, G, untypable	beta (alpha, gamma)	Throat, colon, female genital tract	Group A strains bacitracin resistant PYR negative; Minute colony variants of other groups	Pyogenic infections
Enterococcus sp. (Str. faecalis and other enterococci)	D	Gamma (alpha, beta)	Colon	Growth in 6.5% NaCl; PYR positive	Urinary tract infections, endocarditis, suppurative infections
Nonenterococcal Group D species (Str. bovis)	D	gamma	Colon	No growth in 6.5% NaCl	Endocarditis
Viridans streptococci (many species)	Not typed	alpha (gamma)	Mouth, colon, female genital tract	Optochin resistant, species classification on biochemical properties	Endocarditis (Str. sanguis); dental caries (Str. mutans)

varies within wide limits and is influenced by the nature of the culture medium, chains being longer in liquid than in solid media. Chain formation is due to the cocci dividing in one plane only and the daughter cells failing to separate completely. There is often an appearance of pairing within the chains. Significance was once attached to the length of the chains, and streptococci had been classified accordingly (*Str. longus* and *brevis*) but this has no relevance to virulence or other properties. In fact, some nonpathogenic streptococci form the longest chains, for example, *Str. salivarius*. (Fig. 23.1).

Streptococci are nonmotile and nonsporing. Some strains of *Str. pyogenes* and some group C strains have capsules composed of hyaluronic acid, while polysaccharide capsules are encountered in members of group B and D. These capsules are best seen in very young cultures.

Cultural characteristics: It is an aerobe and a facultative anaerobe, growing best at a temperature of 37 °C (range 22–42 °C). It is exacting in nutritive requirements, growth occurring only in media containing fermentable carbohydrates or enriched with blood or serum. On blood agar, after incubation for 24 hours, the colonies are small (0.5–1.0 mm) circular, semitransparent, low convex discs with an area of clear hemolysis around them. Growth and hemolysis are promoted by 10 per cent CO_2. Virulent strains, on fresh isolation from lesions, produce a 'matt' (finely granular) colony, while avirulent strains form 'glossy' colonies. Strains with well marked capsules produce 'mucoid' colonies, corresponding in virulence to the matt type. Very rarely, nonhemolytic group A streptococci are encountered, which are typical of *Str. pyogenes* in other respects.

In liquid media, such as glucose or serum broth, growth occurs as a granular turbidity with a powdery deposit. No pellicle is formed.

Biochemical reactions: Streptococci ferment several sugars producing acid but no gas.

Streptococci are catalase negative. They are not soluble in 10 per cent bile, unlike pneumococci. Hydrolysis of pyrrolidonyl naphthylamide (PYR test) and failure to ferment ribose are useful in differentiating *Str. pyogenes* from other streptococci.

Resistance: *Str. pyogenes is* a delicate organism, easily destroyed by heat (54 °C for 30 minutes). It dies in a few days in cultures, unless stored at a low temperature (4 °C), preferably in Robertson's cooked meat medium. It can, however, survive in dust for several weeks, if protected from sunlight. It is rapidly inactivated by antiseptics. It is more resistant to crystal violet than many bacteria, including *Staph. aureus.* Crystal violet (1 mg/L), nalidixic acid (15 mg/L) and colistin sulphate (10 mg/L) added to blood agar provide a good selective medium for the isolation of streptococci, including pneumococci. It is susceptible to sulphonamides and many antibiotics but unlike *Staph. aureus* does not develop resistance to drugs. Sensitivity to bacitracin is employed as a convenient method for differentiating *Str. pyogenes* from other hemolytic streptococci.

Antigenic structure: Fig. 23.3 illustrates the disposition of the various antigens in *Str. pyogenes.* The capsule when present inhibits phagocytosis. It is not antigenic in human beings.

The cell wall is composed of an outer layer of protein and lipoteichoic acid, a middle layer of group specific carbohydrate and an inner layer of peptidoglycan.

The peptidoglycan (mucoprotein) is responsible for cell wall rigidity. It has also some biological properties such as pyrogenic and thrombolytic activity.

Serological grouping of streptococci depends on the C carbohydrate. *Str. pyogenes* belongs to group A. As this antigen is an integral part of the cell wall, it has to be extracted for grouping by a precipitation test with group antisera. For the test, streptococci are grown in Todd–Hewitt broth and extracted with hydrochloric acid (Lancefield's acid extraction method), or formamide (Fuller's method) or by an enzyme produced by *Streptomyces albus* (Maxted's method) or by autoclaving (Rantz and Randall's method). The extract and the specific antisera are allowed to react in capillary tubes. Precipitation occurs within five minutes at the interface between the extract and the homologous antiserum. Grouping may also be done by agar gel precipitation.

Several protein antigens have been identified in the outer part of the cell wall. *Str. pyogenes* can be typed, based on the surface proteins M, T and R. The M protein is the most important of these. It acts as a virulence factor by inhibiting phagocytosis. It is antigenic. The antibody to M protein promotes phagocytosis of the coccus and is therefore protective. The M protein is heat and acid stable but susceptible to tryptic digestion. It can be extracted by the Lancefield acid extraction method and typing is done with type specific sera. About 80 M protein types have been recognised.

The T protein is an acid labile, trypsin resistant antigen present in many serotypes of *Str. pyogenes.* It may be specific but many different M types possess the same T antigen. It is usually demonstrated by the slide agglutination test using trypsin-treated whole streptococci. Some types of *Str. pyogenes* (types 2, 3, 28 and 48) and some strains of groups B, C and G contain a third antigen, the R protein. The T and R proteins have no relation to virulence. A nontype-specific protein, associated with the M protein, has been identified. This is known as M associated protein (MAP).

Hair-like pili (fimbria) project through the capsule of group A streptococci. The pili consist partly of M protein and are covered with lipoteichoic acid which is important in the attachment of streptococci to epithelial cells.

Various structural components of *Str. pyogenes* exhibit antigenic cross reaction with different tissues of the human body. Antigenic relationships have been demonstrated between capsular hyaluronic acid and human synovial fluid, cell wall protein and myocardium, group A carbohydrate and cardiac valves, cytoplasmic membrane antigens and vascular intima, and peptidoglycans and skin antigens. It has been postulated that these antigenic cross reactions may account for some of the manifestations of rheumatic fever and other streptococcal diseases, the tissue damage being of an immunological nature.

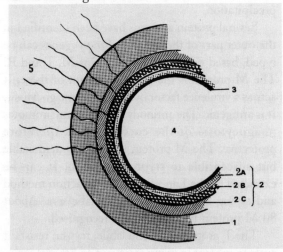

Fig. 23.3 Antigenic structure of *Str. pyogenes*.
1. Hyaluronic acid capsule. 2. Cell wall comprising 2A. peptidoglycan, 2B. group specific carbohydrate and 2C. protein lipoteichoic acid fimbria 3. Cytoplasmic membrane 4. Cytoplasm. 5. Pili covered with lipoteichoic acid.

Toxins and other virulence factors: *Str. pyogenes* forms several exotoxins and enzymes which contribute to its virulence. Besides these, the M protein also acts as a virulence factor by inhibiting phagocytosis. The C polysaccharide has been shown to have a toxic effect on connective tissue in experimental animals.

Hemolysins: Streptococci produce two hemolysins, streptolysin 'O' and 'S'. Streptolysin O is so called because it is oxygen labile. It is inactive in the oxidised form but may be reactivated by treatment with mild reducing agents. On blood agar, streptolysin O activity is seen only in pour plates and not in surface cultures. It may be obtained in the active state by growing streptococci in broth containing reducing agents such as sodium hydrosulphite. It is also heat labile. It appears to be important in contributing to virulence. It is lethal on intravenous injection into animals and has a specific cardiotoxic activity. It has leucotoxic activity also. In its biological action, streptolysin O resembles the oxygen labile hemolysins of *Cl. perfringens, Cl. tetani* and the pneumococcus.

Streptolysin O is antigenic and antistreptolysin O appears in sera following streptococcal infection. Estimation of this antibody (ASO titre) is a standard serological procedure for the retrospective diagnosis of infection with *Str. pyogenes*. The lysin is inhibited by cholesterol but not by normal sera. Following certain chemical treatments or bacterial contamination, sera may develop inhibitory activity due to some changes in the lipoproteins. Such sera are unfit for the ASO test. Because of the complexity of the hemolysis inhibition test, ASO test is now done by the serological method of latex agglutination. An ASO titre in excess of 200 units is considered significant and suggests either recent or recurrent infection with streptococci. Streptolysin S and O are produced by groups A, C and G also.

Streptolysin S is an oxygen stable hemolysin and so is responsible for the hemolysis seen around streptococcal colonies on the surface of blood agar plates. It is called streptolysin S since it is soluble in serum. It is a protein but is not antigenic. Convalescent sera do not neutralise streptolysin S activity. It is inhibited nonspecifically by serum lipoproteins.

Pyrogenic exotoxin (Erythrogenic, Dick, scarlatinal toxin): This toxin was named 'erythrogenic' because its intradermal injection into susceptible individuals produced an erythematous reaction (Dick test, 1924). This test was used to identify children susceptible to scarlet fever, a type of acute pharyngitis with extensive erythematous rash, caused by the *Str. pyogenes* strains producing this toxin. Blanching of the rash on local injection of convalescent serum was used as a diagnostic test for scarlet fever (Schultz Charlton reaction, 1918). The Dick test and Schultz Charlton reaction are now only of historical value as scarlet fever is no longer a common or serious disease.

The primary effect of the toxin is induction of fever and so it was renamed Streptococcal pyrogenic exotoxin (SPE). Three types of SPE have been identified—SPE A,B and C. Types A and C are coded for by bacteriophage genes, while type B gene is chromosomal. SPEs are 'superantigens' (like staphylococcal enterotoxins and TSS toxin), T cell mitogens which induce massive release of inflammatory cytokines causing fever, shock and tissue damage.

Streptokinase (fibrinolysin): This toxin promotes the lysis of human fibrin clots by activating a plasma procursor (plasminogen). It is an antigenic protein and neutralising antibodies appear in convalescent sera. Anti-streptokinase antibody provides retrospective evidence of streptococcal infection. Fibrinolysin appears to play a biological role in streptococcal infections by breaking down the fibrin barrier around the lesions and facilitating the spread of infection. Streptokinase is given intravenously for the treatment of early myocardial infarction and other thromboemboloic disorders.

Deoxyribonucleases (Streptodornase, DNAase): These cause depolymerisation of DNA. Pyogenic exudates contain large amounts of DNA, derived from the nuclei of necrotic cells. Streptodornase helps to liquefy the thick pus and may be responsible for the thin serous character of streptococcal exudates. This property has been applied therapeutically in liquefying localised collections of thick exudates, as in empyema. A preparation containing streptokinase and streptodornase is available for this purpose. Four antigenically distinct DNAases, A, B, C and D, have been recognised, of which type B is the most antigenic in human beings. Demonstration of anti-DNAase B antibody is useful in the retrospective diagnosis of *Str. pyogenes* infection, particularly in skin infections, where ASO titres may be low. Streptodornase B and D also possess ribonuclease activity.

Nicotinamide adenine dinucleotidase (NADase, formerly diphosphopyridine nucleotidase, DPNase): This acts on the coenzyme NAD and liberates nicotinamide from the molecule. It is antigenic and is specifically neutralised by the antibody in convalescent sera. The biological significance of NADase is not known, though it is believed to be leucotoxic.

Hyaluronidase: This enzyme breaks down the hyaluronic acid of the tissues. This might favour the spread of infection along the intercellular spaces. Streptococci possess a hyaluronic acid capsule and also elaborate a hyaluronidase—a seemingly self-destructive process. It is, however, found that strains that form hyaluronidase in large quantities (M types 4 and 22) are noncapsulated. The enzyme is antigenic and specific antibodies appear in convalescent sera.

Serum opacity factor: Some M types of *Str. pyogenes* produce a lipoproteinase which produces opacity when applied to agar gel containing horse or swine serum. This is known as serum opacity factor (SOP).

Many strains also produce proteinase,

phosphatase, esterases, amylase, N acetyl glucosaminidase, neuraminidase and other toxins or enzymes. It is not known whether, and to what extent, these contribute to pathogenesis.

PATHOGENICITY

Str. pyogenes produces pyogenic infections with a tendency to spread locally, along lymphatics and through the bloodstream.

Respiratory infections: The primary site of invasion of the human body by Str. pyogenes is the throat. Sore throat is the most common of streptococcal diseases. It may be localised as tonsillitis or may involve the pharynx more diffusely (pharyngitis). Virulent group A streptococci adhere to the pharyngeal epithelium by means of lipoteichoic acid covering the surface pili. The glycoprotein fibronectin on the epithelial cells probably serves as the lipoteichoic acid ligand. Tonsillitis is more common in older children and adults than in younger children, who commonly develop diffuse pharyngitis. Localisation is believed to be favoured by hypersensitivity due to prior contact.

From the throat, streptococci may spread to the surrounding tissues, leading to suppurative complications, such as otitis media, mastoiditis, quinsy, Ludwig's angina and suppurative adenitis. It may rarely lead to meningitis. Streptococcal pneumonia seldom follows throat infection but may occur as a complication of influenza or other respiratory viral diseases.

Skin and soft tissue infections: Str. pyogenes causes a variety of suppurative infections of the skin, including infection of wounds or burns, with a predilection to produce lymphangitis and cellulitis. Infection of minor abrasions may at times lead to fatal septicemia.

The two typical streptococcal infections of the skin are erysipelas and impetigo. The former is a diffuse infection involving the superficial lymphatics. The affected skin, which is red, swollen and indurated, is sharply demarcated from the surrounding healthy area. While erysipelas is rare and seen only in older patients, impetigo is found mainly in young children. Impetigo is caused by Str. pyogenes belonging to a limited number of serotypes, usually the higher numbered M types, instead of the lower numbered M types which cause throat infections. Impetigo and streptococcal infection of scabies lesions are the main causes leading to acute glomerulonephritis in children in the tropics.

In pyoderma, antibody response to streptolysin O is not high and ASO estimation does not have as much clinical significance as in pharyngeal infections. Antibody to DNAase B and hyaluronidase are more useful in retrospective diagnosis of pyoderma antecendent to acute glomerulonephritis.

Streptococcal subcutaneous infections range from cellulitis to necrotising fasciitis. The latter condition is more commonly caused by a mixed aerobic and anaerobic bacterial infection but some strains of Str. pyogenes (more particularly M types 1 and 3 strains forming pyrogenic exotoxin A) may alone be responsible. This is ordinarily a sporadic condition and has been known since 1883 but small outbreaks in the UK and the USA have recently caused much alarm because of their severity and high fatality. These strains have earned notoriety under the name 'flesh eating bacteria'. In such cases, extensive necrosis of subcutaneous and muscular tissues and adjacent fascia is associated with a severe systemic illness—a toxic shock-like syndrome with disseminated intravascular coagulation and multiple system failure. Str. pyogenes can be isolated from the affected site and rising titres of antistreptolysin and anti-DNAase B demonstrated. Though the isolates are penicillin sensitive in vitro, treatment with penicillin may not be effective. Vancomycin is the drug of choice in life threatening infections.

Soft tissue infections with some M types of Str. pyogenes (1, 3, 12, 28) may sometimes cause a toxic shock syndrome resembling staphylococcal TSS. Streptococcal TSS and necrotising fasciitis occur only in persons nonimmune to the infecting M types.

Genital infections: Both aerobic and anaerobic streptococci are normal inhabitants of the female genitalia. *Str. pyogenes* was an important cause of puerperal sepsis, with the infection usually being exogenous. The emphatic demonstration by Semmelweis in 1847 that hospital outbreaks of puerperal fever could be prevented by the simple measure of handwashing by those attending the labour wards remains a landmark in clinical microbiology. Puerperal fever is now much more commonly due to endogenous infection with anaerobic streptococci. Streptococcal puerperal sepsis used to take a heavy toll of life before antibiotics became available.

Other suppurative infections: *Str. pyogenes* may cause abscesses in internal organs such as the brain, lungs, liver and kidneys, and also septicemia and pyemia.

Nonsuppurative complications: *Str. pyogenes* infections lead to two important nonsuppurative sequelae—acute rheumatic fever and acute glomerulonephritis. These complications ensue 1–3 weeks after the acute infection so that the organism may not be detectable when sequelae set in. They differ in their natural history in a number of respects (Table 23.2).

The pathogenesis of these complications is not clearly understood. The essential lesion in rheumatic fever is carditis, including connective tissue degeneration of the heart valves and inflammatory myocardial lesions characterised by Aschoff nodules. Typically, rheumatic fever follows persistent or repeated streptococcal throat infections with a strong antibody response. The lesions are believed to be the result of hypersensitivity to some streptococcal component. It has also been suggested that there may be an element of autoimmunity involved, and antigenic cross-reactions have been demonstrated between streptococci and heart tissues. Lesions resembling rheumatic fever have been produced experimentally in rabbits by repeated infection with *Str. pyogenes* and in mice by injection of sonic lysates of the cocci.

While rheumatic fever may follow infection with any serotype of *Str. pyogenes*, nephritis is caused by only a few 'nephritogenic' types. In the tropics, skin infections are perhaps more important in this respect than throat infections. The nephritis is usually a self-limited episode that resolves without any permanent damage. The pathogenesis may be due to antigenic cross-reactions between the glomerular membrane antigen and cell membranes of nephritogenic streptococci, or more often it may be an immune complex disease. This condition has been produced in monkeys and rabbits by repeated infection with type 12 *Str. pyogenes* or injection of bacterial products, and in mice with soluble streptococcal products.

Epidemiology: The major source of *Str. pyogenes* is the human upper respiratory tract – throat, nasopharynx or nose – of patients and carriers. Carrier rates of up to 20 per cent have been observed. Symptomless infection is common and helps to maintain the organism in the community. Transmission of infection is either by direct contact or through contaminated fingers, dust or fomites. In the tropics, streptococcal infection of the skin is common and may be spread by nonbiting insects, particularly the eye gnat *Hippelates*.

Streptococcal infections of the respiratory tract are more frequent in children 5–8 years of age than in children below two years or in adults. They are more common in winter in the temperate countries. No seasonal distribution has been identified in the tropics. Crowding is an important factor in the transmission of infection. Outbreaks of infection may occur in closed communities such as boarding schools or army camps.

Immunity is type specific and appears to be associated with antibody to the M protein. Reinfections occur because of the multiplicity of serotypes.

Laboratory diagnosis: In acute infections,

Table 23.2 Comparison of rheumatic fever and glomerulonephritis

	Acute rheumatic fever	*Acute glomerulonephritis*
Site of infection	Throat	Throat or skin
Prior sensitisation	Essential	Not necessary
Serotype of *Str. pyogenes*	Any	Pyodermal types 49, 53–55, 59–61 and pharyngitis strains 1 and 12
Immune response	Marked	Moderate
Complement level	Unaffected	Lowered
Genetic susceptibility	Present	Not known
Repeated attacks	Common	Absent
Penicillin prophylaxis	Essential	Not indicated
Course	Progressive or static	Spontaneous resolution
Prognosis	Variable	Good

diagnosis is established by culture, while in the nonsuppurative complications, diagnosis is mainly based on the demonstration of antibodies.

Presumptive information may be obtained by an examination of Gram stained films from pus and CSF. The presence of Gram positive cocci in chains is indicative of streptococcal infection. However, smears are of no value in infections of the throat or genitalia, where streptococci may form part of the resident flora.

For cultures, swabs should be collected under vision from the affected site and either plated immediately or sent to the laboratory in Pike's medium (blood agar containing 1 in 1,000,000 crystal violet and 1 in 16,000 sodium azide). The specimen is plated on blood agar and incubated at 37 °C anaerobically or under 5–10% CO_2, as hemolysis develops better under these conditions. Sheep blood agar is recommended for primary isolation because it is inhibitory for *Haemophilus haemolyticus*, colonies of which may be confused with those of hemolytic streptococci. Hemolytic streptococci are grouped by the Lancefield technique. The fluorescent antibody technique has been employed for the rapid identification of group A streptococci. A convenient method for the identification of *Str. pyogenes* is based on Maxted's observation that they are more sensitive to bacitracin than other streptococci. A filter paper disc dipped

in a solution of bacitracin (1 unit/ml) is applied on the surface of an inoculated blood agar. After incubation, a wide zone of inhibition is seen with *Str. pyogenes* but not with other streptococci.

Typing of *Str. pyogenes* is required only for epidemiological purposes. If required, this may be done by precipitation or agglutination.

Rapid diagnostic test kits for the detection of streptococcal group A antigen from throat swabs are available commercially. The tests can be completed in 1–4 hours and are nearly as specific as cultures, though less sensitive.

In rheumatic fever and glomerulonephritis, a retrospective diagnosis of streptococcal infection may be established by demonstrating high levels of antibody to streptococcal toxins. The usual test done is antistreptolysin O titration. ASO titres higher than 200 are indicative of prior streptococcal infection. High levels are usually found in acute rheumatic fever but in glomerulonephritis, titres are often low. Antideoxyribonuclease B (anti-DNAase B) estimation is also commonly employed. Titres higher than 300 are taken as significant. Anti-DNAase B and antihyaluronidase tests are very useful for the retrospective diagnosis of streptococcal pyoderma, for which ASO is of much less value.

The streptozyme test, a passive slide hemagglutination test using erythrocytes sensitised with a crude preparation of extracellular antigens of streptococci, is a convenient, sensitive and specific screening test. It becomes positive after nearly all types of streptococcal infections, whether of the throat or the skin.

Prophylaxis: The indication for prophylaxis in streptococcal infection is only in the prevention of rheumatic fever. This is achieved by a long-term administration of penicillin in children who have developed early signs of rheumatic fever. This prevents streptococcal reinfection and further damage to the heart. Antibiotic prophylaxis is not useful for glomerulonephritis as this complication follows a single streptococcal infection, and reinfections do not occur.

Treatment: All beta hemolytic group A streptococci are sensitive to penicillin G, and most are sensitive to erythromycin. In patients allergic to penicillin, erythromycin or cephalexin may be used. Strains resistant to erythromycin have been reported. Tetracylines and sulphonamides are not recommended. Antimicrobial drugs have no effect on established glomerulonephritis and rheumatic fever.

OTHER HEMOLYTIC STREPTOCOCCI

Besides *Str. pyogenes*, streptococci belonging to groups B, C, D, F, G and rarely H, K , O and R may also cause human infections.

Data from Streptococcal Reference Laboratories in India (Lady Hardinge Medical College, New Delhi; Christian Medical College, Vellore) showed that while approximately 45 per cent of hemolytic streptococcal isolates tested belong to group A, 10–15 per cent belong to groups B and C each, about 25 per cent to group G and 5 per cent to group F.

GROUP B

These are important pathogens of cattle, producing bovine mastitis (*Str. agalactiae*). From the 1960s, Group B streptococcus has assumed great clinical importance as the single most common cause of neonatal meningitis in the West. Infection in the newborn is classified as the early onset type

occurring within a week of birth, and the late onset type developing between the second and twelfth weeks of life. The more common early onset type presents as septicemia, meningitis or pneumonia, and is often fatal. Infection is acquired from the maternal vagina during birth. In the late onset type, infection is more often obtained from the environment. Other Group B infections in neonates include arthritis, osteomyelitis, conjunctivitis, respiratory infections, peritonitis, omphalitis and endocarditis. Group B streptococci may also cause adult infections, including puerperal sepsis and pnenmonia.

Their ability to hydrolyse hippurate acts as a presumptive identification method. They may be identified by the CAMP reaction (Christie, Atkins and Munch–Peterson), which can be demonstrated as an accentuated zone of hemolysis when *Str. agalactiae* is inoculated perpendicular to a streak of *Staph. aureus* grown on blood agar. Occasional strains are bacitracin sensitive. Human pathogenic Group B strains possess a polysaccharide capsule which appears to confer virulence. Nine capsular serotypes have been identified, antibodies to which confer type specific protection.

GROUP C

Streptococci of this group are predominantly animal pathogens and may be divided into four species biochemically. Group C strains isolated from human sources usually belong to *Strep. equisimilis* species. It can cause upper respiratory infections, as well as deep infections such as endocarditis, osteomyelitis, brain abscess, pneumonia and puerperal sepsis. Strains are often tolerant to penicillin and serious infections may not respond to penicillin treatment. The addition of gentamicin is recommended in serious cases. It resembles *Str. pyogenes* in fermenting trehalose but differs in fermenting ribose. It produces streptolysin O, streptokinase (antigenically distinct from that produced by *Str. pyogenes*) and other extracellular substances. *Str. equisimilis* is the source of streptokinase used for thrombolytic therapy in patients.

GROUP F

These grow poorly on blood agar unless incubated under CO_2. They have been called the 'minute streptococci'. They are sometimes found in suppurative lesions. One member of this group is *Streptococus* MG which is an alpha lytic strain isolated from cases of primary atypical pneumonia. Demonstration of agglutinins to *Streptococcus* MG in sera of patients had been used as a diagnostic test for primary atypical pneumonia.

GROUP G

These are commensals in the throats of human beings, monkeys or dogs. They may occasionally cause tonsillitis, endocarditis and urinary infections in human beings.

Groups H and K sometimes cause infective endocarditis.

Group O is isolated mainly from the healthy human throat and may cause acute tonsillitis and endocarditis.

Group R strains are natural pathogens of pigs. They have been reported from occasional cases of meningitis, septicemia and respiratory infection in persons in contact with infected pigs or contaminated meat.

GROUP D STREPTOCOCCI

These can be classified into two groups: (1) the enterococcus group (enterococci or fecal streptococci), which have been reclassified as a separate genus called Enterococcus and containing different species for example, *E. faecalis, E. faecium, E. durans;* and (2) the nonenterococcal group, for example, *Str. bovis, Str. equinus.*

The enterococci possess several distinctive features separating them from streptococci. These include their ability to grow in the presence of 40 per cent bile, 6.5 per cent sodium chloride, at pH 9.6, at 45 °C and in 0.1 per cent methylene blue milk. On MacConkey's medium they produce tiny deep pink colonies. They are relatively heat resistant, surviving 60 °C for 30 minutes. Enterococci typically appear as pairs of oval cocci, the cells in a pair arranged at an angle to each other (Fig. 23.4). They are usually nonhemolytic, though some strains may show alpha or beta hemolysis.

The identification of enterococcus species is made on biochemical grounds. *E. faecalis* is the enterococcus most often isolated from human sources. *E. faecalis* can be identified by its ability to ferment mannitol, sucrose, sorbitol and aesculin, and to grow on tellurite blood agar producing black colonies.

Enterococci are present in the intestine, genital tract and saliva. They are frequently isolated from cases of urinary tract infection and wound infection. They may also cause endocarditis, infection of the biliary tract, septicemia, and intraabdominal abscess complicating diverticulitis and peritonitis. Strains resistant to penicillin and other antibiotics occur frequently, so it is essential to perform antibiotic sensitivity for proper therapy.

Nonenterococcal species of group D (*Str. bovis, Str. equinus*) are generally susceptible to penicillin and are inhibited by 6.5 per cent sodium chloride or bile. They may cause urinary infection or endocarditis rarely.

THE VIRIDANS GROUP

This group, formerly called *Streptococcus viridans*, is a miscellany of streptococci normally resident in the mouth and upper respiratory tract, and typically producing greening (alpha lysis) on blood agar— hence the name *viridans*.

Some of them may be nonlytic. They cannot be categorised under the Lancefield antigenic groups.

However, based on sugar fermentation, cell wall composition and production of dextrans and levans, they have been classified into many species, for example, *Str. mitis, Str. mutans, Str. salivarius, Str. sanguis.*

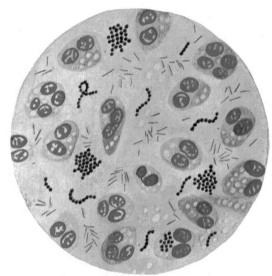

Gram stain of a pus smear. Plate shows Gram positive violet coloured cocci in groups (staphylococci). in chains (streptococci) and pink rods (Gram negative bacilli). Pus cells show up pink stained.

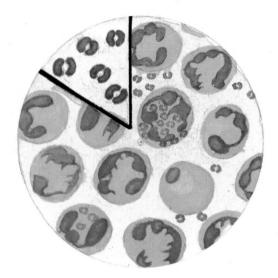

Gonococci in urethral discharge. Gram stain.

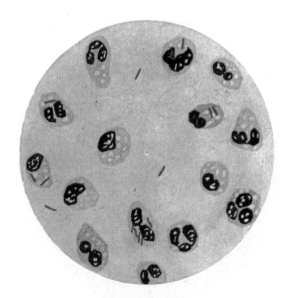

Acid fast stain (Ziehl-Neelsen stain) of sputum. The red rods are *M. tuberculosis.*

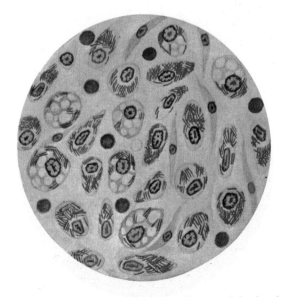

M. leprae: Ziehl-Neelsen stain of section of lepra nodule showing lepra cells and characteristic arrangement of lepra bacilli.

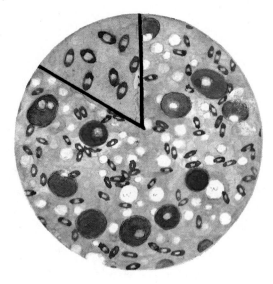

Yersinia pestes. Smear from enlarged lymph gland from a case of plague Leishman stain. Characteristic bipolar staining.

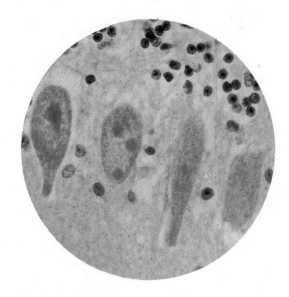

Negri bodies in dog's brain in rabies (hippocampus of dog). Alcoholic eosin and methylene blue stain.

Allantoic membrane showing Variola pocks. Clear cut and white

Allantoic membrane showing Vaccinia pocks. Note irregularity in shape and size

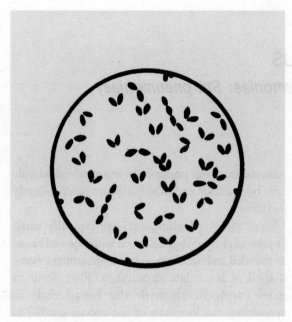

Fig. 23.4 Enterococcus. Oval cells arranged in pairs at an angle, or in short chains.

They are ordinarily nonpathogenic but can on occasion cause disease. In persons with preexisting cardiac lesions, they may cause bacterial endocarditis, *Str. sanguis* being most often responsible. Following tooth extraction or other dental procedures, they cause transient bacteremia and get implanted on damaged or prosthetic valves or in a congenitally diseased heart, and grow to form vegetations. Prophylactic antibiotic cover is advisable in such persons before tooth extraction or similar procedures. While viridans streptococci are generally penicillin sensitive, some strains may be resistant. It is therefore essential that in endocarditis, the causative strain is isolated and its antibiotic sensitivity determined so that appropriate antibiotics in adequate bactericidal concentration can be employed for treatment.

Str. mutans (so called because it assumes a bacillary form in acid environments) is important in the causation of dental caries. It breaks down dietary sucrose, producing acid and a tough adhesive dextran. The acid damages dentine and the dextrans bind together food debris, epithelial cells, mucus and bacteria to form dental plaques, which lead to caries. Experimental caries in monkeys has been prevented by a *Str. mutans* vaccine, but its extention to human use is fraught with problems.

Further Reading

Beighton D et al. 1991. A scheme for identification of viridans streptococci. *J Med Microbiol* 35:367.

Bisno AL. 1991. Group A streptococcal infections and acute rheumatic fever. *New Eng J Med* 325:783.

Bisno AL and DL Stevens 1996. Streptococcal infections of skin and soft tissues. *New Engl J Med* 334:240.

Charles D and B Larsen 1986. Streptococcal puerperal sepsis and obstetric infections: A historical perspective. *Clin Microbiol Rev* 2 : 315.

Moellering RC. 1992. Emergence of Enterococcus as a significant pathogen. *Clin Infect Dis* 14:1173.

Pneumococcus
(*Diplococcus pneumoniae: Str. pneumoniae*)

Pneumococcus, a Gram positive lanceolate diplococcus, formerly classified as Diplococcus pneumomiae, has been reclassified as *Str. pneumoniae* because of its genetic relatedness to streptococcus. Pneumococcus differs from other streptococci chiefly in its morphology, bile solubility, optochin sensitivity and possession of a specific polysaccharide capsule. Pneumococci are normal inhabitants of the human upper respiratory tract. They are the single most prevalent bacterial agent in pneumonia and in otitis media in children. They can also cause sinusitis, bronchitis, infections bacteremia, meningitis and other infections.

Pneumococci were first noticed in 1881 by Pasteur and Sternberg independently. They produced a fatal septicemia in rabbits by inoculating human saliva and isolated pneumococci from the blood of the animals. But the relationship between pneumococci and pneumonia was established only later by Fraenkel and Weichselbaum independently in 1886.

Morphology: Pneumococci are typically small (1 μm), slightly elongated cocci, with one end broad or rounded and the other pointed, presenting a flame shaped or lanceolate appearance. They occur in pairs (diplococci), with the broad ends in apposition, the long axis of the coccus parallel to the line joining the two cocci in a pair. They are capsulated, the capsule enclosing each pair. The capsules are best seen in material taken directly from exudates and may be lost on repeated cultivation. In culture, the typical morphology may not be apparent and the cocci are more rounded, tending to occur in short chains. They are nonmotile and nonsporing.

They are readily stained with aniline dyes and are Gram positive. The capsule may be demonstrated as a clear halo in Indian ink preparations or may be stained directly by special techniques.

Cultural characteristics: Pneumococci have complex growth requirements and grow only in enriched media. They are aerobes and facultative anaerobes, the optimum temperature being 37 °C (range 25–42 °C) and pH 7.8 (range 6.5–8.3). Growth is improved by 5–10% CO_2.

On blood agar, after incubation for 18 hours, the colonies are small (0.5–1 mm), dome shaped and glistening, with an area of green discoloration (alpha hemolysis) around them, resembling colonies of *Str. viridans*. On further incubation the colonies become flat with raised edges and central

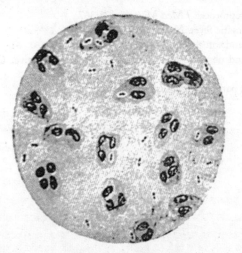

Fig. 24.1 Pneumococci in pus

umbonation, so that concentric rings are seen on the surface when viewed from above (draughtsman or carrom coin appearance). Some strains that develop abundant capsular material (types 3 and 7) form large mucoid colonies.

Under anaerobic conditions, colonies on blood agar are surrounded by a zone of beta hemolysis due to oxygen labile hemolysin O. In liquid media such as glucose broth, growth occurs as uniform turbidity. The cocci readily undergo autolysis in cultures due to the activity of intracellular enzymes. Autolysis is enhanced by bile salts, sodium lauryl sulphate and other surface active agents. Heat killed cultures do not undergo autolysis.

Biochemical reactions: Pneumococci ferment several sugars, forming acid only. Fermentation is tested in Hiss's serum water or serum agar slopes. Fermentation of inulin by pneumococci is a useful test for differentiating them from streptococci as the latter do not ferment it.

Pneumococci are bile soluble. If a few drops of 10% sodium deoxycholate solution are added to 1 ml of an overnight broth culture, the culture clears due to the lysis of the cocci. Alternatively, if a loopful of 10% deoxycholate solution is placed on a pneumococcus colony on blood agar the colony lyses within a few minutes. Bile solubility is a constant property of pneumococci and hence is of diagnostic importance. The bile solubility test is based on the presence in the pneumococci of an autolytic amidase that cleaves the bond between alanine and muramic acid in the peptidoglycan. The amidase is activated by surface active agents such as bile or bile salts, resulting in lysis of the organisms. The test should be carried out at neutral pH using deoxycholate and live young cells in saline suspension.

Pneumococci are catalase and oxidase negative.

Resistance: Pneumococci are delicate organisms and are readily destroyed by heat (thermal death point 52 °C for 15 minutes) and antiseptics. In cultures, they die on prolonged incubation, perhaps due to an accumulation of toxic peroxides. Strains

Fig. 24.2 Pneumococci. Indian ink preparation to show capsules.

may be maintained on semisolid blood agar or by lyophilisation.

They are sensitive to most antibiotics, beta lactams being the drugs of choice. Almost all strains were sensitive to 0.05 mg penicillin till 1967, when resistant strains began to appear. The resistance may be intermediate (MIC 1 µg) or high (2 µg or more) and due to mutation or gene transfer. The mode of resistance is not production of beta lactamase, but alteration in the penicillin binding proteins on the bacterial surface. Such strains are also resistant to multiple drugs. A drug resistant *Strep. pneumoniae* (DRSP) strain originating in Spain has spread to most parts of the world posing problems in treament.

The sensitivity of pneumococci to optochin (ethyl hydrocuprein) 1/500,000 is useful in differentiating them from streptococci. When a disc impregnated with optochin is applied on a plate of blood agar inoculated with pneumococci, a wide zone of inhibition appears on incubation.

Antigenic properties: The most important antigen of the pneumococcus is the type specific capsular polysaccharide. As this polysaccharide diffuses into the culture medium or infective exudates and tissues, it is also called the 'specific soluble substance' (SSS). Pneumococci are classified into types based on the antigenic nature of the capsular polysaccharide. Pneumococci isolated from lobar pneumonia were originally classified into three types, I, II and III, and a heterogeneous group IV. Members of group IV were later classified into types, and now more than 90 different serotypes are recognised, named 1, 2, 3, and so on.

Typing may be carried out by (1) agglutination of the cocci with the type specific antiserum; (2) precipitation of the SSS with the specific serum; or (3) by the capsule swelling reaction described by Neufeld (1902). In the capsule swelling or 'quellung' reaction (quellung = swelling), a suspension of pneumococci is mixed on a slide with a drop of the type specific antiserum and a loopful of methylene blue solution. In the presence of the homologous antiserum, the capsule becomes apparently swollen, sharply delineated and refractile. The quellung test can be done directly with sputum from acute pneumonia cases. It used to be a routine bedside procedure in the past when the specific antiserum was used for the treatment of pneumonia.

The antigenicity of the capsular polysaccharide varies in different species. It is antigenic in human beings and rabbits. But in mice, large doses (500 µg) induce no immunological response (immunological paralysis), while small doses (0.5 µg) are antigenic.

Pneumococci contain other antigens also—a nucleoprotein deep inside the cell and a somatic 'C' carbohydrate antigen, both of which are species specific.

An abnormal protein (beta globulin) that precipitates with the somatic 'C' antigen of pneumococci, appears in the acute phase sera of cases of pneumonia but disappears during convalescence. It also occurs in some other pathological conditions. This is known as the 'C-reactive protein' (CRP). Its apparent antibody-like relation to the 'C' antigen of pneumococcus is only fortuitous. It is not an antibody produced as a result of pneumococcal infection. It is an 'acute phase' substance, produced in hepatocytes. Its production is stimulated by bacterial infections, inflammation, malignancies and tissue destruction. It disappears when the inflammatory reactions subside. CRP is used as an index of response to treatment in rheumatic fever and certain other conditions. CRP testing, by passive agglutination using latex particles coated with anti-CRP antibody is a routine diagnostic procedure.

Variation: On repeated subculture, pneumococci undergo a smooth-to-rough (S–R) variation. In the R form, the colonies are rough and the cocci are noncapsulated, autoagglutinable and avirulent. R forms arise as spontaneous mutants and outgrow the parental S forms in artificial culture; in tissues, such R mutants are eliminated by phagocytosis.

Rough pneumococci derived from capsulated

Fig. 24.3 Draughtsman appearance of pneumococcus colonies. Left: View from above to show concentric rings. Right: side view in cross section.

cells of one serotype may be made to produce capsules of the same or different serotypes, on treatment with DNA from the respective serotypes of pneumococci. This transformation, which may be demonstrated in vivo or in vitro, was discovered by Griffith (1928) and is of considerable historical interest as the first demonstration of genetic exchange of information in bacteria.

Toxins and other virulence factors: Pneumococci produce an oxygen labile hemolysin and a leucocidin but these are weak and make no contribution to virulence. The virulence of pneumococci depends on its capsule and the production of a toxin called pneumolysin. The capsular polysaccharide, because of its acidic and hydrophilic properties, protects the cocci from phagocytosis. Capsulated pneumococci are not phagocytosed efficiently in fluid media or exudates. They are however, susceptible to 'surface phagocytosis', being engulfed against a firm surface, such as fibrin clot or epithelium.

The enhanced virulence of type 3 pneumococcus is due to the abundance of its capsular material. Noncapsulated strains are avirulent. The antibody to the capsular polysaccharide affords protection against infection.

Pneumolysin, a membrane damaging toxin produced by pneumococci has cytotoxic and complement activating properties and so may be a virulence factor. It is immunogenic. Pneumolysin negative mutants show reduced virulence in experimental animals. Pneumococcal autolysins, by releasing bacterial components in infected tissues may also contribute to virulence.

Pathogenicity: Experimentally, fatal infection can be produced in mice or rabbits by intraperitoneal inoculation of pneumococci. Death occurs in 1–3 days, and pneumococci can be demonstrated in large numbers in the peritoneal exudate and heart blood.

Pneumococci colonise the human nasopharynx and may cause infection of the middle ear, paranasal sinuses and respiratory tract by direct spread. Infection of the meninges can also occur, by contiguity or through blood. Pneumococcal bacteremia may also lead to distant infections as in the heart, peritoneum or joints. Infection is commonly endogenous, but exogenous infection may also occur, especially with highly virulent strains.

The commonest pneumococcal infections are otitis media and sinusitis. Prior respiratory infection or allergy causing congestion and blockage predispose to these conditions. Serotypes 6, 14, 19F and 23F are commonly encountered in these conditions, in the West.

Pneumococci are one of the most common bacteria causing pneumonia, both lobar and bronchopneumonia. They also cause acute tracheobronchitis and empyema.

Aspiration of nasopharyngeal secretions containing pneumococci into the lower respiratory tract is a common event and may occur even in sleep. Normal mucosal defence mechanisms such as entrapment, expulsion and the cough reflex, aided by the ciliary escalator effect prevent establishment of infection. When the normal defences are compromised by viral infection, anesthesia, chilling or other factors, pneumococci nultiply, penetrate the bronchial mucosa and spread through the lung along peribronchial tissues and lymphatics. Bacteremia is common during the early stage of lobar pneumonia. Toxemia is due to the diffusion of the capsular polysaccharide into the blood and tissues. The fall of temperature by crisis and relief of symptoms coincide with the neutralisation of the SSS by anticapsular antibodies.

In adults, types 1–8 are responsible for about 75 per cent of cases of pneumococcal pneumonia and for more than 50 per cent of all fatalities due to pneumococcal bacteremia. In children, types 6, 14, 19 and 23 are frequent causes.

Bronchopneumonia is almost always a secondary infection. This may be caused by any serotype of pneumococcus. The damage to the respiratory epithelium and excessive bronchial secretions caused by the primary infection facilitate the invasion of pneumococci along the bronchial tree.

Bronchopneumonia is frequently a terminal event in aged and debilitated patients.

Pneumococci are commonly associated with the acute exacerbations in chronic bronchitis. The copious respiratory secretions in chronic bronchitis aid pneumococcal invasion. Another bacterium commonly associated with this condition is *Haemophilus influenzae*.

Meningitis is the most serious of pneumococcal infections. It is usually secondary to other pneumococcal infections such as pneumonia, otitis media, sinusitis or conjunctivitis but in a proportion of cases, other foci of infection may not be demonstrable. Pneumococcal meningitis occurs at all ages. Untreated cases are almost invariably fatal. Even with antibiotic therapy, the case fatality rate is about 25 per cent.

Pneumococci may also produce suppurative lesions in other parts of the body – empyema, pericarditis, otitis media, sinusitis, conjunctivitis, suppurative arthritis and peritonitis, usually as complications of pneumonia.

Epidemiology: Natural infection with pneumococci has been reported in some species of animals such as guinea pigs but they have little relation to human disease. The source of human infection is the respiratory tract of carriers and less often, of patients. Pneumococci occur in the throat of approximately half the population sampled at any one time. They are transmitted from one to another by fingers or by inhalation of contaminated droplets or droplet nuclei. Dissemination is facilitated by crowding.

Infection usually leads only to pharyngeal carriage. Disease results only when the host resistance is lowered by contributory factors such as respiratory viral infections, pulmonary congestion, stress, malnutrition, immunodeficiency or alcoholism. Splenectomy and sickle cell disease are important predisposing conditions.

Pneumococcal serotypes vary greatly in virulence. The case fatality rates of pneumonia may vary according to the virulence of the infecting serotype. Type 3 is the most virulent.

Lobar pneumonia is usually a sporadic disease but epidemics may occur among closed communities as in army camps. The incidence of bronchopneumonia increases when an epidemic of influenza or other viral infection of the respiratory tract occurs. Cases are more common in winter and affect the two extreme age groups more often.

Laboratory diagnosis: The clinical diagnosis of pneumonia is easy but as the disease may be caused by several different microorganisms, etiological diagnosis should be made by laboratory tests. This is of great importance in treatment.

In the acute phase of lobar pneumonia, the rusty sputum contains pneumococci in large numbers, with hardly any other kind of bacterium. They may be demonstrated by Gram stain. In the preantibiotic era, direct serotyping of pneumococci in wet films of sputum by the quellung test was a routine bedside test because success of treatment depended on administering the specific antiserum. In later stages of the disease, pneumococci are less abundant.

The sputum, after homogenisation if necessary, is inoculated on blood agar plates and incubated at 37 °C under 5–10 per cent CO_2. Growth occurs after overnight incubation. Where sputum is not available, as in infants, serum-coated laryngeal swabs may be used for culture. Isolation from respiratory secretions is facilitated by using blood agar containing gentamicin 5 $\mu g/ml$.

From specimens where pneumococci are expected to be scanty, isolation may be obtained by intraperitoneal inoculation in mice, even if cultures are negative. Inoculated mice die in 1–3 days, and pneumococci may be demonstrated in the peritoneal exudate and heart blood. The test may be negative with occasional strains that are avirulent for mice (type 14 strains).

In the acute stage of pneumonia, the organism may be obtained from blood culture in glucose

Table 24.1 Differentiation between *Str. pneumoniae* and *Str. viridans*.

	Str. pneumoniae	*Str. viridans*
Morphology	Capsulated, lanceolate diplococci	Noncapsulated, oval or round cells in chains
Quellung test	Positive	Negative
Colonies	Initially dome-shaped, later, 'draughtsman' colonies	Dome-shaped
Growth in liquid media	Uniform turbidity	Granular turbidity, powdery deposit
Bile solubility	Invariably positive	Invariably negative
Inulin fermentation	Positive	Negative
Optochin sensitivity	Positive	Negative
Intraperitoneal inoculation in mice	Fatal infection	Nonpathogenic

broth. Isolation of pneumococci from blood indicates bad prognosis.

In acute otitis media pneumococci may be demonstrated in the fluid aspirated from the middle ear.

In case of meningitis, presumptive diagnosis may be made from Gram stained films of CSF. Gram positive diplococci can be seen both inside the polymorphs and extracellularly. Diagnosis is confirmed by culture. In cases which are negative by culture, it may be possible to establish the diagnosis by demonstrating the SSS in CSF by precipitation with antisera.

Capsular polysaccharide can be demonstrated in the blood, urine and cerebrospinal fluid by counterimmunoelectrophoresis. Antibodies can be demonstrated by agglutination, precipitation, mouse protection tests and bactericidal tests with whole blood. Indirect hemagglutination, indirect FA test and radioimmunoassay have been employed.

Prophylaxis: Immunity is type specific and associated with antibody to the capsular polysaccharide. The existence of some 90 serotypes makes a complete polyvalent vaccine impracticable. A polyvalent polysaccharide vaccine representing the capsular antigens of 23 most prevalent serotypes has been stated to give 80–90 per cent protection. It is not meant for general use, but only in persons at enhanced risk of pneumococcal infection such as those with absent or dysfunctional spleen, sickle cell disease, coeliac disease, chronic renal, lung, heart and liver diseases, diabetes mellitus and immunodeficiencies including HIV infection. It is not recommended in children under two years of age and those with lymphoreticular malignancies and immunosuppressive therapy.

Treatment: The antibiotic of choice is parenteral penicillin in serious cases and amoxycillin in milder ones, provided the infecting strain is penicillin sensitive. Many penicillin resistant strains are also resistant to other antibiotics like erythromycin and tetracycline. A third generation cephalosporin is indicated in such cases. Vancomycin is to be reserved for life threatening illnesses with highly resistant strains.

Further Reading

American Academy of Pediatrics. 1997. Therapy for children with invasive pneumococcal infection, *Pediatrics* 99:289.
Jacobs MR and PC Applebaum 1995. Antibiotic resistant pneumococci, *Rev Med Microbiol* 6:77.
Tuomanen EI et al. 1995. Pathogenesis of pneumococcal infection. *New Engl J Med* 332:1280.
Pepys MB. 2001. The renaissance of c-reactive protein. BMJ. 322 : 4.
Quie PG et al. 1981. Symposium on the Pneumococcus. *Rev Infect Dis* 3:183.

Neisseria

25

The genus Neisseria consists of Gram negative aerobic nonsporulating, nonmotile, oxidase positive cocci typically arranged in pairs (diplococci). Besides the two important pathogens, *N. meningitidis* and *N. gonorrhoeae*, the genus contains many other species such as *N. lactamica* that occur as commensals in the mouth or the upper respiratory tract.

NEISSERIA MENINGITIDIS

(Meningococcus; *Diplococcus intracellularis meningitidis*) Meningococcus was first described and isolated in 1887 by Weichselbaum from the spinal fluid of a patient.

N.meningitidis causes meningococcal meningitis (formerly also known as cerebrospinal fever) which may occur sporadically, as localised outbreaks or as epidemics, and also septicemia.

Morphology: Meningococci are Gram negative oval or spherical cocci 0.6–0.8 μm in size, typically arranged in pairs, with the adjacent sides flattened (Fig. 25.1). The long axis of the coccus is at right angles to a line joining the two cocci in a pair. Considerable variations occur in size, shape and staining properties, especially in older cultures, due to autolysis. In smears from lesions, the cocci are more regular and generally intracellular. They are nonmotile. Most fresh isolates are capsulated.

Cultural characteristics: Meningococci have exacting growth requirements and do not grow on ordinary media. Growth occurs on media enriched with blood, serum or ascitic fluid, which promote growth by neutralising certain inhibiting

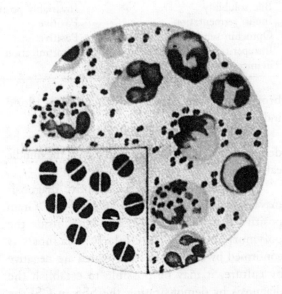

Fig. 25.1 Meningococcus in cerebrospinal fluid. Inset – enlarged view to show flat adjacent sides of the cocci.

substances in culture media rather than by providing additional nutritional needs.

They are strict aerobes, no growth occurring anaerobically. The optimum temperature for growth is 35–36 °C. No growth takes place below 30 °C. Optimum pH is 7.4–7.6. Growth is facilitated by 5–10 per cent CO_2 and high humidity.

On solid media, after incubation for 24 hours, the colonies are small (about 1 mm in diameter) translucent, round, convex, bluish grey, with a smooth glistening surface and with entire edges. The colonies are typically lenticular in shape, butyrous in consistency and easily emulsifiable. Weak hemolysis occurs on blood agar. Smooth and rough types of colonies are found. Growth is poor in liquid media, producing a granular turbidity with little or no surface growth.

Blood agar, chocolate agar and Mueller–Hinton starch casein hydrolysate agar are the media commonly used for culturing meningococci. Modified Thayer–Martin (with vancomycin, colistin and nystatin) is a useful selective medium.

Biochemical reactions: They are catalase and oxidase positive. The prompt oxidase reaction helps the identification of neisseria (both meningococcus and gonococcus) in mixed cultures. When freshly prepared 1% solution of oxidase reagent (tetramethyl paraphenylene diamine hydrochloride) is poured on the culture media, the neisseria colonies turn deep purple. Subcultures should be made immediately, as the organism dies on prolonged exposure to the reagent. The test may also be performed by rubbing a little of the growth with a loop on a strip of filter paper moistened with the oxidase reagent (Kovac's method). A deep purple colour appears immediately.

Indole and hydrogen sulphide are not produced and nitrates are not reduced. Glucose and maltose are utilised, but not sucrose or lactose, producing acid but no gas (gonococci acidify glucose but not maltose). Acid formation by neisseriae is weak, being oxidative and therefore best tested on peptone serum agar slopes containing the sugar and indicator.

Antigenic properties and classification: Meningococci are capsulated, unlike other neisseriae. Based on their capsular polysaccharide antigens, meningococci are classified into at least 13 serogroups, of which Groups A, B and C are the most important. Group A is usually associated with epidemics and Group C mostly with localised outbreaks, while Group B causes both epidemics and outbreaks. Groups 29-E, W-135 and Y also frequently cause meningitis. Any serogroup may colonise the nasopharynx, but these six groups account for the large majority of meningitis. Serogroups are further classified into serotypes and subtypes based on outer membrane proteins and polysaccharides.

Resistance: Meningococci are very delicate organisms, being highly susceptible to heat, dessication, alterations in pH and to disinfectants. They were uniformly sensitive to penicillin and other antibiotics, but resistant strains have emerged and become common in many areas.

Pathogenicity: Cerebrospinal meningitis and meningococcal septicemia are the two main types of meningococcal disease. Meningococci are strict human parasites inhabiting the nasopharynx. Infection is usually asymptomatic. In some, local inflammation ensues, with rhinitis and pharyngitis. Dissemination occurs only in a small proportion.

The manner in which the cocci spread from the nasopharynx to the meninges may be directly along the perineural sheath of the olfactory nerve, through the cribriform plate to the subarachnoid space, or more probably, through the bloodstream. In certain cases the site of entry of the meningococcus may be the conjunctiva. Cases of meningococcal purulent conjunctivitis occur. On reaching the central nervous system, a suppurative lesion of the meninges is set up, involving the surface of the spinal cord as well as the base and cortex of the brain. The cocci are invariably found in the spinal fluid, both free and within the leucocytes. Case fatality is variable but in untreated cases may be as high as 80 per cent. Survivors may have sequelae such as blindness and deafness. Some cases develop chronic or recurrent meningitis.

Meningococcemia presents as acute fever with chills, malaise and prostration. Typically a petechial rash occurs early in the disease. Meningococci may be isolated from the petechial lesions. Metastatic involvement of the joints, ears, eyes, lungs and adrenals may occur. About 10 per cent develop pneumonia.

A few develop fulminant meningococcemia (formerly called Waterhouse–Friderichsen syndrome) which is an overwhelming and usually fatal condition, characterised by shock, disseminated intravascular coagulation and multisystem failure. Rarely chronic meningococcemia may be seen. Meningococcal disease is favoured by deficiency of the terminal complement components (C5–C9).

The pathogenic agent in meningococcal disease appears to be the endotoxin (LPS) released by autolysis. The vascular endothelium is particularly sensitive to the endotoxin. All major inflammatory cascade systems as well as cytokines and nitric oxide are triggered and upregulated. In fulminant cases adrenal hemorrhage and profound shock are present.

Natural infection is limited to human beings. Intraspinal inoculation of large numbers of cocci may produce a picture of meningitis in monkeys. Intraperitoneal inoculation of the cocci suspended in hog gastric mucin brings about a fatal infection in mice.

Epidemiology: The human nasopharynx is the only reservoir of the meningococcus. Asymptomatic nasopharyngeal carriers rarely contract the illness but serve to infect their contacts. Transmission is essentially by airborne droplets or less often by fomites. During interepidemic periods, the carrier rate is about 5–10 per cent. An increase in carrier rate heralds the onset of an epidemic. During epidemics the carrier rates in closed communities may go up to 90 per cent. Meningitis is common in children between 3 months and 5 years of age. Epidemics usually occur in semiclosed communities living in crowded conditions, as in jails and ships formerly, and in army camps in recent times.

Prevalance of meningitis is highest in the 'meningitis belt of Africa' stretching from Ethiopia to Senegal. Frequent epidemics have occurred here. One of the largest was in 1996, when 150,000 cases and 15,000 deaths were reported.

Laboratory diagnosis: The primary agents causing purulent bacterial meningitis are meningococci, pneumococci and *Haemophilus influenzae type b*. Other important causative agents are group B streptococci, staphylococci, *Escherichia coli* and *Listeria monocytogenes*.

It is necessary to establish the specific etiology in purulent meningitis for proper treatment. In meningococcal meningitis, the cocci are present in large numbers in the spinal fluid and, in the early stage, in the blood as well. Demonstration of meningococci in the nasopharynx helps in the detection of carriers.

1. *Examination of CSF:* The fluid will be under pressure and turbid, with a large number of pus cells. For bacteriological examination, if a sufficient quantity is available, the CSF is divided into three portions. One portion is centrifuged and Gram stained smears are prepared from the deposit. Meningococci will be seen mainly inside polymorphs but often extracellularly also. This presumptive diagnosis is sufficient to start antibiotic treatment. The supernatent will contain meningococcal antigen, which may be demonstrated by latex agglutination or counterimmunoelectrophoresis using meningococcal antisera. Similar tests are also available for pneumococcus, *H. influenzae type b* and Group B streptococcus antigens. Antigen detection is particularly useful in partially treated patients in whom smear and culture tests may be negative. The second portion of the CSF is inoculated on blood agar or chocolate agar plates and incubated at 35–36 °C under 5–10%. CO_2. Colonies appear after 18–24 hours and may be identified by morphology and biochemical reactions. It is important to remember that morphologically similar organisms such as *N. flavescens, N. flava* and *Acinetobacter* may also cause purulent meningitis occasionally. The isolated meningococcus may be grouped, if required, by agglutination with the appropriate sera. The third portion of CSF is incubated overnight, either as it is or after adding an equal volume of glucose broth and then subcultured on chocolate agar. This method may sometimes succeed where direct plating fails.

2. *Blood culture:* In meningococcemia and in early

cases of meningitis, blood culture is often positive. Cultures should be incubated for 4–7 days, with daily subcultures. Meningococcal antigens can be found in the blood in active disease.

3. *Nasopharyngeal swab:* This is useful for the detection of carriers. Sampling should be done without contamination with saliva. The swab should be held in a suitable transport medium (for example, Stuart's) till it is plated.

4. *Petechial lesions:* Meningococci may sometimes be demonstrated in petechial lesions by microscopy and culture.

5. *Autopsy:* At autopsy, specimens may be collected from the meninges, lateral ventricles or the surface of the brain and spinal cord for smear and culture. Meningococci may die if specimens are not collected within twelve hours of the death of the patient.

6. *Retrospective evidence:* Retrospective evidence of meningococcal infection may be obtained by detection of antibodies.

7. *Molecular diagnosis:* Group specific diagnosis of infection can be made by detection of meningococcal DNA sequence in CSF or blood by PCR amplifications.

Treatment: Prompt treatment is essential to ensure recovery without sequelae. Sulphonamides, once the mainstay, are not used now due to widespread resistance. Intravenous penicillin G is the treatment of choice. Chloramphenicol is equally effective. One of the later cephalosporins (ceftriaxone, ceftazidime) may be used for the initiation of treatment before the etiology of meningitis is known.

After the initial course of treatment, eradicative therapy is to be given with rifampicin or ciprofloxacin to free the nasopharynx of the cocci and prevent carrier state.

Prophylaxis: Sulphonamides are not effective due to resistance. Penicillin is unable to eradicate the carrier state. Rifampicin or ciprofloxacin is recommended for chemoprophylaxis. As attack rates are very high in the household or close contacts of meningococcal patients, they should be provided with chemoprophylaxis.

Monovalent and polyvalent vaccines are available containing the capsular polysaccharides of groups A, C, W-135 and Y. The vaccines induce good immunity after a single dose in older children and adults but are of little value in children below 3 years. The immunity is group specific. There is no Group B vaccine available at present.

NEISSERIA GONORRHOEAE (GONOCOCCUS)

N. gonorrhoeae causes the venereal disease gonorrhea. The gonococcus was first described in gonorrheal pus by Neisser in 1879. Bumm in 1885 cultured the coccus and proved its pathogenicity by inoculating human volunteers. Gonococci resemble meningococci very closely in many properties.

Morphology: In smears from the urethral discharge in acute gonorrhea, the organism appears as a diplococcus with the adjacent sides concave, being typically kidney-shaped. It is found predominantly within the polymorphs, some cells containing as many as a hundred cocci.

Gonococci possess pili on their surface. Pili facilitate adhesion of the cocci to mucosal surfaces and promote virulence by inhibiting phagocytosis. Piliated gonococci agglutinate human red blood cells but not red cells from other mammals. The hemagglutination is not inhibited by mannose.

Cultural characteristics: Gonococci are more difficult to grow than meningococci. They are aerobic but may grow anaerobically also. Growth occurs best at pH 7.2–7.6 and at a temperature of 35–36 °C. It is essential to provide 5–10% CO_2. They grow well on chocolate agar and Mueller–Hinton agar. A popular selective medium is the Thayer–Martin medium (containing vancomycin, colistin and nystatin) which inhibits most contaminants including nonpathogenic neisseria.

Colonies are small, round, translucent, convex

or slightly umbonate, with finely granular surface and lobate margins. They are soft and easily emulsifiable.

Four types of colonies have been recognised – T1 to T4. Types 1 and 2 form small brown colonies. The cocci are piliated, autoagglutinable and virulent. Types 3 and 4 form larger, granular, nonpigmented colonies. T3 and T4 cocci are nonpiliated, form smooth suspensions and are avirulent. Fresh isolates from acute cases of gonorrhea generally form T1 and T2 colonies. On serial subculture, they change to T3 or T4 colonial morphology. T1 and T2 types are also known as P+ and P++, respectively, while T3 and T4 are known as P−.

Biochemical reactions: Gonococci resemble meningococci except in the effect on maltose. Gonococci acidify only glucose and not maltose.

Antigenic properties: Gonococci are antigenically heterogeneous. They are capable of changing their surface structures in vitro. They probably do so in vivo as well, to avoid host defence. The surface structures include the following:

Pili which are hairlike structures several micrometres long, act as virulence factors by promoting attachment to host cells and inhibiting phagocytosis. Pili are composed of repeating peptide subunits (pilins) consisting of conserved (constant) and variable regions. Pili undergo antigenic and phase variation.

The trilaminar *outer membrane* of gonococci contains many different proteins. Protein I is the major constituent and shows antigenic diversity, which helps in typing gonococcal strains. Protein I of a single strain is antigenically constant, though it shows considerable heterogeneity between different strains. There are two variants of protein I, called IA and IB. Any one strain carries only either IA or IB but not both. Using monoclonal antibodies to protein I epitopes, gonococci can be classified into several serovars, A1 to 24 and B1 to 32.

Proteins I and III act as ligands attaching the coccus to the host cells. They also form transmembrane channels (porins) which play a role in the exchange of molecules across the outer membrane.

Protein II is related to the opacity of the gonococcal colonies and so is called the 'opacity associated' (OPA) outer membrane protein. Strains with the OPA protein form opaque colonies and those lacking it transparent colonies. A strain may express 0 to 3 serological varieties of the OPA protein at a time. OPA may be responsible for attachment to the host cells and also for the clumping of cocci seen in urethral exudate smears.

The outer membrane also contains lipopolysaccharide (endotoxin) which may be responsible for the toxicity in gonococcal infections. Many other proteins of poorly defined roles in pathogenicity have been described. Both gonococci and meningococci elaborate IgA1 protease that splits and inactivates IgA.

Resistance: The gonococcus is a very delicate organism, readily killed by heat, drying and antiseptics. It is a strict parasite and dies in 1–2 hours in exudates outside the body.

In cultures, the coccus dies in 3–4 days but survives in slant cultures at 35 °C if kept under sterile paraffin oil. Cultures may be stored for years if frozen quickly and left at −70 °C.

Pathogenicity: Gonorrhea is a venereal disease which has been known from ancient times. The name gonorrhea (meaning, flow of seed) was first employed by Galen in 130 AD.

The disease is acquired by sexual contact. The first step in infection is adhesion of gonococci to the urethra or other mucosal surfaces. Pili are involved in this adhesion. Adhesion is rapid and firm so that micturition after exposure offers no protection against infection. The cocci penetrate through the intercellular spaces and reach the subepithelial connective tissue by the third day after infection. The incubation period is 2–8 days. In men, the disease starts as an acute urethritis with a mucopurulent discharge containing gonococci in large numbers. The infection extends along the urethra to the prostate, seminal vesicles and epididymis. Chronic urethritis may lead to stricture formation. The infection may spread to the periurethral tissues, causing abscesses and multiple discharging sinuses ('watercan perineum').

In women, the initial infection involves the urethra and cervix uteri. The vaginal mucosa is not usually affected in adults because the stratified squamous epithelium is resistant to infection by the cocci and also because of the acid pH of vaginal secretions. (Vulvovaginitis occurs in prepubertal girls). The infection may extend to Bartholin's glands, endometrium and fallopian tubes. Pelvic inflammatory disease and salpingitis may lead to sterility. Rarely, peritonitis may develop with perihepatic inflammation (Fitz–Hugh–Curtis syndrome). Clinical disease is as a rule less severe in women, many of whom may carry gonococci in the cervix without any symptoms. Asymptomatic carriage of gonococci is rare in men.

Proctitis occurs in both sexes. It may develop by direct contiguous spread in women but in men is usually the result of anal sex. Conjunctivitis may occur, usually due to autoinoculation by the patient's fingers. Blood invasion may occur from the primary site of infection and may lead to metastatic lesions such as arthritis, ulcerative endocarditis and very rarely meningitis. Occasional cases of pyemia have been reported.

A nonvenereal infection is gonococcal ophthalmia in the newborn, which results from direct infection during passage through the birth canal. Gonococcal bacteremia leads to skin lesions, especially hemorrhagic papules and pustules on the hands, forearm, feet and legs, and to tenosynovitis and suppurative arthritis, usually of the knees, ankles and wrists.

Gonococci contain several plasmids. Ninety-five per cent of the strains have a small cryptic plasmid of unknown function. Two other transmissible plasmids contain genes that code for beta lactamase which causes resistance to penicillin.

Epidemiology: Gonorrhea is an exclusively human disease, there being no natural infection in animals. Experimental disease may be produced in chimpanzees by urethral inoculation. A lethal infection can be produced in mice by intracerebral inoculation.

The only source of infection is a human carrier or less often a patient. The existence of asymptomatic carriage in women makes them a reservoir serving to perpetuate infection among their male contacts. The mode of infection is almost exclusively venereal. Fomites do not play any significant role, as the cocci die rapidly outside the human body. The only nonvenereal infection is ophthalmia neonatorum. Once very common, this has been controlled by the practice of instilling 1% silver nitrate solution into the eyes of all newborn babies (Crede's method).

When sulphonamides, and later penicillin, were found very effective for the treatment of gonorrhea, it was hoped that the disease could be eradicated. However, after a temporary decline, its incidence has been rising steeply. In 1970, the global incidence of new cases was estimated at 16 million, making it one of the most common infective diseases. In some areas, gonorrhea has reached epidemic proportions, especially in adolescents and young adults. The reasons for the increase in gonococcal infection are largely social and cultural. In the 1980s, with the AIDS scare, there was a noticeable decline in the incidence of gonorrhea, but this has not been kept up. A higher incidence of gonorrhea has been observed in persons belonging to blood group B. The basis for this is not known.

Laboratory diagnosis: In the acute stage, diagnosis can be established readily but chronic cases sometimes present great difficulties. In acute gonorrhea the urethral discharge contains gonococci in large numbers. The meatus is cleaned with a gauze soaked in saline and a sample of the discharge collected with a platinum loop for culture, or directly on slide for smears. In women, besides the urethral discharge, cervical swabs should also be collected. This should be done carefully, using a speculum. High vaginal swabs are not satisfactory.

In chronic infections, there may not be any

urethral discharge. The 'morning drop' of secretion may be examined or some exudate may be obtained after prostatic massage. It may also be possible to demonstrate gonococci in the centrifuged deposits of urine in cases where no urethral discharge is available.

The demonstration of intracellular Gram negative diplococci in stained smears provides a presumptive evidence of gonorrhea in men. It has to be emphasised that diagnosis of gonorrhea by smear examination is unreliable in women as some of the normal genital flora have an essentially similar morphology. The use of fluorescent antibody techniques for the identification of gonococci in smears has increased the sensitivity and specificity of diagnosis by microscopy.

For culture, specimens should be inoculated on prewarmed plates, immediately on collection. If this is not possible, specimens should be collected with charcoal impregnated swabs and sent to the laboratory in Stuart's transport medium. In acute gonorrhea, cultures can be obtained readily on chocolate agar or Mueller–Hinton agar incubated

at 35–36 °C under 5–10% CO_2. In chronic cases, where mixed infection is usual and in the examination of lesions such as proctitis, however, it is better to use a selective medium such as the Thayer–Martin medium. The growth is identified by morphology and biochemical reactions.

It may not be possible to obtain gonococci in culture from some chronic cases or from patients with metastatic lesions such as arthritis. Serological tests may be of value in such instances. The complement fixation test has been used with varying degrees of success. It becomes positive only some weeks after the infection is established and may remain positive for months or years after the disease has been cured. The test may also be positive following meningococcal infections. It is necessary to use a polyvalent antigen because of the antigenic heterogeneity of the gonococcal strains. The test is not suitable for routine use. Many other serological tests have been attempted, including precipitation, passive agglutination, immunofluorescence, and radioimmunoassay using whole-cell lysate, pilus protein and lipopolysaccharide antigens. However, no serological test has been found useful for routine diagnostic purposes.

Treatment: In 1935, when sulphonamides were introduced for treating gonorrhea, all strains were sensitive to the drug but resistance developed rapidly. Again, when penicillin was introduced, all strains were highly sensitive (MIC 0.005 unit/ml). From 1957, strains with decreased susceptibility (MIC higher than 0.1 unit/ml) became common. As patients infected with such strains did not respond to the usual doses of penicillin, very large doses of penicillin, 2.4–4.8 million units were used. From 1976, gonococci producing β lactamase (penicillinase) have appeared, rendering penicillin treatment ineffective. These penicillinase-producing N. gonorrhoeae (PPNG) have spread widely.

The Centers for Disease Control and Prevention, USA in 1993 recommended the following schedule for uncomplicated gonorrhea: Ceftriaxone 125 mg single IM dose or Ciprofloxacin 500 mg (or

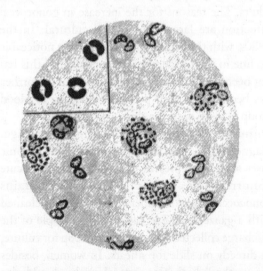

Fig. 25.2 Gonococci in urethral pus. Inset: enlarged view to show kidney shaped cells with adjacent surfaces concave.

Ofloxacin 400 mg) single oral dose, plus Doxycycline 100 mg twice daily for 7 days or Erythromycin 1 g single oral dose. The regimen is costly but works very well against gonococci and the frequently coexisting chlamydial infection.

Prophylaxis: Control of gonorrhea consists of early detection of cases, contact tracing, health education and other general measures. As even clinical disease does not confer any immunity, vaccination has no place in prophylaxis.

NONGONOCOCCAL (NONSPECIFIC) URETHRITIS

Along with an increase in the incidence of gonorrhea, there has also been an increase, in recent years, of cases of chronic urethritis where gonococci cannot be demonstrated. This has been called nongonococcal or nonspecific urethritis. In some of these, urethritis forms part of a syndrome consisting of conjunctivitis and arthritis in addition (Reiter's syndrome). Some of these cases may be due to gonococcal infection, the cocci persisting as L-forms and hence undetectable by routine tests. The majority of such cases are, however, the result of infections of diverse etiology. The most important of these are *Chlam. trachomatis, Ureaplasma urealyticum* and *Mycoplasma hominis.* Herpes virus and cytomegalovirus may also account for some cases. Urethritis may also be caused by other bacteria (for example, *Gardnerella vaginalis, Acinetobacter lwoffi, Ac. calcoaceticus),* fungi *(Candida albicans),* protozoa *(Trichomonas vaginalis),* or even by mechanical or chemical irritation. As etiological diagnosis is seldom achieved, the management of this syndrome is difficult.

COMMENSAL NEISSERIAE

Several species of Neisseriae inhabit the normal respiratory tract. The characteristic features of some of the common species are listed in Table 25.1.

Table 25.1 Differential characteristics of Neisseriae

Species	Colonies	Growth		Fermentation			Serological classification
		On nutrient agar	At 22°C	Glucose	Maltose	Sucrose	
N. menigitidis	Round, smooth, shiny, creamy consistency	–	–	A	A	–	Thirteen antigenic groups
N. gonorrhoeae	Same as above, but smaller and more opalescent	–	–	A	–	–	Antigenically heterogenous
N. flavescens	Resemble meningococcus but pigmented yellow	+	+	–	–	–	Antigenically distinct homogeneous group
N. sicca	Small, dry, opaque, wrinkled, brittle	+	+	A	A	A	Autoagglutinable
N. catarrhalis (*Branhamella catarrhalis*)	Variable, smooth and translucent or adherent and opaque, not easily emulsifiable	+	+	–	–	–	Autoagglutinable

Their pathogenic significance is uncertain though some of them (for example, *N. flavescens, N. catarrhalis*) have been reported occasionally as having caused meningitis.

N. *lactamica*, frequently isolated from the nasopharynx is closely related to meningococci, though it is virtually avirulent. It differs from pathogenic neisseriae in being positive in the ONPG test for beta galactosidase. Nasopharyngeal colonisation by *N. lactamica* in young children may be responsible for the presence in them of antibodies protective against meningococcal infection.

Neisseria catarrhalis is now classified as *Moraxella (Branhamella) catarrhalis*. It is an opportunistic pathogen capable of causing laryngitis, bronchopneumonia, meningitis, sinusitis and middle ear disease.

Further Reading

Britigan BE and PF Sparling 1985. Gonococcal infection. *New Engl J Med.* 312:1683.

Cartwright K (ed) 1995. *Meningococcal Disease*, Chichester: John Wiley.

Morse SA et al 1989. Perspectives on pathogenic Neisseria spp. *Clin Microbiol Rev*, 2 (Suppl.1S).

Rosentstein NC et al. 2001. Meningococcal diseases. *New Engl J Med.* 334:1378

Tunkel AR and MW Scheld 1995. Acute bacterial meningitis. *Lancet*, 346:1675.

26 Corynebacterium

Corynebacteria are Gram positive, nonacid fast, nonmotile rods with irregularly stained segments, and sometimes granules. They frequently show club shaped swellings and hence the name corynebacteria (from *coryne*, meaning club). The most important member of the genus is *C. diphtheriae,* the causative agent of diphtheria.

Diphtheria has been known from ancient times. Aretaeus, the Cappodocian, in the second century, described the Egyptian or Syriac ulcer, which most medical historians agree can be identified as diphtheria. The disease was first recognised as a clinical entity by Bretonneau (1826) who called it 'diphtherite'. The name is derived from the tough, leathery pseudo-membrane formed in the disease (*diphtheros*, meaning leather). The diphtheria bacillus was first observed and described by Klebs (1883) but was first cultivated by Loeffler (1884). It is hence known as the Klebs–Loeffler bacillus or KLB. Loeffler studied the effect of the bacillus in experimental animals and concluded that the disease was due to some diffusible product of the bacillus. Roux and Yersin (1888) discovered the diphtheria exotoxin and established its pathogenic effect. The antitoxin was described by von Behring (1890).

CORYNEBACTERIUM DIPHTHERIAE

Morphology: The diphtheria bacillus is a slender rod with a tendency to clubbing at one or both ends, measuring approximately 3–6 μm × 0.6–0.8 μm. The bacilli are pleomorphic. They are nonsporing, noncapsulated and nonmotile. Cells often show septa, and branching is infrequently observed. They are Gram positive but tend to be decolorised easily. Granules composed of polymetaphosphate are seen in the cells. They are more strongly Gram positive than the rest of the bacterial cell. Stained with Loeffler's methylene blue, the granules take up a bluish purple colour and hence they are called metachromatic granules. They are also called *volutin* or *Babes Ernst granules*. They are often situated at the poles of the bacilli and are called *polar bodies*. Special stains, such as Albert's, Neisser's and Ponder's have been devised for demonstrating the granules clearly. The bacilli are arranged in a characteristic fashion in smears. They are usually seen in pairs, palisades (resembling stakes of a fence) or small groups, the bacilli being at various angles to each other, resembling the letters V or L. This has been called the *Chinese letter* or *cuneiform arrangement*. This is due to the incomplete separation of the daughter cells after binary fission (Fig. 26.1).

Cultural characteristics: Growth is scanty on ordinary media. Enrichment with blood, serum or egg is necessary for good growth. The optimum temperature for growth is 37 °C (range 15–40 °C) and optimum pH 7.2. It is an aerobe and a facultative anaerobe.

The usual media employed for cultivation of the diphtheria bacillus are Loeffler's serum slope and tellurite blood agar. Diphtheria bacilli grow on Loeffler's serum slope very rapidly and colonies can be seen in 6–8 hours, long before other bacteria grow. Colonies are at first small, circular white opaque discs but enlarge on continued incubation and may acquire a distinct yellow tint. Several

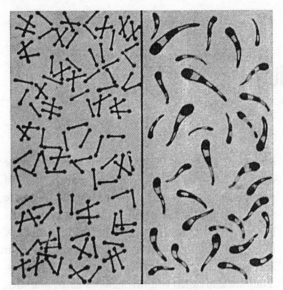

Fig. 26.1 Left: normal forms of *C.diphtheria*
Right: involution forms

modifications of tellurite blood agar have been utilised, such as McLeod's and Hoyle's media. Tellurite (0.04%) inhibits the growth of most other bacteria, acting as a selective agent. Diphtheria bacilli reduce tellurite to metallic tellurium, which is incorporated in the colonies giving them a grey or black colour. The growth of diphtheria bacilli may be delayed on the tellurite medium and colonies may take two days to appear. Based on colonial morphology on the tellurite medium and other properties, McLeod classified diphtheria bacilli into three types – *gravis, intermedius* and *mitis*. The names were originally proposed to relate to the clinical severity of the disease produced by the three types – gravis, causing the most serious, and mitis the mildest variety, with intermedius being responsible for disease of intermediate severity. However, this association is not constant. The necessity for typing an isolate in the laboratory has been superseded by the need to know whether the strain is toxigenic or not. Certain biological characteristics of these individua! types have some value.

The gravis and intermedius types are associated with high case fatality rates, while mitis infections are less lethal. Paralytic complications are most common in gravis, hemorrhagic complications in gravis and intermedius, and obstructive lesions in the air passage in mitis infections. In general, mitis is the predominant strain in endemic areas, while gravis and intermedius tend to be epidemic. The mitis type is better able than the more virulent types to establish a commensal relationship with the host. Wide variations have been noted in the frequency of the different types in different places at different times. There is evidence to show that the gravis and, to a lesser extent, the intermedius strains are able to spread more readily than the mitis in populations naturally immune or artificially immunised. Table 26.1 lists the characteristics of the three types.

Diphtheria bacilli ferment with the production of acid, (but no gas) glucose, galactose, maltose and dextrin (but not lactose, mannitol or sucrose). Some strains of virulent diphtheria bacilli have been found to ferment sucrose. It is necessary to employ Hiss's serum water for testing sugar fermentation. Proteolytic activity is absent. They do not hydrolyse urea or form phosphatase.

TOXIN

Virulent strains of diphtheria bacilli produce a very powerful exotoxin. The pathogenic effects of the bacillus are due to the toxin. Almost all strains of gravis and intermedius (about 95–99 per cent) are toxigenic, while only about 80–85 per cent of the mitis strains are so. The proportions vary with the origin of the cultures tested. Strains of all three types are invariably virulent when isolated from acute cases. Avirulent strains are common among convalescents, contacts and carriers, particularly in those with extrafaucial infection. There is considerable variation in the amount of toxin produced by the different strains, some strains producing it abundantly and others only poorly. But the toxin produced by all the strains of diphtheria

Table 26.1 Type differentiation of diphtheria bacilli

	Gravis	Intermedius	Mitis
Morphology	Usually short rods, with uniform staining, few or no granules. Some degree of pleomorphism, with irregularly barred, snow-shoe and tear-drop forms	Long barred forms with clubbed ends; poor granulation, very pleomorphic	Long, curved, pleomorphic rods with prominent granules
Colony on tellurite blood agar	In 18 hours, colony is 1–2 mm in size, with greyish black centre, paler, semitranslucent periphery and commencing crenation of edge. In 2–3 days, 3–5 mm in size, flat colony with raised dark centre and crenated edge with radial striation – 'daisy head' colony	18 hour colony small, 1mm in size, misty. Does not enlarge in 48 hours, dull granular centre with smoother, more glistening periphery and a lighter ring near the edge – 'frog's egg' colony	Size variable, shiny black. In 2–3 days, colonies become flat, with a central elevation 'poached egg' colony
Consistency of colonies	Like 'cold margarine', brittle, moves as a whole on the plate, not easily picked out or emulsifiable	Intermediate between gravis and mitis	Soft, buttery, easily emulsifiable
Hemolysis	Variable	Nonhemolytic	Usually hemolytic
Growth in broth	Surface pellicle, granular deposit, little or no turbidity	Turbidity in 24 hours, clearing in 48 hours, with fine granular sediment	Diffuse turbidity with soft pellicle later
Glycogen and starch fermentation	Positive	Negative	Negative

bacilli is qualitatively similar. The strain almost universally used for toxin production is the 'Park Williams 8' strain, which has been variously described as a mitis (Topley and Wilson) and an intermedius strain (Cruickshank).

The diphtheria toxin is a protein and has been crystallised. It has a molecular weight of about 62,000. It is extremely potent and the lethal dose for a 250 g guinea pig is 0.0001 mg. It consists of two fragments, A and B, of MW 24,000 and 38,000, respectively. Both fragments are necessary for the toxic effect. When released by the bacterium, the toxin is inactive because the active site on fragment A is masked. Activation is probably accomplished by proteases present in the culture medium and infected tissues. All the enzymatic activity of the toxin is present in fragment A. Fragment B is responsible for binding the toxin to the cells. The antibody to fragment B is protective by preventing the binding of the toxin to the cells. The toxin is labile. Prolonged storage, incubation at 37 °C for 4–6 weeks, treatment with 0.2–0.4 per cent formalin or acid pH converts it to toxoid. Toxoid is toxin that has lost its toxicity but not its antigenicity. It is capable of inducing antitoxin and reacting specifically with it.

The toxigenicity of the diphtheria bacillus depends on the presence in it of corynephages (tox+), which act as the genetic determinant controlling toxin production. Nontoxigenic strains may be rendered toxigenic by infecting them with *beta* phage or some other toxlarger phage. This is known as *lysogenic or phage conversion*. The toxigenicity remains only as long as the bacillus is lysogenic. When the bacillus is cured of its phage, as by growing it in the presence of antiphage serum, it loses the toxigenic capacity.

Toxin production is also influenced by the concentration of iron in the medium. The optimum level of iron for toxin production is 0.1 mg per litre, while a concentration of 0.5 mg per litre inhibits the formation of toxin. The diphtheria toxin acts by inhibiting protein synthesis. Specifically, fragment A inhibits polypeptide chain elongation in the presence of nicotinamide adenine dinucleotide by inactivating the elongation factor, EF-2. It has a special affinity for certain tissues such as the myocardium, adrenals and nerve endings.

Resistance: Cultures may remain viable for two or more weeks at 25–30 °C. It is readily destroyed by heat in 10 minutes at 58 °C and in a minute at 100 °C. It is more resistant to the action of light, desiccation and freezing than most nonsporing bacilli. It has been cultured from dried bits of pseudomembrane after 14 weeks. It remains fully virulent in blankets and floor dust for five weeks. It is easily destroyed by antiseptics. It is susceptible to penicillin, erythromycin and broad spectrum antibiotics.

Antigenic structure: Diphtheria bacilli are antigenically heterogeneous. By agglutination, gravis strains have been classified into 13 types, intermedius into 4 types and mitis into 40 types. Gravis strains of types I and III have been reported to be common in Great Britain, type II worldwide, type IV mainly in Egypt and type V in the USA.

No connection has been established between type specificity and other characters.

Bacteriophage typing: About 15 bacteriophage types have been described. Type I and III strains are mitis, IV and VI intermedius, VII avirulent gravis and the remainder virulent gravis. The phage types are apparently stable. A system of bacteriocin (diphthericin) typing has also been described. Other methods of typing include bacterial polypeptide analysis, DNA restriction patterns and hybridisation with DNA probes.

Pathogenicity: The incubation period in diphtheria is commonly 3–4 days but may on occasion be as short as one day. In carriers, the incubation period may be very prolonged. The site of infection may be (1) faucial; (2) laryngeal; (3) nasal; (4) otitic; (5) conjunctival; (6) genital-vulval, vaginal or prepucial; and (7) cutaneous, which is usually a secondary infection on pre-existing skin lesions. Sometimes diphtheritic whitlow or ulcer may occur. Cutaneous infections are commonly caused by nontoxigenic strains of diphtheria bacilli.

Faucial diphtheria is the commonest type and may vary from mild catarrhal inflammation to very widespread involvement. According to the clinical severity, diphtheria may be classified as:

1. Malignant or hypertoxic in which there is severe toxemia with marked adenitis (bullneck). Death is due to circulatory failure. There is high incidence of paralytic sequelae in those who recover.

2. Septic, which leads to ulceration, cellulitis and even gangrene around the pseudomembrane; and

3. Hemorrhagic, which is characterised by bleeding from the edge of the membrane, epistaxis, conjunctival hemorrhage, purpura and generalised bleeding tendency.

The common complications are:

1. Asphyxia due to mechanical obstruction of the respiratory passage by the pseudomembrane for

which an emergency tracheostomy may become necessary.

2. Acute circulatory failure, which may be peripheral or cardiac.

3. Postdiphtheritic paralysis, which typically occurs in the third or fourth week of the disease; palatine and ciliary but not pupillary paralysis is characteristic, and spontaneous recovery is the rule.

4. Septic, such as pneumonia and otitis media. Relapse may occur in about 1% of cases.

Diphtheria is a toxemia. The bacilli remain confined to the site of entry, where they multiply and form the toxin. The toxin causes local necrotic changes and the resulting fibrinous exudate, together with the disintegrating epithelial cells, leucocytes, erythrocytes and bacteria, constitute the pseudomembrane, which is characteristic of diphtheritic infection. The mechanical complications of diphtheria are due to the membrane, while the systemic effects are due to the toxin.

Nontoxigenic strains of diphtheria bacilli may cause infection even in immunised individuals, as immunity with the toxoid does not confer antibacterial immunity. Such infection is mild though pseudomembrane formation may sometimes occur.

Diphtheria does not occur naturally in animals but infection can be produced experimentally. Susceptibility varies in different species. Subcutaneous inoculation of a guinea pig with a culture of virulent diphtheria bacillus will cause death in 1–4 days. At autopsy, the following features can be observed:

1. gelatinous, hemorrhagic edema and, often, necrosis at the site of inoculation;

2. swollen and congested draining lymph nodes;

3. peritoneal exudate which may be clear, cloudy or bloodstained;

4. congested abdominal viscera;

5. enlarged hemorrhagic adrenals, which is the pathognomonic feature;

6. clear, cloudy or bloodstained pleural exudate; and

7. sometimes, pericardial effusion.

Laboratory diagnosis: Laboratory confirmation of diphtheria is necessary for the initiation of control measures and for epidemiological purposes but not for the treatment of individual cases. Specific treatment should be instituted *immediately* on suspicion of diphtheria without waiting for laboratory tests. Any delay may be fatal.

Laboratory diagnosis consists of isolation of the diphtheria bacillus and demonstration of its toxicity. One or two swabs from the lesions are collected under vision, using a tongue depressor. Diphtheria bacilli may not always be demonstrable in smears from the lesion, nor can they be confidently differentiated from some commensal corynebacteria normally found in the throat. Hence smear examination alone is not sufficient for diagnosing diphtheria but is important in identifying Vincent's angina. For this, a Gram or Leishman stained smear is examined for Vincent's spirochetes and fusiform bacilli. Toxigenic diphtheria bacilli may be identified in smears by immunofluorescence. For culture, the swabs are inoculated on Loeffler's serum slope, tellurite blood agar and a plate of ordinary blood agar, the last for differentiating streptococcal or staphylococcal pharyngitis, which may simulate diphtheria. If the swab cannot be inoculated promptly it should be kept moistened with sterile serum so that the bacilli remain viable. The serum slope may show growth in 4–8 hours but if negative, will have to be incubated for 24 hours. Smears stained with methylene blue or one of the special stains (Neisser or Albert stain) will show the bacilli with metachromatic granules and typical arrangement. Tellurite plates will have to be incubated for at least two days before being considered negative, as growth may sometimes be delayed. The tellurite medium is particularly important in the isolation of diphtheria bacilli from convalescents, contacts and carriers as in these cases they may be outnumbered by other bacteria.

VIRULENCE TESTS

Any isolate of the diphtheria bacillus should be tested for virulence or toxigenicity for the bacteriological diagnosis to be complete. Virulence testing may be by in vivo or in vitro methods, the former by the subcutaneous or intradermal test and the latter by the precipitation test or the tissue culture test.

In vivo tests

1. *Subcutaneous test:* The growth from an overnight culture on Loeffler's slope is emulsified in 2–4 ml broth and 0.8 ml of the emulsion injected subcutaneously into two guinea pigs, one of which has been protected with 500 units of the diphtheria antitoxin 18–24 hours previously. If the strain is virulent, the unprotected animal will die within four days, showing the autopsy appearance described earlier. The method is not usually employed as it is wasteful of animals.

2. *Intracutaneous test:* The broth emulsion of the culture is inoculated intracutaneously into two guinea pigs (or rabbits) so that each receives 0.1 ml in two different sites. One animal acts as the control and should receive 500 units of antitoxin the previous day. The other is given 50 units of antitoxin intraperitoneally four hours after the skin test, in order to prevent death. Toxigenicity is indicated by inflammatory reaction at the site of injection, progressing to necrosis in 48–72 hours in the test animal and no change in the control animal. An advantage in the intracutaneous test is that the animals do not die. As many as ten strains can be tested at a time on a rabbit.

In vitro test

1. *Elek's gel precipitation test:* A rectangular strip of filter paper impregnated with diphtheria antitoxin (1000 units/ml) is placed on the surface of a 20% normal horse serum agar in a petri dish while the medium is still fluid. If horse serum is not available, sheep or rabbit serum may be used. When the agar has set, the surface is dried and narrow streaks of the strains are made at right angles to the filter paper strip. A positive and negative control should be put up. The plate is incubated at 37 °C for 24–48 hours. Toxins produced by the bacterial growth will diffuse in the agar and where it meets the antitoxin at optimum concentration will produce a line of precipitation (Fig. 26.2). The presence of such arrowhead lines of precipitates indicates that the strain is toxigenic. No precipitate will form in the case of nontoxigenic strains. This test is very convenient and economical but some brands of peptone and some samples of serum do not give satisfactory results.

2. *Tissue culture test:* The toxigenicity of diphtheria bacilli can be demonstrated by incorporating the strains in the agar overlay of cell culture monolayers. The toxin produced diffuses into the cells below and kills them.

Epidemiology: Diphtheria was formerly an

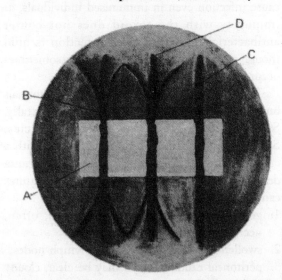

Fig.26.2 Elek's test. A. Filter paper strip impregnated with A. *diphtheriae* antitoxin. B. Toxigenic strain. C. Nontoxigenic strain. D. Test strain showing toxigenicity.

important pediatric disease all over the world but following the development of effective prophylactics and mass immunisation, the disease has been virtually eradicated from most advanced countries. In those developing countries where childhood immunisation programmes have been implemented effectively, diphtheria has become rare but in others it continues to be a serious problem. The prolonged and extensive epidemic of diphtheria in parts of the erstwhile Soviet Union in the 1990s, involving several thousands, with a mortality of up to 20 per cent is a warning of what can befall countries that neglect immunisation and let living conditions deteriorate.

In endemic areas, it is mainly a disease of childhood. It is rare in the first year of life due to the passive immunity obtained from the mother, reaches a peak between two and five years, falls slowly between five and 10 years, and rapidly between 10 and 15 years with only very low incidence afterwards because of active immunity acquired by repeated subclinical infections.

Asymptomatic carriers who outnumber cases by a hundredfold or more in endemic areas are the most important source of infection. In the temperate regions, carriage is mainly in the nose and throat. Nasal carriers harbour the bacilli for longer periods than pharyngeal carriers. In the tropics, diphtheria bacilli infect the skin more often than the respiratory tract. Toxigenic diphtheria bacilli may persist in the skin for over three years. Cutaneous infections may stimulate natural immunity to diphtheria but may also lead to faucial diphtheria in nonimmune contacts. Fomites do not seem to play an important role though in special situations toys and pencils may act as vehicles of infection.

In nature, diphtheria is virtually confined to human beings, though cows may on occasion be found to have diphtheritic infection of the udder. The infection in such cases is invariably transmitted by the milker. The infection may be spread through the milk of infected cows.

PROPHYLAXIS

Diphtheria can be controlled by immunisation. Three methods of immunisation are available: active, passive and combined. Of these, only active immunisation can provide herd immunity and lead to eradication of the disease. Passive and combined immunisation can only provide emergency protection to susceptible individuals exposed to risk.

The objective of immunisation is to increase protective levels of antitoxin in circulation. Early in the development of diphtheria prophylactics, when immunising agents were scarce and not free from risk, it was customary to test for susceptibility before active immunisation was given. The susceptibility test used was the Schick test introduced in 1913. The Schick test is no longer in use. (Older editions of this textbook may be consulted for details of Schick test, if required). The availability of safe and effective toxoid preparations has made susceptibility tests unnecessary. If, for any special reason, the circulating antitoxin level is to be assayed, it can now be done by serological tests such as passive hemagglutination or by neutralisation in cell culture. Antitoxin level of 0.01 unit or more per ml of blood is considered as index of immunity.

Active immunisation: Diphtheria immunisation in children was initiated in 1913 by von Behring using a toxin–antitoxin mixture containing only enough antitoxin to leave the toxin just underneutralised. This was a hazardous preparation because the final toxicity of such mixtures was determined not merely by the relative proportions of toxin and antitoxin but also by other variables, including the manner in which the toxin and antitoxin were mixed. If to a given amount of antitoxin, the equivalent amount of toxin was added all at once, the mixture remained nontoxic. If instead, the same amount of toxin was added in two or more instalments at intervals of 15 minutes or more, the resultant mixture was toxic. This paradoxical occurrence was known as the *Danysz phenomenon* and was due to the ability of the toxins and antitoxins to combine in varying proportions. When the toxin was added in instalments, the toxin added first combined with more than its equivalent of antitoxin, leaving insufficient antitoxin behind to neutralise the toxin added subsequently.

Several other preparations were introduced for active immunisation (for details, the third edition of this textbook may be consulted). Only two preparations are in use now, Formol toxoid (also known as fluid toxoid) and adsorbed toxoid. Formol toxoid is prepared by incubating the toxin with formalin at pH 7.4–7.6 for three to four weeks at 37 °C until the product is devoid of toxicity while retaining immunogenicity. Adsorbed toxoid is purified toxoid adsorbed onto insoluble aluminium compounds—usually aluminium phosphate, less often the hydroxide. Adsorbed toxoid is much more immunogenic than the fluid toxoid. Due to anxiety about an enhanced risk of provocative poliomyelitis, it was replaced by fluid toxoid for some time. However, as the risk is considered small and as the immunogenicity of fluid toxoid was unacceptably low, adsorbed toxoid is now used almost universally as the preferred agent. It is advisable to give adsorbed toxoid by intramuscular injections as subcutaneous injection may be painful.

Diphtheria toxoid is usually given in children as a trivalent preparation containing tetanus toxoid and pertussis vaccine also, as the DTP, DPT or triple vaccine. A quadruple vaccine containing in addition the inactivated poliovaccine is also available. For young children, diphtheria toxoid given in a dose of 10–25 Lf units is recommended. Smaller doses (1–2 Lf units) are used for older children and adults to minimise adverse reactions. In toxoid preparations the lower dose of toxoid is indicated by the small letter 'd' and the full dose by capital 'D'. For example, the tetanus diphtheria vaccine for adults containing low dose diphtheria toxoid is referred to as 'Td'.

The schedule of primary immunisation of infants and children consists of three doses of DPT given at intervals of at least four weeks, and preferably six weeks or more, followed by a fourth dose about a year afterwards. A further booster dose is given at school entry.

Passive immunisation: This is an emergency measure to be employed when susceptibles are exposed to infection, as when a case of diphtheria is admitted to general pediatric wards. It consists of the subcutaneous administration of 500–1000 units of antitoxin (antidiphtheritic serum, ADS). As this is a horse serum, precaution against hypersensitivity should be observed.

Combined immunisation: This consists of administration of the first dose of adsorbed toxoid on one arm, while ADS is given on the other arm, to be continued by the full course of active immunisation. Ideally, all cases that receive ADS prophylactically should receive combined immunisation.

STANDARDISATION OF TOXINS AND ANTITOXINS

The toxin content of culture filtrates varies considerably from batch to batch. As such their standardisation or measurement should be with reference to their biological activity. Ehrlich defined the minimum lethal dose (MLD) of the diphtheria toxin as the least amount of the toxin required to kill a guinea pig weighing 250 g within 96 hours after subcutaneous inoculation. One unit of antitoxin was defined as the smallest amount of antitoxin required to neutralise 100 MLD of toxin. Keeping a labile substance like the toxin as the standard led to inaccuracies. Toxin undergoes spontaneous denaturation into toxoid which will combine equally well with the antitoxin. Thus, any sample of toxin will contain a variable quantity of toxoid which will vitiate standardisation of antitoxin. The antitoxin, on the other hand, is permanently stable in the freeze-dried state. Therefore, the antitoxin has been adopted as the reference preparation. Ehrlich's original antitoxin is accepted as the international standard. One antitoxin unit (AU) is defined as the amount of antitoxin that has the same total combining capacity, for toxin and toxoid together as one unit of Ehrlich's original antitoxin.

Since toxin always contains some toxoid, two other units for measurement of toxin have been introduced, the L0 and L+ doses. The L0 (*Limes nul*) dose of the diphtheria toxin is the largest amount of toxin that, when mixed with one unit of antitoxin and injected subcutaneously into a 250 g guinea pig, will on the average cause no observable reaction. As 'no reaction' is not a definite end point, in actual practice, the end point is taken as minimum local edema. The L+ (*Limes tod*) dose of diphtheria toxin is the smallest amount of toxin that when mixed with one unit of antitoxin and injected subcutaneously into a 250 g guinea pig will on the average kill the animal within 96 hours. If toxin combines with antitoxin in constant proportions, it would be expected that the difference between the L+ dose and the L0 dose would be equal to 1 MLD. But when the estimations are actually made, it is found to vary from 10–100 MLD or more. This discrepancy is due to the presence in toxin preparations of varying amounts of toxoid and to the ability of the toxin and antitoxin to combine in varying proportions. This is known as the *Ehrlich phenomenon*.

The use of death as an end point for the titration of toxin is wasteful of animals. Romer introduced a method of titration employing the erythematous swelling produced by the intradermal injection of toxin, and its neutralisation by antitoxin. The minimum reacting dose (MRD) is the least amount of toxin that when injected intradermally in a guinea pig, causes an erythematous flush 5 mm in diameter visible after 36 hours. The Lr dose is the smallest amount of toxin which, after mixing with 1 unit of antitoxin, will produce a minimal skin reaction when injected intradermally into a guinea pig.

Ramon introduced a test tube method for titrating toxin and antitoxin based on flocculation. The flocculating or Lf unit of diphtheria toxin is the amount of toxin which flocculates most rapidly with one unit of antitoxin. The Lf unit has several advantages. It is inexpensive and rapid and does not need animals. It is also the only method available for the titration of toxoids. The amount of toxoid in prophylactics is expressed in Lf units. Many other in vitro tests have been developed for antigen assay. These include cell culture neutralisation tests using rabbit kidney cells, passive hemagglutination test with toxin coated tanned sheep RBC, and RIA.

Treatment: Specific treatment of diphtheria consists of antitoxic and antibiotic therapy. Antitoxin should be given immediately when a case is suspected as diphtheria, as the fatality rate increases with delay in starting antitoxic treatment. The dosage recommended is 20,000 to 1,00,000 units for serious cases, half the dose being given intravenously. Antitoxin treatment is generally not indicated in cutaneous diphtheria as the causative strains are usually nontoxigenic.

C. diphtheriae is sensitive to penicillin and can be cleared from the throat within a few days by penicillin treatment. Diphtheria patients are given a course of penicillin though it only supplements and does not replace antitoxin therapy. Erythromycin is more active than penicillin in the treatment of carriers.

OTHER PATHOGENIC CORYNEBACTERIA

C. ULCERANS

This bacillus related to *C. diphtheriae* can cause diphtheria-like lesions. It resembles the gravis type of the diphtheria bacillus but it liquefies gelatin, ferments trehalose slowly and does not reduce nitrate to nitrite. It produces two types of toxins, one probably identical with the diphtheria toxin and the other resembling the toxin of *C. pseudotuberculosis*. It is pathogenic to guinea pigs, the lesions produced resembling those caused by *C. diphtheriae*. It has been found to cause infection in cows, and human infections may be transmitted through cow's milk. It is sensitive to erythromycin. Diphtheria antitoxin is protective.

It has been suggested that *C. ulcerans* may be considered a subgroup of diphtheria bacilli rather than a separate species.

Arcanobacterium (formerly *Corynebacterium*) *haemolyticum* can cause pharyngitis and skin ulcers. *C. jakeium* can cause cutaneous and blood infections in immunocompromised hosts. It is usually multiresistant, responding only to vancomycin.

Corynebacteria of veterinary importance are the Preisz Nocard bacillus (*C. pseudotuberculosis*), which causes pseudotuberculosis in sheep and suppurative lymphadenitis in horses, *C. renale* causing cystitis and pyelonephritis in cattle and *C. equi*, isolated from pneumonia in foals.

CORYNEBACTERIA CAUSING SUPERFICIAL SKIN INFECTIONS

Erythrasma, a localised infection of the stratum corneum usually affecting the axilla and groin, is caused by *C. minutissimum*. This is a lipophilic corynebacterium and can be grown readily in media containing 20 per cent fetal calf serum.

C. tenuis has been associated with trichomycosis axillaris, characterised by the formation of pigmented nodules around axillary and pubic hair shafts.

DIPHTHEROIDS

Corynebacteria resembling *C. diphtheriae* occur as normal commensals in the throat, skin, conjunctiva and other areas. These may sometimes be mistaken for diphtheria bacilli and are called diphtheroids. In general, diphtheroids stain more uniformly than diphtheria bacilli, possess few or no metachromatic granules and tend to be arranged in parallel rows (palisades) rather than cuneiform pattern. However, some diphtheroids may be indistinguishable from diphtheria bacilli microscopically. Differentiation is by biochemical reactions and more reliably by virulence tests. The common diphtheroids are *C. pseudodiphtheriticum* (*C. hofmannii*) found in the throat and *C. xerosis* found in the conjunctival sac. The former is unease positive and does not ferment glucose, while the latter is unease negative and ferments glucose. Both are pyrazinamidase positive, unlike diphtheria bacilli.

OTHER CORYNEFORM BACTERIA

Besides genus *Corynebacterium*, a number of other genera of coryneform bacteria have been defined. Among them, the genus *Propionibacterium* is of medical interest as three species, *P. acnes*, *P. granulosum* and *P. avidum*, are constantly present on human skin. They are anaerobic and aerotolerant, growing well in lipid containing media. *P. acnes* is often isolated from acne lesions but its pathogenic role is uncertain.

Corynebacterium parvum which is frequently used as an immunomodulator is a mixture of Propionibacterium species.

Further Reading

Coyle MB and BA Lipsky 1990. Coryneform bacteria in infectious disease. *Clin Microbiol Rev* 3:227.

Hardy ERB et al. 1996. Resurgence of diphtheria in the former Soviet Union. *Lancet* 347:1991.

Hofler W. 1991. Cutaneous diphtheria. *Int J Dermatol.* 30:845.

Zamiri I. 1996. Corynebacterium. In Collee, JG et al (eds). *Practical Medical Microbiology.* 14th edn. Edinburgh: Churchill-Livingstone.

Bacillus

Sporogenous, rod-shaped bacteria are classified into two genera, the aerobic *Bacilli* and the anaerobic *Clostridia*. The genus *Bacillus* consists of aerobic bacilli forming heat resistant spores. They are Gram positive but tend to be decolourised easily so as to appear Gram variable, or even frankly Gram negative. They are generally motile with peritrichous flagella, the anthrax bacillus being a notable exception. Members of this group exhibit great diversity in their properties. The genus includes psychrophilic, mesophilic and thermophilic species, the maximum temperatures for vegetative growth ranging from about 25 °C to above 75 °C and the minimum from about 5 °C to 45 °C. Their salt tolerance varies from less than 2% to 25% NaCl.

Their spores are ubiquitous, being found in soil, dust, water and air and constitute the commonest contaminants in bacteriological culture media. *Bacillus anthracis*, the causative agent of anthrax, is the major pathogenic species. *B. cereus* can cause foodborne gastroenteritis. Some species may be responsible for opportunistic infections.

BACILLUS ANTHRACIS

Considerable historical interest is attached to the anthrax bacillus. It was the first pathogenic bacterium to be observed under the microscope (Pollender, 1849), the first communicable disease shown to be transmitted by inoculation of infected blood (Davaine, 1850), the first bacillus to be isolated in pure culture and shown to possess spores (Koch, 1876) and the first bacterium used for the preparation of an attenuated vaccine (Pasteur, 1881).

Anthrax was for long feared as a potential tool in biological warfare. This fear became an actual fact in 2001, when anthrax in the form of weapons grade spores, having enhanced dispersability and virulence was sent by mail to various destinations in the USA, causing disease and death in many persons.

Morphology: The anthrax bacillus is one of the largest of pathogenic bacteria, measuring 3–10 μm × 1–1.6 μm. In tissues, it is found singly, in pairs or in short chains, the entire chain being surrounded by a capsule. The capsule is polypeptide in nature, being composed of a polymer of d(–) glutamic acid. Capsules are not formed under ordinary conditions of culture but only if the media contain added bicarbonate or are incubated under 10–25% CO_2. If grown in media containing serum, albumin, charcoal or starch, capsule formation may occur in the absence of CO_2.

In cultures, the bacilli are arranged end to end in long chains. The ends of the bacilli are truncated or often concave and somewhat swollen so that a chain of bacilli presents a 'bamboo stick' appearance. Spores are formed in culture or in the soil but never in the animal body during life. Sporulation occurs under unfavourable conditions for growth and is encouraged by distilled water, 2% NaCl or growth in oxalated agar. Oxygen is required for sporulation, but not for germination. Sporulation is inhibited by calcium chloride. Spores are central or subterminal, elliptical or oval in shape, and are of the same width as the bacillary body so that they do not cause bulging of the vegetative cell (Fig. 27.1).

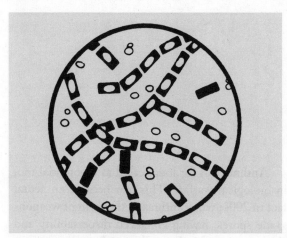

Fig. 27.1 Anthrax bacilli

The anthrax bacillus is Gram positive and nonacid fast. The spores do not stain by ordinary methods but can be stained differentially by special techniques. When stained with Sudan black B, fat globules may be made out within the bacilli. When blood films containing anthrax bacilli are stained with polychrome methylene blue for a few seconds and examined under the microscope, an amorphous purplish material is noticed around the bacilli. This represents the capsular material and is characteristic of the anthrax bacillus. This is called the M'Fadyean's reaction and is employed for the presumptive diagnosis of anthrax in animals.

The anthrax bacillus is nonmotile, unlike most other members of this genus.

Cultural characteristics: It is an aerobe, and a facultative anaerobe, with a temperature range for growth of 12–45 °C (optimum 35–37 °C). The optimum temperature for sporulation is 25–30 °C. Good growth occurs on ordinary media.

On agar plates, irregularly round colonies are formed, 2–3 mm in diameter, raised, dull, opaque, greyish white, with a frosted glass appearance. Under the low power microscope, the edge of the colony is composed of long, interlacing chains of bacilli, resembling locks of matted hair. This is called the 'Medusa head appearance' (Fig. 27.2). Virulent capsulated strains form rough cultures,

while avirulent or attenuated strains form smooth colonies. On gelatin stab culture, a characteristic 'inverted fir tree' appearance is seen, with slow liquefaction commencing from the top (Fig. 27.3). On blood agar, the colonies are nonhemolytic, though occasional strains produce a narrow zone of hemolysis. In broth growth occurs as floccular deposit, with little or no turbidity.

When *B. anthracis* is grown on the surface of a solid medium containing 0.05–0.50 units of penicillin/ml, in 3–6 hours the cells become large, spherical, and occur in chains on the surface of the agar, resembling a string of pearls. This 'string of pearls reaction' differentiates clearly *B. anthracis* from *B. cereus* and other aerobic spore bearers. Another useful test to differentiate between the two is the susceptibility of *B. anthracis* to gamma phage.

A selective medium (PLET medium), consisting of polymyxin, lysozyme, ethylene diamine tetra acetic acid (EDTA) and thallous acetate added to heart infusion agar, has been devised to isolate *B. anthracis* from mixtures containing other spore-bearing bacilli.

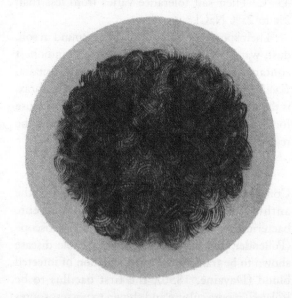

Fig. 27.2 Medusa head appearance of anthrax bacilli

Biochemical reactions: Glucose, maltose and sucrose are fermented producing acid but no gas. Nitrates are reduced to nitrites. Catalase is formed.

Resistance: The vegetative bacilli are not particularly resistant and are destroyed at 60 °C in 30 minutes. In the carcasses of animals which have died of anthrax, the bacilli remain viable in the bone marrow for a week and in the skin for two weeks. Normal heat fixation of smears may not kill the bacilli in blood films. The spores are highly resistant to physical and chemical agents. They have been isolated from naturally infected soil after as long as 60 years. They resist dry heat at 140 °C for 1–3 hours and boiling for 10 minutes. They survive in 5% phenol for weeks. $HgCl_2$ in a 1/1000 solution may fail to kill anthrax spores in less than 70 hours. Four per cent potassium permanganate kills them in 15 minutes. Destruction of the spores in animal products imported into nonendemic countries is achieved by 'duckering' in which formaldehyde is used as 2% solution at 30–40 °C for 20 minutes for disinfection of wool and as 0.25 per cent at 60 °C for six hours for animal hair and bristles. The anthrax bacillus is susceptible to sulphonamides, penicillin, erythromycin, streptomycin, tetracycline and chloramphenicol. Occasional strains resistant to penicillin have been met with.

Pathogenicity: In nature, anthrax is primarily a disease of cattle and sheep, and less often of horses and swine but experimentally most animals are susceptible to a greater or lesser degree. Rabbits, guinea pigs and mice are susceptible. Infection can be produced with difficulty in birds. Frogs are resistant, while toads are very susceptible.

Following the subcutaneous inoculation of a culture into a guinea pig, the animal dies in 24–72 hours, showing a local, gelatinous, hemorrhagic edema at the site of inoculation, extensive subcutaneous congestion and characteristically, an enlarged, dark red, friable spleen. The blood is dark red and coagulates less firmly than normally. The bacilli are found in large numbers in the local

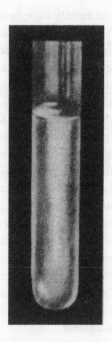

Fig. 27.3 Anthrax bacillus in gelatin stab culture showing inverted fir tree appearance

lesion, heart blood and spleen (more than 10^8 bacilli/ml). The bacilli are seen confined to the interior of the capillaries, where their numbers may be so great as to obstruct the flow of blood.

Two virulence factors have been identified—the *capsular polypeptide* and the *anthrax toxin*, each of which is encoded by a separate plasmid.

The capsular polypeptide aids virulence by inhibiting phagocytosis. Loss of the plasmid (px02) which controls capsule production leads to loss of virulence. This is how the live attenuated anthrax spore vaccine (Sterne strain) was obtained.

Anthrax toxin was identified by the finding that the injection of sterile plasma of guinea pigs dying of anthrax into healthy guinea pigs killed them and that death could be prevented by immune serum. The toxin is a complex of three fractions: the edema factor (OF or Factor I), the protective antigen factor (PA or Factor II) and the lethal factor (LF or Factor III). They are not toxic individually but the whole complex produces local edema and generalised shock. The three factors have been characterised and cloned. PA is the fraction which binds to the receptors on the target cell surface, and in turn provides attachment sites for OF or LF, facilitating their entry into the cell. Antibody to PA is protective because it blocks the first step in toxin activity, namely, its binding to target cells. OF is an adenyl cyclase which is activated only inside the target cells, leading to intracellular accumulation of cyclic AMP. This is believed to be responsible for the edema and other biological effects of the toxin. Entry of LF into the target cell causes cell death but the mechanism of action is not known. Loss of the plasmid (p×01) which encodes the anthrax toxin renders the strain avirulent. This is believed to have been the basis for the original anthrax vaccine developed by Pasteur. The avirulent Sterne vaccine strain is devoid of the plasmid coding for the capsular polysaccharide.

ANTHRAX

Anthrax is a zoonosis. Animals are infected by ingestion of the spores present in the soil. Direct spread from animal to animal is rare. The disease is generally a fatal septicemia but may sometimes be localised, resembling the cutaneous disease in human beings. Infected animals shed in the discharges from the mouth, nose and rectum, large numbers of bacilli, which sporulate in soil and remain as the source of infection.

Human anthrax is contracted from animals, directly or indirectly. The disease may be (1) cutaneous; (2) pulmonary; or (3) intestinal, all types leading to fatal septicemia or meningitis.

Cutaneous anthrax follows entry of the infection through the skin. The face, neck, hands, arms and back are the usual sites. The lesion starts as a papule 1–3 days after infection and becomes vesicular, containing fluid which may be clear or bloodstained. The whole area is congested and edematous, and several satellite lesions filled with serum or yellow fluid are arranged round a central necrotic lesion which is covered by a black eschar.

(The name anthrax, which means coal, comes from the black colour of the eschar.) The lesion is called a *malignant pustule*. The disease used to be common in dock workers carrying loads of hides and skins on their bare backs and hence was known as the *hide porter's disease*. Cutaneous anthrax generally resolves spontaneously, but 10–20 per cent of untreated patients may develop fatal septicemia or meningitis.

Pulmonary anthrax is called the *wool sorter's disease* because it used to be common in workers in wool factories, due to inhalation of dust from infected wool. This is a hemorrhagic pneumonia with a high fatality rate. Hemorrhagic meningitis may occur as a complication.

Intestinal anthrax is rare and occurs mainly in primitive communities who eat the carcasses of animals dying of anthrax. A violent enteritis with bloody diarrhea occurs, with high case fatality.

Human anthrax may be industrial or non-industrial (agricultural). The former is found in workers in industries such as meat packing or wool factories. Non-industrial anthrax is often an occupational disease in those who associate frequently with animals, such as veterinarians, butchers and farmers. It may also be found in the general population. Cutaneous anthrax used to be caused by shaving brushes made with animal hair. Stomoxys calcitrans and other biting insects may occasionally transmit infection mechanically.

Anthrax is enzootic in India, the number of animals infected running into tens of thousands annually. The disease is rare in some countries such as Britain, where infection is imported through contaminated hides, bone meal fertiliser and other animal products. The extent of anthrax in human beings is not clear but about 20,000 to 100,000 cases are believed to occur annually throughout the world, mostly in rural areas. Large epidemics of anthrax were reported from Russia and Zimbabwe during 1978–80. An epizootic of anthrax in sheep has been active near the Andhra–Tamil Nadu border, causing many cutaneous and meningoencephalitic human infections, with high mortality rate. There have been outbreaks in Karnataka and West Bengal. Anthrax infection in human beings provides permanent immunity and second attacks are extremely rare.

Laboratory diagnosis: Anthrax may be diagnosed by microscopy, culture, animal inoculation and serological demonstration of the anthrax antigen in infected tissues. Acute and convalescent phase sera should be obtained, since antibodies to the organism can be demonstrated by gel diffusion, complement fixation, antigen coated tanned red cell agglutination and ELISA techniques. The type of test to be employed depends on the nature of the material available.

When an animal is suspected to have died of anthrax, autopsy is not permissible, as the spilt blood will lead to contamination of the soil. An ear may be cut off from the carcass and sent to the laboratory. Alternatively, swabs soaked in blood or several blood smears may be sent. The demonstration of Gram positive bacilli with the morphology of anthrax bacilli and a positive M'Fadyean's reaction will enable the presumptive diagnosis to be made. Immunofluorescent microscopy can confirm the identification. Isolation of the bacillus is easy if gross contamination has not occurred. The anthrax bacillus can often be isolated from contaminated tissues by applying them over the shaven skin of a guinea pig. It is able to penetrate through minute abrasions and produce fatal infection. If the sample received is putrid so that viable bacilli are unlikely, diagnosis may be established by Ascoli's thermoprecipitin test by demonstration of the anthrax antigen in tissue extracts.

After the bioterrorism experience in the USA in 2001, the CDC (Centers for Disease Control) have prepared guidelines for identification of anthrax bacillus. Any large Gram positive bacillus with the general morphology and cultural features of anthrax; nonmotile, nonhemolytic on blood agar and catalase positive can be given a presumptive report of anthrax. For initial confirmation, lysis by gammaphage and direct fluorescent antibody test (DFA) for capsule specific staining and for polysaccharide cell wall antigen are sufficient.

For a further confirmation, PCR for anthrax bacillus specific chromosomal markers can be done.

For epidemiological studies and strain characterisation, MLVA (multiple locus variable number tandem repeat analysis) or AFLP (amplified fragment length polymorphism) can be used.

Prophylaxis: Prevention of human anthrax is mainly by general methods such as improvement of factory hygiene and proper sterilisation of animal products like hides and wool. Carcasses of animals suspected to have died of anthrax are buried deep in quicklime or cremated to prevent soil contamination.

Prevention of anthrax in animals is aided by active immunisation. The original Pasteur's anthrax vaccine is of great historical importance. It was Pasteur's convincing demonstration of the protective effect of his anthrax vaccine in a public experiment at Pouilly-le-Fort in 1881 that marked the beginning of scientific immunoprophylaxis. Pasteur's vaccine was the anthrax bacillus attenuated by growth at 42–43 °C.

As the spore is the common infective form in nature, vaccines consisting of spores of attenuated strains were developed. The Sterne vaccine contained spores of a noncapsulated avirulent mutant strain. The Mazucchi vaccine contained spores of stable attenuated Carbazoo strain in 2% saponin. The spore vaccines have been used extensively in animals with good results. They give protection for a year following a single injection. They are not considered safe for human use, though they have been used for human immunisation in Russia. Alum precipitated toxoid prepared from the protective antigen has been shown to be a safe and effective vaccine for human use. It has been used in persons occupationally exposed to anthrax infection. Three doses intramuscularly at intervals of six weeks between first and second, and six months between second and third doses induce good immunity, which can be reinforced if necessary with annual booster injections.

Treatment: Antibiotic therapy is effective in human cases but rarely succeeds in animals as therapy is not started sufficiently early. Antibiotics have no effect on the toxin once it is formed. Penicillin and streptomycin are no longer used for treatment. They have been replaced by doxycycline and ciprofloxacin, which are effective in prophylaxis and treatment.

ANTHRACOID BACILLI

Many members of the genus bacillus, other than the anthrax bacillus have occasionally caused human infections. Of them, the most important is *B. cereus* which from 1970 has been recognised as a frequent cause of foodborne gastroenteritis. It has also been associated with septicemia, meningitis, endocarditis, pneumonia, wound infections and other suppurative lesions, particularly as an opportunist pathogen. *B. subtilis*, *B. licheniformis* and a few other species have also been occasionally isolated from such lesions. These and a large number and variety of nonpathogenic aerobic spore bearing bacilli appearing as common contaminants in cultures and

having a general resemblance to anthrax bacilli have been collectively called *pseudoanthrax* or *anthracoid bacilli*. Table 27.1 lists the main differentiating features between them.

BACILLUS CEREUS

B. cereus has become important as a cause of food poisoning. It is widely distributed in nature and may be readily isolated from soil, vegetables and a wide variety of foods including milk, cereals, spices, meat and poultry. *B. cereus* is generally motile but nonmotile strains may occur. It resembles *B. anthracis* except that it is not capsulated and not susceptible to gamma phage and does not react with anthrax fluorescent antibody conjugate. Animal pathogenicity test also differentiates between the two.

B. cereus produces two patterns of foodborne disease. One is associated with a wide range of foods including cooked meat and vegetables. It is characterised by diarrhea and abdominal pain, 8–16 hours after ingestion of contaminated foods. Vomiting is rare. *B. cereus* is not found in large numbers in fecal specimens from these patients. The second type is associated almost exclusively

Table 27.1 Differentiating features between anthrax and anthracoid bacilli

	Anthrax bacilli	*Anthracoid bacilli*
1.	Nonmotile	Generally motile
2.	Capsulated	Noncapsulated
3.	Grow in long chains	Grow in short chains
4.	Medusa head colony	Not present
5.	No growth in penicillin agar (10 units/ml)	Grow usually
6.	Hemolysis absent or weak	Usually well marked
7.	Inverted fir tree growth and slow gelatin liquefaction	Rapid liquefaction
8.	No turbidity in broth	Turbidity usual
9.	Salicin fermentation negative	Usually positive
10.	No growth at 45 °C	Grows usually
11.	Growth inhibited by chloral hydrate	Not inhibited
12.	Susceptible to gamma phage	Not susceptible
13.	Pathogenic to laboratory animals	Not pathogenic

with the consumption of cooked rice, usually fried rice from Chinese restaurants. The illness is characterised by acute nausea and vomiting 1–5 hours after the meal. Diarrhea is not common. *B. cereus* is present in large numbers in the cooked rice and fecal samples from these patients. Both types of illness are mild and self limited, requiring no specific treatment.

It has been shown that the two types of disease are caused by strains of *B. cereus* belonging to different serotypes. The diarrheal disease is mostly caused by serotypes 2, 6, 8, 9, 10 or 12, while the rice associated emetic illness is caused by serotypes 1, 3 or 5. Isolates from the diarrheal type of disease produce an enterotoxin which causes fluid accumulation in ligated rabbit ileal loop, resembling the heat labile enterotoxin of *Escherichia coli*. Strains causing the emetic type of disease produce a toxin which causes vomiting when fed to Rhesus monkeys, resembling staphylococcal enterotoxin. The emetic toxin was produced only when *B. cereus* was grown in rice but not in other media. Two mechanisms of action have been described for the enterotoxin of *B. cereus*, one involving stimulation of CAMP system and the other independent of it.

A special mannitol–egg yolk–phenol red–polymyxin agar (MYPA) medium is useful in isolating *B. cereus* from feces and other sources. *B. cereus* produces lecithinase and ferments glucose but not mannitol.

Further Reading

Aksaray N et al. 1990. Cutaneous anthrax. *Trop Geograph Med* 42:168.
Brachman PS. 1980. Inhalation anthrax. *Ann New York Acad Sci* 353:83.
Dixon TC et al. 1999. Anthrax. *New Eng J Med* 341:815
Indira Devi K. 2001. Anthrax J. *Acad Clin Microb* 3:55.
Lalitha MK and A Kumar 1996. Anthrax in South India. *Lancet* 348:553.
Laforce FM. 1994. Anthrax. *Clin Infect Dis* 19:1009.
Maselson, M et al 1994. The Sverdlovsk anthrax outbreak of 1979. *Science* 266:1202.
Mock M and A Fovet 2001 Anthrax. *Ann Rev Microbiol* 55:647.

Clostridium

The genus Clostridium consists of Gram positive, anaerobic, spore forming bacilli. The spores are wider than the bacillary bodies, giving the bacillus a swollen appearence, resembling a spindle. Hence the name Clostridium (*kloster*, meaning a spindle). The genus contains bacteria responsible for three major diseases of human beings – gas gangrene, food poisoning and tetanus. Some of the pathogens, for example, *Cl. perfringens* and *Cl. tetani* are found normally in human and animal intestines. Many species are pathogenic but most are saprophytes found in soil, water and decomposing plant and animal matter. Intestinal clostridia rapidly invade the blood and tissues of the host after death and initiate decomposition of the cadaver. Some (for example, *Cl. acetobutylicum*) are of industrial importance, used for the production of chemicals such as acetone and butanol.

Clostridia are highly pleomorphic. They are rod shaped, usually 3–8 μm × 0.4–1.2 μm in size. Long filaments and involution forms are common. Spore formation occurs with varying frequency in different species. Some (*Cl. sporogenes*) sporulate readily while others (*Cl. perfringens*) do so inconstantly. Sporulation takes place in the animal body also. The shape and position of spores vary in different species and these are of use in the identification and classification of clostridia. Spores may be:

1. Central or equatorial, giving the bacillus a spindle shape (*Cl. bifermentans*).
2. Subterminal, the bacillus appearing club shaped (*Cl. perfringens*).
3. Oval and terminal, resembling a tennis racket (*Cl. tertium*).
4. Spherical and terminal, giving a drumstick appearance (*Cl. tetani*).

Clostridia are motile with peritrichate flagella, with few exceptions such as *Cl. perfringens* and *Cl. tetani* type VI which are nonmotile. The motility is slow and has been described as 'stately'. *Cl. perfringens* and *Cl. butyricum* are capsulated, while others are not.

Clostridia are easily stained. They are Gram positive but in older cultures, cells are often Gram variable, or even frankly Gram negative.

Clostridia are anaerobic. The sensitivity to oxygen varies in different species. Some (for example, *Cl. novyi*) are exacting anaerobes and die on exposure to oxygen, while some others (for example, *Cl. histolyticum*) are aerotolerant and may even grow aerobically. More important than the absence of oxygen is the provision of a sufficiently low redox potential (Eh) in the medium. This can be achieved by adding reducing substances such as unsaturated fatty acids, ascorbic acid, glutathione, cysteine, thioglycollic acid, alkaline glucose, sulphites or metallic iron. A small concentration of CO_2 appears to enhance growth. The optimum temperature for pathogenic clostridia is 37 °C. Some saprophytic clostridia are thermophilic and others psychrophylic. The optimum pH is 7–7.4.

Growth is relatively slow on solid media. Colonial characteristics are variable. Some species are hemolytic on blood agar. A very useful medium is Robertson's cooked meat broth. It contains unsaturated fatty acids which take up oxygen, the reaction being catalysed by hematin in the meat, and also sulphydril compounds which bring about a reduced OR potential. Clostridia grow in the medium, rendering the broth turbid. Most species produce gas. Saccharolytic species turn the meat pink. Proteolytic species turn the meat black and produce foul and pervasive odours. In litmus milk medium, the production of acid, clot and gas can be detected.

The vegetative cells of clostridia do not differ from nonsporing bacilli in their resistance to physical and chemical agents. The spores exhibit a pronounced but variable resistance to heat, drying and disinfectants. Spores of *Cl. botulinum* survive boiling after 3–4 hours and even at 105 °C are not killed completely in less than 100 minutes. Spores of most strains of *Cl. perfringens* are destroyed by boiling for less than five minutes but spores of some Type A strains that cause food poisoning survive for several hours. *Cl. tetani* spores persist for years in dried earth. Spores of some strains of *Cl. tetani* resist boiling for 15–90 minutes, though in most cases, they are destroyed within five minutes. All species are killed by autoclaving at 121 °C within 20 minutes. Spores are particularly resistant to phenolic disinfectants. Formaldehyde is not very active and spores may sometimes survive immersion in 2% solution for upto five days. Halogens are effective and 1% aqueous iodine solution kills spores within three hours. Glutaraldehyde (2% at pH 7.5–8.5) is very effective in killing spores. In general, clostridia are susceptible to metronidazole, penicillin, cephalosporins and chloramphenicol; less so to tetracyclines, and resistant to aminoglycosides and quinolones.

Clostridia can produce disease only when the conditions are appropriate. Their invasive powers are limited. Pathogenic clostridia form powerful exotoxins. *Cl. botulinum* is virtually noninvasive and noninfectious. Botulism is due to the ingestion of preformed toxin in food. *Cl. tetani* has little invasive property and is confined to the primary site of lodgement. Tetanus results from the action of the potent exotoxin it produces. The gas gangrene clostridia, besides being toxigenic, are also invasive

and can spread along tissues and even cause septicemia.

Many methods have been adopted for the classification of clostridia. These include morphological features such as the shape and position of spores and biochemical features such as saccharolytic and proteolytic capacities (Table 28.1). Clostridia of medical importance may also be considered under the diseases they produce (see classification below).

CLOSTRIDIUM PERFRINGENS

(*Cl. welchii, Bacillus aerogenes capsulatus, B. phlegmonis emphysematosae*)

The bacillus was originally cultivated by Achalme (1891) but was first described in detail by Welch and Nuttall (1892), who isolated it from the blood and organs of a cadaver. This is the most important of the clostridia causing gas gangrene. It also produces food poisoning and necrotic enteritis in human beings and many serious diseases in animals.

Cl. perfringens is a normal inhabitant of the large intestines of human beings and animals. It is found in the feces and it contaminates the skin of the perineum, buttocks and thighs. The spores are commonly found in soil, dust and air.

Morphology: It is a plump, Gram positive bacillus with straight, parallel sides and rounded or truncated ends, about 4–6 μm × 1 μm, usually occurring singly or in chains or small bundles. It is pleomorphic, and filamentous and involution forms are common. It is capsulated and nonmotile. Spores are central or subterminal but are rarely seen in artificial culture or in material from pathological lesions, and their absence is one of the characteristic morphological features of *Cl. perfringens*.

Cultural characteristics: It is an anaerobe but can also grow under microaerophilic conditions. Oxygen is not actively toxic to the bacillus and cultures do not die on exposure to air, as happens with some fastidious anaerobes. It grows over a pH range of 5.5–8.0 and temperature range of 20°C–50 °C. Though usually grown at 37 °C, a temperature of 45 °C is optimal for many strains. The generation time at this temperature may be as short as ten minutes. This property can be utilised for obtaining pure cultures of *Cl. perfringens*. Robertson's cooked meat broth inoculated with mixtures of *Cl. perfringens* and other bacteria and incubated at 45 °C for 4–6 hours serves as an enrichment. Subcultures from this onto blood agar plates yield pure or predominant growth of *Cl. perfringens.*

Good growth occurs in Robertson's cooked meat medium. The meat is turned pink but is not digested. The culture has an acid reaction and a sour odour.

In litmus milk, fermentation of lactose leads to formation of acid, which is indicated by the change in the colour of litmus from blue to red. The acid coagulates the casein (acid clot) and the clotted milk is disrupted due to the vigorous gas production. The paraffin plug is pushed up and shreds of clot are seen sticking to the sides of the tube. This is known as 'stormy fermentation'.

After overnight incubation on rabbit, sheep or human blood agar, colonies of most strains show a 'target hemolysis', resulting from a narrow zone of complete hemolysis due to theta toxin and a much wider zone of incomplete hemolysis due to the alpha toxin. This double zone pattern of hemolysis may fade on longer incubation.

Biochemical reactions: Glucose, maltose, lactose and sucrose are fermented with the production of acid and gas. It is indole negative, MR positive and VP negative. H_2S is formed abundantly. Most strains reduce nitrates.

Resistance: Spores are usually destroyed within five minutes by boiling but those of the 'food poisoning' strains of Type A and certain Type C strains resist boiling for 1–3 hours. Autoclaving of 121 °C for 15 minutes is lethal. Spores are resistant to the antiseptics and disinfectants in common use.

Classification: *Cl. perfringens* strains are classified into five types, A to E, based on the toxins they produce. Though the bacillus produces a large number of toxins, typing depends on the four 'major toxins'. Typing is done by neutralisation tests with specific antitoxins by intracutaneous injections in guinea pigs or intravenous injection in mice.

Toxins: *Cl. perfringens* is one of the most prolific of toxin-producing bacteria, forming at least 12 distinct toxins, besides many other enzymes and biologically active soluble substances. The four 'major toxins', alpha, beta, epsilon and iota, are predominantly responsible for pathogenicity. The

Table 28.1 A morphological and biochemical classification of Clostridia

Position of spores	Both proteolytic and saccharolytic		Slightly proteolytic but not saccharolytic	Saccharolytic but not proteolytic	Neither proteolytic nor saccharolytic
	Proteolytic predominating	*Saccharolytic predominating*			
Central or subterminal	*Cl. bifermentans* *Cl. botulinum* A.B.F. *Cl. histolyticum* *Cl. sordelli* *Cl. sporogenes*	*Cl. perfringens* *Cl. septicum* *Cl. chauvoei* *Cl. novyi*		*Cl. fallax* *Cl. botulinum* C.D.E	
Oval and terminal	—	*Cl. difficile*	—	*Cl. tertium*	*Cl.cochlearum*
Spherical and terminal	—	—	*Cl . tetani*	*Cl. tetanomorphum* *Cl. sphenoides*	

Clostridia as human pathogens

A. The gas gangrene group:

1. Established pathogens	*Cl.perfringens* *Cl. septicum* *Cl. novyi*
2. Less pathogenic	*Cl. histolyticum* *Cl. fallax*
3. Doubtful pathogens	*Cl. bifermentans* *Cl. sporogenes*

B. Tetanus: *Cl. tetani*

C. Food poisoning:

1. Gastroenteritis	*Cl. perfringens* (Type A)
2. Necrotising enteritis	*Cl. perfringens* (Type C)
3. Botulism	*Cl. botulinum*

D. Acute colitis   *Cl. difficile*

alpha (α) toxin is produced by all types of *Cl. perfringens* and most abundantly by Type A strains. This is the most important toxin biologically and is responsible for the profound toxemia of gas gangrene. It is lethal, dermonecrotic and hemolytic. It is a phospholipidase (lecithinase C) which, in the presence of Ca^{++} and Mg^{++} ions, splits lecithin into phosphoryl choline and diglyceride. This reaction is seen as an opalescence in serum or egg yolk media and is specifically neutralised by the antitoxin. When *Cl. perfringens* is grown on a medium containing 6% agar, 5% Fildes' peptic digest of sheep blood and 20% human serum, with the antitoxin spread on one half of the plate, colonies on the other half without the antitoxin will be surrounded by a zone of opacity. There will be no opacity around the colonies on the half of the plate with the antitoxin, due to the specific neutralisation of the alpha toxin. This specific lecithinase effect, known as the Nagler reaction, is a useful test for the rapid detection of *Cl. perfringens* in clinical specimens (Fig. 28.1). The incorporation of neomycin sulphate in the medium makes it more selective, inhibiting coliforms and aerobic spore bearers. Human serum may be replaced by 5% egg

yolk. The opalescence in the egg yolk media may be produced by other lecithinase forming bacteria also (*Cl. novyi*, *Cl. bifermentans*, some vibrios, some aerobic spore bearers). In the case of these bacteria, the reaction is not neutralised by the *Cl. perfringens* antitoxin, except with *Cl. bifermentans* which produces a serologically related lecithinase.

The alpha toxin is hemolytic for the red cells of most species, except horse and goat, due to its action on the phospholipids on the erythrocyte membranes. The lysis is of the hot–cold variety, being best seen after incubation at 37 °C followed by chilling at 4 °C. It is relatively heat stable and is only partially inactivated by boiling for five minutes.

Beta (β), epsilon (ϵ) and iota (ι) toxins have lethal and necrotising properties. Gamma (γ) and eta (η) toxins have minor lethal actions. The delta (δ) toxin has a lethal effect and is hemolytic for the red cells of even-toed ungulates (sheep, goats, pigs, cattle). The theta (θ) toxin is an oxygen labile hemolysin antigenically related to streptolysin O. It is also lethal and a general cytolytic toxin. The kappa (κ) toxin is a collagenase. The lambda (λ) toxin is a proteinase and gelatinase. The mu (μ) toxin is a hyaluronidase and the nu (ν) toxin a deoxytribonuclease.

Besides the toxins, *Cl. perfringens* also produces other soluble substances, some of which possess enzymatic properties. These include the enzymes which destroy the blood group substance, A and H, a neuraminidase which destroys myxovirus receptors on red blood cells, a substance which renders red blood cells panagglutinable by exposing their T antigens, a hemagglutinin active against the red blood cells of human beings and most animals, a fibrinolysin, a hemolysin distinct from alpha, theta and delta toxins, histamine, a 'bursting factor' which has a specific action on muscle tissue and may be responsible for the characteristic muscle lesions in gas gangrene and a 'circulating factor' which can cause an increase in the adrenaline sensitivity of the capillary bed and also inhibit phagocytosis.

PATHOGENICITY

Cl. perfringens produces the following human infections:

Gas gangrene: *Cl. perfringens* Type A is the predominant agent causing gas gangrene. It may occur as the sole etiological agent but is more commonly seen in association with other clostridia as well as nonclostridial anaerobes and even aerobes. All clostridial wound infections do not result in gas gangrene. More commonly, they lead only to wound contamination, or anaerobic cellulitis. It is only when muscle tissues are invaded that gas gangrene (anaerobic myositis) results.

Food poisoning: Some strains of Type A (food poisoning strains) can produce food poisoning. They are characterised by the marked heat resistance of their spores and the feeble production of alpha and theta toxins. They have been shown to produce a heat labile enterotoxin which, like the enterotoxins of *V. cholerae* and enterotoxigenic *E. coli*, leads to fluid accumulation in the rabbit ileal loop.

Food poisoning by *Cl. perfringens* is usually caused by a cold or warmed up meat dish. When contaminated meat is cooked, the spores in the interior may survive. During storage or warming they germinate and multiply in the anaerobic environment in the cooked meat. Large numbers of clostridia may thus be consumed, which may pass unharmed by the gastric acid due to the high protein in the meal and reach the intestines where they produce the enterotoxin. After an incubation period of 8–24 hours, abdominal pain, diarrhea and vomiting set in. The illness is self-limited and recovery occurs in 24–48 hours. Diagnosis is made by isolating heat resistant *Cl. perfringens* Type A from the feces and food. As this may be present in normal intestines, isolation from feces, except in large numbers is not meaningful. Isolation from food has to be attempted by direct plating on selective media, as the bacillus is present in food mainly as the vegetative cells.

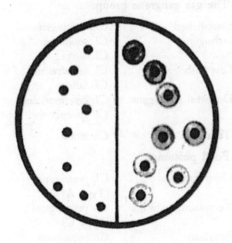

Fig. 28.1 Nagler reaction. *Cl. perfringens* colonies on the right half of the plate are surrounded by haloes, while colonies on the left half (containing antiserum to alpha toxin) have no haloes around them.

Gangrenous appendicitis: *Cl. perfringens* Type A (and occasionally Type D) strains have been isolated from gangrenous appendicitis. The demonstration of antitoxin in these patients and the beneficial effects of the administration of antitoxin also suggest the etiological role of the bacillus in this condition. It has been proposed that the toxemia and shock in some cases of intestinal obstruction and peritonitis may be due to the toxins of *Cl. perfringens*.

Necrotising enteritis: This is a severe and often fatal enteritis known by different names in different countries: Germany (Darmbrand), New Guinea (pigbel), East Africa, Thailand and Nepal. It is caused by *Cl. perfringens* type C strains with heat resistant spores which germinate in the intestine producing beta toxin causing mucosal necrosis. The evocative name 'pigbel' is New Guinea pidgin for abdominal pain and diarrhea following unaccustomed feasting on pig meat along with trypsin inhibitors like sweet potatoes. Immunisation with type C toxoid has been shown to protect against this condition.

Table 28.2 : Toxins produced by Cl. perfringens types

Type	Pathogenicity	Major toxins				Minor toxins							
		α	β	ε	ι	γ	δ	η	θ	κ	λ	μ	ν
A	Gas gangrene: wound infections, septicemia	+++	−	−	−	−	−	−	++	+++	−	+	+
	Food poisoning	+++	−	−	−	−	−	−	+++	++	−	+++	++
B	Lamb dysentery	+++	+++	++	−	−	−	−	+++	+++	+++	+++	+++
C	Enteritis in animals	+++	+++	−	−	+	−	−	+++	+++	−	−	−
	Enteritis necroticans in human beings	+++	+++	−	−	−	++	−	−	++	−	−	+++
D	Enterotoxemia of sheep	+++	−	+++	−	−	−	−	++	++	++	++	++
E	Doubtful pathogen of sheep and cattle	+++	−	−	+++	−	−	−	++	++	++	+++	+++

Biliary tract infection: *Cl. perfringens* has been reported to produce two rare but serious infections of the biliary tract – acute emphysematous cholecystitis and postcholecystectomy septicemia.

Endogenous gas gangrene of intra-abdominal origin: Gas gangrene of the abdominal wall has been reported as an infrequent complication of abdominal surgery. The infection is endogenous, the organism being derived from the gut and contaminating the abdominal wall during surgery. Gas gangrene of the thigh as a result of infection tracking from the abdomen has also been reported.

Brain abscess and meningitis: Brain abscess and meningitis due to *Cl. perfringens* have been reported very rarely.

Panophthalmitis: Panophthalmitis due to *Cl. perfringens* has occasionally followed penetrating eye injuries.

Thoracic infections: Clostridial infection of the chest cavity may follow penetrating wounds of the thorax. This is more often seen in battle casualties than in civilian situations.

Urogenital infections: Infection of the urinary tract may occasionally follow surgical procedure such as nephrectomy. Clostridial infection of the uterus is a serious and not infrequent condition, commonly associated with septic abortion. Septicemia is common in this condition.

CLOSTRIDIUM SEPTICUM

This bacillus was first described by Pasteur and Joubert (1887) and called *Vibrion septique*. It is a pleomorphic bacillus, about 3–8 μm × 0.6 μm in size, forming oval, central or subterminal spores. It is motile by peritrichate flagella. Growth occurs anaerobically on ordinary media. The colonies are irregular and transparent initially, turning opaque on continued incubation. Hemolysis occurs on horse blood agar. Growth is promoted by glucose. It is saccharolytic and produces abundant gas.

Six groups have been recognised, based on somatic and flagellar antigens. *Cl. septicum*

produces at least four distinct toxins and a fibrinolysin. The alpha toxin is hemolytic, dermonecrotic and lethal, the beta toxin is a leucotoxic deoxyribonuclease, the gamma toxin a hyaluronidase and the delta toxin an oxygen labile hemolysin.

Cl. septicum is found in the soil or in animal intestines. It is associated with gas gangrene in human beings, usually with other clostridia. It also causes 'braxy' in sheep and 'malignant edema' in cattle and sheep.

CLOSTRIDIUM NOVYI

(*Cl. oedematiens*)

This is a large, stout, pleomorphic, Gram positive bacillus with large, oval, subterminal spores. It is widely distributed in soil. It is a strict anaerobe, readily inactivated by exposure of cultures to air. Four types (A to D) are recognised, based on the production of toxins. Only type A is of medical importance, as it causes gas gangrene. Gas gangrene caused by *Cl. novyi* is characterised by high mortality and large amounts of edema fluid with little or no observable gas in infected tissue. Other types produce veterinary disease. There was a lethal outbreak of *Cl. novyi* type A infection in heroin addicts in Britain in 2000.

CLOSTRIDIUM HISTOLYTICUM

This is an actively proteolytic clostridium, forming oval, subterminal, bulging spores. This is aerotolerant and some growth may occur even in aerobic cultures. It forms at least five distinct toxins. It is infrequently associated with gas gangrene in humans.

GAS GANGRENE

Oakley (1954) defined gas gangrene as a rapidly spreading, edematous myonecrosis, occurring characteristically in association with severe wounds of extensive muscle masses that have been contaminated with pathogenic clostridia, particularly with *Cl. perfringens*. The disease has been referred to in the past as 'malignant edema'. Other descriptive terms that have been used are 'anaerobic (clostridial) myositis' and 'clostridial myonecrosis'.

Gas gangrene is characteristically a disease of war, in which extensive wounds with heavy contamination are very common. In civilian life, the disease generally follows road accidents or other types of injury involving crushing of large muscle masses. Rarely, it may even follow surgical operations.

The bacteriology of gas gangrene is varied. Rarely is this due to infection with a single clostridium. Generally, several species of clostridia are found in association with anaerobic streptococci and facultative anaerobes such as *E. coli*, proteus and staphylococci. Among the pathogenic clostridia, *Cl. perfringens* is the most frequently encountered (approximately 60 per cent), and *Cl. novyi* and *Cl. septicum* being the next common (20–40 per cent), and *Cl. histolyticum* less often. Other clostridia usually found are *Cl. sporogenes*, *Cl. fallax*, *Cl. bifermentans*, *Cl. sordellii*, *Cl. aerofoetidum* and *Cl. tertium*. These may not be pathogenic by themselves. The relative incidence of the different species varies in different series of cases and may be a reflection of the distribution of the species in different soils.

Clostridia usually enter the wounds along with implanted foreign particles such as soil (particularly manured or cultivated soil), road dust, bits of clothing or shrapnel. Clostridia may also be present on the normal skin, especially on the perineum and thighs. Infection may at times be endogenous. Gas gangrene may occasionally follow clean surgical procedures (especially amputations for vascular disease) and even injections (especially adrenaline).

The mere presence of clostridia in wounds does not constitute gas gangrene. MacLennan has distinguished three types of anaerobic wound infections:

Simple wound contamination with no invasion of the underlying tissue, resulting in little more than some delay in wound healing.

Anaerobic cellulitis in which clostridia invade the fascial planes, with minimal toxin production and no invasion of muscle tissues. The disease is gradual in onset and may vary from a limited 'gas abscess' to the extensive involvement of a limb.

Anaerobic myositis or gas gangrene, which is the most serious, associated with clostridial invasion of healthy muscle tissues and abundant formation of exotoxins. Gas gangrene results only if the conditions favourable for clostridial multiplication exist in the wound. The most important of these is low oxygen tension. This is achieved ideally in battle wounds in which there are implanted bullets or shell fragments, along with bits of clothing and soil particles. The ionised calcium salts and silicic acid in the soil cause necrosis. Crushing tissue or tearing of the arteries produces anoxia of the muscle. Extravasation of blood increases the pressure on the capillaries, reducing the blood supply still further. The Eh and pH of the damaged tissues fall, and these changes along with the chemical changes that occur within the damaged and anoxic muscles, including breakdown of carbohydrates and liberation of aminoacids from proteins, provide an ideal pabulum for the proliferation of anaerobes. Extravasated hemoglobin and myohemoglobin are reduced and cease to act as oxygen carriers. As a result, aerobic oxidation is halted and anaerobic reduction of pyruvate to lactate leads to a further fall in Eh.

The clostridia multiply and elaborate toxins which cause further tissue damage. The lecithinases damage cell membranes and increase capillary permeability, leading to extravasation and increased tension in the affected muscles, causing further anoxic damage. The hemolytic anemia and hemoglobinuria seen in *Cl. perfringens* infections are due to the lysis of erythrocytes by the alpha toxin. The collagenases destroy collagen barriers in the tissues and hyaluronidases break down the intercellular substances furthering invasive spread by the clostridia. The abundant production of gas reduces the blood supply still further by pressure effects, extending the area of anoxic damage. It thus becomes possible for the infection to spread from the original site, making the lesion a progressive one.

The incubation period may be as short as seven hours or as long as six weeks after wounding, the average being 10–48 hours with *Cl. perfringens*, 2–3 days with *Cl. septicum* and 5–6 days with *Cl. novyi* infection. The disease develops with increasing pain, tenderness and edema of the affected part along with systemic signs of toxemia. There is a thin watery discharge from the wound, which later becomes profuse and serosanguinous. Accumulation of gas makes the tissues crepitant. In untreated cases, the disease process extends rapidly and inexorably. Profound toxemia and prostration develop and death occurs due to circulatory failure.

Laboratory diagnosis: The diagnosis of gas gangrene must be made primarily on clinical grounds, and the function of the laboratory is only to provide confirmation of the clinical diagnosis as well as identification and enumeration of the infecting organisms. Bacteriological examination also helps to differentiate gas gangrene from anaerobic streptococcal myositis, which may be indistinguishable from it clinically in the early stages. In the latter, Gram stained films show large numbers of streptococci and pus cells, but not bacilli, contrasting with the scanty pus cells and diverse bacterial flora seen in films from gas gangrene.

The specimens to be collected are: (1) films from the muscles at the edge of the affected area, from the tissue in the necrotic area and from the exudate in the deeper parts of the wound; (2) exudates from the parts where infection appears to be most active and from the depths of the wound, to be collected with a capillary pipette or a swab; and (3) necrotic tissue and muscle fragments.

Gram stained films give presumptive information about the species of clostridia present and their relative numbers. The presence of large numbers of regularly shaped Gram positive bacilli without spores is strongly suggestive of *Cl. perfringens* infection. 'Citron bodies' and boat or leaf shaped pleomorphic bacilli with irregular staining suggest *Cl. septicum*. Large bacilli with oval, subterminal spores indicate *Cl. novyi*. Slender bacilli with round, terminal spores may be *Cl. tetani* or *Cl. tetanomorphum*.

Aerobic and anaerobic cultures are made on fresh and heated blood agar, preferably on 5–6 per cent agar to prevent swarming. A plate of serum or egg yolk agar, with *Cl. perfringens* antitoxin spread on one half is used for the 'Nagler reaction'. Four tubes of Robertson's cooked meat broth are inoculated and heated at 100 °C for 5, 10, 15 and 20 minutes, incubated and subcultured on blood agar plates after 24–48 hours, to differentiate the organisms with heat resistant spores. Blood cultures are often positive, especially in *Cl. perfringens* and *Cl. septicum* infections. However *Cl. perfringens* bacteremia may occur without gas gangrene. The isolates are identified based on their morphological, cultural, biochemical and toxigenic characters.

Prophylaxis and therapy: Surgery is the most important prophylactic and therapeutic measure in gas gangrene. All damaged tissues should be removed promptly and the wounds irrigated to remove blood clots, necrotic tissue and foreign materials. In established gas gangrene, uncompromising excision of all affected parts may be life-saving. Where facilities exist, hyperbaric oxygen may be beneficial in treatment.

Antibiotics are effective in prophylaxis, in combination with surgical methods. The drug of choice is metronidazole given IV before surgery and repeated 8 hourly for 24 hours. As mixed aerobic and anaerobic infections are usual, a more broadspectrum antibiotic prophylaxis, such as a combination of metronidazole, gentamicin and amoxycillin is advisable.

Passive immunisation with 'anti-gas gangrene serum' (equine polyvalent antitoxin in a dose of 10,000 IU *Cl. perfringens*, 10,000 IU *Cl. novyi* and

5,000 IU *Cl. septicum* antitoxin given IM or in emergencies IV) used to be the common practice in prophylaxis. However, in view of its uncertain efficacy and availability, its use has become rare.

CLOSTRIDIUM TETANI

Cl. tetani is the causative organism of tetanus. Tetanus has been known from very early times, having been described by Hippocrates and Aretaeus. Carle and Rattone (1884) transmitted the disease to rabbits. Nicolaier (1884), studying the experimental disease, suggested that the manifestations of tetanus were due to a strychnine-like poison produced by the bacillus multiplying locally. Rosenbach (1886) demonstrated a slender bacillus with round terminal spores in a case of tetanus. The final proof of the etiological role of the bacillus in tetanus was furnished by Kitasato (1889) who isolated it in pure culture and reproduced the disease in animals by inoculation of pure cultures.

Cl. tetani is widely distributed in soil and in the intestines of human beings and animals. It is ubiquitous and has been recovered from a wide variety of other sources, including street and hospital dust, cotton wool, plaster of Paris, bandages, catgut, talc, wall plaster and clothing. It may occur as an apparently harmless contaminant in wounds.

Morphology: It is a Gram positive, slender bacillus, about 4–8 μm × 0.5 μm though there may be considerable variation in length. It has a straight axis, parallel sides and rounded ends. It occurs singly and occasionally in chains. The spores are spherical, terminal and bulging, giving the bacillus the characteristic 'drumstick' appearance (Fig. 28.2). The morphology of the spore depends on its stage of development and the young spore may be oval rather than spherical. It is noncapsulated and motile by peritrichate flagella. Young cultures are strongly Gram positive but older cells show variable staining and may even be Gram negative.

Cultural characteristics: It is an obligatory anaerobe that grows only in the absence of oxygen.

The optimum temperature is 37 °C and pH 7.4. It grows on ordinary media. Growth is improved by blood and serum but not by glucose. Surface colonies are difficult to obtain as the growth has a marked tendency to swarm over the surface of the agar, especially if the medium is moist. An extremely fine, translucent film of growth is produced that is practically invisible, except at the delicately filamentous advancing edge. This property enables the separation of *Cl. tetani* from mixed cultures. If the water of condensation at the bottom of a slope of nutrient agar is inoculated with the mixed cell culture, after incubation anaerobically for 24 hours, subcultures from the top of the tube will yield a pure growth of the tetanus bacillus (Fildes' technique).

In deep agar shake cultures, the colonies are spherical fluffy balls, 1–3 mm in diameter, made up of filaments with a radial arrangement. In gelatin stab cultures a fir tree type of growth occurs, with slow liquefaction.

It grows well in Robertson's cooked meat broth, with turbidity and some gas formation. The meat is not digested but is turned black on prolonged incubation.

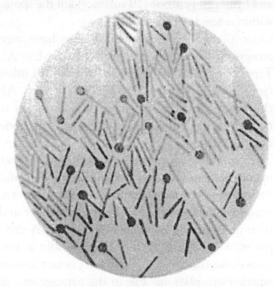

Fig. 28.2 *Cl. tetani,* some with spores and some without

On blood agar, α hemolysis is produced, which later develops into β hemolysis, due to the production of hemolysin (tetanolysin).

Biochemical reactions: *Cl. tetani* has feeble proteolytic but no saccharolytic property. It does not attack any sugar. It forms indole. It is MR and VP negative. H_2S is not formed. Nitrates are not reduced. Gelatin liquefaction occurs very slowly. A greenish fluorescence is produced on media containing neutral red (as on MacConkey's medium).

Resistance: The resistance of tetanus spores to heat appears to be subject to strain differences. Most are killed by boiling for 10–15 minutes but some resist boiling for upto three hours. When destruction of spores is to be ensured, autoclaving at 121 °C for 20 minutes is recommended. On the other hand, when heat is applied in order to free cultures of *Cl. tetani* from nonsporing contaminants, it is important not to exceed 80 °C for 10 minutes, as even this mild treatment can cause considerable destruction. Spores are able to survive in soil for years, and are resistant to most antiseptics. They are not destroyed by 5% phenol or 0.1% mercuric chloride solution in two weeks or more. Iodine (1% aqueous solution) and hydrogen peroxide (10 volumes) kill the spores within a few hours.

Classification: Ten serological types have been recognised based on agglutination (types I to X). Type VI contains nonflagellated strains. All other types possess type specific flagellar antigens. All the types produce the same toxin, which is neutralised by antitoxin produced against any one type.

Toxins: *Cl. tetani* produces at least two distinct toxins—a hemolysin (*tetanolysin*) and a powerful neurotoxin (*tetanospasmin*). The two are antigenically and pharmacologically distinct and their production is mutually independent. A third toxin, a nonspasmogenic, peripherally active neurotoxin, has been identified. It is not known whether this plays any role in the pathogenesis of tetanus.

Tetanolysin is a heat labile, oxygen labile hemolysin, antigenically related to the oxygen labile hemolysins produced by *Cl. perfringens*, *Cl. novyi* and *Str. pyogenes*. It is not relevant in the pathogenesis of tetanus.

Tetanospasmin is the toxin responsible for tetanus. It is oxygen stable but relatively heat labile, being inactivated at 65 °C in five minutes. It is plasmid coded. It gets toxoided spontaneously or in the presence of low concentrations of formaldehyde. It is a good antigen and is specifically neutralised by the antitoxin. The toxin has been crystallised. It is a simple protein composed of a single polypeptide chain. On release from the bacillus, it is autolysed to form a heterodimer consisting of a heavy chain (93,000 MW) and a light chain (52,000 MW) joined by a disulphide bond. Tetanus and botulinum toxins resemble each other in their aminoacid sequences.

The purified toxin is active in extremely small amounts and has an MLD for mice of about 50–75 $\times 10^{-6}$ mg. The amount of toxin produced depends on the strain of bacillus and the type of culture medium used. Its MLD for human beings is about 130 nanograms. There is considerable variation in the susceptibility of different species of animals to the toxin. The horse is the most susceptible. Guinea pigs, mice, goats and rabbits are susceptible in that descending order. Birds and reptiles are highly resistant. Frogs, which are normally insusceptible, may be rendered susceptible by elevating their body temperature.

Pathogenicity: *Cl. tetani* has little invasive power. Washed spores injected into experimental animals do not germinate and are destroyed by phagocytes. Germination and toxin production occur only if favourable conditions exist, such as reduced O-R potential, devitalised tissues, foreign bodies or concurrent infection. The toxin produced locally is absorbed by the motor nerve endings and transported to the central nervous system intraxonally. The toxin is specifically and avidly fixed by gangliosides of the grey matter of the nervous tissue. Tetanospasmin resembles strychnine in its effects. The tetanus toxin specifically blocks synaptic inhibition in the spinal cord, presumably at inhibitory terminals that use glycine and GABA as neurotransmitters. The toxin acts presynaptically, unlike strychnine which acts postsynaptically. The abolition of spinal inhibition causes uncontrolled spread of impulses initiated anywhere in the central nervous system. This results in muscle rigidity and spasms due to the simultaneous contraction of agonists and antagonists, in the absence of reciprocal inhibition. The convulsion pattern is determined by the most powerful muscles at a given point, and in most animals is characterised by tonic extension of the body and of all limbs.

The toxicity of tetanospasmin is influenced by the route by which it is administered. Given orally, it is destroyed by the digestive enzymes and is without effect. Subcutaneous, intramuscular and intravenous injections are equally effective. Intraneural injections are more lethal and injections directly into the central nervous system very much more so. The route of administration also modifies the clinical picture. Experimental tetanus may accordingly, be of the 'local', 'ascending' or 'descending' variety. These differences are related to the manner in which the toxin reaches and is disseminated in the central nervous system.

When the toxin is inoculated intramuscularly in one of the hindlimbs, tonic spasms of the muscles of the inoculated limb appear first. This is known as *local tetanus* and is due to the toxin acting on the segment of the spinal cord containing the motor neurons of the nerve supplying the inoculated area. Subsequent spread of the toxin up the spinal cord causes 'ascending tetanus'. The opposite hindlimb, trunk and forelimbs are involved in an ascending fashion. If the toxin is injected intravenously, spasticity develops first in the muscles of the head and neck and then spreads downwards (descending tetanus). This type resembles the naturally occurring tetanus in human beings.

TETANUS

Tetanus is characterised by tonic muscular spasms, usually commencing at the site of infection and in all but the mildest cases becoming generalised, involving the whole of the somatic muscular system. Most frequently, the disease follows injury, which may even be too trivial to be noticed. Puncture wounds are particularly vulnerable as they favour the growth of the anaerobic bacillus. Rarely, it may follow surgical operations, usually due to lapses in asepsis. Sometimes the disease may be due to local suppuration, such as otitis media (otogenic tetanus). Tetanus is an important complication of septic abortion. It may be caused by unhygienic practices, such as application of cowdung on the umbilical stump or rituals such as earboring or circumcision. Tetanus may also be caused by unsterile injections.

The incubation period is variable, from two days to several weeks, but is commonly 6–12 days. This is influenced by several factors, such as the site and nature of the wound, the dose and toxigenicity of the contaminating organism and the immune status of the patient. The incubation period is of prognostic significance, the prognosis being grave when it is short. Of similar significance is the interval between the first symptom of the disease, usually trismus, and the onset of spasms (period of onset).

Tetanus was a serious disease with a high rate of mortality, 80–90 per cent, before specific treatment became available. Even with proper treatment the case fatality rate varies from 15–50 per cent. Tetanus neonatorum and uterine tetanus have very high fatality rates (70–100 per cent), while otogenic tetanus is much less serious.

Tetanus is more common in the developing countries, where the climate is warm, and in rural areas where the soil is fertile and highly cultivated, where human and animal populations are substantial and live in close association and where unhygienic practices are common and medical facilities poor. In rural India, tetanus was a common cause of death, particularly in the newborn. But immunisation of infants and expectant mothers has reduced the incidence to a large extent.

Laboratory diagnosis: The diagnosis of tetanus should always be made on clinical grounds. Laboratory tests only help in confirmation. Not infrequently, it may not be possible to establish a laboratory diagnosis at all.

Laboratory diagnosis may be made by demonstration of *Cl. tetani* by microscopy, culture or by animal inoculation. Microscopy is unreliable and the demonstration of the typical 'drumstick' bacilli in wounds in itself is not diagnostic of tetanus. The bacilli may be present in some wounds without tetanus developing. It may not also be possible to distinguish by microscopy between *Cl. tetani* and morphologically similar bacilli such as *Cl. tetanomorphum* and *Cl. sphenoides*. Diagnosis by culture is more dependable. Isolation is more likely from excised bits of tissue from the necrotic depths of wounds than from wound swabs. The material is inoculated on one half of a blood agar plate. *Cl. tetani* produces a swarming growth which may be detected on the opposite half of the plate after 1–2 days incubation anaerobically. The material is also inoculated into three tubes of cooked meat broth, one of which is heated to 80 °C for 15 minutes, the second for 5 minutes, and the third left unheated. The purpose of heating for different periods is to kill vegetative bacteria, while leaving undamaged tetanus spores, which vary widely in heat resistance. The cooked meat tubes are incubated at 37 °C and subcultured on one half of blood agar plates daily for upto four days. *Cl. tetani* may be isolated in pure culture by subculturing from the swarming edge of the growth. The incorporation of polymyxin B, to which clostridia are resistant, makes the medium more selective.

For identification and toxigenicity testing, blood agar plates (with 4% agar to inhibit swarming), having tetanus antitoxin (1500 units per ml) spread over one half of the plate are used. The *Cl. tetani*

strains are stab-inoculated on each half of the plate, which is then incubated anaerobically for two days. Toxigenic *Cl. tetani* strains show hemolysis around the colonies, only on the half without the antitoxin. Lysis is inhibited by the antitoxin on the other half. This may help in identification of the culture as *Cl. tetani* but is unreliable as a test of toxigenicity since it indicates the production only of tetanolysin and not necessarily of tetanospasmin, which is the pathogenic toxin.

Toxigenicity is best tested in animals. A two-to four-day-old cooked meat culture (0.2 ml) is inoculated into the root of the tail of a mouse. A second mouse that has received the tetanus antitoxin (1000 units) an hour earlier serves as the control. Symptoms develop in the test animal in 12–24 hours, beginning with stiffness in the tail. Rigidity proceeds to the leg on the inoculated side, the opposite leg, trunk and forelimbs, in that order. The animal dies within two days but may be killed earlier as the appearance of ascending tetanus is diagnostic.

Prophylaxis: Tetanus is a preventable disease. As the spores are ubiquitous, wound contamination is unavoidable. The disease is due to the action of the toxin. Therefore the obvious and most dependable method of prevention is to build up antitoxic immunity by active immunisation by routine immunisation of children and booster doses where appropriate.

The nature of prophylaxis depends largely on the type of the wound and the immune status of the patient. The available methods of prophylaxis are (1) surgical attention; (2) antibiotics; and (3) immunisation—passive, active or combined.

Surgical prophylaxis aims at removal of foreign bodies, necrotic tissue and blood clots, to prevent an anaerobic environment favourable for the tetanus bacillus. The extent of surgical treatment may vary from simple cleansing to radical excision, depending on the type of wound.

Antibiotic prophylaxis aims at destroying or inhibiting tetanus bacilli and pyogenic bacteria in wounds so that the production of toxin is prevented. In experimentally infected animals tetanus can be prevented by antibiotics when administered four hours after infection but not after eight hours. This emphasises the need for prompt administration of antibiotics. Long-acting penicillin injection is the drug of choice. An alternative is erythromycin 500 mg b.d. for five days. Antibiotics are to be started before wound toilet. Bacitracin or neomycin may be applied locally also. Antibiotics have no action on the toxin. Hence, antibiotic prophylaxis does not replace immunisation but serves as a useful adjunct.

Passive immunisation is by injection of tetanus antitoxin. Antitetanus serum (ATS) from hyperimmune horses was the preparation originally used. The dose employed was 1500 IU given subcutaneously or intramuscularly in nonimmune persons soon after receiving any tetanus prone injury. ATS was useful not only in reducing the incidence of tetanus but also in prolonging the incubation period and reducing the mortality when it did not prevent the disease. However, equine ATS carried two disadvantages implicit in the use of any heterologous serum – 'immune elimination' and hypersensitivity. The half-life of ATS in human beings is normally about seven days but in persons who have had prior injections of horse serum, it is eliminated much more quickly by combination with pre-existing antibodies. Prior sensitisation also leads to hypersensitivity reactions which may range from mild local reactions to serum sickness, and even fatal anaphylaxis. It is, therefore, obligatory that a test for hypersensitivity should invariably be made before administration of ATS. The intradermal test for hypersensitivity, which is in common use, has been reported to be unreliable. A 'trial' dose given subcutaneously would be a better index of hypersensitivity. A dose of 0.5 ml of ATS is given subcutaneously and the patient observed for at least half an hour for general reactions. As even this dose may precipitate anaphylaxis in some cases, *a syringe loaded with adrenaline (1/1000) must be kept ready.* In persons with a history of any allergy, the trial dose should be 0.05 ml of a 1/10 dilution of ATS.

Bovine and ovine ATS were introduced to overcome reactions to horse serum but these in turn can also produce hypersensitivity. Passive immunity without risk of hypersensitivity can be obtained by the use of human antitetanus immunoglobulin (TIG). This is effective in smaller doses (250 units) and has a longer half-life (3–5 weeks). As TIG is prepared by immunisation of human volunteers, its availability is limited.

Passive immunisation is an emergency procedure to be used only once. The former practice of persons receiving ATS every time they are wounded was not only useless and wasteful but also positively dangerous. It is better to eliminate the use of ATS altogether, tetanus being controlled by active immunisation, with human TIG being reserved for emergency use in the nonimmune.

Active immunisation is not only the most effective method of prophylaxis but also the only means whereby tetanus following unnoticed injuries can be prevented. This is achieved by spaced injections of formol toxoid, which is available either as 'plain toxoid', or adsorbed on aluminium hydroxide or phosphate. The adsorbed toxoid is a better antigen. The tetanus toxoid is given either alone or along with the diphtheria toxoid and the pertussis vaccine as the 'triple vaccine', in which pertussis vaccine acts as an adjuvant also. A course of immunisation consists of three doses of tetanus toxoid given intramuscularly, with an interval of 4–6 weeks between the first two injections and the third dose 6 months later (or as per recommendations of the National Immunisation Programme). A full course of immunisation confers immunity for a period of at least ten years. A 'booster dose' of toxoid is recommended after ten years. ATS or TIG should not be given to an immunised individual. Instead, a booster dose of toxoid is given if wounding occurs three years or more after the full course of immunisation. Too frequent injection of toxoid should be avoided as hypersensitivity reactions may occur occasionally.

An illustration of the efficacy of active immunisation is that in World War II, only 12 cases of tetanus occurred in 2,734,819 hospital admissions for wounds or injuries, among the American soldiers who had been previously immunised.

Combined immunisation consists of administering to a nonimmune person exposed to the risk of tetanus TIG injection at one site, along with the first dose of toxoid at the contralateral site, followed by the second and third doses of toxoid at monthly intervals. It is important to use adsorbed toxoid as the immune response to plain toxoid may be inhibited by TIG. Ideally, combined immunisation should be employed whenever passive immunisation is called for.

Table 28.3 shows the recommended integrated prophylaxis of tetanus following injury.

Treatment: Tetanus patients should be treated in hospitals, preferably in special units. The reason for isolating them is to protect them from noise and light which may provoke the convulsions.

However, because the patients are isolated, there is a common impression that they are highly infectious. This is not true. Tetanus patients are hardly ever infectious, and person to person transmission does not occur at all.

Treatment consists of ensuring quiet, controlling spasms, maintaining airway by tracheostomy with intermittent positive pressure respiration and attention to feeding. Human TIG 10,000 IU suitably diluted may be given by slow IV infusion, followed, if needed, by another 5,000 IU later. Even though TIG may not neutralise the toxin already bound to the nervous tissue, it can inactivate the unbound toxin and any further toxin that may be produced. Antibacterial therapy with penicillin or metronidazole should be started at once and continued for a week or more. ATS used to be given intravenously in massive doses as part of the treatment. Several controlled trials have been undertaken to assess the value of antitoxin and the optimum dose. The results indicate that antitoxin is of value in treatment but that 10,000 IU intravenously gives as good results as much higher doses.

Table 28.3 Tetanus prophylaxis in the wounded

Nature of wound	Immune status of the person		
	Immune	Partially immune	Nonimmune
Clean (wound toilet performed within six hours)	Toxoid × 1 *	Toxoid × 1	Toxoid × 3
Contaminated (soil or other foreign or necrotic material present)	Toxoid × 1 *	Toxoid × 1 TIG antibiotics	Toxoid × 3 TIG antibiotics
Infected	Toxoid × 1 * Antibiotics	Toxoid × 1 TIG antibiotics	Toxoid × 3 TIG antibiotics

Note: Immune – Patient has had a full course of three injections of toxoid.
Partially immune – Patient has had two injections of toxoid.
Nonimmune – Patient has had one or no injection of toxoid, or immunisation status is notknown.
TIG – Tetanus Immune Globulin.
* The toxoid needs to be given only if three years or more have elapsed after active immunisation or the last booster injection.

Patients recovering from tetanus should receive a full course of active immunisation, as an attack of the disease does not confer immunity. Second attacks of tetanus have been recorded.

CLOSTRIDIUM BOTULINUM

Cl. botulinum causes botulism, a paralytic disease usually presenting as a form of food poisoning. The name botulism is derived from 'sausage' (*botulus*, Latin for sausage) formerly associated with this type of food poisoning. *Cl. botulinum* was first isolated by van Ermengem (1896) from a piece of ham that caused an outbreak of botulism. The bacillus is a widely distributed saprophyte, occurring in virgin soil, vegetables, hay, silage, animal manure and sea mud.

Morphology: It is a Gram positive bacillus about 5 μm × 1 μm, noncapsulated, motile by peritrichate flagella, producing subterminal, oval, bulging spores.

Cultural characteristics: It is a strict anaerobe. Optimum temperature is 35 °C but some strains may grow even at 1–5 °C. Good growth occurs on ordinary media. Surface colonies are large, irregular, semitransparent, with fimbriate border. Biochemical reactions vary in different types. Spores are produced consistently when grown in alkaline glucose gelatin media at 20–25 °C. They are not usually produced at higher temperatures.

Resistance: Spores are heat and radiation resistant, surviving several hours at 100 °C and for upto 10 minutes at 120 °C. Spores of nonproteolytic types of B, E and F are much less resistant to heat.

Classification: Eight types of *Cl. botulinum* have been identified (Types A, B, C1, C2, D, E, F, G) based on the immunological difference in the toxins produced by them. The toxins produced by the different types are identical in their pharmacological activity but are neutralised only by the homologous antiserum. An exception is C2 toxin, which shows enterotoxic activity, while all the others are neurotoxins.

Toxin: *Cl. botulinum* produces a powerful exotoxin that is responsible for its pathogenicity. The toxin differs from other exotoxins in that it is not released during the life of the organism. It is produced intracellularly and appears in the medium only on the death and autolysis of the cell. It is believed to be synthesised initially as a nontoxic protoxin or progenitor toxin. Trypsin and other proteolytic enzymes activate progenitor toxin to active toxin.

The toxin has been isolated as a pure crystalline protein which is probably the most toxic substance known. It has a MW 70,000 and a lethal dose for mice of 0.000,000,033 mg. The lethal dose for human beings is probably 1–2 μg. It is a neurotoxin and acts slowly, taking several hours to kill.

The toxin is relatively stable, being inactivated only after 30–40 minutes at 80 °C and 10 minutes at 100 °C. Food suspected to be contaminated with botulinum toxin can be rendered completely safe by pressure cooking or boiling for 20 minutes. It resists digestion and is absorbed through the small intestines in active form. It acts by blocking the production or release of acetylcholine at the synapses and neuromuscular junctions. The onset is marked by diplopia, dysphagia and dysarthria due to cranial nerve involvement. A symmetric descending paralysis is the characteristic pattern, ending in death by respiratory paralysis.

A small quantity of *Cl. botulinum* type A toxin injected into a muscle selectively weakens it by blocking the release of acetylcholine at the neuromuscular junction. Muscles so injected atrophy but recover in 2–4 months as new terminal axon sprouts form and restore transmission. Intramuscular injection of the toxin, first used to treat strabismus, is now recognised as a safe and effective symptomatic therapy for many neuromuscular diseases.

The botulinum toxin can be toxoided. It is specifically neutralised by its antitoxin and is a good antigen. The toxins produced by the different types of *Cl. botulinum* appear to be identical, except for immunological differences. Toxin production appears to be determined by the presence of bacteriophages, at least in types C and D.

Pathogenicity: *Cl. botulinum* is noninvasive and virtually noninfectious. Its pathogenicity is due to the action of its toxin, the manifestations of which are collectively called botulism. Botulism is of three types – foodborne botulism, wound botulism and infant botulism.

Foodborne botulism is due to the ingestion of preformed toxin. The types of the bacillus and the nature of the food responsible vary in different regions. Human disease is usually caused by types A, B, E and very rarely F. Types C and D are usually associated with outbreaks in cattle and wild fowl. Type G has been associated with sudden death in a few patients. The source of botulism is usually preserved food—meat and meat products in Europe, canned vegetables in America and fish in Japan. Type E is associated with fish and other seafoods. Proteolytic varieties of *Cl. botulinum* can digest food, which then appears spoiled. The cans are often inflated and show bubbles on opening. Nonproteolytic varieties leave food unchanged.

Symptoms begin usually 12–36 hours after ingestion of food. Vomiting, thirst, constipation, ocular paresis, difficulty in swallowing, speaking and breathing constitute the common features. Coma or delirium may supervene. Death is due to respiratory failure and occurs 1–7 days after onset. Case fatality varies from 25–70 per cent.

Wound botulism is a very rare condition resulting from wound infection with *Cl. botulinum*. Toxin is produced at the site of infection and is absorbed. The symptoms are those of foodborne botulism except for the gastrointestinal components which are absent. Type A has been responsible for most of the cases studied.

Infant botulism was recognised as a clinical entity in 1976. This is a toxico-infection. *Cl. botulinum* spores are ingested in food, get established in the gut and there produce the toxin. Cases occur in infants below six months. Older children and adults are not susceptible. The manifestations are constipation, poor feeding, lethargy, weakness, pooled oral secretions, weak or altered cry, floppiness and loss of head control. Patients excrete toxin and spores in their feces. Toxin is not generally demonstrable in blood. Management consists of supportive care and assisted feeding. Antitoxins and antibiotics are not indicated. Degrees of severity vary from very mild illness to fatal disease. Some cases of sudden infant death syndrome have been found to be due to infant botulism. Honey has been incriminated as a likely food item through which the bacillus enters the gut.

Laboratory diagnosis: Diagnosis may be confirmed by demonstration of the bacillus or the toxin in food or feces. Gram positive sporing bacilli may be demonstrable in smears made from the food. *Cl. botulinum* may be isolated from the food or the patient's feces. The food is macerated in sterile saline, and the filtrate inoculated into mice or guinea pigs intraperitoneally. Control animals protected by polyvalent antitoxin remain healthy. Typing is done by passive protection with type specific antitoxin. The toxin may occasionally be demonstrable in the patient's blood, or in the liver postmortem.

A retrospective diagnosis may be made by detection of antitoxin in the patient's serum but it may not be seen in all cases.

Control: As most cases of botulism follow consumption of inadequately canned or preserved food, control can be achieved by proper canning and preservation. When an outbreak occurs, a prophylactic dose of antitoxin should be given intramuscularly to all who consumed the article of food.

Active immunisation has been shown to be effective. If immunisation is needed, as in laboratory workers exposed to the risk, two injections of aluminium sulphate adsorbed toxoid may be given at an interval of ten weeks, followed by a booster a year later. Antitoxin may be tried for treatment. Polyvalent antiserum to types A, B and E may be administered as soon as a clinical diagnosis is made.

Supportive therapy with maintenance of respiration is of equal or greater importance.

CLOSTRIDIUM DIFFICILE AND ANTIBIOTIC ASSOCIATED COLITIS

Cl. difficile was first isolated in 1935 from the feces of newborn infants. It was so named because of the unusual difficulty in isolating it. It is a long, slender, Gram positive bacillus with a pronounced tendency to lose its Gram reaction. Spores are large, oval and terminal. It is nonhemolytic, saccharolytic and weakly proteolytic. It was not considered pathogenic till 1977 when it was found to be responsible for antibiotic associated colitis.

Acute colitis, with or without membrane formation, is an important complication of oral antibiotic therapy. Many antibiotics have been incriminated including ampicillin, tetracycline and chloramphenicol but lincomycin and clindamycin are particularly prone to cause pseudomembranous colitis.

It has now been shown that antibiotic associated colitis is due to the active multiplication of *Cl. difficile* and its production of an enterotoxin as well as a cytotoxin. Diagnosis can be made by demonstrating the toxin in the feces of patients by its characteristic effect on Hep-2 and human diploid cell cultures or by ELISA. The toxin is specifically neutralised by the *Cl. sordelli* antitoxin. *Cl. difficile* can also be grown from the feces of patients.

Cl. difficile strains are usually resistant to most antibiotics. Metronidazole is the drug of choice. Vancomycin and bacitracin are also useful.

Further Reading

Bartlett JG. 1994. Clostridium difficile. *Clin Infect Dis*, 18:S265.
Brazier JS. 1995. Laboratory diagnosis of Cl. difficile associated disease. *Rev Med Microbiol* 6:236.
Duerden BI and BS Drasar (eds). 1991. *Anaerobes in human disease*. London: Arnold.
Hathava CL. 1995. Botulism. *Curr Topics Microbiol Immunol*. 195:55.
Sakurai J. 1995. Toxins of *Cl. Perfringens*. *Rev Med Microbiol*. 6:175.
Sanford JP. 1995. Tetanus – forgotten, but not gone. *New Engl J Med*. 332:812.

Nonsporing Anaerobes

Anaerobic bacteria have been known since the original observation of Pasteur that bacteria which produce butyric acid, his *Vibrion butyrique*, were rendered nonmotile on exposure to air (1863). Though many anaerobic bacteria may be pathogenic for human beings, they are generally neglected in diagnostic laboratories. This neglect is not because they are uncommon. Indeed, they outnumber aerobic bacteria in many habitats, including most sites of the human or animal body. Even in such seemingly aerobic situations as the mouth and the skin, anaerobic bacteria are ten to thirty times more frequent than aerobes. In the human intestines, they outnumber aerobic bacteria a thousandfold. The numbers of anaerobes present have been estimated to be $10^4 - 10^5$/ml in the small intestine, 10^8/ml in saliva and 10^{11}/g in the colon.

Anaerobic bacteria differ widely in the degree of anaerobiosis required for their growth. Some species fail to grow if the atmosphere contains as little as 0.03 per cent oxygen, while at the other extreme, some are aerotolerant and may grow sparsely on the surface of aerobic plates. Consequently the techniques employed for the propagation and study of anaerobes vary in complexity.

Early methods of classification used such unstable criteria as cell and colony morphology, biochemical reactions and antibiotic sensitivity patterns. Current classification is based on DNA base composition and analysis of the fatty acid end products of metabolism. Medically important anaerobes may be broadly classified as follows:

I. Cocci
  A. Gram positive
    a. Peptostreptococcus
    b. Peptococcus
  B. Gram negative
    Veillonella

II. Bacilli
  1. Endospore forming
    Clostridia
  2. Nonsporing
  A. Gram positive
    a. Eubacterium
    b. Propionibacterium
    c. Lactobacillus
    d. Mobiluncus
    e. Bifidobacterium
    f. Actinomyces
  B. Gram negative
    a. Bacteroides
    b. Prevotellla
    c. Porphyromonas
    d. Fusobacterium
    e. Leptotrichia

III. Spirochetes
    a. Treponema
    b. Borrelia

Besides the medically important species listed above, there are several anaerobes that occur in soil and water and which may be of industrial and agricultural importance (for example, methanobacteria, butyrivibrios).

ANAEROBIC COCCI

Anaerobic cocci represent a heterogeneous

collection of cocci whose classification and nomenclature have undergone several modifications. They can be divided into Gram positive and Gram negative groups.

Anaerobic Gram positive cocci had been classified into the genera *Peptostreptococcus* and *Peptococcus* originally, based on morphology, chain-forming and paired cocci placed in the former and cluster-forming cocci in the latter. However, DNA base ratio studies have led to most of the species formerly considered as peptococci being reclassified as peptostreptococci. They are cocci of small size (0.2–2.5 µm). Many of them are aerotolerant and grow well under 10% CO_2 in an aerobic atmosphere.

They are normal inhabitants of the vagina, intestines and mouth. They may cause several clinical infections such as puerperal sepsis and other genital infections, wound infections, gangrenous appendicitis, urinary tract infections, osteomyelitis and abscesses in the brain, lungs and other internal organs. They are often seen in large numbers in pus from suppurative lesions, so a Gram stained smear may be helpful in diagnosis. Infections are usually mixed, the cocci being present along with clostridia or anaerobic Gram negative bacilli. *Peptostreptococcus anaerobius* is most often responsible for puerperal sepsis and *Pst. magnus* for abscesses. *Pst. asaccharolyticus*, *Pst. tetradius* and *Pst. prevoti* are some other species commonly present in clinical specimens.

Veillonellae are Gram negative cocci of varying sizes occurring as diplococci, short chains or groups. They are normal inhabitants of the mouth, intestinal and genital tracts. *Veillonella parvula* has been reported from clinical specimens but its pathogenic role is uncertain.

All anaerobic cocci are generally sensitive to penicillin, chloramphenicol and metronidazole, and resistant to streptomycin and gentamicin.

ANAEROBIC GRAM POSITIVE BACILLI

This group contains many genera, of which the medically relevant are *Eubacterium*, *Propionibacterium*, *Lactobacillus*, *Mobiluncus* and *Bifidobacterium*. Other genera in this group, *Actinomyces* and *Arachnia*, are dealt with elsewhere.

Members of the genus *Eubacterium* are strictly anaerobic and grow very slowly. They are members of the normal mouth and intestinal flora. Some species (*E. brachy, E. timidum, E. nodatum*) are commonly seen in periodontitis. *E. lentum* is commonly isolated from nonoral clinical specimens.

Propionibacterium is constantly present on the skin. *P. acnes* is a common contaminant in blood and CSF cultures.

Lactobacillus is present in the mouth, intestines and, typically, in the adult vagina (Doderlein's bacilli). It is generally nonpathogenic, though *L. catenaforme* has been associated with bronchopulmonary infections.

Bifidobacterium is a pleomorphic rod that shows true and false branching. It is present in large numbers in the intestines and in the mouth.

Mobiluncus species are motile, curved, anaerobic bacilli that may appear as Gram variable rods. *M. mulieris* and *M. curtisii* have been isolated from the vagina in bacterial vaginosis, along with *Gardnerella vaginalis*. Bacterial vaginosis is a polymicrobial infection characterised by a thin malodorous vaginal discharge. Its 'rotten fish' smell is accentuated by mixing it with a drop of KOH solution. The vaginal pH is more than 4.5. Clue cells (epithelial cells with surface covered by adherent bacilli) are seen in stained or unstained films.

ANAEROBIC GRAM NEGATIVE BACILLI

Medically important anaerobic Gram negative bacilli belong to the family *Bacteroidaceae* and are classified into the genera *Bacteroides*, *Fusobacterium* and *Leptotrichia*.

Bacteroides are the most common anaerobes isolated from clinical specimens. They are nonsporing, nonmotile, strict anaerobes, usually very pleomorphic, appearing as slender rods, branching forms or coccobacilli, seen singly, in pairs or in short chains. They grow well on media such as brain heart infusion agar in an anaerobic atmosphere containing 10% CO_2. They possess capsular polysaccharides which appear to be virulence factors, and antibodies to them can be detected in patients. They are normal inhabitants of the intestinal, respiratory and female genital tracts.

Bacteroides species have been classified based on their saccharolytic effects. Asaccharolytic pigmented species have been separated as the genus Porphyromonas, containing P. gingivalis responsible for periodontal disease, P. endodontalis causing dental root canal infections and other species. Moderately saccharolytic species inhibited by 20% bile are placed in the genus Prevotella, containing P. melaninogenica, P. buccalis, P. denticola and others. The genus Bacteroides proper now includes the important species B. fragilis, and others such as B. vulgatus, B. distasonis and B. thetaiotaomicron.

B. fragilis is the most frequent of the nonsporing anaerobes isolated from clinical specimens. It is often recovered from blood, pleural and peritoneal fluids, CSF, brain abscesses, wounds and urogenital infections. P. melaninogenica is easy to recognise because of the black or brown colour of the colonies. The colour is not due to the melanin pigment as was once thought but to a hemin derivative. It has been isolated from various infections including lung or liver abscess, mastoiditis, intestinal lesions and lesions of the mouth and gums. Cultures of P. melaninogenica and even dressings from wounds infected with the bacillus give a characteristic red fluorescence when exposed to ultraviolet light.

The genus Fusobacterium contains long, thin or spindle shaped bacilli with pointed ends. F. nucleatum is a normal inhabitant of the mouth and is found in oral infection and pleuropulmonary sepsis. F. necrophorum produces a wide range of exotoxins and has been responsible for liver abscess

and other abdominal infections in animals and less often in humans.

The genus Leptotrichia contains the single species, L. buccalis which was formerly known as Vincent's fusiform bacillus or Fusobacterium fusiforme. They are long, straight or slightly curved rods, often with pointed ends. They are part of the normal oral flora and are seen in acute necrotising lesions in the mouth.

A common condition is Vincent's angina, which may resemble diphtheria, with the inflamed pharyngeal mucosa showing a greyish membrane which peels easily. Stained smears show large fusiform and spiral bacilli.

ANAEROBIC INFECTIONS

There has been a reawakening of interest in anaerobic infections during recent years. This is due to the availability of improved and simplified techniques for the isolation and identification of anaerobes.

Anaerobic infections are usually endogenous and are caused by tissue invasion by bacteria normally resident on the respective body surfaces. Anaerobic bacteria are normally present on the skin, mouth, nasopharynx and upper respiratory tract, intestines and vagina (Table 29.1). Anaerobic infections generally follow some precipitating factor such as trauma, tissue necrosis, impaired circulation, hematoma formation or the presence of foreign bodies. Diabetes, malnutrition, malignancy or prolonged treatment with aminoglycoside antibiotics may act as predisposing factors. Anaerobic infections are typically polymicrobial, more than one anaerobe being responsible besides aerobic bacteria. While the infection is usually localised, general dissemination may occur by bacteremia. Table 29.2 lists the common sites and type of anaerobic infections and the bacteria responsible.

There are some clinical features which suggest the presence of anaerobic infection. Pus produced by anaerobes is characteristically putrid, with a

Table 29.1 Normal anaerobic flora of the human body

Anaerobe	Skin	Mouth–nasopharynx	Intestine	Vagina
Clostridium			+ +	
Actinomyces		+		
Bifidobacterium		+	+ +	+
Propionibacterium	+ +			
Bacteroides fragilis			+ +	
P. melaninogenica		+ +	+	+ +
Fusobacterium		+ +	+	
Gram positive cocci		+ +	+ +	+ +
Gram negative cocci		+ +	+	+ +
Spirochetes		+		

pervasive, nauseating odour. However, there may be exceptions; infections solely due to B. fragilis may be free of this smell. Pronounced cellulitis is a common feature of anaerobic wound infections. Toxemia and fever are not marked.

Laboratory diagnosis: As anaerobes form part of the normal flora of the skin and mucous surfaces, their isolation from specimens has to be interpreted cautiously. The mere presence of an anaerobe does not prove its causal role. Specimens should be collected in such a manner as to avoid resident flora. For example, the sputum is unsatisfactory for culture from a suspected case of lung abscess; only material collected by aspiration would be acceptable.

As some anaerobes die on exposure to oxygen, care should be exercised to minimise contact with air during collection, transport and handling of specimens. A satisfactory method of collection is to aspirate the specimen into an airtight syringe, plunge the needle into a sterile rubber cork to seal it and send it immediately to the laboratory. Pus and other fluids may be collected in small bottles with airtight caps and transported quickly, ensuring that the specimens fill the bottles completely. Swabs are generally unsatisfactory but where they are to

be used, they should be sent in Stuart's transport medium.

In the laboratory, exposure should be limited to the minimum. Examination of a Gram stained smear is useful. Pus in anaerobic infection usually shows a large variety of different organisms and numerous pus cells. Rarely, as in brain abscess, a single type of organism alone may be seen. Examination of the specimen under ultraviolet light may show the bright red fluorescence of *P. melaninogenica*. Gas liquid chromatography of the specimen may yield presumptive information on the types of anaerobes present.

Several special media have been described for anaerobes but for routine diagnostic work, freshly prepared blood agar with neomycin, yeast extract, hemin and vitamin K is adequate. Plates are incubated at 37 °C in an anaerobic jar, with 10% CO_2. The Gaspak system provides a convenient method of routine anaerobic cultures. Plates are examined after 24 or 48 hours. Some anaerobes, such as fusobacteria, require longer periods of incubation. Parallel aerobic cultures should always be set up. This is necessary as a control for the growth on anaerobic plates and also because in most anaerobic infections aerobic bacteria are also involved.

Table 29.2 Common anaerobic infections and the bacteria responsible

Site and type of infection	Bacteria commonly responsible
Central nervous system:	
Brain abscess	*B. fragilis; Peptostreptococcus*
Ear, nose, throat:	
Chronic sinusitis, otitis media,	
mastoiditis, orbital cellulitis	Fusobacteria (aerobes frequently responsible)
Mouth and jaw:	
Ulcerative gingivitis (Vincent's)	Fusobacteria, spirochetes
Dental abscess, cellulitis;	Mouth anaerobes,
Abscess and sinus of jaw	Actinomyces, other mouth anaerobes.
Respiratory:	
Aspiration pneumonia, lung abscess,	Fusobacteria, *P. melaninogenica*,
bronchiectasis, empyema	anaerobic cocci; *B. fragilis* rarely
Abdominal:	
Subphrenic, hepatic abscess;	
appendicitis, peritonitis;	
ischiorectal abscess;	*B. fragilis*
wound infection after	
colorectal surgery	
Female genitalia:	
Wound infection following	
genital surgery;	
Puerperal sepsis;	*P. melaninogenica,*
tubo-ovarian abscess;	anaerobic cocci; *B. fragilis*
Bartholin's abscess,	
septic abortion	Genital anaerobes and *Cl. perfringens*
Skin and soft tissue:	
Infected sebacious cyst.	Anaerobic cocci
Breast abscess, axillary abscess	Anaerobic cocci; *P.melaninogenica* (*Staph. aureus* commonest cause)
Cellulitis, diabetic ulcer, gangrene	*B. fragilis* and others.

Further Reading

Duerden DL and BS Drasar (eds). 1991. *Anaerobes in Human Disease*. London: Arnold.
Finegold M. 1995. Overview of clinically important anaerobes. *Clin Infect Dis*. 20: S205.
Kasper DL. 1998. Infections due to mixed anaerobic organisms. In *Harrison's Principles of Internal Medicine*, 14th edn. New York: McGraw Hill.

Enterobacteriaceae I: Coliforms - Proteus

The predominant aerobic bacterial flora of the large intestines of human beings and animals is composed of nonsporing, nonacid fast, Gram negative bacilli. They exhibit general morphological and biochemical similarities and are grouped together in the large and complex family *Enterobacteriaceae*. Members of this family may or may not be capsulated and are motile by peritrichate flagella, or are nonmotile. They are aerobic and facultatively anaerobic, grow readily in ordinary media, ferment glucose producing acid and gas or acid only, reduce nitrates to nitrites and form catalase but not oxidase. Within the family, they exhibit very wide biochemical and antigenic heterogeneity. Though the family is subdivided into groups or tribes, genera, subgenera, species and types, many strains are met with that possess every conceivable combination of characters and do not fall into any such arbitrary taxonomic category. The frequency of genetic mechanisms such as conjugation and transduction in these bacteria contributes to their infinite variety. Classification of these bacteria into well demarcated compartments, though necessary for their systematic study, would therefore be artificial. The classification of *Enterobacteriaceae* has been controversial and there have been successive changes in their grouping and nomenclature.

The oldest method was to classify these bacteria into three groups based on their action on lactose.

I. Lactose fermenters (for example Escherichia, Klebsiella)

II. Late lactose fermenters (for example Shigella sonnei 'Paracolons')

III. Nonlactose fermenters (for example Salmonella, Shigella)

This method of classification was derived from the use of lactose in MacConkey's medium, the most popular medium for the isolation of fecal bacilli. Though taxonomically unacceptable, this scheme had practical value in diagnostic bacteriology. The majority of the commensal intestinal bacilli are lactose fermenting (LF). As the most common member of this group is the colon bacillus, or *Escherichia coli*, all lactose fermenting, enteric bacilli were called *coliform* bacilli. The major intestinal pathogens, *Salmonella* and *Shigella* are nonlactose fermenters (NLF), and hence readily detectable by the colourless colonies they form on MacConkey's medium. There remained a small group which showed delayed fermentation of lactose and with the exception of *Shigella sonnei*, they were all commensals. This heterogenous group of late lactose fermenters was called *paracolon bacilli*.

Classification based on a single property, such as lactose fermentation, is contrary to modern taxonomical concepts. The current practice is to group together bacteria that possess a number of common morphological and biochemical properties, and similar DNA base compositions. While the three widely used systems for the classification of *Enterobacteriaceae* (Bergey's manual, Kauffmann, Edwards–Ewing) have certain differences, the general approach is the same. The family is first classified into its major subdivision –

group or tribe. Each tribe consists of one or more genera and each genus one or more subgenera and species. The species are classified into types— biotypes, serotypes, bacteriophage types, colicin types.

ENTEROBACTERIACEAE

Tribe I: Escherichiae
    Genus   1. Escherichia
            2. Edwardsiella
            3. Citrobacter
            4. Salmonella
            5. Shigella
Tribe II: Klebsielleae
    Genus   1. Klebsiella
            2. Enterobacter
            3. Hafnia
            4. Serratia
Tribe III : Proteeae
    Genus   1. Proteus
            2. Morganella
            3. Providencia
Tribe IV: Erwinieae
    Genus   1. Erwinia

The genus *Yersinia*, including the plague bacillus, has been placed in the family *Enterobacteriaceae* but because of the special importance of plague, the major disease caused by yersiniae and its lack of similarity to enteric disease, it is dealt with separately.

ESCHERICHIA COLI

This genus is named after Escherich who was the first to describe the colon bacillus under the name *Bacterium coli commune* (1885). Based on minor differences in biochemical characteristics, colon bacilli were described under various names but in view of the mutability of the biochemical properties in this group, they have all been included in one species *Escherichia coli* which is further subdivided into biotypes and serotypes. A few other species have been described in the genus but they are of little medical importance. These include *E.*

fergusonii, E. hermanii and *E. vulneris* which have been isolated infrequently from clinical specimens. *E. blattae* found in the gut of cockroaches is biochemically different in being indole and beta-galactosidase negative. It has not been isolated from clinical specimens.

Unlike other coliforms, *E. coli* is a parasite living only in the human or animal intestine. Voided in feces, it remains viable in the environment only for some days. Detection of *E. coli* in drinking water, therefore, is taken as evidence of recent pollution with human or animal feces.

Morphology: *E. coli* is a Gram negative, straight, rod measuring $1–3 \times 0.4–0.7$ μm arranged singly or in pairs. It is motile by peritrichate flagella, though some strains may be nonmotile. Capsules and fimbriae are found in some strains. Spores are not formed.

Cultural characteristics: It is an aerobe and a facultative anaerobe. The temperature range is 10–40 °C (optimum 37 °C). Good growth occurs on ordinary media. Colonies are large, thick, greyish white, moist, smooth opaque or partially translucent discs. This description applies to the smooth (S) form seen on fresh isolation, which is easily emulsifiable in saline. The rough (R) forms give rise to colonies with an irregular dull surface and are often autoagglutinable in saline. The S-R variation occurs as a result of repeated subcultures and is associated with the loss of surface antigens and usually of virulence. Many pathogenic isolates have polysaccharide capsules. Some strains may occur in the 'mucoid' form.

Many strains, especially those isolated from pathologic conditions, are hemolytic on blood agar. On MacConkey's medium, colonies are bright pink due to lactose fermentation. Growth is largely inhibited on selective media such as DCA or SS agar used for the isolation of salmonellae and shigellae. In broth, growth occurs as general turbidity and a heavy deposit, which disperses completely on shaking.

Biochemical reactions: Glucose, lactose,

mannitol, maltose and many other sugars are fermented with the production of acid and gas. Typical strains do not ferment sucrose. The four biochemical tests widely employed in the classification of enterobacteria are the indole, methyl red (MR), Voges–Proskauer (VP) and citrate utilisation tests, generally referred to by the mnemonic 'IMViC'. *E. coli* is indole and MR positive, and VP and citrate negative (IMViC + + – –). Gelatin is not liquified, H_2S is not formed, urea is not split and growth does not occur in KCN medium.

Antigenic structure: Serotyping of *E. coli* is based on three antigens – the somatic antigen O, the capsular antigen K and the flagellar antigen H. So far some 170 types of O antigens, 100 K antigens and 75 H antigens have been recognised. The antigenic pattern of a strain is recorded as the number of the particular antigen it carries, as for example 0111: K58: H2.

The K antigen is the acidic polysaccharide antigen located in the 'envelope' or microcapsule. (K for *Kapsel*, German for capsule). It encloses the O antigen and renders the strain inagglutinable by the O antiserum. It may also contribute to virulence by inhibiting phagocytosis. Formerly K antigens were subdivided into three kinds – the thermolabile L antigens, the thermostable A antigens and the B antigens found on enteropathogenic strains associated with infantile diarrhea. Later it was shown that the B antigen was not a separate entity. K antigens are therefore currently classified into two groups, I and II, generally corresponding to the former A and L antigens.

Several different serotypes of *E. coli* are found in the normal intestine. Most of them do not have K antigens. The normal colon strains belong to the 'early' O groups (1, 2, 3, 4 etc.), while the enteropathogenic strains belong to the 'later' O groups (26, 55, 86, 111, etc.).

Virulence factors: Two types of virulence factors have been recognised in *E. coli*—surface antigens and toxins.

The somatic lipopolysaccharide surface O antigen, besides exerting endotoxic activity, also protects the bacillus from phagocytosis and the bactericidal effects of complement. The envelope or K antigens also afford protection against phagocytosis and antibacterial factors in normal serum, though it is not effective in the presence of antibody to O or K antigen. Most strains of *E. coli* responsible for neonatal meningitis and septicemia carry the KI envelope antigen which is a virulence factor resembling the group B antigen of meningococci.

Fimbriae also promote virulence. The common fimbriae seen in most enterobacteria, which are chromosomally determined, present in large numbers and causing mannose sensitive hemagglutination, are probably not relevant in pathogenesis. A different kind of fimbriae which are plasmid coded, found only in small numbers and mediating mannose resistant hemagglutinins have been shown to act as virulence factors. Some of them may not occur as morphologically separate structures but only as surface antigens – for example, K88 and K99 antigens in strains causing diarrhea in animals, or the *Colonisation Factor Antigens* (CFA) in enterotoxigenic *E. coli* causing human diarrhea. Fimbriae are also of importance in urinary tract infection, as for example the P fimbria which binds specifically to the P blood group substance on human erythrocytes and uroepithelial cells.

E. coli produce two kinds of exotoxins – *hemolysins* and *enterotoxins*. Hemolysins do not appear to be relevant in pathogenesis though they are produced more commonly by virulent strains than by avirulent strains. Enterotoxins are important in the pathogenesis of diarrhea. Three distinct types of *E. coli* enterotoxins have been identified – heat labile toxin (LT), heat stable toxin (ST) and verotoxin (VT) also known as Shiga-like toxin (SLT).

The *E. coli* enterotoxin LT was discovered in 1956 by De and colleagues in isolates from adult diarrhea cases in Calcutta, by the rabbit ileal loop

Table 30.1 Enterobacteriaceae: Important distinguishing features of the different genera

	Escherichia	*Edwardsiella*	*Citrobacter*	*Salmonella*[1]	*Shigella*[2]	*Klebsiella*	*Enterobacter*	*Hafnia*	*Serratia*	*Proteus*	*Morganella*	*Providencia*
Motility	+	+	+	+	−	−	+	+	+	+	+	+
Gas from glucose	+	+	+	+	−	+	+	+	d	d	+	+
Acid from lactose	+	−	+	−	−	+	+	−	−	−	−	−
Acid from sucrose	d	−	d	−	−	+	+	−	+	d	−	d
Growth in KCN	−	−	+	d	−	+	+	+	+	+	+	+
Indole	+	+	d	−	d	−	−	−	−	d	+	+
MR	+	+	+	+	+	−	−	−	−	+	+	+
VP	−	−	−	−	−	+	+	+	+	−	−	−
Citrate	−	−	+	+	−	+	+	+	+	d	d	d
H2S	−	+	+	+	−	+	−	−	−	+	−	−
Urease	−	−	−	−	−	+	d	−	−	+	+	d
Phenylalanine deaminase (PPA)	−	−	−	−	−	−	−	−	−	+	+	+
Arginine dehydrolase	d	−	d	+	−	−	d	−	−	−	−	−
Lysine decarboxylase	+	+	−	+	−	d	d	+	+	−	−	−
Ornithine decarboxylase	d	+	d	+	d	−	+	+	+	d	+	−

(d = results different in different species or strains.)
Important exceptions:
[1]S. typhi does not produce gas from sugars.
[2]Sh. sonnei ferments lactose and sucrose late

method which they had earlier used for identifying the cholera enterotoxin (CT), viz. injection of *E. coli* culture filtrates into closed ligated loops of rabbit ileum induced outpouring of fluid and ballooning of the loops. *E. coli* LT resembles the cholera toxin in its structure, antigenic properties and mode of action. It is a complex of polypeptide subunits – each unit of the toxin consisting of one subunit A (A for *active*) and five subunits B (B for *binding*). The toxin binds to the Gm1 ganglioside receptor on intestinal epithelial cells by means of subunit B, following which the subunit A is activated to yield two fragments – A1 and A2. The A1 fragment activates adenyl cyclase in the enterocyte to form cyclic adenosine 5' monophosphate (cAMP),

leading to increased outflow of water and electrolytes into the gut lumen, with consequent diarrhea. Though the mechanism of action of LT and CT is the same, the latter is about a hundred times more potent than the former. LT is a powerful antigen and can therefore, be detected by a number of serological as well as biological tests (Table 30.2).

The heat stable toxins of *E. coli* (ST), first identified in 1970, are low molecular weight polypeptides which are poorly antigenic. Two types of ST are known, ST_A (or ST 1) and ST_B (or ST II). ST_A acts by activation of cyclic guanosine monophosphate (cGMP) in the intestine. It acts very rapidly and induces fluid accumulation in the intestines of infant mice within four hours of intragastric administration. This infant mouse test is the standard method for demonstration of ST_A. It also induces fluid accumulation in the intestinal loops of neonatal but not weaned piglets. ST_A is methanol soluble. ST_B causes fluid accumulation in young piglets (upto nine weeks) but not in infant mice. The mode of action of ST_B is not known but it is not through cAMP or cGMP. It is not methanol soluble. ST genes are carried on plasmids which may also carry other genes, such as for LT and drug resistance. However, ST_A and ST_B genes are not seen to be carried on the same plasmid.

E. coli Verocytotoxin or Verotoxin (VT) was so named because it was first detected (1977) by its cytotoxic effect on Vero cells, a cell line derived from African green monkey kidney cells. It is also known as Shiga-like toxin (SLT) because it is similar to the *Shigella dysenteriae* type 1 toxin in its physical, antigenic and biological properties. Besides cytotoxicity in Vero or HeLa cells, VT also shows enterotoxicity in rabbit ileal loops and mouse paralytic-lethality as does the Shiga toxin. VT is also composed of A and B subunits. VT genes appear to be phage encoded. An antigenically different VT, called VT_2 has been identified, which is not neutralised by the Shiga antitoxin, unlike VT_1.

CLINICAL INFECTIONS

Four main types of clinical syndromes are caused by E. coli: 1) urinary tract infection, 2) diarrhea, 3) pyogenic infections, and 4) septicemia.

Urinary tract infection: *E. coli* and other coliforms account for the large majority of naturally acquired urinary tract infections. Those acquired in the hospital, following instrumentation, are more often caused by other bacteria such as *Pseudomonas* and *Proteus*.

The *E. coli* serotypes commonly responsible for urinary tract infections are those normally found in the feces, O groups 1, 2, 4, 6, 7, etc. Only one serotype is generally isolated from infected urine at

a time, though recurrences may be due to different serotypes.

Infection may be precipitated by urinary obstruction due to prostatic enlargement, calculi or pregnancy. About 5–7 per cent of pregnant women have been reported to have urinary infection without any symptoms. Such *asymptomatic bacteriuria* undetected and untreated may lead to symptomatic infection later in pregnancy, pyelonephritis and hypertension in the pregnant woman, as well as to prematurity and perinatal death of the fetus.

While infections of the lower urinary tract seem to be 'ascending infection' caused by fecal coliforms, pyelonephritis is probably due to hematogenous infection. Strains carrying K antigens are more commonly responsible for pyelonephritis, while most isolates from cystitis lack K antigens.

Bacteriological diagnosis of urinary tract infection has undergone a marked change following the development by Kass of the concept of 'significant bacteriuria'. Normal urine is sterile but during voiding may become contaminated with genital commensals. In order to avoid such contamination, urine used to be collected by catheterisation for culture. Any bacterial growth from catheterised urine was considered to denote infection. Even under ideal conditions, catheterisation leads to urinary infection in at least two per cent, and when precautions are inadequate, the risk is much higher. Hence catheterisation is no longer considered justifiable for diagnostic purposes. Instead, clean-voided midstream samples of urine are employed for culture. Such specimens should be collected carefully to reduce contamination to the minimum. In men, it is sufficient if midstream urine is collected after the prepuce is retracted and the glans penis cleaned with wet cotton. In women, anogenital toilet is more important and should consist of careful cleaning with soap and water. Nonirritant antiseptics such as chlorhexidine have been recommended for vulval cleaning. Urine should be passed keeping the labia

Table 30.2 Methods for detection of ETEC enterotoxins

Assay	LT	ST
In vivo tests		
Ligated rabbit ileal loop		
Read at 6 hours	±	+
Read at 18 hours	+	−
Infant rabbit bowel	+	+
Infant mouse intragastric (4 hours)	−	+
Adult rabbit skin (vascular permeability factor)	+	−
In vitro tests		
Tissue culture tests		
Rounding of Y1 mouse adrenal cells	+	−
Elongation of Chinese hamster ovary (CHO) cells	+	−
Serological tests		
`ELISA	+	(ST-ELISA with mono-colonial antibody −
Passive agglutination tests, passive immune hemolysis, precipitin (Eiken's) test	+	
Genetic tests		+
DNA probes	+	

separated by fingers. The first portion of urine that flushes out commensal bacteria from the anterior urethra is discarded. The next portion of the urine (midstream sample) is collected directly into a sterile wide mouthed container and transported to the laboratory without delay. Urine is a good medium for the growth of coliforms and other urinary pathogens, and hence delay in processing will vitiate the results of quantitative culture. If delay of more than 1–2 hours is unavoidable, the specimen should be refrigerated.

In quantitative cultures, midstream urine samples will give a biphasic distribution of colonies, most specimens containing either less than 10,000 or more than 100,000 bacteria per ml. Kass and other investigators have established that in the presence of active infection in the urinary tract the urine will contain 100,000 bacteria or more per ml. This level is, therefore, considered to represent *significant bacteriuria*. Counts of 10,000 bacteria or less per ml are due to contamination during voiding and are of no significance. Counts between the two levels are infrequent when the sample is collected properly and processed promptly. Such results should be considered equivocal and the culture repeated. Needless to say, interpretation of bacteriuria, should always be with reference to the condition of the patient. In patients on antibacterial or diuretic drugs and with some bacteria like *Staph. aureus*, even low counts may be significant.

For quantitative culture, serial ten fold dilutions of urine are tested by the pour plate or surface culture methods. This, however, is too complicated for routine diagnostic work, for which semiquantitative techniques are more convenient. The most widely used technique employs a standard loop which transfers a fixed, small volume of urine. One loopful of urine is placed on a noninhibitory medium (blood agar) and another loopful on an indicator medium (MacConkey). The former medium gives a quantitative measurement of bacteriuria, while the latter enables a presumptive diagnosis of the bacterium. The isolates are identified by their properties.

Bacteriological investigation of urinary tract infection is not complete without an antibiotic sensitivity test of the isolate. *E. coli* and other common urinary pathogens develop drug resistance so frequently that no antibacterial therapy can be instituted meaningfully without testing individual strains. Resistance is often to multiple drugs and is of the transferable variety. Antibiotic sensitivity tests may be done directly using the urine samples as inocula and the results confirmed by repeating the test with individual isolates.

Because urinary tract infection is such a common problem and bacteriological facilities are not always available, several screening techniques have been introduced for the presumptive diagnosis of significant bacteriuria. These include the following: 1) Griess nitrite test – based on the absence of nitrite in normal urine. The presence of nitrite, detectable by a simple test, indicates the presence of nitrate-reducing bacteria in urine, 2) catalase test – the presence of catalase as evidenced by frothing on addition of hydrogen peroxide indicates bacteriuria, though a positive result is obtained also in hematuria, 3) triphenyltetrazolium chloride (TTC) test – based on the production of a pink-red precipitate in the reagent caused by the respiratory activity of growing bacteria, 4) microscopic demonstration of bacteria in Gram stained films of urine, 5) glucose test paper – based on the utilisation of the minute amounts of glucose present in normal urine, by bacteria causing the infection, and 6) dip slide culture methods – agar coated slides are immersed in urine or even exposed to the stream of urine during voiding, incubated and the growth estimated by colony counting or by colour change of indicators. None of the screening methods is as sensitive or reliable as a culture.

The antibody coated bacteria test has been employed for the localisation of the site of urinary infection. This is based on the assumption that bacteria coated with specific antibodies are present in the urine only when the kidneys are infected and not when the infection is confined to the bladder. Antibody coated bacteria are detected by immunofluorescence using fluorescent tagged antihuman globulin or by staphylococcal coagglutination.

Diarrhea: Right from 1885 when Escherich first isolated the bacillus from the feces of infants with enteritis, *E. coli* had been suspected to be a causative agent of diarrhea. However, as there was no way then of differentiating diarrheagenic *E. coli* strains from the welter of commensal strains invariably present in normal feces, it remained unconfirmed till serotyping schemes for *E. coli* were developed. It was only in 1945 that Bray established the etiological role of a specific type of *E.coli*(subsequently recognised as type 0111) during a hospital outbreak of childhood diarrhea in London. Soon many other enteropathogenic serotypes of *E. coli* came to be recognised as responsible for infantile diarrhea. Subsequently, other varieties of *E. coli* diarrhea came to be identified in children as well as in adults. At least five different types of diarrheagenic *E. coli* are now recognised – enteropathogenic, enterotoxigenic, enteroinvasive, entero-hemorrhagic (Shigatoxigenic or Verotoxigenic) and entero-aggregative *E. coli.*

Enteropathogenic E. coli (EPEC): These have been associated mainly with diarrhea in infants and children usually occurring as institutional outbreaks but they can also cause sporadic diarrhea in children and less often in adults. EPEC diarrhea was common worldwide from the late 1940s to the 1960s. Afterwards, it has become less common.

EPEC were identified by serotyping, initially by their O and B antigens (for example, 026:B6, 055:B5, 0111:B4 and so on). After the existence of the B antigens became suspect, only O typing is practised.

The diagnosis of EPEC diarrhea is relatively easy during outbreaks but very difficult in sporadic cases. Fresh diarrheal feces is plated on blood agar and MacConkey media. After overnight incubation, *E. coli* colonies are emulsified in saline on a slide and tested for agglutination by polyvalent and monovalent EPEC O antisera. At least ten colonies per plate should be tested as many serotypes are present in a single culture. If isolated colonies are negative, the confluent growth is emulsified and tested. During outbreaks, if the causative serotype is known, cultures need be tested only with the particular antiserum. EPEC antisera are now difficult to obtain and so specific diagnosis is available only in few laboratories. When the outbreak is caused by a strain with some readily demonstrable feature such as failure to ferment sorbitol, rapid identification is possible by using appropriate culture media.

The pathogenesis of EPEC diarrhea is not fully understood. EPEC do not ordinarily produce enterotoxins, nor are they invasive. In infantile enteritis, the bacilli are seen to be adherent to the mucosa of the upper small intestine, intimately attached to cup-like projections ('pedestals') of the enterocyte membrane, causing disruption of the brush border microvilli. The name *enteroadherent E. coli* has been proposed for these strains, which can be identified by their adhesion to HEp-2 cells.

Enterotoxigenic E. coli (ETEC): Diarrhea caused by ETEC is endemic in the developing countries in the tropics, among all age groups in the local population. Its severity varies from mild watery diarrhea to fatal disease indistinguishable from cholera. Persons from developed countries visiting endemic areas often suffer from ETEC diarrhea – a condition known as 'traveller's diarrhea'. ETEC diarrhea came into prominence from the late 1960s.

Though plasmids with enterotoxin genes may be present in any strain of *E. coli*, in practice only a small number of serotypes become enterotoxigenic (for example, 06, 08, 015, 025, 027, 0167). Toxin production alone may not lead to illness. The strains should first be able to adhere to intestinal mucosa. This adhesion is mediated by fimbrial or colonisation factor antigens, of which a number have been identified (CFA I, II, III,IV).

Diagnosis of ETEC diarrhea depends on the demonstration of enterotoxin in *E. coli* isolates by any of the methods listed in Table 30.2. A strain of ETEC may produce either LT or ST or both. Detection of LT is easy as many in vitro methods are available, such as tissue culture tests (rounding of Y_1 mouse adrenal cells and elongation of CHO cells due to intracellular increase of cAMP concentration), and serological tests (ELISA, passive agglutination and immunolysin tests). In vivo tests such as rabbit loop or intradermal tests may be used when in vitro tests are not available. The detection of ST is more difficult. The infant mouse test is still widely employed. The poor antigenicity of ST has prevented the development of serological tests, though ST ELISA using monoclonal antibody has been introduced. Genetic probes are available for detection of ST and LT in *E. coli* cultures, or directly in feces, food or water.

Enteroinvasive E. coli (EIEC): These resemble shigellae in many respects. Many of these strains are nonmotile, do not ferment lactose or ferment it late with acid, but without producing any gas and do not form lysine decarboxylase. Many of these show O antigen cross reaction with shigellae. These 'atypical' *E. coli* strains had earlier been grouped under the 'Alkalescens–Dispar Group' and given names such as *'Shigella alkalescens'* (resembling *Sh. flexneri* except in fermenting dulcitol and forming alkali in litmus milk) and *'Sh. dispar'* (late lactose fermenter like Sh. sonnei but indole positive). Besides these 'atypical strains' many typical *E. coli* strains can also cause clinical illness resembling shigellosis. These have been termed *enteroinvasive E. coli* because they have the capacity to invade interstitial epithelial cells in vivo and penetrate HeLa cells in tissue culture. EIEC strains usually belong to serogroups 028 ac, 0112 ac, 0124, 0136, 0143, 0114, 0152, 0154.

Clinically EIEC infection resembles shigellosis, ranging from mild diarrhea to frank dysentery, and occurs, in children as well as adults. For laboratory diagnosis of EIEC, the Sereny test used to be employed (that is, instillation of a suspension of freshly isolated EIEC or shigella into the eyes of guinea pigs leads to mucopurulent conjunctivitis and severe keratitis). Mice may be used instead of guinea pigs. Cell penetration of HeLa or HEP-2 cells in culture is a more humane diagnostic test. This ability to penetrate cells is determined by a large plasmid, detection of which can also be a diagnostic test. The plasmid codes for outer membrane antigens called the *virulence marker antigens'* (VMA) which can be detected by the ELISA (VMA ELISA) test.

Enterohemorrhagic E.coli (EHEC) Shigatoxigenic E. coli (STEC) or Verotoxigenic E. coli (VTEC): *E.coli* strains producing verocytotoxin (VT) or Shiga-like toxin (SLT) can give rise to diarrheal disease ranging in severity from mild diarrhea to fatal hemorrhagic colitis and hemorrhagic uremic syndrome (HUS) particularly in young children and the elderly. The primary target for VT appears to be the vascular endothelial cells. This may explain the pathogenesis of HUS, in which a characteristic renal lesion is capillary microangiopathy. VTEC also produces diarrhea in cattle and pigs. The typical EHEC is serotype O157: H7, but a few others such as O26: H1 also belong to this category.

The disease may occur sporadically or as outbreaks of food poisonong. The source of infection is contamination by human or animal feces, directly or indirectly. Changing life styles and eating habits, with growing popularity of fast foods have led to a remarkable increase in EHEC food poisoning. In the USA, about 20,000 cases of 0:157 food poisoning occur every year, many with hemorrhagic complications. A large outbreak of food poisoning caused by *E. coli* O:157 , with over 10,000 cases occurred in Japan in 1996, mostly affecting school children. Investigation of this epidemic revealed the source of infection to be salad vegetables such as radish and alfalfa sprouts, in which the bacteria were found beneath the skin and in the deeper tissues. Washing would not remove the bacteria from such vegetables and cooking alone may ensure safety. This finding extends the scope of EHEC food poisoning to vegetarians also.

Laboratory diagnosis of VTEC diarrhea can be made by demonstration of the bacilli or VT in feces directly or in culture. As VTEC forms only a minority of fecal coliforms in infected cases, testing individual colonies may not be successful. The sensitivity can be considerably increased by using DNA probes for VT_1 and VT_2 genes. VT can be detected by its cytotoxic effects on Vero or HeLa cells. Demonstration of VT neutralising antibodies in convalescent sera may help in retrospective diagnosis.

Most VTEC strains belong to the serotype 0157:H7 which does not ferment sorbitol, unlike the majority of *E. coli.* So the use of sorbitol MacConkey medium helps in screening for 0:157 VTEC.

Enteroaggregative E. coli (EAEC): These strains are so named because they appear aggregated in a 'stacked brick' formation on Hep-2 cells or glass. They have been associated with persistent diarrhea, especially in developing countries. Most of the are O-untypable, but many are H-typable. In animal experiments they cause shortening of villi, hemorrhagic necrosis and mild edema with mononuclear infiltration of the submucosa. They form a low molecular weight heat stable enterotoxin called EAST1 ('enteroaggregative heat stable enterotoxin-1).

Pyogenic infections:*E. coli* form the most common cause of intra-abdominal infections, such as peritonitis and abscesses resulting from spillage of bowel contents. They also cause pyogenic infections in the perianal area. They are an important cause of neonatal meningitis.

Septicemia: Blood stream invasion by *E. coli* may lead to fatal conditions like septic shock and 'systemic inflammatory response syndrome' (SIRS).

As *E. coli* commonly show multiple drug resistance, antibiotic sensitivity testing of strains is important in treatment.

EDWARDSIELLA

The genus contains the species *Edwardsiella tarda* which is a noncapsulated, motile bacillus with weak fermentative powers. The name *tarda* refers to its tardy or weak fermentation of sugars. Of the sugars commonly used, only glucose and maltose are fermented. It forms indole and H_2S, utilises citrate and decarboxylates lysine and ornithine.

E. tarda is a normal intestinal inhabitant of snakes and other cold blooded animals. It has been cultured from normal and diarrheaic human feces. Its pathogenic role is uncertain but it has been isolated from wounds, urine, blood, and from CSF in cases of fatal meningitis.

CITROBACTER

These are motile bacilli which utilise citrate, grow in KCN medium, produce H_2S and ferment lactose late or not at all. Three species are recognised, *Citro. freundii* which gives typical reactions and *Citro. koseri* (formerly *Citro. diversus*) and *Citro. amalonaticus* which do not form H_2S. *Citro. freundii* strains were formerly classified as the 'Ballerup–Bethesda group'. They exhibit extensive antigenic sharing with salmonellae. This may cause confusion in the diagnostic laboratory. Some strains (for exmaple, the Bhatnagar strain) have a Vi

antigen serologically identical to the antigen of *S. typhi* and *S. paratyphi* C. These may be used for the estimation of Vi antibodies or for raising Vi antisera.

Citrobacter is a normal intestinal inhabitant. Many strains formerly called paracolons belong to this group. It has been isolated from a few cases of enteric fever but its etiological role is not established. It may cause infections of the urinary tract, gall bladder, middle ear and meninges.

KLEBSIELLA

The genus *Klebsiella* consists of nonmotile, capsulated rods that grow well on ordinary media forming large, dome shaped, mucoid colonies of varying degrees of stickiness. They are short, plump, straight rods, about 1-2 x 0.5-0.8 mm in size. The capsule is often prominent and can be made out even in Gram stained smears as haloes around the bacilli. Klebsiellae are widely distributed in nature, occurring both as commensals in the intestines and as saprophytes in soil and water. Their classification has undergone various modifications. They have been classified into three species based on biochemical reactions and into over 80 serotypes based on the capsular (K) antigens (Table 30.3).

KLEBSIELLA PNEUMONIAE

(*Friedlander's bacillus, Bacillus mucosus capsulatus*)

This bacillus was first isolated by Friedlander

Table 30.3 Differentiation of Klebsiella species

	K. pneumoniae	K. ozaenae	K. rhinoscleromatis
Gas from glucose	+	d	–
Acid from lactose	+	d	–
MR	–	+	+
VP	+	–	–
Citrate	+	d	–
Urease	+	d	–
Malonate	+	–	+
Lysine	+	d	–

(1883) from fatal cases of pneumonia. It ferments sugars (glucose, lactose, sucrose, mannitol) with the production of acid and abundant gas. It is indole and MR negative and VP and citrate positive (IM Vic − − + +). Biochemically variant strains are common. It forms urease. Strains, formerly labelled as nonmotile *Aerobacter aerogenes* (*K. aerogenes*), are now considered to be *K. pneumoniae* subspecies aerogenes. It is the second most populous member of the aerobic bacterial flora of the human intestine. It has become a very important cause of nosocomial infections, even replacing *E. coli* in some centres. It causes pneumonia, urinary infection, other pyogenic infections, septicemia and rarely diarrhea.

Klebsiella pneumonia is a serious disease with high case fatality. It occurs in middle aged or older persons who have medical problems such as alcoholism, chronic bronchopulmonary disease or diabetes mellitus. The disease is characterised by massive mucoid inflammatory exudate of lobar or lobular distribution, involving one or more lobes of the lung. Necrosis and abscess formation are more frequent than in pneumococcal pneumonia. Serotypes 1, 2 and 3 are usually responsible for pneumonia. Positive blood cultures can be obtained in about 25 per cent of the cases.

K. pneumoniae is a frequent cause of urinary infection. As most strains are resistant to antibiotics, treatment poses serious problems. It also causes pyogenic infections such as abscesses, meningitis and septicemia.

Some strains of *K. pneumoniae* isolated from cases of diarrhea have been shown to produce an enterotoxin very similar to the heat stable toxin of *E. coli*. The production of this toxin is determined by the presence of a plasmid.

Diagnosis is made by culturing appropriate specimens and identifying the isolate by biochemical reactions. Antibiotic sensitivity should invariably be done. Many strains carry plasmids determining multiple drug resistance.

K. ozaenae is a bacillus associated with ozena, a disease characterised by foul smelling nasal discharge. Identification is difficult due to wide variations in the biochemical reactions of individual strains. *K. ozaenae* belongs to capsular types 3–6.

K. rhinoscleromatis causes rhinoscleroma, a chronic granulomatous hypertrophy of the nose prevalent in southeastern Europe, India and Central America. The bacilli are seen intracellularly in lesions. It can be identified by biochemical reactions and belongs to capsular type 3.

The species *K. oxytoca* may be rarely isolated from clinical specimens.

ENTEROBACTER

Formerly known as Aerobacter, these are motile, capsulated, lactose fermenting bacilli which are indole and MR negative and VP and citrate positive. Two clinically relevant species are *E. cloacae* and *E. aerogenes* (Table 30.4).

They are normally found in feces, sewage, soil and water and rarely in urine, pus and other pathological materials. They may be responsible for hospital infections.

HAFNIA

This is a motile, nonlactose-fermenting bacillus which is indole and MR negative and VP and citrate

Table 30.4 Differentiation between E. cloacae and E. aerogenes

	E. cloacae	*E. aerogenes*
Gas from glycerol	−	+
Aesculin hydrolysis	−	+
Lysine decarboxylase	−	+
Arginine dihydrolase	+	+

positive. Biochemical reactions are evident best at 22 °C; at 37 °C they may be negative or irregular. Only one genus is recognised, *H. alvei*. It is found in human and animal feces, sewage, soil and water.

SERRATIA

This differs from *Hafnia* in forming a pink, red or magenta, nondiffusible pigment called prodigiosin which is formed optimally at room temperature. Only one species is of medical importance – *S. marcescens* ('*Bacillus prodigiosus*'). It is pleomorphic, with minute coccobacillary and normal bacillary forms. It is a saprophyte found in water, soil and food. It may grow in sputum after collection and may suggest hemoptysis because of the pigment formed ('pseudohemoptysis'). Nosocomial infections due to *S. marcescens* are being reported with increasing frequency. The bacillus has been associated with meningitis, endocarditis, septicemia, peritonitis, respiratory infection and many other conditions. Multiple drug resistance is common in hospital strains.

TRIBE PROTEEAE

(Proteus bacilli)

Proteus bacilli constituting the tribe *Proteeae* are lactose nonfermenters and so do not strictly belong to the group of 'coliform bacilli'. However, they are also normal intestinal commensals and opportunistic pathogens like coliforms, and so are included in this chapter. The name 'Proteus' refers to their pleomorphism, after the Greek god Proteus who could assume any shape.

The tribe *Proteeae* is classified into three genera – *Proteus, Morganella* and *Providencia*. Most of them except for some Provindencia strains, produce a powerful urease which rapidly hydrolyses urea to ammonia and carbon dioxide. A characteristic feature which distinguishes *Proteeae* from other enterobacteria is the presence, in all members of the tribe, of the enzyme phenyl alanine deaminase which converts phenyl alanine to phenyl pyruvic acid (PPA reaction). All of them with few exceptions show the following features:

Gram negative, noncapsulated, pleomorphic, motile rods,

- resistant to KCN;
- degrade tyrosine;
- fail to acidify lactose, dulcitol or malonate;
- do not form arginine or lysine decarboxylase or beta galactosidase;
- MR positive, VP negative.

The major differentiating features of medically important species of proteus bacilli are shown in Table 30.5.

Proteus bacilli possess somatic O and flagellar H antigens, which are of considerable historical interest. Weil and Felix (1916) studying Proteus bacilli observed that flagellated strains growing on agar formed a thin surface film resembling the mist produced by breathing on glass and named this variety the 'Hauch' form (from *Hauch*, meaning film of breath). Nonflagellated variants grew as

Table 30.5 Biochemical features of Proteus bacilli

Test	Pr. mirabilis	Pr. vulgaris	Morg. morganii	Prov. alcalifaciens	Prov. stuartii	Prov. rettgeri
Urease	+	+	+	−	±	+
Ornithine decarboxylase	+	−	+	−	−	−
Indole	−	+	+	+	+	+
Fermentation of adonitol	−	−	−	+	±	±
Fermentation of trehalose	+	±	±	−	+	

isolated colonies without the surface film and were called 'Ohne Hauch' (meaning without film of breath). These names came to be abbreviated as the H and O forms. Subsequently, the H and O were extended to refer to the flagellar and somatic antigens of other bacilli as well. The terms are also used to designate the type of bacterial agglutination, the H type referring to the loose, fluffy masses formed when flagellated cells are agglutinated, and the O type to the fine granular appearance of somatic agglutination.

Weil and Felix also observed that certain nonmotile strains of *Pr. vulgaris*, called the 'X strains', were agglutinated by sera from typhus fever patients. This heterophilic agglutination due to the sharing of a carbohydrate hapten by certain strains of Proteus and rickettsiae forms the basis of the Weil–Felix reaction for the diagnosis of some rickettsial infections. Three nonmotile Proteus strains OX2, OX19 and OXK are used in the agglutination test.

Proteus bacilli are widely distributed in nature as saprophytes, being found in decomposing animal matter, in sewage, in manured soil and in human and animal feces. They are frequently present on the moist areas of the skin. They are opportunistic pathogens, commonly responsible for urinary and septic infections, often nosocomial.

The genus *Proteus* contains two species of medical importance – *Pr. mirabilis*, which is an important urinary and nosocomial pathogen, and *Pr. vulgaris* which is found much less commonly in human infections. *Pr. mirabilis* is indole negative and *Pr. vulgaris* indole positive.

Cultures of proteus bacilli have a characteristic putrefactive odour described as 'fishy' or 'seminal'. *Pr. mirabilis* and *Pr. vulgaris* swarm on solid culture media. Discrete colonies are seen in young cultures but thereafter actively motile cells spread on the surface of the plate in successive waves to form a thin filmy layer in concentric circles. Swarming growth is a problem in the laboratory when mixed growth is obtained in which proteus bacilli are present with other bacteria. Several methods have been used to inhibit swarming – increased (6%) concentration of agar, incorporation of chloral hydrate (1:500), sodium azide (1:500), alcohol (5–6%), sulphonamide, surface active agents or boric acid (1:1000). Swarming does not occur on MacConkey's medium, on which smooth colourless colonies are formed.

The genus *Morganella* has only one species, *M. morganii* (formerly *Pr. morganii*). It does not swarm in culture. It is commonly found in human and animal feces and causes urinary infection infrequently. Nosocomial wound infections also occur.

The genus *Providencia* (formerly known as *Proteus inconstans*) contains three species seen in clinical infections. *Prov. alcalifaciens* is sometimes seen in normal human feces but far more frequently in diarrheal stools though its etiological role is uncertain. *Prov. stuartii* is a common cause of urinary infection and of infection in burns. *Prov. rettgerii* is part of the normal fecal flora of reptiles and amphibians, and sometimes causes nosocomial infection of the urinary tract, wounds, burns and blood.

Proteus bacilli are resistant to many of the common antibiotics. An exception is *Pr. mirabilis* which is sensitive to ampicillin and cephalo-sporins. Providencia are the most resistant, particularly *Prov. stuartii* which is also resistant to disinfectants such as chlorhexidine, cetrimide, benzalkonium chloride and heavy metal compounds such as silver sulphonamide, making it a major pathogen in burns units. It is sensitive to phenol and glutaraldehyde. Amikacin and ciprofloxocin are generally effective in treatment.

ERWINIA

These are anaerogenic bacilli forming a yellowish pigment, usually found in soil and causing plant infections. *E. herbicola* has occasionally been isolated from respiratory and urinary infections in predisposed or hospitalised patients.

Further Reading

Baldwin TJ. 1998. The pathogenicity of enteropathogenic *Escherichia coli. J Med Microbiol.* 47:283.

Banwell JG. 1990. Pathophysiology of diarrheal disorders. *Rev Infect Dis.* 12:S.30.

Cooke EM. 1985. *Escherichia coli*, an overview. *J Hyg (Camb) 95:*523.

Ewing WH. 1986. *Edwards and Ewing's Identification of Enterobacteriaceae*, 4th edn. New York: Elsevier.

Feng P. 1995 *E. coli* serotye O157: Novel vehicle of infection. *Emerging Infect Dis.* 1:2.

Fitzpatrick M. 1999. Haemolytic uremic syndrome and *E. coli* 0157. *BMJ.* 318:684.

Graham JC and A Galloway. 2001. Laboratory diagnosis of urinary tract infection. *J Clin Path* 54:911.

Gransden WR. 1990. Bacteremia due to *Escherichia coli. Rev Infect Dis.* 12:008.

Gross RJ. 1991. The pathogenesis of *Escherichia coli* diarrhea. *Rev Med Microbiol.* 2:37.

Natara P and JB Kaper. 1998. Diarrhiagenic *E.coli. Clin Microbial Rev.* 11:742.

Enterobacteriaceae II: Shigella

Dysentery is a clinical condition of multiple etiology, characterised by the frequent passage of blood stained, mucopurulent stools. The two common types of dysentery are bacillary and amebic. The causative agents of bacillary dysentery belong to the genus *Shigella*, so named after Shiga, who in 1896 isolated the first member of this genus from epidemic dysentery in Japan. Some other bacilli, such as enteroinvasive *E. coli*, *Vibrio parahaemolytius* and *Campylobacter*, can also cause the clinical picture of dysentery.

Morphology: Shigellae are short, Gram negative rods, about 0.5 μm × 1–3 μm in size. They are nonmotile, nonsporing and noncapsulated. Fimbriae may be present.

Cultural characteristics: They are aerobes and facultative anaerobes, with a growth temperature range of 10–40 °C and optima of 37 °C and pH 7.4. They grow on ordinary media but less readily than other enterobacteria. After overnight incubation, colonies are small, about 2 mm in diameter, circular, convex, smooth and translucent. Occasionally on primary isolation and frequently in subcultures, a proportion of the colonies may be of the rough type. Colonies on MacConkey agar are colourless due to the absence of lactose fermentation. An exception is *Sh. sonnei* which ferments lactose late and forms pale pink colonies. Deoxycholate citrate agar (DCA) is a useful selective medium. Growth is inhibited on Wilson and Blair's bismuth sulphite medium.

Resistance: Shigellae are not specially resistant. They are killed at 56 °C in one hour and by 1% phenol in 30 minutes. In ice they last for 1–6 months. They remain viable in moist environments for days, but die rapidly on drying. In feces they die within a few hours due to the acidity produced by the growth of coliforms. *Sh. sonnei* is in general more resistant than other shigella species.

Biochemical reactions: Shigellae are MR positive and reduce nitrates to nitrites. They cannot utilise citrate as the sole source of carbon, do not form H_2S and are inhibited by KCN. Catalase is produced, except by *Sh. dysenteriae* type 1. Glucose is fermented with the production of acid, without gas, except for the Newcastle and Manchester biotypes of *Sh. flexneri* type 6, and some strains of *Sh. boydii* types 13 and 14, which form gas. Fermentation of mannitol is of importance in classification and shigellae have traditionally been divided into mannitol fermenting and nonfermenting species. *Sh. flexneri*, *Sh. boydii* and *Sh. sonnei* ferment mannitol, while *Sh. dysenteriae* does not. Exceptions are not infrequent. Lactose and sucrose are not fermented, except by *Sh. sonnei* which ferments them late. Adonitol, inositol and salicin are not fermented.

Antigenic structure: Shigellae possess one or more 'major' antigens and a large number of 'minor' somatic O antigens. Some strains possess K antigens. These are not relevant in typing but may sometimes interfere with agglutination by O antisera. Fimbrial antigens are also present. In general, the antigenic structure of shigellae is simple, compared to the complex structure of salmonellae. There is considerable antigenic sharing between some members of the genus as well as between shigellae and *E. coli*. Common fimbrial antigens may also occur, particularly in *Sh. flexneri*. It is, therefore, important that the identification of shigellae should be made by a combination of antigenic and biochemical properties and not by slide agglutination alone.

CLASSIFICATION

Shigellae are classified into four species or subgroups based on a combination of biochemical and serological characteristics. Serotypes are distinguished within the species. *Sh. sonnei* is serologically homogeneous and is classified by colicin typing.

Sh. dysenteriae (subgroup A): This species of mannitol nonfermenting bacilli consists of ten serotypes. Type 1 is the bacillus originally described by Shiga (*Sh. shigae*). It is indole negative and is the only member of the family that is always catalase negative. (*Sh. schmitzi* and *Sh. sonnei* are invariably catalase positive, while among other shigella species, some strains may be catalase negative.)

Sh. dysenteriae type 1 forms a toxin (Shiga toxin), the earliest example of an exotoxin produced by a Gram negative bacillus. Three types of toxic activity have been demonstrated in shigella culture filtrates: (1) neurotoxicity, demonstrable by paralysis and death on injection into mice or rabbits. Though known as 'neurotoxin', the primary site of its action appears to be not the nervous tissue but the blood vessels, mainly of the central nervous system, with the neurological effects being secondary; (2) enterotoxicity, with induction of fluid accumulation in ligated rabbit ileal loop. Two new shigella enterotoxins have been identified, designated as Sh. ET-1 and 2, the former confined to *Sh. flexneri* 2a and the latter more widespread; and (3) cytotoxicity, causing cytopathic changes in cultured Vero cells. This appears to be the same as Verotoxin 1 (or Shiga-like toxin) produced by certain strains of *E. coli* (VTEC). The toxin consists of binding (B) and active (A) subunits. Subunit A is divided into two fragments A1 and

A2. Fragment A1 appears to inactivate host cell 60 S ribosome, interfering with protein synthesis.

Sh. dysenteriae type 2 (*Sh. schmitzi*) forms indole and ferments sorbitol and rhamnose. Serotypes 3–7 were described by Large and Sachs in India and hence used to be known as the Large–Sachs group. Three further serotypes have been described making a total of ten.

Sh. flexneri (subgroup B): This group is named after Flexner, who described the first of the mannitol fermenting shigellae from Philippines (1900). This group is biochemically heterogeneous and antigenically the most complex among shigellae. Based on type specific and group specific antigens, they have been classified into six serotypes (1–6) and several subtypes (1a; 1b; 2a, 2b; 3a, 3b, 3c, 4a, 4b, 5a, 5b). In addition, two antigenic 'variants' called X and Y are recognised, which lack the type specific antigens. Serotype 6 is always indole negative and occurs in three biotypes, some of which form gas from sugars.

Sh. boydii (subgroup C): This group consists of dysentery bacilli that resemble *Sh. flexneri* biochemically but not antigenically. The group is named after Boyd, who first described these strains from India (1931). Fifteen serotypes have been identified. *Sh. boydii* are isolated least frequently from cases of bacillary dysentery.

Sh. sonnei (subgroup D): This bacillus, first described by Sonne (1915) in Denmark, ferments lactose and sucrose late. It is indole negative. It is antigenically homogeneous but may occur in two forms – phase I and phase II – the latter forming colonies that are larger, flatter and more irregular. On subculture, phase I produces both types of colonies but phase II is considered to be a loss variation. Organisms in phase II may be isolated from patients but are more common in convalescents and carriers.

Sh. sonnei causes the mildest form of bacillary dysentery. In many cases the disease may only be a mild diarrhea. However, *Sh. sonnei* infection persists as the most common shigellosis in the advanced countries. For epidemiological purposes, *Sh. sonnei* has been classified into many colicin types.

PATHOGENICITY

Shigellae cause bacillary dysentery. Infection occurs by ingestion. The minimum infective dose is low, as few as 10–100 bacilli being capable of initiating the disease, probably because they survive gastric acidity better than other enterobacteria. Their pathogenic mechanisms resemble those of enteroinvasive *E. coli*. The bacilli infect the epithelium cells of the villi in the large intestine and multiply inside them, spreading laterally to involve adjacent cells and penetrating into the lamina propria. Inflammatory reaction develops with capillary thrombosis, leading to necrosis of patches of epithelium, which slough off, leaving behind transverse superficial ulcers. Bacteremia may occur in severe infections, particularly in malnourished children and in AIDS.

Though *Sh. dysenteriae* type 1 forms an exotoxin, it appears to be much less important in pathogenesis than the ability of the bacillus to penetrate and multiply in colonic mucosa. Nontoxigenic mutants can still cause dysentery but not noninvasive ones. The invasive property of the bacillus can be demonstrated by its ability to penetrate cultured HeLa or Hep-2 cells or by the Congo red binding test. Invasive property is related to the presence in the bacillus of large plasmids (M.W. 140×10^6) coding for the outer membrane protein responsible for cell penetration. These proteins are called 'virulence marker antigens' (VMA). Detection of VMA by ELISA serves as a virulence test for Shigellae, as for enteroinvasive *E. coli*.

Bacillary dysentery has a short incubation period (1–7 days, usually 48 hours). The onset and clinical course are variable and are largely determined by the virulence of the infecting strain. The main clinical features are frequent passage of loose, scanty feces containing blood and mucus, along with abdominal cramps and tenesmus. Fever and vomiting may be present. Complications are most often seen in infection with *Sh. dysenteriae* type 1 and include arthritis, toxic neuritis, conjunctivitis, parotitis and, in children, intussusception. Hemolytic uremic syndrome may occur as a complication in severe cases. The severity of the disease may vary from acute fulminating dysentery to mild diarrhea. As the term bacillary dysentery refers only to the more severe cases, the term 'shigellosis' has been employed to include the whole spectrum of disease caused by shigellae.

Human beings are the only natural hosts for shigellae. Captive monkeys have been found

Table 31.1 Distinguishing features of Shigella species

Subgroup	A	B	C	D
Species	*Sh. dysenteriae*	*Sh. flexneri*	*Sh. boydii*	*Sh. sonnei*
Mannitol	–	A	A	A
Lactose	–	–	–	A Late
Sucrose	–	–	–	A Late
Dulcitol	–	–	d	–
Indole	d	d	d	–
Ornithine decarboxylase	–	–	–	+
Serotypes	10	6 + variants	15	Only one

A = Acid   d=Variable

Table 31.2 Biotypes of Sh. flexneri Type 6

Biotype	Fermentation of	
	Glucose	Mannitol
Boyd 88	A	A
Manchester	AG	AG
Newcastle	A or AG	–

A=Acid   AG=Acid and Gas

infected but such infections may have been of human origin. Experimentally, dysentery can be produced only in monkeys. Human volunteer studies have clarified the spectrum of shigellosis. Of a group of volunteers ingesting 10,000 *Sh. flexneri* 2a bacilli, a quarter remained asymptomatic, another quarter had transient fever a day or two later, a quarter developed fever with watery diarrhea, while only one quarter developed typical dysentery.

Epidemiology: Epidemics of bacillary dysentery have always accompanied wars and often influenced their outcome. In several campaigns, more men have died of dysentery than were killed in battle. A recent instance was the major epidemic affecting many thousands, with high case fatality, which occurred during the Rwandan civil war in 1994. Epidemics in civilian communities are associated with poverty and lack of sanitation.

The only source of infection are human beings – cases, or less often carriers. Chronic carriage is rare, the bacilli disappearing from feces within a few weeks, except in some malnourished chidren or AIDS patients. Shigellae exhibit a high rate of secondary household transmission. The modes of transmission may be as follows: (1) direct, through contaminated fingers: 'hand-to-mouth' infection; (2) through fomites such as door handles, water taps, lavatory seats; (3) through water; (4) through contaminated food or drink. Shigellosis, especially *Sh. sonnei* infection, may occur as food poisoning; and (5) through flies which may transmit the infection as mechanical vectors; (6) Shigellosis may occur in young male homosexuals as part of the gay bowel syndrome.

Shigellosis is worldwide in distribution but epidemiologically, there are a number of differences between the nature and extent of the infection in the affluent and in the poor countries. Where environmental sanitation is good, as in Britain, shigellosis is mainly seen in young children and in special situations like mental hospitals (asylum dysentery). *Sh. sonnei* is the predominant infecting agent. In the USA, *Sh. sonnei* is the main type in the north, while *Sh. flexneri* is more common in the south. In countries where environmental sanitation is poor, endemic shigellosis is found in all age groups and is caused by all species. In India, *Sh. flexneri* has been the predominant species, having formed 50–85 per cent of isolates in different series. *Sh. dysenteriae* (8–25 per cent) and *Sh. sonnei* (2–24 per cent) are the next common species. *Sh. boydii* (0–8 per cent) has been isolated least frequently.

The picture has changed in recent years. After a long period of quiescence, *Sh. dysenteriae* type I suddenly appeared in an extensive and virulent epidemic form in Central America in 1968. In 1973, a similar outbreak started in Bangladesh and later in Sri Lanka. Several localised outbreaks were observed in India from 1974, followed by extensive epidemics in various states from the early 1980s. The epidemic strains showed plasmidborne multiple drug resistance.

Laboratory diagnosis: Diagnosis is made by isolating the bacillus from feces. Fresh feces should be inoculated without delay or transported in a suitable medium such as Sachs' buffered glycerol saline, pH 7.0–7.4. Highly alkaline transport media used for vibrios are inhibitory for shigellae. Rectal swabs are not satisfactory.

For inoculation it is best to use mucus flakes if they are present in the sample. MacConkey and DCA plates are inoculated. After overnight incubation at 37 °C, the plates are inspected for nonlactose fermenting colonies, which are tested for motility and biochemical reactions. Any nonmotile bacillus that is urease, citrate, H_2S and

KCN negative should be further investigated by biochemical tests (Table 31.1). Identification is confirmed by slide agglutination with polyvalent and monovalent sera. Demonstration of antibodies in sera is not useful.

Treatment: Uncomplicated shigellosis is a self limited condition in which the patient usually recovers spontaneously in a few days. However, in acute cases, particularly in infants and young children, dehydration has to be corrected promptly. Oral rehydration is adequate in most cases.

Routine antibacterial treatment is not indicated in dysentery. Multiple drug resistance plasmids are widely prevalent in shigellae. Indiscriminate antibiotic treatment will only worsen the problem of drug resistance in intestinal bacteria. Antibiotics should therefore be limited to severe or toxic cases, and in the very young, debilitated and the aged. The choice of antibiotic should be based on the sensitivity of the prevailing strain. Many strains are still susceptible to nalidixic acid or norfloxacin and other fluoroquinolones.

Control: Control consists essentially in improving personal and environmental sanitation. Antibiotics have no place in prophylaxis. No effective vaccine is available.

Further Reading

Hale TH. 1998. Bacillary dysentery. In *Topley and Wilson's Microbiology and Microbial Infections*. 9th edn. vol. 3. London: Arnold.

Keusch GT. 1998. Shigellosis. In *Harrison's Principles of Internal Medicine*, Vol.1, 14th edn., New York: McGraw Hill.

Lewis MJ. 1997. Shigella. In Greenwood D (ed). *Medical Microbiology*, 15th edn. Edinburgh: Churchill-Livingstone.

Enterobacteriaceae III: Salmonella

The genus *Salmonella* consists of bacilli that parasitise the intestines of a large number of vertebrate species and infect human beings, leading to enteric fever, gastroenteritis, septicemia with or without focal suppuration, and the carrier state.

The most important member of the genus is *Salmonella typhi*, the causative agent of typhoid fever. The typhoid bacillus was first observed by Eberth (1880) in the mesenteric nodes and spleen of fatal cases of typhoid fever and was isolated by Gaffky (1884). It came to be known as the Eberth–Gaffky bacillus or *Eberthella typhi*. Salmon and Smith (1885) described a bacillus which was believed to cause hog cholera (mistakenly, as it is a virus disease). This bacillus, later called *S. cholerae-suis*, was the first of a series of similar organisms to be isolated from animals and human beings – the genus *Salmonella*. It was subsequently realised that the typhoid bacillus also belonged to this group, in spite of minor biochemical differences, and it was redesignated *S. typhi*, the genus *Eberthella* having been abolished.

Salmonellae currently comprise above 2000 serotypes or species, all of them potentially pathogenic. For practical purposes, they may be divided into two groups: (1) The enteric fever group, consisting of the typhoid and paratyphoid bacilli that are exclusively or primarily human parasites; and (2) the food poisoning group, which are essentially animal parasites but which can also infect human beings, producing gastroenteritis, septicemia or localised infections.

Morphology: Salmonellae are Gram negative rods, about 1–3 μm × 0.5 μm in size. They are motile with peritrichate flagella, except for one type, *S. gallinarum-pullorum*, which is always nonmotile. Nonmotile mutants of other types may sometimes be found. They do not form capsules or spores but may possess fimbriae.

Cultural characteristics: Salmonellae are aerobic and facultatively anaerobic, growing readily on simple media over a range of pH 6–8 and temperature 15–41 °C (optimum 37 °C).

Colonies are large, 2–3 mm in diameter, circular, low convex and smooth. They are more translucent than coliform colonies. On MacConkey and deoxycholate citrate media, colonies are colourless due to the absence of lactose fermentation. On Wilson and Blair bismuth sulphite medium, jet black colonies with a metallic sheen are formed due to production of H_2S. *S. paratyphi* A and other species that do not form H_2S produce green colonies.

Selenite F and tetrathionate broth are commonly employed as enrichment media.

Biochemical reactions: Salmonellae ferment glucose, mannitol and maltose, forming acid and gas. An important exception is *S. typhi* which is anaerogenic. Lactose, sucrose and salicin are not fermented. Indole is not produced. They are MR positive, VP negative and citrate positive. *S. typhi* and a few other salmonellae do not grow in Simmons' citrate medium as they need tryptophan as the growth factor. Urea is not hydrolysed. H_2S is produced, except by *S. paratyphi* A, *S. cholerae-suis* and some other species.

The enteric fever group may be separated biochemically (Table 32.1).

Resistance: The bacilli are killed at 55 °C in one hour or at 60 °C in 15 minutes. Boiling or chlorination of water and pasteurisation of milk destroy the bacilli. In polluted water and soil, they survive for weeks and in ice for months. Cultures may be viable for years if prevented from drying. They are killed within five minutes by mercuric chloride (1:500) or 5% phenol.

Antigenic structure: Salmonellae possess the following antigens based on which they are classified and identified: (1) flagellar antigen H, (2) somatic antigen O, and (3) a surface antigen Vi, found in some species. Several strains carry fimbriae. Fimbrial antigens are not important in identification but may cause confusion due to their nonspecific nature and widespread sharing among enterobacteria.

H antigen: This antigen present on the flagella is a heat labile protein. It is destroyed by boiling or by treatment with alcohol but not by formaldehyde. When mixed with antisera, H suspensions agglutinate rapidly, producing large, loose, fluffy clumps. The H antigen is strongly immunogenic and induces antibody formation rapidly and in high titres following infection or immunisation. The flagellar antigen is of a dual nature, occurring in one of two phases.

O antigen: The somatic O antigen is a phospholipid–protein–polysaccharide complex which forms an integral part of the cell wall. It is identical with endotoxin. It can be extracted from the bacterial cell by treatment with trichloracetic acid, as first shown by Boivin (and therefore called the Boivin antigen). Treatment with phenol splits off the protein moiety, removing the antigenicity but retaining the toxicity of the complex.

The O antigen is unaffected by boiling, alcohol or weak acids. When mixed with antisera, O antigen suspensions form compact, chalky, granular clumps. O agglutination takes place more slowly and at a higher temperature optimum (50–55 °C) than H agglutination (37 °C). The O antigen is less immunogenic than the H antigen and the titre of the O antibody induced after infection or immunisation is generally lower than that of the H antibody.

The O antigen is not a single factor but a mosaic of two or more antigenic factors. Salmonellae are classified into a number of groups based on the presence of characteristic O antigens on the bacterial surface.

Vi antigen: Many strains of *S. typhi* fail to agglutinate with the O antiserum when freshly isolated. This is due to the presence of a surface polysaccharide antigen enveloping the O antigen. Felix and Pitt, who first described this antigen, believed that it was related to virulence and gave it the name 'Vi antigen'. It is analogous to the K antigens of coliforms. It is heat labile. Bacilli inagglutinable with the O antiserum become agglutinable after boiling or heating at 60 °C for one hour. It is also destroyed by N HCl and 0.5 N NaOH. It is unaffected by alcohol or 0.2% formol.

Originally observed in *S. typhi*, the Vi antigen with similar antigenic specificity is present in *S. paratyphi C* and *S. dublin*, as well as in certain strains of *Citrobacter* (the Ballerup–Bethesda group). The Vi antigen tends to be lost on serial subculture. The Vi polysaccharide acts as a virulence factor by inhibiting phagocytosis, resisting complement activation and bacterial lysis by the alternative pathway and peroxidase mediated killing.

Table 32.1 Biochemical characters of typhoid and paratyphoid bacilli

	Glucose	Xylose	d-Tartrate	Mucate
S. typhi	A	d	A	d
S. paratyphi A	AG	–	–	–
S. paratyphi B	AG	AG	–	AG
S. paratyphi C	AG	AG	AG	–

In human volunteer experiments, strains possessing the Vi antigen were found to cause clinical disease more consistently than those lacking it.

The Vi antigen is poorly immunogenic and only low titres of antibody are produced following infection. No Vi antibody is induced by the phenolised vaccine though low titres are produced by the alcoholised vaccine. The protective efficacy of the Vi antigen is demonstrated by the success of the purified Vi vaccine for typhoid now in routine use. Detection of the Vi antibody is not helpful for the diagnosis of cases and hence the Vi antigen is not employed in the Widal test. It has been stated that the total absence of the Vi antibody in a proven case of typhoid fever indicates poor prognosis. The antibody disappears early in convalescence. Its persistence indicates the development of the carrier state. The Vi antigen affords a method of epidemiological typing of the *S. typhi* strains based on specific Vi bacteriophages.

Antigenic variations: The antigens of salmonellae undergo phenotypic and genotypic variations.

H–O variation: This variation is associated with the loss of flagella. When salmonellae are grown on agar containing phenol (1:800), flagella are inhibited. This change is phenotypic and temporary. Flagella reappear when the strain is subcultured on media without phenol. Rarely, salmonellae may lose their flagella by mutation. A stable nonmotile mutant of *S. typhi* is the 901-0 strain which is widely employed for the preparation of O-agglutinable bacterial suspensions. Generally, the loss of flagella is not total and there occurs only a diminution in the number of flagella and the quantity of the H antigen. Flagellated cells are found in small numbers in such cultures. To obtain a population of motile cells, rich in H antigen, from such cultures, selection may be carried out by using Craigie's tube. This consists of a wide tube containing soft agar (0.2%) at the centre of which is embedded a short, narrow tube open at both ends, in such a way that it projects above the agar. The strain is inoculated carefully into the inner tube.

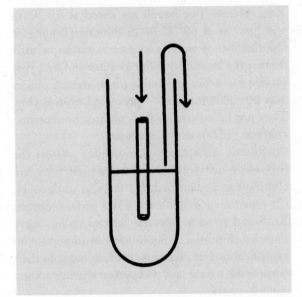

Fig.32.1 Craigie's tube. Inoculation is made inside the inner tube and after incubation, subculture is taken from the surface of the medium in the outer tube.

After incubation, subcultures withdrawn from the top of the agar outside the central tube will yield a population of motile cells (Fig. 32.1). Instead of Craigie's tube, a U-tube of soft agar may be employed, inoculation being made into one limb and subculture taken from the other.

Phase variation: The flagellar antigens of most salmonellae occur in one of two phases, that is, the flagella may exhibit one or the other of two alternative sets of antigens, defined by two separate sets of genes in the bacterial genome. Phase 1 antigens are either specific for a species or shared by a few species only. Hence phase 1 is called the 'specific' phase. Phase 2 antigens are widely shared and hence phase 2 is called the 'nonspecific' or 'group' phase. Phase 1 antigens are designated a, b, c, d, etc., and after z, as z1, z2, etc. Phase 2 antigens are far fewer and are termed 1, 2, etc. In some species, antigens belonging to phase 1 may occur as the phase 2 antigens (for example, e, n, x, z15). Strains that possess both phases are called *diphasic*. Some, like *S. typhi*, occur in phase 1 only and are called monophasic.

A culture will contain cells with the flagellar antigens of both phases but generally one or the other phase will predominate so that the culture is agglutinated only by one of the phase antisera. For serotyping of Salmonella isolates, it may be necessary to identify the flagellar antigens of both phases. A culture in phase 1 can be converted to phase 2 by passing it through a Craigie's tube containing specific phase 1 antiserum, and the reverse conversion achieved by using phase 2 antiserum.

V–W variation: Fresh isolates of *S. typhi* generally carry a surface layer of Vi antigen that completely masks the O antigen. Such bacilli are agglutinable with the Vi antiserum but not with the O antiserum. This is called the *V form*. After a number of subcultures, the Vi antigen is completely lost. Such cultures are inagglutinable with the Vi antiserum but readily agglutinable with the O antiserum. This is called the *W form*. Intermediate stages during the loss of the Vi antigen, when the bacillus is agglutinable with both Vi and O antisera, are called 'VW forms'.

Other Vi-containing bacilli such as *S. paratyphi C* and *S. dublin* seldom have the O antigen completely masked by the Vi antigen.

S–R variation: The smooth-to-rough variation is associated with the change in the colony morphology and loss of the O antigen and of virulence. The colony becomes large, rough and irregular. Suspensions in saline are autoagglutinable. Conversion into R forms occurs by mutation. R forms may be common in laboratory strains maintained by serial subcultivation. S-R variation may be prevented to some extent by maintaining cultures on Dorset's egg media in the cold, or ideally by lyophilisation.

Mucoid colonies, associated with the development of a new mucoid or 'M' antigen, have been described with *S. paratyphi B* and some other species.

Variations in O antigen: Changes in the structural formulae of the O antigen may be induced by lysogenisation with some converting phages, resulting in the alteration of serotypes. Thus, *S. anatum* is converted into *S. newington* by one phage and the latter into *S. minneapolis* by another phage (Fig. 32.2).

Classification and nomenclature: The classification and nomenclature of salmonellae have undergone several modifications over the years. Inclusion in the genus is based on common biochemical properties. Classification within the genus is on antigenic characterisation based on the Kauffmann–White scheme. This scheme depends on the identification, by agglutination, of the

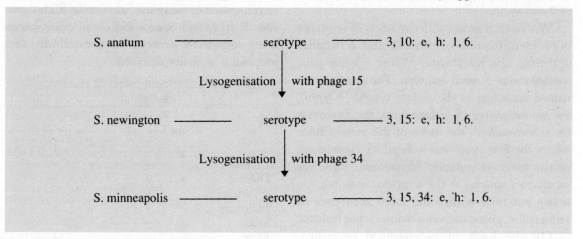

Fig. 32.2 Phage conversion of Salmonella serotypes

Table 32.2 Kaufmann–White scheme—illlustrative examples

Serogroups	Serotype	Antigen O	Antigen H Phase I	Antigen H Phase II
2 - A	S. paratyphi A	1, 2, 12	a	–
4 - B	S. paratyphi B	1, 4, 5, 12	b	1.2
	S. typhimurium	1, 4, 5, 12	i	1.2
	S. chester	4, 5, 12	e, h	e, n, x
7 - C1	S. paratyphi C	6, 7, (Vi)	c	1.5
	S. cholerae-suis	6, 7	c	1.5
8 - C2	S. muenchen	6, 8	d	1.2
9 - D	S. typhi	9, 12, (Vi)	d	–
	S. enteritidis	1, 9, 12	g, m	–
	S. gallinarum	1, 9, 12	–	–
10 - E1	S. anatum	3, 10	e, h	1. 6

structural formulae of the O and H antigens of the strains (Table 32.2).

Salmonellae are initially classified into serological groups, based on the presence of distinctive O antigen factors, which are designated 1, 2, 3, etc. Strains possessing factor 2 belong to group A, factor 4 to group B, factor 9 to group D and so on. Serogroups were originally designated by capital letters, A to Z, and afterwards by numbers – currently upto 67. It would be more logical to name the serogroups according to their characteristic O antigen factor numbers, rather than by letters. It has therefore been proposed to designate group A as 2, B as 4, C1 as 7, C2 as 8, D as 9 and so on.

Within each group, differentiation of serotypes is by identification of phase 1 and 2 flagellar antigens. The Kauffmann–White scheme gave species status to each serotype. The species were named according to the disease caused (S.typhi), the animal source (S. gallinarium), the discoverer (S. schottmulleri), the name of the patient from whom the first strain was isolated (S. thompson), or the place of isolation (S. poona). This was satisfactory so long as the serotypes were not too many but now with some 2400 serotypes of salmonellae, giving individual names is not realistic.

On the basis of biochemical reactions, Kauffmann proposed that salmonellae be classified into four subgenera (Table 32.3):

Subgenus I, the largest and medically the most important group contains all the species which commonly cause human and animal infections.

Subgenus II contains mostly species isolated from reptiles.

Subgenus III contains bacilli, formerly designated Arizona, originally isolated from lizards but subsequently found in reptiles, birds, domestic animals and human beings. Many of them are prompt lactose fermenters.

Subgenus IV strains are rarely encountered and may be considered atypical members of subgenus II.

Ewing proposed that only three species should be recognised in the genus Salmonella–S. cholerae-suis, S. typhi and S. enteritidis – all other species being considered serotypes of S. enteritidis. This proposal is now not followed.

Table 32.3 Biochemical reactions of Salmonella subgenera

Test	Subgenera I	II	III	IV
Lactose	–	–	+	–
Dulcitol	+	+	–	–
d-Tartrate	+	–	–	–
Malonate	–	+	+	–
Salicin	–	–	–	+
KCN	–	–	–	+

Modern taxonomical techniques, especially DNA studies, have shown that all the members of the genus *Salmonellae* and of the former genus *Arizona* are so closely related that they should all be considered as belonging to a single species, in a genetic, phylogenetic and evolutionary sense. Variations in properties such as antigenic structure, biochemical reactions and host preferences exhibited by different strains can be considered intraspecies divergences. A new species name *S. enterica* has been coined to include all salmonellae. *S. enterica* is classified into seven subspecies based on DNA–reassociation tests. These subspecies are named *enterica*, *salamae*, *arizonae*, *diarizonae*, *houtenae*, *bongori* and *indica*. Subspecies *enterica* corresponds to the former subgenus I.

Such classification and nomenclature, while being taxonomically correct, would be too complicated for use in clinical bacteriology. For example, the taxonomically correct name for the typhoid bacillus would be 'Salmonella enterica, subspecies enterica, serotype typhi'. Therefore, the old practice of referring to clinically important salmonellae serotypes by the species name continues in clinical bacteriology.

Sometimes serotypes may have to be further differentiated. Thus, *S. gallinarum* and *S. pullorum* cannot be distinguished serologically but they can be identified by biochemical reactions. (*S. gallinarum* is anaerogenic and ferments dulcitol unlike *S. pullorum*). Important pathogens such as *S. typhi*, *S. paratyphi A* and *B*, and *S. typhimurium* can be further typed for epidemiological purposes by phage susceptibility, biochemical properties, bacterocin production and antibiogram.

Pathogenicity: Salmonellae are strict parasites of animals or humans. *S. typhi*, *S. paratyphi A* and usually, but not invariably *S. paratyphi B* are confined to human beings. Other salmonellae are parasitic in various animals – domestic animals, rodents, reptiles – and birds. Some species are host adapted – *S. abortus-equi* found only in horses, *S.*

abortus-ovis in sheep and *S. gallinarum* in poultry. Others such as *S. typhimurium*, have a wide host range affecting animals, birds and humans. Infection in animals may vary from an asymptomatic condition to fatal, and sometimes epizootic disease. *S. typhimurium* and *S. enteritidis* cause a fatal septicemia in rats and mice. *S. pullorum* causes 'white diarrhea' in chicks and *S. gallinarum* fowl typhoid.

Salmonellae cause the following clinical syndromes in human beings: (1) enteric fever; (2) septicemia, with or without local suppurative lesions; and (3) gastroenteritis or food poisoning.

ENTERIC FEVER

The term enteric fever includes typhoid fever caused by *S. typhi* and paratyphoid fever caused by *S. paratyphi* A, B and C.

Typhoid fever was once prevalent all over the world and was not well demarcated from other prolonged fevers. A detailed study of the disease was presented by Bretonneau (1826) who identified the intestinal lesions. The name typhoid was given by Louis (1829) to distinguish it from typhus fever. Budd (1856) pointed out that the disease was transmitted through the excreta of patients. Eberth (1880) described the typhoid bacillus and Gaffky (1884) isolated it in pure culture. Its causative role was confirmed by Metchnikoff and Besredka (1900) by infecting apes experimentally. *S. paratyphi* A was isolated by Gwyn (1898), *S. paratyphi* B (*S. schottmulleri*) by Achard and Bensaude (1896) and *S. paratyphi* C (*S. hirschfeldii*) by Uhlenhuth and Hubener (1908) from cases resembling typhoid fever.

The infection is acquired by ingestion. In human volunteer experiments, the ID50 was found to be about 10^3 to 10^6 bacilli. On reaching the gut, the bacilli attach themselves to microvilli of the ileal mucosa and penetrate to the lamina propria and submucosa. They are phagocytosed there by polymorphs and macrophages. The ability to resist intracellular killing and to multiply within these cells is a measure of their virulence. They enter the mesenteric lymph nodes, where they multiply and, via the thoracic duct, enter the bloodstream. A transient bacteremia follows, during which the bacilli are seeded in the liver, gall bladder, spleen, bone marrow, lymph nodes, lungs and kidneys, where further multiplication takes place. Towards the end of the incubation period, there occurs massive bacteremia from these sites of multiplication, heralding the onset of clinical disease.

As bile is a good culture medium for the bacillus, it multiplies abundantly in the gall bladder and is discharged continuously into the intestine where it involves the Peyer's patches and lymphoid follicles of the ileum. These become inflamed, undergo necrosis and slough off, leaving behind the characteristic typhoid ulcers. Ulceration of the bowel leads to the two major complications of the disease – intestinal perforation and hemorrhage. During the 3–4 weeks that normally constitute the course of the disease, the intestinal lesions undergo healing.

The incubation period is usually 7–14 days but may range from 3–56 days and appears to be related to the dose of infection. The clinical course may vary from a mild undifferentiated pyrexia (ambulant typhoid) to a rapidly fatal disease. The onset is usually gradual, with headache, malaise, anorexia, a coated tongue and abdominal discomfort with either constipation or diarrhea. The typical features are a step-ladder pyrexia, with relative bradycardia and toxemia. A soft, palpable spleen is a constant finding. Hepatomegaly is also common. 'Rose spots' that fade on pressure appear on the skin during the second or third week but are seldom noticeable in dark skinned patients.

The most important complications are intestinal perforation, hemorrhage and circulatory collapse. Some degree of bronchitis or bronchopneumonia is always found. Some develop psychoses, deafness or meningitis. Cholecystitis, arthritis, abscesses, periosteitis, nephritis, hemolytic anemia, venous thromboses and peripheral neuritis are other complications found. Osteomyelitis is a rare sequel.

Convalescence is slow. In about 5–10 per cent of cases, relapse occurs during convalescence. The relapse rate is higher in patients treated early with chloramphenicol (15–20 per cent).

S. paratyphi A and B cause paratyphoid fever which resembles typhoid fever but is generally milder. *S. paratyphi* C may also cause paratyphoid fever but more often it leads to a frank septicemia with suppurative complications. Other salmonellae have on occasion been reported to cause enteric fever. These have included *S. dublin, S. barielly, S. sendai, S. enteritidis, S. typhimurium, S. eastbourne, S. saintpaul, S. oranienburg* and *S. panama.* Infection with *Alkaligenes faecalis* also may sometimes cause a similar clinical picture.

Epidemiology: Typhoid fever has been virtually eliminated from the advanced countries during the last several decades mainly as a result of improvements in water supply and sanitation but it continues to be endemic in the poor nations of the world. The control of paratyphoid fever has not been so successful. The distribution of paratyphoid bacilli shows marked geographical differences. *S. paratyphi* A is prevalent in India and other Asian countries, Eastern Europe and South America, *S. paratyphi* B in Western Europe, Britain and North America; and S. paratyphi C in Eastern Europe and Guyana.

Enteric fever is endemic in all parts of India. An incidence of 980 per 100,000 was recorded in the late 1990s in a 5-year community based study of children in Delhi. Worldwide, 16 million cases are estimated to occur annually with 600,000 deaths! The proportion of typhoid to paratyphoid A is about 10:1. Paratyphoid B is rare and C very rare. The disease occurs at all ages but is probably most common in the 5–20 years age group. The age incidence is related to the endemicity of the disease and the level of sanitation.

The source of infection is a patient, or far more frequently, a carrier. Patients who continue to shed typhoid bacilli in feces for three weeks to three months after clinical cure are called *convalescent carriers*. Those who shed the bacilli for more than three months but less than a year are called 'temporary carriers' and those who shed the bacilli for over a year are called 'chronic carriers'. About 2–4 per cent of patients become chronic carriers. The development of the carrier state is more common in women and in the older age groups (over 40 years). Some persons may become carriers following inapparent infection (symptomless excretor). The shedding of bacilli is usually intermittent. The bacilli persist in the gall bladder or kidney and are eliminated in the feces (fecal carrier) or urine (urinary carrier), respectively. Urinary carriage is less frequent and is generally associated with some urinary lesion such as calculi or schistosomiasis.

Food handlers or cooks who become carriers are particularly dangerous. The best known of such typhoid carriers was Mary Mallon ('Typhoid Mary'), a New York cook who, over a period of 15 years, caused at least seven outbreaks affecting over 200 persons.

Carriers occur with paratyphoid bacilli also. While *S. paratyphi* A occurs only in human beings, *S. paratyphi* B can infect animals such as dogs or cows, which may act as sources of human disease.

Typhoid fever occurs in two epidemiological types. The first is endemic or residual typhoid that occurs throughout the year though seasonal variations may sometimes be apparent. The second is epidemic typhoid, which may occur in endemic or nonendemic areas. Typhoid epidemics are water, milk or foodborne.

Laboratory diagnosis: Bacteriological diagnosis of enteric fever consists of the isolation of the bacilli from the patient and the demonstration of antibodies in his serum. A positive blood culture is diagnostic, while the same significance cannot be attached to isolation from feces or urine. Demonstration of antibodies is not conclusive evidence of current infection. A third method is the demonstration of typhoid bacillus antigen in blood or urine.

Blood culture: Bacteremia occurs early in the disease and blood cultures are positive in approximately 90 per cent of cases in the first week of fever. The popular belief that blood culture for diagnosis of typhoid fever is useful only in the first week is erroneous. Blood culture is positive in approximately 75 per cent of cases in the second week, 60 per cent in the third week and 25 per cent thereafter till the subsidence of pyrexia. Blood cultures rapidly become negative on treatment with antibiotics.

About 5–10 ml of blood is collected by venepuncture and inoculated into a culture bottle containing 50–100 ml of 0.5 per cent bile broth. Blood contains substances that inhibit the growth of the bacilli and hence it is essential that the broth be taken in sufficient quantity to provide at least fourfold dilution of blood. The addition of liquoid (sodium polyanethol sulphonate) counteracts the bactericidal action of blood.

After incubation overnight at 37 °C, the bile broth is subcultured on MacConkey agar. Pale nonlactose fermenting colonies that may appear on this medium are picked out for biochemical tests and motility. Salmonellae will be motile, indole and urease negative and ferment glucose, mannitol and maltose but not lactose or sucrose. The typhoid bacillus will be anaerogenic, while paratyphoid bacilli will form acid and gas from sugars. Identification of the isolate is by slide agglutination. A loopful of the growth from an agar slope is emulsified in two drops of saline on a slide. One emulsion acts as a control to show that the strain is not autoagglutinable. If *S. typhi* is suspected (that is, when no gas is formed from glucose), a loopful of typhoid O antiserum (factor 9/group D) is added to one drop of bacterial emulsion on the slide, and agglutination looked for after rocking the slide gently. Prompt agglutination indicates that the isolate belongs to Salmonella group D. Its identity as *S. typhi* is established by agglutination with the flagellar antiserum (anti-d serum). Quite often, fresh isolates of *S. typhi* are in the V form and do not agglutinate with the O antiserum. Such strains may be tested for agglutination against anti-Vi serum. Alternatively, the growth is scraped off in a small amount of saline, boiled for 20 minutes and tested for agglutination with the O antiserum. Where the isolate is a nontyphoid Salmonella (producing gas from sugars), it is tested for agglutination with O and H antisera for groups A, B and C. For identification of unusual serotypes, the help of the National Salmonella Reference Centre should be sought. The National Salmonella Reference Centre in India is located at the Central Research Institute, Kasauli. The reference centre for salmonellae of animal origin is at the Indian Veterinary Research Institute, Izatnagar.

If salmonellae are not obtained from the first subculture from bile broth, subcultures should be repeated every other day till growth is obtained. Cultures should be declared negative only after incubation for ten days. To eliminate the risk of introducing contamination during repeated subcultures, and also for economy and safety, Castaneda's method of culture may be adopted. In this, a double medium is used. The bottle of bile broth has an agar slant on one side. After inoculation of blood, the bottle is incubated in the upright position. For subculture, the bottle is merely tilted so that the broth runs over the surface of the agar. It is reincubated in the upright position. If salmonellae are present, colonies will appear on the slant.

An alternative to blood culture is the clot culture. Here, 5 ml of blood is withdrawn from the patient into a sterile test tube and allowed to clot. The serum is pipetted off and used for the Widal test. The clot is broken up with a sterile glass rod and added to a bottle of bile broth. The incorporation of streptokinase (100 units per ml) in the broth facilitates lysis of the clot. Clot cultures yield a higher rate of isolation than blood cultures as the bactericidal action of the serum is obviated.

Another advantage is that a sample of serum also becomes available. Even though agglutinins may be absent in the early stages of the disease, a Widal test provides a baseline titre against which the results of tests performed later may be evaluated.

Feces culture: Salmonellae are shed in feces throughout the course of the disease and even in convalescence, with varying frequency. Hence fecal cultures are almost as valuable as blood cultures in diagnosis. A positive fecal culture, however, may occur in carriers as well as in patients. The use of enrichment and selective media and repeated sampling increase the rate of isolation. Fecal culture is particularly valuable in patients on antibiotics as the drug does not eliminate the bacilli from the gut as rapidly as it does from the blood.

Fecal samples are plated directly on MacConkey, DCA and Wilson–Blair media. The last is highly selective and should be plated heavily. On MacConkey and DCA media, salmonellae appear as pale colonies. On the Wilson-Blair medium, *S. typhi* forms large black colonies, with a metallic sheen. *S. paratyphi* A produces green colonies due to the absence of H_2S production.

For enrichment, specimens are inoculated into one tube each of selenite and tetrathionate broth, and incubated for 12–18 hours before subculture onto plates.

Urine culture: Salmonellae are shed in the urine irregularly and infrequently. Hence urine culture is less useful than the culture of blood or feces. Cultures are generally positive only in the second and third weeks and then only in about 25 per cent of cases. Repeated sampling improves the rate of isolation. Clean voided urine samples are centrifuged and the deposit inoculated into enrichment and selective media as for fecal culture.

Other materials for culture: Isolation may be obtained from several other sources but they are not usually employed. Bone marrow culture is valuable as it is positive in most cases even when blood cultures are negative. Culture of bile obtained by duodenal aspiration is usually positive and may be employed for the detection of carriers. Other materials which may yield isolation at times are rose spots, pus from suppurative lesions, CSF and sputum. At autopsy, cultures may be obtained from the gall bladder, liver, spleen and mesenteric lymph nodes.

Widal reaction: This is a test for the measurement of H and O agglutinins for typhoid and paratyphoid bacilli in the patient's sera. Two types of tubes are generally used for the test—a narrow tube with a conical bottom (Dreyer's agglutination tube) for the H agglutination, and a short round bottomed tube (Felix tube) for the O agglutination. Equal volumes (0.4 ml) of serial dilutions of the serum (from 1/10 to 1/640) and the H and O antigens are mixed in Dreyer's and Felix agglutination tubes, respectively, and incubated in a water bath at 37 °C overnight. Some workers recommend incubation at 50–55 °C for two hours, followed by overnight incubation at room temperature. Control tubes containing the antigen and normal saline are set to check for autoagglutination. The agglutination titres of the serum are read. H agglutination leads to the formation of loose, cotton woolly clumps, while O agglutination is seen as a disclike pattern at the bottom of the tube. In both, the supernatant fluid is rendered clear.

The antigens used in the test are the H and O antigens of *S. typhi* and the H antigens of *S. paratyphi* A and B. The paratyphoid O antigens are not employed as they cross-react with the typhoid O antigen due to their sharing of factor 12. The H agglutinable suspension is prepared by adding 0.1% formalin to a 24-hour broth culture or saline suspension of an agar culture. For preparing the O suspension, the bacillus is cultured on phenol agar (1:800) and the growth scraped off in a small volume of saline. It is mixed with 20 times its volume of absolute alcohol, heated at 40–50 °C for 30 minutes, centrifuged and the deposit resuspended in saline to the appropriate density. Chloroform

may be added as a preservative. It is important to use standard smooth strains for antigen preparation. The strains used usually are the *S. typhi* 901, 'O' and 'H' strains. Each batch of antigen should be compared with a standard. Readymade Widal kits of stained antigens available commercially are now widely used.

The results of the Widal test should be interpreted taking into account the following:

1. The agglutination titre will depend on the stage of the disease. Agglutinins usually appear by the end of the first week, so that blood taken earlier may give a negative result. The titre increases steadily till the third or the fourth week, after which it declines gradually.

2. Demonstration of a rise in titre of antibodies, by testing two or more serum samples, is more meaningful than a single test. If the first sample is taken late in the disease, a rise may not be demonstrable. Instead, a fall in titre may be seen in some cases.

3. The results of a single test should be interpreted with caution. It is difficult to lay down levels of significance though it is generally stated that titres of 1/100 or more for O agglutinins and 1/200 or more for H agglutinins are significant. It is necessary to obtain information on the distribution of agglutinin levels in 'normal sera' in different areas.

4. Agglutinins may be present on account of prior disease, inapparent infection or immunisation. Therefore, the mere presence of agglutinin in the Widal test should not be taken as proof of typhoid fever.

   H agglutinins persist longer than O agglutinins. Serum from an individual immunised with TAB vaccine will generally have antibodies to *S. typhi, S. paratyphi* A and B, while in case of infection antibodies will be seen only against the infecting species.

5. Persons who have had prior infection or immunisation may develop an anamnestic response during an unrelated fever. This may

be differentiated by repetition of the test after a week. The anamnestic response shows only a transient rise, while in enteric fever the rise is sustained.

6. Bacterial suspensions used as antigens should be free from fimbria. False positive results may otherwise occur.

7. Cases treated early with chloramphenicol may show a poor agglutinin response.

Other serological methods of diagnosis include indirect hemagglutination, CIE and ELISA.

DEMONSTRATION OF CIRCULATING ANTIGEN

Typhoid bacillus antigens are consistently present in the blood in the early phase of the disease, and also in the urine of patients. The antigen can be demonstrated by sensitised staphylococcal coagglutination test. *Staph. aureus* (Cowan I strain) which contains protein A, is stabilised with formaldehyde and coated with *S. typhi* antibody. When a 1% suspension of such sensitised staphylococcal cells is mixed on a slide with serum from patients in the first week of typhoid fever, the typhoid antigen present in the serum combines with the antibody attached to staphylococcal cells producing visible agglutination within two minutes. The test is rapid, sensitive and specific but is not positive after the first week of the disease.

Other laboratory tests: A white cell count is useful. Leucopenia with a relative lymphocytosis is seen. Eosinophils are said to be absent but in the tropics, with a high incidence of helminthic infestation, eosinophils are usually present.

DIAGNOSIS OF CARRIERS

The detection of carriers is important for epidemiological and public health purposes. Laboratory tests are also useful in screening food handlers and cooks to detect carrier state.

The identification of fecal carriers is by isolation of the bacillus from feces or from bile. The frequency and intensity of bacillary shedding vary widely and it is essential, therefore, to test repeated samples. Cholagogue purgatives increase the chance of isolation. For the detection of urinary carriers, repeated urine cultures should be carried out.

The Widal reaction is of no value in the detection of carriers in endemic countries. The demonstration of Vi agglutinins has been claimed to indicate the carrier state. While this is useful as a screening test, confirmation should be made by culture.

The tracing of carriers in cities may be accomplished by the 'sewer-swab' technique. Gauze pads left in sewers and drains are cultured, and by tracing positive swabs, one may be led to the house harbouring a carrier. Another technique of isolating salmonellae from sewage is filtration through millipore membranes and culturing the membranes on highly selective media such as Wilson and Blair media.

BACTERIOPHAGE TYPING

Intraspecies classification of *S. typhi* for epidemiological purposes was made possible by bacteriophage typing, first developed by Craigie and Yen (1937). They found that a bacteriophage acting on the Vi antigen of the typhoid bacillus (Vi phage II) was highly adaptable. The parent phage is called *phage A*. It could be made specific for a particular strain of typhoid bacillus by serial propagation in the strain. Such adaptation was obtained by phenotypic or genotypic variation. At present, 97 Vi II phage types of *S. typhi* are recognised. As phage typing of *S. typhi* depends on the presence of Vi antigens, a proportion of strains (Vi negative) will be untypable. The phage type is stable. Apart from helping in tracing the source of epidemics, phage typing also provides information on the trends and patterns in the epidemiology of typhoid at the local, national and international levels. Phage typing is carried out at the National Phage Typing Centres and is coordinated by the International Reference Centre. The National Salmonella Phage Typing Centre for India is located at the Lady

Hardinge Medical College, New Delhi. Phage types A and E1 are the most common and are present throughout India. However, the relative prevalence in different regions is subject to change from time to time.

The preponderance of one or two phage types in a region limits the utility of phage typing as an epidemiological tool. Additional markers have, therefore, been employed for the subdivision of strains belonging to a phage type. These include (1) Nicolle's complementary phage typing of type A strains into 10 types; (2) Kristensen's biotyping based on fermentation of xylose and arabinose; (3) production of tetrathionate reductase; (4) bacteriocin production; and (5) antibiogram.

Currently, more discriminating genotyping methods like phasmid finger printing, multilocus enzyme electrophoresis, IS-200 profiling and random amplified polymorphic DNA analysis have been employed for epidemiological characterisation in advanced centres.

Phage typing has been applied also to *S. paratyphi* A and B, *S. typhimurium*, *S. enteritidis* and *S. dublin*. Among the *S. paratyphi* A isolated from India, phage types 1 and 2 are the most common.

Prophylaxis: Typhoid fever can be effectively controlled by general measures, such as improvements in sanitation and provision of protected water supply. Many developed countries have been able to eliminate the risk by these measures, but occasional outbreaks do appear due to unforeseen lapses.

Specific prophylaxis with heat killed typhoid bacillus vaccine was developed and successfully field tested by Almroth Wright during the Boer war in South Africa. The TAB vaccine which came into general use later contained *S. typhi*, 1000 million and *S. paratyphi* A and B, 750 million each per ml killed by heating at 50–60 °C and preserved in 0.5 % phenol.

The use of polyvalent TAB vaccine was an accident of history. It was introduced in that form in World War I, as British troops had to serve in various parts of Europe, Africa and Asia where typhoid and paratyphoid fevers were endemic. No controlled field trial has been conducted with the TAB vaccine. In civilian practice, protection is mainly required against typhoid fever. If paratyphoid components are considered necessary either A or B may be added, but not both, as only one of them is found in any one area. Therefore, in India, instead of the TAB vaccine, a divalent typhoid–paratyphoid A vaccine (eliminating paratyphoid B which is very rare in the country) or the monovalent typhoid vaccine is preferred.

The vaccine is given in two doses of 0.5 ml subcutaneously at an interval of 4–6 weeks. Local and general reactions lasting for one or two days are quite frequent. Such reactions may be avoided if the vaccine is administered in a dose of 0.1 ml intradermally. In nonendemic areas, vaccination is recommended for troops, medical and paramedical personnel. In endemic areas vaccination is recommended for all children, in whom a single dose might give adequate protection, which may

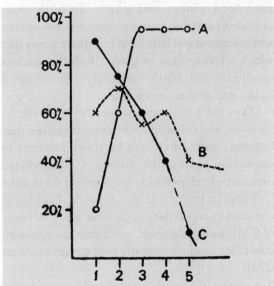

Fig.32.3 Laboratory diagnosis of typhoid fever. The approximate percentages of tests found positive during different stages of the disease (from 1st to 5th week). A. Widal agglutination. B. Feces culture. C. Blood culture.

be maintained for several years by the booster effect of repeated natural subclinical infections.

Two new typhoid vaccines, one oral and the other injectable, have been introduced after successful field trials. The live oral vaccine (*typhoral*) is a stable mutant of *S. typhi* strain Ty2 1a, lacking the enzyme UDP-galactose-4-epimerase (Gal E mutant). On ingestion, it initiates infection but 'self destructs' after four or five cell divisions, and therefore cannot induce any illness. The vaccine is an enteric coated capsule containing 10^9 viable lyophilised mutant bacilli. The course consists of one capsule orally, taken an hour before food, with a glass of water or milk, on days 1, 3 and 5. No antibiotic should be taken during this period.

The injectable vaccine (*typhim-Vi*) contains purified Vi polysaccharide antigen (25 μg per dose) from *S. typhi* strain Ty2. It is given as a single subcutaneous or intramuscular injection, which causes only minimal local reaction.

Both these vaccines are recommended only in those over five years of age, the same dose being used for children and adults. In both cases protection is stated to commence 2–3 weeks after administration and lasts for at least three years, after which a booster may be given. Both the vaccines are effective and only their relatively high cost stands in the way of their wider use.

Typhoid bacilli are primarily intracellular parasites, and cell mediated immunity rather than humoral antibodies may be more relevant in protection against the disease. Cell mediated immunity develops during the course of the disease. Cellular immunity to the typhoid bacillus is common in populations in endemic areas. Absence of CMI has been claimed to indicate susceptibility. The killed vaccines currently used do not stimulate CMI.

Treatment: Specific antibacterial therapy for enteric fever became available only in 1948 with the introduction of chloramphenicol, which continued as the sheet anchor against the disease till the 1970s when resistance became common.

Though *S. typhi* is susceptible in vitro to many antibiotics such as streptomycin and tetracycline, these are ineffective in vivo. Ampicillin, amoxycillin, furazolidone, and cotrimoxazole were the other drugs that had been found useful in the treatment of typhoid fever.

While antibacterial therapy has been so effective in the treatment of cases, it has been disappointing in the treatment of carriers. A combination of antibacterial therapy along with the vaccine has been tried in the eradication of carrier state. This combination has also been used to prevent relapses. Elimination of the carrier state may require heroic measures such as cholecystectomy, pyelolithotomy or nephrectomy.

Drug resistance: Though occasional resistant strains had been identified in the laboratory, resistance to chloramphenicol did not pose any problem in typhoid fever till 1972, when resistant strains emerged in Mexico and in Kerala (India). In Mexico, the resistant strain caused an explosive epidemic, with high mortality. Travellers who got infected in Mexico had, on occasion, conveyed the resistant strain to North America and Europe but it did not get established in these areas. Chloramphenicol resistant typhoid fever has become a problem in many countries in Asia.

In India, chloramphenicol resistant typhoid fever appeared in epidemic form first in Calicut (Kerala) in early 1972. It became endemic and was confined to Kerala till 1978. Subsequently such strains carrying drug resistance plasmids appeared in many other parts of India. Though resistant to chloramphenicol, such strains were initially sensitive to ampicillin, amoxycillin, cotrimoxazole and furazolidone, which were successfully used for treatment. By late 1980s, typhoid bacillus strains resistant to many or all of these drugs began to spread in most parts of India. At present, the drugs useful in treatment of such multiresistant typhoid cases are the later fluoroquinolones (such as ciprofloxacin, pefloxacin, oflaxacin) and the third generation cephalosporins (such as ceftazidime, ceftrioxone, cefotaxime). Furozolidone is still active against most isolates but its action is too slow for it to be used alone in treatment. Recently many strains have become resistant to fluoroquinolones, but several isolates of typhoid bacilli are now sensitive to chloramphenicol.

SALMONELLA GASTROENTERITIS

Salmonella gastroenteritis (more appropriately enterocolitis) or food poisoning is generally a zoonotic disease, the source of infection being animal products. It may be caused by any salmonella except *S. typhi*. The first instance of salmonella food poisoning to have been identified was in 1888, when Gaertner in Germany isolated a bacillus (*S. enteritidis)* from the meat of an emergency-slaughtered cow and from the cadaver of a fatal case of food poisoning caused by the meat. In 1898, Durham in England and de Nobele in Belgium isolated *S. typhimurium* from meat and from food poisoning cases. A very large number of salmonellae have since been identified from cases of gastroenteritis and food poisoning but a few species account for the majority of cases. In most parts of the world, *S. typhimurium* is the most common species. Some other common species have been *S. enteritidis, S. haldar, S. heidelberg, S. agona, S. virchow, S. seftenberg, S. indiana, S. newport* and *S. anatum.*

Human infection results from the ingestion of contaminated food. The most frequent sources of salmonella food poisoning are poultry, meat, milk and milk products. Of great concern are eggs and egg products. Salmonellae can enter through the shell if eggs are left on contaminated chicken feed or feces, and grow inside. Human carriers do occur but their role is minimal when considered in relation to the magnitude of infection from animals. Even salads and other uncooked vegetables may cause infection if contaminated through manure or by handling. Food contamination may also result from the droppings of rats, lizards or other small animals. Gastroenteritis may occur without food poisoning as in cross infection in hospitals.

Clinically, the disease develops after a short incubation period of 24 hours or less, with diarrhea, vomiting, abdominal pain and fever. It may vary in severity from the passage of one or two loose stools to an acute cholera-like disease. It usually subsides in 2–4 days but in some cases a more prolonged enteritis develops, with passage of mucus and pus in feces, resembling dysentery. In a few, typhoidal or septicemic type of fever may develop.

Laboratory diagnosis is made by isolating the salmonella from the feces. In outbreaks of food poisoning, the causative article of food can often be identified by taking a proper history. Isolation of salmonellae from the article of food confirms the diagnosis.

Control of salmonella food poisoning requires the prevention of food contamination. Food may become contaminated at various levels, from natural infection in the animal or bird, to contamination of the prepared food. Proper cooking of food destroys salmonellae.

While enteric fever is a major problem only in the developing countries, salmonella food poisoning is largely a problem for the developed nations. This is due to the differences in food habits and living conditions between them and also because food production, packaging, storage and marketing have become industries in the rich countries while they still remain agricultural in the developing world.

Treatment of uncomplicated, noninvasive salmonellosis is symptomatic. Antibiotics should not be used. Not only do they not hasten recovery but they may actually increase the period of fecal shedding of the bacilli. But for the serious invasive cases, antibiotic treatment is needed.

SALMONELLA SEPTICEMIA

Certain salmonellae, *S. choleraesuis* in particular, may cause septicemic disease with focal suppurative lesions, such as osteomyelitis, deep abscesses, endocarditis, pneumonia and meningitis. Antecedent gastroenteritis may or may not be present. The case fatality may be as high as 25 per cent.

Salmonellae may be isolated from the blood or from the pus from the suppurative lesion. Feces culture may also sometimes be positive. Septicemic salmonellosis should be treated with chloramphenicol or other appropriate antibiotics as determined by sensitivity tests.

MULTIRESISTANT SALMONELLAE

R factors conferring multiple drug resistance have become widely disseminated among salmonellae. The clinical significance of this phenomenon was first observed during the studies of human and veterinary infections with drug resistant

S.typhimurium phage type 29 in England in the 1960s. Human infections were initially gastroenteritis due to spread from infected animals, through food. Subsequently, some salmonellae appear to have changed their ecology in some ways. From being responsible for zoonotic infections only, as in the past, some multiresistant salmonellae have now become important agents of hospital cross infections. Such nosocomial salmonellosis manifests particularly in neonates as septicemia, meningitis and suppurative lesions. Diarrhea may not always be present.

In India, several hospital outbreaks of neonatal septicemia caused by multiresistant salmonellae have occurred in recent years. Mortality in neonates is very high unless early treatment is started with antibiotics to which the infecting strain is sensitive.

Further Reading

Christie AB. 1987. *Infectious Diseases: Epidemiology and Clinical Practice*, 4th edn. Edinburgh: Churchill-Livingstone.
Forsyth JRL. 1998. *Typhoid and Paratyphoid*. In *Topley and Wilson's Microbiology and Mircrobial Infections*, 9th edn. vol.3. London: Arnold.
Ivanoff B et al. 1994. Vaccination against typhoid fever: Present status, *Bull Wld Hlth Org*: 72:957.
Mandel BK. 1994. Salmonella typhi and other salmonellas. *Gut* 35:726.
Mirza SH et al. 1996. Multidrug resistant Salmonella typhi: A global problem. *J Med Micriobiol.* 44:317.
WHO, 1994. Control of Salmonella infections in animals, *Bull Wld Hlth Org*, 72, 831.

33

Vibrio

Vibrios are Gram negative, rigid, curved rods that are actively motile by means of a polar flagellum. The name 'vibrio' is derived from the characteristic vibratory motility (from *vibrare*, meaning to vibrate). They are asporogenous and noncapsulated. Vibrios are present in marine environments and surface waters worldwide. The most important member of the genus is *Vibrio cholerae*, the causative agent of cholera. It was first isolated by Koch (1883) from cholera patients in Egypt, though it had been observed earlier by Pacini (1854) and others.

VIBRIO CHOLERAE

Morphology: The cholera vibrio is a short, curved, cylindrical rod, about 1.5 μm × 0.2–0.4 μm in size, with rounded or slightly pointed ends. The cell is typically comma shaped (hence the old name *V. comma*) but the curvature is often lost on subculture. S-shaped or spiral forms may be seen due to two or more cells lying end to end. Pleomorphism is frequent in old cultures. In stained films of mucous flakes from acute cholera cases, the vibrios are seen arranged in parallel rows, described by Koch as the 'fish in stream' appearance. It is actively motile, with a single sheathed polar flagellum. The motility is of the darting type, and when acute cholera stool or a young culture is examined under the microscope, the actively motile vibrios suggest a 'swarm of gnats'. The vibrios stain readily with aniline dyes and are Gram negative and nonacid fast (Fig. 33.1).

Cultural characteristics: The cholera vibrio is strongly aerobic, growth being scanty and slow anaerobically. It grows within a temperature range of 16–40 °C (optimum 37 °C). Growth is better in an alkaline medium the range of pH being 6.4–9.6 (optimum 8.2). NaCl (0.5–1%) is required for optimal growth though high concentrations (6% and above) are inhibitory.

It grows well on ordinary media. On nutrient agar, after overnight growth, colonies are moist, translucent, round discs, about 1–2 mm in diameter, with a bluish tinge in transmitted light. The growth has a distinctive odour. On MacConkeys agar, the colonies are colourless at first but become reddish on prolonged incubation due to the late fermentation of lactose. On blood agar, colonies are initially surrounded by a zone of greening,

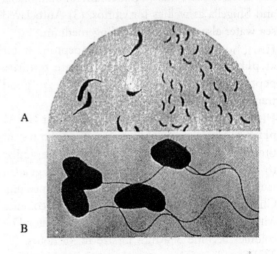

A

B

Fig. 33.1   A.   Cholera vibrios. Right – Gram stain. Left – Flagellar stain showing single polar flagellum. B. Electron micrograph showing single polar flagellum (x 1600) (Source: AN Ghosh, NICED)

which later becomes clear due to hemodigestion. In gelatin stab culture, infundibuliform (funnel-shaped) or napiform (turnip-shaped) liquefaction occurs in three days at 22 °C. In peptone water, growth occurs in about six hours as a fine surface pellicle, which on shaking breaks up into membranous pieces. Turbidity and a powdery deposit develop on continued incubation.

A number of special media have been employed for the cultivation of cholera vibrios. They may be classified as follows:

Holding or transport media: (1) Venkat-raman–Ramakrishnan (VR) medium: A simple modified form of this medium is prepared by dissolving 20 g crude sea salt and 5 g peptone in one litre of distilled water and adjusting the pH to 8.6–8.8. It is dispensed in screwcapped bottles in 10–15 ml amounts. About 1–3 ml stool is to be added to each bottle. In this medium vibrios do not multiply but remain viable for several weeks. (2) Cary–Blair medium: This is a buffered solution of sodium chloride, sodium thioglycollate, disodium phosphate and calcium chloride at pH 8.4. It is a suitable transport medium for Salmonella and Shigella as well as for vibrios. (3) Autoclaved sea water also serves as a holding medium.

Enrichment media: (1) Alkaline peptone water at pH 8.6; (2) Monsur's taurocholate tellurite peptone water at pH 9.2. Both these are good transport as well as enrichment media.

Plating media: (1) Alkaline bile salt agar (BSA) pH 8.2: This simple medium has stood the test of time and is still widely used. The colonies are similar to those on nutrient agar. (2) Monsur's gelatin taurocholate trypticase tellurite agar (GTTA) medium: Cholera vibrios produce small, translucent colonies with a greyish black centre and a turbid halo. The colonies become 3–4 mm in size in 48 hours. (3) TCBS medium: This medium, containing thiosulfate, citrate, bile salts and sucrose, is available commercially and is very widely used at present. Cholera vibrios produce large yellow convex colonies which may become green on continued incubation.

Vibrio colonies may be identified by the 'string test'. A loopful of the growth is mixed with a drop of 0.5% sodium deoxycholate in saline on a slide. If the test is positive, the suspension loses its turbidity, becomes mucoid and forms a 'string' when the loop is drawn slowly away from the suspension. **Biochemical reactions:** Carbohydrate metabolism is fermentative, producing acid, but no gas. Cholera vibrios ferment glucose, mannitol, maltose, mannose and sucrose but not inositol, arabinose, or lactose, though lactose may be split very slowly. Indole is formed and nitrates are reduced to nitrites. These two properties contribute to the 'cholera red reaction' which is tested by adding a few drops of concentrated sulphuric acid to a 24-hour peptone water culture. With cholera vibrios, a reddish pink colour is developed due to the formation of nitroso-indole. Catalase and oxidase tests are positive. Methyl red and urease tests are negative. Vibrios decarboxylate lysine and ornithine but do not utilise arginine. Gelatin is liquefied. Vibrios elaborate several enzymes including collagenase, elastase, chitinase, nucleotidase, decarboxylase, lipase, mucinase and neuraminidase (receptor destroying enzyme).

Resistance: Cholera vibrios are susceptible to heat, drying and acids, but resist high alkalinity. They are destroyed at 55 °C in 15 minutes. Dried on linen or thread, they survive for 1–3 days but die in about three hours on cover slips. Survival in water is influenced by its pH, temperature, salinity, presence of organic pollution and other factors. In general, the El Tor vibrio survives longer than the classical cholera vibrio. In the laboratory, vibrios survive for months in sterile sea water, and this has been suggested as a method for the survival of vibrios in nature. In grossly contaminated water, such as the Ganges water of India, the vibrios do not survive for any length of time, due to the apparently large amounts of vibriophages present. They survive in clean tap water for thirty days. In untreated night soil, they may survive for several days. Vibrios are susceptible to the common disinfectants.

On fruits, they survive for 1–5 days at room temperature and for a week in the refrigerator. In general, food materials left at room temperature do not act as an important source of infection for longer than a day or two but those stored in the cold may harbour vibrios for more than two weeks.

They are killed in a few minutes in the gastric juice of normal acidity but they may survive for 24 hours in achlorhydric gastric juice.

Classification: In the past, many oxidase positive, motile, curved rods were rather loosely grouped as vibrios. Precise criteria have been laid down for differentiating vibrios from related genera (Table 33.1).

Heiberg (1934) classified vibrios into six groups based on the fermentation of mannose, sucrose and arabinose. Two more groups were added later. Cholera vibrios belong to Group I (Table 33.2).

A serological classification was introduced by Gardner and Venkatraman (1935). Cholera vibrios and biochemically similar vibrios, possessing a common flagellar (H) antigen were classified as Group A vibrios, and the rest as Group B vibrios comprising a heterogeneous collection. Based on the major somatic (O) antigen, Group A vibrios were classified into 'subgroups' (now called O serogroups or serovars), 139 of which are currently known (Table 33.3). All isolates from epidemic cholera (till 1992) belonged to serogroup O-1. Therefore in the diagnostic laboratory group O-1 antiserum (commonly called 'cholera nondifferential serum') came to be used for identifying pathogenic cholera vibrios (which are referred to as 'agglutinable vibrios'). Other vibrio isolates which were not agglutinated by the O-1 antiserum came to be called nonagglutinable or NAG vibrios. They were considered nonpathogenic and hence also called noncholera vibrios (NCV).

Both these terms are not strictly appropriate. Though NAG vibrios are not agglutinable by the O-1 antiserum, they are readily agglutinable by their own antisera. The term noncholera vibrio is not correct as some of them can cause a disease clinically indistinguishable from cholera. However, by and large, NAG vibrios were nonpathogenic and commonly isolated from environmental sources and healthy human intestines.

While all isolates from epidemic cholera belonged to group O-1, not all members of the group were capable of causing clinical cholera. The first such members which acquired prominence were the vibrios isolated by Gottschlich (1905) from six Haj pilgrims who died at the Tor quarantine station on the Sinai Peninsula. They had died not from cholera but from dysentery or gangrene of the colon. These came to be called the El Tor vibrios. They were identical to cholera vibrios in all laboratory tests except that they were hemolytic to sheep erythrocytes and gave a positive Voges–Proskauer reaction. As the El Tor vibrios were subsequently isolated from water sources and normal human intestines, they were considered to be nonpathogenic. In 1937, El Tor vibrios were recognised as endemic in Celebes (Sulawesi), Indonesia, causing a choleraic disease (paracholera). However, outside this endemic area, El Tor vibrios were considered nonpathogenic.

The situation changed in 1961 when El Tor vibrios gave rise to the seventh pandemic of cholera. Besides increased virulence and invasiveness, the pandemic El Tor strains showed altered laboratory reactions. The new El Tor strains were often nonhemolytic and V–P negative. New differentiating properties were defined such as chick cell agglutination, polymyxin sensitivity and phage susceptibility tests (Table 33.4). It was accepted that El Tor vibrios were indeed cholera vibrios, which contained two biotypes, the old or 'classical' cholera vibrios, and the El Tor vibrios.

Based on minor surface antigenic characteristics both classical and El Tor biotypes of cholera vibrios were classified into three serotypes, Ogawa, Inaba, and Hikojima (Table 33.5). The Ogawa and Inaba strains are agglutinated by their own respective specific sera only, while the Hikojima strains are agglutinated by both Ogawa and Inaba antisera.

Table 33.1 Differentiation of vibrios from allied genera

Genus	Oxidation–Fermentation (Hugh–Liefson Test)		Utilisation of aminoacids			String test
	Oxidation	Fermentation	Lysine	Arginine	Ornithine	
Vibrio	+	+1	+	–	+	+
Aeromonas	+	+2	–	+	–	V
Pseudomonas	+	–	V	V	V	–
Plesiomonas	+	+	+	+	+	–

Note : 1 = no gas produced;　2 = gas may or may not be produced;　V = reaction variable.

There is no difference in pathogenicity between the three serotypes. Serotyping is only of epidemiological significance.

The non-01 vibrios (the so called NAG vibrios) have been classified into many serogroups, currently upto 139. The latest serogroup O-139, identified in 1992 causes epidemics of cholera, emphasising that they can no longer be considered as noncholera vibrios.

Modern taxonomical criteria, particularly DNA studies, have led to the recognition that all the cholera vibrios that belong to Gardner and Venkatraman's group A and share similar biochemical properties and a common H antigen are so closely related that they constitute a single species *Vibrio cholerae,* which can be classified into serogroups (or serovars), biotypes and serotypes. Accordingly the present nomenclature will be indicative of all these features, as for example, *V. cholerae* serovar 01, biotype El Tor, serotype Ogawa.

Further classification can be made by phage typing. Phage typing schemes have been standardised for classical and El Tor biotypes as as well as for O-139 vibrios. New molecular methods like ribotyping have added further refinements to strain typing.

CHOLERA

Cholera is an acute diarrheal disease caused by *V. cholerae.* In its most severe form, cholera is a dramatic and terrifying illness in which profuse painless watery diarrhea and copious effortless vomiting may lead to hypovolemic shock and death in less than 24 hours. In treated cases, the disease may last 4–6 days, during which period the patient may pass a total volume of liquid stool equal to twice his body weight. All the clinical features of severe cholera result from this massive loss of fluid and electrolytes. The cholera stool is typically a colourless watery fluid with flecks of mucus, said to resemble water in which rice has been washed

Table 33.2 Heiberg grouping of vibrios

Group	Fermentation of mannose	Sucrose	Arabinose
I	A	A	–
II	–	A	–
III	A	A	A
IV	–	A	A
V	A	–	–
VI	–	–	–
VII	A	–	A
VIII	–	–	A

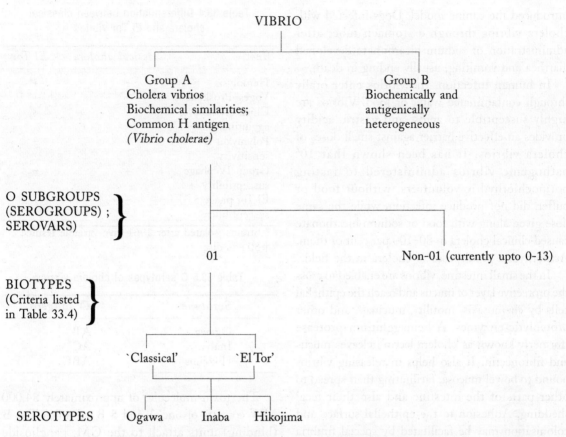

VIBRIO

Group A
Cholera vibrios
Biochemical similarities;
Common H antigen
(Vibrio cholerae)

Group B
Biochemically and
antigenically
heterogeneous

O SUBGROUPS
(SEROGROUPS) ;
SEROVARS)

01

Non-01 (currently upto 0-13)

BIOTYPES
(Criteria listed
in Table 33.4)

`Classical'          `El Tor'

SEROTYPES   Ogawa   Inaba   Hikojima

Table 33.3 Gardner and Venkatraman's classification (updated)

(hence called 'rice water stools'). It has a characteristic inoffensive sweetish odour. In composition it is a bicarbonate-rich isotonic electrolyte solution, with little protein. Its outpouring leads to diminution of extracellular fluid volume, hemoconcentration, hypokalemia, base-deficit acidosis and shock. The common complications are muscular cramps, renal failure, pulmonary edema, cardiac arrhythmias and paralytic ileus. The clinical severity of cholera varies widely, from the rapidly fatal disease to a transient asymptomatic colonisation of the intestine by the vibrios. The incidence of mild and asymptomatic infections is more with El Tor vibrios than with the classical cholera vibrios.

The incubation period varies from less than 24 hours to about five days. The clinical illness may begin slowly with mild diarrhea and vomiting in 1–3 days or abruptly with sudden massive diarrhea.

Pathogenesis: Natural infection with cholera occurs only in humans and not in animals. A number of animal models have been developed which have helped in understanding the pathogenic mechanisms in cholera. The first of these was the rabbit ileal loop model of De and Chatterjee (1953). Injection of cholera culture or culture filtrate into the ligated ileal loop caused fluid accumulation and ballooning. Intestinal loops of many other animals and also of chickens have been shown to behave in a similar manner. Dutta and Habbu (1955) showed that a fatal diarrhea could be induced in infant rabbits infected with vibrios perorally or intraintestinally. Sack and Carpenter (1966) introduced the canine model. Dogs infected with cholera vibrios through a stomach tube, after administration of sodium bicarbonate developed diarrhea and vomiting, usually ending in death.

In human infection, the vibrios enter orally through contaminated water or food. Vibrios are highly susceptible to acids, and gastric acidity provides an effective barrier against small doses of cholera vibrios. It has been shown that 10^6 pathogenic vibrios administered to fasting normochlorhydric volunteers, without food or buffer, did not produce infection, while the same dose given along with food or sodium bicarbonate caused clinical cholera in 80–100 per cent of them. Achlorhydria predisposes to cholera in the field.

In the small intestine, vibrios are enabled to cross the protective layer of mucus and reach the epithelial cells by chemotaxis, motility, mucinase and other proteolytic enzymes. A hemagglutinin-protease (formerly known as 'cholera lectin') cleaves mucus and fibronectin. It also helps in releasing vibrios bound to bowel mucosa, facilitating their spread to other parts of the intestine and also their fecal shedding. Adhesion to the epithelial surface and colonisation may be facilitated by special fimbria such as the 'toxin co-regulated pilus' (TCP). Throughout the course of infection, the vibrios remain attached to the epithelium but do not damage or invade the cells. The changes induced are biochemical rather than histological.

Vibrios multiplying on the intestinal epithelium produce a toxin (choleragen, cholera enterotoxin, cholera toxin, CT, or CTX) which is very similar to the heat labile toxin (LT) of *E. coli* in structural, chemical, biological and antigenic properties, though CT is far more potent than LT in biological activity. CT production is determined by a filamentous phage integrated with the bacterial chromosome. It can also replicate as a plasmid which can be transmitted to nontoxigenic strains, rendering them toxigenic. CT, TCP and other virulence factors are regulated by the ToxR gene product, ToxR protein.

Table 33.4 Differentiation between classical cholera and El Tor vibrios

Test	Classical cholera	El Tor
Hemolysis	–	+*
Voges–Proskauer	–	+*
Chick erythrocyte agglutination	–	.	+
Polymyxin B sensitivity+	+	–
Group IV phage susceptibility	+	–
El Tor phage 5 susceptibility	–	+

* Strains isolated after 1961 give variable results;
† 50 i. u. disc.

Table 33.5 O serotypes of cholera vibrios

Serotype	O antigens
Ogawa	AB
Inaba	AC
Hikojima	ABC

The toxin molecule, of approximately 84,000 MW consists of one A and 5 B subunits. The B (binding) units attach to the GM_1 ganglioside receptors on the surface of jejunal epithelial cells. The A (active) subunit, on being transported into the enterocyte dissociates into two fragments A_1 and A_2. The A_2 fragment only links the biologically active A_1 to the B subunit. The A1 fragment causes prolonged activation of cellular adenylate cyclate and accumulation of cAMP, leading to outpouring into the small intestinal lumen, of large quantities of water and electrolytes and the consequent watery diarrhea. The fluid secreted is isotonic with plasma but contains much more of potassium and bicarbonate. The toxin also inhibits intestinal absorption of sodium and chloride. All clinical manifestations and complications in cholera result from the massive water and electrolyte depletion thus caused.

CT also exhibits other biological effects which can be used for its detection and estimation. These include activation of lipolysis in rat testicular tissue, elongation of Chinese hamster ovary (CHO) cells in culture and histological changes in adrenal tumour (Y_1) cell culture and vero cells. It also increases skin capillary permeability, and so has been called the 'permeability factor' (PF). It can be demonstrated by the 'skin blueing test' when CT is injected intradermally in rabbits or guinea pigs and pontamine sky blue injected intravenously afterwards, the site of toxin injection becomes blue. CT can also be estimated by ELISA. CT is antigenic and induces production of neutralising antitoxins. CT can be toxoided.

Cholera vibrios also possess the lipopolysaccharide O antigen (LPS, endotoxin), as in Gram negative intestinal bacilli. This apparently plays no role in the pathogenesis of cholera but is responsible for the immunity induced by killed vaccines. It may cause the fatal illness produced experimentally by peritoneal inoculation in mice.

Epidemiology: Cholera can occur in many forms – sporadic, endemic, epidemic or pandemic. India, more specifically the large deltaic area of the Ganges and Brahmaputra in Bengal, is its homeland, where it has been known from very ancient times. Till early in the nineteenth century, cholera was virtually confined to India, periodically causing large epidemics in different parts of the country.

From 1817 to 1923 cholera vibrios had spread from Bengal, in six separate pandemic waves, involving most parts of the world. It was largely due to the threat of pandemic cholera that international health organisations came into being. After the end of the 6th pandemic in 1923, till 1961 the disease remained confined to its endemic areas, except for an isolated epidemic in Egypt in 1947.

The seventh pandemic originated from Sulawesi (Celebes), Indonesia, in 1961 when the El Tor vibrios which had been smouldering there for many decades suddenly became more virulent. After spreading to Hongkong and the Philippines, it spread steadily westwards, invading India in 1964. By 1966, it had spread throughout the Indian subcontinent and West Asia. In the 1970s the pandemic extended to Africa and parts of Southern Europe.

During the course of the pandemic, the vibrios had invaded affluent countries also. In the 1970s small outbreaks had occurred in Queensland, Australia and the Gulf Coast in the USA from special environmental foci in the coastal waters. However, they remained localised and were soon controlled, in contrast to the outbreaks in the poor nations, which developed into prolonged and extensive epidemics.

In January, 1991, the pandemic reached Peru, thus encircling the globe in thirty years time (Fig 33.2). For the first time in the century, cholera had invaded South America. The epidemic spread rapidly through many Central and South American countries, and by mid-1992 over half a million cases and 5000 deaths had been reported. By 1994 most parts of Central and South America had been involved and rendered endemic.

The seventh pandemic of cholera has been different from all the others. It is the first to have originated from outside the Indian subcontinent. It is also the first to have been caused by the El Tor biotype, in contrast to all the earlier ones caused by the classical cholera vibrios. The severity of illness was much less, with a large proportion of mild and asymptomatic infections. Mortality was low and the carrier rate high. El Tor vibrios tended to remain endemic in many new geographic areas, causing periodic epidemic bursts. The El Tor vibrio has proved to be much hardier than the classical vibrios, capable of surviving in the environment much longer. A peculiar phenomenon has been the replacement of the classical biotype by the El Tor vibrios following the pandemic spread. Thus, in India the classical vibrio is hardly ever encountered after the El Tor epidemic took root, though in Bangladesh, the classical vibrio had staged a comeback.

An event of great significance was the sudden emergence of non-01 *V. cholerae* (former NAG vibrio) as the cause of epidemic cholera. In October 1992, a new non-01 vibrio was isolated from a cholera outbreak in Madras (Chennai). Similar outbreaks soon followed in different parts of India. By January, 1993, the new strain had become epidemic in Bangladesh also. In the affected areas, this strain replaced the E1 Tor vibrios as the epidemic and environmental serovar. It also showed a tendency to be more invasive, causing bacteremic illness in some. The new epidemic strain was designated Serovar O-139 (or O-139 Bengal). Unlike the O-1 cholera vibrio, the O-139 vibrio is capsulated. As it possessed novel surface antigens, the O-1 strain vaccines could not protect against O-139 infection. There was no natural antibody against the strain in any human population then. It was therefore considered likely that the O-139 strain

may initiate the next pandemic of cholera. The new strain continued spreading, eastwards to the South East Asian countries, and westwards to Pakistan, China and some parts of Europe. But surprisingly, by 1994 the El Tor strain regained its dominance and the threat of an O-139 pandemic diminished. Both O-1 El Tor and O-139 strains began to coexist in endemic areas.

Cholera is an exclusively human disease. Infection originates from the patient or the carrier. Carriers may be incubatory, convalescent, healthy or chronic. Incubatory carriers shed vibrios only during the brief incubation period of 1–5 days. Convalescents may excrete them for 2–3 weeks. The healthy or contact carrier who has had subclinical infection usually sheds the vibrios for less than 10 days. The chronic carrier continues to be active for months or years—the longest duration recorded being 10 years. Chronic carriers were rare in

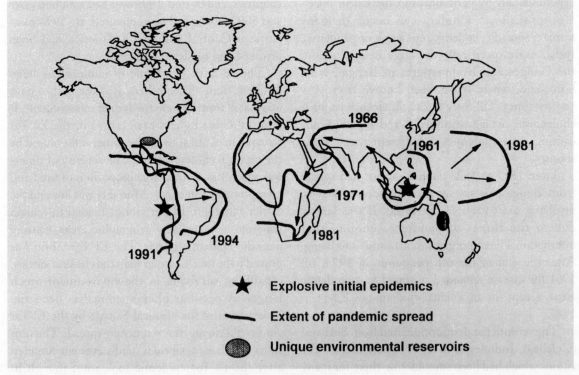

Fig. 33.2 Spread of El Tor Cholera, 1961–1994. Recently identified special environmental reservoirs of toxigenic El Tor Cholera vibrio 01 are also indicated. (Source: WHO).

classical cholera but with El Tor infection they are seen more often. Persistent infection of the gall bladder accounts for chronic carriage.

Infection is acquired through fecally contaminated water or food. Direct person-to-person spread by contact may not be common but hand contamination of stored drinking water has been shown to be an important method of domestic spread of infection. Large scale movement of persons, as occurs during fairs and festivals, has traditionally been associated with the spread of cholera.

The persistence of the vibrio during the interepidemic periods was a matter of controversy. In the endemic areas it may be maintained by continuous transmission of subclinical or mild infection. It is now known that the natural habitat of cholera vibrios is the saline waters of coastal seas and brackish estuaries, where they can persist for long periods, particularly in association with small crustaceans such as copepods, crabs or plankton.

A significant difference in susceptibility to cholera has been reported in relation to blood groups, group O persons being the most susceptible and group AB the least. The reason for this is not known.

Laboratory diagnosis: Stool, collected in the acute stage of the disease, before the administration of antibiotics, is the most useful specimen for laboratory diagnosis. Isolation of cholera vibrios from such stools is a simple matter as they are present in very large numbers, 10^6–10^9 vibrios per ml. The specimen is best collected by introducing into the rectum a lubricated catheter and letting the liquid stool flow directly into a screwcapped container. Rectal swabs may be used, provided they are made with good quality cotton wool, absorbing about 0.1–0.2 ml of fluid. They are useful in collecting specimens from convalescents who no longer have watery diarrhea. In such cases, the swabs should be moistened with transport medium before sampling. Collection of stools from pans is not recommended. Vomitus is not useful.

As cholera vibrios may die in a few hours at tropical temperatures, it is necessary to preserve the specimen at 4 °C or in some appropriate holding medium. Stool samples may be preserved in VR fluid or Cary-Blair medium for long periods. If the specimen can reach the laboratory in a few hours, it may be transported in enrichment media such as alkaline peptone water or Monsur's medium, thus saving the time required for isolation. If transport media are not available, strips of blotting paper may be soaked in the watery stool and sent to the laboratory packed in plastic envelopes. Whenever possible, specimens should be plated at the bedside and the inoculated plates sent to the laboratory.

Diagnosis by direct microscopic examination of cholera stool is not recommended as the results are not reliable. For rapid diagnosis, the

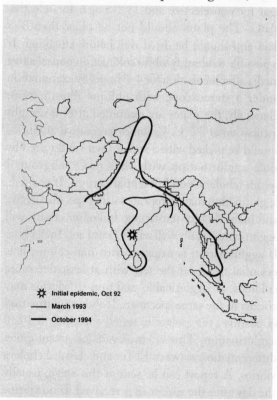

☀ Initial epidemic, Oct 92

—— March 1993

━━ October 1994

Fig. 33.3 Spread of vibrio cholerae O-139 epidemic in Asia (1992–1994) (Source: WHO)

characteristic motility of the vibrio and its inhibition by antiserum can be demonstrated under the dark field or phase contrast microscope, using cholera stool from acute cases, or more reliably after enrichment for six hours. Demonstration of vibrios in stools by direct immunofluorescence has been attempted but nonspecific fluorescence is common and the technique is too complicated for use in the field.

On arrival in the laboratory, the specimens sent in enrichment media should be incubated for 6–8 hours including transit time. The specimens sent in holding media should be inoculated into enrichment media, to be incubated for 6–8 hours before being streaked on a selective and a nonselective medium. It is also desirable to do direct plating before enrichment. The plating media used vary in different laboratories but the media employed usually are bile salt agar, MacConkey agar for nonselective and TCBS agar for selective plates. The plates should not be older than 3–5 days and should be dried well before streaking. It is possible to identify vibrio colonies on nonselective media after incubation for 4–5 hours by examination under a stereoscope with oblique illumination. Generally, the plates are examined after overnight incubation at 37 °C. Colonies suggestive of vibrios should be picked with a straight wire and tested by slide agglutination with cholera O subgroup I serum (cholera 'nondifferential' serum). If positive, agglutination may be repeated using specific Ogawa and Inaba sera for serotyping. Hikojima strains will agglutinate equally well with Ogawa and Inaba sera. If agglutination is negative with one colony, it is essential to repeat the test with at least five more colonies, as 'agglutinable' and non-01 vibrios may coexist in the same specimen. If slide agglutination is positive, the isolate is tested for chick red cell agglutination. This is employed for presumptive differentiation between El Tor and classical cholera vibrios. A report can be sent at this stage, usually the day after the specimen is received. If no vibrios are isolated, a second cycle of enrichment and plating may succeed in some cases.

The isolate may then be subjected to detailed study, if desired, including the oxidase test, utilisation of aminoacids, lysine, arginine and ornithine, fermentation of sugars including sucrose, mannose and arabinose, hemolysis, VP, polymyxin B sensitivity and susceptibility to cholera phage IV. The strain may be sent to the International Reference Centre for vibrio phage typing at the National Institute of Cholera and Enteric Disease (NICED) at Kolkata.

Isolates of vibrios that are not agglutinated by the O subgroup I serum should not be ignored as non-01 vibrios are known to produce cholera-like disease. An antiserum to the H antigen which is shared by all cholera virios has been found to be a useful reagent. Any vibrio which is agglutinated by this H antiserum, but not by O-I serum is considered to be non-O1 cholera vibrio. Specific antiserum against O-139 is available. In the fully equipped laboratory, diagnostic tests in cholera and other diarrheal diseases should consist of a battery of tests designed to isolate other known pathogens also.

For isolation of vibrios from carriers, essentially the same techniques are to be followed, except that more than one cycle of enrichment may be necessary. As vibrio excretion is intermittent, repeated stool examination will yield better results. Examination of stools after a purgative (magnesium sulphate 15–30 g or Mannitol 30 g), or of bile after duodenal intubation is of special value.

Serological examination is of little use in the diagnosis of cases though it may be helpful in assessing the prevalence of cholera in an area. The tests available are agglutination using live or killed vibrio suspensions, indirect hemagglutination, vibriocidal test and antitoxin assay. Of these, the complement dependent vibriocidal antibody test is the most useful.

For examination of water samples for vibrios, enrichment or filtration methods may be employed. In the former, 900 ml of water are added to 100 ml tenfold concentrated peptone water at pH 9.2, incubated at 37 °C for 6–8 hours and a second enrichment done before plating on selective media. For the filtration technique the water to be tested should be filtered through the Millipore membrane filter, which is then placed directly on the surface of a selective medium and incubated. Colonies appear after overnight incubation. Sewage should be diluted in saline, filtered through gauze and treated as for water.

Immunity: In cholera, the vibrios remain confined to the intestine, where they multiply and elaborate the enterotoxin which is responsible for the disease. Immunity, therefore, may be directed against the bacterium or against the toxin— antibacterial or antitoxic. Natural infection confers some amount of immunity but it does not seem to last for more than 6–12 months and reinfections are known after this period.

Immunisation with killed vaccines induces only antibacterial immunity. The protective effect of these vaccines, especially purified somatic antigens used as vaccines, though short-lived, proves that antibacterial immunity can protect against infection. The protection appears to be serotype specific but not biotype specific.

Immunity may be local, in the intestine, or systemic. The appearance of local antibodies in the intestine has been known for a long time. These are known as 'coproantibodies' as they appear in the feces. They consist of IgG, IgM and IgA.

Prophylaxis: The prevention of cholera requires essentially general measures such as provision of protected water supply and improvement of environmental sanitation. As these are not easily attainable, vaccination continues to be the most widely used method of prevention in endemic areas.

Cholera vaccines were introduced by Ferran within a year of the discovery of the vibrio. The original vaccines were live suspensions of vibrios. As they gave rise to adverse reactions, they were replaced by killed vaccines. The vaccines used traditionally are killed suspensions containing 8000 million *V. cholerae* per ml, composed of equal numbers of Ogawa and Inaba serotypes, given by subcutaneous or intramuscular injection. Many laboratories employ classical cholera and El Tor vibrios in equal numbers in the vaccine. Strain O-139 vaccine has also been prepared. The concentration of the vaccine has been increased to 12,000 million per ml, in order to improve the antigenic stimulus.

Several controlled field trials in endemic areas with various types of injected vaccines have shown that the protection afforded by them does not exceed 50–60 per cent; the duration of protection is only 3–6 months; the rate of protection in endemic areas increases with age; a single dose of vaccine is ineffective in children below five years of age while two doses at 1–4 week intervals are protective; a single dose confers good protection in adults due to its acting as a booster on top of prior natural immunisation; cell-free somatic antigen preparations are as effective as whole cell vaccine; there is good cross-protection between classical and El Tor vibrios; the cross-protection between Ogawa and Inaba serotypes is doubtful and requires further study, pending which vaccine containing the homologous serotype is to be employed. Aluminium hydroxide and phosphate adjuvant vaccines produced better immunity, particularly in young children. Toxoid vaccines have not been been successful. Injectable vaccines do not provide any local immunity in the intestinal mucosa. They are also unacceptably reactogenic. Hence attention has been directed to oral vaccines.

Two types of oral vaccines have been tried recently: *killed oral whole cell* vaccines with and without the inclusion of the B subunit of CT, and *live oral vaccines* with classical, El Tor and O-139 strains, with their toxin genes deleted. While the results have been promising, problems remain to be solved before they are cleared for general use.

An ideal cholera vaccine is yet to be found. Cholera vaccination was a compulsory requirement for international travel, but now very few countries insist on this.

Treatment: The treatment of cholera consists essentially of the prompt and adequate replacement of lost fluid and electrolytes. Oral administration of fluid containing glucose and electrolytes, either alone or supplemented by intravenous fluids is a highly successful and freely available method of treating cholera. Cereal based preparations are equally effective and usually more acceptable. Antibacterial therapy is of secondary importance. Oral tetracycline was recommended for reducing the period of vibrio excretion and the need for parenteral fluids. Initially cholera vibrios were uniformly susceptible to all antibiotics active against Gram negative bacilli, but since 1979, multiple drug resistant strains have become increasingly common.

VIBRIO MIMICUS

So named because it closely resembles cholera vibrios in biochemical features, *V. mimicus* can be differentiated by its failure to ferment sucrose. Like *V. cholerae*, it grows best at low salt concentrations (0.5–1%). It has been responsible for many sporadic cases of diarrheal disease on the Gulf Coast of the USA. Infection is acquired from eating seafood, especially oysters. The disease is self-limited. Clinical manifestations resemble those caused by *V. parahaemolyticus*.

HALOPHILIC VIBRIOS

Vibrios that have a high requirement of sodium chloride are known as halophilic vibrios. Their natural habitat is sea water and marine life. Some halophilic vibrios have been shown to cause human disease—*V. parahaemolyticus, V. alginolyticus* and *V. vulnificus*.

VIBRIO PARAHAEMOLYTICUS

V. parahaemolyticus is an enteropathogenic halophilic vibrio originally isolated in 1951 in Japan as the causative agent of an outbreak of food poisoning due to sea fish. Gastroenteritis due to this vibrio has since been identified in several countries and it is now considered an important cause of food poisoning throughout the world. It inhabits the coastal seas, where it is found in fishes, arthropods such as shrimps and crabs, and molluscs such as oysters. In Calcutta, it has also been found in small pond fishes.

In morphology, it resembles the cholera vibrio, except that it is capsulated, shows bipolar staining and has a tendency to pleomorphism, especially when grown on 3% salt agar and in old cultures. Unlike other vibrios, it produces peritrichous flagella when grown on solid media. Polar flagella are formed in liquid cultures.

It grows only in media containing NaCl. It can tolerate salt concentration upto 8 per cent but not 10 per cent. The optimum salt concentration is 2–4 per cent. On TCBS agar, the colonies are green with an opaque, raised centre and flat translucent periphery. The string test is positive.

It is oxidase, catalase, nitrate, indole and citrate positive. Glucose, maltose, mannitol, mannose and arabinose are fermented producing acid only. Lactose, sucrose, salicin, xylose, adonitol, inositol and sorbitol are not fermented.

It is killed at 60 °C in 15 minutes. It does not grow at 4 °C but can survive refrigeration and freezing. Drying destroys it. It dies in distilled water or vinegar in a few minutes.

Three antigenic components have been recognised—somatic O, capsular K and flagellar H antigens. Serotyping is based on O and K antigens; 12 O groups have been recognised and 59 distinct K antigens.

Not all strains of *V. parahaemolyticus* are pathogenic for human beings. It has been found that strains isolated from environmental sources (such as water, fish, crabs or oysters) are nearly always nonhemolytic when grown on a special high salt blood agar (Wagatsuma agar), while strains from human patients are almost always hemolytic. This is called the Kanagawa phenomenon and is due to a heat stable hemolysin. The significance of

Table 33.6 Some characteristics of *V. parahaemolyticus* and *V. alginolyticus*

	V. parahaemolyticus	*V. alginolyticus*
Indole	+	+
V.P.	−	+
Nitrate reduction	+	+
Urease	−	−
Sucrosefermentation	−	+
Swarming	−	+
Growth in 0% NaCl	−	−
7% NaCl	+	+
10% NaCl	−	+

this hemolysis is not known but it is used as a laboratory test for pathogenicity; Kanagawa positive strains being considered pathogenic for human beings and negative strains nonpathogenic. No enterotoxin has been identified. The vibrio is believed to cause enteritis by invasion of the intestinal epithelium. *V. parahaemolyticus* causes food poisoning associated with marine food. It also causes acute diarrhea, unassociated with food poisoning. Abdominal pain, diarrhea, vomiting and fever are the usual signs. Feces contains cellular exudate and often also blood. Dehydration is of moderate degree and recovery occurs in 1–3 days. Cases are more common in summer, and in adults than in children. In Calcutta, *V. parahaemolyticus* could be isolated from 5–10 per cent of diarrhea cases admitted to the Infectious Diseases Hospital. *V. parahaemolyticus* is common in sea fish in some other parts of India but human cases are much less frequent.

VIBRIO ALGINOLYTICUS

This halophilic vibrio resembles *V. parahaemolyticus* in many respects and was formerly considered a biotype of the latter. It has a higher salt tolerance, is VP positive and ferments sucrose (Table 33.6). It is frequently found in sea fish. Its status as a human pathogen is uncertain. It has been associated with infections of eyes, ears and wounds in human beings exposed to sea water.

VIBRIO VULNIFICUS

V. vulnificus, previously known as L+ vibrio or *Beneckea vulnifica*, is a marine vibrio of medical importance. It is VP negative and ferments lactose but not sucrose. It has a salt tolerance of less than eight per cent. It causes two types of illness. The first is wound infection following contact of open wounds with seawater. The second type occurs in compromised hosts particularly those with liver disease. Following ingestion of the vibrio, usually in oysters, it penetrates the gut mucosa without causing gastrointestinal manifestations and enters the bloodstream, rapidly leading to septicemia with high mortality.

AEROMONAS AND PLESIOMONAS

Besides the genus *Vibrio*, the family Vibrionaceae also contains the genera *Aeromonas* and *Plesiomonas*, some members of which have been associated with human lesions.

Aeromonas hydrophila, originally isolated from frogs, in which it causes the 'red leg disease', has been reported from many cases of diarrhea and from some pyogenic lesions in human beings. *Plesiomonas shigelloides* also has been reported from diarrheal disease. Both these are oxidase positive, polar flagellated, Gram negative rods and may be mistaken for vibrios. They may be differentiated from vibrios by biochemical tests such as utilisation of aminoacids.

Further Reading

Barua D and WB Greenough 1992. *Cholera*. New York:Plenum.

Collier L et al (eds). 1998. *Topley and Williams Microbiology and Microbial Infections*, 9th edn. London : Arnold Vols. 2 and 3.

Colwell RR and A Huq 1994. Environmental reservoir of Vibrio cholerae. Annals Acad Sci 740:44.

Faruq SM et al. 2003. Emergence and evolution of V. cholerae O-139. *Proc Nat Acad Sci* (USA) 100:1304.

Honda T and T Iida 1993. The pathogenicity of *Vibrio parahaemolyticus*. *Rev Med Microbiol*. 4:106.

Kaper JB et al. 1995. Cholera. *Clin Microbiol Rev.* 8:48.

Lacey SW. 1995. Cholera. *Clin Infect Dis.* 20:1409.

Mekalanos JJ and JC Sadoff 1994. Cholera vaccines. *Science* 265:1387.

Nair GB et al. 1996. *Vibrio cholerae* O139-Bengal. *Rev Med Microbiol* 7:43.

Pseudomonas

Pseudomonas are a large group of aerobic, nonsporing Gram negative bacilli, motile by polar flagella. They are ubiquitous, mostly saprophytic, being found in water, soil or other moist environments. Some of them are pathogenic to plants, insects and reptiles. A few cause human infection, typically opportunistic.

Based on molecular analysis, pseudomonads have been reclassified and many former *Pseudomonas* species reallocated to new genera such as *Burkholderia, Stenotrophomonas* and others.

PSEUDOMONAS AERUGINOSA

Ps. pyocyanea: Bacillus pyocyaneus

Morphology: It is a slender Gram negative bacillus, 1.5–3 μm × 0.5 μm, actively motile by a polar flagellum. Occasional strains have two or three flagella. Clinical isolates are often piliated. It is noncapsulated but many strains have a mucoid slime layer. Mucoid strains, particularly isolates from cystic fibrosis patients have an abundance of extracellular polysaccharides composed of alginate polymers. This forms a loose capsule (glycocalyx) in which microcolonies of the bacillus are enmeshed and protected from host defences.

Cultural characteristics: It is an obligate aerobe, but can grow anaerobically if nitrate is available. Growth occurs at a wide range of temperatures, 6–42 °C, the optimum being 37 °C. It grows well on ordinary media, producing large, opaque, irregular colonies, with a distinctive, musty, mawkish or earthy smell. Iridescent patches with a metallic sheen are seen in cultures on nutrient agar. Crystals are seen beneath the patches. It grows on MacConkey and DCA media, forming non–lactose-fermenting colonies. Many strains are hemolytic on blood agar. In broth, it forms a dense turbidity with a surface pellicle.

Ps. aeruginosa produces a number of pigments, the best known being pyocyanin and fluorescin. Pyocyanin is a bluish green phenazine pigment soluble in water and chloroform. Fluorescin (pyoverdin) is a greenish yellow pigment soluble in water but not in chloroform. In old cultures it may be oxidised to a yellowish brown pigment. Pyocyanin is produced only by *Ps. aeruginosa* but fluorescin may be produced by many other species also. Other pigments produced are pyorubin (red) and pyomelanin (brown) in various combinations. Some strains may be nonpigmented. It is not known whether the pigments have any role in pathogenesis. Some of the pigments particularly pyocyanin, inhibit the growth of many other bacteria and may therefore contribute to *Ps. aeruginosa* emerging as the dominant bacterium in mixed infections.

Biochemical reactions: The metabolism is oxidative and nonfermentative. Peptone water sugars are unsuitable for detecting acid production, since this is weak and gets neutralised by alkali produced from peptone. An ammonium salts medium in which the sugar is the only carbon source is the best. Glucose is utilised oxidatively, forming acid only. Indole, MR, VP and H_2S tests are negative. Nitrates are reduced to nitrites and further to gaseous nitrogen. Catalase, oxidase and arginine dihydrolase tests are positive.

Classification: As *Ps. aeruginosa* has become

a very important cause of hospital infections, its classification is essential for epidemiological purposes. Serotyping, bacteriocin (pyocin, aeruginosin) typing and bacteriophage typing have been used but are not entirely satisfactory. Restriction endonuclease typing with pulsed-field gel electrophoresis is the most reliable method available.

Resistance: The bacillus is not particularly heat resistant, being killed at 55 °C in one hour but exhibits a high degree of resistance to chemical agents. It is resistant to the common antiseptics and disinfectants such as quaternary ammonium compounds, chloroxylenol and hexachlorophane and may even grow profusely in bottles of such antiseptic lotions kept for use in hospitals. Indeed, selective media have been devised for *Ps. aeruginosa* incorporating dettol or cetrimide. It is sensitive to acids, beta glutaraldehyde, silver salts and strong phenolic disinfectants. Its susceptibility to silver has been applied clinically in the use of silver sulphonamide compounds as topical cream in burns.

Ps. aeruginosa possesses a considerable degree of natural resistance to antibiotics. Examples of clinically effective antibiotics are aminoglycosides (gentamicin, amikacin), cephalosporins (cefotaxime, ceftazidime, cefoperazone), fluoroquinolones (ciprofloxacin, ofloxacin, pefloxacin), penicillins (piperacillin, ticarcillin, azlocillin). For localised infetions, topical colistin, polymyxin B or 1% acetic acid may be useful.

Pathogenicity: 'Blue pus' was known as a surgical entity long before Gessard (1882) isolated *Ps. aeruginosa* from such cases. Both the specific names of the bacillus refer to its capacity to cause 'blue pus', the term aeruginosa, meaning verdigris which is bluish green in colour and *pyocyanea,* being a literal translation of 'blue pus'.

The pathogenic importance of the bacillus was not adequately recognised till recently, when it has established itself as one of the most troublesome agents causing nosocomial infections. In the community outside the hospital, the most common infection caused by *Ps. aeruginosa* is suppurative otitis, which is chronic though not disabling. In the hospital, it may cause localised or generalised infections. Localised lesions are commonly infections of wounds and bedsores, eye infections and urinary infections following catheterisation. *Ps. aeruginosa* is the most common and most serious cause of infection in burns. It is also one of the agents responsible for iatrogenic meningitis following lumbar puncture. It frequently causes post-tracheostomy pulmonary infection. Septicemia and endocarditis may occur in patients who are debilitated due to concomitant infection, malignancy or immunosuppressive therapy. Ecthyma gangrenosum and many other types of skin lesions have been described occurring either alone or as part of generalised infection, mainly in patients with leukemia and other types of malignancy. Infection of the nail bed is not uncommon following excessive exposure of hands to detergents and water.

Ps. aeruginosa has been described as one of the agents responsible for infantile diarrhea and sepsis. Strains isolated from outbreaks of diarrhea may form a heat labile enterotoxin and give a positive rabbit ileal loop reaction. *Ps. aeruginosa* has been reported to cause a self-limited febrile illness (*Shanghai fever*) resembling typhoid fever in some tropical areas.

The pre-eminent role of *Ps. aeruginosa* in hospital infection is due to its resistance to common antibiotics and antiseptics, and its ability to establish itself widely in hospitals. Being an extremely adaptable organism it can survive and multiply even with minimal nutrients, if moisture is available. Equipment such as respirators and endoscopes, articles such as bed pans and medicines such as lotions, ointments and eye drops and even stocks of distilled water or plants and flowers may be frequently contaminated. *Ps. aeruginosa* is present on the skin of the axilla and perineum in some persons. Fecal carriage is not common but may be frequent following oral antibiotic treatment or hospitalisation.

The mechanisms of pathogenesis are not clearly understood. Several toxic extracellular products have been identified in the culture filtrates, such as exotoxins A and S. Exotoxin A acts as an NADase, resembling the diphtheria toxin. Good antibody response to exotoxin A is considered a favourable sign in severe infections with *Ps. aeruginosa*. Other toxic products include proteases, elastases, hemolysins and enterotoxin. The slime layer acts as a capsule in enhancing virulence.

Laboratory diagnosis: The bacterium grows readily on most media. The identification of pigmented strains of the bacillus from clinical specimens is easy. But about 10 per cent of isolates may be nonpigmented. Prompt oxidase reaction and arginine hydrolysis help in their identification. It may be necessary to use selective media such as cetrimide agar for isolation from feces or other samples with mixed flora. As *Ps. aeruginosa* is a frequent contaminant, isolation of the bacillus from a specimen should not always be taken as proof of its etiological role. Repeated isolations help to confirm the diagnosis.

Control: Prevention of *Ps. aeruginosa* cross-infection in hospitals requires constant vigilance and strict attention to asepsis. Antibiotic treatment is not always satisfactory. Animals with experimentally infected burns have been protected by prior immunisation with the homologous strains. Immunotherapy in human burns cases with antiserum to *Ps. aeruginosa* may be useful. Pseudomonas vaccines are being tried in cystic fibrosis patients who are highly vulnerable to pseudomonas infection.

Specific antibacterial therapy constitutes only one aspect of the management of serious pseudomonas infections. Treatment of the underlying diseases, correction of granulopenia and appropriate supportive therapy need attention.

Occasional opportunist infections may be caused by a few other species, such as *Ps. fluorescens, Ps. putida* and *Ps. stutzeri*.

STENOTROPHOMONAS MALTOPHILA (FORMERLY *PSEUDOMONAS MALTOPHILA*)

This is a saprophyte and opportunistic pathogen, causing wound infection, urinary tract infection and septicemia. It is usually oxidase negative and acidifies maltose in addition to glucose, lactose and sucrose. Infections usually respond to cotrimoxazole and chloramphenicol.

BURKHOLDERIA CEPACIA (FORMERLY *PSEUDOMONAS CEPACIA*)

This is a plant pathogen causing onion rot (*cepia*, Latin for onion). It is increasingly being recognised as an opportunist environmental pathogen, particularly in those with cystic fibrosis or chronic granulomatous disease, in whom it causes fatal necrotising pneumonia. It is nutritionally very versatile. It can grow in many common disinfectants and can even use penicillin G as a sole source of carbon! It is oxidase positive and acidifies mannitol, sorbitol and sucrose. It can cause urinary, respiratory and wound infections, peritonitis, endocarditis and septicemia. It is inherently resistant to most antibiotics.

GLANDERS

BURKHOLDERIA MALLEI (FORMELY *PSEUDOMONAS MALLEI*)

The bacillus had also been classified variously as *Loefflerella, Pfeifferella, Malleomyces, Actinobacillus* and *Acinetobacter*. It is the causative agent of glanders (*malleus*, in Latin), a disease primarily of equine animals – horses, mules and asses – but capable of being transmitted to other animals and to human beings. The bacillus was discovered by Loeffler and Schutz (1882).

Ps. mallei is a slender, nonmotile, Gram negative bacillus, 2–5 μm × 0.5 μm staining irregularly and often giving a beaded appearance. It is an aerobe and facultative anaerobe, growing on ordinary media under a wide range of temperature. Colonies which are small and transluscent initially become yellowish and opaque on ageing. On potato, a characteristic amber, honey-like growth appears, becoming greenish yellow resembling Ps. aeruginosa. It is quite inactive biochemically, attacking only glucose.

The natural disease in equines occurs in two forms—glanders and farcy. In glanders, the respiratory system is involved, with the formation of firm, round nodules and a profuse catarrhal discharge from the nose. Farcy follows infection through the skin and is an involvement of the lymph vessels and nodes, which stand out as hard cords beneath the skin.

Guinea pigs are susceptible and intraperitoneal injection into male guinea pigs induces the Straus reaction. This consists of swelling of the testes, inflammation of tunica vaginalis and ulceration of the scrotal skin. The Straus reaction is not diagnostic of glanders, as it may also be produced by inoculation of other bacteria such as Brucella species, Preisz–Nocard bacillus, Actinobacillus ligniersi and Ps. pseudomallei.

Human infection is usually occupational, found in ostlers, grooms and veterinarians. It may be acute or chronic and is protean in character, with localisation in the respiratory tract, skin or subcutaneous tissues. In acute glanders, there is fever, mucopurulent nasal discharge and severe prostration. The fatality rate is high. While human infection is acquired only rarely from infected animals, laboratory cultures are highly infectious and Ps. mallei is one of the most dangerous bacteria to work with.

Animals suffering from glanders develop a delayed hypersensitivity to the bacterial protein. This is the basis of the mallein test used for diagnosing glanders. This is analogous to the tuberculin test and may be performed by the subcutaneous, intracutaneous or conjunctival methods.

MELIOIDOSIS

BURKHOLDERIA PSEUDOMALLEI (FORMERLY PSEUDOMONAS PSEUDOMALLEI)

Also known as Whitmore's bacillus, Actinobacillus whitmori, Malleomyces pseudomallei, Loefflerella pseudomallei).

This is the causative agent of melioidosis, a glanders-like disease, epizootic in rodents in southeast Asia, India and North Australia. (The name is derived from melis, a disease of asses [glanders], and eidos meaning resemblance). The disease was first described in human beings by Whitmore and Krishnaswami (1912) in Rangoon. Whitmore (1913) isolated the bacillus. It resembles Ps. mallei but differs in being motile, liquefying gelatin and forming acid from several sugars. Two thermolabile exotoxins, one lethal and the other necrotising have been identified in culture filtrates.

The human disease may take different forms. It may be an acute septicemia, a subacute typhoid-like disease, or pneumonia and hemoptysis resembling tuberculosis. In chronic form, there may be multiple caseous or suppurative foci, with abscess formation in the skin and subcutaneous tissues, bones and internal organs. Acute melioidosis has a high case fatality rate. Serological evidence indicates that inapparent infection is common in endemic areas. Long latency and reactivation may occur as the bacillus can survive intracellularly in the reticuloendothelial system. The bacillus has been isolated from water and soil in endemic areas. It is a soil saprophyte that causes infection in rodents and humans accidentally. Human infection occurs commonly through skin abrasions or by inhalation.

Diagnosis may be made by demonstration of the bacillus in exudates by microscopy (small irregularly staining Gram negative bacilli, showing typical bipolar 'safety pin' appearance with methylene blue stain), isolation by culture from sputum, pus, blood or urine, or by serology (ELISA for IgM and IgG antibody, indirect hemagglutination). A PCR test has also been developed.

Ceftazidime is the drug of choice, along with cotrimoxazole, tetracycline, amoxycillin clavulanate, or chloramphenicol. Prolonged treatment, for many months may be necessary.

Further Reading

Baltch AL and Smith RP (eds). 1994. *Pseudomonas aeruginosa infections.* New York: Marcel Dekker.

Dance DAB. 1991. Melioidosis. *Clin Microbiol Rev.* 4:52.

Fick RB (ed). 1992. *Pseudomonas aeruginosa: The Opportunist: Pathogenesis and Disease.* Boca Raton:CRC.

Gilligan PR. 1995. Pseudomanas and Burkholderia. In Murray PR et al *Manual of Clinical Microbiology.* Washington:American Society of Microbiology.

Gould IM and R. Rise 1985. Pseudomonas aeruginosa – Clinical manifestations and management. *Lancet* 2:1224.

Leelarasamee A and S. Bovoronkitti 1989. Melioidosis. *Rev Infect Dis.* 11:413.

Morrison AJ Jr. and RP. Werzel 1984. Epidemiology of infections due to Pseudomonas aeruginosa. *Rev Infect Dis.* 6: Suppl 5-627.

Patamasucon P et al. 1982. Melioidosis. *J Pediatr* 100:175.

Yersinia, Pasteurella, Francisella

The plague bacillus and many other Gram negative, short bacilli that are primary pathogens of rodents were grouped together in the genus *Pasteurella*. Based on cultural and biochemical differences, this group has been divided into three genera – *Yersinia, Pasteurella* and *Francisella*. The genus *Yersinia,* containing the medically important species *Y. pestis* (the causative agent of plague), *Y. pseudo tuberculosis* (a primary pathogen of rodents) and *Y. enterocolitica* (which causes enteric and systemic diseases in animals and human beings) was so named after Alexandre Yersin, who discovered the plague bacillus. The genus *Yersinia* is now assigned to the family Enterobacteriaceae. The genus *Pasteurella* contains several related bacteria causing hemorrhagic septicemia in different species of animals and occasionally producing local and systemic infections in human beings, grouped under a common species named *P. multocida*. One of these, *P. aviseptica* is the chicken cholera bacillus used by Pasteur for the development of the first attenuated bacterial vaccine. Hence the name Pasteurella. The genus *Francisella,* consisting of *F. tularensis*, is named after Francis for his pioneering studies on tularemia, caused by this bacillus.

YERSINIA PESTIS (FORMERLY PASTEURELLA PESTIS)

The plague bacillus was discovered independently and simultaneously by Yersin and Kitasato (1894) in Hong Kong at the beginning of the last pandemic of the disease.

Morphology: *Y. pestis* is a short, plump, ovoid, Gram negative bacillus, about 1.5 μm × 0.7 μm in size, with rounded ends and convex sides, arranged singly, in short chains or in small groups. In smears stained with Giemsa or methylene blue, it shows bipolar staining (safety pin appearance) with the two ends densely stained and the central area clear (Fig. 35.1). Pleomorphism is very common and in old cultures, involution forms are seen—coccoid, club-shaped, filamentous and giant forms. Pleomorphism is characterically enhanced in media containing 3% NaCl.

The bacillus is surrounded by a slime layer (envelope or capsule). It is nonmotile, nonsporing and non-acid fast.

Cultural characteristics: The plague bacillus is aerobic and facultatively anaerobic. Growth occurs over a wide range of pH (pH 5–9.6, optimum pH 7.2) and temperature (range 2–45 °C). The optimum temperature for growth (unlike most pathogens) is 27 °C but the envelope develops best at 37 °C.

It is not nutritionally exacting and grows on ordinary media. On nutrient agar, colonies are small, delicate, transparent discs, becoming opaque on continued incubation. Colonies on blood agar or other hemin containing media are dark brown due to the absorption of the hemin pigment. Colourless colonies are formed on MacConkey's agar. In broth, a flocculent growth occurs at the bottom and along the sides of the tube, with little or no turbidity. A delicate pellicle may form later. If grown in a flask of broth with oil or ghee (clarified butter) floated on top (ghee broth) a characteristic growth occurs which hangs down into the broth from the surface, resembling stalactites (*stalactite growth*) (Fig. 35.2).

Biochemical reactions: Glucose, maltose and mannitol but not lactose, sucrose or rhamnose are fermented with the production of acid but no gas. Indole is not produced. It is MR positive and VP and citrate negative, catalase positive and aesculin positive and oxidase and urease negative. Gelatin is not liquefied. Based on the fermentation of glycerol and reduction of nitrate, Devignat has distinguished three physiological varieties of *Y. pestis.* This typing appears to be of epidemiological significance because of the different geographical distribution of the types (Table 35.1).

Resistance: The plague bacillus is easily destroyed by exposure to heat, sunlight, drying and chemical disinfectants. It is destroyed by heat at 55 °C or by 0.5% phenol in 15 minutes. It remains viable for long periods in cold, moist environments. It can survive for several months, and even multiply, in the soil of rodent burrows. All strains are lysed by a specific antiplague bacteriophage at 22 °C.

Antigens, toxins and other virulence factors: Plague bacilli are antigenically homogeneous and serotypes do not exist. The antigenic structure is complex. At least 20 antigens have been detected by gel diffusion and biochemical analysis. Many of them have been claimed to be virulence factors. They include the following:

1. A heat labile protein envelope antigen (Fraction I or F-I) best formed in cultures incubated at 37 °C. It inhibits phagocytosis and is generally present only in virulent strains. This plasmid encoded antigen has been considered a virulence determinant but occasional strains deficient in Fraction I antigen have been isolated from fatal human cases. The antibody to this antigen is protective in mice.

2. Two antigens designated V and W and always produced together have been considered to be the virulence factors as they inhibit phagocytosis and intracellular killing of the bacillus. Production of V and W antigens is plasmid mediated.

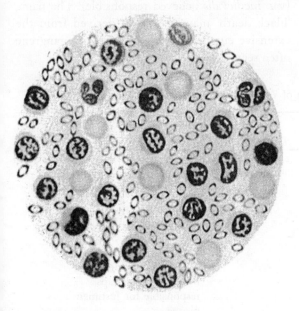

Fig.35.1 Smear from gland puncture in a case of plague showing *Y. pestis* with bipolar staining (safety pin appearance), a few red blood cell and leucocytes.

Fig.35.2 *Y. pestis* in ghee broth culture. Stalactite growth.

3. Virulent strains produce a bacteriocin (Pesticin I), coagulase and fibrinolysin. Pesticin I inhibits strains of *Y. pseudotuberculosis, Y. entero colitica* and *E. coli*.

4. The term 'plague toxins' refers to at least two classes of toxins found in culture filtrates or cell lysates. The first is the endotoxin, a lipopolysaccharide similar to the endotoxins of enteric bacilli. The second class of toxins is protein in nature, possessing some properties of both exotoxins and endotoxins. They are thermolabile and may be toxoided but do not diffuse freely into the medium and are released only by the lysis of the cell. They are called *murine toxins* as they are active in rats and mice but not in guinea pigs, rabbits and primates. On injection into experimental animals, plague toxins produce local edema and necrosis with systemic effects on the peripheral vascular system and liver. The role of plague toxins in natural disease in human beings is not known.

5. Virulence also appears to be associated with an unidentified surface component which absorbs hemin and basic aromatic dyes in culture media to form coloured colonies.

6. Virulence has also been associated with the ability for purine synthesis.

PLAGUE

Plague is an ancient scourge of mankind. The disease was familiar to the ancient civilisations of Asia. The *Bhagavatha Purana* urged householders to flee when rat falls were noticed.

Central Asia or the Himalayas is believed to have been the original home of plague, from where it has, in wave after wave, spread far and wide, causing epidemics and pandemics, exacting a toll of human life surpassing any other disease. The identity of the Biblical plague of the Philistines (1320 BC) is in doubt but the pandemic that occurred during the reign of Emperor Justinian (AD 542) was undoubtedly bubonic plague (believed to have been caused by *Y. pestis, var. antiqua*) and caused a hundred million deaths. In the fourteenth century, pandemic plague known as the 'black death' is believed to have killed a quarter of all mankind. (*var. medievalis* believed responsible). The name 'black death' may have been derived from the extensive cutaneous hemorrhages and gangrene often seen in fatal cases of plague.

Table 35.1 Biotypes of Yersinia pestis

Variety	Glycerol fermentation	Nitrate reduction	Geographical distribution
Y. pestis var. orientalis	−	+	Primary foci in India, Myanmar, and China. Causative agent of 1894 pandemic. Responsible for wild plague in Western USA, South America, South Africa.
Y. pestis var. antiqua	+	+	Transbaikalia, Mongolia, Manchuria, perhaps responsible for Justinian plague.
Y. pestis var. medievalis	+	−	Southeast Russia.

Historians of plague identify 41 epidemics before the birth of Christ and 109 epidemics in the next 15 centuries. There are records of 45 pandemics between AD 1500 and 1720. The disease was quiescent in the eighteenth and nineteenth centuries and confined to endemic foci. The last pandemic started in Hong Kong in 1894 and spread throughout the world. (caused by *Y.pestis var. orientalis*). India was one of the countries worst hit by this pandemic. Plague reached Bombay in 1896 and spread all over the country during the next few years, causing more than 10 million deaths by 1918. It gradually receded thereafter, though occasional cases continued to occur in endemic foci till 1967. No further plague cases were seen in India till 1994, when in August a nonfatal outbreak of bubonic plague was reported from Maharashtra (Beed district). In September pneumonic plague was reported in Surat and adjoining areas of Gujarat and Maharashtra, causing much panic and consternation. A few cases were reported from different parts of north India also, probably caused by the exodus from affected areas. During the outbreak which subsided in two months, there were over 6000 *suspected* plague cases and 60 deaths. In February 2002, plague struck again causing a short outbreak near Simla, claiming 4 lives.

Plague survives in several scattered natural foci in many countries (Fig. 35.3) in wild rodents, occasionally causing infection in human contacts. In India at least four foci of plague are known. One is the region near Kolar at the trijunction of Tamil Nadu, Andhra and Karnataka. The second is the Beed-Latur belt in Maharashtra from where the Surat epidemic emanated. The third is in Rhoru in Himachal Pradesh where the 2002 outbreak took place, and the fourth is a small pocket in Uttaranchal.

In human beings, plague occurs in three major forms: bubonic, pneumonic and septicemic. In **bubonic plague**, after an incubation period of 2–5 days, the lymph nodes draining the site of entry of the bacillus become infected. In some, the infection remains localised at the site of flea bite, with only minor constitutional symptoms (pestis minor). As the plague bacillus usually enters through flea bites on the legs, the inguinal nodes are involved and hence the name 'bubonic' (**bubon** meaning groin). The glands become enlarged and suppurate. The bacilli enter the bloodstream and produce septicemia. Sometimes there are hemorrhages into the skin and mucosa. Disseminated intravascular coagulation is common and may lead to gangrene of the skin, fingers and penis. The case fatality in untreated cases may be 30–90 per cent.

Pneumonic plague may be seen sometimes during epidemics of bubonic plague. Rarely, primary pneumonic plague may occur in epidemic form, as happened in Manchuria during 1910–1912, causing some 60,000 deaths. Pneumonic plague is spread by droplet infection. The bacilli spread through the lungs producing hemorrhagic pneumonia. Cyanosis is very prominent. The bloody mucoid sputum that is coughed out contains bacilli in enormous numbers. Pneumonic plague is highly infectious and in untreated patients, almost invariably fatal.

Septicemic plague is usually the terminal event in the bubonic or pneumonic plague but may sometimes occur primarily. Meningitic involvement may occur rarely. Human carriers have not been recorded but asymptomatic oropharyngeal infection has been observed in some contacts.

Epidemiology: Plague is a zoonotic disease. The plague bacillus is naturally parasitic in rodents. Infection is transmitted among them by rat fleas. The fleas acquire the infection by feeding on infected rodents. In the flea, the bacilli multiply in the stomach to such an extent that they block the proventriculus. The interval between the ingestion of infected blood and blocking in the proventriculus is the extrinsic incubation period, which is usually about two weeks in *Xenopsylla cheopis*. When such a 'blocked flea' bites another rodent, it cannot suck in blood because the bacterial mass blocks the passage mechanically. The blood, mixed with the

YERSINIA, PASTEURELLA, FRANCISELLA

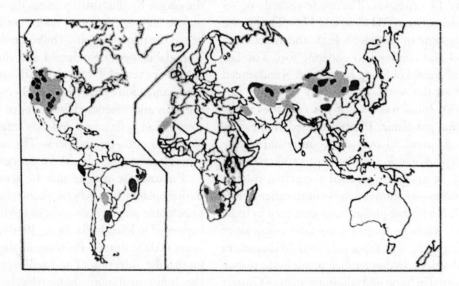

Fig. 35.3 Natural foci of plague, known and suspected (Known areas – dark; Suspected – shaded)

bacteria is regurgitated into the bite, transmitting the infection. Infection may also be transferred by contamination of the bite wound with the feces of infected fleas. When a diseased rat dies (rat fall), the fleas leave the carcass and in the absence of another rat, may bite human beings, causing bubonic plague.

Several species of fleas may act as vectors, the most important being *Xenopsylla cheopis, X. astia* and *Ceratophyllus fasciatus. X. cheopis*, the predominant species in north India is a more efficient vector than the south Indian species *X. astia*. This has contributed to the more extensive nature of plague outbreaks in the north as compared to south India. Plague epidemics generally occur in the cool, humid seasons that favour the multiplication of fleas, leading to a high 'flea index' (mean number of fleas per rat). In the hot, dry weather, fleas do not thrive and the transmission of infection is interrupted.

The studies of the various governmental Plague Commissions in Bombay, during the early years of the twentieth century, helped to clarify the epidemiology of plague. It was found that plague produced epizootics first in *Rattus norvegicus* (sewer rat). When their number dwindled, the disease passed to the domestic rat, *R. rattus*. It was from the domestic rat that the infection spread to human beings.

Two natural cycles of plague exist, the domestic and the wild. The term 'urban or domestic plague' refers to plague that is intimately associated with human beings and rodents living with them, possessing a definite potential for producing epidemics. 'Wild or sylvatic plague' occurs in nature and in wild rodents, independent of human beings. The rodents involved vary in different regions. Over 200 species and subspecies are involved. In Western USA prairie dogs, ground squirrels, wood rats and mice are found infected. In the endemic areas of the USA, cases of human plague have occurred following contact with wild animals, and even with domestic carnivores, particularly pet cats. In Java, the field rat is the reservoir. In India, the gerbil

(*Tatera indica*) and the bandicoot are infected. Human infection may occur during skinning and handling of carcasses of infected wild animals. Carnivores, including cats and dogs can get infected by eating infected rodents or through their fleas. Clinical plague is seldom seen in dogs, but may develop in cats. Human infection from inhalation of respiratory droplets from infected cats has been reported.

In enzootic foci, plague may persist for long periods. Infected fleas may survive for over a year. The bacilli can remain alive and even multiply in the soil of abandoned rodent burrows. They can infect new rodents that may reoccupy such burrows. This may account for the long period of quiescence and subsequent re-emergence characteristic of plague. Attenuated strains of plague bacilli have been isolated from natural foci. They may regain virulence when plague becomes active. Eradication of plague is an unlikely prospect as it is a disease of the earth—of rodents that live in burrows and of the fleas that live on them. Only when human beings or domestic animals trespass on these natural foci do human infections set in.

In the 1990s, there has been a re-emergence of plague in countries where it had ceased to be noticed for many years. This has happened in the developing and the developed countries—India and China in Asia, Malawi and Zimbabwe in Africa, the erstwhile USSR in Europe and in the USA. Plague bacillus strains carrying plasmid borne resistance to multiple antibiotics were reported from Madagascar in 1995. These have the potential to spread and pose a great threat.

Laboratory diagnosis: The laboratory should be able to diagnose plague not only in humans, but in rodents also, as timely detection of infection in rats may help to prevent epidemic spread.

A rat which died of plague may carry infected fleas and should be handled with care. Pouring kerosene oil over the carcass is a simple method of eliminating the fleas. In the laboratory, the carcass should be dipped in 3% lysol to destroy ectoparasites.

During epizootics, it is easy to diagnose plague in rats. Buboes are usually present in the cervical region. They are hard and can be moved under the skin. On section, the bubo may show congestion, hemorrhagic points or grey necrosis. Smears from the bubo stained with methylene blue show the bipolar stained bacilli. The fluorescent antibody technique may be of use in identifying plague bacilli in the impression films of the tissues. Bacilli in bubo show considerable pleomorphism. The liver is mottled, with red, yellow or grey stippling. The spleen is enlarged, and moulded over the stomach, with granules or nodules on the surface. A characteristic feature is pleural effusion which may be clear, abundant and straw coloured or, less often, bloodstained. Bacilli may be demonstrated microscopically in spleen smears and heart blood. Cultures may be made from the buboes, spleen, heart blood and particularly, from bone marrow in decomposed carcasses.

In badly putrified carcasses, microscopy and culture may not be successful. The putrified tissue rubbed on the shaven abdomen of a guinea pig can infect the animal. Diagnosis may also be established by demonstrating the F-I antigen by immmo-flumescent staining.

In human bubonic plague, the bacilli may be readily demonstrated in buboes by microscopy, culture or animal inoculation. Blood cultures are often positive.

In pneumonic plague, the bacilli can be demonstrated in the sputum by microscopy, culture or animal inoculation.

Serological tests are sometimes useful in diagnosis. Antibodies to the F-I antigen may be detected by passive hemagglutination. Rise in titre of antibodies in paired sera or titre of 128 or above in a single serum sample can be considered positive. IgG and IgM ELISA tests have been developed. PCR is a rapid and sensitive method for presumptive diagnosis of plague in clinical material and fleas.

Prophylaxis: In the prevention of domestic plague, general measures such as control of fleas and rodents are of great importance. Two types of vaccine have been in use: killed and live attenuated vaccines. The killed vaccine used in India (prepared at the Haffkine Institute, Mumbai) is a whole culture antigen. A virulent strain of the plague bacillus is grown in casein hydrolysate broth for 2–4 weeks at 32°C and killed by 0.05 per cent formaldehyde and preserved with phenyl mercuric nitrate (Sokhey's modification of Haffkine's vaccine). Standardisation is by immunogenic potency rather than by bacterial counts. The vaccine is given subcutaneously, two doses at an interval of 1–3 months, followed by a third six months later. Vaccination gives some protection against bubonic plague but not against pneumonic plague. The protection does not last for more than six months. In contrast, an attack of plague provides more lasting immunity. A person exposed to definite risk of infection, whether vaccinated or not, should be given chemoprophylaxis—cotrimoxazole or tetracycline orally for at least five days.

The vaccine is recommended only in those exposed occupationally or otherwise to infection, such as plague laboratory or hospital personnel and troops deployed in known plague areas. It is of no value in plague outbreaks and mass vaccination is not advised.

Live attenuated plague vaccines (Otten's Tjiwidej strain from Indonesia and Girard's EV strain from Malagasy) cause severe reactions and are not in use now.

Treatment: Early treatment with antibiotics has reduced plague mortality from 30–100 per cent to 5–10 per cent. Streptomycin, deoxycyclene and, chloramphenicol are effective.

YERSINIOSIS

The term yersinosis denotes infections with yersiniae other than *Y. pestis*. These include zoonotic infections by *Y. pseudotuberculosis* and *Y. enterocolitica,* which appear to be acquired accidentally from disease cycles of wild or domestic animals.

YERSINIA PSEUDOTUBERCULOSIS (*formerly Pasteurella pseudotuberculosis*)

This bacillus resembles the plague bacillus closely but can be distinguished by its relatively poor growth on MacConkey's agar, motility at 22 °C (but not at 37 °C), production of urease, fermentation of rhamnose and melibiose and failure to be lysed by the antiplague bacteriophage at 22 °C. Distinction between *Y. pseudotuberculosis* and *Y. pestis* becomes important when the former is isolated from rats.

Y. pseudotuberculosis is antigenically heterogeneous, six serological groups and many serotypes being distinguished, based on somatic and flagellar antigens. It shows antigenic cross relationships with *Y. pestis* as well as salmonellae. Most human infections are caused by serogroup.

The natural mode of infection in animals is probably through the alimentary tract. In infected guinea pigs, the liver, spleen and lungs show multiple nodules resembling tuberculosis lesions (hence the name *pseudotuberculosis*). Human infection occurs rarely and may present as a fatal typhoid-like illness with hepatosplenomegaly and purpura or as mesenteric lymphadenitis simulating acute appendicitis. It has also been reported to cause erythema nodosum and gastroenteritis.

YERSINIA ENTEROCOLITICA

This bacillus resembles *Y. pseudotuberculosis* in being motile at 22 °C but differs from it in fermenting sucrose and cellobiose and decarboxylating ornithine. It does not ferment rhamnose or melibiose. Many strains give a positive VP test and form indole. Six biotypes have been identified based on cultural and biochemical characteristics. The antigenic structure of *Y. enterocolitica* is distinct from that of *Y. psuedo tuberculosis.* More than 60 O serotypes have been reported. Most human isolates belong to serotypes, 03, 08 and 09. Serological cross reactions between serotype 9 and brucella strains occur.

Table 35.2 Some differentiating features among Yersinia and Pasteurella

	Y. pestis	Y. pseudotuberculosis	Y. enterocolitica	P. multocida
Motility at 22 °C	−	+	+	−
Growth on MacConkey's agar		+	+	−
Acid from sucrose	+	−	+	+
Acid from maltose	−	+	+	−
Indole	+	−	+	+
Oxidase	−	−	−	+
Urease	−	+	+	−
Ornithine decarboxylase	−	−	+	+

Y. enterocolitica has been isolated from a wide range of domestic and wild animals and, in recent years, is increasingly being reported from human clinical material. It produces three types of disease in human beings. The first type occurs in young children as self-limited gastroenteritis or enterocolitis which may be either inflammatory or noninflammatory. The second is mesenteric adenitis and inflammatory terminal ileitis in older children that may mimic appendicitis. The third category is a systemic disease typically in adults, often characterised by bacteremia, meningitis, arthralgia or erythema nodosum. Persons belonging to HLA - B 27 group are prone to develop reactive arthritis.

PASTEURELLA MULTOCIDA
(formerly Pasteurella Septica)

A group of related bacteria isolated from hemorrhagic septicemia in a variety of animals and birds had, in the past, been named according to their species of origin—*P. boviseptica, lepiseptica, aviseptica,* etc. Though they show some degree of host specificity, they are so alike in other respects that they are now considered strains of a single species designated *P. multocida.*

P. multocida is a nonmotile, Gram negative bacillus generally resembling *Yersinia* but differing in being oxidase positive, producing indole and failing to grow on MacConkey's agar.

The bacillus is often carried in the upper respiratory tract of a variety of animals such as dogs, cats, rats, cattle and sheep. It may sometimes occur as a commensal in the human respiratory tract also. Human infection is rare but may occur following animal bites or trauma. The clinical manifestations may be local suppuration following animal bites (wound infection, cellulitis, abscess, osteomyelitis), meningitis following head injury, respiratory tract infection (pneumonia, bronchitis, sinusitis) or appendicitis and appendicial abscess.

The bacillus is sensitive to tetracycline and streptomycin and most strains to penicillin as well.

FRANCISELLA TULARENSIS
(PASTEURELLA TULARENSIS, BRUCELLA TULARENSIS)

This is the causative agent of tularemia, a disease of rabbits and other rodents, originally described in Tulare county, California. Infection is transmitted by ticks and several other arthropod vectors. Human infection may occur by direct contact with infected rodents such as rabbits or through tick bites. It can also be acquired by ingestion of contaminated meat or water and inhalation of infective aerosols.

It is a minute, capsulated, nonmotile Gram negative bacillus, about 0.3–0.7 μm × 0.2 μm in size. It resembles mycoplasma in being filterable and in multiplying by filament formation and budding, besides binary fission. In infected animals, it acts as an intracellular parasite, being found in large masses inside the liver and spleen cells. It has fastidious growth requirements and special media such as Francis' blood dextrose cystine agar have to be employed for its isolation. Minute transparent colonies appear after incubation for 3–5 days.

Strains of *S.tularensis* have been subdivided into biotypes based on their virulence and epidemiological behaviour. Highly virulent strains are found only in N. America, while strains of low virulence are seen in Europe and Asia also.

In human beings, tularemia may present as a local ulceration with lymphadenitis, a typhoid like fever with glandular enlargement or an influenza like respiratory infection. The disease may also be waterborne, as a result of water pollution by the excreta of infected rodents. The bacillus is highly infectious and laboratory infection has been quite common. Diagnosis may be made by culture or by inoculation into guinea pigs or mice. Agglutinating antibodies may be demonstrated in sera from patients.

An attenuated vaccine is available which can be administered by scarification to persons who are subject to high risk of infection.

Further Reading

Brubaker BR. 1991. Factors promoting infections caused by yersiniae. *Clin Microbiol Rev.* 4:309.

Butler T. 1994. Yersinia infections. *Clin Infect Dis.* 19:655.

Campbell and JM Hughes 1995. Plague in India. *Ann Int Med.* 122:155.

Cover TL and RC Aber 1989. Yersinia enterocolitica. *New Engl J Med* 321:16.

Gage KI. 1998. Plague. In *Topley and Wilson's Microbiology and Microbial Infections,* 9th edn. London: Arnold.

Pollitzer R. 1954. *Plague.* WHO Monograph series No. 22.

Haemophilus

The genus *Haemophilus* contains small, nonmotile, nonsporing, oxidase positive, pleomorphic, Gram negative bacilli that are parasitic on human beings or animals. They are characterised by their requirement of one or both of two accessory growth factors (X and V) present in blood (*Haemophilus*, meaning blood loving).

Pfeiffer (1892) observed that a small, Gram negative bacillus was 'constantly present' in the sputum of patients from the influenza pandemic of 1889–92 and mistakenly proposed this as the causative agent of human influenza. This came to be known as the 'influenza bacillus' (Pfeiffer's bacillus), later renamed *Haemophilus influenzae*. The causal relationship between this bacillus and human influenza could not be substantiated and was finally disproved when Smith, Andrewes and Laidlaw (1933) isolated the influenza virus.

HAEMOPHILUS INFLUENZAE
(Influenza bacillus, Pfeiffer's bacillus)

Morphology: *H. influenzae* is a small (1.0 μm × 0.3 μm), Gram negative, nonmotile, nonsporing bacillus, exhibiting considerable pleomorphism (Fig. 36.1). In sputum, it usually occurs as clusters of coccobacillary forms, while in the CSF from meningitis cases, long, bacillary and filamentous forms predominate. Cells from young cultures (18–24 hours) are usually coccobacillary, while older cultures are distinctly pleomorphic. Strains isolated from acute infections are often capsulated.

The bacilli are relatively difficult to stain. Staining for 5–15 minutes with Loeffler's methylene blue or dilute carbol fuchsin gives good results.

Cultural characteristics: The bacillus has fastidious growth requirements. The accessory growth factors, named X and V, present in blood are essential for growth. The heat stable X factor is hemin or other porphyrins required for the synthesis of cytochrome and other heme enzymes such as catalase and peroxidase involved in aerobic respiration. The X factor is not required for anaerobic growth. The V factor was so named because it was originally thought to be a bacterial vitamin. It is heat labile being destroyed at 120 °C in a few minutes. It is present in red blood cells and in many other animal and plant cells. It is synthesised by some fungi and bacteria (for example, *Staph. aureus*) in excess of their requirements and released into the surrounding medium. The V factor is a coenzyme, nicotinamide adenine dinucleotide (NAD) or NAD phosphate (NADP) which acts as a hydrogen acceptor in the metabolism of the cell.

It is aerobic but grows anaerobically also. The optimum temperature is 37 °C. It does not grow below 20°C. Some strains require 10% CO_2. It grows on blood agar but growth is scanty, as the V factor is not freely available, being imprisoned inside the red blood cells. Growth is, therefore, better if a source of the V factor is also provided. When *Staph. aureus* is streaked across a plate of blood agar on which a specimen containing *H. influenzae* has been inoculated, after overnight incubation, the colonies of *H. influenzae* will be large and well developed alongside the streak of staphylococcus, and smaller farther away. This phenomenon is called **satellitism** and demonstrates the dependence of

H. influenzae on the V factor, which is available in high concentrations near the staphylococcal growth and only in smaller quantities away from it. This is a routine test in clinical bacteriology for the identification of *H. influenzae* (Fig 36.2). It is, however, not very specific as it will also be positive with other V factors requiring hemophili as well as with occasional strains cf neisseriae and diphtheroids.

When blood agar is heated to 80–90 °C or boiled for a few minutes (boiled blood agar), the V factor is released from within the erythrocytes and hence these media are superior to plain blood agar for growing *H. influenzae*. Clear transparent media may be prepared by boiling and filtering a mixture of blood and nutrient broth (Levinthal's medium) or by adding a peptic digest of blood to nutrient agar (Fildes agar). Fildes agar is best for primary isolation of *H. influenzae* and gives a copious growth. Capsulated strains produce transluscent colonies with a distinctive iridescence on Levinthal's agar.

Biochemical reactions: Glucose and xylose are fermented with acid production but not lactose, sucrose and mannitol. Catalase and oxidase reactions are positive. Nitrates are reduced to nitrites. Eight biotypes have been identified on the basis of indole production, urease and ornithine decarboxylase activity. Biotype I is most frequently responsible for meningitis.

Resistance: H. influenzae is a delicate bacterium, destroyed by heating (55°C for 30 minutes), refrigeration (0–4 °C), drying and disinfectants. In culture, the cells die within two or three days due to autolysis. Cultures may be preserved for about a month on chocolate agar slopes in screw capped bottles. For longterm preservation, the culture may be lyophilised.

Antigenic properties: There are three major surface antigens – the capsular polysaccharide, the outer membrane proteins (OMP) and lipooligosaccharide (LOS).

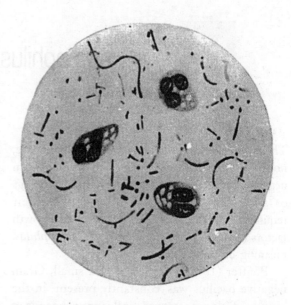

Fig. 36.1 *H. influenzae* in cerebrospinal fluid showing pleomorphism

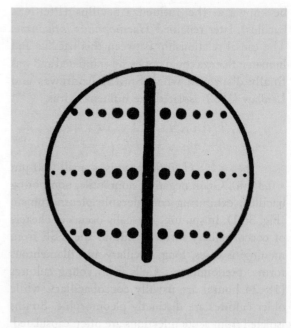

Fig. 36.2 Satellitism. *H. influenzae* colonies are large near growth of staphylococcus, and smaller away from it.

The major antigenic determinant of capsulated strains is the capsular polysaccharide based on which *H. influenzae* strains have been classified by Pittman into six capsular types – types a to f. Typing was originally done by agglutination but other methods such as Quellung reaction, precipitation, coagglutination, CIE and ELISA may also be used. Capsular typing is of medical importance as about 95 per cent of *H. influenzae* isolates from acute invasive infections such as meningitis belong to type b. Diagnostic kits for the identification of *H. influenzae* type b (Hib) are commercially available.

The type b capsular polysaccharide has a unique chemical structure, containing the pentose sugars ribose and ribitol instead of the hexoses and hexosamines as in the other five serotypes. The capsular polyribosyl ribitol phosphate (PRP) antigen of Hib induces IgG, IgM and IgA antibodies which are bactericidal, opsonic and protective. Hib PRP is therefore employed for immunisation. Hib capsular antigen shows cross reaction with the capsular antigens of some Gram positive and Gram negative bacteria.

H. influenzae strains lacking a capsule can not be typed and are called 'nontypable strains'. Next to Hib, the nontypable strains are the most relevant in clinical infections.

The outer membrane protein antigens show considerable variation. OMP antigens of Hib have been classified into at least 13 subtypes. *H. influenzae* lipooligosaccharides are antigenically complex. OMP and LOS subtyping may be of epidemiological value.

H. influenzae is the first freeliving organism whose complete genome has been sequenced.

Pathogenicity: *H. influenzae* is an exclusively human pathogen. It is not naturally pathogenic for animals but intraperitoneal inoculation of large doses is fatal in mice, guinea pigs and rabbits.

Diseases due to *H. influenzae* may be considered under two groups, invasive and noninvasive diseases. In the first group, the bacillus acts as a primary pathogen, causing acute invasive infections. The bacilli spread through blood, being protected from phagocytes by their capsule. Haemophilus meningitis is the most important infection in this group, others being laryngoepiglottitis, conjunctivitis, bacteremia, pneumonia, arthritis, endocarditis and pericarditis. These infections are usually seen in children and are caused by the capsulated strains, type b accounting for most cases. In the second group, the bacillus spreads by local invasion along mucosal surfaces and causes secondary or superadded infections, usually of the respiratory tract. These include otitis media, sinusitis and exacerbations of chronic bronchitis and bronchiectasis. These are usually seen in adults and are often caused by the noncapsulated strains.

Meningitis: This is the most serious disease produced by *H. influenzae* with case fatality rates up to 90 per cent in the untreated. The bacilli reach the meninges from the nasopharynx through the bloodstream. The disease is more common in children between two months and three years of age. This age incidence has been correlated with the absence of bactericidal anti-PRP antibodies. Older children develop immunity as a result of subclinical infection. It has been reported that in the tropics, non-type b strains may be responsible for meningitis more often than in the temperate zones.

Laryngoepiglottitis (croup): This is an acute inflammation of the epiglottis, with obstructive laryngitis, seen in children above two years. Untreated cases may be fatal within hours. Tracheostomy is often necessary to relieve respiratory obstruction caused by the grossly enlarged uvula. This condition is always associated with bacteremia and blood cultures are usually positive.

Pneumonia: Haemophilus pneumonia typically occurs in infants and is accompanied by empyema and sometimes meningitis as well. In older children and adults, the picture is of lobar pneumonia. While these are primary infections due to capsulated strains, bronchopneumonia may occur as a secondary infection with the noncapsulated strains. *H. influenzae* was a frequent cause of fatal pneumonia in the pandemic of influenza in 1918–19 but this association has not been found later.

Suppurative lesions: Suppurative lesions such as arthritis, endocarditis and pericarditis may result from hematogenous dissemination. Otitis media occurs by direct spread from the nasopharynx. Cellulitis, particularly in the buccal and periorbital areas is seen in young children.

Bronchitis: *H. influenzae* is an important pathogen associated with pneumococci in the acute exacerbations of chronic bronchitis and bronchiectasis.

Laboratory diagnosis: In meningitis, the presence in the CSF of pleomorphic, Gram negative bacilli that do not stain well should arouse suspicion of *H. influenzae* infection. Capsular polysaccharide antigen may be present in the CSF in meningitis and in urine in systemic infection. Its demonstration by latex particle agglutination or CIE is useful in diagnosis.

For isolation, CSF should be plated promptly on a suitable medium such as blood agar or chocolate agar and incubated in an environment of 5–10 per cent CO_2 and high humidity. (As the bacillus is very sensitive to low temperatures, specimens should never be refrigerated before inoculation.) A strain of staphylococcus should be streaked across the plate. After overnight incubation at 37 °C, small opaque colonies appear that show satellitism. Iridescence may be demonstrated on Levinthal's medium. Typing may be done if antisera are available.

Blood cultures are often positive in cases of laryngoepiglottitis and pneumonia. Cultures may be done in nutrient broth as the patient's blood affords sufficient enrichment.

Isolation from sputum requires special care. It has been demonstrated that very large variations in the rates of isolation occur when different parts of the sputum are sampled. Sputum should therefore be homogenised by treatment with pancreatin or by shaking with sterile water and glass beads for 15–30 minutes. Culturing several samples of sputum from the patient increases the rate of isolation.

Treatment: Cefotaxime or ceftazidime is the drug of choice for the treatment of haemophilus meningitis. Ampicillin and cotrimoxazole were popular for respiratory infection, but as plasmid borne resistance to these drugs is now common, amoxycillin-clavulanate or clarithromycin is more effective.

Epidemiology and prevention: There is considerable similarity between the epidemiology of *H. influenzae* and pneumococci. Both are indigenous to human beings, primarily parasitic in

Table 36.1 Growth characteristics of Haemophilus species

Species	Growth requirements			Hemolysis on horse blood agar
	X	V	CO_2	
H. influenzae	+	+	–	–
H. aegyptius	+	+	–	–
H. ducreyi	+	–	Variable	Variable
H. parainfluenzae	–	+	–	–
H. haemolyticus	+	+	–	+
H. parahaemolyticus	–	+	–	+
H. aphrophilus	+	–	+	–
H. paraphrophilus	–	+	+	–

the upper respiratory tract. Infection is transmitted by the respiratory route. Carriage in the upper respiratory tract is common particularly in young children but such strains are usually noncapsulated and not responsible for acute invasive infection.

Immunity is type specific. As the large majority of serious infections are caused by type b strains, active immunisation with Hib PRP vaccine is indicated. Purified PRP is immunogenic in older children and adults. However, in common with other polysaccharide antigens, PRP is poorly immunogenic in children below two years. Its immunogenicity can be improved by coupling with protein carriers like diphtheria and tetanus toxoids or meningococcus outer membrane protein. Such conjugate Hib PRP are available for use in young children.

Young household contacts of patients with systemic *H. influenzae* infection have increased risk of getting infected. Rifampicin given for four days prevents secondary infection in contacts and also eradicates carrier state.

HAEMOPHILUS AEGYPTIUS

(*Koch–Weeks bacillus,* formerly *H. aegypticus*)
Even before Pfeiffer described the 'influenza bacillus', Koch (1883) had observed a small bacillus in conjunctivitis cases in Egypt. It was first cultivated by Weeks (1887) in New York and came to be known as Koch–Weeks bacillus. Recent DNA studies have shown that the bacillus is identical with non-capsulated *H. influenzae*. Therefore, the former *H. aegypticus* has lost its separate species status and is now considered as a biotype of *h. influenzae*. It is worldwide in distribution and causes a highly contagious form of conjunctivitis ('pink eye'). It is especially common in the tropics and subtropics and may occur in epidemic forms. It responds to local sulphonamides or gentamicin.

It has also been identified as the causative agent of Brazilian purpuric fever (BPF), in which conjunctivitis proceeds to a fulminant septicemia in infants and children with high fatality. First recognised in Brazil in 1984, BPF is now endemic in South America.

HAEMOPHILUS DUCREYI

Ducrey (1890) demonstrated this bacillus in chancroid lesions and by inoculation into the skin on the forearm, was able to transmit the lesion through several generations.

Chancroid or soft sore is a venereal disease characterised by tender nonindurated irregular ulcers on the genitalia. This infection remains localised, spreading only to the regional lymph nodes which are enlarged and painful. Autoinoculation lesions may be produced by contact. There is no immunity following infection but a hypersensitivity results, which can be demonstrated by intradermal inoculation of killed bacilli.

H. ducreyi is a short, ovoid bacillus (1–1.5 μm × 0.6 mm) with a tendency to occur in end to end pairs or short chains. It is Gram negative but often may appear Gram positive and frequently shows bipolar staining. The bacilli may be arranged in small groups or whorls or in parallel chains giving a 'school of fish' or 'rail road track' appearance.

Primary isolation is difficult. It can be grown on fresh clotted rabbit blood. Smears made after 24–48 hours incubation show tangled chains of bacilli. It may also be grown on the chorioallantoic membrane of the chick embryo. On chocolate agar, enriched with isovitalex and fetal calf serum, and containing vancomycin as a selective agent, *H. ducreyi* forms small, grey translucent colonies after incubation at 35 °C under 10 per cent CO_2 and high humidity in 2–8 days.

The species is antigenically homogeneous and cultures may be identified by agglutination with the antiserum. Intradermal inoculation of the culture into rabbits produces a local ulcerative lesion.

H. ducreyi is susceptible to sulphonamides and many antibiotics. Cases resistant to sulphonamides and tetracyclines have been reported. Erythromycin, cotrimoxazole, ciprofloxacin or ceftriaxone may be used for treatment.

HAEMOPHILUS PARAINFLUENZAE

This differs from *H. influenzae* in requiring only the V factor and not the X factor. It is a commensal in the upper respiratory tract and has been reported to cause subacute bacterial endocarditis, urethritis and acute pharyngitis.

HAEMOPHILUS HAEMOLYTICUS

This actively hemolytic species occurs as a commensal in the upper respiratory tract. Colonies on blood agar may be mistaken for those of hemolytic streptococci. It requires both X and V factors, and is not pathogenic. Strains that do not require the X factor have been designated *H. parahaemolyticus*.

HAEMOPHILUS APHROPHILUS

It requires the X factor but not the V factor. Its name refers to its high CO_2 requirement for optimal growth. It has been reported to cause bacterial endocarditis, brain abscess, sinusitis, pneumonia and abscesses elsewhere. Similar strains requiring the V factor but not the X factor have been termed *H. paraphrophilus*.

HACEK GROUP BACTERIA

The acronym HACEK refers to a group of fastidious slow growing bacteria, normally resident in the mouth, which can sometimes cause severe infections, particularly endocarditis. The group includes *Haemophilus* species (*parainfluenzae, aphrophilus, paraphrophilus*), *Actinobacillus actinomycetemcomitans, Cardiobacterium hominis, Eikenella corrodens* and *Kingella kingae*. Blood cultures from HACEK patients take 7 to 30 days to become positive. Antibiotic sensitivity tests are essential for effective therapy as drug resistance is very common.

Further Reading

BPF Study group. 1987. Brazilian purpuric fever. *Lancet.* 2:757.

Farley MM et al. 1992. Invasive *H. influenzae* disease in adults, *Annals Int Med.* 116:806.

Jordan JZ and MPE. Slack 1995. *Haemophilus influenzae* then and now. *Eur J Clin Microbiol.* 14:935.

Katz SL and EA. Mortimer 1987. *Haemophilus influenzae* type b. The disease and its prevention. *Paediatr Infec Dis J* 6:773.

Murphy TF and MA. Apicella 1987. Nontypable *Haemophilus influenzae*. A review. *Rev Infect Dis* 9: 1.

Tree DL and SA. Morse 1995. Chancroid and *H. ducreyi. Clin Microbiol Rev.* 8:357.

37 Bordetella

The genus *Bordetella* is named after Jules Bordet, who along with Gengou identified the small ovoid bacillus causing whooping cough, in the sputum of children suffering from the disease (1900) and succeeded in cultivating it in a complex medium (1906). The bacillus is now known as *Bordetella pertussis* (*pertussis* meaning intense cough). A related bacillus, *Bord. parapertussis* was isolated from mild cases of whooping cough (1937). *Bord. bronchiseptica* originally isolated from dogs with broncho-pneumonia (1911) may occasionally infect human beings, producing a condition resembling pertussis. It has been suggested that *Bord. bronchiseptica* represents the ancestral form from which the other two species have evolved. The fourth member of the genus is *Bord. avium* which causes respiratory disease in turkeys.

BORDETELLA PERTUSSIS

(Bordet–Gengou bacillus;
formerly *Haemophilus pertussis*)

Morphology: *Bord. pertussis* is a small, ovoid coccobacillus (mean length 0.5 μm). In primary cultures, cells are of uniform size and shape but on subculture they may become longer and thread like. It is nonmotile and nonsporing. It is capsulated but tends to lose the capsule on repeated cultivation. The capsule can be demonstrated by special stains but does not swell in the presence of the antiserum. In culture films, the bacilli tend to be arranged in loose clumps, with clear spaces in between giving a 'thumb print' appearance. Freshly isolated strains of *Bord. pertussis* have fimbriae.

It is Gram negative. Bipolar metachromatic granules may be demonstrated on staining with toluidine blue.

Cultural characteristics: It is aerobic. No growth occurs anaerobically. It grows best at 35–36 °C.

Complex media are necessary for primary isolation. The medium in common use is the Bordet–Gengou glycerine-potato-blood agar. Blood is required not to provide additional nutritive factors but rather to neutralise inhibitory materials formed during bacterial growth. Charcoal or ion exchange resins incorporated in culture media may serve the same purpose. Charcoal blood agar is a useful medium. It does not grow on simple media like nutrient agar.

Growth is slow. After incubation for 48–72 hours, colonies on Bordet–Gengou medium are small, dome shaped, smooth, opaque, viscid, greyish white, refractile and glistening, resembling 'bisected pearls' or 'mercury drops'. Colonies are surrounded by a hazy zone of hemolysis. Confluent growth presents an 'aluminium paint' appearance.

Biochemical reactions: It is biochemically inactive. It does not ferment sugars, form indole, reduce nitrates, utilise citrate or split urea. It produces oxidase and usually catalase also.

Resistance: It is a delicate organism, being killed readily by heat (55 °C for 30 minutes), drying and disinfectants. But unlike *H. influenzae* it retains viability at low temperatures (0–4 °C).

Outside the body, *Bord. pertussis* in dried droplets is said to survive for five days on glass, three days on cloth and a few hours on paper.

Antigenic constituents and virulence factors: Several antigenic fractions and putative virulence factors have been described but their role in the pathogenesis of pertussis remains to be clarified. They include the following:

1.Agglutinogens: Bordetellae possess genus specific and species specific surface agglutinogens associated with the capsular K antigens or fimbriae. By agglutinin absorption tests, 14 agglutinating factors have been identified. Factor 7 is common to all three mammalian species of bordetellae. Factor 12 is specific for *Bord. bronchiseptica* and Factor 14 for *Bord. parapertussis*. Factors 1 to 6 are found only in strains of *Bord. pertussis*, all of which carry Factor 1 and one or more of the other factors. Bordetellae are classified into various types based on the agglutinogens they carry. As strains causing infections belong to types 1, 2 and 3, it is essential that pertussis vaccine strains should have factors 1, 2 and 3 . Factor specific antibodies are present in the sera of convalescent and immunised persons. Agglutinogens promote virulence by helping bacteria to attach to respiratory epithelial cells. They are useful in serotyping strains and in epidemiological studies.

2. Pertussis toxin (PT): This is present only in *Bord. pertussis.* It plays an important role in the pathogenesis of whooping cough. PT is expressed on the surface of the bacillus and secreted into the surrounding medium. The toxin exhibits diverse biological and biochemical activities, which formerly had been believed to be caused by different substances that had been named accordingly. Examples are the *lymphocytosis producing factor* or LPF causing profound lymphocytosis in pertussis patients as well as in experimental animals; and two effects seen only in experimental animals, but not in patients, such as the histamine *sensitising factor* or HSF responsible for heightened sensitivity to histamine in experimental animals, and the *islet activating protein* or IAP inducing excessive insulin secretion by the pancreatic islet cells. It is now known that all these are manifestations of the pertussis toxin. PT is a 117,000 molecular weight hexamer protein composed of six subunits with an A-B structure (the A portion being the enzymatically active moiety and B the binding component). It can be toxoided. PT toxoid is the major component of acellular pertussis vaccines. Antibody to PT can protect mice against intranasal, intraperitoneal or intracerebral challenge.

3. Filamentous hemagglutinin (FHA): This is one of the three hemagglutinins produced by *Bord. pertussis*, the others being PT and a lipid factor. Purified FHA appears as a filamentous structure in the electron microscope and hence the name. It is present on the bacillary surface and is readily shed. It adheres to the cilia of respiratory epithelium and to erythrocytes. Besides facilitating adhesion of *Bord. pertussis* to respiratory epithelium, FHA and PT hemagglutinins also promote secondary infection by coating other bacteria such as *Haemophilus influenzae* and pneumococci and assisting their binding to respiratory epithelium. This phenomenon has been termed *piracy of adhesins.*

Antibody to FHA can protect mice against aerosol challenge. FHA is used in acellular pertussis vaccines along with PT toxoid.

4. Adenylate cyclase (AC): All mammalian bordetellae but not *Bord. avium* produce adenylate cyclase. At least two types of AC are known, only one of which has the ability to enter target cells and act as a toxin. This is known as AC toxin (ACT). It acts by catalysing the production of cAMP by various types of cells.

5. Heat labile toxin (HLT): It is a cytoplasmic protein present in all bordetellae. It is inactivated in 30 minutes at 56 °C. It is dermonecrotic and lethal in mice. Its pathogenic role is not known.

6. Tracheal cytotoxin (TCT): It is a low molecular weight peptidoglycan produced by all bordetellae. It induces ciliary damage in hamster tracheal ring cultures and inhibition of DNA synthesis in epithelial cell cultures. Its role in disease is not known.

7. *Lipopolysaccharide (LPS) or the heat stable toxin* is present in all bordetellae and exhibits features of Gram negative bacterial endotoxins. It is present in the whole cell pertussis vaccine but is not considered to be a protective antigen.

8. *Pertactin:* Pertactin is an outer membrane protein (OMP) antigen present in all virulent strains of *B. pertussis.* Mice immunized with pertactin resist respiratory challenge with the bacillus. Antibody to pertactin can be seen in the blood of children after infection or immunization. Pertactin is included in acellular pertussis vaccines.

Variation: *Bord. pertussis* undergoes a smooth to rough variation. All fresh isolates are in the smooth form (Phase I). On subculture, they undergo progressive loss of surface antigens, and pass through phases II and III, finally becoming phase IV which is the rough, avirulent form.

A reversible change in the capsular antigen has been described as 'modulation'. The bacillus may occur in one of three potential 'modes', X, I and C, each of which has a characteristic surface antigen. X, I and C refer to the colour of the confluent colonies on the Bordet–Gengou medium – X for *Xanthic* (yellow), C for *cyanic* (blue) and I for *intermediate*. Modulation is influenced by the nature of the culture medium. On the Bordet–Gengou medium, fresh isolates always occur in the X mode.

Pathogenicity: *Bord. pertussis* is an obligate human parasite but infection can be produced experimentally in several species of animals, the white mouse being most often employed. Intranasal inoculation in mice induces a characteristic patchy interstitial pneumonia, histologically resembling the human disease. Intraperitoneal inoculation of large doses is fatal due to toxemia. Intracerebral inoculation causes a fatal infection. Immunised mice are protected. This forms the basis for the intracerebral mouse potency assay for pertussis vaccines.

In human beings, after an incubation period of about 1–2 weeks, the disease takes a protracted course comprising three stages – the catarrhal, paroxysmal and convalescent – each lasting approximately two weeks. The onset is insidious, with low grade fever, catarrhal symptoms and a dry irritating cough. Clinical diagnosis in the catarrhal stage is difficult. This is unfortunate as this is the stage at which the disease can be arrested by antibiotic treatment. This is also the stage of maximum infectivity. As the catarrhal stage advances to the paroxysmal stage, the cough increases in intensity and comes on in distinctive bouts. During the paroxysm, the patient is subjected to violent spasms of continuous coughing, followed by a long inrush of air into the almost empty lungs, with a characteristic whoop (hence the name). The paroxysmal stage is followed by convalescence, during which the frequency and severity of coughing gradually decrease.

The disease usually lasts 6–8 weeks though in some it may be very protracted. Complications may be 1) due to pressure effects during the violent bouts of coughing (subconjunctival hemorrhage, subcutaneous emphysema), 2) respiratory (broncho-pneumonia, lung collapse), or 3) neurological (convulsions, coma). Respiratory complications are self limited, the atelectasis resolving spontaneously but the neurological complications may result in permanent sequelae such as epilepsy, paralysis, retardation, blindness or deafness.

The infection is limited to the respiratory tract and the bacilli do not invade the bloodstream. In the initial stages, the bacilli are confined to the nasopharynx, trachea and bronchi. Clumps of bacilli may be seen enmeshed in the cilia of the respiratory epithelium. As the disease progresses, inflammation extends into the lungs, producing a diffuse bronchopneumonia with desquamation of the alveolar epithelium.

Blood changes in the disease are distinctive and helpful in diagnosis. A marked leucocytosis occurs, with relative lymphocytosis (total leucocytic counts 20,000–30,000 per mm^3 with 60–80 per cent lymphocytes). The erythrocyte sedimentation rate is not increased, except when secondary infection is present.

Epidemiology: Whooping cough is predominantly a pediatric disease, the incidence and mortality being highest in the first year of life. Maternal antibodies do not seem to give protection against the disease. Immunisation should, therefore, be started early. The disease is commoner in the female than in the male at all ages. It is worldwide in distribution. It occurs in epidemic form periodically but the disease is never absent from any community.

The source of infection is the patient in the early stage of the disease. Infection is transmitted by droplets and fomites contaminated with oropharyngeal secretions. Whooping cough is one of the most infectious of bacterial diseases and nonimmune contacts seldom escape the disease.

The secondary attack rates are highest in close household contacts. In adolescents and adults the disease is often atypical and may present as bronchitis. They may serve as a source of infection in infants and children. Chronic carriers are not known. Natural infection confers protection though it may not be permanent, and second attacks have been reported.

Bord. pertussis causes 95 per cent of whooping cough cases. About 5 per cent of the cases are caused by *Bord. parapertussis*. This is generally a milder disease and the incidence varies in different countries. Very infrequently whooping cough may be caused by *Bord. bronchiseptica*. A clinical syndrome resembling whooping cough (pseudo-whooping cough) may also be produced by some other respiratory pathogens, such as adenoviruses and *Mycoplasma pneumoniae*.

Laboratory diagnosis: The bacilli are present in the upper respiratory tract most abundantly in the early stage of the disease. They may be demonstrated by microscopy or more reliably by culture. In the paroxysmal stage, the bacilli are scanty and during convalescence they are not demonstrable. Antibodies develop late and help only in retrospective diagnosis.

Microscopic diagnosis depends on demonstration of the bacilli in respiratory secretions by the fluorescent antibody technique.

For culture, specimens may be collected by different methods.

1. The cough plate method: Here a culture plate is held about 10–15 cm in front of the patient's mouth during a bout of spontaneous or induced coughing so that droplets of respiratory exudates impinge directly on the medium. This has the advantage that specimens are directly inoculated at the bedside.

2. The postnasal (peroral) swab: Secretions from the posterior pharyngeal wall are collected with a cotton swab on a bent wire passed through the mouth. Salivary contamination should be avoided. A West's postnasal swab may be conveniently employed.

3. The pernasal swab: Here a swab on a flexible nichrome wire is passed along the floor of the nasal cavity and material collected from the pharyngeal wall. Nasopharyngeal aspirate collected through a soft catheter attached to a syringe is a better source. It can be used for PCR also.

Some fatty acids present in cotton may inhibit growth of the bacilli and so it is preferable to use dacron or calcium alginate swabs for specimen collection. The swabs are to be plated without delay, or transported in 0.25–0.5 ml casamino acid solution, at pH 7.2, in modified Stuart's medium or Mischulow's charcoal agar. The medium employed is the glycerine-potato-blood agar of Bordet and Gengou or one of its modifications. Incorporation of diamidine fluoride and penicillin (Lacey's DFP medium) makes it more selective. Plates are incubated in high humidity at 35–36 °C. Colonies appear in 48–72 hours. Identification is confirmed by microscopy and slide agglutination.

Immunofluorescence is useful in identifying the bacillus in direct smears of clinical specimens and of cultures. The differentiating features of bordetellae are listed in Table 37.1.

Serological diagnosis is not helpful. Rise in antibody titre may be demonstrated in paired serum samples by agglutination, gel precipitation or complement fixation tests. As antibodies appear late, the second sample of serum should be collected some weeks after the onset of the disease. Demonstration of specific secretory IgA antibody in nasopharyngeal secretions by ELISA has been proposed as a diagnostic method in culture negative cases.

Prophylaxis: Preventing the spread of infection by isolation of cases is seldom practicable, as infectivity is highest in the earliest stage of the disease when clinical diagnosis is not easy.

Specific immunisation with killed *Bord. pertussis* vaccine has been found very effective. It is of utmost importance to use a smooth phase I strain for vaccine production. The method of inactivation should be such that antigenic potency is unaffected. Detoxication with 0.2% merthiolate during several months' storage at 4 °C has been recommended as a satisfactory procedure. The alum absorbed vaccine produces better and more sustained protection and less reaction than the plain vaccines. Pertussis vaccine is usually administered in combination with diphtheria and tetanus toxoid (triple vaccine). Not only is this more convenient, but *Bord. pertussis* also acts as an adjuvant for the toxoids, producing better antibody response.

In view of the high incidence and severity of the disease in the newborn, it is advisable to start immunisation as early as possible. Three injections at intervals of 4–6 weeks are to be given before the age of six months, followed by a booster at the end of the first year of life.

Children under four years who are contacts of patients should receive a booster even if they had been previously immunised. They should also receive chemoprophylaxis with erythromycin. Nonimmunised contacts should receive erythromycin prophylaxis for ten days after contact with the patient has ceased. Pertussis vaccination may induce reactions ranging from local soreness and fever, to shock, convulsions and encephalopathy. Provocation poliomyelitis is a rare complication.

Factors contributing to toxicity or postvaccinal encephalopathy have not been defined. The latter complication is estimated to occur in one in 5–10

Table 37.1 Differentiating features of Bordetella species

	Bord. pertussis	Bord. parapertussis	Bord. bronchisepica	Bord. avium
Motility	−	−	+	+
Growth on nutrient agar	−	+	+	+
Growth on Bordet–Gengou medium (days)	3–6	1–2	1	1
Urease	−	+	+	−
Nitrate to nitrite	−	−	+	−
Citrate utilisation	−	V	+	V
Oxidase	+	−	+	+
Toxins:				
HLT and TCT	+	+	+	+
ACT	+	+	+	−
PT	+	−	−	−

V = Variable

million injections. Estimated neurological complications of natural disease have ranged from 1.5–14 per cent in hospitalised cases; a third of these recover, a third have sequelae and a third die or have severe defects.

If severe complications such as encephalopathy, seizures, shock or hyperpyrexia develop following the vaccine, subsequent doses of the vaccine are contraindicated. Routine pertussis vaccination is not advisable after the age of seven years as adverse reactions are likely and the risk of severe disease is low. Acellular vaccines containing the protective components of the pertussis bacillus (PT, FHA, agglutinogens 1, 2, 3), first developed in Japan, are now used in some other countries also as they cause far fewer reactions, particularly in older children. Both whole cell and acellular vaccines have a protection rate of about 90 per cent. With whole cell vaccines, the protection declines to 50 per cent in about five years and is absent after 12 years. The duration of protection with acellular vaccines is not known. Even fully immunised subjects may develop pertussis but the disease will be very mild in them.

Treatment: *Bord. pertussis* is susceptible to several antibiotics (except penicillin) but antimicrobial therapy is beneficial only if initiated within the first ten days of the disease. Erythromycin or one of the newer macrolides is the drug of choice. Chloramphenicol and cotrimoxazole are also useful.

BORDETELLA PARAPERTUSSIS

This is an infrequent cause of whooping cough. The disease is mild. The pertussis vaccine does not protect against *Bord. parapertussis* infection.

BORDETELLA BRONCHISEPTICA

(*Bord. bronchicanis*)

This is motile by peritrichate flagella. It is antigenically related to *Bord. pertussis* and *Brucella abortus*. It occurs naturally in the respiratory tract of several species of animals. It has been found to cause a very small proportion (0.1 per cent) of cases of whooping cough.

Further Reading

Cherry JD et al. 1988. Report of the task force on Pertussis. *Pediatr* 81:939.

Editorial. 1992. Pertussis: adults, infants and herds. *Lancet,* 339:526.

Friedman RL. 1988. Pertussis. The disease and new diagnostic methods. *Clin Microbiol Rev* 1:365.

Gustaffson L et al. 1996. A controlled trial of acellular pertussis vaccines. *New Engl J Med.* 333:349.

Pittman M. 1984. The concept of pertussis as a toxin mediated disease. *Pediatr Infect Dis.* 3:467.

Weiss AA and EL Hewlett 1986. Virulence factors of *Bordetella pertussis. Ann Rev Microbiol* 40:661.

Hewlett EL. 1997. Pertussis: Current concepts of pathogenesis. *Pediatric Infect Dis.* J 16:578

Brucella

The genus *Brucella* consists of very small, nonmotile, aerobic, Gram negative coccobacilli that grow poorly on ordinary media and have little or no fermentative powers. They are strict parasites of animals and may also infect humans.

Brucellosis is a zoonosis, primarily affecting goats, sheep, cattle, buffaloes, pigs and other animals and transmitted to humans by contact with infected animals or through their products. The human disease was recognised along the Mediterranean littoral from very early times and has been known under various names such as Mediterranean fever, Malta fever and undulant fever.

A British army doctor, David Bruce (1886) isolated a small microorganism from the spleen of fatal cases in Malta and transmitted the disease to monkeys experimentally. This was named *Brucella melitensis* (Brucella after *Bruce*, *melitensis* after *Melita*, the Roman name for Malta). A Maltese bacteriologist Zammit (1905) showed that *Br. melitensis* was transmitted to humans by goat's milk. Following this, the disease was eliminated from British soldiers by prohibiting them from using goat's milk and milk products, while the disease remained undiminished in the civilian population, which continued to use them. Bang (1897) described *Br. abortus*, the cause of contagious abortion in cattle. The third major species in the genus, *Br. suis* was isolated by Traum (1914) from pigs in the USA. These three species cause human *brucellosis*.

Other species causing animal infections include *Br. canis*, isolated from cases of canine abortion, *Br. ovis* from abortion in sheep and *Br. neotomae*

from desert wood rats. *Br. canis* may occasionally cause a mild human disease, but the other two are not pathogenic for humans.

Morphology: Brucellae are coccobacilli or short rods 0.5–0.7 µm × 0.6–1.5 µm in size, arranged singly or in short chains. The cells are so small that they may be mistaken for cocci, as was done by Bruce who called them *Micrococcus melitensis*. In older cultures, irregular forms appear. They are nonmotile, noncapsulated and nonsporing. They are Gram negative and nonacid fast. Bipolar staining is not uncommon.

Cultural characteristics: Brucellae are strict aerobes and do not grow anaerobically. *Br. abortus* is capnophilic, many strains requiring 5–10% CO_2 for growth. The optimum temperature is 37 °C (range 20–40 °C) and pH 6.6–7.4. They may grow on simple media, though growth is slow and scanty. Growth is improved by the addition of serum or liver extract. Liver infusion media were widely used for the cultivation of brucellae. The media employed currently are serum dextrose agar, serum potato infusion agar, trypticase soy agar, or tryptose agar. The addition of bacitracin, polymyxin and cycloheximide to the above media makes them selective.

In liquid media, growth is uniform, and a powdery or viscous deposit is formed in old cultures. On solid media, colonies are small, moist, translucent and glistening. Mucoid, smooth and rough types of colonies appear, associated with changes in antigenic structure and virulence.

Erythritol has a specially stimulating effect on the growth of brucellae.

Biochemical reactions: No carbohydrates are ordinarily fermented, though they possess oxidative capacity. Brucellae are catalase positive, oxidase positive (except for *Br. neotomae* and *Br. ovis* which are negative) and urease positive. Nitrates are reduced to nitrites. Citrate is not utilised. Indole is not produced and MR and VP tests are negative.

Resistance: Brucellae are destroyed by heat at 60 °C in 10 minutes and by 1% phenol in 15 minutes. They are killed by pasteurisation. They may survive in soil and manure for several weeks. They remain viable for 10 days in refrigerated milk, one month in ice cream, four months in butter and for varying periods in cheese depending on its pH. They may also survive for many weeks in meat. They are sensitive to direct sunlight and acid, and tend to die in buttermilk. *Br. melitensis* may remain alive for six days in urine, six weeks in dust and ten weeks in water.

Antigenic structure: The somatic antigens of brucellae contain two main antigenic determinants, A and M which are present in different amounts in the three major species. *Br. abortus* contains about 20 times A as M: *Br. melitensis* about 20 times M as A. *Br. suis* has an intermediate antigenic pattern. Absorption of the minor antigenic component from an antiserum will leave most of the major antibody component and such absorbed A and M monospecific sera are useful for species identification by the agglutination test. The species identification of brucella strains is not, however, so straightforward and strains are often seen that behave biochemically as abortus and serologically as melitensis and vice versa. Species and biotype identification depends on a variety of other factors besides antigenic structure (Table 38.1).

Antigenic cross-reactions exist between brucellae and *V. cholerae* and persons receiving the cholera vaccine may develop brucella agglutinins lasting for about three years. Antigenic cross-reactions also exist with *E. coli* 0:116; 0:157, Salmonella serotypes group N (0:30 antigen Kauffman and White), *Ps. maltophila, Y.* *enterocolitica* and *F. tularensis.* A superficial L antigen resembling Salmonella Vi antigen has been described.

Brucella bacteriophage: Several bacteriophages that lyse the Brucella strains have been isolated. All these phages are serologically similar. The Tblisi (Tb) phage has been designated as the reference phage and at RTD lyses only *Br. abortus. Br. suis* is lysed at 10,000 RTD, while *Br. melitensis* is not lysed at all.

Classification: Brucellae may be classified into different species, based on CO_2 requirements, H_2S production, sensitivity to dyes (basic fuchsin and thionin), agglutination by monospecific sera, phage lysis and oxidative metabolic tests with amino acids and carbohydrates. The three major species are *Br. melitensis, Br. abortus,* infecting primarily goats or sheep, cattle and swine, respectively. Many biotypes have been recognised in these species.

Br. suis strains that produce H_2S are known as 'American' strains and those that do not as 'Danish' strains.

Pathogenicity: All three major species of brucellae are pathogenic to human beings. *Br. melitensis* is the most pathogenic, *Br. abortus* and *Br. suis* of intermediate pathogenicity. The incubation period is usually about 10–30 days, but may sometimes be very prolonged. Human infection may be of three types:

1. latent infection with only serological but no clinical evidence;
2. acute or subacute brucellosis; and
3. chronic brucellosis.

Acute brucellosis is mostly due to *Br. melitensis.* (It is usually known as *undulant fever,* but this is misleading as only some cases show the undulant pattern.) It is associated with prolonged bacteremia and irregular fever. The symptomatology is varied, consisting of muscular and articular pains, asthmatic attacks, nocturnal drenching sweats, exhaustion, anorexia, constipation, nervous irritability and chills. The usual complications are articular, osseous, visceral or neurological.

Chronic brucellosis, which may be nonbacteremic, is a low grade infection with periodic exacerbations. The symptoms are generally related to a state of hypersensitivity in the patient, the common clinical manifestations being sweating, lassitude and joint pains, with minimal or no pyrexia. The illness lasts for years.

Brucellosis is primarily an intracellular pathogen affecting the reticuloendothelial system. Brucellae have a special predilection for intracellular growth and may be demonstrated inside phagocytic cells. This accounts for their refractoriness to chemotherapy and the coexistence of viable bacilli with high levels of circulating antibodies. Immunity in brucellosis is mainly cell mediated. Activated macrophages can kill the bacteria. This is probably the most important mechanism in recovery and immunity in brucellosis. Tissue reaction to brucella consists of granuloma formation with epithelial cells, giant cells, lymphocytes and plasma cells. Granulomas heal with fibrosis and sometimes get calcified.

The brucellae spread from the initial site of infection through lymphatic channels to the local lymph glands, in the cells of which they multiply. They then spill over into the bloodstream and are disseminated throughout the body. They have a predilection for the placenta, probably due to the presence in it of erythritol, which has a stimulating effect on brucellae in culture.

Table 38.1 Differential characteristics of Brucella species and biotypes

species	biotypes	Lysis by phage RTD	Lysis by phage RTD × 10^4	CO_2 requirement	H_2S production	Basic Fuchsin 1:50,000	Thionin 1:25,000	Thionin 1:50,000	Mono specific sera A	Mono specific sera M	Anti-rough serum	Most common host
Br. melitensis	1	–	–	–	–	+	–	+	–	+	–	sheep, goats
	2	–	–	–	–	+	–	+	+	+	–	
	3	–	–	–	–	+	–	+	+	+	–	
Br. abortus	1	+	+	±	+	+	–	–	+	–	–	Cattle
	2	+	+	+	+	–	–	–	+	–	–	
	3	+	+	±	+	+	+	+	+	–	–	
	4	+	+	±	+	+	–	–	–	+	–	
	5	+	+	–	–	+	–	+	+	–	–	
	6	+	+	–	±	+	–	+	+	–	–	
	9	+	+	±	+	+	–	+	+	–	–	
Br. suis	1	–	+	–	+	–	+	+	+	–	–	Pigs
	2	–	+	–	–	–	+	+	+	–	–	Pigs, hare
	3	–	+	–	+	+	+	+	+	–	–	Pigs
	4	–	+	–	–	+	+	+	+	+	–	Reindeer
Br. neotomae		–	+	–	+	–	–	–	+	–	–	Wood rat
Br. ovis		–	–	+	–	+	+	+	–	–	+	Sheep
Br. canis		–	–	–	–	–	+	+	–	–	+	Dogs

Of the laboratory animals, the guinea pig is the most susceptible. The Straus reaction can be elicited in male guinea pigs.

Epidemiology: Human brucellosis is acquired from animals, directly or indirectly. The animals that commonly act as sources of human infection are goats, sheep, cattle, buffaloles, and swine. In some parts of the world, infection may also come from dogs, reindeer, caribou, camels and yaks. The modes of infection are by ingestion, contact, inhalation or accidental inoculation. Person to person spread does not ordinarily occur, but very rarely transmission has been reported through the placenta, breast feeding and sex.

The most important vehicle of infection is raw milk. Milk products, meat from infected animals and raw vegetables or water supplies contaminated by the feces or urine of infected animals may also be responsible. Infection by contact occurs when brucellae in vaginal discharges, fetuses, placenta, urine, manure or carcasses enter through the skin, mucosa or conjunctiva. Contact infection is especially important as an occupational hazard in veterinarians, butchers, and animal handlers, and is particularly common during the calving season. Infection is transmitted by inhalation of dried material of animal origin such as dust from wool. Infection by inhalation is a serious risk in laboratory workers handling brucellae. Infection by accidental inoculation is not infrequent among veterinarians and laboratory workers.

Brucellae have a wide host range but exhibit a degree of host preference in natural infections – *Br. melitensis* predominantly in goats and sheep, *Br. abortus* in cattle and *Br. suis* in swine. Foci of infection with brucellae may occur also in wild animal populations independent of domesticated animals. Infection is transmitted among animals directly or through blood-sucking arthropods, particularly ticks.

Brucellosis is worldwide in distribution and is endemic in certain areas such as the Mediterranean countries. Human infections are caused by different

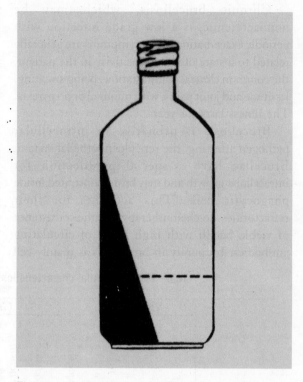

Fig. 38.1 Castaneda's method of blood culture

species of brucellae in different areas. In Great Britain, *Br. abortus* is the only species responsible for human infection, while in the swine rearing areas of the USA, most cases are due to *Br. suis*. Most human infections in various parts of India are due to *Br. melitensis* acquired from goats and sheep. In a serological survey of over 30,000 goats and sheep from Haryana, Mathur (1968) found evidence of infection in about 6.5 per cent of the animals. Of the 88 strains isolated from sheep and goats, 71 were *Br. melitensis* and 17 *Br. abortus*. Cows and buffaloes in rural areas were free from infection but those in organised farms were found infected. All the isolates from cattle were *Br. abortus*.

Laboratory diagnosis: The clinical manifestations of human brucellosis are variable, and only if a high index of suspicion is maintained will the disease be identified. Clinical diagnosis is almost impossible and laboratory aid is therefore essential.

Laboratory methods for diagnosis include culture, serology and hypersensitivity tests.

Blood culture is the most definitive method for the diagnosis of brucellosis. Blood is inoculated into a bottle of trypticase soy broth and incubated at 37 °C under 5–10% CO_2. As bacteria in blood are usually scanty, large volumes of blood (5 ml) should be inoculated. Subcultures are made on solid media every 3–5 days, beginning on the fourth day. Growth may often be delayed and cultures should not be declared negative in less than 6–8 weeks. BACTEC cultures may become positive in 5 to 6 days.

The Castaneda method of blood culture has several advantages and is recommended. Here, both liquid and solid media are available in the same bottle. The blood is inoculated into the broth and the bottle incubated in the upright position. For subculture, it is sufficient if the bottle is tilted so that the broth flows over the surface of the agar slant. It is again incubated in an upright position. Colonies appear on the slant. This method minimises materials and manipulation, reducing chances of contamination and risk of infection to laboratory workers.

Blood cultures are positive only in about 30–50 per cent of cases, even when repeated samples are tested. *Br. melitensis* and *Br. suis* are isolated more readily than *Br. abortus*. Bone marrow cultures yield a higher rate of isolation and remain positive long after the blood culture has become negative. Cultures may also be obtained from lymph nodes, cerebrospinal fluid, urine and abscesses, if present, and, on occasion, also from sputum, breast milk, vaginal discharges and seminal fluid.

As cultures are often unsuccessful, serological methods are important in diagnosis. Several serological tests have been developed, including agglutination, complement fixation and ELISA.

The standard agglutination test (SAT) is performed most often. This is a tube agglutination test in which equal volumes of serial dilutions of the patient's serum and the standardised antigen (a killed suspension of a standard strain of *Br. abortus*) are mixed and incubated at 37 °C for 24 hours or 50 °C for 18 hours. A titre of 160 or more is considered significant. Most patients with acute brucellosis develop titres of 640 or more by 3–4 weeks of illness. Titres tend to decline after the acute phase of the illness.

Several sources of error have to be guarded against. Sera often contain 'blocking' or 'nonagglutinating' antibodies. The blocking effect may sometimes be removed by prior heating of the serum at 55 °C for 30 minutes or by using 4% saline as the diluent for the test. The most reliable method for obviating the blocking effect and detecting the 'incomplete' antibodies is the antiglobulin (Coombs) test. As the prozone phenomenon to high titres (upto 1/640) is very frequent in brucellosis, it is essential that several serum dilutions be tested. A positive agglutination test may be produced by cholera, tularemia or yersinia infection, or immunisation. Cholera induced agglutinins may be differentiated by the agglutinin absorption test and also as they are removed by treatment with 2-mercapto-ethanol. In order that results from different laboratories are comparable, it is the practice to express agglutinin titres in International Units. This is done by using a standard reference serum for comparison.

In brucellosis, both IgM and IgG antibodies appear in 7–10 days after the onset of clinical infection. As the disease progresses, IgM antibodies decline, while the IgG antibodies persist or increase in titre. In chronic infections, IgM may often be absent and only IgG can be demonstrated. The agglutination test identifies mainly the IgM antibody, while both IgM and IgG fix complement. The IgG and IgA antibodies may act as 'blocking' or 'nonagglutinating' antibodies. It is thus evident that the agglutination test is usually positive in acute infection but may be only weakly positive or even negative in chronic cases. The results of the agglutination tests therefore have to be evaluated carefully. While a high titre of agglutinins, and especially demonstration of a rise in titre, can be taken as diagnostic, even a negative agglutination test may not exclude the possibility of brucellosis.

The complement fixation test is more useful in chronic cases as it detects IgG antibody also. ELISA is sensitive, specific and can detect IgM and IgG antibody separately. It is therefore useful for differentiation between the acute and chronic phases of brucellosis and also for screening large numbers of sera.

Delayed hypersensitivity type skin tests with brucella antigens ('brucellins') are not useful in diagnosing acute brucellosis. They parallel the tuberculin test in indicating only prior sensitisation with the antigens, and may remain positive for years. Brucellin testing may lead to a rise in titre of antibodies.

The methods used for the laboratory diagnosis of human brucellosis may also be employed for the diagnosis of animal infections. In addition, brucellae may be demonstrated microscopically in pathological specimens by suitable staining or by immunofluorescence. Several rapid methods have been employed for the detection of brucellosis in herds of cattle. These include the *rapid plate agglutination test* and the *Rose Bengal card test*. For the detection of infected animals in dairies, pooled milk samples may be tested for bacilli by culture and for antibodies by several techniques. In the *milk ring test* a sample of whole milk is mixed well with a drop of the stained brucella antigen (a concentrated suspension of killed *Br. abortus* stained with hematoxylin) and incubated in a water bath at 70 °C for 40–50 minutes. If antibodies are present in the milk, the bacilli are agglutinated and rise with the cream to form a blue ring at the top, leaving the milk unstained. If antibodies are absent, no coloured ring is formed and the milk remains uniformly blue. The whey agglutination test is another useful method for detecting the antibodies in milk.

Prophylaxis: As the majority of human infections are acquired by consumption of contaminated milk, prevention consists of checking brucellosis in dairy animals. In many advanced countries, this is achieved by the detection of infected animals, their elimination by slaughter and the development of certified brucella-free herds. Pasteurisation of milk is an additional safeguard.

Vaccines have been developed for use in animals. *Br. abortus* strain 19 vaccine is protective in cattle. No suitable vaccine is available for human use.

Treatment: The usual regimen is a combination of doxycycline for 45 days with streptomycin IM daily for the first 2 weeks in adults, and in children cotrimoxazole along with rifampicin or gentamycin.

Further Reading

Corbel MJ. 1997. Brucellosis, an overview. *Emerging Infect Dis.* 3:No. 2.

Corbel MJ. 1997. Vaccines against bacterial zoonoses. *J Med Microbiol* 46:267.

Expert Committee on Brucellosis. 1986. Sixth Report, Technical Report Series No. 740. Geneva:WHO.

Young EJ. 1995. An overview of human brucellosis. *Clin Infect Dis.* 21:283.

Mycobacterium I: Tuberculosis

Mycobacteria are slender rods that sometimes show branching filamentous forms resembling fungal mycelium. In liquid cultures they form a mold-like pellicle. Hence the name 'mycobacteria', meaning fungus-like bacteria. They do not stain readily, but once stained, resist decolourisation with dilute mineral acids. Mycobacteria are therefore called 'acid fast bacilli' or AFB. They are aerobic, nonmotile, noncapsulated and nonsporing. Growth is generally slow. The genus includes obligate parasites, opportunistic pathogens and saprophytes.

The first member of this genus to be identified was the lepra bacillus discovered by Hansen in 1868. Koch (1882) isolated the mammalian tubercle bacillus and proved its causative role in tuberculosis by satisfying Koch's postulates. Tuberculosis in humans was subsequently shown to be caused by two types of the bacillus—the human and bovine types, designated *Mycobacterium tuberculosis* and *M. bovis,* respectively. The term *M. tuberculosis* complex includes, besides the human and bovine types, two other mammalian types also: *M. africanum* causing human tuberculosis in tropical Africa and possessing properties intermediate between human and bovine types; and *M. microti* (the vole bacillus pathogenic for voles and other small mammals but not for humans).

The second human pathogenic mycobacterium is the lepra bacillus causing leprosy. Though this was the mycobacterium first described, it is the least understood because it has not been possible to convincingly culture it in vitro so far.

The third group of mycobacterium is a mixed group of isolates from diverse sources: from birds, cold blooded and warm blooded animals, from skin ulcers, and from soil, water and other environmental sources. They were initially called *atypical mycobateria* and broadly categorised into four categories: photochromogens, scotochromogens, non-photochromogens and rapid growers, based on their growth rates and pigmentation. They are opportunistic pathogens and can lead to many types of diseases; they are described in Chapter 40.

Saprophytic mycobacteria were isolated from a number of sources. These included *M. butyricum* from butter, *M. phlei* from grass, *M. stercoris* from dung and *M. smegmatis* from smegma. (Contrary to common belief, *M. smegmatis* is seldom found in smegma, though other rapidly growing mycobacteria occur frequently there, contaminating urine cultures).

MYCOBACTERIUM TUBERCULOSIS

Morphology: *M. tuberculosis* is a straight or slightly curved rod, about 3 µm x 0.3 µm, occurring singly, in pairs or as small clumps. The size depends on conditions of growth, and long filamentous, club shaped and branching forms may be sometimes seen. *M. bovis* is usually straighter, shorter and stouter.

Tubercle bacilli have been described as Gram positive, though strictly speaking this is not correct, as after staining with basic dyes they resist decolourisation by alcohol even without the mordanting effect of iodine. When stained with carbol fuchsin by the Ziehl–Neelsen method or by fluorescent dyes (auramine O, rhodamine), they resist decolourisation by 20 per cent sulphuric acid and absolute alcohol for 10 minutes (acid and alcohol fast). Acid fastness has been ascribed variously to the presence in the bacillus of an unsaponifiable wax (mycoloic acid) or to a semipermeable membrane around the cell. It is related to the integrity of the cell and appears to be a property of the lipid-rich waxy cell wall. Staining may be uniform or granular. Beaded or barred forms are frequently seen in *M. tuberculosis*, but *M. bovis* stains more uniformly.

Electron micrographs of thin sections show that the thick cell wall is composed of three layers enclosing a trilaminar plasma membrane. Spheroplasts are formed when grown in the presence of lysozyme. L-forms are also seen.

Cultural characteristics: The bacilli grow slowly, the generation time in vitro being 14–15 hours. Colonies appear in about two weeks and may sometimes take up to eight weeks. Optimum temperature is 37 °C and growth does not occur below 25 °C or above 40 °C. Optimum pH is 6.4–7.0. *M. tuberculosis* is an obligate aerobe, while *M. bovis* is microaerophilic on primary isolation, becoming aerobic on subculture. *M. tuberculosis* grows luxuriantly in culture as compared to *M. bovis* which grows sparsely. They are therefore termed *eugonic* and *dysgonic* respectively. The addition of 0.5% glycerol improves the growth of *M. tuberculosis*, but has no effect on or may even impair the growth of *M. bovis*. Sodium pyruvate helps the growth of both types. Human tubercle bacilli do not grow in presence of P-nitrobenzoic acid, unlike other slow growing nonchromogens.

Tubercle bacilli do not have exacting growth requirements but are highly susceptible even to traces of toxic substances like fatty acids in culture media. The toxicity is neutralised by serum albumin or charcoal. Koch originally grew the bacillus on heat coagulated bovine serum. Several media, both solid and liquid have been described for the cultivation of tubercle bacilli. The solid media contain egg (Lowenstein–Jensen, Petragnini, Dorset), blood (Tarshis), serum (Loeffler) or potato (Pawlowsky). The solid medium most widely employed for routine culture is Lowenstein–Jensen (LJ) medium without starch, as recommended by the International Union Against Tuberculosis (IUAT). This consists of coagulated hens' egg, mineral salt solution, asparagine and malachite green, the last acting as a selective agent inhibiting other bacteria. Among the several liquid media described, Dubos', Middlebrook's, Proskauer and Beck's, Sula's and Sauton's media are the more common. Liquid media are not generally employed for routine cultivation, but are used for sensitivity testing, chemical analyses and preparation of antigens and vaccines.

On solid media, *M. tuberculosis* forms dry, rough, raised, irregular colonies with a wrinkled surface. They are creamy white, becoming yellowish or buff coloured on further incubation. They are tenacious and not easily emulsified. *M. bovis* colonies, in comparison are flat, smooth, moist, white and break up easily when touched.

In liquid media without dispersing agents the growth begins at the bottom, creeps up the sides and forms a prominent surface pellicle which may extend along the sides above the medium. Diffuse growth is obtained in Dubos' medium containing Tween-80 (sorbitan monooleate). Virulent strains tend to form long serpentine cords in liquid media, while avirulent strains grow in a more dispersed manner. The cord factor itself is not a virulence factor as it is present in some avirulent strains as well.

Resistance: Mycobacteria are not specially heat resistant, being killed at 60 °C in 15–20 minutes. Survival is influenced by the material in which the bacteria are present. Cultures may be killed by exposure to direct sunlight for two hours, but bacilli in sputum may remain alive for 20–30 hours. Bacilli in droplet nuclei may retain viability for 8–10 days under suitable conditions. Cultures remain viable at room temperature for 6–8 months and may be stored for up to two years at −20 °C.

Tubercle bacilli are relatively resistant to chemical disinfectants, surviving exposure to 5%

phenol, 15% sulphuric acid, 3% nitric acid, 5% oxalic acid and 4% sodium hydroxide. They are sensitive to formaldehyde and gluteraldehyde. They are destroyed by tincture of iodine in five minutes and by 80% ethanol in 2–10 minutes. Ethanol is a suitable disinfectant for skin, gloves and clinical thermometers.

Biochemical reactions

Several biochemical tests have been described for the identification of mycobacterial species.

Niacin test: Human tubercle bacilli form niacin when grown on an egg medium. When 10% cyanogen bromide and 4% aniline in 96% ethanol are added to a suspension of the culture, a canary yellow colour indicates a positive reaction. The test is positive with human type and negative with bovine type of bacilli. The test is useful in identifying human strains as no other mycobacterium is positive, except for *M. simiae* and a few strains of *M. cheloneii*.

Aryl sulphatase test: This test is positive only with atypical mycobacteria. The bacilli are grown in a medium containing 0.001 M tripotassium phenolphthalein disulphate. 2 N. NaOH is added drop by drop to the culture. A pink colour indicates a positive reaction.

Neutral red test: Virulent strains of tubercle bacilli are able to bind neutral red in alkaline buffer solution, while avirulent strains are unable to do so.

Catalase–Peroxidase tests: These help in differentiating tubercle bacilli from atypical mycobacteria and provide an indication of the sensitivity of the strain to isoniazid. Most atypical mycobacterial strains are strongly catalase positive, while tubercle bacilli are only weakly positive in comparison. On the other hand, tubercle bacilli are peroxidase positive, but not atypical mycobacteria. Catalase and peroxidase activities are lost when tubercle bacilli become INH resistant. Catalase negative strains of tubercle bacilli are not virulent for guinea pigs.

A mixture of equal volumes of 30 vol. H_2O_2 and 0.2% catechol in distilled water is added to 5 ml of the test culture and allowed to stand for few minutes. Effervescence indicates catalase production and browning indicates peroxidase activity.

Amidase tests: The ability to split amides has been used to differentiate mycobacteria. A useful pattern is provided by testing five amides, viz., acetamide, benzamide, carbamide, nicotinamide and pyrazinamide. A 0.00165 M solution of the amide is incubated with the bacillary suspension at 37 °C and 0.1 ml of $MnSO_4.4 H_2O$, 1.0 ml of phenol solution and 0.5 ml of hypochlorite solution are added. The tubes are placed in boiling water for 20 minutes. A blue colour indicates a positive test.

Nitrate reduction test: This is positive with *M. tuberculosis* and negative with *M. bovis*.

Antigenic properties: Many antigens have been identified in mycobacteria. Group specificity is due to polysaccharide and type specificity to protein antigens. Following infection by tubercle bacilli, delayed hypersensitivty is developed to the bacillary protein (tuberculin). Tuberculins from human, bovine and murine bacilli appear to be indistinguishable. Some degree of antigenic relationship exists between tubercle bacilli and atypical mycobacteria, as shown by weak cross reactions in skin testing with different tuberculins. There is also some antigenic relationship between lepra and tubercle bacilli.

By various serological tests it has been established that *M. tuberculosis* strains are antigenically homogeneous and very similar to *M. bovis* and *M. microti*, but distinct from other species. Antibodies against polysaccharide, protein and phosphatide antigens of tubercle bacilli have been demonstrated in sera of patients, but they have not been found useful in diagnosis or relevant in immunity.

Bacteriophage: Many mycobacteriophages have been isolated from soil, water and other environmental sources as well as from lysogenic strains. Many mycobacteria infected with temperate phages are not truly lysogenic. Instead of being integrated with the bacterial chromosome, the phage genome appears free, like a plasmid. This is called *pseudolysogeny*.

Tubercle bacilli have been classified into four phage types—A, B, C, and a type intermediate between A and B, and therefore designated I (for 'intermediate'). Phage type A is the commonest and is present worldwide. Type B is common in Europe and N. America. Type C is seen rarely. Type I is common in India and neighbouring countries.

Phage 33 D isolated from an environmental mycobacterium lyses all variants of *M. tuberculosis*, but not BCG.

Bacteriocins: *M. tuberculosis* is divisible into two types by means of bacteriocins produced by rapidly growing mycobacteria.

Molecular typing: DNA fingerprinting provides a method for differentiating between strains of tubercle bacilli. Restriction endonulease treatment yields nucleic acid fragments of varying lengths, the patterns of which are strain specific. This 'restriction fragment length polymorphism' (RFLP) enables strain typing for epidemiological purposes. Fingerprinting can also be done with a chromosomal insertion sequence, IS 6110, which is present in most strains of tubercle bacilli.

As the entire genome of tubercle bacillus has been sequenced, more molecular typing methods may become available.

Host range: *M. tuberculosis* causes natural infection in humans, other primates, dogs and some other animals which have close contact with humans. Experimentally it is highly infectious for guinea pigs and hamsters, but virtually nonpathogenic for rabbits, cats, goats, bovines and fowl. Mice are moderately susceptible and develop progressive infection following intraperitoneal, intravenous or intracerebral inoculation. Variation in virulence among strains is frequent. Isolates from cutaneous and urogenital tuberculosis are often of low virulence for experimental animals.

M. bovis is more pathogenic for animals. It produces tuberculosis in cattle, humans, other primates, carnivores including dogs and cats, badgers, swine, parrots and some birds of prey. Experimentally it is highly pathogenic for guinea pigs and calves, moderately pathogenic for dogs, cats, horses and rats, and nonpathogenic for fowl. BCG, the tuberculous vaccine, is an attenuated strain of *M bovis*.

Strains of tubercle bacilli isolated from parts of Africa, that show properties intermediate between human and bovine types have been called 'African strains' or *M. africanum*. The name *'Asian type'* has been given to strains of tubercle bacilli originally isolated from south India, which are of low virulence for guinea pigs, susceptible to hydrogen peroxide, isoniazid sensitive and usually of phage type I. Such strains have also been isolated from some other Asian countries and from Asian expatriates abroad. Though species names are sometimes used for different varieties of tubercle bacilli infecting humans, they are not considered independent entities, but only variants of the *M. tuberculosis* complex.

M. microti is a natural pathogen of voles. It does not cause natural infection in humans, but can cause ulcers after experimental infection. Because it is antigenically identical with human tubercle bacilli, it was tried as a substitute for BCG for human vaccination. It was given up because of serious local reactions.

Pathogenesis: The source of infection is usually an open case of pulmonary tuberculosis. It is estimated that an open case of tuberculosis in India may infect on an average some 25 contacts before death or cure. Other forms of tuberculosis are of much less importance in public health. The mode of infection is by direct inhalation of aerosolised bacilli contained in droplet nuclei of expectorated sputum. Coughing, sneezing and speaking release numerous droplets—as many as 3000 infectious nuclei per cough. Dried bacilli in dust are much less infectious. Spread occurs most often among household or other close and prolonged contacts of open cases, whose sputum may have over 10,000 bacilli per ml. Infection also occurs infrequently by ingestion, for example, through infected milk, and rarely by inoculation.

The majority of inhaled bacilli are arrested by the natural defenses of the upper respiratory tract. Bacilli reaching the lungs are ingested by the alveolar macrophages. Several factors – the number and virulence of the infecting bacilli, and host factors including genetic susceptibility, age, immuno competence, stress, nutrition and coexisting illness – influence the outcome of the infection.

Tubercle bacilli do not contain or secrete a toxin. The exact basis of their virulence is not understood, but seems to be related to their ability to survive and multiply in macrophages. Various components of the bacillus have been shown to possess different biological activities which may influence the pathogenesis, allergy and immunity in the infection. Humans are evidently able to mount an effective defence against the infection as only about a tenth of the infected develop active tuberculosis. The only specific immune mechanism effective is the cell mediated type. Humoral immunity appears to be irrelevant. The key cell is the activated CD4+ helper T cell which can develop along two different paths—the Th-1 or Th-2 cells, releasing cytokines such as interferon γ (gamma) interleukins 1 and 2, toxic necrosis factor α (alpha) and others exerting different biological effects. Th-1 dependent cytokines activate macrophages resulting in protective immunity and containment of the infection. Th-2 cytokines induce delayed type hypersensitivity (DTH), tissue destruction and progressive disease.

The essential pathology in tuberculosis is the production in infected tissues of a characteristic lesion, the *tubercle*. This is an avascular granuloma composed of a central zone containing giant cells, with or without caseation, and a peripheral zone of lymphocytes and fibroblasts. Tuberculous lesions are primarily of two types—exudative and productive. The exudative type is an acute inflammatory reaction with accumulation of edema fluid, polymorphonuclear leucocytes, and later of lymphocytes and mononuclear cells. This is typically seen when the bacilli are many and virulent and the host response is more in the nature of DTH than of protective immunity. The productive type of lesion is predominantly cellular, associated more with protective immunity than DTH.

Depending on the time of infection and the type of response, tuberculosis may be classified as 'primary' and 'post-primary'.

Primary tuberculosis is the initial infection by tubercle bacilli in a host. In endemic countries like India this usually occurs in young children. In them the bacilli engulfed by alveolar macrophages multiply and give rise to a subpleural focus of tuberculous pneumonia, commonly located in the lower lobe or the lower part of the upper lobe (Ghon focus). The hilar lymph nodes are involved. The Ghon focus together with the enlarged hilar lymph node constitutes the 'primary complex'. This occurs about 3–8 weeks from the time of infection and is associated with the development of tuberculin hypersensitivity. In the majority of cases the lesion heals spontaneously in 2–6 months leaving behind a calcified nodule. However, a few bacilli may survive in the healed lesion and remain latent. In a few, particularly in children with impaired immunity or other risk factors, the primary lesion may enlarge and cause miliary, meningeal or other forms of disseminated tuberculosis.

The post-primary (secondary or adult) type of tuberculosis is due to reactivation of latent infection (post-primary progression, endogenous reactivation) or exogenous reinfection and differs from the primary type in many respects. It affects mainly the upper lobes of the lungs, the lesions undergoing necrosis and tissue destruction, leading to cavitation. Lymph node involvement is unusual. The necrotic materials break out into the airways, leading to expectoration of bacteria-laden sputum, which is the main source of infection to contacts. In the immunodeficient, cavity formation is unusual.

Instead there is widespread dissemination of lesions in the lungs and other organs.

Epidemiology: Tuberculosis is an ancient disease. Evidence of spinal tuberculosis is present in some Egyptian mummies. Tubercle bacillus DNA has been detected by molecular analysis in a mummy dated circa 1550–1080 BC. Tuberculosis has been for many centuries the most important of human infections, in its global prevalence, devastating morbidity and massive mortality. It has been called the 'white plague' and 'the captain of all the men of death'.

It is estimated that a third of the world's population, about two billion people are infected with tubercle bacilli. Every year between eight and nine million new cases of tuberculosis appear and three million persons die from the disease. The large majority of the cases and deaths are from the poor nations. India is one of the worst affected countries. More than 40 per cent of the population are infected and some 15 million suffer from tuberculosis in the country, of whom over three million are highly infectious open cases. Half a million people die from the disease every year in India—one every minute.

Poverty and tuberculosis go together. With improvements in standards of living, tuberculosis had declined rapidly in the affluent nations, though it continued unabated in the poor countries. But with the progress of the AIDS pandemic, tuberculosis became a problem for the rich nations also, with cases and even outbreaks among the HIV infected. A close relationship has emerged between tuberculosis and HIV. Not only does HIV infection reactivate a latent tuberculosis infection, but it also makes the disease more serious and renders treatment ineffective. Tuberculosis in turn may hasten the development of HIV infection into active disease. A third complication that has made the situation more grave is the emergence and spread of multiple drug resistance among tubercle bacilli. So serious is the global threat of tuberculosis combined with multidrug resistance and concomitant HIV infection that the World Health Organization in 1993 took the unprecedented step of declaring this disease a global emergency.

Human infection with *M. bovis* used to be common worldwide. In many advanced countries, as in the UK it has been almost eliminated by regular tuberculin testing of herds and slaughter of affected cattle. The infection spreads between animals through aerosolised bacilli in moist cough sprays. A few infected cows shed the bacilli in milk, which is infectious in humans when consumed raw. The primary infection, mostly in children would occur in the cervical and mesenteric lymph nodes, from where it could spread to bone and joints and other extrapulmonary sites. Human infection with *M. bovis* could be prevented by drinking only pasteurised or heated milk. Person-to-person transmission of of *M. bovis* is very rare.

Laboratory diagnosis: Laboratory diagnosis of tuberculosis may be established by demonstrating the bacillus in the lesion by microscopy, isolating it in culture or by transmitting the infection to experimental animals. Demonstration of hypersensitivity to tuberculoprotein may be helpful in some cases. Molecular diagnostic methods have also been introduced.

PULMONARY TUBERCULOSIS

The specimen tested is the sputum. Bacillary shedding in sputum is abundant in cases with caseation, but relatively scanty in organised lesions that do not communicate with airways. Sputum is best collected in the morning before any meal. If sputum is scanty, a 24-hour sample may be tested. Sputum sampling on three days increases chances of detection. Where sputum is not available, laryngeal swabs or bronchial washings may be collected. In small children who tend to swallow the sputum, gastric lavage can be examined.

Microscopy: Direct or concentration smears of sputum are examined. Sputum microscopy is the most reliable single method in diagnosis and control of tuberculosis. New slides should be used for smears and they should not be reused, as acid fast bacilli may not always be removed from slides by cleaning. Smears should be prepared from the thick purulent part of the sputum. Smears are dried, heat fixed and stained by the Ziehl–Neelsen technique. The smear is covered with strong carbol fuchsin and gently heated to steaming for 5–7 minutes, without letting the stain boil and become dry. The slide is then washed with water and decolourised with 20% sulphuric acid till no more stain comes off and then with 95% ethanol for two minutes. Decolourisation may be carried out as a single step with acid alcohol (3% HCl in 95% ethanol). After washing, the smear is counterstained with Loeffler's methylene blue, 1% picric acid or 0.2% malachite green for one minute. Under the oil immersion objective, acid fast bacilli are seen as bright red rods while the background is blue, yellow or green depending on the counterstain used. At least 10,000 acid fast bacilli should be present per ml of sputum for them to be readily demonstrable in direct smears. A negative report should not be given till at least 300 fields have been examined, taking about 10 minutes. A positive report can be given only if two or more typical bacilli have been seen. Smears are graded depending on the number of bacilli seen: (Table 39.1)

When several smears are to be examined daily, it is more convenient to use fluorescent microscopy. Smears are stained with auramine phenol or auramine rhodamine fluorescent dyes and when examined under ultraviolet illumination, the bacilli will appear as bright rods against a dark background. Because of the contrast, the bacilli can be seen even under the high dry objective, enabling large areas of the smear to be screened rapidly.

Microscopic demonstration of acid fast bacilli provides only presumptive evidence of tuberculous infection, as even saprophytic mycobacteria may present a similar appearance. However most saprophytic species stain uniformly without appearing barred or beaded and are usually only acid fast without being alcohol fast. As saprophytic mycobacteria may be present in tap water, rubber tubes, cork or bark, they can get into clinical materials unless scrupulous care is taken in their collection. Saprophytic bacilli are not ordinarily present in respiratory secretions, but they may be a problem with gastric aspirates, feces and urogenital specimens.

Concentration methods: Several methods have been described for the homogenisation and concentration of sputum and other specimens. They can be classified as methods useful for microscopy only and those useful for culture and animal inoculation as well. To the former group belong treatment with antiformin, sodium carbonate or hypochlorite, detergents like tergitol, flotation methods using hydrocarbons, and the autoclave method. These methods kill the bacilli without altering their morphology or staining reaction. Concentration methods that do not kill the bacilli and so can be used for culture and animal inoculation include the following:

Petroff's method: This simple method is widely used. Sputum is incubated with an equal volume of 4% sodium hydroxide solution at 37 °C with frequent shaking till it becomes clear, on an average for 20 minutes. It is then centrifuged at 3000 rpm for 20 minutes and the sediment neutralised with N/10 HCl and used for smear, culture and animal inoculation. Excessive exposure to alkali is deleterious and should be avoided.

Table 39.1 ZN smear evaluation and AFB report

No. of AFB	Seen in (oil immersion field)	Report
0	300 F	AFB not seen
1 – 2	300 F	Doubtful, repeat smear
1 – 9	100 F	1 +
1 – 9	10F	2 +
1 – 9	1F	3 +
10 or more	1F	4 +

NB: F-oil immersion field

A simpler method has been described eliminating centrifugation and neutralisation. Sputum is treated with an approximately equal volume of a sterile solution containing 20 g cetrimonium bromide and 40 g of NaOH per litre of distilled water. The contents are mixed with a cotton swab and let stand for five minutes. About 0.2 ml of the inoculum is smeared firmly with the swab over the entire surface of acid buffered medium (IUAT-LJ medium with 20.5 g KH_2PO_4 per litre). The same swab is used for inoculating a second slope after stirring the contents again. The results are as good as with Petroff's method.

Instead of alkali, homogenisation can be achieved by treatment with dilute acids (6% sulphuric acid, 3% hydrochloric acid or 5% oxalic acid), N acetyl cysteine with NaOH, pancreatin, desogen, zephiran and cetrimide. Flocculation methods have also been described.

Culture: Culture is a very sensitive diagnostic technique for tubercle bacilli, detecting as few as 10 to 100 bacilli per ml. The concentrated material is inoculated onto at least two bottles of IUAT-LJ medium. If the specimen is positive by microscopy, a direct drug sensitivity test may also be set up. Cultures are examined for growth after incubation at 37 °C for four days (for rapid growing mycobacteria, fungi and contaminant bacteria) and at least twice weekly thereafter. A negative report is given if no growth occurs after 8–12 weeks. Any growth seen is smeared and tested by ZN staining. For routine purposes, a slow growing, nonpigmented, niacin positive acid fast bacillus is taken as *M. tuberculosis*. Confirmation is by detailed biochemical studies. When the isolate is niacin negative, a battery of tests may be needed for identification, including growth at 25 °C and 45 °C, animal pathogenicity and biochemical tests (Tables 39.2, 39.3).

The use of liquid media with radiometric growth detection (such as BACTEC-460) and the identification of isolates by nucleic acid probes have simplified culture methods greatly and enabled results to be given in 2–3 weeks. But these are available only in advanced laboratories.

Sensitivity tests: As drug resistance is an important problem in tuberculosis, it is desirable to have sensitivity of isolates tested as an aid to treatment. Sensitivity tests for tubercle bacilli are mainly of three types. The first is the absolute concentration method in which a number of media containing serial concentrations of the drugs are inoculated and the minimum inhibitory concentrations calculated. The second is the resistance ratio method in which two sets of media containing graded concentrations of the drugs are inoculated, one set with the test strain and the other with a standard strain of known sensitivity. The third is the proportion method which indicates the average sensitivity of the strain, taking into account the fact that any population will contain cells with varying degrees of sensitivity to a drug.

Animal inoculation: The concentrated material is inoculated intramuscularly into the thigh of two healthy guinea pigs about 12 weeks old. Subcutaneous inoculation is not recommended as it leads to a local ulcer which may be infectious. The animals are weighed before inoculation and at intervals thereafter. Progressive loss of weight is an indication of infection. Infected animals show a positive tuberculin skin reaction. One animal is killed after four weeks and autopsied. If it shows no evidence of tuberculosis, the other is autopsied after eight weeks.

At autopsy a positive animal will show a caseous lesion at the site of inoculation. Sometimes the local lesion may contain pus under tension, which may spurt on incision. The draining and internal lymph nodes are enlarged and caseous. The spleen is enlarged, with irregular necrotic areas. Tubercles are seen in the peritoneum and sometimes in the lung, but the kidneys are unaffected. The autopsy lesions have to be confirmed as tuberculous by acid fast staining of smears, to exclude *Y. pseudotuberculosis* and other bacterial infections which may resemble

Table 39.2 : Identification of tubercle bacilli and related mycobacteria

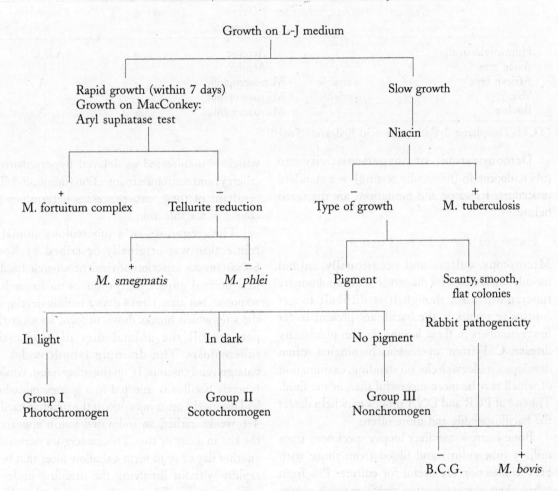

the lesions of tuberculosis, but will be smear negative.

Guinea pig inoculation, once so commonly used, is now seldom resorted to because it is cumbersome, costly and less sensitive than culture, particularly with catalase negative, INH resistant strains isolated from south India.

Nucleic acid technology: Polymerase chain reaction (PCR) and ligase chain reaction (LCR) are used as diagnostic techniques. Transcription mediated amplification, targeting ribosomal RNA has been introduced as an improvement on PCR

based DNA amplification. The use of RFLP and IS fingerprinting for epidemiological typing of strains has been referred to. Demonstration of mutation in specific drug sensitivity genes is a useful indicator of drug resistance. Such tests for rifampicin resistance are already available.

Immunodiagnosis: Serological tests are not useful in diagnosis, though antibodies to many bacillary antigens have been demonstrated in the sera of patients. Detection of antibody to mycobacterial lipo-arabinomannan has been reported to be of some value.

Table 39.3

Type	Niacin	Nitrate reduction	Oxygen Preference	Growth in TCH*	Phage type
Human(classical)	+	+	Aerobic	+	A.B.C
Asian type	+	+	Aerobic	-	I
African type	+/-	variable	Microaerophilic	-	A
Vole	+/-	variable	Microaerophilic	-	?
Bovine	-	-	Microaerophilic	-	A

*TCH=Thiophene-2-Carboxylic acid hydrazide(5mg/l)

Demonstration of hypersensitivity to tuberculoprotein (tuberculin testing) is a standard procedure. Its scope and limitations are discussed below.

Extrapulmonary Tuberculosis

Microscopy, culture and occasionally animal inoculation are used for diagnosis of extrapulmonary tuberculosis also, though it is difficult to get conclusive results as the bacilli are present in far fewer numbers in these lesions than in pulmonary disease. CSF from tuberculous meningitis often develops a spider web clot on standing, examination of which may be more successful than of the fluid. The use of PCR and DNA probes may help detect the bacilli speedily and more often.

Bone marrow and liver biopsy specimens from miliary tuberculosis and blood from those with HIV coinfection are useful for culture. Pus from tuberculous abscesses often yields positive results in smear and culture.

Pleural effusion and other exudates may be collected with citrate to prevent coagulation. If free from other bacteria, they may be used for culture after centrifugation. If other bacteria are present, prior concentration is necessary.

Urinary excretion of bacilli in renal tuberculosis is intermittent. Hence it is advisable to test 3–6 morning samples of urine. Each sample is centrifuged for 3000 rpm for 30 minutes and the sediment used for culture after concentration.

Allergy and immunity: Infection with tubercle bacillus induces cell mediated immunity which is manifested as delayed hypersensitivity (allergy) and resistance to infection (immunity). The resultant of these two processes determines the course of the infection.

The response of a tuberculous animal to reinfection was originally described by Koch. Subcutaneous injection of virulent tubercle bacillus in a normal guinea pig produces no immediate response, but after 10–14 days a nodule develops at the site, which breaks down to form an ulcer that persists till the animal dies of progressive tuberculosis. The draining lymph nodes are enlarged and caseous. If on the other hand, virulent tubercle bacillus is injected in a guinea pig which had received a prior injection of the tubercle bacillus 4–6 weeks earlier, an indurated lesion appears at the site in a day or two. This undergoes necrosis in another day or so to form a shallow ulcer that heals rapidly without involving the draining nodes or other tissues. This is known as the *Koch phenomenon* and is a combination of hypersensitivity and immunity. The Koch phenomenon has three components—a 'local' reaction, a 'focal' response manifested as congestion and even hemorrhage around the tuberculous foci in tissues, and a 'constitutional' or 'systemic' response of fever which may sometimes be fatal.

Allergy can be induced by infection with virulent as well as avirulent tubercle bacilli, but not ordinarily by injection of killed bacilli or bacterial proteins. However, for demonstrating allergy, live or killed bacilli or tuberculoprotein can be employed.

Allergic tests: Koch prepared a protein extract of tubercle bacillus by concentrating tenfold by evaporation, a 6–8 week culture filtrate of the bacillus grown in 5% glycerol broth. This was called 'original' or 'old tuberculin' (OT). Initially Koch employed OT in the treatment of tuberculosis but it was soon given up as it was not only of no benefit but also caused serious reactions in some due to the focal and systemic components of the Koch phenomenon.

OT was first used for allergic (tuberculin) testing by von Pirquet (1906). However, as OT was a crude product and batches tended to vary in purity and potency, it was replaced by a partially purified protein antigen introduced by Seibert. This is known as the *purified protein derivative* (PPD). One large batch of PPD made by Seibert in 1939 (PPD-S) was recognised by the WHO as the international standard PPD-tuberculin and arbitrarily designated to contain 50,000 tuberculin units (TU) per mg, 1 TU equal to 0.01 ml of OT or 0.00002 mg of PPD-S. More highly purified preparations of PPD have since been developed.

Many methods had been described for tuberculin testing. The method used routinely is the technique of Mantoux (1910). In the Mantoux test, 0.1 ml of PPD containing 5 TU is injected intradermally on the flexor aspect of the forearm with a tuberculin syringe raising a wheal. It is essential that the injection be given between the layers of the skin and not subcutaneously. The site is examined 48–72 hours later and induration measured at its widest point transversely to the long axis of the forearm. Erythema is not taken into account. Induration of diameter 10 mm or more is considered positive, 5 mm or less negative and 6–9 mm equivocal. A PPD dose of 1 TU is used when extreme hypersensitivity is suspected; and doses of 10 or 100 when 5 TU test is negative.

Multiple puncture testing, as in the Heaf test, is satisfactory for screening and surveys, but not accurate enough as a diagnostic test. The Heaf gun has to be sterilised between tests to prevent cross infection. Disposable prongs carrying dried PPD (Tine test) are also available for individual testing.

A positive tuberculin test indicates hypersensitivity to tuberculoprotein denoting infection with tubercle bacillus or BCG immunisation, recent or past, with or without clinical disease. The test becomes positive 4–6 weeks after infection or immunisation. Tuberculin allergy wanes gradually and disappears after 4–5 years in the absence of subsequent contact with the bacillus. In endemic areas the allergy is maintained by repeated contacts with the bacillus.

Persons who have never had contact with tubercle bacilli are tuberculin negative. False negative tests (anergy) may be seen in certain situations like miliary tuberculosis, convalescence from some viral infections like measles, lymphoreticular malignancy, sarcoidosis, severe malnutrition, immunosuppressive therapy or impaired cell mediated immunity. False negative results may also be due to inactive PPD preparations and improper injection technique. False positive reactions may be seen in infections with some related mycobacteria ('atypical' mycobacteria).

Repeated tuberculin testing will not cause a positive reaction in a noninfected person, but may enhance the intensity of response in reactive individuals. This booster effect is useful in persons showing a negative or equivocal test due to waning allergy, in whom retesting after a week may induce a positive response ('two step testing'). Retesting is to be done at a site different from the earlier one.

Tuberculin testing may be used as an aid in diagnosing active infection in infants and young children, to measure prevalence of infection in an area, to select susceptibles or as an indication of successful vaccination. Tuberculin testing of cattle has been of great value in the control of bovine tuberculosis.

Prophylaxis: In the prevention of tuberculosis general measures such as adequate nutrition, good housing and health education are as important as specific antibacterial measures. The latter consist of early detection and treatment of cases, chemoprophylaxis and immunoprophylaxis.

Immunoprophylaxis is by intradermal injection of the live attenuated vaccine developed by Calmette and Guerin (1921), the Bacille Calmette Guerin or BCG. This is a strain of *M. bovis* attenuated by 239 serial subcultures in a glycerine-bile-potato medium over a period of 13 years. Injection of BCG in animals induces self limited infection, with multiplication and dissemination of the bacillus in different organs and production of small tubercles. Within a few weeks the bacilli stop multiplying although they survive in the tissues for long periods. This gives rise to delayed hypersensitivity and immunity. Following BCG vaccination, a tuberculin negative recipient is converted to a positive reactor. The immunity may last for 10–15 years and is similar to the immunity following natural infection, except that it does not carry any risk of disease due to reactivation, as in the latter case.

Several field trials have been conducted to assess the efficacy of the BCG vaccine. The results have varied widely, from 80 per cent protection to a total absence of protection. In south India, a trial conducted at Madanapalle showed 60 per cent efficacy while a later large trial in Chingalpattu did not reveal any protection in adults, though a 15-year follow up showed some protection in young persons. The reasons for such wide disparity are not clear but have been attributed to several factors such as the differences in the prevalence and virulence of tubercle bacilli in various communities, the type and potency of vaccines used and the presence of 'atypical mycobacteria' in the areas.

The BCG vaccine aroused much criticism and it has been suggested that it may regain its virulence, though there has not been any evidence of it so far. The Lubeck disaster in which several children developed fatal tuberculosis following oral immunisation earned the vaccine much notoriety in the early days of the vaccine. This was due to a mix-up by which live virulent tubercle was given instead of BCG. Stringent safety measures have

since been enforced in the manufacture of BCG vaccine. The recognised complications of BCG vaccine are the following:

Local: Abscess, indolent ulcer, keloid, tuberculides, confluent lesions, lupoid lesions, lupus vulgaris.

Regional: Enlargement and suppuration of draining lymph nodes.

General: Fever, mediastinal adenitis, erythema nodosum, tendency to keloid formation after wounding at other sites, and very rarely nonfatal meningitis. The very few cases of progressive tuberculosis reported are believed to have been in immunodeficient subjects.

The consensus opinion is that BCG may not protect from the risk of tuberculosis infection, but gives protection to infants and young children against the more serious types of the disease, such as meningitis and disseminated tuberculosis. The recommendation therefore is that in endemic countries such as India, BCG vaccine be administered to babies by intradermal injection on the deltoid immediately after birth, or as early as possible thereafter, before the age of 12 months. The vaccine need not be administered after the age of two years. BCG should not be given to infants and children with active HIV disease, though it may be given with benefit to asymptomatic HIV positives. Babies born to mothers with AFB positive sputum should not be given BCG at birth, but only after a course of preventive chemotherapy.

BCG induces a nonspecific stimulation of the immune system providing some protection against leprosy and leukemia. Multiple injection of BCG has been tried as adjunctive therapy in some malignancies. Some workers have reported that BCG is superior to PPD for tuberculin testing.

Chemoprophylaxis or preventive chemotherapy is the administration of antituberculous drugs (usually only isoniazid) to persons with latent tuberculosis (asymptomatic tuberculin positive) and a high risk of developing active tuberculosis, or to the uninfected exposed to high risk of infection. It is particularly indicated in infants of mothers with active tuberculosis and in children living with a case of active tuberculosis in the house. Isoniazid 5 mg/kg daily for 6–12 months is the usual course. Trials have shown that this reduces the risk of developing active disease by 90 per cent. HIV infected contacts of active tuberculosis also benefit from this prophylaxis.

THERAPY

Chemotherapy has revolutionised the management of tuberculosis. It has been established that sanatorium regimens, bed rest, fresh air and rich food, as well as operative interventions, such as artificial pneumothorax and thoracoplasty are not essential for cure if domiciliary treatment with effective antituberculous drugs is given in optimal dose and duration.

Antituberculous drugs are of two types, bactericidal and bacteristatic. Of the bactericidal drugs, rifampicin (R) and pyrazinamide (Z) are called sterilising drugs because they are able to effectively kill the bacilli in the lesions. Of the other bactericidal drugs, isoniazid (H) is effective only against replicating bacilli and streptomycin (S) only against extracellular bacilli and so are not by themselves able to sterilise the lesions. The bactericidal drugs, along with the bacteristatic drug ethambutol (E) constitute the first line drugs in antituberculous therapy. The old practice of daily administration of drugs for two years or so has been replaced by short course regimens of 6–7 months, which are effective and convenient. A typical example of such a schedule for a new smear positive case is a combination of four drugs (HRZE) given three times a week during an initial intensive phase of two months, followed by 4–5 months of continuing phase with only two drugs (HR) three times a week.

The major problem in chemotherapy is drug resistance, which in tubercle bacilli is due to mutation, with an approximate rate of once in 10^8 cell divisions. This could have been effectively checked by multiple drug therapy, which was introduced for this very purpose. Unfortunately this was not implemented properly. Due to a combination of lapses in prescribing practices, drug delivery and patient compliance, resistance has built up in tubercle bacilli over the years, reducing the efficacy of treatment.

Drug resistance may be 'primary' (pretreatment, initial), when the patient is infected with a strain of tubercle bacillus which is already resistant, or 'acquired' (secondary, post-treatment), when the infecting strain initially sensitive becomes resistant, usually as a result of improper or inadequate treatment. This is the more common type of resistance. When acquired resistant strains become increasingly common in an area, the chance of new patients presenting with primary resistance increases. When an infecting strain acquires resistance to one drug, the chance of its becoming resistant to other drugs increases, unless the treatment schedule contains an adequate number of effective drugs. At present the spectrum of strains prevalent in the community covers resistance to all available antituberculous drugs.

A very serious consequence of unchecked drug resistance has been the emergence and spread of **multidrug resistant tuberculosis** (MDR-TB). Though the term multidrug resistance means only resistance to two or more drugs, in the context of tuberculosis, it specifically refers to resistance to rifampicin and isoniazid, with or without resistance to one or more other drugs. This is because R and H form the sheet anchor of short-term chemotherapy and any strain resistant to both these drugs is unlikely to respond to treatment.

MDR-TB is a global problem, menacing the poor and the rich nations alike. It may be primary or acquired. Its presence in those with concomitant HIV infection makes it more dangerous. When first line drugs become ineffective, second line drugs have to be tried. Large numbers of old and new drugs are being used – quinolones, aminoglycosides, macrolides, para amino salicylic acid, thiacetazone, cycloserine, capreomycin and others. They are unsatisfactory, being much less effective, costlier, more toxic and requiring prolonged treatment schedules.

It is in this context that the directly observed therapy under supervision (DOTS) becomes important. This strategy can prevent deterioration of the resistance problem by ensuring the patient's compliance.

Restoration of cellular immune capacity by 'transfer factor' had been shown, many years ago, to help recovery in immunodeficient patients. A vaccine containing heat killed *M. vaccae*, an environmental mycobacterium from Uganda is being tested as an immunomodulator for stimulation of Th-1 cells which promote protective immunity.

Further Reading

American Thoracic Society Workshop. 1997. Rapid Diagnostic Tests for Tuberculosis. *Am J Respir Crit Care Med.* 155:1804.

Bloom BR and CJ Murray 1992. Tuberculosis, Commentary on a reemerging killer, *Science.* 257:1055.

Chan EA and MD Isman 2002. Current medical treatment for tuberculosis. *BMJ* 325:1282.

Collins CH et al. 1997. *Tuberculosis Bacteriology: Organisation and Practice*, 2nd edn. London: Butterworth.

Grange JM. 1996. *Mycobacteria and Human Disease*, 2nd edn. London: Arnold.

Khatri GR and TR Frieden 2002. Controlling tuberculosis in India. *New Eng J Med* 347:1420.

Revigleone MC and RJ O'Brien 1998. Tuberculosis, in *Harrison's Principles of Internal Medicine*, 14th edn. New York: McGraw Hill.

Reichman LB and ES Hershfield 2000. *Tuberculosis.* New York: Marcel Dekker.

Rom WN and SM Gray (eds). 1996. *Tuberculosis.* Boston: Little Brown.

Suri JC and MK Sen 1998. Multidrug Resistant Tuberculosis. *JAMA India.* 1:27.

Valway SE et al. 1998. An outbreak involving extensive transmission of a virulent strain of mycobacterium tuberculosis. *New Engl J Med.* 338:633.

Zumla A and JM Grange 1998. Tuberculosis. *BMJ* 316:1962.

Mycobacterium II: Non-Tuberculous Mycobacteria (NTM)

Mycobacteria other than manmalian tubercle bacilli, which may occasionally cause human disease resembling tuberculosis, have been called 'atypical', 'anonymous' or 'unclassified' mycobacteria. The names 'environmental' or 'opportunistic mycobacteria' are better suited as their natural habitat appears to be soil or water and they cause opportunistic infections in human beings. The name 'nontuberculous mycobacteria' (NTM) has gained wide acceptance in recent years. They have also been called 'paratubercle', 'tuberculoid' and 'MOTT' (mycobacteria other than tubercle) bacilli. They are distinct from the saprophytic mycobacteria such as *M. phlei* which are incapable of infecting human beings or animals. While human infection with them is common in some areas, disease is rare. They are unable to cause progressive disease when injected into guinea pigs.

Non-tuberculous mycobacteria have been classified into four groups by Runyon (1959) based on pigment production and rate of growth: Group I photochromogens, Group II scotochromogens, Group III nonphotochromogens and Group IV rapid growers. Though other methods of classification have been described, Runyon's classification has found universal acceptance. Species identification depends on several additional characteristics (Table 40.1).

Group I—photochromogens: These strains form colonies that produce no pigment in the dark but when the young culture is exposed to light for one hour in the presence of air, and reincubated for 24–28 hours, a yellow orange pigment appears. They are slow growing, though growth is faster than that of tubercle bacilli. The important species in this group are *M. kansasii, M. marinum* and *M. simiae.*

M. kansasii causes chronic pulmonary disease resembling tuberculosis, usually affecting the upper lobes, with cavity formation and scarring. *M.kansasii* has been isolated from tap water samples around the world and this is believed to be the main reason and source of infection. It is the second most common NTM seen in lung diseases after *M. avium complex.*

M. marinum which causes a warty skin lesion ('swimming pool or fish tank granuloma'), closely resembles *M. kansasii* but can be differentiated by its poor growth at 37 °C, negative nitratase, positive pyrazinamide hydrolase and L-fucosidase activities.

Several photochromogenic mycobacteria were isolated in 1964 from monkeys exported from India. They have been classified into two species: niacin positive *M. simiae* and niacin negative *M. asiaticum.* They have subsequently been associated with pulmonary disease in human beings.

Group II—scotochromogens: These strains form pigmented colonies (yellow-orange-red) even in the dark. They are widely distributed in the environment and sometimes contaminate cultures of tubercle bacilli. *M. scrofulaceum* may cause scrofula (cervical adenitis) in children.

M. gordonae, often found in tap water (hence called 'the tap water scotochromogen'), is a common contaminant in clinical specimens and a rare cause of pulmonary disease. It differs from *M. scrofulaceum* in failing to hydrolyse urea, nicotinamide and pyrazinamide.

Table 40.1 Differentiation between tubercle bacilli and some species of atypical mycobacteria

Test	M. tuberculosis	M. bovis	M. microti	M. kansasii	M. marinum	M.scrofulaceum	M. avium-intracellulare complex	M. fortuitum	M.chelonei	M. phlei	M.smegmatis
Growth in 7 days	-	-	-	-	-	-	-	+	+	+	+
Growth at 25 °C	-	-	-	+	+	+	±	+	+	+	+
Growth at 37 °C	+	+	+	+	±	+	+	+	+	+	+
Growth at 45 °C	-	-	-	-	-	-	±	-	-	+	+
Pigment in dark	-	-	-	-	-	+	-	-	-	+	-
Pigment in light	-	-	-	+	+	+	-	-	-	+	-
Urease	+	+	+	+	+	+	-	+	+	-	+
Niacin	+	-	±	-	-	-	-	-	-	-	-
Nitrate reduction	+	-	-	+	-	-	-	+	-	+	+

M. szulgai is scotochromogenic when grown at 37 °C and photochromogenic at 25 °C.

Group III—nonphotochromogens: These strains do not form pigment even on exposure light. Colonies may resemble those of tubercle bacilli. The medically important species are *M. avium*, *M. intracellulare*, *M. xenopi* and the skin pathogen *M. ulcerans*.

M. avium, which causes natural tuberculosis in birds and lymphadenopathy in pigs is one of the most common opportunist human pathogens. *M. intracellulare* is commonly known as the 'Battey bacillus' because it was first identified as a human pathogen at the Battey State Hospital for Tuberculosis, Georgia, USA.

M. avium and *M. intracellulare* are so closely similar that they have been considered as one group, the *M. avium* complex (MAC). They cause lymphadenopathy, pulmonary lesions or disseminated disease, particularly in AIDS patients. They are related to the animal pathogens *M. paratuberculosis* and *M. lepraemurium*.

M. malmoense which may cause pulmonary disease is a slow grower, taking 8–12 weeks to form colonies.

M. xenopi, originally isolated from toads, may

Table 40.2 Differentiation between *M. ulcerans* and *M. marinum*

Character	M. ulcerans	M. marinum
Distribution	Tropics	Temperate zone
Clinical course	Chronic progressive ulcer	Self-limited ulcer
Bacilli in ulcer	Abundant	Scanty
Rate of growth	Slower; 4–8 weeks	Faster, 1–2 weeks
Growth at 25 °C	-	+
Growth at 37 °C	-	+
Culture film	Bacilli in cords	No cord formation
Pigment in light	-	+
Mouse footpad lesion	Edema, rarely ulcer	Marked inflammation—purulent ulcer

occasionally cause chronic lung disease in human beings. *M. xenopi* and *M. avium* are thermophiles, capable of growth at 45 °C.

Though usually classified as a nonphoto-chromogen, *M. xenopi* may form scoto-chromogenic yellow colonies. *M. xenopi* has been isolated from water taps, mostly hot water taps, in hospitals. It has also been isolated from main water supplies.

Group IV—rapid growers: This is a heterogeneous group of mycobacteria capable of rapid growth, colonies appearing within seven days of incubation at 37 °C or 25 °C. Within the group, photochromogenic, scotochromogenic, and nonchromogenic species occur. Chromogenic rapid growers are mostly saprophytes (for example, *M. phlei*). The medically important species are *M. fortuitum* and *M. chelonae* both of which can cause chronic abscesses in human beings. Outbreaks of abscesses following injection of vaccines and other preparations contaminated by these mycobacteria have been reported on a number of occasions. The bacilli are found in the soil, and infection usually follows some injury.

M. fortuitum and *M. chelonei* do not produce any pigment. Pulmonary lesions caused by *M. fortuitum* cannot be distinguished radiologically from typical tuberculosis. No effective chemotherapy is available. *M. smegmatis*, commonly considered as saprophyte in smegma, is seldom seen in that location. It is a frequent isolate from soft tissue lesions following trauma or surgery.

Some noncultivable or poorly growing mycobacteria identified from the blood of AIDS patients have been characterised by their 16S RNA base sequences. They grow sparsely in some liquid media. Examples are *M. genevense, M. confluentis* and *M. intermedium*.

A rapid grower, *M. vaccae* is reported to be an immunomodulator capable of inhibiting tissue destroying hypersensitivity responses and stimulating protective immune processes in tuberculosis. Clinical trials of *M. vaccae* vaccine as an adjuvant to chemotherapy in tuberculosis are on.

Skin Pathogens

Cutaneous lesions may occur in leprosy or tuberculosis, either as localised disease or as part of a generalised infection. In a different class are two species of mycobacteria, *M. ulcerans* and *M. marinum,* which are exclusively skin pathogens, causing chronic ulcers and granulomatous lesions on the skin. Systemic invasion does not occur and the regional lymph glands are not involved. Cutaneous localisation is because they multiply optimally at skin temperature.

M. ulcerans: This was originally isolated from human skin lesions in Australia (1948) but has subsequently been recovered from similar lesions from Uganda (Buruli ulcer), Congo, Nigeria, Mexico, Malaysia and New Guinea. Ulcers are usually seen on the legs or arms and are believed to follow infection through minor injuries. After an incubation period of a few weeks, indurated nodules appear, which break down forming indolent ulcers which slowly extend under the skin.

Initially, smears from the edge of the ulcer show large clumps of bacilli which are acid fast and alcohol fast. Later, the immunoreactive phase sets in and the bacilli disappear. The ulcers then heal with disfiguring scars.

The bacillus grows on Lowenstein–Jensen medium slowly, in 4–8 weeks. The temperature of incubation is critical; growth occurs between 30 °C and 33 °C but not at 25 °C or 37 °C. Inoculation into the foot pad of mice leads to edema of the limb though ulceration is infrequent. A toxin is produced by *M. ulcerans* that causes inflammation and necrosis when injected into the skin of guinea pigs. This is the only known instance of toxin produced by any mycobacterium species.

M. marinum: This is a natural pathogen of coldblooded animals, causing tuberculosis in fish and amphibia. It may also occur as a saprophyte in fresh or salt water. Human infection originates from

Table 40.3 Atypical mycobacteria associated with human disease

Species	Natural habitat	Type of infection
M. africanum	Animals, soil	Pulmonary
M. asiaticum	Primates	Pulmonary
M. avium intracellulare	Soil, seawater animals	Pulmonary, systemic, gastrointestinal, lymphadenitis
M. chelonae	Soil, seawater, animals	Porcine heart valves, surgical wound, pulmonary
M. chelonae, s.s.	Soil, seawater animals	Cutaneous, surgical abscessus wound - pulmonary-systemic
M. fallax	Water, soil	Pulmonary
M. fortuitum	Water, soil animals	Pulmonary, surgical wound cutaneous, systemic, bone and joint
M. haemophilum	Unknown	Cutaneous, subcutaneous
M. kansasii	Water, animals	Pulmonary, systemic, skin joints, lymphnodes
M. malmoense	Unknown	Pulmonary
M. marinum	Aquarium water, fish	Cutaneous (swimming pool granuloma), joints
M. scrofulaceum	Soil, water, fomites	Lymphadenitis (usually cervical); pulmonary disseminated
M. schimoidei	Unknown	Pulmonary
M. simiae	primates, water	Pulmonary
M. szulgai	Unknown	Pulmonary, lymphadenitis, cutaneous, subcutaneous bursitis
M. ulcerans	Unknown	Cutaneous
M. xenopi	Soil, water	Pulmonary, epididymitis

contaminated swimming pools or fish tanks. The lesion, beginning as a papule and breaking down to form an indolent nuclear, usually follows abrasions and therefore occurs on the prominences —elbows, knees, ankles, nose, fingers or toes. It was first described from Sweden under the name 'swimming pool granuloma', and the bacillus was named M. balnei (from balneum meaning bath). It has since been reported from other European countries and from North America. Its distribution is in temperate areas in contrast to M. ulcerans, which has a tropical prevalence. Human infection may occur in epidemic form. The ulcers are self-limited and undergo spontaneous healing.

Bacilli are scanty in smears from ulcers. Growth occurs in about two weeks at 30 °C (range 25–35 °C) and primary cultures do not grow at 37 °C but they do so after adaptation. Colonies are nonpigmented in the dark; however, they become intense orange yellow to red on exposure to light.

M. marinum is not pathogenic for guinea pigs but intradermal inoculation in rabbits leads to a superficial granulomatous lesion. Footpad inoculation in mice leads to a more severe lesion than with M. ulcerans, local inflammation being followed by a purulent ulcer formation.

Infection with M. marinum, but not M. ulcerans, may cause a low-grade tuberculin reaction.

M. haemophilum, first described in 1978, causes skin lesions. It requires hemin for growth. It grows at 32 °C in 2–4 weeks but not at 37 °C.

Table 40.3 shows the range of human infections produced by different species of atypical mycobacteria.

Ecology and epidemiology: As environmental bacteria are widely distributed in nature, infection with them is quite common, from soil, water and air. Person-to-person infection does not seem to occur. Infection is mainly asymptomatic, though it may result in sensitisation, causing weak positive Mantoux reaction, due to cross-reaction with tubercle bacillus protein. Tuberculins prepared from different environmental mycobacteria induce reactions of appropriate specificity. Sensitisation with environmental mycobacteria is believed to influence the protective response to BCG vaccination. This may be one of the reasons for the wide variation in protective effect of the vaccine observed in field trials in different parts of the world.

An inverse relation seems to exist between tuberculosis and disease caused by NTM. Where tuberculosis is endemic, opportunist mycobacterial disease is rare. Where tuberculosis is rare, NTM disease is more common.

Some opportunist species may colonise tap water (for example, *M. avium*, *M. kansasii*, *M. xenopi*). These may cause problems in the laboratory where they may be mistaken for tubercle bacilli in acid fast smears, and false positive reports given.

Treatment: Most environmental mycobacteria are resistant to the usual antituberculous drugs, though pulmonary disease caused by *M. avium* complex or *M. kansasii* may respond to prolonged treatment with rifampicin, isoniazid and ethambutol. Various combinations of drugs including rifabutin, clofazimine, quinolones, newer macrolides and others are used in treatment, with selection of drugs based on sensitivity studies, where feasible.

Further Reading

Diagnosis and treatment of disease caused by nontuberculous mycobacteria 1990. *Amer Rev Resp Dis* 142:940.

Falkinham JO. 1996. Epidemiology of infection by nontuberculous mycobacteria. *Clin Microbiol Rev* 9:173.

Grange JM. 1996. *Mycobacteria and human disease*, 2nd ed. London:Arnold.

Grange JM and MD Yates 1986. Infections caused by opportunist mycobacteria. A Review. *J Royal Soc Med* 79:226.

Horsburgh CR. 1991. Mycobacterium avium infection in AIDS. *New Engl J Med* 324:1332.

Wolinsky E. 1995. Mycobacterial lymphadenitis in children. *Clin Infect Dis* 20:954.

Mycobacterium III: M. Leprae

Handwritten note:

Mycobacterium leprae :–
→ straight or slightly curved rods, Gram +ve, acid fast.
→ It has not been possible to cultivate lepra bacilli, either in bacteriological media or in tissue culture.

Leprosy :–
→ Is a chronic disease of humans involving the skin, peripheral nerves & nasal mucosa but capable of affecting any tissue or organ.
→ There are two forms of leprosy :–
    Tuberculoid   lepromatous.

TREATMENT — Rifampicin.

Leprosy is [...] n singly and in groups,
recognised [...] ree outside the cells. They
Biblical ti [...] lomerates, the bacilli being
originated [...] id-like substance, the glia.
the world [...] n as 'globi'. The parallel
superstitiou [...] bi present a 'cigar bundle'
leprosy cor [...] tions, the clumps of bacilli
The lepra b [...] ls. The globi appear in
1868. Thou [...] r 'foamy cells' which are
of humans [...] stiocytes.
least under [...] t so far been possible to
possible to [...] er in bacteriological media
[...] e have been several reports
of successful cultivation but none has been
confirmed. One of the best known of such reports
(1962) came from the Indian Cancer Research
Centre, Bombay, where an acid fast bacillus was
isolated from leprosy patients, employing human
fetal spinal ganglion cell culture. This ICRC
bacillus has been adapted for growth on
Lowenstein–Jensen medium. Its relation to the lepra
bacillus is uncertain.

Morphology: *M. leprae* is a straight or slightly
curved rod, 1–8 μm × 0.2–0.5 μm in size, showing
considerable morphological variations. Polar bodies
and other intracellular elements may be present.
Clubbed forms, lateral buds or branching may be
observed. It is Gram positive and stains more readily
than the tubercle bacillus. It is acid fast, but less so
than tubercle bacillus. Hence 5% sulphuric acid
instead of 20% is employed for decolourisation after
staining with carbol fuchsin. It is the practice to
differentiate between live and dead bacilli in stained
smears, assuming without conclusive proof that the
former appear solid and uniformly stained, while
the latter are fragmented and granular. The
percentage of uniformly stained bacilli in tissues
(*morphological index*) provides a method of
assessing the progress of patients on chemotherapy
and is more meaningful than the old criterion of
bacteriological index (the number of bacilli in
tissues).

There have been many attempts to transmit
leprosy to experimental animals. However, the real
break through was the discovery by Shepard (1960)
that lepra bacilli could multiply in the footpads of
mice kept at a low temperature (20 °C). This
observation has been confirmed and has become
the standard procedure for experimental work with
the bacillus. Following intradermal inoculation into
the footpads of mice, a granuloma develops at the
site in 1–6 months. If cell mediated immunity is
suppressed by thymectomy or the administration
of antilymphocyte serum, a generalised infection is

produced, simulating lepromatous leprosy. The nine-banded armadillo (*Dasypus novemcinctus*) is highly susceptible to infection with lepra bacilli. Following inoculation into armadilloes, a generalised infection occurs with extensive multiplication of the bacilli and production of lesions typical of lepromatous leprosy. Some wild armadilloes in captivity have been observed to be naturally infected with a mycobacterium resembling the lepra bacillus. 'Natural disease' has also been identified in chimpanzees and mangabey monkeys from West Africa but it is not known whether they have any relevance to human infection.

In animal experiments, the generation time of the lepra bacillus has been found to be exceptionally long, 12–13 days on the average but may vary from 8–42 days, in comparison with about 14 hours in the case of the tubercle bacillus and about 20 minutes in the case of coliform bacilli.

M. leprae genome has been mapped and the genes for its major protein antigens cloned and sequenced.

Resistance: Lepra bacilli have been found to remain viable in a warm humid environment for 9–16 days and in moist soil for 46 days. They survive exposure to direct sunlight for two hours and ultraviolet light for 30 minutes.

LEPROSY

Leprosy is a chronic granulomatous disease of humans primarily involving the skin, peripheral nerves and nasal mucosa but capable of affecting any tissue or organ. The disease may be classified into four types – *lepromatous, tuberculoid, dimorphous* and *indeterminate* (Madrid classification, 1953). The type of disease is a reflection of the immune status of the host. It is therefore not permanent and varies with chemotherapy and alterations in host resistance. Bacilli isolated from different types of leprosy do not differ in virulence or other properties.

The two extreme or 'polar' forms of the disease are the lepromatous and tuberculoid types. The lepromatous type is seen where the host resistance is low. The bacilli are seen in large numbers or as globi inside lepra cells or extracellularly. This is known as 'multibacillary disease'. Superficial nodular lesions (lepromata) develop which consist of granulation tissue containing a dense collection of vacuolated cells in different stages of development from mononuclear cells to lepra cells. The nodules ulcerate, become secondarily infected and cause distortion and mutilation. Bacilli invade the mucosa of the nose, mouth and upper respiratory tract and are shed in large numbers in nasal and oral secretions. The reticuloendothelial system, eyes, testes, kidneys and bones are also involved. Bacillemia is common. The lepromatous type is more infective than the other types. The prognosis is poor. Cell mediated immunity is deficient and the lepromin test is negative in lepromatous leprosy. On the other hand, there is an exaggerated and broad humoral immune response. Antibodies in high titres are seen against mycobacterial as well as several other antigens. Autoantibodies are common. Most cases show biological false positive reaction in standard serological tests for syphilis.

At the other end of the spectrum is tuberculoid leprosy, which is seen in patients with a high degree of resistance. The skin lesions are few and sharply demarcated, consisting of macular anesthetic patches. Neural involvement occurs early and may be pronounced, leading to deformities, particularly in the hands and feet. Bacilli are scanty in the lesions and infectivity is minimal. This is known as 'paucibacillary disease'. Cell mediated immunity is adequate and the lepromin test is positive. Antimycobacterial and autoimmune antibodies are rare. The prognosis is good.

The term borderline or dimorphous type refers to lesions possessing characteristics of both tuberculoid and lepromatous types. It may shift to the lepromatous or tuberculoid part of the spectrum depending on chemotherapy or alterations in host resistance.

The indeterminate type is the early unstable

tissue reaction which is not characteristic of either the lepromatous or the tuberculoid type. In many persons, the indeterminate lesions undergo healing spontaneously. In others, the lesions may progress to the tuberculoid or lepromatous types. The Indian classification of leprosy has an additional type, the pure neuritic type, which is bacteriologically negative and shows neural involvement without any skin lesion.

Ridely and Jopling (1966) have introduced a scale for classifying the spectrum of leprosy into five groups – tuberculoid (TT), borderline tuberculoid (BT), borderline (BB), borderline lepromatous (BL) and lepromatous (LL).

Epidemiology: Leprosy is an exclusively human disease and the only source of infection is the patient. The exact mode of infection is not clear. Very large numbers of bacilli are shed in the nasal secretions It is recorded that a patient with untreated lepromatic leprosy may discharge upto 8×10^8 bacilli in one nose blow. The mode of entry may be either through the respiratory tract or through the skin. Asymptomatic infection appears to be quite common in endemic areas. It is not uncommon for an infectious patient, who appears quite normal and is unaware that he has leprosy, to continue to shed bacilli from his nose and skin for 2–3 years before more obvious signs appear and the disease is recognised. It has been suggested but not proved that insect vectors may have a role in the transmission of leprosy. Mosquitoes which had fed on lepromatous patients were shown to be capable of infecting mice but it is not known whether this holds good for human beings.

Leprosy is not highly communicable. The disease develops in only about five per cent of spouses living with leprosy patients. However, contacts of patients show a high rate of sensitisation to M. leprae by lymphocyte transformation tests. The incubation period is very long and averages 2–5 years. It has been estimated to vary from a few months to as long as 30 years. As both the time of exposure and the onset of disease are difficult to identify, estimates of incubation period are only approximations. Exceptionally, the disease may follow a single exposure such as tattooing. It is generally held that intimate and prolonged contact is necessary for infection to take place. The disease is more likely if contact occurs during childhood.

Once worldwide in distribution, leprosy is now confined mainly, but not exclusively, to the underdeveloped areas of the tropics and the southern hemisphere. There has been a considerable decline in the number of cases, from about 12 million in the 1980s to less than two million in 1996, partly as a result of control programs. South and South East Asia and Brazil are the most affected areas. India has the maximum prevalence, with about a third of the global total. Leprosy is present in all states and territories of India, but with marked regional variations – Orissa and Bihar having the highest prevalence (> 5 per 1000 population) and Haryana the least (< 0.1 per 1000).

Immunity: A high degree of innate immunity against lepra bacilli seems to exist in human beings so that only a minority of those infected develop clinical disease. Infection with lepra bacilli induces both humoral and cellular immune responses. Humoral antibodies do not have deleterious effect on the bacilli, while cellular immune mechanisms are capable of destroying them. The type of leprosy in an individual is determined by the status of cell mediated immunity in that person. When it is adequate, the lesions are of the tuberculoid type. The patient exhibits delayed hypersensitivity to the lepra bacillus protein. The macrophages phagocytose the bacilli and destroy them. Specific humoral antibodies are not prominent. There is no increase in the immunoglobulin level and the albumin:globulin ratio in the serum is not altered.

When cell mediated immunity is deficient, the lepromatous type of disease develops. Delayed hypersensitivity to the lepra bacillus protein is absent. The macrophages are able to phagocytose the bacilli but instead of being destroyed, the bacilli proliferate inside the cells.

The deficiency in cell mediated immunity is specific to the lepra bacillus antigens. Lepromatous patients are not more susceptible to viruses, parasites and other pathogens against which CMI is important. Tuberculin reactivity may be suppressed in untreated lepromatous patients but it becomes positive following treatment, unlike the lepromin response which remains negative Lepromatous patients have large numbers of CD8+ (suppressor) lymphocytes in circulation, which can be specifically activated by the lepra bacillus antigens. The lymphocytes present in skin granulomas are almost exclusively CD8+ cells, in contrast to tuberculoid lesions which contain predominantly CD4+ cells. In lepromatous leprosy, there is extensive polyclonal B cell activation with large amounts of antibodies being produced, both antimycobacterial and autoimmune. The albumin:globulin ratio is reversed. The antimyco-bacterial antibodies are not beneficial. On the other hand, they may have an enhancing effect.

There is evidence of genetic effect in the pattern of response to lepra bacillus infection. HLA-DR2 is seen preponderantly in persons with the tuberculoid type of reaction, while HLA-MTI and HLA-DQ1 are associated with lepromatous disease.

Though leprosy is a chronic disease, its course may be interspersed with acute exacerbations which are of an allergic nature. Two types of such reactions occur.

Type 1 or the 'reversal reaction' or the 'lepra reaction' is seen mostly in borderline leprosy, occurring spontaneously or more often during chemotherapy. It is a cell mediated immune reaction, with an influx of lymphocytes into lesions, and a shift to tuberculoid morphology. The lesions develop erythema and swelling, along with pain and tenderness. A similar clinical picture is seen in the 'downgrading reaction' which occurs usually in untreated or pregnant patients. Here, biopsy of the lesions shows a shift to the lepromatous pattern, reflecting a decrease of CMI.

Type 2 reaction or Erythema Nodosum Leprosum (ENL) occurs in the LL and BL types, usually a few months after institution of chemotherapy. Crops of tender, inflamed subcutaneous nodules appear, with fever, lymphadenopathy and arthralgia. This is an Arthus type response to antigens released from dead lepra cells and is characterised by neutrophil infiltration and IgG and complement deposition in the lesions.

LEPROMIN TEST

Till recently, the only method for studying immunity in leprosy was a skin test for delayed hypersensitivity, the lepromin test first described by Mitsuda in 1919. The original antigen (lepromin) was boiled, emulsified, lepromatous tissue rich in lepra bacilli. The response to the intradermal injection of lepromin is typically biphasic, consisting of two separate events. The first is the early reaction of Fernandez, which consists of erythema and induration developing in 24–48 hours and usually remaining for 3–5 days. This is analogous to the

Table 41.1 Characterisation of the different types of leprosy

	Tuberculoid	Indeterminate Borderline	Lepromatous
Lepra bacilli in tissues	±	+	+++
Lepromin test	++	±	−
Mycobacterial antibodies	±	+	+++
Lymphocytic infiltration of lesions	+++	+	−
Plasma cells in lymphoid tissue	+	+	+++

tuberculin reaction. This is usually poorly defined and carries little significance. The second and more meaningful is the late reaction of Mitsuda, starting in 1–2 weeks, reaching a peak in four weeks and gradually subsiding in the next few weeks. The reaction consists of an indurated skin nodule, which may ulcerate. Histologically, there is infiltration with lymphocytes, epithelioid cells and giant cells. The Mitsuda late reaction does not indicate pre-existing DTH but is a measure of the CMI induced by the injected lepromin itself. It thus distinguishes between persons who can mount a CMI response against the lepra bacillus antigens and those who cannot.

The original crude Mitsuda antigens extracted from skin lesions of lepromatous patients (integral lepromins) were standardised on the basis of tissue content. Modern antigens are standardised according to their lepra bacillus content (4 x 10^7 lepra bacilli per ml). Standard lepromins are being prepared increasingly from armadillo derived lepra bacilli (lepromin-A), replacing human derived lepromin-H.

The lepromin test is not used to diagnose leprosy, nor does it indicate prior contact with the lepra bacillus. Healthy persons in nonendemic areas with no chance of contact with the bacillus may give a positive lepromin test. The test is employed for the following purposes:

1. To classify the lesions of leprosy patients. The lepromin test is positive in tuberculoid, negative in lepromatous and variable in dimorphous and indeterminate types of disease.

2. To assess the prognosis and response to treatment. A positive reaction indicates good prognosis and a negative one bad prognosis. Conversion to lepromin positivity during treatment is evidence of improvement.

3. To assess the resistance of individuals to leprosy. It is desirable to recruit only lepromin positive persons for work in leprosaria as lepromin

negative persons are more prone to develop the disease.

4. To verify the identity of candidate lepra bacilli. Cultivable acid fast bacilli claimed to be lepra bacilli should give matching results when tested in parallel with standard lepromin.

Laboratory diagnosis: Bacteriological diagnosis is easy in the lepromatous but may be difficult in the tuberculoid cases. The diagnosis consists of demonstration of acid fast bacilli in the lesions. For routine examination, specimens are collected from the nasal mucosa, skin lesions and ear lobules. A blunt, narrow scalpel is introduced into the nose and the internal septum scraped sufficiently to remove a piece of mucus membrane, which is transferred to a slide and teased out into a uniform smear. Samples from the skin should be obtained from the edges of the lesion rather than from the centre. The skin is pinched up tight to minimise bleeding and a cut about 5 mm long made with a scalpel, deep enough to get into the infiltrated layers. After wiping off blood or lymph that may have exuded, the scalpel blade is turned transversely to scrape the sides and bottom of the cut so as to obtain a little tissue pulp which is smeared uniformly on a slide. About 5–6 different areas of the skin should be sampled, including the skin over the buttocks, forehead, chin, cheek and ears. The smears are stained by the Ziehl–Neelsen technique using 5% instead of 20% sulphuric acid for decolourisation. Biopsy of the nodular lesions and thickened nerves, and lymph node puncture may be necessary in some cases.

The smears are graded, based on the number of bacilli as follows:

1–10 bacilli in 100 fields	= 1+
1–10 bacilli in 10 fields	= 2+
1–10 bacilli per field	= 3+
10–100 bacilli per field	= 4+
100–1000 bacilli per field	= 5+
More than 1000 bacilli, clumps and globi in every field	= 6+

The bacteriological (bacterial) index (BI) is calculated by totalling the number of pluses (+s) scored in all the smears and divided by the number of smears. Thus, if eight smears examined have a total of sixteen pluses, the BI will be 2. For calculating BI, a minimum of four skin lesions, a nasal swab and both the ear lobes have to be examined.

The morphological index (MI) is expressed as the percentage of uniformly stained bacilli out of the total number of bacilli counted.

Mouse foot pad inoculation has been reported to be more sensitive than skin slit smears for detection of lepra bacilli in tissues. But this is unsuitable for routine diagnosis and feasible only for drug potency or resistance testing and research studies.

Detection of antibody against *M. leprae* phenolic glycolipid antigen has been claimed to be a specific diagnostic test. Attempts to develop molecular diagnostic methods are in progress. Meanwhile, microscopic demonstration of lepra bacilli and histology remain the most useful diagnostic procedures.

Treatment: Dapsone was the first effective chemotherapeutic agent against leprosy. Its use as a monotherapy for several years led to the development of resistant strains of lepra bacilli. In view of this, multiple drug therapy (MDT) is now recommended in leprosy, as in tuberculosis. The current recommendations for patients with paucibacillary lesions (I, TT, BT) is the concurrent administration of rifampicin 600 mg once a month and dapsone100 mg daily for six months. For multibacillary lesions (BB, BL, LL), the recommendation is rifampicin 600 mg once a month, dapsone 100 mg daily and clofazimine 50 mg daily for two years or until skin smears are negative. Ethionamide or prothionamide may be added to this negimen or substituted for clofazimine. A minimum follow-up of four years for paucibacillary and eight years for multibacillary cases would be necessary to detect any relapse.

An immunotherapeutic vaccine (Mycobacterium W) developed at the National Institute of Immunology, New Delhi is claimed to enhance the effect of MDT.

Prophylaxis: Case finding and adequate therapy have been the methods employed for prophylaxis. Long-term chemoprophylaxis has given encouraging results in child contacts of infectious cases in India and the Philippines.

There is some degree of antigenic relationship between the lepra and tubercle bacilli. It is an old clinical observation that leprosy and tuberculosis do not usually coexist. BCG vaccine was observed to induce lepromin positivity and hence its use in the prevention of leprosy was suggested by Fernandez as early as in 1939. Shepard found that lepra bacilli did not multiply in the footpads of mice immunised with BCG. Controlled trials gave divergent results, from high to no protection. Field trials with different leprosy vaccines (BCG + killed lepra bacilli; ICRC bacillus) have not given conclusive results so far.

MYCOBACTERIUM LEPRAE MURIUM

This is the causative agent of rat leprosy. It was first described by Stefansky in 1901 at Odessa. It has been subsequently reported from several countries. Rat leprosy is characterised by subcutaneous indurations, lymphadenopathy, emaciation, ulcerations and loss of hair. Acid fast bacilli resembling lepra bacilli are found in the lesions in large numbers. However, the disease differs from human leprosy in that the nerves are not affected. *M. leprae* and *M. leprae murium* are not closely related by DNA studies.

Further Reading

Blake L et al. 1987. Environmental nonhuman sources of leprosy. *Rev Infect Dis* 9:562.

Cambau E et al. 1997. Multidrug resistance in *M. leprae*. *Lancet* 349:103.

Dharmendra. 1985. *Leprosy* Vol. 1 and 2. Bombay: Samant & Co.

Editorial. 1986. Serological tests for leprosy. *Lancet* 1:532.

Editorial. 1987. Vaccines against leprosy. *Lancet* 1:1183.

Fine PEM. 1982. Leprosy. the epidemiology of a slow bacterium. *Epidemiol Rev* 4:161.

Karonga Prevention Trial Group. 1996. Randomised controlled trial of BCG and *M. leprae* vaccines in Malawi. *Lancet* 348:17.

Spirochetes ... are structurally more complex than other bacteria. A characteristic feature is the presence of varying numbers of *endoflagella,* which are polar flagella wound along the helical protoplasmic cylinder, and situated between the outer membrane and cell wall. *Endoflagella* are believed to be responsible for motility but the exact mechanisms of locomotion are not understood.

Spirochetes vary widely in size, some being as long as 500 μm and others as short as 5 μm. They are Gram negative. Many are free-living saprophytes, while some are obligate parasites. They may be aerobic, anaerobic or facultative. Reproduction is by transverse fission.

Spirochetes belong to the order Spirochetales, comprising two families—Spirochetaceae containing the genera *Spirochaeta, Cristispira, Treponema and Borrelia;* and Leptospiraceae containing the genus *Leptospira.* Human pathogens are found in the genera *Treponema, Borrelia* and *Leptospira.* Members of the genus *Spirochaeta* are saprophytes found in water and sewage, while *Cristispira* are found in molluscs.

TREPONEMA

Treponemes *(trepos,* meaning to turn, and *nema,* meaning thread) are relatively short slender spirochetes with fine spirals and pointed or rounded ends. Some of them are pathogenic, while others occur as commensals in the mouth, intestines, and genitalia. Pathogenic treponemes have not been cultivated in cell free media though ... may be grown in artificial media. ...ponemes cause the following diseases in humans:

1. Venereal syphilis caused by *T. pallidum*
2. Endemic syphilis caused by *T. pallidum* (*T. endemicum*)
3. Yaws caused by *T. pertenue*
4. Pinta caused by *T. carateum*

They are almost identical in their morphology, antigenic structure and other features, though there are differences in the clinical features and natural history of the diseases they produce. It has been suggested that the pathogenic treponemes represent only evolutionary variations of a single species and that the diseases caused by them, though different clinically and epidemiologically, should be considered parts of a continuous spectrum of *treponematoses.* Accordingly, the species *T. pallidum* is now considered to include three subspecies—subspecies *pallidum* causing venereal syphilis, *endemicum* causing endemic syphilis and *pertenue* causing yaws.

TREPONEMA PALLIDUM

Treponema pallidum, the causative agent of syphilis, was discovered by Schaudinn and Hoffmann (1905) in the chancres and inguinal lymph nodes of syphilitic patients. The name *pallidum* refers to its pale staining.

Morphology: It is a thin, delicate spirochete with tapering ends, about 10 μm long (range 4–14 μm) and 0.1–0.2 μm wide. It has about ten regular spirals, which are sharp and angular, at regular intervals of about 1 μm. It is actively motile, exhibiting rotation around the long axis, backward and forward movements, and flexion of the whole body. During motion, secondary curves appear and disappear in succession but the primary spirals are unchanged (Fig. 42.1).

T. pallidum cannot be seen under the light microscope in wet films but can be made out by negative staining with Indian ink. Its morphology and motility can be seen under the dark ground or phase contrast microscope. It does not take ordinary bacterial stains but stains light rose red with prolonged Giemsa staining. It can be stained by silver impregnation methods. Fontana's method is useful for staining films and Levaditi's method for tissue sections.

Ultrastructurally, the cytoplasm of T. pallidum is surrounded by a trilaminar cytoplasmic membrane, enclosed by a cell wall containing peptidoglycan which gives the cell rigidity and shape. External to this is the lipid rich outer membrane layer. Originating from each end of the cell, three or four endoflagella wind round the axis of the cell in the space between the cell wall and outer membrane layer, to interdigitate at its centre. Unlike the flagella of other bacteria, these endoflagella do not protrude outside, but remain within the outer membrane layer.

Saprophytic spirochetes are generally coarser in appearance, lack the uniform spirals with regular spacing, and show lashing motility.

Cultivation: Pathogenic treponemes do not grow in artificial culture media. Limited growth of T. pallidum has been reported in cocultivation with tissue culture cells. It is possible to maintain T. pallidum in motile and virulent form for 10–12 days in complex media under anaerobic conditions. Virulent T. pallidum strains have been maintained for many decades by serial testicular passage in rabbits. One such strain (Nichol's strain) isolated from the brain of a fatal case of general paralysis of the insane in 1912 is still being propagated and used for diagnostic and research purposes.

There have been many claims of cultivation of T. pallidum in cultures but none has been substantiated. The isolates have been nonpathogenic treponemes, showing morphological and antigenic similarities with T. pallidum. The best known of these is the Reiter strain, which has been widely used as the antigen in group specific treponemal tests for the diagnosis of syphilis. The Reiter treponeme grows well in thioglycollate medium containing serum. The Reiter treponeme is now classified as T. phagedenis.

Resistance: T. pallidum is very delicate, being readily inactivated by drying or by heat (41–42 °C in one hour). Hence fomites are of little importance in the transmission of infection. Susceptibility of T. pallidum to heat was the basis of the 'fever therapy' for syphilis. It is killed in 1–3 days at 0–4 °C, so that transfusion syphilis can be prevented by storing blood for at least four days in the refrigerator before transfusion. Stored frozen at −70 °C in 10% glycerol, or in liquid nitrogen (−130 °C), it remains viable for 10–15 years. It is inactivated by contact with oxygen, distilled water, soap, arsenicals, mercurials, bismuth, common antiseptic agents and antibiotics.

Antigenic structure: The antigenic structure

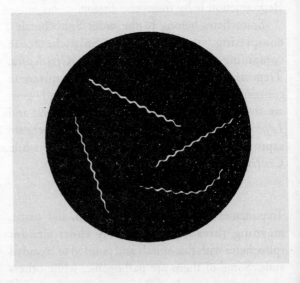

Fig. 42.1 Treponema pallidum – dark ground illumination

of *T. pallidum* is complex. Treponemal infection induces at least three types of antibodies. The first is the *reagin* antibody that reacts in the standard or nonspecific tests for syphilis, such as Wassermann, Kahn and VDRL, in which a hapten extracted from the beef heart is used as the antigen. This lipid hapten is known as *cardiolipin* and is chemically a diphosphatidyl glycerol. This lipid has been detected in *T. pallidum* but it is not known whether the reagin antibody is induced by cardiolipin that is present in the spirochete or released from damaged host tissues.

The second is a group antigen found in *T. pallidum* as well as in nonpathogenic cultivable treponemes like the Reiter treponeme.

The third antigen, probably polysaccharide in nature, is species specific. The antibody to this antigen is demonstrated by the specific *T. pallidum* tests which are positive only with sera of patients infected with pathogenic treponemes.

Pathogenicity: Natural infection with *T. pallidum* occurs only in human beings. Experimentally, monkeys may be infected. A disease resembling syphilis can be produced experimentally in chimpanzees, with typical lesions of primary and secondary syphilis. Rabbits can be infected by intradermal or intratesticular inoculation, the former giving rise to chancre and the latter to syphilomas. Serial passage in rabbits does not appear to reduce the virulence of the spirochete to human beings, as evidenced by several accidental infections in laboratory workers caused by the Nichol's strain. Hamsters are also susceptible.

SYPHILIS

The origin of syphilis is not definitely known. Towards the end of the fifteenth century, syphilis spread widely throughout Europe in a particularly virulent form called the **pox**. The name 'syphilis' was derived from a poem written by Fracastorius of Verona in 1530 describing the legend of a shepherd named Syphilus, who had been struck with the disease. It was widely held that syphilis was a new disease brought from America by Columbus's crew. The natural history of the disease has undergone alterations since then but syphilis continues to be one of the most important and widespread of human infections.

Venereal syphilis is acquired by sexual contact. The spirochete enters the body through minute abrasions on the mucosa or skin. Infectivity of a patient to the sexual partner is maximum during the first two years of the disease—the primary, secondary and early latent stages. After five years, the risk is considered minimal. The infective dose is small, as few as 60 treponemes being capable of infecting 50 per cent of human volunteers. It multiplies at the site of entry. Its generation time is 30–33 hours. Clinical disease sets in after an incubation period of about a month (range 10–90 days). The clinical manifestations fall into three stages—primary, secondary and tertiary.

The primary lesion in syphilis is the chancre at the site of entry of the spirochete. In all but a few, the chancre is genital. Other common sites are the mouth and nipples. In some cases the chancre may not be visible, as when it occurs on the uterine cervix. The chancre is a painless, relatively avascular, circumscribed, indurated, superficially ulcerated lesion. It is known as 'hard chancre' to distinguish it from the nonindurated lesions of 'soft sore' caused by *H. ducreyi*, and as Hunterian chancre named after John Hunter who produced the lesion on himself experimentally and described the evolution of the disease. The chancre is covered by a thick, glairy exudate very rich in spirochetes. The regional lymph nodes are swollen, discrete, rubbery and nontender. Even before the chancre appears, the spirochetes spread from the site of entry into the lymph and bloodstream, so the patient may be infectious during the late incubation period. The chancre invariably heals in about 10–40 days, even without treatment, leaving a thin scar. Persistent or multiple chancres may be seen in HIV infected or other immunodeficient patients.

Secondary syphilis sets in 1–3 months after the

primary lesion heals. During this interval the patient is asymptomatic. The secondary lesions are due to widespread multiplication of the spirochetes and their dissemination through the blood. Roseolar or papular skin rashes, mucous patches in the oropharynx and condylomata at the mucocutaneous junctions are the characteristic lesions. Spirochetes are abundant in the lesions and consequently the patient is most infectious during the secondary stage. There may also be ophthalmic, osseous and meningeal involvement. Secondary lesions are highly variable in distribution, intensity and duration but they usually undergo spontaneous healing, in some instances taking as long as four or five years.

After the secondary lesions disappear, there is a period of quiescence known as 'latent syphilis'. Diagnosis during this period is possible only by serological tests. In many cases, this is followed by natural cure but in others, after several years, manifestations of tertiary syphilis appear. These consist of cardiovascular lesions including aneurysms, chronic granulomata (gummata) and meningovascular manifestations. Tertiary lesions contain few spirochetes and may represent manifestations of delayed hypersensitivity. In a few cases, neurological manifestations such as tabes dorsalis or general paralysis of the insane develop several decades after the initial infection. These are known as late tertiary or quaternary syphilis.

In syphilis acquired nonvenereally (as occupationally in doctors or nurses), the natural evolution is as in venereal syphilis, except that the primary chancre is extragenital, usually on the fingers. In the rare instances where syphilis is transmitted by blood transfusion, the primary chancre does not occur. In congenital syphilis, where infection is transmitted from mother to fetus transplacentally, the manifestations and course are different. Transplacental transmission can take place at any stage of pregnancy. A woman with early syphilis can infect her fetus much more commonly (75–95 per cent) than one with syphilis of over two years duration (35 per cent). The lesions of congenital syphilis usually develop only after the fourth month of gestation, the time when fetal immune competence starts appearing. This suggests that the pathogenesis requires immune response from the fetus. Congenital syphilis can be prevented if the mother is given adequate treatment before the fourth month of pregnancy. The obstetric history in an untreated syphilitic woman is typically one of abortions and stillbirths followed by live births of infants with stigmata of syphilis and finally of healthy infants.

Laboratory diagnosis: As the manifestations of syphilis are protean and as there are asymptomatic periods during the natural course of the disease, laboratory aid is essential for the diagnosis of the disease. It is also important in assessing the cure after treatment. Because of the social and emotional overtones of the disease, the diagnosis of syphilis should impose a great sense of responsibility on the laboratory. Laboratory diagnosis consists of demonstration of the spirochetes under the microscope and of antibodies in serum or CSF.

Microscopy: Diagnosis by microscopy is applicable in primary and secondary stages and in cases of congenital syphilis with superficial lesions. Specimens should be collected with care as the lesions are highly infectious. The lesion is cleaned with a gauze soaked in warm saline and the margins gently scraped so that the superficial epithelium is abraded. Gentle pressure is applied to the base of the lesion and the serum that exudes is collected preventing admixture with blood. Wet films are prepared with the exudate and after applying thin coverslips, examined under the dark ground microscope. *T. pallidum* is identified by its slender spiral structure and slow movement. Differentiation from saprophytic spirochetes commonly present in the genital area needs experience.

Dark ground examination is useful but negative results do not exclude the diagnosis of syphilis, because of its low sensitivity. A treponemal concentration of 10^4 per ml in the exudates is required for the test to be positive.

The direct fluorescent antibody test for *T. pallidum* (DFA-TP) is a better and safer method for microscopic diagnosis. Smears of the exudate are fixed with acetone and sent to the laboratory, where the DFA-TP test is done using fluorescent tagged anti-*T. pallidum* antiserum. The use of specific monoclonal antibody has made the test more reliable.

Serological tests: These tests form the mainstay of laboratory diagnosis. A large number of tests have been described, of which only a few are now employed .

Serological tests for syphilis may be classified as follows:

1. tests for antibodies reacting with cardiolipin antigen reagin tests; standard tests for syphilis; STS

2. tests for antibodies reacting with group specific treponemal antigen

3. tests for specific antibodies to pathogenic treponema (*T. pallidum*).

1. Reagin antibody tests: These tests use the lipoidal or cardiolipin antigens and are known as 'standard tests for syphilis' or STS. (The antibody reacting with cardiolipin is known as *reagin*. This can be misleading, as the IgE antibody in atopy is also called reagin, though there is no connection between the two.)

The first of the reagin antibody tests was the Wassermann complement fixation test (1906), which originally used a watery extract of the liver of a syphilitic fetus as the antigen. This was later substituted by an alcoholic extract of ox heart tissue, to which lecithin and cholesterol were added. This crude extract was subsequently replaced by a purified lipid extract of beef heart (called *cardiolipin*), with added lecithin and cholesterol, as standardised by Pangborn (1945). The complement fixation test remained the principal serological test for syphilis, till it was replaced by the simpler flocculation tests which also use the cardiolipin antigen. The Wassermann test is no longer in use now.

The first flocculation test used widely was the tube flocculation test of Kahn. The Kahn test has been replaced by the simpler and more rapid VDRL test, which gives more quantitative results (VDRL, for Veneral Disease Research Laboratory, USPHS, New York, where the test was developed). In the VDRL test, the inactivated serum (that is, serum heated at 56 °C for 30 minutes) is mixed with cardiolipin antigen on a special slide and rotated for four minutes. Cardiolipin remains as uniform crystals in normal serum but forms visible clumps on combining with reagin antibody. The reaction is read under a low power microscope. By testing serial dilutions, the antibody titre can be determined. The results are reported qualitatively as 'reactive', 'weak reactive' or 'not reactive'. For quantitative reporting, the reciprocal of the end point is given as the titre, for example 'reactive 4 dilution' or 'titre 4'.

VDRL test can be used for testing CSF also, but not plasma. CSF need not be heated prior to the test.

A number of modifications of the VDRL test have been developed, of which the Rapid Plasma Reagin (RPR) test is the most popular. The RPR test uses VDRL antigen containing fine carbon particles, which make the result more clear cut and evident to the naked eye. RPR test can be done with unheated serum or plasma, but is not suitable for testing CSF. Automated RPR test (ART) is available for large scale tests. An automated VDRL-ELISA test has been developed which can measure IgG and IgM antibodies separately and is suitable for large scale testing of sera.

As cardiolipin antigen is present both in *T. pallidum* and in mammalian tissues, reagin antibodies may be induced by treponemal or host tissue antigens. This accounts for the biological false positive (BFP) reactions, which constitute the major disadvantage of STS. BFP reactions are defined as **positive reactions** obtained in cardiolipin tests, with negative results in specific treponemal tests, in the absence of past or present treponemal infections— and not caused by technical faults. They represent nontreponemal cardiolipin antibody responses.

BFP reactions may occur in about one per cent of normal sera. BFP antibody is usually IgM, while reagin antibody in syphilis is mainly IgG. Clinically, BFP reactions may be classified as acute or chronic. Acute BFP reactions last only for a few weeks or months and are usually associated with acute infections, injuries or inflammatory conditions. Chronic BFP reactions persist for longer than six months and are typically seen in SLE and other collagen diseases. Leprosy, malaria, relapsing fever, infectious mononucleosis, hepatitis and tropical eosinophilia are examples of other conditions associated with BFP reactions.

Reagin antibody becomes detectable 7–10 days after the appearance of primary chancre (or 3–5 weeks after acquiring the infection). The sensitivity in the primary stage is 60–75 per cent with the titres being low, upto eight. In the secondary stage, the sensitivity is 100 per cent and titres range from 16 to 128 or more. Prozone phenomenon may be a problem in high titre sera and it is therefore essential to test sera in dilutions. Another stage of syphilis in which such high titres are seen is congenital syphilis. After the secondary stage, titres diminish and about a third of patients with late syphilis are seronegative. The titres may rise in patients developing cardiovascular, neurological or gummatous lesions. In some cases of neurosyphilis, reagin tests may be negative with serum but positive with the CSF. Reagin tests usually become negative 6–18 months after effective treatment of syphilis, depending on the stage at which treatment is given. However, if treatment is started late, the tests may remain positive in low titres.

2. Group-specific treponemal tests: In order to avoid BFP reactions, tests using cultivable treponemes as antigens were developed. These employed the Reiter treponemes (originally believed to be an adapted strain of *T. pallidum*). The test most commonly employed in this group was the Reiter protein complement fixation (RPCF) test, using a lipopolysaccharide-protein complex antigen derived from the treponeme. Its sensitivity and specificity were lower than those of tests using *T. pallidum*. Though RPCF was generally free from BFP reactions, it still gave some false positive reactions. RPCF and other Reiter treponeme tests are not now in general use.

3. Specific T. pallidum tests: These tests use the virulent Nichol's strain of *T. pallidum* maintained by serial inoculation in rabbit testes.

The first in this group is the *Treponema pallidum* immobilisation (TPI) test introduced in 1949. The test serum is incubated with complement and *T. pallidum* maintained in a complex medium anaerobically. If antibodies are present, the treponemes are immobilised, that is, rendered nonmotile, when examined under dark ground illumination.

In its time, TPI was the most specific test available for diagnosis of syphilis and was considered the gold standard in syphilis serology. However, because of its extreme complexity, it was available only in a few laboratories. The TPI test has now been supplanted by other tests such as FTA-ABS and TPHA which are quite as specific and much simpler.

The fluorescent treponemal antibody (FTA) test is an indirect immunofluorescence test using as antigen, smears prepared on slides with Nichol's strain of *T. pallidum*. The slides can be stored for several months in deep freeze. The currently used modification of the test is the FTA-absorption (FTA-ABS) test in which the test serum is preabsorbed with a sonicate of the Reiter treponemes (*sorbent*) to eliminate group specific reactions. FTA-ABS is as specific as the TPI test and is now accepted as a standard reference test. However, as it can be done only in suitably equipped laboratories, it is not available for routine testing.

The *T. pallidum* hemagglutination Assay (TPHA) uses tanned erythrocytes sensitised with a sonicated extract of *T. pallidum*, as antigen. The procedure now employed is a micro-hemagglutination test (MHA-TP), which is capable of being automated.

The test sera for TPHA are absorbed with a diluent containing components of the Reiter treponeme, rabbit testis and sheep erythrocytes. Sera are screened in an initial dilution of 1:80 but titres of 5120 or more are common in the secondary stage. TPHA is just as specific as FTA-ABS and almost as sensitive, except in the primary stage. It is also much simpler and more economical. No special equipment is needed. Kits are available commercially. These advantages have made TPHA a standard confirmatory test.

Table 42.1 shows the relative sensitivities of the serological tests in common use.

Enzyme immunoassays (EIA) have been developed using *T. pallidum* antigens and are available commercially (Bio-Enza Bead test; Captia Syphilis-G test). A rapid agglutination test has been developed, using latex particles coated with three immunodominant proteins of *T. pallidum*, obtained by recombinant technology. It is claimed to be as specific as TPHA, and more sensitive.

The practice for serological screening for syphilis varies in different countries. In the UK, a combination of VDRL and TPHA tests is used. This is an efficient combination for the detection or exclusion of syphilis at all stages, except the early primary stage. A repeat test 1–3 months later will bring even this to light. In the USA, screening is by VDRL or RPR test alone. This may fail to detect about one per cent of secondary syphilis due to the prozone effect and about 30 per cent of latent or late syphilis.

Table 42.1 Frequency of reactive serological tests in untreated syphilis (percentage)

Stage	VDRL/RPR	FTA-ABS	TPHA
Primary	70–80	85–100	65–85
Secondary	100	100	100
Latent/late	60–70	95–100	95-100

Quantitative tests are useful in monitoring the patient's response to treatment, indicating the stage of the disease and in detecting reinfection. Reagin tests are preferred because they usually become negative following treatment. If treatment is given very early, the serum may not become positive at all. Treatment in the primary stage leads to seroreversal in about four months; in the secondary and early latent stages, it takes 12–18 months; in later stages, it may take five years or more. In some cases low titre reactivity may persist indefinitely, in spite of effective treatment. Specific treponemal tests are of little value as indicators of clinical cure, as they tend to remain positive in spite of treatment. TPHA titres may fall rapidly following treatment in secondary syphilis but remain positive for life in low titres.

TPHA and FTA-ABS are helpful in excluding or confirming the diagnosis of syphilis and for identifying BFP reactions. Though false positive reactions were believed to have been eliminated with the introduction of these specific tests, it is not truly so. Both TPHA and FTA-ABS can give false positive results, though very rarely. All serological tests for syphilis may be positive in nonvenereal treponematoses, and some in a few other spirocheatal infections as well. In Lyme disease, VDRL test is negative, but FTA-ABS may be positive.

A negative TPHA virtually excludes the diagnosis of syphilis, past or present, except in the very early stages. In neurosyphilis, a negative CSF VDRL test may not be conclusive but a negative TPHA test eliminates the possibility of neurosyphilis.

Detection of specific IgM antibody may be helpful in some situations. Being the initial type of antibody to appear, IgM is detectable by the second week of infection. IgM antibody production ceases soon after elimination of infection by treatment. Persistence of IgM antibody indicates continuing active disease and the need for treatment. As IgM does not cross the placenta, its presence in neonatal serum confirms congenital syphilis and helps differentiate it from seropositivity due to passively transferred maternal antibody (syphilotoxemia). Many techniques have been developed for the selective detection of IgM antibodies. These include modifications of the FTA-ABS, TPHA, EIA and VDRL tests, using whole sera or separated IgM fractions. When such tests are not available, parallel tests of maternal and neonatal sera may settle the diagnosis of congenital syphilis, in which the neonatal serum may show a higher titre of antibody than the maternal serum. Serial testing is also useful because the titre of passively transferred antibody decreases rapidly, the VDRL test becoming negative by three months.

Epidemiology: Venereal syphilis is worldwide in distribution. During the five centuries that it has been recorded and studied, the disease has undergone much variation in its natural history and clinical features. As originally described, it was a highly virulent disease with florid cutaneous manifestations. With the discovery of the dramatic therapeutic response to penicillin, it was hoped that it may even be possible to eradicate syphilis, as the disease has no extra human reservoir. However, not only has it not been possible to eliminate the disease but an increase has occurred in its incidence, due to the changing customs, habits and values in society.

The advent of the AIDS pandemic has had an impact on syphilis. In most places, fear of AIDS and safer sex practices led to a fall in the incidence of syphilis and all STDs initially, but this trend did not continue everywhere. Concurrent infection with syphilis and HIV is common and may lead to earlier evolution of neurosyphilis.

Immunity: The immune mechanisms in syphilis are not adequately understood. Humoral immune response against the treponeme does not appear to be effective as the disease progresses unhindered for decades even in the presence of a vigorous antibody response. Cell mediated immunity may be more relevant. T lymphocytes and macrophages are predominant in early syphilitic lesions. Specifically sensitised Th1 cells secrete cytokines favouring clearance of spirochetes by activated macrophages.

Reinfections do not appear to occur in a person already having active infection. It was believed that *premunition* or infection immunity, as seen in some parasitic infections, holds good in syphilis also and that a patient becomes susceptible to reinfection only when his original infection is cured. However, it has been shown that some degree of immunity to reinfection occurs in experimental animals and persons whose infection has been completely eliminated by treatment.

Prophylaxis: As transmission is by direct contact, it is possible to protect against syphilis by avoidance of sexual contact with an infected individual. When this is not complied with, the use of physical barriers (such as condoms), antiseptics (potassium permanganate) or antibiotics may minimise the risk. The use of prophylactic penicillin carries the danger that it may suppress the primary lesion without eliminating the infection so that recognition and treatment of the disease may become more difficult. No vaccine is available.

Treatment: Penicillin is uniformly effective in syphilis but it is necessary to give an adequate dose and maintain the drug level for a sufficiently long period to establish cure. A single injection of 2.4 million units of benzathine penicillin G is adequate in early cases. For late syphilis, this amount may be repeated weekly for three weeks. In patients allergic to penicillin, doxycycline may be used. Ceftriaxone is effective, particularly in neurosyphilis Penicillin treatment in syphilis sometimes induces a reaction, the Jarisch–Herxheimer reaction, consisting of fever, malaise and exacerbation of symptoms. It is frequent, but harmless, in primary and secondary syphilis, and can be managed with bed rest and aspirin. It is rare in late syphilis but can be dangerous in some cases of gummatous, cardiovascular or neurosyphilis. It is believed to be due to the liberation of toxic products like tumor necrosis factors from the massive destruction of treponemes or due to hypersensitivity.

It has been reported that *T. pallidum* may sometimes survive in the brain and other tissues of patients clinically cured after adequate treatment with penicillin. The significance of such persistent treponemes is not clear.

NONVENEREAL TREPONEMATOSES

Nonvenereal treponemal diseases occur in endemic foci in several parts of the world, in communities with poor standards of hygiene. The diseases have been given different names in different regions and vary somewhat in clinical manifestations but the treponemes responsible are virtually indistinguishable from *T. pallidum* and are now considered as its subspecies. Infection is usually transmitted by direct body to body contact. It has been suggested that endemic treponematoses represent the ancient patterns of association between human beings and treponemes. When civilisation and the general use of clothing limited the chances of bodily contact among persons, the treponemes may have become adapted for transmission through sexual intercourse, resulting in venereal syphilis.

Three distinct forms of endemic treponematoses are recognised—endemic syphilis, yaws and pinta.

ENDEMIC SYPHILIS

Syphilis, transmitted nonvenereally, was endemic in several foci. With recognition of such foci and mass treatment with penicillin under WHO auspices, endemic syphilis has become very rare. Under the name of *sibbens,* it was present in Scotland in the last century. It is known as *bejel* in the Middle East, *njovera* in Zimbabwe, *dichuchwa* in Bechuanaland, *Skerljevo* in Eastern Europe and *siti* in Gambia. It has also been reported from India. The causative agent is the *T. pallidum* subspecies *endemicum.*

The disease is common in young children. The primary chancre is not usually seen, except sometimes on the nipples of mothers infected by their children. The disease is usually seen with manifestations of secondary syphilis, such as mucous patches and skin eruptions. The disease progresses to tertiary lesions, particularly gummatous lesions. Cardiovascular and neurological involvement is rare. Congenital syphilis also is not found.

The laboratory diagnosis and treatment are as for venereal syphilis.

YAWS

Yaws, also known as frambesia, pian, parangi and by many other synonyms, is endemic in the tropical areas of Africa, Asia and America. Yaws eradication campaigns by mass penicillin injections in endemic areas led to the virtual eradication of the disease. However, it has subsequently reappeared in some areas. In India cases have been identified in Andhra Pradesh, Orissa and Madhya Pradesh. The causative agent is *T. pallidum* subspecies *pertenue* (*T. pertenue*) which is morphologically and antigenically indistinguishable from *T. pallidum.* The primary lesion (mother yaw) is an extragenital papule which enlarges and breaks down to form an ulcerating granuloma. As in syphilis, secondary and tertiary manifestations follow but, cardiovascular or neurological involvement is rare. Destructive gummatous lesions of the bones are common.

Infection is by direct contact. Flies may act as mechanical vectors. The small fly, *Hippolates pallippes,* has been found feeding on open sores but its epidemiological importance is not known.

Laboratory diagnosis and treatment are as for syphilis. There appears to be some cross-immunity between yaws and syphilis, in that venereal syphilis is rare in communities where yaws is endemic.

PINTA

Pinta (carate, mal del pinto) is endemic in Central and South America and the neighbouring islands. The primary lesion is an extragenital papule, which does not ulcerate but develops into a lichenoid or psoriaform patch. Secondary skin lesions are characterised by hyperpigmentation or hypopigmentation. Tissues other than skin are seldom affected.

The causative agent is *T. carateum*. It is very closely related to *T. pallidum* but is not antigenically identical so cross immunity between pinta and syphilis is only partial.

NONPATHOGENIC TREPONEMES

Several commensal treponemes occur on the buccal and genital mucosa and may cause confusion in the diagnosis of syphilis by dark field examination. They are a heterogeneous group and have not been adequately characterised. Best known among them is the oral spirochete, *T. denticole,* which can be readily cultivated. Treponemes also occur on the surface of gastric and colonic epithelium in human beings and animals.

During early attempts to grow the syphilis spirochete in cultures, several treponemes had been grown and mistakenly called *T. pallidum*—for example, the Reiter and Kazan strains which have been identified as *T. phagedenis* and the avirulent Nichols and Noguchi strains which have been recognised as *T. refringens.*

In experimental work on *T. pallidum* in rabbits, *T. paraluiscuniculi* (formerly *T. cuniculi*), which has a very similar appearance and causes natural venereal infection in rabbits, may pose problems.

BORRELIA

Borreliae are large, motile, refractile spirochetes with irregular, wide, open coils. They are usually 5–30 μm long and 0.3–0.7 μm wide. They are readily stained by ordinary methods and are Gram negative. Several species of Borrelia occur as commensals on the buccal and genital mucosa. Borreliae of medical importance are those causing relapsing fever, *B. vincenti* which sometimes causes fusospirochetosis and *B. burgdorferi*, the causative agent of Lyme disease.

RELAPSING FEVER

Relapsing fever (RF) has been known since the time of Hippocrates and has occurred in epidemic, endemic or sporadic form throughout the world. RF is an arthropod-borne infection, two types of which occur – louseborne and tickborne. The borreliae causing them are indistinguishable in morphology and many other features but differ in their arthropod hosts.

The causative agent of epidemic or louseborne RF is *B. recurrentis*, first observed by Obermeier (1873) in the blood of patients during an epidemic in Berlin. It is an exclusive human pathogen, being transmitted from person to person through body lice (*Pediculus humanus corporis*). No extrahuman reservoir is known.

Borreliae causing endemic or tickborne RF normally live in their natural hosts—rodents or other mammals on which the vector ticks feed. Human infection is only an accidental event. Borrelliae have been assigned to various species based on the ticks that carry them. Over ten species of borreliae are known to infect human beings and cause RF (*B. duttonii, B. hermsii, B. parkeri*, etc.) They are generally confined to certain geographic areas. There is evidence from DNA homology studies to indicate that all of them may belong to a single species, with separate host adaptation. The descriptions that follow apply to all of them, unless stated otherwise.

Morphology: *B. recurrentis* is an irregular spiral with one or both ends pointed. It is 8–20 μm long and 0.2–0.4 μm wide. It possesses 5–10 loose spiral coils at intervals of about 2 mm. It stains well with Giemsa and bacterial stains and is Gram negative.

Cultural characteristics: Borrelia are microaerophilic. Optimum temperature for growth is 28–30 °C. Cultivation is difficult but has been successful in complex media containing serous fluids. Growth occurs on the chorioallantoic membrane of chick embryos. For primary isolation, the best method is to inoculate mice or rats intraperitoneally. When using experimental animals, great care has to be taken to ensure that the animals are free from pre-existing borreliosis.

Antigenic properties: Borrelia readily undergoes antigenic variations in vivo and this is believed to be the reason for the occurrence of relapses in the disease. Antigenic variations have been shown to be caused by DNA rearrangements in linear plasmids present in borrelia. Ultimate recovery after a number of relapses may be due to the development of immunity to all the antigenic variants. Agglutinating, complement fixing and lytic antibodies develop during infection but their demonstration is not possible as a routine diagnostic test due to the difficulty in preparing satisfactory antigens.

Pathogenicity: After an incubation period of 2–10 days relapsing fever sets in as fever of sudden onset. During this period, borreliae are abundant in the patient's blood. The fever subsides in 3–5 days. After an afebrile period of 4–10 days during which borreliae are not demonstrable in blood, another bout of fever sets in. The borreliae reappear in blood during the relapses of fever. The disease ultimately subsides after 3–10 relapses.

Experimentally, rodents such as rats, mice and, less readily, guinea pigs may be infected by intraperitoneal injection. Borreliae may survive in the brains of infected animals after they have disappeared from the blood.

Epidemiology: Louseborne relapsing fever tends to occur as epidemics whenever poverty, overcrowding and lack of personal hygiene encourage louse infestation. Epidemic relapsing fever used to be very common during wars and in jails of former days but with improvements in hygiene and the discovery of insecticides, it has now become rare. It survives in some areas, as in parts of Africa and appears as outbreaks whenever civil strife and famine encourage large scale louse infestation. The louseborne disease presents a more severe clinical picture than the tickborne variety and is associated with jaundice, hemorrhages and,

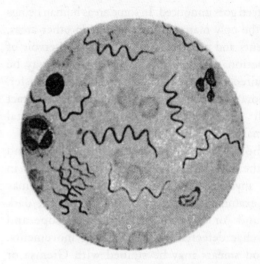

Fig. 42.2 Borrelia recurrentis in peripheral blood smear

in some outbreaks, a high rate of fatality. In lice, the borrelia is confined to the hemolymph and is not shed in saliva or excreta. So the infection is transmitted not by the bite of lice but by their being crushed and rubbed into abraded skin. *B. recurrentis* is not transmitted transovarially in lice.

Tickborne relapsing fever occurs as sporadic cases in endemic areas. It is a 'place disease' and is frequently associated with certain dwellings or other locations that are inhabited by infected ticks. The disease is milder but relapses are more frequent than in louseborne fever. The borrelia persists in the body of infected ticks throughout their life and is also transmitted transovarially so that the ticks act as reservoirs as well as vectors. The borrelia invades all parts of the body of the tick and is shed in its saliva and feces. So the infection is transmitted to humans through the bite of ticks or their discharges. Several species of soft ticks belonging to the genus Ornithodorus act as vectors, different species being responsible in different regions. In India, the vector species are *O. tholozoni*, *O. crossi*, *O. lahorensis* and the fowl tick, *Argas persicus*. These soft ticks can live for ten years or more with only an occasional blood meal. They feed usually while the host is sleeping, and painlessly so that the feed goes unnoticed. In some areas human beings are the only mammal infected but in other areas, rodents and other animals act as the reservoir of infection. Relapsing fever very rarely may be acquired congenitally by transplacental transfer. Laboratory infection may occur through contact with the blood of patients or experimental animals.

Laboratory diagnosis: Borreliae are found in the blood during the fever but seldom in the apyrexial intervals. A drop of blood may be examined as a wet film under the dark ground or phase contrast microscope and borreliae detected by their lashing movements. Blood smears may be stained with Giemsa or Leishman stain or with dilute carbol fuchsin and examined for borreliae.

A more successful method is to inoculate 1–2 ml of blood from the patient into white mice intraperitoneally. The borreliae multiply in the animals and appear in large numbers in peripheral blood within two days. Smears are prepared from blood collected from the tail vein and examined daily for two weeks.

Cultivation of the borreliae and demonstration of antibodies are too difficult and unreliable to be used in diagnosis. Patients with relapsing fever sometimes develop false positive serological tests for syphilis. Agglutinins for Proteus OXK are sometimes seen in high titres in louse-borne relapsing fever.

Prophylaxis: Prevention of louseborne relapsing fever consists of prevention of louse infestation along with the use of insecticides whenever necessary. Prevention of tickborne disease is less easy and consists of identification of tick infested places and their avoidance, or eradication of the vectors. No vaccine is available.

Treatment: Tetracyclines, chloramphenicol, penicillin and erythromycin are effective.

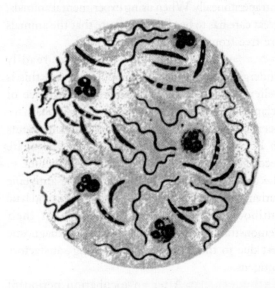

Fig. 42.3 Throat swab from a case of Vincent's angina showing Vincent's spirochetes and fusiform bacilli

BORRELIA VINCENTI
(Treponema Vincenti)

Borrelia vincenti is a motile spirochete, about 5–20 μm long and 0.2–0.6 μm wide, with 3–8 coils of variable size. It is easily stained with dilute carbol fuchsin and is Gram negative. It is a normal mouth commensal but may, under predisposing conditions such as malnutrition or viral infections, give rise to ulcerative gingivostomatitis or oropharyngitis (Vincent's angina). In these cases, *B. vincenti* is always associated with fusiform bacilli (*Fusobacterium fusiforme*). This symbiotic infection is known as *fusospirochetosis*. Large numbers of spirochetes and fusiform bacilli may also be demonstrated in some cases of lung abscess, phagedenous skin ulcers and gangrenous balanitis. Their significance is uncertain. They are not primary pathogens but may cause opportunistic disease in devitalised tissues.

Diagnosis may be made by demonstrating spirochetes and fusiform bacilli in stained smears of exudates from the lesions. *B. vincenti* may be cultivated with difficulty in enriched media anaerobically. Fusiform bacilli also grow in the culture and it is very difficult to obtain a pure growth. Penicillin and metronidazole are effective in treatment.

Fusospirochetal infection of the intestine has been reported to cause choleraic diarrhea or dysentery but this needs further confirmation.

LYME DISEASE: BORRELIA BURGDORFERI

A new spirochetal disease identified in 1975, while studying a cluster of suspected juvenile rheumatoid arthritis cases, was named *Lyme disease* or *Lyme borreliosis* (originally *Lyme arthritis*), as it was first observed in Lyme, Connecticut, USA. The disease is widespread in USA, where it is the most common vector-borne infection. It has been reported from other parts of the world also. It is caused by *Borrelia burgdorferi* transmitted by the bite of Ixodid ticks.

Lyme disease occurs in three stages. After an incubation period of 3–30 days, the first stage of 'localised infection' appears as an expanding annular skin lesion (*erythema migrans* or EM). A few weeks later, the second stage of 'disseminated infection' develops with fever, headache, myalgia, arthralgia and lymphadenopathy. Some develop meningeal or cardiac involvement. The third stage of 'persistent infection' sets in months or years later with chronic arthritis, polyneuropathy, encephalopathy and acrodermatitis.

B. burgdorferi is a fastidious bacterium which can be grown in a modified Kelley's (BSK) medium, after incubation for two weeks or more, optimally at 33 °C. Three species of the borrelia have been identified (named *B. burgdorferi*, *garinii* and *afzelii*) each of which is prevalent in different geographical regions, causing regional variations in clinical features.

The natural reservoir hosts are rodents, deer and other mammals. Ixodes dammini and related species are the vectors. The borrelia grows mainly in the midgut of the tick. Infection occurs by regurgitation of the gut contents during biting.

Laboratory diagnosis can be made by isolation of the borrelia or by serology. The borrelia has been isolated from ticks as well as from skin lesions, CSF and the blood of patients, but culture is too slow and difficult to be of use in diagnosis. Serological tests such as ELISA and IF have been described and immunoblotting recommended for confirmation. Antibodies take 1–2 months to appear, with initial IgM response followed by IgG. False positive syphilis serology may be seen, with FTA-ABS being positive and VDRL test negative.

Doxycycline, amoxycillin and cefuroxine are useful for treatment.

LEPTOSPIRA

Leptospires are actively motile, delicate spirochetes, possessing a large number of closely wound spirals and characteristic hooked ends. They are too thin to be seen under the light microscope (*leptos*, meaning fine or thin). Several leptospires are saprophytic, while many are parasitic in rodents and other animals.

The first recognised leptospiral disease of human beings was the spirochetal jaundice described by Weil (1886). Stimson (1907) observed slender spirochetes in silver stained sections of kidneys from a fatal case of jaundice. He named the organism *Spirochaeta interrogans* from a fancied resemblance of its shape to an interrogation (question) mark (Fig. 42.4). The causative agent of Weil's disease was isolated in 1915 by Inada and named *L.icterohaemorrhagiae*. Subsequently, large numbers of leptospires have been isolated from human patients and animals from different parts of the world. These were given different names and considered different species of leptospires. Several saprophytic leptospires were also isolated from water, sewage and other sources.

The genus *Leptospira* is now classified into two species: *L. interrogans* containing pathogenic leptospires and *L. biflexa* containing saprophytic leptospires found predominantly in surface waters. Within each species are serogroups, which are

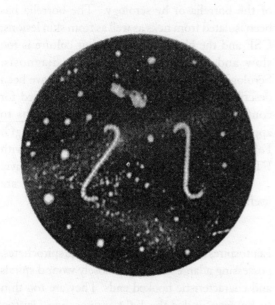

Fig. 42.4 Leptospira– dark ground illumination

further classified into serotypes (serovars). For example, *L. interrogans* is classified into several serogroups (Icterohaemorrhagiae, Canicola, Pyrogenes, Autumnalis, Australis, Pomona, Hebdomadis, Grippotyphosa, etc). Within each serogroup several serovars are recognised, for example, the serogroup Icterohaemorrhagiae contains the serovars *icterohaemorrhagiae, copenhageni, smithi,* etc). Over 200 serovars have been identified and assembled into 22 serogroups.

Morphology: Leptospires are delicate flexible helical rods about 6–20 μm long and 0.1 μm thick. They possess numerous coils set so close together that they can be distinguished only under dark ground illumination in the living state or by electron microscopy. Their ends are hooked and resemble umbrella handles. They are actively motile. They stain poorly with aniline dyes. They may be stained with Giemsa stain. Better results are obtained by the silver impregnation methods.

Cultural characteristics: Leptospires can be grown in media enriched with rabbit serum. Several liquid and semisolid media, such as Korthof's, Stuart's and Fletcher's media, have been described. Semisynthetic media, such as EMJH (Ellinghausen, McCullough, Johnson, Harris) medium are now commonly used. They are aerobic and microaerophilic. In semisolid media, growth occurs characteristically a few millimetres below the surface. Optimum temperature is 25–30 °C and optimum pH 7.2–7.5. The generation time in laboratory media is 12–16 hours and 4–8 hours in inoculated animals.

Leptospires may be grown on the chorioallantoic membrane of chick embryos. They may be demonstrated in the blood of allantoic vessels 4–5 days after inoculation. Bacterial contamination is a serious problem in isolating and maintaining leptospires in culture. The use of 5-fluorouracil has been recommended for the inhibition of contaminating bacteria in cultures. A simple method for obtaining cultures free of contaminants is to inoculate the material intraperitoneally in guinea pigs and culture the heart blood collected ten minutes later. Leptospires are able to invade the bloodstream more rapidly than other bacteria.

Resistance: Leptospires are very susceptible to heat, being killed in ten minutes at 50 °C and in 10 seconds at 60 °C. They are also sensitive to acid and are destroyed by gastric juice in 30 minutes. Bile destroys them rapidly. They are also readily destroyed by chlorine and most other antiseptics and disinfectants. Their survival in water or soil depends on temperature, acidity, salinity and nature and amount of pollution, dying rapidly in acid urine, nonaerated sewage, saltish or brackish water. They can survive for days in moist conditions at pH 6.8–8.

Antigenic properties: Leptospires exhibit considerable antigenic cross-reaction. A genus specific somatic antigen is present in all members of the genus. Classification into serogroups and serotypes is based on surface antigens. Determination of serotypes is based on agglutination and cross absorption reactions using immune rabbit sera or more recently with monoclonal antibodies. Genetic methods, such as restriction endonuclease analysis and DNA pairing are used for further classification into serotypes.

Pathogenicity: In natural reservoir hosts, leptospiral infection is asymptomatic. However, when infection is transmitted to other animals, clinical disease may result. Humans are infected when the leptospires in water contaminated by the urine of carrier animals enters the body through cuts or abrasions on the skin or through intact mucosa of mouth, nose or conjunctiva. The incubation period is usually about 10 days (range 2–26 days). The clinical picture varies from mild undifferentiated pyrexia to severe or fatal illness with hepatorenal damage (Weil's disease). In severe cases, the onset is acute, with rigor, vomiting, headache and intense injection of the eyes. The fever is irregular and usually subsides in about ten days. Jaundice occurs in about 10–20 per cent of cases by the second or third day. Purpuric hemorrhages sometimes occur on the skin and mucosa. Albuminuria is a constant feature.

This typical presentation is unusual. Leptospirosis is now classified into two clinical types —*icteric* and *nonicteric*. Many cases present as aseptic meningitis and in some, abdominal symptoms predominate. Clinical diagnosis is impossible in the majority of cases and unless a high index of suspicion is maintained and laboratory assistance sought, leptospirosis will be missed in all but a few instances.

Leptospires are seen in the blood during the acute phase of the disease but can seldom be demonstrated after 8–10 days. They persist in the internal organs, and most abundantly in the kidneys, so that they may be demonstrated in the urine in the later stages of the disease.

Serious cases of leptospirosis are caused most often by serotype icterohaemorrhagiae, though they may also be due to copenhageni and less often bataviae, grippotyphosa, pyrogenes and some others.

Aseptic meningitis is common in canicola infection and abdominal symptoms in grippotyphosa infections. However, clinical syndromes are not serotype specific and any type of illness can be produced by any serotype.

Laboratory diagnosis: Diagnosis may be made by demonstration of the leptospires microscopically in blood or urine, by isolating them in culture or by inoculation of guinea pigs, or by serological tests.

1. Examination of blood: As leptospires disappear from the blood after the first week, blood examination is helpful only in the early stages of the disease, before antibiotics are given. Leptospires may be demonstrated by examination of the blood under the dark field microscope or by immunofluorescence but this is of little practical value.

Three or four drops of blood are inoculated into each of several bijou bottles containing EMJH or similar medium. The bottles are incubated at 37 °C for two days and left thereafter at room temperature in the dark for two weeks. Samples from the cultures are examined every third day for the presence of leptospires under dark ground illumination. Primary isolation may be delayed and may take many weeks to months. Chances of isolation are increased by culturing blood daily at the early stage of the disease. Leptospires may sometimes be isolated from the CSF also.

The blood from the patient is also inoculated intraperitoneally into young guinea pigs. With virulent serotypes like icterohaemorrhagiae, the animals develop fever and die within 8–12 days with jaundice and hemorrhage into the lungs and serous cavities. With other serotypes such as canicola and pomona the animal may not become ill and infection will have to be identified by demonstration of the leptospires in the peritoneal fluid, by blood culture or by serology. From the third day after inoculation, the peritoneal fluid is examined daily under dark ground illumination and when leptospires are detected, the blood withdrawn by cardiac puncture is inoculated into culture media.

2. Examination of urine: Leptospires appear in the urine in the second week of the disease and intermittently thereafter for 4–6 weeks. The urine should be examined immediately after voiding as leptospires readily undergo lysis in acid urine. Centrifuged deposit of the urine may be examined under dark ground illumination. Direct culture of urine is seldom successful because of contamination but isolation is usually possible by inoculation into guinea pigs.

The identification of the isolates of leptospires is made by agglutination with type specific sera. Due to the large number of serotypes and the high degree of antigenic cross reactions between them, identification of isolates is a complicated procedure and is generally confirmed by one of the WHO/FAO Reference Laboratories.

3. Serological diagnosis: Antibodies appear in serum towards the end of the first week of the disease and increase till the fourth week, declining thereafter. Agglutinins may, however, be demonstrable years after the infection. Two types of serological tests are available, the broadly reactive screening tests and the serotype specific tests.

The broadly reactive or genus specific tests identify leptospiral infection without indicating the exact infecting serovar. The antigens for these tests are prepared from the nonpathogenic *L. biflexa* Patoc 1 strain. The tests employed include sensitised erythrocyte lysis (SEL), complement fixation, agglutination and indirect immunofluorescence. ELISA has been used to detect IgM and IgG antibodies separately, in order to indicate the stage of infection. A simple and rapid dip-stick assay has been developed for the assay of leptospira-specific IgM antibody in human sera.

The type specific tests identify the infecting serovar by demonstrating specific antibodies. Macroscopic and microscopic agglutination tests are used for this purpose. In the former,

formalinised suspensions of prevalent leptospira serovars are tested for macroscopic agglutination with serial dilutions of the test serum. The microscopic agglutination test (MAT) generally uses live cultures of different serotypes and agglutination is observed under the low power dark field microscope. This test is more specific and is usually done only in reference laboratories. Due to the presence of some degree of cross reaction between different serovars, agglutinin absorption tests may sometimes become necessary for accurate diagnosis.

4. Diagnosis of leptospirosis in animals: Infection in rodents and other animals may be diagnosed by serological tests or by culturing pieces of kidneys.

5. Examination of water for pathogenic leptospires: If a shaved and scarified area of the skin of a young guinea pig is immersed in water for an hour, infection takes place through the abrasions.

Epidemiology: Leptospirosis is considered to be the most widespread of zoonoses, being regularly present in all continents except Antarctica. Pathogenic leptospires survive for long periods in the convoluted tubules of the kidneys in natural hosts, multiply and are shed in the urine. Animal carriers often excrete upto 100 million leptospires per ml of urine. If the infected urine contaminates the water or mud that is neutral or slightly alkaline, the leptospires survive for weeks. When people come into contact with such water, the leptospires enter the body through abraded skin or mucosa and initiate infection. Certain occupational groups such as agricultural workers in rice or cane fields, miners and sewer cleaners are more often exposed to infection, and so leptospirosis is more common in them. Leptospires may be shed in the milk of lactating animals. However, they die rapidly in milk, and human infection through milk is not known. They are not shed in saliva, and so animal bites are not infectious. Arthropods are not known to transmit the infection.

Several animals act as carriers. Rats are particularly important as they are ubiquitous and carry the most pathogenic serotype icterohaemorrhagiae. Field mice carry grippotyphosa, pigs pomona and dogs canicola serotypes. However, the same serotype may be carried by different mammals and one mammal may carry different serotypes. While leptospires are generally nonpathogenic in the reservoir animal, leptospirosis is of veterinary importance as infection of cattle and pigs cause considerable economic loss. Infection among animals is also transmitted by urinary contamination of water and fodder. Human beings are an aberrant or 'end' host. There is no evidence that human patients infect others.

From being predominantly a rural disease of agricultural workers, leptospirosis has, in recent times also become an urban problem in the developing countries. This is perhaps due to overcrowding, insanitation, increasing rat population and the habit of walking barefooted.

Prophylaxis: As leptospirosis results from contact of skin or mucosa with contaminated water, general measures of prevention such as rodent control, disinfection of water and the wearing of protective clothing contribute to its prevention. Vaccination has been attempted with some success in dogs, cattle and pigs. Immunity following vaccination or infection is serotype specific. Vaccination has also been tried in persons at high risk such as agricultural workers.

Therapy: Leptospires are sensitive to penicillin and tetracyclines, but the treatment to be effective should be started early in the course of the disease. Penicillin is given IV, 1–2 million units 6 hourly for 7 days in serious cases. A mild Jarisch–Herxheimar reaction may occur in some. Doxycycline 200 mg orally once a week is effective in prophylaxis.

Table 42.2 Important leptospiral infections

Serotype	Disease	Clinical picture	Animal reservoir	Distribution
Icterohaemorrhagiae	Weil's disease	Fever, jaundice, hemorrhages	Rat	Worldwide
Canicola	Canicola fever	Influenza like, aseptic-meningitis	Dog	Worldwide
Grippotyphosa	Swamp or marsh fever	Fever, prostration, aseptic-meningitis	Field mice	Europe, Africa, S.E. Asia, USA
Pomona	Swineherd's disease	Fever	Pig	America, Europe, Middle East, Indonesia, Australia
Hebdomadis	Seven day fever	Fever, lymphadenopathy	Field mice	Japan, Europe, USA
Fortbragg	Pretibial fever, Fort Bragg fever	Fever, rash over tibia	Not known	Japan, S.E. Asia, USA
Pyrogenes	Febrile spirochetosis	Fever	Pig	S.E. Asia, Europe, USA
Bataviae	Indonesian Weil's disease	Fever	Rat	S.E. Asia, Africa, Europe
Hardjo	Dairy farm fever	Fever	Cattle	UK, USA, New Zealand

Further Reading

Barbour AG. 1990. Antigenic variation of relapsing fever Borrelia. species *Ann Rev Microbiol* 44:155.

Farr RW. 1995. Leptospirosis. *Clin Infect Dis* 21:1.

Gussenhoven GC. 1997. Lepto–dipstick assay for leptospira–specific IgM antibody in human sera. *J Clin Microbiol* 35:92.

Koff AB and T Rosen 1993. Nonvenereal treponematoses. *J Amer Acad Dermatol* 29:519.

Larsen SA et al. 1995. Laboratory diagnosis and interpretation of tests for syphilis, *Clin Microbol Rev* 8:1.

O'Connell S. 1995. Lyme disease in the UK. *BMJ* 310:303.

Rahn DW and SE Malawista 1991. Lyme disease. *Ann Intern Med* 114:472.

Sandra AL et al. 1995. Laboratory diagnosis and interpretation of tests for syphilis *Clin Microbiol Rev* 8:1.

wall precursors like muramic acid or diaminopimelic acid. The cells are bounded by a soft trilaminar unit membrane containing sterols. Because of their plasticity, they can pass through bacterial filters and have often been mistaken for viruses. The first member of the group was the organism causing bovine pleuropneumonia, isolated by Nocard and Roux (1898). A similar organism was found to cause contagious agalactia in sheep. When many similar isolates were obtained from animals, human beings, plants and environmental sources, they came to be called *pleuropneumonia-like organisms*' (PPLO). This unsatisfactory name has been replaced by the term Mycoplasma (*Myco*, from the fungus-like form of the branching filaments; *plasma*, denoting their plasticity of shape).

Mycoplasmas have been placed in the class Mollicutes (literally meaning soft skin), order ...matales, which contains the following ...nd genera:

... *Mycoplasmataceae*, to which belong parasitic mycoplasmas requiring cholesterol or other sterols as an essential growth factor. This contains two genera:

a. Genus *Mycoplasma* which utilise glucose or arginine but do not split urea, and

b. Genus *Ureaplasma* which hydrolyse urea.

2. Family *Acholeplasmataceae*, mostly saprophytic mycoplasmas, which do not require sterols as growth factor.

3. Family *Spiroplasmataceae*, containing the Genus *Spiroplasma*, which parasitise arthropods and plants. They are sterol dependent. These are helical in shape.

4. Family *Anaeroplasmataceae*, containing the genus *Anaeroplasma*, which are strict anaerobes, found in the rumen of cattle and sheep.

Mycoplasmas may be saprophytic, parasitic or pathogenic. More than 100 species of mycoplasma are known to cause disease in a variety of

Table 43.1 Mycoplasmas of Humans

A. Parasitic:
1. *Established pathogen:*
   M. pneumoniae causing pneumonia
2. *Presumed pathogens:*
   M. hominis and U.urealyticum associated with genital infections
3. *Non-pathogenic:*
   M, orale, M. buccale, M. salivarium, M. faucium in oropharynx
   M. fermentans, M. genitalium, M. penetrans, M. primatum,
   M. spermatophilum in genital tract
B. Saprophytic
   Acholeplasma laidlawii on skin and in mouth.

MYCOPLASMA

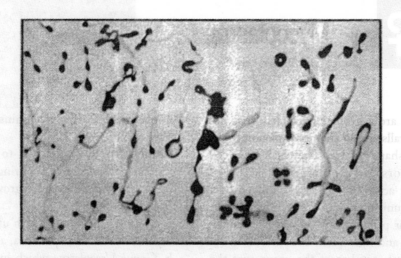

Fig. 43.1 Morphology of mycoplasma—extreme pleomorphism

mammalian, insect and plant hosts. About sixteen species, belonging to three families are found in human beings (Table 43.1).

Morphology: Mycoplasmas are the smallest free-living microorganisms, and one of the most pleomorphic (Fig. 43.1). They occur as granules and filaments of various sizes. The granules may be coccoid, balloon, disc, ring or star forms. The filaments are slender, of varying lengths and show true branching. Multiplication is by binary fission, but as genomic replication and cell division are often asynchronous, budding forms and chains of beads are produced. A distinctive feature seen in some species is a bulbous enlargement, with a differentiated tip structure, by means of which the organisms get attached to suitable host cells carrying neuraminic acid receptors. They may be responsible for the hemadsorption shown by some species.

Mycoplasmas do not possess spores, flagella or fimbria. Some species exhibit a gliding motility. Mycoplasmas are Gram negative but are better stained by Giemsa stain.

Mycoplasmas may be cultivated in fluid or solid media. They are generally facultative anaerobes, growth being better aerobically. They grow within a temperature range of 22–41 °C, the parasitic species growing optimally at 35–37 °C and the saprophytes at lower temperatures. Media for cultivating mycoplasma are enriched with 20 per cent horse or human serum and yeast extract. Penicillin and thallium acetate are added as selective agents. The high concentration of serum is necessary as a source of cholesterol and other lipids. Colonies appear after incubation for 2–6 days and are about 10–600 μm in size. The colony is typically biphasic, with a 'fried egg' appearance, consisting of a central opaque granular area of growth extending into the depth of the medium, surrounded by a flat, translucent peripheral zone (Fig. 43.2). Colonies may be seen with a hand lens but are best studied after staining by Dienes method. For this, a block of agar containing the colony is cut and placed on a slide. It is covered with a cover slip on which has been dried an alcoholic solution of methylene blue and azure.

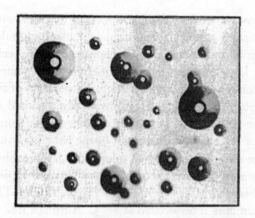

Fig.43.2 'Fried egg' appearance of mycoplasma colonies

Colonies cannot be picked with platinum loops. Subculture is done by cutting out an agar block with colonies and rubbing it on fresh plates. Most mycoplasma colonies are hemolytic.

Biochemical reactions: Mycoplasmas are chemo-organotrophs, the metabolism being mainly fermentative. Most species utilise glucose or arginine as the major sources of energy. Urea is not hydrolysed, except by ureaplasmas. They are generally not proteolytic.

Unique among procaryotes is the requirement of most mycoplasmas for cholesterol and related sterols, which are incorporated in their surface membranes. Mycoplasmas also lack the ability to synthesise purines and pyrimidines.

Resistance: Mycoplasmas generally resemble nonsporing bacteria in heat resistance but some strains are more sensitive, being destroyed at 45 °C in 15 minutes. They are relatively resistant to lysis by osmotic shock but are very sensitive to lysis by surface active agents and lipolytic agents such as taurocholate and digitonin. They are resistant to penicillin and cephalosporin as well as to lysozymes that act on the bacterial cell walls but are sensitive to tetracycline and many other antibiotics. Susceptibility to erythromycin and some other macrolide antibiotics is useful for species differentiation. Growth is inhibited by gold salts. *M. pneumoniae* can grow in the presence of 0.002 per cent methylene blue in agar, while many other species are inhibited.

Antigenic properties: Serological tests such as complement fixation, agglutination, passive hemagglutination, ELISA, and immuno-fluorescence have been employed for detection of antibodies in sera and for the identification of isolates. Mycoplasmal surface antigens are mainly glycolipids and proteins. Glycolipid antigens are identified by complement fixation and protein antigens by ELISA. A particularly useful technique for the identification of isolates is the growth inhibition test based on the ability of antisera to specifically inhibit the growth of the homologous species on solid media.

Pathogenicity: Parasitic mycoplasmas exhibit host specificity. They generally produce surface infections by adhering to the mucosa of the respiratory, gastrointestinal and genitourinary tracts. Mycoplasma cause two types of diseases in humans – pneumonia and genital infections.

Mycoplasmal pneumonia (*primary atypical pneumonia*) is caused by *M. pneumoniae*. The disease is typically a tracheobronchitis. Acute pharyngitis is uncommon and only a third of the patients develop pneumonia. Incubation period is 1–3 weeks. The onset is gradual, with fever, malaise, headache and sore throat. Paroxysmal cough may occur with blood tinged sputum. The disease is characterised by paucity of respiratory signs on physical examination but radiological evidence of consolidation, which is usually patchy, involving one of the lower lobes, starting at the hilum, and fanning out to the periphery. The disease is usually self-limited, recovery occurring in 1–2 weeks, but can be prolonged. Bullous myringitis and otitis are common complications. Rashes, meningitis, encephalitis and hemolytic anemia are other complications seen.

The disease is worldwide and is found at all ages. Transmission is by droplets of nasopharyngeal secretion. Spread is favoured by close contact, as in families and most typically among military recruits.

The mycoplasma may remain in the throat for two or more months after recovery from the disease.

Eaton (1944) was the first to isolate the causative agent of the disease in hamsters and cotton rats. He was able to transmit the infection later to chick embryos by amniotic inoculation. Because it was filterable, it was considered to be a virus (Eaton agent), but was subsequently shown to be a mycoplasma and named *M. pneumoniae.*

Laboratory diagnosis of mycoplasmal primary atypical pneumonia may be established either by isolation of the mycoplasma or by serological methods. For isolation, throat swabs or respiratory secretions are inoculated into mycoplasma medium containing glucose and phenol red. Growth is slow on primary isolation and may take 1–3 weeks. Growth is indicated by acid production in the medium. *M. pneumoniae* produces beta hemolysis and agglutinates guinea pig erythrocytes. Colonies on agar adsorb erythrocytes. The hemadsorption is enzymatic and occurs optimally at 37 °C. The cell receptors are destroyed by neuraminidase. It inhibits ciliary motility in hamster trachea organ cultures. *M. pneumoniae* is unrelated to other human mycoplasmas and may be identified by growth inhibition by specific antisera. As isolation is difficult and delayed, PCR assay which is rapid and specific is being used where feasible.

Serological diagnosis may be made by specific tests using mycoplasmal antigens or by nonspecific methods. Among the former, immunofluorescence, hemagglutination inhibition and metabolic inhibition are the most sensitive tests. Complement fixation and indirect hemagglutination tests are less sensitive.

The nonspecific serological tests are *Streptococcus* MG and cold agglutination tests. The former is done by mixing serial dilutions of the patient's unheated serum and a heat killed suspension of *Streptococcus MG*, and observing agglutination after overnight incubation at 37 °C. A titre of 1:20 or over is considered suggestive.

The cold agglutination test is based on the appearance in a high proportion of cases with primary atypical pneumonia, of macroglobulin antibodies that agglutinate human group O cells at low temperature. The patient's blood sample should not be refrigerated before separation of the serum, as the agglutinins are readily absorbed by the homologous erythrocytes at low temperatures. For the test, serial dilutions of the patient's serum are mixed with an equal volume of a 0.2% washed human O group erythrocytes, and clumping observed after leaving at 4 °C overnight. The clumping is dissociated at 37 °C. A titre of 1:32 or over is suggestive but demonstration of rise in titre in paired serum samples is more reliable. The indirect Coombs test may also be positive in some cases.

UREAPLASMA UREALYTICUM

Some strains of mycoplasma frequently isolated from the urogenital tract of human beings and animals form very tiny colonies, generally 15–50 μm in size. They were called T strain or T form mycoplasmas (T for tiny). They are peculiar in their ability to hydrolyse urea, which is an essential growth factor in addition to cholesterol. Human T strain mycoplasmas have been reclassified as *Ureaplasma urealyticum.*

Genital infections are caused by *M. hominis* and *U. urealyticum*. They are transmitted by sexual contact, and may cause urethritis, proctitis, balanoposthitis and Reiter's syndrome in men, and acute salphingitis, pelvic inflammatory disease, cervicitis and vaginitis in women. They have also been associated with infertility, abortion, postpartum fever, chorioamnionitis and low birthweight of infants.

Mycoplasma and HIV infection: Mycoplasmas tend to cause more severe and prolonged infections in the HIV infected and other immunodeficient subjects.

Mycoplasma as cell culture contaminants: Continuous cell cultures maintained in many laboratories have been found to be contaminated with different species of mycoplasma. The contamination may originate from the worker or from animal sera or trypsin used in cell culture. Contamination generally does not produce cytopathic effects but may interfere with the growth of viruses in such cell cultures and may also produce misleading results in serological tests. Mycoplasmas growing in cell cultures have often been mistaken for viruses. Eradication of mycoplasmas from infected cells is difficult.

Treatment are the drugs of choice for the treatment of mycoplasmal infections. Some ureaplasmas are resistant to tetracycline, doxycycline, the newer macrolides and quinolones.

Mycoplasmas and L forms of bacteria: Kleineberger (1935) found pleuropneumonia-like forms in a culture of *Streptobacillus* *moniliformis* and termed them L forms, after Lister Institute, London, where the observation was made. It was subsequently shown that many bacteria, either spontaneously or induced by certain substances like penicillin, lost part or all of their cell wall and develop into L forms. Such L forms may be 'unstable', when they revert to their normal morphology, or 'stable' when they continue in the cell wall deficient state permanently. Cell wall deficient forms (L forms, protoplasts, spheroplasts) may not initiate disease but may be important in bacterial persistence during antibiotic therapy and subsequent recurrence of the infection. It has been suggested that mycoplasmas may represent stable L forms of bacteria but genetic, antigenic and biochemical evidence are against the possibility.

Further Reading

Lin JS. 1985. Human mycoplasmal infections. Serologic observations. *Rev Infect Dis* 7:216.

Symposium. 1993. The changing role of mycoplasmas in respiratory disease and AIDS. *Clin Infect Dis* 17:(Suppl.1).

Taylor-Robinson D and J Bradbury 1998. Mycoplasma diseases. In *Topley and Wilson's Microbiology and Microbial Infections*, 9th edn. London:Arnold.

44 Actinomycetes

Actinomycetes are tra[...] [...]tinomycosis in
transitional forms betw[...] [...] is a chronic
fungi they form a my[...] [...] human beings
filaments but, like bac[...] [...]e development
cell walls containi[...] [...]he connective
prokaryotic nuclei [...] [...]ge of 'sulphur
antibacterial antibioti[...] [...]wards the skin,
bacteria, bearing a sup[...]
Actinomycetes are re[...] [...]beings is an
corynebacteria. They a[...] [...]yces species are
nonsporing, noncapsul[...] [...]tine and vagina
into bacillary and cocc[...] [...]ies or poor oral
living, particularly in [...]

Handwritten note:

Actinomycetes –
→ are transitional forms between bacteria & fungi.
→ They are Gram +ve, nonmotile, non-sporing, non-encapsulated filaments.
→ They are anaerobic & non-acid fast.

Actinomycosis –
→ chronic inf. occurring in human beings & animals.
→ characterized by the dev. of swellings in the connective tissue & the discharge of 'sulphur granules' which often points tells the skin leading to multiple sinuses.
→ Actinomycosis occurs in 4 main clinical forms.
1. cervicofacial 2. Thoracic 3. Abdominal 4. Pelvic

Treatment — Ampicilline or penicilline & tetracycline
Personal hygiene is main prevention.

Actinomycetes include many genera of medical interest such as the anaerobic *Actinomyces*, *Arachnia*, *Bifidobacterium*, *Rothia* and aerobic *Nocardia*, *Actinomadura*, *Dermatophilus* and *Streptomyces*. The major pathogenic genus *Actinomyces* is anaerobic or microaerophilic and nonacid fast, while *Nocardia* species are aerobic and may be acid fast. Some species of *Streptomyces* may cause disease rarely, but their importance is as the major source of antibiotics.

ACTINOMYCES

Bollinger (1877) found a mould-like organism in the lesion of 'lumpy jaw' (actinomycosis) in cattle. The name actinomyces was coined by Harz to refer to the raylike appearance of the organism in the granules that characterise the lesions (*actinomyces*, meaning ray fungus). Wolff and Israel (1891) isolated an anaerobic bacillus from human lesions and produced experimental infection in rabbits and guinea pigs. This was named *Actinomyces israelii*.

hygiene may favour tissue invasion. *A. israelii* is the most common causative agent. However, other actinomycetes such as *A. naeslundii*, *A. viscosus*, *A. odontolyticum*, *A. meyeri*, *A. gerencsonei* and *Propionibacterium propionicum* may sometimes be responsible. Actinomycosis is usually a co-operative disease, the actinomyces being accompanied by other associated bacteria which may enhance the pathogenic effect. These include *Bifidobacterium dentium*, *Actinobacillus actinomycetemcomitans*, *Eikenella corrodens*, *Haemophilus aphrophilus*, bacteroides, fusobacteria, staphylococci and anaerobic streptococci.

Actinomycosis in human beings occurs in four main clinical forms: (1) *cervicofacial* with indurated lesions on the cheek and submaxillary regions; (2) *thoracic*, with lesions in the lung that may involve the pleura and pericardium and spread outwards through the chest wall; (3) *abdominal* where the lesion is usually around the cecum, with the involvement of the neighbouring tissues and the abdominal wall. Sometimes the infection spreads to the liver via the portal vein. (4) *Pelvic*. Many cases of pelvic actinomycosis have been reported in association with the use of intrauterine devices.

Actinomyces have been incriminated in inflam...

[Handwritten note overlaying text:]

Nocardia
→ Resemble actinomycetes but are aerobic.
→ cause cutaneous, subcutaneous or systemic lesions in humans.
→ may lead to local abscesses, cellulitis or lymphocutaneous lesions.
→ Nocardiosis manifests primarily as pulmonary disease, pneumonia, lung abscess or other lesions resembling tuberculosis.

TREATMENT - cotrimoxazole, minocycline, amikacin & cefotaxime.

are examined microscopically under a cover slip. They are crushed between slides and stained by Gram stain and examined. The granules are, in fact, bacterial colonies and will be found to consist of a dense network of thin Gram positive filaments, surrounded by a peripheral zone of swollen radiating club shaped structures, presenting a sun ray appearance. The 'clubs' are believed to be antigen–antibody complexes (Fig. 44.1).

Sulphur granules or pus containing actinomycetes are washed and inoculated into thioglycollate liquid medium or streaked on brain–heart infusion agar and incubated anaerobically at 37 °C. In thioglycollate *A. bovis* produces general turbidity whereas *A. israelii* grows as fluffy balls at the bottom of the tube. On solid media *A. israelii* produces small 'spidery colonies' in 48–72 hours that become heaped up, white and irregular or smooth, large colonies in 10 days. Other species have different types of colonies.

The isolate is identified by microscopy, biochemical reactions and fluorescent antibody

methods. Gel diffusion and immunofluorescence can differentiate *A. israelii* from other actinomycete species and from other filamentous anaerobes that may produce granules in tissues.

Epidemiology. The disease occurs throughout ... cidence in the advanced countries ... probably as a result of the ... antibiotics. Actinomycosis is ... rural areas and in agricultural ... persons (10–30 years old) are ... affected. The reason for this ... known. About 60 per cent of ... cofacial and some 20 per·cent ... actinomyces is seen mainly in ... uterine devices.

... disease responds to prolonged ... cillin or tetracycline. Treatment ... tinued for several months and ... rgery where necessary.

NOCARDIA

Nocardia resemble Actinomycetes morphologically but are aerobic. All species are Gram positive and

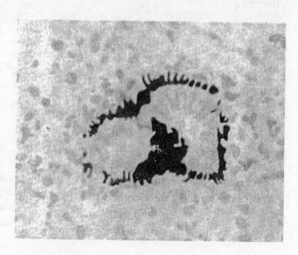

Fig. 44.1 Sulphur granule. Section of tissue showing an actinomycotic clolony, the clubs at the periphery giving a 'sun ray' appearance.

some such as *N. astroides* and *N. brasiliensis* also acid fast. Nocardia are frequently found in soil and infection may be exogenous. Infection with nocardia causes cutaneous, subcutaneous or systemic lesions in humans. The species usually responsible are *N. asteroides, N. brasiliensis* and *N. caviae*. Cutaneous infection may lead to local abscesses, cellulitis or lymphocutaneous lesions. The subcutaneous lesion is actinomycotic mycetoma (described below). Systemic nocardiosis usually caused by *N. asteroides* manifests primarily as pulmonary disease, pneumonia, lung abscess or other lesions resembling tuberculosis. Metastatic manifestations may involve the brain, kidneys and other organs. Systemic nocardiosis occurs more often in immunodeficient persons.

Diagnosis is by demonstration of branching filaments microscopically and by isolation in culture. Nocardia grow readily on ordinary media forming dry, granular, wrinkled colonies, which produce pigment ranging from yellow to red.

Cotrimoxazole given for several months may be useful. Minocycline, amikacin and cefotaxime are effective.

ACTINOMYCOTIC MYCETOMA

Mycetoma is a localised chronic, granulomatous involvement of the subcutaneous and deeper tissues, commonly affecting the foot and less often the hand and other parts, and presenting as a tumour with multiple discharging sinuses. This clinical syndrome was first described from Madura by Gill (1842) and came to be known as *Maduramycosis*. Mycetomas are usually caused by fungi but may be caused by bacteria as well. Even *Staph. aureus* and other pyogenic bacteria may occasionally cause a mycetoma-like lesion (*botryomycosis*). Bacterial mycetomas are usually caused by actinomycetes— *Actinomyces* (*A. israelii, A. bovis*), *Nocardia* (*N. asteroides, N. brasiliensis, N. caviae*), *Actinomadura* (*A. madurae, A. pelletierii*), *Streptomyces* (*S. somaliensis*).

Etiological diagnosis of mycetoma is important in choosing appropriate treatment. The colour of the granules gives some indication. In actinomycotic mycetoma, the granules are white to yellow, while in eumycotic mycetomas, the granules are generally black. Examination of crushed smears of the granules helps to differentiate actinomycotic from mycotic mycetomas. In the former, the filaments are thin (about 1 µm), while in the latter they are stout (about 4–5 µm). Isolation of the agent in culture establishes the diagnosis.

ACTINOMYCETES AND HYPERSENSITIVITY PNEUMONITIS

Spores of some thermophilic actinomycetes such as *Faenia* and *Saccharomonosporia* species, present in mouldy hay, when inhaled may induce allergic alveolitis leading to chronic obstructive pulmonary disease (COPD, farmer's lung).

Further Reading

Collins CH et al. 1988. Presumptive identification of nocardias. *J Applied Bact* 65:55.
Curry WH. 1980. Human nocardiosis. *Arch Int Med* 140:818.
Schaal KP and HJ Lee 1995. Actinomycete infections in humans. *Gene* 115:201.
Schaal KP. 1998. Actinomycoses. In *Topley and Wilson's Microbiology and Microbial Infections*, 9th edn. London: Arnold.

Miscellaneous Bacteria

LISTERIA MONOCYTOGENES

Listeria monocytogenes is a small, coccoid, Gram positive bacillus, with a tendency to occur in chains. Rough forms may be seen as long filaments. It exhibits a characteristic, slow, tumbling motility when grown at 25 °C but at 37 °C is nonmotile. This is because peritrichous flagella are produced by the bacillus optimally at 20–30 °C but only scantily or not at all at 37 °C. It is aerobic or microaerophilic. Growth is improved when cultures are incubated at reduced oxygen tension and with 5–10% CO_2. It grows best between 30 °C and 37 °C, but slow growth occurs even at 4 °C. Colonies are hemolytic on blood agar. *L. monocytogenes* ferments glucose, maltose, L rhamnose and alpha methyl D-mannoside, producing acid without gas. It is catalase positive. It grows in the presence of 0.1% potassium tellurite, 10% salt and at pH 9.6. Many serovars have been recognised.

L. monocytogenes is widely distributed in nature. It has been isolated from a wide range of mammals, birds, fish, ticks and crustacea. It occurs as a saprophyte in soil, water and sewage. Listeriosis in human beings may present in many forms. It may cause meningitis or meningoencephalitis, particularly in neonates and in the elderly. Infection of pregnant women may lead to abortion or stillbirth. Asymptomatic infection of the female genital tract may cause infertility. Listeriosis may also present as abscesses, conjunctivitis, pharyngitis, urethritis, pneumonia, infectious mononucleosis-like syndrome, endocarditis or septicemia.

Most human infections are caused by serovar 1/2a or 1/2b and 4b. Experimental inoculation in rabbits causes a marked monocytosis (hence the name *monocytogenes*). Monocytosis is a feature of human listeriosis also. Instillation into the eyes of rabbits produces keratoconjunctivitis (*Anton test*). Human infection is believed to result from contact with infected animals, inhalation of contaminated dust or ingestion of contaminated milk or food. Outbreaks of foodborne listeriosis have been known.

Laboratory diagnosis is established by the isolation of the bacillus from appropriate clinical material such as cervical and vaginal secretions, lochia, meconium, cord blood, blood and cerebrospinal fluid. Greater success in isolation is achieved if the materials are stored in tryptose phosphate or thioglycollate broth at 4 °C and subcultures are done at weekly intervals for 1–6 months (*cold enrichment*). Listeriosis in human beings is being increasingly reported. Isolates are likely to be missed as nonpathogenic diphtheroids unless properly investigated. Ampicillin, cotrimoxazole and gentamicin are effective. Cephalosporins are not recommended.

Table 45.1 lists some distinguishing features of nonsporing Gram positive bacilli found in clinical specimens.

ERYSIPELOTHRIX RHUSIOPATHIAE

Erysipelothrix rhusiopathiae is a slender, nonmotile, nonsporing, noncapsulated Gram positive rod, with a tendency towards formation of long filaments. It is microaerophilic on primary isolation but on subculture, grows as an aerobe or facultative anaerobe. It grows on ordinary media. Black colonies are developed in tellurite media. It ferments glucose and lactose, producing acid without gas; sucrose and mannitol are not fermented. Different antigenic types have been recognised.

E. rhusiopathiae is a natural parasite of many animals. It causes swine erysipelas and human erysipeloid. Human infection usually occurs on the hand or fingers of persons handling animals fish or animal products. The lesions are painful, edematous and erythematous, usually involving the local lymphnodes and joints. Occasional cases of endocarditis have been reported. The bacillus is sensitive to penicillin, erythromycin and broad spectrum antibiotics.

ALCALIGENES FAECALIS

The name Bacterium faecalis alkaligenes was originally applied to an ill defined group of Gram negative bacilli isolated from human feces, which did not ferment sugars but produced an alkaline reaction in litmus milk. The term Alcaligenes faecalis now refers to Gram negative, short, nonsporing bacilli, which are strict aerobes and do not ferment sugars. They are motile by means of peritrichous flagella. They are usually oxidase positive. Nitrate reduction is variable.

Alc. faecalis is a saprophyte found in water and soil contaminated with decaying organic matter. They are also commensals in human and animal intestines. They have been isolated from a variety of clinical specimens such as urine, pus and blood. They have been considered responsible for a typhoid-like fever, urinary infections, infantile gastroenteritis and suppuration in various parts of the body.

CHROMOBACTERIUM VIOLACEUM

Chromobacterium violaceum is a Gram negative, nonsporing bacillus, motile by means of polar and lateral flagella. They are facultative anaerobes growing on ordinary media and producing violet pigment soluble in ethanol and insoluble in water and chloroform. They are oxidase negative and

saprophytic in water and soil. Human infections have been recorded mainly in the tropics and consist of skin lesions with pyemia and multiple abscesses.

FLAVOBACTERIUM MENINGOSEPTICUM

Flavobacterium meningosepticum is a Gram negative nonmotile rod, producing a yellowish pigment. It is oxidase positive, proteolytic and weakly fermentative. It is a ubiquitous saprophyte capable of causing opportunistic infections. It has been responsible for outbreaks of meningitis in newborn infants. Infection in adults leads to a mild febrile illness.

DONOVANIA GRANULOMATIS
(Calymmatobacterium granulomatis)

Donovan (1905) described the presence of characteristic intracellular bodies in smears from ulcerated lesions of a disease now known as Donovanosis. He considered the bodies to be parasites. Donovanosis is a venereal disease, first described by McLeod in India in 1882 and seen mainly in the tropics. The incubation period ranges from 1 to 12 weeks. It begins as a painless papule on the genitalia, which leads to a slowly progressive, autoinoculable ulcers. The disease runs a chronic course. Donovan's intracellular bodies have since been identified as bacteria and named Donovania granulomatis.

Diagnosis can be made by demonstration of Donovan bodies in Wright–Giemsa stained impression smears from the lesions. They appear as rounded cocobacilli, 1–2 μm, within cystic spaces in large mononuclear cells. They show bipolar condensation of chromatin, giving a closed safety pin appearance in stained smears. Capsules are usually seen as dense acidophilic areas around the bacilli. They are nonmotile and Gram negative. They can be grown on egg yolk medium and on a modified Levinthal agar. It is morphologically and antigenically related to klebsiellae.

Pathogenicity is limited to human beings. Intradermal inoculation of whole cultures or of an

Table 45.1 Differential features of nonsporing Gram positive bacilli

	L. monocytogenes	E. rhusiopathiae	Diphtheroids	Lactobacilli
Beta hemolysis	+	-	±	-
Catalase	+	-	±	-
Motility	+	-	-	-
H₂S production	-	+	-	-

alkaline extract of cultures in patients produces a red edematous reaction in 24 hours. Tetracycline given for at least three weeks is usually curative. Cotrimoxazole, chloramphenicol, gentamycin, quinolones and the newer macrolides are also effective.

ACINETOBACTER

The genus *Acinetobacter* contains strictly aerobic, nonmotile, gram negative, coccobacillary rods that are oxidase negative, nitrate negative and do not ferment sugars. They are 1–1.5 μm x 1.5–2.5 μm in size, often appearing in pairs, mimicking neisseriae in appearance. Hence the name *Mimeae* was applied to them for a time. The earliest member of the group was a soil bacterium isolated in 1911 by Beijerinck, who named it *Micrococcus Calcoaceticus*. Subsequently many similar bacteria isolated from clinical and other sources were given a variety of names.

Strains which acidified sugars oxidatively were called *Herellea vaginicola, Bacterium antitratum, Acinetobacter anitratum* and so on. Strains which were asaccharolytic were called mima *polymorpha, acinetobacter lwoffi*, and so on.

By DNA hybridization studies, they have been assigned to different DNA homology groups, called *genomo species*, within the genes *acinetobacter*. Strains commonly isolated in clinical laboratories are called the *Acinetobacter calcoaceticus-baumannii complex* subdivided as follows: glucose oxidising, nonhemolytic clinical strains as *A. baumannii* (corresponding to the former *A.antitratus*); the glucose negative nonhemolytic strain as *A. lwoffi* (corresponding to the form *Mima polymorpha*); and the hemolytic strain as *A. hemolyticus.*

A. baumannii: These form pinkish colonies on MacConkey medium. Acid without gas is formed in glucose, arabinose, xylose, and occasionally in rhamnose. A characteristic reaction is the formation of acid in 10%, but not 1% lactose. Several serotypes have been identified by capsule swelling and immunofluorescence.

A. lowffi: This forms yellow colonies on MacConkey medium and does not acidify sugars. Some strains are oxidase positive.

Acinetobacters are opportunistic pathogens and are often found in hospital infections, particularly in iatrogenic meningitis. They are frequently present on the normal skin. All strains are resistant to penicillin but most strains are sensitive to one or the other of the broad spectrum antibiotics.

RAT BITE FEVER
(Streptobacillus moniliformis and Spirillum minus)

Rat bite fever (RBF) is characterised by relapsing fever, rash and arthralgia occurring days or weeks after a rat bite. Two different bacteria can cause this condition—*Streptobacillus moniliformis* and *Spirillum minus*, both of which are natural parasites of rodents.

Str. moniliformis is a highly pleomorphic, Gram negative, nonmotile bacillus. In cultures it grows as tangled chains of rods of various lengths, with beaded or fusiform swellings, readily developing into L-forms. Growth requires the presence of blood or other body fluids. It is catalase, oxidase, nitrate, urease and indole negative. It ferments glucose and a few other sugars forming acid but no gas.

Streptobacillary RBF develops 2–10 days after exposure, with abrupt onset of fever, headache and myalgia, followed by a petechial rash and arthritis.

Relapses are common in untreated cases.. The disease can also occur as outbreaks, in the absence of rat bite. This condition, first observed in Haverhill, USA, is called *Haverhill fever* or *erythema arthriticum epidemicum*. It is believed to be caused also by consumption of raw milk or water contaminated by rats.

Laboratory diagnosis is by isolation of the bacillus from blood or other body fluids. Smears of the joint fluid may show pleomorphic Gram negative rods. Agglutination, CF and fluorescent antibody tests have been used for serological diagnosis.

Spirillum minus is a short, actively motile bacterium, $3-5 \times 0.2-0.5$ µm in size, with two or three regular spirals and $1-7$ amphitrichous flagella. It is Gram negative but is better visualised by Giemsa or Fontana stains or by dark field microscopy. It was first observed in a rat by Carter (1888) in India. Japanese workers identified it as the causative agent of one type of RBF, called *Sodoku*. It has not been cultivated in laboratory media.

Spirillary RBF has an incubation period of $1-4$ weeks. The rat bite wound which may have healed, suppurates at the onset of fever, with regional lymphadenopathy. The subsequent course is similar to the streptobacillary type. Mortality rates of up to 10 per cent have been reported, mainly due to endocarditis.

Laboratory diagnosis is by the microscopic examination of the blood and exudates from the lesion, by intraperitoneal inoculation into guinea pigs and mice and by demonstration of the spirilla in their blood and peritoneal fluid. Biological false positive reactions for syphilis serology occurs in a proportion of RBF patients, more in the spirillary form.

Both types of RBF respond to penicillin and tetracycline. Oral penicillin or doxycycline after rat bite is effective in prophylaxis.

CAMPYLOBACTER

The genus *Campylobacter* (Greek, meaning curved rod) contains slender spirally curved Gram negative rods, $0.2-0.5$ µm thick and $0.5-5$ µm long. They are typically comma shaped but may occur as 'S' or multispiral chains. Old cultures are coccoid and pleomorphic. They are nonsporing and motile with a single unsheathed polar flagellum at one or both poles. Growth occurs under microaerophilic conditions, 5% oxygen concentration being optimal. Many pathogenic species are thermophilic, growing well at 42 °C. Campylobacters do not attack carbohydrates but are strongly oxidase positive.

Campylobacters first gained prominence in the 1970s as a common cause of human diarrheal disease, affecting children and adults. They can, on occasion, also cause systemic infections. They are important veterinary pathogens. Campylobacters of medical importance are the following:

Causing diarrheal disease: *C. jejuni, C. coli, C. lari.*

Causing extraintestinal infection: *C. fetus*

Causing abscesses: *C. sputorum, C. conciscus*

CAMPYLOBACTER JEJUNI

Medically, this is the most important campylobacter species as it causes attacks of diarrhea worldwide. The infection is zoonotic, the source being food of animal origin, especially raw milk. It is part of the normal intestinal flora of domestic animals and birds, and is shed in their feces. It can be isolated frequently from surface waters.

Infection occurs by ingestion. The jejunum and ileum are the primary sites of colonisation, but it may spread down to the colon and rectum. It is an invasive pathogen and may involve mesenteric lymph nodes and cause bacteremia. The incubation period is $1-7$ days. The illness starts with fever, abdominal pain and watery diarrhea. Stool contains leucocytes and blood. The disease is usually self-limited, though campylobacter shedding may continue for weeks after recovery. Fluid and electrolyte replacement is all that is generally required. When needed, erythromycin is the best antibiotic.

Laboratory diagnosis depends on isolation of the campylobacter from feces. Direct microscopic examination – phase contrast or dark field microscopy to detect the darting or tumbling motility of the spiral rods, or demonstration of the small curved rods in stained smears – may be useful for presumptive rapid diagnosis. Feces or rectal swabs are plated on selective media. In case of delay in culturing, a transport medium has to be employed. Campylobacters survive for 1–2 weeks at 4 °C in Cary–Blair transport medium but glycerol-saline is not satisfactory. The plating media commonly used are Skirrow's, Butzler's or Campy BAP selective media. *C. jejuni*, as well as *C. coli* and *C. lari*, are thermophilic and do not grow at 25 °C. Inoculated plates are incubated at 42 °C in an atmosphere of 5% oxygen, 10% carbon dioxide and 85% nitrogen. Thermophilic campylobacters can grow well at 37 °C also but incubation at higher temperatures suppresses normal fecal flora to some extent.

Colonies appear usually by 48 hours. They are nonhemolytic, grey or colourless, moist, and flat or convex. Suggestive colonies are screened by Gram staining, motility and oxidase tests. Confirmation is by further biochemical tests, including positive catalase and nitrate reduction tests.

C. coli causes an infection clinically indistinguishable from that due to *C. jejuni*. *C. coli* is commonly found in healthy pigs. It is differentiated from *C. jejuni* by the hippurate hydrolysis test which is positive only in the case of *C. jejuni*.

C. lari also causes a similar diarrheal disease. It can be distinguished from *C. jejuni* and *C. coli* by its resistance to nalidixic acid.

C. jejuni and *C. coli* can be serotyped for epidemiological purposes.

C. jejuni is the most common bacterial cause of diarrheal disease in many developed countries – more common than salmonellae or shigellae. In the developing countries, *C. jejuni* is endemic, asymptomatic infection being widely prevalent in humans, as well as domestic animals and birds. In this situation, clinical disease is infrequent and usually confined to children, while older age groups are immune due to subclinical infections.

The related genus Arcobacteria species (*A. butzleri*, *A. cryaerophila*) also cause diarrheal disease. They are capable of aerobic growth.

CAMPYLOBACTER FETUS

This organism was isolated in 1918 by Theobald Smith from infectious abortion in cattle and named *Vibrio fetus*. It is a very important veterinary pathogen. Human infection by *C. fetus* may lead to bacteremia, sepsis and meningitis.

HELICOBACTER

Spiral, campylobacter-like bacteria were observed in close apposition to the gastric mucosa in several cases of gastritis and peptic ulcer, by Warren and Marshall in Australia in 1983. They were originally named *Campylobacter pylori*. As they differed in many respects from campylobacters, they have been redesignated as *Helicobacter pylori*. It now appears that helicobacters have caused human infection from ancient times. By enzyme immunoassay, helicobacter antigens have been detected in the intestines of pre-Columbian mummies in the USA. Today, helicobacters colonise the stomachs of half the human population of the world!

Helicobacters inhabit the stomachs of different animals, each with its own helicobacter species. *H. pylori* is adapted to the human gastric mucosa. The only animal it infects is the monkey. A larger spiral bacterium of uncertain taxonomy, '*H. heilmanii*' can occasionally infect humans and some animals like cats and dogs also. *H. cinaedi* and *H. fennelliae* are associated with proctitis in the HIV infected.

HELICOBACTER PYLORI

H. pylori is a Gram negative spiral rod, motile by a unipolar tuft of lophotrichous flagella. It grows on chocolate agar or campylobacter media under microaerophilic conditions, with 5–20% CO_2, and pH 6–7. At 37 °C, colonies take 2–7 days to develop. Coccoid forms appear in old cultures. It produces oxidase, catalase, phosphatase and H$_2$S. A distinctive feature is the production of abundant urease, and this property has been used as a rapid diagnostic test in gastric biopsy samples. It does not metabolise carbohydrates or reduce nitrate.

H. pylori is global, with a prevalence of 30–60 per cent—more in the developing than in the developed countries. The sole source of H. pylori is the human gastric mucus. The exact mechanism of transmission is not clear, but it is likely to be oral–oral or fecal–oral. Poverty, overcrowding and poor hygiene favour transmission. With improvements in lifestyle, the prevalence of childhood infections has declined in the developed countries.

After an incubation period of a few days, H. pylori causes, in some persons, a mild acute gastritis which may last for about two weeks. The infection may be transient in some, but in most, it persists for years or decades. Such colonisation is usually asymptomatic, though chronic superficial gastritis may be demonstrable histologically. The bacteria are present only in the overlying mucus and do not invade the mucosa. Gastric antrum is the commonest site of colonisation, though any part of the stomach may be involved. The infection is strictly confined to the gastric mucosa, in the stomach, as well as in areas of gastric metaplasia and heterotopia in the duodenum. The exact pathogenic mechanisms are not clearly understood. Bacterial protease, toxins or ammonia released by urease activity or autoimmune responses to gastric antigens may all contribute.

Peptic ulcer disease occurs in a proportion of the infected. Chronic atrophic gastritis may be seen in the later stages. The infection is recognised as a risk factor for gastric malignancies such as adenocarcinoma and 'mucosa associated lymphoid tissue' (MALT) lymphomas. Such MALTomas appear to be antigen driven and are found to regress after elimination of H. pylori by treatment. Infection induces IgM, IgG, IgA and cellular immune responses, but they do not seem to be protective.

H. pylori shows considerable genetic diversity, as evident in molecular typing. The complete genome of the bacterium has been mapped. Virulence has been associated with certain alleles in genes, such as cag (cytotoxin associated gene) and vac (vacuolating cytotoxin gene).

Diagnostic tests are of two kinds, invasive and noninvasive. Invasive tests involve endoscopic biopsy of gastric mucosa, for examination by microscopy, culture and urease tests. Microcopy of biopsy sections by silver staining or of Gram stained smears is a useful method. Culture is more sensitive, but requires expertise and takes 3–7 days. A bit of the biopsy material put in a urease indicator medium shows positive result in minutes. Noninvasive tests include serology (ELISA) and the 'urease breath test'. In the latter, the subject drinks a urea solution containing labelled carbon, which can be detected in the breath. It is sensitive and reliable, but needs isotope assay facilities.

H. pylori is sensitive to several antibiotics and to bismuth salts. The standard treatment is a combination of bismuth subsalicylate, tetracycline (or amoxycillin) and metronidazole for two weeks. An alternative schedule employs a proton pump inhibitor like omeprazole and clarithromycin. Treatment is indicated only for H. pylori related gastric or duodenal ulceration and not for asymptomatic colonisation. Drug resistance and recurrences are frequent.

LEGIONELLA PNEUMOPHILA

The name Legionnaires' disease was given to an apparently new illness which broke out among members of the American Legion who attended a convention in Philadelphia in 1976. The disease was characterised by fever, cough and chest pain, leading on to pneumonia and often ending fatally. The causative agent has been called Legionella pneumophila. Subsequent investigations have revealed that the disease is neither new nor localised.

Infection with *L. pneumophila* is now known to cause protean manifestations. Two distinct clinical patterns have been identified and designated as Legionnaires' disease and Pontiac fever, together known as *legionellosis.*

Legionnaire's disease may be either epidemic or sporadic. The incubation period is 2–10 days. The disease presents with fever, nonproductive cough and dyspnea, rapidly progressing, if untreated, to pneumonia. Diarrhea and encephalopathy are common. Case fatality may be 15–20 per cent, the cause of death being progressive respiratory failure and shock. All age groups are susceptible, though more cases have occurred in the elderly.

Pontiac fever is a milder, nonfatal 'influenza-like' illness with fever, chills, myalgia and headache. Outbreaks with high attack rates may occur.

The discovery of *L. pneumophila* led to the isolation of many related bacteria, which have been placed in the genus *Legionella*, under the family Legionellaceae. Some 40 species of legionellae have been recognised, many of them with multiple serogroups. The original isolate in this genus is designated *L. pneumophila* serogroup 1 (SG1), which accounts for nearly all severe infections. Examples of other species that cause human infection less often are *L. micdadei*, *L. bozemanii*, *L. dumoffii* and *L. gormanii.*

Legionellae are thin, noncapsulated bacilli, 2–5 μm × 0.3–0.1 μm, coccobacillary in clinical material and assuming longer forms in culture. Most are motile with polar or subpolar flagella. They are Gram negative but stain poorly, particularly in smears from clinical specimens. They stain better by silver impregnation, but are best visualised by direct fluorescent antibody (DFA) staining with monoclonal or polyclonal sera.

They have fastidious requirements and grow on complex media such as buffered charcoal, yeast extract (BCYE) agar, with L-cysteine and antibiotic supplements, with 5% CO_2, at pH 6.9, 35 °C and 90% humidity. Growth is slow and colonies take 3–6 days to appear.

Legionellae are widely distributed in natural water sources, such as stagnant waters, mud and hot springs, where the nutritional and growth requirements for these fastidious bacteria are provided by some types of algae. Legionellae survive and multiply inside free-living amebae and other protozoa. They also multiply in some artificial aquatic environments, which serve as amplifiers. Human infection is typically by inhalation of aerosols produced by cooling towers, air conditioners and shower heads which act as disseminators. Aerosolised legionellae can survive for long and can be carried over long distances. No animal reservoir exists, and infection is limited to human beings. No carrier state is established. Man-to-man transmission does not occur.

The outcome of inhalation of legionellae depends on the size of the infecting dose, virulence of the strain and resistance of the host. Known risk factors are smoking, alcohol, advanced age, intercurrent illness, hospitalisation and immuno-deficiency. Men are more often affected than women. In the developed countries, legionellosis accounts for 1–3 per cent of community acquired, and 10–30 per cent of hospital acquired pneumonias. Its prevalence in the developing countries is not adequately known.

Following entry into the alveoli through aerosols, legionellae multiply inside the monocytes and macrophages. Dissemination occurs by endobronchial, hematogenous, lymphatic and contiguous spread. Because of their intracellular location, humoral antibodies are ineffective. Cellular immunity is responsible for recovery.

Laboratory diagnosis is by the demonstration of legionellae in clinical specimens, such as sputum, bronchial aspirate, and lung biopsy, by direct fluorescent antibody test and culture, by the identification of legionella antigens in urine by latex agglutination or ELISA, and by the detection of serum antibody by ELISA or indirect immunofluorescent assay.

For treatment, the newer macrolides,

ciprofloxacin, and tetracyclines are effective. Rifampicin is employed in severe cases. Beta lactamase antibiotics and aminoglycosides are ineffective.

EIKENELLA CORRODENS

This is an oxidase positive, facultatively anaerobic, capnophilic, Gram negative bacillus. The name 'corrodens' refers to the characteristic pitting or corroding of blood agar by colonies of the bacterium. It is present in the mouth, upper respiratory tract and gastrointestinal tract of human beings. Infection follows salivary or fecal contamination and usually involves the skin and subcutaneous tissues, though rarely osteomyelitis, pneumonia, endocarditis and meningitis may occur. It is sensitive to penicillin and tetracycline.

CARDIOBACTERIUM HOMINIS

This Gram negative, pleomorphic bacillus which occurs commonly as a commensal in the human nose and throat may cause endocarditis, particularly in those with pre-existing cardiovascular disease. It grows on blood agar under 3–5% CO_2 high humidity. It ferments a wide range of sugars, forms indole and is oxidase positive, but catalase and nitrate negative. It is sensitive to many antibiotics, penicillin and streptomycin being the recommended drugs.

CAPNOCYTOPHAGA

The Capnocytophaga species are Gram negative fusiform gliding bacilli which form part of the normal mouth flora. They may occasionally cause systemic infections in the immunodeficient.

GARDNERELLA VAGINALIS

Gardnerella vaginalis is a small, Gram negative, nonmotile, pleomorphic rod which shows metachromatic granules. It was formerly known as Haemophilus vaginalis or Corynebacterium vaginale. It grows on blood or chocolate agar aerobically under 5% CO_2. Minute colonies appear in 24–48 hours and are hemolytic on human or rabbit blood agar. It is catalase, oxidase, indole and urease negative.

G. vaginalis is considered responsible for bacterial vaginosis, a mild but common condition characterised by raised vaginal pH > 4.5, foul smelling discharge and the presence of 'clue cells', which are vaginal epithelial cells with their surface studded with numerous small bacteria. Bacterial vaginosis is also associated with anaerobic bacteria, particularly Mobiluncus. Metronidazole is effective in treatment.

MORAXELLA
(BRANHAMELLA) CATARRHALIS

Gram negative cocci, usually arranged in pairs, growing readily on nutrient agar at 18–42 °C, producing nonpigmented colonies and not fermenting sugars were formerly known as Neisseria catarrhalis. They have been reclassified as Branhamella, and again as Moraxella catarrhalis. They form part of the normal pharyngeal flora but can cause respiratory infections, including otitis media, sinusitis, tracheobronchitis and pneumonia. As many strains produce beta lactamases, penicillins are not useful in treatment unless given in combination with clavulanate or sulbactam.

MORAXELLA LACUNATA

These are short, plump, Gram negative bacilli usually arranged in pairs. They are nonflagellated but have been reported to be sluggishly motile. Strictly aerobic, they grow on ordinary media. They are oxidase and catalase positive, indole and H_2S negative and nonfermentative.

M. lacunata was first reported as the cause of angular conjunctivitis by Morax and Axenfeld. Hence it is also known as the Morax – Axenfeld bacillus.

KINGELLA

The genus Kingella, comprising some species of

oxidase positive, nonmotile, Gram negative rods, with a tendency to occur as coccobacillary and diplococcal forms, was formerly grouped under the genus *Moraxella*. They are part of the normal oral flora. *K. kingae* has been associated with endocarditis and infections of bones, joints and tendons.

Further Reading

Bergone-Berezin E and KJ Towner 1996. *Acinetobacter* spp. As nosocomial pathogens. *Clin Microbiol Rev* 9:148.

Blaser MJ. 1998. *Helicobacter pylori* and gastric diseases, *BMJ,* 316, 1507.

Blaser MJ. 1990. Epidemiology and pathophysiology of *Camp. pylori* infections. *Rev Infect Dis* 12:(Suppl.1),99.

Catlin BW. 1992. *Gardnerella vaginalis, Clin Microbiol Rev,* 5, 213.

Fang GD et al. 1989. Disease due to the Legionallaeceae, *Medicine* (Baltimore), 68:116.

GrahamD et al. 1990. Infections caused by Moraxellae. *Rev Infect Dis* 12:423.

Ionnides JPA et al. 1995. *Morxella catarrhalis* bacteremia. *Clin Infect Dis* 2:390.

Levett PN. 1992. Bacterial vaginosis. *Rev Med Microbiol* 3:15.

Mishu-Allos B and MJ Blaser 1995. *Campylobacter jejuni. Clin Infect Dis* 20:1092.

Morrison VA and KF Wagner 1989. *Kingella kingae* infections. *Rev Infect Dis* 11:776.

Parenti DM and DR Syndinan 1985. Capnocytophaga species infections. *J Infect Dis* 151:140.

Peterson WJ. 1991. *Helicobacter pylori* and peptic ulcer disease. *New Engl J Med* 324:1043.

Schuchat A et al. 1991. Epidemiology of human listeriosis. *Clin Microbiol Rev* 4:169.

Sherertz RJ and MI Sullivan 1985. Infections with *Acinetobacter calcoaceticus, J Infect Dis* 151:252.

Verghese A and SL Berk 1991. *Moraxella catarrhalis. Infect Dis Clin N America* 5:523.

Wormser GP and EJ Bottone 1983. *Cardiobacterium hominis. Rev Infect Dis* 5:680.

Stout JE and VE Yo 1997. Legionella. *New Eng J Med* 337:682.

Rickettsiaceae

Rickettsiae are small, Gram negative bacilli adapted to obligate intracellular parasitism, and transmitted by arthropod vectors. They are primary parasites of arthropods such as lice, fleas, ticks and mites, in which they are found in the alimentary canal. In vertebrates, including humans, they infect the vascular endothelium and reticuloendothelial cells. The family Rickettsiaceae is named after Howard Taylor Ricketts who discovered the spotted fever rickettsia (1906) and died of typhus fever contracted during his studies.

The family currently comprises three genera—Rickettsia, Orientia and Ehrlichia which appear to have descended from a common ancestor. Former members of the family, *Coxiella burnetii*, which causes Q fever and *Rochalimaea quintana* causing trench fever have been excluded because the former is not primarily arthropod-borne and the latter not an obligate intracellular parasite, being capable of growing in cell-free media, besides being different in genetic properties.

GENUS RICKETTSIA

The genus Rickettsia consists of the causative agents of two groups of diseases—typhus fevers and spotted fevers.

Morphology: In smears from infected tissues, rickettsiae appear as pleomorphic coccobacilli, 0.3–0.6 μm × 0.8–2 μm in size. They are nonmotile and noncapsulated. They are Gram negative, though they do not take the stain well. They stain bluish purple with Giemsa and Castaneda stains and deep red with Machiavello and Gimenez stains.

Under the electron microscope, rickettsiae are seen to have a three layered cell wall, a trilaminar plasma membrane and an outer slime layer.

Cultivation: Rickettsiae are unable to grow in cell-free media. Growth generally occurs in the cytoplasm of infected cells but in the case of the spotted fever rickettsiae, growth may take place in the nucleus as well. Rickettsiae grow best in cells that are not metabolising actively. The optimum temperature for growth is 32–35 °C.

They are readily cultivated in the yolk sac of developing chick embryos, as first shown by Cox. They also grow on mouse fibroblast, HeLa, HEp-2, Detroit 6 and other continuous cell lines but tissue cultures are not satisfactory for primary isolation. Laboratory animals such as guinea pigs and mice are useful for the isolation of rickettsiae from patients. They may also be propagated in arthropods.

Resistance: Rickettsiae are readily inactivated by physical and chemical agents. They are rapidly destroyed at 56 °C and at room temperature when separated from host components, unless preserved in skimmed milk or a suspending medium containing sucrose, potassium phosphate and glutamate (SPG medium).

Rickettsiae are susceptible to tetracycline, chloramphenicol and ciprofloxacin. Penicillin and sulphonamides are ineffective but para-aminobenzoic acid has an inhibitory action on rickettsiae. Sulphonamides may actually enhance the growth of rickettsiae and worsen the condition if administered to patients.

Antigenic structure: Rickettsiae have species and group specific antigens. The immunodominant surface protein antigens (SPA) of *R. prowazekii* and *R. typhi* have both species specific and cross reactive epitopes, Spotted fever rickettsiae have dominant outer membrane proteins (OMP) A and B, the former being a species specific antigen acting as an adhesin for host cells, and the latter showing limited cross reaction with SPA of typhus rickettsiae. The third surface antigen is an alkali stable polysaccharide found in some rickettsiae and in some strains of Proteus bacilli. This sharing of antigens between rickettsiae and proteus is the basis for the Weil–Felix reaction used for the diagnosis of rickettsial infections by the demonstration of agglutinins to Proteus strains OX 19, OX 2 and OX K.

Pathogenesis: Rickettsiae are transmitted to humans by arthropod vectors through their bite or feces. On entry into the human body, the rickettsiae multiply locally and enter the blood. They become localised chiefly in the vascular endothelial cells, which enlarge, degenerate and cause thrombus formation, with partial or complete occlusion of the vascular lumen. The overall pathological features of the rickettsial diseases are similar and can be explained by the damage to the vascular endothelium.

The long survival of rickettsiae in various organs and lymphatic tissues of infected men and animals is a distinctive feature in pathogenesis and is of importance in the epidemiology of some rickettsial diseases.

TYPHUS FEVER GROUP

This group of diseases consists of epidemic typhus, recrudescent typhus (Brill–Zinsser disease) and endemic typhus.

Epidemic typhus: (Louseborne typhus, Classical typhus, Gaol fever) has been one of the great scourges of mankind, occurring in devastating epidemics during times of war and famine, so vividly described by Hans Zinsser in his book, **'Rats, Lice and History'**. The disease has been reported from all parts of the world but has been particularly common in Russia and Eastern Europe. Napoleon's retreat from Moscow was forced by typhus fever breaking out among his troops. During 1917–1922, there were some 25 million cases in Russia, with about three million deaths. Lenin is said to have remarked, in reference to the outbreaks of louseborne typhus and relapsing fever rampant during the Russian revolution, that 'either socialism will defeat the louse or the louse will defeat socialism'! In recent times, the main foci have been Eastern Europe, Africa, South America and Asia. In India, the endemic spot is Kashmir.

The causative agent of epidemic typhus is *R. prowazekii* named after von Prowazek, who died of typhus fever while investigating the disease. Humans are the only natural vertebrate hosts. Several animals – guinea pigs, mice, cotton rats and gerbils – may be infected experimentally. Natural infection in flying squirrels has been reported from south-eastern USA. They may possibly act as reservoir hosts, infection being spread by the squirrel louse and flea.

The human body louse *Pediculus humanus corporis* is the vector. The head louse may also transmit the infection but not the pubic louse. The lice become infected by feeding on rickettsiaemic patients. The rickettsiae multiply in the gut of the lice and appear in the feces in 3–5 days. Lice succumb to the infection within 2–4 weeks, remaining infective till they die. They can transmit the infection after about a week of being infected. The lethal nature of the infection in the louse suggests that the association between *R. prowazekii* and its vector is relatively recent and not well established. Lice may be transferred from person to person. Being sensitive to temperature changes in the host, they leave the febrile patient or the cooling carcass and parasitise other persons. Lice defecate while feeding. Infection is transmitted when the contaminated louse feces is rubbed through the minute abrasions caused by scratching. Occasionally, infection may also be transmitted by aerosols of dried louse feces through inhalation or through the conjunctiva.

4

Table 46.1 Human diseases caused by Rickettsia and Orientia species

Group	Species	Disease	Vector	Vertebrate reservoir	Distribution
Typhus group	R.prowazekii	Epidemic typhus	Louse	Human beings	World wide
	"	Brill-Zinsser disease	"	Human beings	America, Europe, Australia
	R. typhi	Endemic typhus	Rat flea	Rat	World wide
	R. felis	"	Cat flea	Opossum	USA
Spotted Fever group	R. rickettsii	Rocky Mountain spotted fever	Tick	Rabbit, dog Small rodents	N. America
	R. siberica	Siberian tick typhus	"	Wild Animals cattle	Russia, Mongolia
	R. conori	Fever Boutonneuse	"	Dog, rodents	Mediterranean
	"	S. African tick typhus	"	"	S. Africa
	"	Kenyan tick typhus	"	Rodents	Kenya
	"	Indian tick typhus	"	? Rodents	India
	R. australis	Queensland tick typhus	"	Bush rodents	N. Australia
	R. japonica	Oriental spotted fever	"	?	Japan
	R. akari	Rickettsial pox	Gamasid mite	Mouse	USA, Russia
Scrub typhus	O. tsutsugamushi	Scrub typhus	Trombiculid mite	Small rodents, birds	East Asia, Pacific Islands, Australia

The incubation period is 5–15 days. The disease starts with fever and chills. A characteristic rash appears on the fourth or fifth day, starting on the trunk and spreading over the limbs but sparing the face, palms and soles. Towards the second week, the patient becomes stuporous and delirious. The name typhus comes from the cloudy state of consciousness in the disease (from *typhos,* meaning cloud or smoke, cognate with *dhupa,* the Sanskrit word for smoke). The case fatality may reach 40 per cent and increases with age. In some who recover from the disease, the rickettsiae may remain latent in the lymphoid tissues, or organs for years. Such latent infection may, at times, be reactivated leading to *recrudescent typhus (Brill–Zinsser disease).*

Brill (1898) noticed a mild, sporadic, typhus-like disease in New York, among Jewish immigrants from southeastern Europe. Zinsser (1934) isolated *R. prowazekii* from such cases and proved that they were recrudescences of infections acquired many years previously. Brill–Zinsser disease explains the manner in which the rickettsia is able to survive without extrahuman reservoirs. In itself, the disease is not important but such cases occurring in louse ridden communities may initiate epidemics of typhus fever.

Endemic typhus: (murine or fleaborne typhus) is a milder disease than epidemic typhus. It is caused by *R. typhi (R. mooseri)* which is maintained in nature as a mild infection of rats, transmitted by the rat flea *Xenopsylla cheopis.* The rickettsia multiplies in the gut of the flea and is shed in its feces. The flea is unaffected but remains infectious for the rest of its natural span of life. A related species *R. felis,* maintained in a cycle involving opossums and the cat flea (*Ctenocephalus felis*), has been found to cause endemic typhus in the USA.

Humans acquire the disease usually through the bite of infected fleas, when their saliva or feces is rubbed in or through aerosols of dried feces. Ingestion of food recently contaminated with infected rat urine or flea feces may also cause infection. Human infection is a dead end. Man to man transmission does not occur. In Kashmir and China, lice have been known to transmit endemic typhus in human beings, producing smouldering outbreaks.

R. typhi and *R. prowazekii* are closely similar but may be differentiated by biological and immunological tests. When male guinea pigs are inoculated intraperitoneally with blood from a case of endemic typhus or with a culture of *R. typhi,* they develop fever and a characteristic scrotal inflammation. The scrotum becomes enlarged and the testes cannot be pushed back into the abdomen because of inflammatory adhesions between the layers of the tunica vaginalis. This is known as the *Neill–Mooser* or the tunica reaction. The Neill–Mooser reaction is negative with *R. prowazekii.* Other methods used include IFA, ELISA and PCR-based DNA tests.

Endemic typhus is worldwide in prevalence but is not of much public health importance as the disease is mild and sporadic and can be easily controlled now.

SPOTTED FEVER GROUP

Rickettsiae of this group possess a common soluble antigen and multiply in the nucleus as well as in the cytoplasm of host cells. They are all transmitted by ticks, except *R. akari,* which is miteborne.

Tick typhus: Many species have been recognised in this group. *R. rickettsii,* the causative agent of Rocky Mountain spotted fever, discovered by Ricketts in 1906 was the first insect transmitted bacterial pathogen to be recognised. *R. siberica* causes Siberian tick typhus, *R. conori* Indian, Mediterranean, Kenyan and South African tick typhus and *R. australis* the Queensland tick typhus and *R. japonica* the Oriental spotted fever. *R. africae,* reported recently from subsaharan Africa as the cause of tick bite fever has been observed in the Carribean islands also. *R. akari* causes miteborne rickettsial pox.

The rickettsiae are transmitted transovarially in

ticks, which therefore act as both vectors and reservoirs. The infection may be transmitted to vertebrate hosts by any of the larval stages or by adult ticks. Ticks are not harmed by the rickettsiae and remain infected for life. The rickettsiae are shed in tick feces but transmission to human beings is primarily by bite, as the rickettsiae also invade the salivary glands of the ticks. All rickettsiae of this group pass through natural cycles in domestic and wild animals or birds.

Rocky Mountain spotted fever is the most serious type of spotted fever and is the first to have been described. It is prevalent in many parts of North and South America and is transmitted by *Dermacentor andersoni* and related species of ticks.

Tick typhus in several parts of Europe, Africa and Asia is caused by *R. conori*, strains of which isolated from the Mediterranean littoral, Kenya, South Africa and India are indistinguishable. The species is named after Conor, who provided the first description of the Mediterranean disease 'fievre boutonneuse' (1910). The disease was first observed in India by Megaw (1917) in the foothills of the Himalayas. The investigation of Kalra, Rao, Soman, Helig and Naidu had established that the disease is found in many parts of India. The tick *Rhipicephalus sanguineus* is the most important vector. *Haemaphysalis leachi, Amblyomma* and *Hyalomma* ticks can also transmit the infection.

Rickettsial pox: The mildest rickettsial disease of humans is a self-limited, nonfatal, vesicular exanthem first observed in New York (1946). The name is derived from the resemblance of the disease to chickenpox. It is also called vesicular or varicelliform rickettsiosis. The causative agent is *R. akari* (from *akari*, meaning mite). The reservoir of infection is the domestic mouse, Mus musculus and the vector is the mite, *Liponyssoides* (formerly *Allodermanyssus*) *sanguineus*, in which transovarial transmission occurs. *R. akari* has also been isolated from wild rodents in Korea. The disease has also been reported from Eastern Europe and Korea.

GENUS ORIENTIA
SCRUB TYPHUS (CHIGGER-BORNE TYPHUS)

Scrub typhus is caused by Orientia tsutsugamushi (formerly *R. tsutsugamushi, R. orientalis*). It occurs all along east Asia, from Korea to Indonesia, and in the Pacific Islands including Australia. It was first observed in Japan where it was found to be transmitted by mites. The disease was therefore called *tsutsugamushi* (from *tsutsuga*, meaning dangerous, and mushi meaning insect or mite). It is a place disease and is found only in areas with a suitable climate, plenty of moisture and scrub vegetation. The vectors are trombiculid mites belonging to the genus *Leptotrombidium—L. akamushi* in Japan and *L. deliensis* in India. The mites inhabit sharply demarcated areas in the soil where the microecosystem is favourable (*mite islands*). Human beings are infected when they trespass into these mite islands and are bitten by the mite larvae (*chiggers*). The mite feeds on the serum of warm blooded animals only once during its cycle of development, and adult mites feed only on plants. The microbes are transmitted transovarially in mites. Various rodents and birds act as reservoirs and also help in spreading the orientiae to fresh areas.

Scrub typhus, originally found in scrub jungles has also been identified in a variety of other habitats, such as sandy beaches, mountain deserts and equatorial rain forests. The term *chigger–borne typhus* has therefore been suggested as a more apt designation. Four factors are essential for the establishment of a microfocus of infection, viz., coexistence and intimate relationship among *O. tsutsugamushi*, chiggers, rats and secondary or transitional forms of vegetation (known as the *zoonotic tetrad*).

The incubation period is 1–3 weeks. Patients typically develop a characteristic eschar at the site of the mite bite, with regional lymphadenopathy and a maculopapular rash. The disease sets in with fever, headache and conjunctival injection.

Encephalitis and pneumonia may be seen in severe cases. The disease is not a serious problem in civilian practice but assumes great importance in military medicine, especially during jungle warfare, as was recognised in the Indo-Burmese theatre in the Second World War.

Considerable differences exist among different strains of *O. tsutsugamushi* in antigenic properties and virulence, a factor that complicates serodiagnosis and immunoprophylaxis. Three major antigenic types have been recognised—Karp, Gilliam and Kato.

GENUS EHRLICHIA

Ehrlichiae are small, Gram negative, obligately intracelluar bacteria which have an affinity towards blood cells. In the cytoplasm of infected phagocytic cells, they grow within phagosomes as mulberry-like clusters called *morula* (morula, meaning mulberry). They are tick-borne. Similar organisms under the names of *Anaplasma, Cowdria* and *Neorickettsia,* had long been known to veterinary scientists as etological agents of tickborne infections of cattle and sheep. Three human infections caused by this group of organisms have been identified.

The first of these human diseases, reported from Japan in 1954, was a case resembling glandular fever who showed serological response against the agent of canine ehrlichiosis. The etiological agent has been named *Ehrlichia sennetsu* (from 'sennetsu', the Japanese word for glandular fever). It is endemic in Japan and parts of South East Asia. It causes lymphoid hyperplasia and atypical lymphocytosis. No arthropod vector has been identified. Human infection is suspected to be caused by ingestion of fish carrying infected flukes.

The second type of infection is 'human monocytic ehrlichiosis' caused by *E. chaffeensis*. It is transmitted by Amblyomma ticks. Deer and rodents are believed to be reservoir hosts. Human disease is associated with leucopenia, thrombocytopenia and elevated liver enzymes. Multisystem involvement and fatality may occur.

The third is 'human granulocytic ehrlichiosis' caused by an organism either identical with or closely related to the equine pathogen, *E. equi* (probably *E. phagocytophila*). It is transmitted by Ixodes ticks. Deer, cattle and sheep are the suspected reservoir. Leucopenia and thrombocytopenia are seen in patients. Giemsa stained blood films may show morula form of the ehrlichia.

Doxycycline is recommended for treatment of ehrlichioses.

Laboratory diagnosis: Rickettsial diseases may be diagnosed in the laboratory either by isolation of the rickettsiae or by serology. As rickettsiae are highly infectious and have caused several serious and fatal infections among laboratory workers, their isolation should be attempted with utmost care and only in laboratories equipped with appropriate safety provisions.

Rickettsiae may be isolated in male guinea pigs or mice from patients in the early phase of the disease. Blood clot ground in skimmed milk or any suitable suspending medium is inoculated intraperitoneally. The animals have to be observed for 3–4 weeks and their temperature recorded daily. Their response to rickettsial infection varies. In Rocky Mountain spotted fever, guinea pigs develop fever, scrotal necrosis and may even die. With *R. typhi, R. conori* and *R. akari,* they develop fever and tunica reaction. *R. prowazekii* produces only fever without any testicular inflammation. Smears from the peritoneum, tunica and spleen of infected animals may be stained by Giemsa or Gimenez methods to demonstrate the rickettsiae.

Though laboratory strains of rickettsiae grow profusely in the yolk sac of chick embryos, this method and tissue culture are not suitable for primary isolation. Egg and animal inoculation methods have been replaced by the faster and more sensitive cell cultures. Rickettsiae grow well in 3 to 5 days on Verocell MRC 5 cell cover slip cultures and can be identified by immunofluorescence using group and strain specific monoclonal antibodies.

Serological diagnosis may be by the heterophile Weil–Felix reaction or by specific tests using rickettsial antigens. The Weil–Felix reaction is an agglutination test in which sera are tested for agglutinins to the O antigens of certain nonmotile Proteus strains OX 19, OX 2 and OX K. The test was developed from the chance observation of Weil and Felix (1916) that a Proteus strain isolated from the urine of a patient of epidemic typhus was agglutinated by the patient's serum as well as by the sera of other typhus patients. The basis of the test is the sharing of an alkali-stable carbohydrate antigen by some rickettsiae and by certain strains of Proteus, *P. vulgaris* OX 19, and OX 2 and *P. mirabilis* OX K. The test is usually done as a tube agglutination, though rapid slide agglutination methods have been employed for screening.

Sera from epidemic and endemic typhus agglutinate OX 19 and sometimes OX 2 also. The test is negative or only weakly positive in Brill-Zinsser disease. In tickborne spotted fever both OX 19 and OX 2 are agglutinated. OX K agglutinins are found only in scrub typhus. The test is negative in rickettsial pox, trench fever, and Q fever (Table 46.2).

The Weil–Felix reaction is a simple and useful test for the diagnosis of some rickettsial diseases. The antibody appears rapidly during the course of the disease, reaches peak titres of upto 1:1000 or 1:5000 by the second week and declines rapidly during convalescence. False positive reaction may occur in some cases of urinary or other infections by Proteus and at times in typhoid fever and liver diseases. Hence it is desirable to demonstrate a rise in titre of antibodies for the diagnosis of rickettsial infection.

The most frequently used serological method using rickettsial antigens is the complement fixation test. This may be done using the group specific soluble antigen, or the type specific washed rickettsial antigen. The former test is in routine use but the latter is necessary for differentiation between epidemic and endemic typhus. Other serological tests include agglutination of rickettsial suspensions, passive hemagglutination of red cells sensitised by ESS (erythrocyte sensitising substance), toxin neutralisation, immuno-fluorescence and radioisotope precipitation.

Immunoprophylaxis: Rickettsial diseases may be prevented by general measures such as control of vectors and animal reservoirs. Immunisation is useful in special situations. Killed and live vaccines have been prepared against epidemic typhus. The earliest of these was phenolised intestinal contents of lice infected per rectum with *R. prowazekii* (Weigl's vaccine). This was too complicated for mass production. Castaneda developed a formalinised mouse lung vaccine. Effective vaccination became possible only after Cox developed the inactivated yolk sac vaccine. A live vaccine using the attenuated *strain E* has been found to be highly immunogenic but a proportion of vaccinees develop mild disease. The Cox type vaccine has also been prepared against Rocky

Table 46.2 Weil-Felix reaction in rickettsial diseases

Disease	Agglutination pattern with		
	OX 19	OX 2	OX K
Epidemic typhus	+++	+	–
Brill–Zinsser disease	Usually negative or week positive		–
Endemic typhus	+++	±	–
Tickborne spotted fever	++	++	–
Scrub typhus	–	–	+++

Mountain spotted fever. However, there is no satisfactory vaccine available against any of the rickettsial diseases.

GENUS COXIELLA: Q FEVER

Derrick (1935) investgating an outbreak of typhoid-like fever in abattoir workers in Brisbane, Australia, transmitted the infection to guinea pigs by inoculation of blood from patients. As the etiological agent of the disease was unknown, it was referred to as 'Query' or Q fever. As Burnet identified the causative agent as a rickettsia, it was named *R. burnetii*. At about the same time, the same agent was isolated independiently by Cox in the USA from ticks, and was called *R. diaporica*, the name referring to its ability to pass through pores of filters impermeable to other rickettsiae. The Australian and American strains were subsequently shown to be identical. As the Q fever agent differed from other rickettsiae in many features (smaller size, greater resistance to heat and drying, major transmision route being inhalation or ingestion, idependent of arthropod vectors), it has been separated from rickettsiae into a special genus and renamed *Coxiella burnetii*. It has been assigned to the group *Protobacteria* along with other genera like *Legionella* and *Francisella*

Q fever is distributed worldwide, as a zoonosis solidly established in domestic livestock. Wild animals such as the bandicoot may be the primary reservoir. It is transmitted among them, and to cattle, sheep and poultry by ixodid ticks. Transovarial transmission occurs in ticks. Coxiella are abundant in tick feces and survive in dried feces for long periods. They are shed in the milk of infected animals. They are particularly abundant in their products of conception and contaminate the environment at parturition..

Human infection may occur occupationally through handling wool or hides, meat or other animal products contaminated with the organism. Drinking infected milk can transmit the infection. Coxiella may enter through abraded skin, mucosa,

lungs or intestinal tract. Person-to-person transmission is a rarity. Ticks do not seem to be important in human infection.

Cox. burnetii is widely prevalent in birds and animals in India, as shown by serological surveys, but human disease has been identified only rarely. The human disease is an acute systemic infection characterised by an interstitial pneumonia. The clinical picture is very variable and asymptomatic infections very common. In chromic Q feve, the coxiella spreads through almost all organs and may cause hepatitis, meningoencephalitis or endocarditis. Spontaneous recovery is usual. The coxiella may remain latent in the tissues of patients for 2–3 years.

Cox. burnetii is an obligate intracellular pathogen, primarily infecting the monocyte-macrophage cells. It occurs as rods 0.2–0.4 μm x 0.4–1.0 μm or as spheres 0.3–0.4 μm in diameter. It is filterable. Generally regarded as Gram negative, A. it is better stained with Giminez and other rickettsiae strains

In dried feces or wool it survives for a year or more at 4 °C and in meat at least for one month. It is not completely inactivated at .60 °C or by 1% phenol in one hour. In milk it may survive pasteurisation by the holding method, but the flash method is effective. It grows well in the yolk sac of chick embryos and in various cell cultures.

Cox. burnetii shows phase variation. Fresh isolates are in Phase I. It becomes Phase II on repeated passage in yolk sac, but reverts to Phase I by passaging in guinea pigs. Phase I cells are autoagglutinable and are phagocytosed in the absence of antibody. Phase I activity is due to a periodate-sensitive trichloracetic acid-soluble surface carbohydrate. Phase I is a more powerful immunogen than Phase II and elicits good antibody response to both I and II antigens. Phase II antigen is more suitable for complement fixation tests. Q fever sera do not cross-react with rickettsial or proteus bacillus antigens.

Laboratory diagnosis is by serology, by

complement fixation or indirect immuno-fluorescence assay. Isolation of the coxiella from blood, sputum or other clinical specimens is possible, but is not recommended due to the hazard of laboratory infection.

Vaccines have been prepared from formalin killed whole cells, trichloracetic acid extracts and attenuated strains, but they are not for general use. Treatment is with doxycycline. In endocarditis prolonged treatment with combinations of tetracycline, cotrimoxazole or rifampicin may be required.

BARTONELLA

Bartonellae are tiny Gram negative bacilli, usually transmitted by arthropods, which invade mammalian endothelial cells and blood cells. Human pathogenic strains are *B. bacilliformis, B. quintana* and *B. henselae*. The genus contains species causing a number of tickborne fevers of animals. Identification and classification of members of bartonellae, rickettsiae, chlamydiae and related bacteria often depend on sophisticated molecular methods like 16S RNA analysis.

BARTONELLA BACILLIFORMIS

In 1870, when the railway line from Lima to Oroya in Peru was being built, an outbreak of fever killed thousands of workmen. The disease was called *Oroya fever*, which was seen in the mountainous parts of Peru, Columbia and Ecuador in South America. Some of the survivors developed nodular ulcerating skin lesions, called *verruga peruana*. The common etiology of these two conditions was established tragically in 1885 by the Peruvian medical student Daniel Carrion. He inoculated himself with material from verruga and developed Oroya fever from which he died. Oroya fever is therefore also known as Carrion's disease.

Oroya fever presents as fever and progressive anemia due to bacterial invasion of erythrocytes. Mortality is high in untreated cases. A late sequel

in survivors or in those with asymptomatic infection is verruga peruana. *B. bacilliformis* is seen inside erythrocytes and in the skin lesions. It is a pleomorphoic Gram negative rod, which is motile by a tuft of polar flagella. It can be cultivated in semisolid agar with rabbit or human blood.

BARTONELLA (ROCHALIMAEA) QUINTANA

During the First World War, over a million cases of a disease known as *trench fever* or *five-day fever* occurred among soldiers fighting in the trenches in Europe. The disease was not fatal but because of its slow course and prolonged convalescence, it caused very considerable loss of manpower.

Trench fever is an exclusively human disease and no animal reservoir is known. It is transmitted by the body louse. The feces of lice becomes infectious 5–10 days after an infectious meal. The lice are unharmed and remain infective throughout their lives. Vertical transmission does not occur in lice. The causative agent was identified as a rickettsia and named *R. quintana* (from *quintana*, meaning fifth, referring to 'five-day fever', a synonym for trench fever). As it was found to differ from rickettsiae in a number of respects, including its ability to grow in cell-free culture media such as blood agar, it was separated into a new genus Rochalimaea (after da Rocha Lima, an early investigator of rickettsial diseases). In a subsequent taxonomical shift, it has been reclassified as Bartonella and named *B. quintna*.

The disease frequently leads to a chronic or latent infection. Recrudescence may occur as in Brill–Zinsser disease and relapses have been reported as long as 20 years after the primary disease. The chronic infection and late relapses help to maintain the bartonella in the absence of animal reservoirs.

Trench fever was thought to have vanished with the world wars. But isolation of *B. quintana* from Tunisia and Mexico recently suggests that the disease may be more widely distributed than is realised. Trench fever cases have been identified in some homeless persons living in unsanitary conditions in the USA.

BARTONELLA HENSELAE

A febrile illness with lymphadenopathy following a cat scratch had been known for long under the name 'cat scratch disease', but its etiology remained elusive. B. henselae has been isolated from the blood of patients, in blood media after prolonged incubation and is now considered as its etiological agent. It can be demonstrated in lymph node biopsy smears and sections by Warthin–Starry staining.

B. henselae has been also linked with two other conditions, seen more commonly in HIV infected and other immunodeficient persons. These are *bacillary angiomatosis,* in which vascular nodules or tumours appear on the skin, mucosa and other locations, and *bacillary peliosis* involving the liver and spleen.

Angiomatosis may also be due to B. quintana in some cases. Another organism *Afipia felis* had also been proposed as a cause of cat scratch disease.

Further Reading

Adal KA. 1995. Bartonella: New species and new disease. *Rev Med Microbiol* 6:155.
Baca OG and D Paretsky 1983. Q fever and *Coxiella burnetii. Microbiol Rev* 47:127.
Buqui P et al. 1995. Human granulocyte ehrlichiosis. *Lancet* 346:782.
Fishbein DB et al. 1994. Human Ehrlichiosis. *Ann Int Med* 120:736.
Koehlar JE et al. 1994. *Rochalimaea henselae* infection. *J Am Med Assoc* 271:531.
Mourin M and D Raoult 1999. Q fever. *Clin Microbial Rev* 12:518.
Raoult D and V Roux 1997. Rickettsoses as paradigms of new or emerging infectious diseases. *Clin Microbiol Rev* 10:694.
Schultz MG. 1968. A history of bartonellosis (Carrions' disease). *Am J Trop Med* 17:503.
Walker DH and JS Dumler 1996. Emergence of Ehrlichiosis as a human health problem. *Emerging Infect Dis* 2:No1.
Woodward TE. 1973. A historical account of rickettsial diseases with a discussion of the involved problems. *J Inf Dis* 127:585.
Zinsser H. 1935. *Rats, Lice and History.* London: George, Routledge and Sons Ltd.

Chlamydiae

Chlamydiae are obligate intracellular bacterial parasites of humans, animals and birds with tropism for squamous epithelial cells and macrophages of the respiratory and gastrointestinal tracts. Due to their filterability and failure to grow in cell-free media, they were considered to be viruses. Based on the human diseases they were then known to cause, they were called psittacosis-lymphogranuloma-trachoma (PLT) viruses, or noncommittally as 'PLT agents'. However, they differ from viruses in many respects. They possess both DNA and RNA, have cell walls and ribosomes, replicate by binary fission without an 'eclipse phase', and are susceptible to the usual antibiotics and chemotherapeutic agents. They are therefore accepted as bacteria. Unlike other bacteria, they do not have peptidoglycan cell walls. They lack enzymes of the electron transport chain and so require ATP and nutrient resources from host cells. They have therefore been called *energy parasites*.

In recognition of the pioneering studies of Sir Samuel Bedson on psittacosis, the name *Bedsonia* was proposed for this group. However, they are now officially classified as bacteria belonging to the genus *Chlamydia*, in the family Chlamydiaceae, under the order Chlamydiales.

The genus *Chlamydia* contains four species: —*C. trachomatis, C. psittaci, C. pneumoniae*, which can affect humans; and the fourth species, *C. pecorum* created recently to include some strains affecting ruminants. Species differentiation is based on growth characters, nucleic acid profile, antigens, plasmids and nature of the inclusion body.

C. trachomatis strains form compact inclusions with the glycogen matrix, are sensitive to sulphonamides, and are natural parasites of humans, usually causing localised infections of the eyes and genitals. *C. psittaci* strains form diffuse vacuolated inclusions without the glycogen matrix, are resistant to sulphonamides and are natural parasites of birds and animals, capable of causing pneumonia and generalised infections in humans. *C. pneumoniae* is an exclusive human pathogen with no animal or avian host. It is a common cause of acute respiratory disease worldwide.

Morphology and growth cycle: Chlamydiae occur in two forms, the *elementary body* and the *reticulate body* (formerly also called the 'initial body'). The elementary body is the extracellular, infective form. It is a spherical particle, 200–300 nm in diameter, with a rigid trilaminar cell wall similar to the cell walls of Gram negative bacteria, and an electron dense nucleoid. The reticulate body is the intracellular growing and replicative form, 500–1000 nm in size. Its cell wall is fragile and pliable, leading to pleomorphism.

Infection is initiated by the attachment of the elementary body to the surface of a susceptible epithelial cell, followed by its endocytosis (Fig. 47.1). Inside the host cell, the elementary body lies within the endosome, being separated from the host cell cytoplasm by the endosomal membrane throughout its active growth cycle. By about eight hours, the elementary body within the endosome undergoes spheroplast-like transformation to the large reticulate body, which begins to divide by binary fission by 12 hours. By 20–24 hours, the

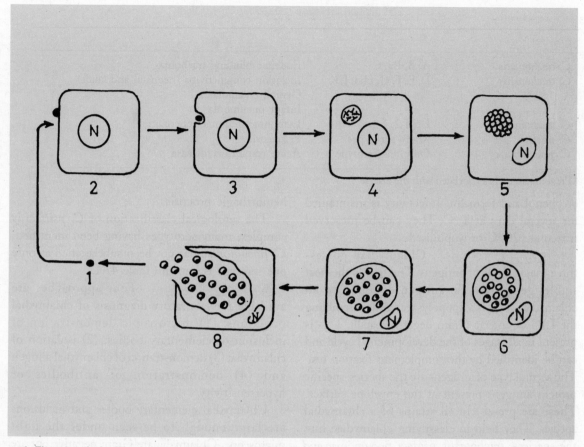

1. Elementary body (EB); 2. EB attaches to cell receptor; 3. EB enters cell by endocytosis. By 8 hours; 4. EB reorganised into retiulate (RB); 5. Host cell growth arrested by 12 hours, RB undergoing fission; 6. By 24 hours, inclusion body with RB and developing EB; 7. By 30 hours, inclusion body containing infectious EB. Nucleus pushed to periphery; 8. By 48 hours, death and lysis of cell releasing EB.

Fig. 47.1 Reproductive cycle of Chlamydia

pleomorphic progeny show central condensation and are converted to elementary bodies. Binary fission continues till about 40 hours. The developing chlamydial microcolony within the host cell is called the *inclusion body*. The mature inclusion body contains 100–500 elementary bodies which are ultimately released from the host cell. In *C. psittaci* infections, the host cell is severely damaged and release of the elementary bodies occurs within 48 hours by host cell lysis. With *C. trachomatis,* the mature inclusion appears to be exocytosed in 72–96 hours, the host cell being left with a scar (Fig. 47.1).

During the active intracellular growth of the organism, the chlamydia specific lipopolysaccharides accumulate on the host cell surface. This highly antigenic material induces inflammatory and immunological responses which contribute to the pathogenesis of chlamydial diseases.

Chlamydiae can be propagated in the mouse, chick embryo or in cell culture though they show individual variations in susceptibility.

Resistance: Chlamydiae are heat labile, being inactivated within minutes at 56 °C. They are susceptible to ethanol, ether and low concentrations

Table 47.1 Human diseases caused by Chlamydiae

Species	Serotype*	Disease
C. trachomatis	A, B, Ba, C	Endemic blinding trachoma
C. trachomatis	D, E, F, G, H, I, J, K	Inclusion conjunctivitis (neonatal and adult)
		Genital chlamdiasis
		Infant pneumonia
C. trachomatis	L1, L2, L3	Lymphogranuloma venereum
C. psittaci	Many serotypes	Psittacosis
C. pneumoniae	Only one serotype	Acute respiratory disease

*Predominamt types associated with the disease

of phenol and formalin. Infectivity is maintained for several days at 4 °C. They can be preserved frozen at −70 °C or lyophilised.

Antigenic properties: Chlamydiae possess three major kinds of antigens. The first is the heat stable, genus specific antigen common to all chlamydiae. This is a lipopolysaccharide resembling the LPS of enteric Gram negative bacilli. This is present in all stages of the developmental cycle and can be identified by the complement fixation test. The second type of antigens are the species-specific protein antigens present at the envelope surface. These are present in all strains of a chlamydial species. They help in classifying chlamydiae into the species—*trachomatis, psittaci, pneumoniae and pecorum*. The third kind of antigens help in intraspecies typing, as they are found only in some members of a species. They are located on the major outer membrane proteins (MOMP) and can be demonstrated by microimmunofluorescence. By micro-IF, chlamydiae have been classified into many serological variants (serovars, serotypes).

C. trachomatis is classified into two broad *biovars* (biological variants) which cause trachoma, inclusion conjunctivitis (TRIC) and lymphogranuloma venereum (LGV), respectively. The TRIC biovar has been classified into 12 serovars—A, B, Ba and C causing blinding trachoma in endemic areas, and serovars D to K associated with the less serious occular infection, inclusion conjunctivitis and with various genital infections. Serovars L1, L2 and L3 cause LGV and

hemorrhagic proctitis.

The serological classification of C. psittaci is complex, many serotypes having been identified. C. pneumoniae has not been subclassified as only one serotype is known (Table 47.1).

Laboratory diagnosis: Four approaches are available for laboratory diagnosis of chlamydial infections: (1) microscopic demonstration of inclusion or elementary bodies; (2) isolation of chlamydia; (3) demonstration of chlamydial antigen and (4) demonstration of antibodies or hypersensitivity.

Chlamydial elementary bodies and inclusions are large enough to be seen under the light microscope. Chlamydia are Gram negative but are stained better by Giemsa, Castaneda, Machiavello or Giminea stains. Microscopic examination of Giemsa stained conjunctival scrapings for the inclusion bodies is useful in the diagnosis of ocular infections particularly in neonatal inclusion conjunctivitis. Because of the glycogen matrix of C. trachomatis inclusions, they can be stained with Lugol's iodine. Iodine staining of conjunctival scrapings has been used as a rapid and simple screening method for trachoma and inclusion conjunctivitis. However, its sensitivity is poor as iodine staining occurs only in certain stages of development of the inclusions. It is, however, useful in the rapid screening for chlamydial inclusions in cell cultures inoculated with clinical samples. Iodine staining is not applicable in C. psittaci because its inclusions do not contain glycogen.

A more sensitive and specific method of microscopic examination is immunofluorescence using monoclonal antibody. Immunofluorescence can identify not only inclusions but also extracellular elementary bodies. Besides ocular infections, IF is useful also in examination of cervical or urethral specimens, which may contain elementary bodies but few intact intracellular inclusions. It is also more sensitive than iodine staining for detection of inclusions in infected cell cultures.

Isolation of chlamydia can be done by inoculation into embryonated eggs, experimental animals (mice) and tissue cultures. Chlamydia can grow in the yolk sac of 6–8 days old chick embryos. The group–specific CF antigen as well as the elementary and inclusion bodies can be demonstrated in the yolk sac. However, as isolation by egg inoculation is tedious and relatively insensitive, it has been replaced by tissue cultures.

Chlamydiae differ in their infectivity to mice. *C. psittaci* strains infect mice by intracerebral, intranasal, intraperitoneal and subcutaneous routes. Among *C. trachomatis* strains, only the LGV serovars (L1, L2, L3) infect mice when injected intracerebrally. The TRIC serovars do not infect mice by any route, though they can kill mice infected intravenously due to toxic effect. Mice can be protected against infection and toxic effect by prior injection of type specific antisera. Mouse inoculation is no longer in use for isolation of chlamydia.

Cell culture is the preferred mode of isolation now. Many cell lines are susceptible but those commonly used are McCoy and HeLa cells. *C. trachomatis* strains vary in their infectivity to cell cultures. LGV strains grow well, while TRIC strains are less infective. Cell cultures used for isolation are pretreated by irradiation or chemicals such as 5-iodo-2-deoxyuridine or cycloheximide to enhance chlamydial replication and facilitate detection of inclusion bodies. Pretreatment of cells with DEAE dextran or centrifugation after inoculation promotes contact between chlamydial

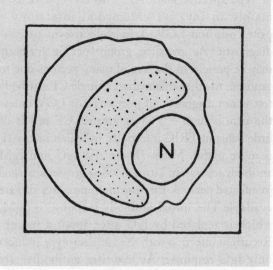

Fig. 47.2 Halberstaedter–Prowazek body in trachoma. Conjuncival epithelial cell containing a large reniform inclusion body surrounding the nucleus (N).

particles and cell monolayer, thereby increasing the chances of isolation. *C. psittaci* strains grow well on cell cultures, but because of the risk of laboratory infection their isolation should be attempted only where appropriate containment facilities are available.

For diagnosis by demonstration of chlamydial antigens, the method commonly used is micro-IF. The infected ocular or genital samples are smeared on a slide, stained with fluorescent conjugated antibody and examined under the UV microscope. This test approaches cultures in sensitivity. The ELISA method is preferred for screening as it enables rapid testing for LPS antigen in large numbers of specimens. Molecular methods like DNA probes and amplification techniques (polymerase chain reaction, ligase chain reaction) have greatly increased the sensitivity and specificity of antigen detection. Another advantantage of molecular techniques is that noninvasive samples like urine can be used, thus simplifying specimen collection and transport.

Diagnosis by demonstration of antibody in serum may be done by the group-specific CF test or type-specific micro-IF. The CF test is used mainly in invasive chlamydial infections—psittacosis and LGV. A fourfold rise in titres is diagnostic. As low titre, group-specific antibody may be present in the sera of many persons due to exposure to other chlamydiae, a single CF antibody test is not diagnostic of psittacosis or LGV unless the titre is high – 1:64 or greater. CF test is of little value in TRIC infections, in which micro-IF is more useful. Micro-IF can test IgG and IgM antibody separately. Titres of 1:8 or greater are usual in infected persons. Enzyme immunoassays also are available. The initial antibody response is IgM, which is replaced by IgG after about a month. Recurrent infection with the same serotype induces only IgG response. As low titre antibodies are frequently seen in healthy individuals, the diagnostic criteria for serology are seroconversion, fourfold rise in IgG titre or presence of IgM antibody. High titre antibodies are usually seen only in infant pneumonia, salpingitis and LGV.

Demonstration of hypersensitivity by skin testing (Frei's test) was widely used formerly for diagnosis of LGV but has been given up because false positive results are very frequent.

CHLAMYDIA TRACHOMATIS

C. trachomatis is a leading cause of ocular and genital infections worldwide.

Trachoma: Trachoma is a chronic keratoconjunctivitis characterised by follicular hypertrophy, papillary hyperplasia, pannus formation and in the late stages, cicatrisation. The name trachoma is derived from the Greek *trakhus* (rough) referring to the roughness of the conjunctiva in the disease. Though Halberstaedter and Prowazek in 1907 transmitted the infection to orangutans and demonstrated in conjunctival smears the characteristic inclusion body that bears their names, cultivation of the chlamydia became possible only half a century later, when Tang and colleagues (1957) grew it in the yolk sac of eggs.

Infection is transmitted from eye-to-eye by fingers or fomites. Flies may transmit the infection mechanically. It may also be carried by dust, in which case infection may be facilitated by minor abrasions caused by dust particles. The incubation period is variable and influenced by the dose of infection. Onset is insidious.

Trachoma has been classified into several stages. The earliest is trachoma dubium, where the disease is just a suspicion. Protrachoma is the stage of conjunctival lesion before follicles become visible. The inclusion bodies are not usually demonstrable in these early stages. Established trachoma progresses through stages I–IV. Infectivity is maximum in the early cases. Stage IV is noninfectious.

Laboratory diagnosis: The characteristic inclusions (*Halberstaedter Prowazek* or *HP bodies*) may be demonstrated in conjunctival scrapings, after staining by Giemsa, Castaneda or Machiavello methods. Because they possess a glycogen matrix they may be stained with iodine which enhances the sensitivity of smear diagnosis.

The chlamydia may be grown in the yolk sac of 6–8 days old eggs. The material is treated with streptomycin or polymyxin B before inoculation. The eggs are incubated at 35 °C in a humid atmosphere. Blind passages may be necessary for isolation. This method is seldom used now as it is time consuming, cumbersome and relatively insensitive.

Tissue culture using stationary phase cells (nonreplicating cells) is the method of choice for isolation. McCoy cells rendered nonreplicating by irradiation or antimetabolites are used. HeLa or HL cells treated with DEAE dextran may also be used. The inoculum has to be driven into the cells by centrifugation upto 15,000 g to get a good growth.

Treatment: Local application and oral administration of erythromycin and tetracycline or other suitable antibiotics should be continued for several weeks. A single-dose azitromycin treatment has been used with good results.

Epidemiology and control: Trachoma is worldwide in distribution and about 500 million people are estimated to be affected. It is particularly prevalent in the developing nations because of overcrowding and unhygienic conditions. It is endemic in the Middle East, Africa, India and the Far East. Control of the disease involves mass education and chemotherapy. Vaccination has not proved to be an effective or practicable method of control.

INCLUSION CONJUNCTIVITIS

The epidemiology of this condition, first recognised by Halberstaedter and Prowazek in 1910 had to be reestablished in recent years. The natural habitat of *C. trachomatis* types D to K is the genital tract in both sexes.

'Inclusion blenorrhea', the neonatal form of inclusion conjunctivitis, develops when the infant is infected in the birth passage. It usually becomes apparent between 5–12 days after birth. It was considered to be benign and self limited but has a high incidence of micropannus, conjunctival scars and late recurrences. These can be prevented by local application of antibiotics.

In the adult form of the disease, there is follicular hypertrophy with scanty nonpurulent discharge. It was known as 'swimming pool conjunctivitis' as infection was associated with bathing in community swimming pools which presumably get contaminated with chlamydia from the genital secretions of bathers. Contamination of the eye with the patient's own genital secretion may be the cause more often.

INFANT PNEUMONIA

C. trachomatis can cause pneumonia in infants, usually around 4–16 weeks of age. Characteristically, they develop prominent respiratory symptoms with cough and wheezing but fever and toxicity are minimal. Conjunctivitis often precedes pneumonia. They show eosinophilia and high titre IgM antibodies to the infecting serovar. Immune response

is believed to have a role in pathogenesis of this condition.

GENITAL INFECTIONS

C. trachomatis causes two types of genital infections – miscellaneous urogenital syndromes caused by the occulogenital serotypes D to K collectively referred to as 'genital chlamydiasis', and LGV caused by serotypes L1, L2 and L3.

Genital chlamydiasis: Chlamydial infections have become the most common sexually transmitted disease worldwide. Their clinical spectrum parallels that of gonococcal infections. Indeed the two infections may often coexist.

In men, they cause urethritis ('nongonococcal urethritis'), epididymitis, proctitis, conjunctivitis and Reiter syndrome. (Reiter syndrome is a triad of recurrent conjunctivitis, polyarthritis and urethritis or cervicitis, associated with many infections but most commonly with *C. trachomatis*). Women develop acute urethral syndrome, bartholinitis, mucopurulent cervicitis, endometritis, salpingitis, pelvic inflammatory disease, conjunctivitis, perihepatitis (Fitz–Hugh Curtis syndrome) and Reiter syndrome. Genital chlamydiasis may cause infertility, ectopic pregnancy, premature deliveries, perinatal morbidity and postpartum fever.

The true prevalence of genital chlamydiasis is not known in the developing countries as laboratory diagnosis is not widely available. In India, chlamydial infection has been reported in 20–30 per cent of women with mucopurulent cervicitis and 30–60 per cent of those with salpingitis and pelvic inflammatory disease.

In the laboratory, chlamydial infection is to be suspected if Gram stained smears of urogenital exudates show significant number of neutrophils (more than four per oil immersion field in urethritis, more than 30 in cervicitis), in the absence of gonococcal infection. Confirmatory tests are chlamydial cultivation and antigen detection by micro-IF. Antigen detection by ELISA and by molecular techniques are also useful.

LYMPHOGRANULOMA VENEREUM

This sexually transmitted disease, characterised by suppurative inguinal adentitis, has been known in the tropics for a long time under various names: lymphogranuloma inguinale, poradenitis, climatic or tropical bubo. It is caused by the LGV serovars of *Chlam. trachomatis*, L1, L2 and L3—most commonly L2. LGV serovars are more invasive than the other immunotypes of *Chlam. trachomatis*. Their preferred site of multiplication is the regional lymph nodes, in contrast to TRIC serovars which grow in epithelial cells.

The primary lesion is a small painless papulovesicular lesion appearing on the external genitalia (or rarely extragenital sites) after an incubation period of three days to five weeks. The secondary stage developing about two weeks later results from lymphatic spread to the draining lymph nodes. In men the inguinal lymph nodes are involved most often and in women the intrapelvic and pararectal nodes. Women and homosexual men may develop hemorrhagic proctitis with regional lymphadenitis. The nodes enlarge, suppurate, become adherent to the skin and break down to form sinuses discharging pus. Metastatic complications may sometimes occur, with involvement of joints, eyes, and meninges. The tertiary stage is chronic, lasting for several years, representing the sequelae of scarring and lymphatic blockage. Late sequelae are more distressing in women leading to rectal strictures and elephantiasis of the vulva (esthiomene).

Laboratory diagnosis: The primary lesion usually goes unnoticed and the disease is seen commonly first in the stage of inguinal adenitis (bubo). Smears of material aspirated from the bubos may show the elementary bodies (Miyagawa's granulocorpuscles). The sensitivity of microscopic diagnosis is very low. Isolation of the chlamydia by intracerebral inoculation into mice and into yolk sac of eggs has been replaced by cell cultures. LGV patients develop high titres of circulating antibodies, with titres of 1:64 or more in CF test and 1:512 or more in micro-IF. Serological diagnosis is therefore feasible.

An intradermal test originally described by Frei in 1925 was commonly used formerly. The crude chlamydial antigen originally obtained from the bubo pus, and later from mouse brain or yolk sac cultures (Lygranum), was inoculated intradermally in the forearm, with a control on the other arm. Induration of 7 mm or more in 2–5 days was considered positive. Due to the frequent occurrence of false positive reactions, Frei's test is now not in use. Treatment is with tetracycline, which should be given for at least three weeks.

CHLAMYDIA PSITTACI

PSITTACOSIS

Psittacosis is a disease of parrots (*psittacos* means parrot) and other psittacine birds, transmissible to human beings. A similar disease acquired by nonpsittacine birds was called ornithosis (*ornithos* meaning birds) but the distinction is now no longer employed, both conditions being called psittacosis.

Infection in birds is usually subclinical leading to a carrier state. Overt disease may be precipitated by caging or overcrowing and is manifested as diarrhea, mucopurluent respiratory discharge and emaciation. Chlamydia are shed in the droppings or nasal discharge and aerosols are liberated. Human infections are mostly occupational, as in poultry workers, pigeon farmers, petshop owners, bird fanciers and veterinarians. Infection is by inhalation. Rare cases of infection by parrot bites have been reported. Consumption of poultry products does not lead to infection. Case to case transmission in humans is rare but has been recorded. The high infectivity of psittacosis is indicated by the frequency of laboratory infections. Strains from parrots and turkeys are more virulent than those from other avian sources.

The incubation period is about ten days. Clinical disease varies from a mild influenza-like syndrome to a fatal pneumonia. Though pneumonia is the usual clinical manifestation, psittacosis is a septicemia and may lead to meningoencephalitis, endocarditis, pericarditis, arthritis or a typhoid-like syndrome.

Laboratory diagnosis: The chlamydia can be isolated from blood during the early stages of the disease and from sputum later on. Infected cells, including alveolar macrophages from patients, and mouse brain, yolk sac and cell cultures show inclusion bodies (Levinthal–Cole–Lillie or LCL bodies). These differ from *C. trachomatis* inclusion in being more diffuse and irregular, not stained by iodine and not inhibited by sulphadiazine or cycloserine. It is generally difficult to recover the chlamydia from patients treated with antibiotics. Isolation should be attempted only in laboratories where special containment facilities are available, as laboratory infection is a serious hazard. Serological diagnosis may be made by the group specific CF test or type specific micro-IF.

CHLAMYDIA PNEUMONIAE

Grayston and colleagues (1986) isolated a chlamydial strain from acute respiratory disease in adults in Taiwan and designated it as *C. psittaci* strain TWAR (from Taiwan Acute Respiratory). It possessed the group-specific antigen in common with *C. psittaci* and *C. trachomatis* but could be distinguished from both of them by species-specific antigens, DNA hybridisation and restriction endonuclease analysis. This appears to be an exclusively human chlamydia transmitted from human to human without any avian or animal host. It grows poorly in cell cultures. Because of these properties it has been classified as a separate species

called *C. pneumoniae*.

It appears to be a common cause of respiratory disease in older children and adults worldwide. Antibodies have been demonstrated in the sera of about 50 percent of adults from different parts of the world. Its clinical spectrum includes pharyngitis, sinusitis, bronchitis and pneumonia, which resembles *Mycoplasma* pneumonia. It has also been associated with adult onset asthma. The incubation period is 1–3 weeks. Outbreaks have been reported in closed communities. Primary infections occur in young children. Reinfections are common. Serum antibodies do not appear to be protective.

Diagnosis is by antigen detection by EIA, direct immunofluorescence or molecular methods, as isolation of the organism is very difficult. Serodiagnosis is by CF, ELISA or micro-IF. Treatment is by one of the new macrolide antibiotics like clarithromycin or azithromycin.

Considerable interest has been aroused by recent reports linking *C. pneumoniae* with atherosclerosis and its clinical effects like coronary, carotid and cerebral arterial disease. Apart from seroepidemiological evidence, the finding of the chlamydial antigens in, the isolation of the organism from coronary artery atheromatous plaques, and the experimental induction of atheroma in rabbits infected with the chlamydia strengthen the association. Early results of anti-chlamydial intervention studies in experimental animals and human volunteers also are consistent with a causative role of *C. pneumoniae* in vascular atheromatous disease. However, more work will have to be done before the issue is finally settled.

Further Reading

Beatty WL et al. 1994. Persistent Chlamydiae. *Microbiol Rev* 58:686.
Kauppinen M and P Saikku 1995. Pneumonia due to Chlamydia pneumoniae. *Clin Infect Dis* 21:Suppl.3, S-244.
Peeling RW and RC Brunham 1996. Chlamydiae as pathogens. *Emerging Infect Dis* 2:4.
Weinstock H et al. 1994. *C. trachomatis* infections. *Infect Dis Clin N Am* 8:797.

General Properties of Viruses

Unicellular microorganisms may be classified in descending order of complexity as *eukaryotes,* such as protozoa and fungi, and *prokaryotes,* such as bacteria, mycoplasmas, rickettsiae and chlamydiae. Viruses do not fall strictly into the category of unicellular microorganisms as they do not possess a cellular organisation. Even the simplest of microorganisms are cells enclosed within a cell wall, containing both types of nucleic acid (DNA and RNA), synthesising their own macromolecular constituents and multiplying by binary fission. Viruses, on the other hand, do not have a cellular organisation and contain only one type of nucleic acid, either DNA or RNA but never both. They are obligate intracellular parasites. They lack the enzymes necessary for protein and nucleic acid synthesis and are dependent for replication on the synthetic machinery of host cells. They multiply by a complex process and not by binary fission. They are unaffected by antibacterial antibiotics. The major differences between viruses and microorganisms are shown in Table 48.1. In spite of these basic differences, viruses are generally considered microorganisms in medical microbiology.

Viruses occupy the twilight zone that separates the 'living' from the 'nonliving'. The demonstration by Stanley (1935) that viruses could be crystallised like chemicals, and the extraction by Geirer and Schramm (1956) of 'infectious nucleic acid' from a virus that could infect host cells and yield complete virus progeny made it appear that viruses were only 'living chemicals'. Recent advances in molecular biology seem to make the distinction between 'life' and 'nonlife' little more than a semantic exercise. As the smallest 'living units', viruses offer the best models for understanding the chemistry of 'life'.

The medical importance of viruses lies in their ability to cause a very large number of human diseases. Viral diseases range from minor ailments such as the common cold to terrifying diseases such as rabies or AIDS. They may be sporadic like mumps, endemic like infectious hepatitis, epidemic lke dengue fever or pandemic like influenza. They may be localised to circumscribed areas (as some arbovirus diseases) or worldwide (as Herpes simplex). The control of bacterial infection with antibiotics has enhanced the role of viral infections in human disease. Viruses can cause cancer in animals and birds, as well as in humans.

Table 48.1 Properties of prokaryotes and viruses

	Cellular organisation	Growth on inanimate media	Binary fission	Both DNA and RNA	Ribosomes	Sensitivity to antibacterial antibiotics	Sensitivity to interferon
Bacteria	+	+	+	+	+	+	-
Mycoplasmas	+	+	+	+	+	+	-
Rickettsiae	+	-	+	+	+	+	-
Chlamydiae	+	-	+	+	+	+	-
Viruses	-	-	-	-	-	-	+

MORPHOLOGY

Size: The extracellular infectious virus particle is called the *virion*. Viruses are much smaller than bacteria. It was their small size and 'filterability' (ability to pass through filters that can hold back bacteria) that led to their recognition as a separate class of infectious agents. Hence they were for a time known as 'filterable viruses'. As they were too small to be seen under the light microscope, they were called 'ultramicroscopic'. Some of the larger viruses, such as poxviruses, can be seen under the light microscope when suitably stained. The virus particles seen in this manner are known as '*elementary bodies*'.

Viruses vary widely in size. The largest among them (for example poxviruses) measuring about 300 nm, are as large as the smallest bacteria (mycoplasma). The smallest viruses (for example parvovirus) measuring about 20 nm are nearly as small as the largest protein molecules such as hemocyanin.

The earliest method of estimating the size of virus particles was by passing them through collodion membrane filters of graded porosity (gradocol membranes). The average pore diameter of the finest filter that permitted passage of the virion gave an estimate of its size. With the development of the ultracentrifuge, a second method became available. From the rate of sedimentation of virus in the ultracentrifuge, the particle size could be calculated using Stokes' law. The third and the most direct method of measuring virus size is electron microscopy. Purified preparations of virions may be examined under the electron microscope either unstained or stained. By this method, both the shape and size of virions can be studied.

Structure and shape: The virion consists essentially of a nucleic acid surrounded by a protein coat, the *capsid* . The capsid with the enclosed nucleic acid is known as the *nucleocapsid*. The function of the capsid is to protect the nucleic acid from inactivation by nucleases and other deleterious

agents in the environment. The capsid is composed of a large number of *capsomers* which form its morphological units. The chemical units of the capsid are polypeptide molecules which are arrranged symmetrically to form an impenetrable shell around the nucleic acid core (Fig. 48.1). One of the major functions of the capsid is to introduce viral genome into host cells by adsorbing readily to cell surfaces.

Two kinds of symmetry are encountered in the capsid, *icosahedral* (cubical) and *helical*. An icosahedron is a polygon with 12 vertices or corners and 20 facets or sides. Each facet is in the shape of an equilateral triangle. Two types of capsomers constitute the icosahedral capsid. They are the pentagonal capsomers at the vertices (pentons) and the hexagonal capsomers making up the facets (hexons). There are always 12 pentons but the number of hexons varies with the virus group. In the nucleocapsids with helical symmetry, the capsomers and nucleic acid are wound together to form a helical or spiral tube. The tube may be rigid, as in the tobacco mosaic virus but in the case of animal viruses, the tubular nucleocapsid is pliable and may be coiled on itself. Not all viruses show the typical icosahedral or helical symmetry. Some, like the poxviruses, exhibit a complex symmetry.

Virions may be enveloped or nonenveloped (naked). The envelope or outer covering of viruses is derived from the host cell membrane when the progeny virus is released by budding. The envelope is lipoprotein in nature. The lipid is largely of host cell origin while the protein is virus coded. Protein subunits may be seen as projecting spikes on the surface of the envelope. These structures are called *peplomers* (from *peplos*, meaning envelope). A virus may have more than one type of peplomer. The influenza virus carries two kinds of peplomers – the hemagglutinin which is a triangular spike and the neuraminidase which is a mushroom shaped structure. Envelopes confer chemical, antigenic and biological properties on viruses. Enveloped viruses are susceptible to the action of lipid solvents like

GENERAL PROPERTIES OF VIRUSES

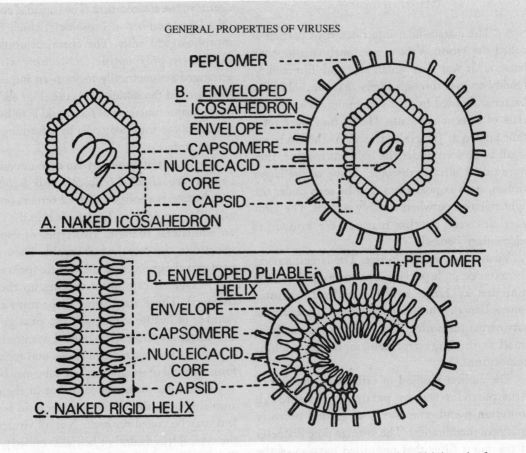

A - naked icosahedral virus, consisting of an inner core of nucleic acid enclosed by a capsid, which is made of capsomers.

B - differs from A in possessing an envelope.

C - naked helical virus composed of capsomers wound round the nucleic acid to form a tubular structure.

D - envelope helical virus in which the tubular capsid is pliable and is enclosed within an envelope.

Fig. 48.1. Design and structure of virions

ether, chloroform and bile salts. Specific neutralisation of virus infectivity depends on antibodies to the surface antigens. Biological properties such as attachment to host cellsurface or hemagglutination depend on the envelope. Some viruses possess additional structural features. For example, fibrils protrude from the vertices of adenovirus particles.

The overall shape of the virus particle varies in different groups of viruses. Most animal viruses are roughly spherical. Some are irregular and pleomorphic. The rabies virus is bullet shaped,

Ebolvirus filamentous and poxviruses are brick shaped; the tobacco mosaic virus is rod shaped. Bacterial viruses have a complex morphology (Fig. 48.2).

Chemical properties: Viruses contain only one type of nucleic acid, either single or double stranded DNA or RNA. In this respect, viruses are unique, for nowhere else in nature is genetic information solely carried by RNA. Viral nucleic acids may be extracted by treatment with detergents or phenol and, in the case of some viruses (for example picornavirus, papovavirus), the extracted

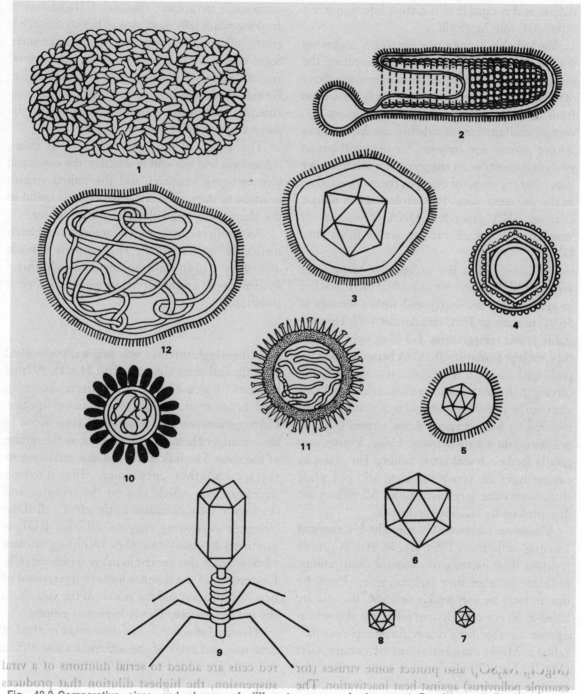

Fig. 48.2 Comparative sizes and shapes of different groups of viruses. 1. Poxviruses 2. Rhabdovirus 3. Herpesvirus 4. Retrovirus 5. Togavirus 6. Adenovirus 7. Parvovirus 8. Picornavirus 9. Bacteriophage 10. Coronavirus 11. Orthomyxovirus 12. Paramyxovirus.

nucleic acid is capable of initiating infection when introduced into host cells.

Viruses also contain protein which makes up the capsid. Viral protein, besides protecting the nucleic acid, also determines the antigenic specificity of the virus. Enveloped viruses contain lipids derived from the host cell membrane. Some viruses also contain small amounts of carbohydrate. Most viruses do not possess any enzymes for the synthesis of viral components or for energy production but some have other enzymes, for example, the neuraminidase in the influenza virus. Retrovirues have a unique enzyme, RNA-dependent-DNA polymerase or 'transcriptase' which can transcribe RNA into DNA.

Resistance: With few exceptions, viruses are very heat labile. There are individual variations but in general, they are inactivated within seconds at 56 °C, minutes at 37 °C and days at 4 °C. They are stable at low temperatures. For long term storage, they are kept frozen at −70 °C. A better method for prolonged storage is lyophilisation or freeze drying (drying the frozen virus under vacuum). Lyophilised virus can be stored for years and reconstituted when required by adding water. Some viruses (such as poliovirus) do not stand freeze drying. Viruses vary greatly in their resistance to acidity. For example, enteroviruses are very resistant to acid pH while rhinoviruses are very susceptible. All viruses are disrupted under alkaline conditions.

Viruses are inactivated by sunlight, UV rays and ionising radiations. They are, in general, more resistant than bacteria to chemical disinfectants, probably because they lack enzymes. Phenolic disinfectants are only weakly virucidal. Bacteria are killed in 50 per cent glycerol saline but this acts as a preservative for many viruses (for example vaccinia, rabies). Molar concentrations of certain salts ($MgCl_2$, Na_2SO_4) also protect some viruses (for example poliovirus) against heat inactivation. The most active antiviral disinfectants are oxidising agents such as hydrogen peroxide, potassium permanganate and hypochlorites. Organic iodine compounds are actively virucidal. Chlorination of drinking water kills most viruses but its efficacy is greatly influenced by the presence of organic matter. Some viruses (such as hepatitis virus, polioviruses) are relatively resistant to chlorination. Formaldehyde and beta propiolactone are actively virucidal and are commonly employed for the preparation of killed viral vaccines.

The action of lipid solvents such as ether, chloroform and bile salts is selective, the enveloped viruses being sensitive and the naked viruses resistant to them. The selective action is useful in the identification and classification of viruses.

Antibiotics active against bacteria are completely ineffective against viruses. This property is made use of in eliminating bacteria from clinical specimens by antibiotic treatment before virus isolation.

VIRAL HEMAGGLUTINATION

Viral hemagglutination was originally observed with the influenza virus by Hirst (1941). A large number of viruses have since been shown to agglutinate erythrocytes from different species. Hemagglutination by the influenza virus is due to the presence of hemagglutinin spikes on the surface of the virus. The influenza virus also carries on its surface another peplomer, the enzyme neuraminidase which acts on the receptor and destroys it. Neuraminidase is, therefore, called the 'receptor destroying enzyme' (RDE). RDE is produced by many microbes including cholera vibrios, and is also present in many vertebrate cells. Destruction of the receptor leads to the reversal of hemagglutination and the release of the virus from the red cell surface. This is known as *elution*.

Hemagglutination is as a convenient method of detection and assay of the influenza virus. When red cells are added to serial dilutions of a viral suspension, the highest dilution that produces hemagglutination provides the hemagglutination titre. The hemagglutination test can be carried out in test tubes or special plastic trays. Red cells which are not agglutinated settle at the bottom in the form of a 'button', while the agglutinated cells are seen spread into a shield-like pattern (Fig. 48.3). As the inactivated virus can also hemagglutinate, the test serves to titrate killed influenza vaccines. As hemagglutination is specifically inhibited by the antibody to the virus, hemagglutination inhibition provides a convenient test for the antiviral antibody. Hemagglutination and elution also help in purifying and concentrating the virus.

Elution is found only in the myxoviruses that possess neutraminidase. With other viruses, hemagglutination is stable. In the case of arboviruses, hemagglutination appears to be a reversible state of equilibrium between the virus and erythrocytes, being influenced by slight variations in pH and temperature. Poxviruses agglutinate red cells from only some fowls. The hemagglutinin of poxvirus is distinct from the virion and can be separated by centrifugation. Table 48.2 shows the characteristics of hemagglutination by different viruses.

VIRAL MULTIPLICATION

The genetic information necessary for viral replication is contained in the viral nucleic acid , but lacking biosynthetic enzymes, the virus depends on the synthetic machinery of the host cell for replication. Early studies on viral replication employed the bacteriophage as the model. While there are general similarities in the pattern of multiplication of bacterial and animal viruses, there are also important differences. The viral multiplication cycle can be divided into six sequential phases, though the phases may sometimes be overlapping: (1) adsorption or attachment; (2) penetration; (3) uncoating; (4) biosynthesis; (5) maturation, and (6) release.

Adsorption: Virions may come into contact with cells by random collision but adsorption takes place only if there is an affinity between the two. The cell surface should contain specific receptor sites to which the virus can gain attachment.

In the case of influenza viruses, the hemagglutinin on the virus surface gets attached to glycoprotein receptor sites on the surface of the respiratory epithelium. Destruction of the receptor sites by RDE prevents viral adsorption. With the human immunodeficiency virus, attcahment is between the CD4 receptor on host cells and the viral surface glycoprotein gp 120. In the case of polioviruses, the receptor is the lipoprotein present on the surface of primate but not rodent cells. The poliovirus can, therefore, attach itself to primate cells but not to rodent cells. Differences in susceptibility to viral infection are to a large extent based on the presence or absence of receptors on cells. If the phase of adsorption can be bypassed, cells normally insusceptible to virus may be rendered susceptible to it. Thus, infectious nucleic acid extracted from picornaviruses can infect rodent cells, which are resistant to infection by the whole virus.

Penetration: Bacteria possess rigid cell walls. Bacterial viruses cannot, therefore, penetrate into bacterial cells and only the nucleic acid is introduced intracellularly by a complex mechanism. Animal cells do not have rigid cell walls and the whole virus can enter into them. Virus particles may be engulfed by a mechanism resembling phagocytosis, a process known as 'viropexis'. Alternatively, in the case of the enveloped viruses, the viral envelope may fuse with the plasma membrane of the host cell and release the nucleocapsid into the cytoplasm.

Uncoating: This is the process of stripping the virus of its outer layers and capsid so that the nucleic acid is released into the cell. With most viruses, uncoating is effected by the action of lysosomal enzymes of the host cell. In poxviruses, uncoating is a two-step process. In the first step, the outer coat is removed by lysosomal enzymes in the phagocytic vacuole. The inner core of the virus, containing the internal protein and nucleic acid, is released into the cytoplasm where the second step of uncoating is effected by a viral uncoating enzyme and the DNA is liberated.

Biosynthesis: This phase includes synthesis not

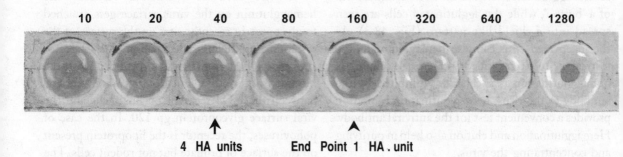

| 10 | 20 | 40 | 80 | 160 | 320 | 640 | 1280 |

↑ 4 HA units   ▲ End Point 1 HA . unit

Fig.48.3 Viral hemagglutination. Virus continuing fluid is diluted in doubling dilutions and 0.5% suspension of chick red cells added. Where virus is present there is diffuse widespread even patter on the bottom of the wells in the plastic plate. Where no virus is present the cells settle down to a button like aggregate with sharp edges.

merely of the viral nucleic acid and capsid protein but also of enzymes necessary in the various stages of viral synthesis, assembly and release. In addition, certain 'regulator proteins' are also synthesised which serve to shut down the normal cellular metabolism and direct the sequential production of viral components. The site of viral synthesis depends on the type of virus. In general, most DNA viruses synthesise their nucleic acid in the host cell nucleus. The exceptions are the poxviruses, which synthesise all their components in the host cell cytoplasm. Most RNA viruses synthesise all their components in the cytoplasm. Exceptions are orthomyxoviruses and some paramyxoviruses and

retroviruses which are synthesised partly in the nucleus. Viral protein is synthesised only in the cytoplasm.

Biosynthesis consists essentially of the following steps:

1. Transcription of messenger RNA (mRNA) from the viral nucleic acid.

2. Translation of the mRNA into 'early proteins'. These 'early or nonstructural proteins' are enzymes which initiate and maintain synthesis of virus components. They may also induce shutdown of host protein and nucleic acid synthesis.

3. Replication of viral nucleic acid.

Table 48.2 Characteristics of hemagglutination by viruses

Virus	Erythrocyte species and other conditions
Influenza virus	Fowl, human, guinea pig, others; Elution at 37 °C
Parainfluenza, mumps, NDV	Fowl, human, guinea pig, others; Elution at 37 °C; Hemolysin present
Measles	Monkey, 37 °C
Togavirus—several groups of Arbovirus	Goose, pigeon, one day old chick; pH and temperature critical
Rubella	Goose, pigeon, oneday old chick; 4×C
Enterovirus, some Coxsackie and ECHO	Human; 4 °C and 37 °C
Rhinovirus, some serotypes	sheep; 4 °C
Rabies	Goose; 4 °C, pH 6.2
Reovirus	Human; 37 °C

4. Synthesis of 'late' or structural proteins, which are the components of daughter virion capsids.

The critical step in viral biosynthesis is the transcription of mRNA from the viral nucleic acid. Once this is achieved, the host cell resources can be utilised for translating mRNA into viral components. Depending on the structure of their genome, viruses use different strategies for the transcription of mRNA. Viruses have been categorised into six classes by Baltimore (1970) based on thier replication mechanisms.

Class 1: In the case of fully double stranded DNA viruses (such as adeno-, herpes-, papovaviruses), the DNA enters the host cell nucleus and uses the host cell enzymes for transcription. The extracted DNA from these viruses is infectious. With hepadnaviruses which have a partially double stranded DNA, the duplex is completed by a viral DNA polymerase, inside the host cytoplasm. The mature DNA then moves into the nucleus, to be transcribed by host transcriptases. Extracted hepadnavirus DNA is not infectious. Poxviruses which replicate in the cytoplasm form mRNA using polymerases contained in the virion itself. Poxvirus DNA is not infectious.

Class 2: With single stranded DNA viruses (for example parvovirus), the DNA molecule moves into the host cell nucleus and is converted into the duplex form. Transcription is achieved by host enzymes.

Class 3: In reoviruses, the double stranded RNA is transcribed to mRNA by viral polymerases.

Class 4: Depending on the method of mRNA transcription, single stranded RNA viruses are classified into two categories. In the *positive strand* (*plus strand, positive sense*) RNA viruses, the viral RNA itself act as the mRNA. Viral RNA is infectious by itself and is translated directly into viral proteins in the host cell cytoplasm (for example picorna-, togaviruses).

Class 5: The *negative strand* (*minus sense*) RNA viruses (for example rhabdo-, orthomyxo-, paramyxoviridae) the RNA is 'antisense', with polarity opposite to mRNA. They possess their own RNA polymerases for mRNA transcription. Extracted nucleic acids from these viruses are not infectious.

Class 6: Retroviridae exhibit a unique replicative strategy. Their single stranded RNA genome is converted into an RNA:DNA hybrid by the viral *reverse transcriptase* (RNA directed DNA polymerase) enzyme. Double stranded DNA is then synthesised from the RNA:DNA hybrid. The double stranded DNA form of the virus (provirus) is integrated into the host cell chromosome. This integration may lead to transformation of the cell and development of neoplasia.

Maturation: Assembly of daughter virions follows the synthesis of viral nucleic acid and proteins. Virion assembly may take place in the host cell nucleus or cytoplasm. Herpes and adenoviruses are assembled in the nucleus, while picorna and poxviruses are assembled in the cytoplasm. At this stage, the nonenveloped viruses are present intracellularly as fully developed virions but in the case of enveloped viruses, only the nucleocapsid is complete. Envelopes are derived from the host cell membrane during the process of budding. The host cell membrane which becomes the envelope is modified by incorporation of virus-specific antigens. Herpes viruses assembled in the nucleus acquire their envelope from the nuclear membrane as they are released into the cytoplasm enclosed in a vesicle. Myxoviruses bud from the cell surface and their envelope is formed by the modified cytoplasmic membrane of the host cell. The incorporation of viral antigen (hemagglutinin) on the cell membrane endows the cell with the property of hemadsorption.

Release: In the case of bacterial viruses, the release of progeny virions takes place by the lysis of the infected bacterium. However, in the case of animal viruses, release usually occurs without cell lysis. Myxoviruses are released by a process of budding from the cell membrane over a period of time. The host cell is unaffected and may even divide, the daughter cells continuing to release virions. Progeny virions are released into the surrounding medium and may infect other cells. In the case of some viruses (for example varicella), transmission occurs directly from cell to cell, very little free virus being demonstrable extracellularly in the medium. Not all animal viruses spare the host cell. The poliovirus causes profound damage to the host cell and may be released by cell lysis.

From the stage of penetration till the appearance of mature daughter virions, the virus cannot be demonstrated inside the host cell. This period during which the virus seems to disappear or go 'underground' is known as the 'eclipse phase'. The time taken for a single cycle of replication is about 15–30 minutes for bacteriophages and about 15–30 hours for animal viruses. A single infected cell may release a large number of progeny virions. While this can be determined readily in bacteriophages (burst size), it is difficult to assess in the case of animal viruses that are released over a prolonged period.

ABNORMAL REPLICATIVE CYCLES

A proportion of daughter virions that are produced may not be infective. This is due to defective assembly. Such 'incomplete viruses' are seen in large proportions when cells are infected with a high dose of the influenza virus. The virus yield will have a high hemagglutinin titre but low infectivity. This is known as the *von Magnus phenomenon*.

Virus infection in some cells does not lead to production of infectious progeny. In such cells (nonpermissive cells), the viral components may be synthesised but maturation or assembly is defective, and either no release occurs or the progeny is noninfectious. This is known as *abortive infection*. Here, the defect is in the type of cell and not in the parental viruses.

Some viruses are genetically defective in that when they infect cells, they are unable to give rise to fully formed progeny. Yield of progeny virions occurs only if the cells are simultaneously infected with a helper virus, which can supplement the genetic deficiency. For example, some strains of the Rous sarcoma virus (RSV) cannot code for the synthesis of the viral envelope. When RSV infects a cell that harbours a helper virus (for example avian leukosis virus), infectious progeny results, the helper virus contributing to the synthesis of the envelope. The envelope antigen of progeny RSV will therefore be determined by the type of helper virus. Other examples of defective viruses are hepatitis D virus and adeno-associated satellite viruses which replicate only in the presence of their helper viruses—hepatitis B and adenoviruses respectively. Viruses which are genetically deficient and therefore incapable of producing infectious daughter virions without the helper activity of another virus are known as *'defective viruses'*.

CULTIVATION OF VIRUSES

As viruses are obligate intracellular parasites, they cannot be grown on any inanimate culture medium. Three methods are employed for the cultivation of viruses – inoculation into animals, embryonated eggs or tissue cultures.

Animal inoculation: The earliest method for the cultivation of viruses causing human diseases was inoculation into human volunteers. Reed and colleagues (1900) used human volunteers for their pioneering work on yellow fever. Due to the serious risk involved, human volunteers are used only when no other method is available and when the virus is relatively harmless. Monkeys were used for the isolation of the poliovirus by Landsteiner and Popper (1909). However, due to their cost and risk to handlers, monkeys find only limited application in virology. In some instances, nonhuman primates provide the only method for virus cultivation. The use of white mice, pioneered by Theiler (1903) extended the scope of animal inoculation greatly. Mice are still the most widely employed animals in virology. Infant (suckling) mice are very susceptible to coxsackie and arboviruses, many of which do not grow in any other system. Mice may be inoculated by several routes—intracerebral, subcutaneous, intraperitoneal or intranasal. Other animals such as guinea pigs, rabbits and ferrets are used in some situations.

The growth of the virus in inoculated animals may be indicated by death, disease or visible lesions. Serial blind passages may sometimes be necessary before evidence of virus growth can be obtained. Disadvantages of animal inoculation are that immunity may interfere with viral growth and that animals often harbour latent viruses. Animal inoculation is also used for the study of pathogenesis, immune response, epidemiology and oncogenesis.

Embryonated eggs: The embryonated hen's egg was first used for the cultivation of viruses by Goodpasture (1931) and the method was further developed by Burnet. The embryonated egg offers several sites for the cultivation of viruses (Fig. 48.4). Inoculation on the chorioallantoic membrane (CAM) produces visible lesions (pocks). Different viruses have different pock morphology. Under optimal conditions, each infectious virus particle can form one pock. Pock counting, therefore, can be used for the assay of pock-forming viruses such as variola or vaccinia. Inoculation into the allantoic cavity provides a rich yield of influenza and some paramyxoviruses. Inoculation into the amniotic sac is employed for the primary isolation of the influenza virus. Yolk sac inoculation is used for the cultivation of some viruses, chlamydiae and rickettsiae.

Allantoic inoculation is employed for growing the influenza virus for vaccine production. Other chick embryo vaccines in routine use are the yellow fever (17D strain) and rabies (Flury strain) vaccines. Duck eggs are bigger and have a longer incubation period than hen's eggs. They therefore provide a better yield of rabies virus and were used for the preparation of the inactivated non-neural rabies vaccine.

Cell culture: Cultivation of bits of tissues and organs in vitro had been used by physiologists and surgeons for the study of morphogenesis and wound healing. Probably, the first application of tissue culture in virology was by Steinhardt and colleagues (1913) who maintained the vaccinia virus in fragments of rabbit cornea. Maitland (1928) used chopped tissues in nutrient media for the cultivation of vaccinia virus. The major obstacle to the development of tissue culture was the presence of bacterial contamination. It was only when antibiotics became available for the prevention of bacterial contamination that tissue culture became a routine laboratory method. The turning point which made tissue culture the most important method for the cultivation of viruses was the demonstration by Enders, Weller and Robbins (1949) that poliovirus, till then considered a strictly neurotropic virus, could be grown in tissue culture of non-neural origin. Since then almost every human virus has been grown in tissue culture.

Three types of tissue cultures are available

1. *Organ culture:* Small bits of organs can be maintained in vitro for days and weeks, preserving their original architecture and function. Organ cultures are useful for the isolation of some viruses which appear to be highly specialised parasites of certain organs. For example, the tracheal ring organ culture is employed for the isolation of coronavirus, a respiratory pathogen.

2. *Explant culture:* Fragments of minced tissue can be grown as 'explants' embedded in plasma clots. They may also be cultivated in suspension. This was what was originally known as 'tissue culture'. This method is now seldom employed in virology. Adenoid tissue explant cultures were used for the isolation of adenoviruses.

3. *Cell culture:* This is the type of culture routinely employed for growing viruses. Tissues are dissociated into the component cells by the action of proteolytic enzymes such as trypsin and mechanical shaking. The cells are washed, counted and suspended in a growth medium. The essential constituents of the growth medium are physiologic amounts of essential aminoacids and vitamins, salts, glucose, and a buffering

system generally consisting of bicarbonate in equilibrium with atmosphere containing about 5% carbon dioxide. This is supplemented with upto 5% calf or fetal calf serum. Antibiotics are added to prevent bacterial contaminants and phenol red as indicator. Such media will enable most cell types to multiply with a division time of 24–48 hours. The cell suspension is dispensed in bottles, tubes or Petri dishes. The cells adhere to the glass surface and on incubation, divide to form a confluent monolayer sheet of cells covering the surface within about a week.

Cell culture tubes may be incubated in a sloped horizontal position, either as 'stationary culture' or may be rolled in special 'roller drums' to provide better aeration. Some fastidious viruses grow only in such roller cultures.

Based on their origin, chromosomal characters and the number of generations through which they can be maintained, cell cultures are classified into three types (Table 48.3):

1. *Primary cell cultures:* These are normal cells freshly taken from the body and cultured. They are capable of only limited growth in culture and cannot be maintained in serial culture. Common examples of primary cell cultures are monkey kidney, human embryonic kidney, human amnion and chick embryo cell cultures. Primary cell cultures are useful for the isolation of viruses and their cultivation for vaccine production.

2. *Diploid cell strains:* These are cells of a single type that retain the original diploid chromosome number and karyotype during serial subcultivation for a limited number of times. After about fifty serial passages, they undergo 'senescence'. Diploid strains developed from human fibroblasts are susceptible to a wide range of human viruses and are very useful for the isolation of some fastidious pathogens. They are also employed for the production of viral vaccines.

3. *Continuous cell lines:* These are cells of a single type, usually derived from cancer cells, that are capable of continuous serial cultivation indefinitely. Standard cell lines derived from human cancers, such as HeLa, Hep-2 and KB cell lines have been used in laboratories throughout the world for many years. These cell lines may be maintained by serial subcultivation or stored in the cold (–70 °C) for use when necessary. Some cell lines are now permitted to be used for vaccine manufacture, for example Verocell for rabies vaccine.

Detection of virus growth in cell cultures: Virus growth in cell cultures can be detected by the following methods:

1. *Cytopathic effect:* Many viruses cause morphological changes in cultured cells in which they grow. These changes can be readily observed by microscopic examination of the cultures. These changes are known as 'cytopathic effects' (CPE) and the viruses causing CPE are called 'cytopathogenic viruses'. The CPE produced by different groups of viruses are characteristic and help in the presumptive identification of virus isolates. For example, enteroviruses produce rapid CPE with crenation of cells and degeneration of the entire cell sheet; measles virus produces syncytium formation; herpes virus causes discrete focal degeneration; adenovirus produces large granular clumps resembling bunches of grapes; and SV_{40} produces prominent cytoplasmic vacuolation.

2. *Metabolic inhibition:* In normal cell cultures, the medium turns acid due to cellular metabolism. When viruses grow in cell cultures, cell metabolism is inhibited and there is no acid production. This can be made out by the colour of the indicator (phenol red) incorporated in the medium.

3. *Hemadsorption:* When hemagglutinating viruses (such as influenza and parainfluenza viruses) grow in cell cultures, their presence can be indicated by the addition of guinea pig erythrocytes to the cultures. If the viruses are

multiplying in the culture, the erythrocytes will adsorb onto the surface of cells. This is known as 'hemadsorption'.

4. *Interference:* The growth of a non-cytopathogenic virus in cell culture can be tested by the subsequent challenge with a known cytopathogenic virus. The growth of the first will inhibit infection by the second virus by interference.

5. *Transformation:* Tumour forming (oncogenic) viruses induce cell 'transformation' and loss of contact inhibition, so that growth appears in a piled-up fashion producing 'microtumours'.

6. *Immunofluorescence:* Cells from virus infected cultures can be stained by fluorescent conjugated antiserum and examined under the UV microscope for the presence of virus antigen. This gives positive results earlier than other methods and, therefore, finds wide application in diagnostic virology.

VIRAL ASSAY

The virus content of a specimen can be assayed in two ways: either with reference to the total virus particles or with reference to the infectious virions only. Two methods employed for total particle enumeration are electron microscopy and hemagglutination. By simple negative staining, the virus particles in a suspension can be counted directly under the electron microscope. The virus suspension can be mixed with a known concentration of latex particles The ratio between the virus and latex particles under the electron microscope gives an indication of the virus count. With hemagglutinating viruses, a convenient method of quantitation is the determination of hemagglutination titres. Hemagglutination is not a very sensitive indicator of the presence of small amounts of virus particles. Thus, approximately 10^7 influenza virions are required to produce macroscopic agglutination of a convenient quantity of chicken erythrocytes (0.5 ml of 0.5 per cent suspension). However, because of its simplicity, hemagglutination is a very convenient method of virus assay.

ASSAY OF INFECTIVITY

Two types of infectivity assays can be carried out – quantitative and quantal assays. Quantitative assays measure the actual number of infectious particles in the inoculum, while quantal assays only indicate the presence or absence of infectious viruses. Using

Table 48.3 Some cell cultures in common use

a. Primary cell cultures
  1. Rhesus monkey kidney cell culture
  2. Human amnion cell culture
  3. Chick embryo fibroblast cell culture
b. Diploid cell strains
  1. WI-38   Human embryonic lung cell strain
  2. HL-8   Rhesus embryo cell strain
c. Continuouscell lines
  1. HeLa   Human carcinoma of cervix cell line
  2. HEP-2   Human epithelioma of larynx cell line
  3. KB   Human carcinoma of nasopharynx cell line
  4. McCoy   Human synovial carcinoma cell line
  5. Detroit-6   Sternal marrow cell line
  6. Chang C/I/L/K   Human conjunctiva (C)
                             Intestine (I), Liver (L) and Kidney (K) cell lines
  7. Vero   Vervet monkey kidney cell line
                             Baby hamster kidney cell line

GENERAL PROPERTIES OF VIRUSES

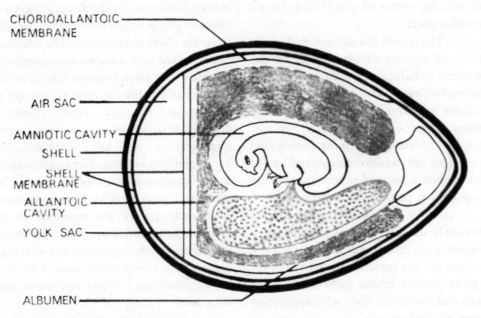

CHORIOALLANTOIC MEMBRANE
AIR SAC
AMNIOTIC CAVITY
SHELL
SHELL MEMBRANE
ALLANTOIC CAVITY
YOLK SAC
ALBUMEN

Fig. 48.4 Cross section of a ten day old egg

serial dilutions of virus suspensions and with the aid of statistical methods, reasonably accurate estimates of infectivity can be obtained in quantal assays.

Quantal assays of infectivity can be carried out in animals, eggs or tissue culture. Examples of endpoints used for infectivity titration are the death of the animal, production of hemagglutinin in allantoic fluid or the appearance of CPE in cell cultures. The titre is usually expressed as the '50 per cent infectious dose' (ID_{50}) per ml, which indicates the highest dilution of the inoculum that would produce an effect in 50 per cent of animals, eggs or cell cultures inoculated. ID_{50} is calculated by the application of statistical methods, such as that of Reed and Muench.

The *quantitative infectivity* assay of viruses is similar to the estimation of bacterial viable counts by colony counting. Two methods are available – plaque assay in monolayer cell culture and pock assay on chick embryo CAM. *Plaque assay* was introduced in animal virology by Dulbecco (1952)

as a modification of the bacteriophage plaque assay. A viral suspension is added to a monolayer of cultured cells in a bottle or Petri dish, and after allowing time for absorption, the medium is removed and replaced with a solid agar gel, to ensure that the spread of progeny virions is confined to the immediate vicinity of infected cells. In this system, each infectious viral particle gives rise to a localised focus of infected cells that can be seen with the naked eye. Such foci are known as 'plaques' and each plaque indicates an infectious virus (Fig. 48.5). Some viruses which are transmitted directly from cell to cell (for example herpesvirus) may form plaques even without an agar overlay. Oncogenic viruses produce cell transformation which can be seen as micro-tumours. Hence they can be enumerated by the transformation assay.

Viruses that form pocks on CAM (for example vaccinia) can be assayed by counting the number of pocks formed on CAM by appropriate inocula of virus. This is known as pock assay.

VIRAL GENETICS

Like all other 'living beings', viruses obey the laws of genetics. Several properties of viruses, such as virulence and antigenicity, that are of great concern to human beings in the context of infections at the level of the cell, individual and community, are under genetic control. Genetic studies, therefore, have contributed to a better understanding of virus–host interactions and the development of better viral vaccines. Genetic mechanisms such as mutation and selection were utilised in the past without recognising the biological mechanisms involved. The development of the 'fixed' rabies virus by Pasteur (1885) is a case in point.

The two main mechanisms for genetic modification in viruses are mutation and recombination. In addition, viruses may exhibit many nonheritable variations due to gene product interactions.

Mutation: The frequency of mutation in viruses is about 10^{-4} to 10^{-8}, approximately the same as in bacteria. Mutations, therefore, occur during every viral infection. Most mutations are lethal. A mutant becomes evident only if the mutation confers some readily observable property or survival advantage. Mutation may occur spontaneously or may be induced by mutagens, physical agents such as irradiation or chemical agents such as 5-fluorouracil.

The mutants may be of various types. Some mutations of clinical and laboratory interest are those affecting virulence, host range, antigenicity and pock or plaque morphology. A class of mutants that are of great importance in laboratory studies is the *conditional lethal mutant*. These are mutants which are able to grow under certain conditions (called permissive conditions), but are lethal, that is it cannot grow under certain other specified conditions (called nonpermissive or restrictive conditions). There are different types of conditional lethal mutants but the types most widely employed in genetic studies are the 'temperature sensitive' (ts)

mutants. These can grow at a low (permissive) temperature (28–31°C), but not at a higher (restrictive) temperature (37 °C). The advantage here is that by using a single selective test (temperature sensitivity), large numbers of mutants with lesions in different genes may be obtained. The *ts* mutants have not only contributed largely to fundamental studies on viral genetics but also, because of their low virulence, offer prospects of better live viral vaccines.

Recombination: Genetic recombination may occur when two different, but related, viruses infect a cell simultaneously. The two viruses exchange segments of nucleic acid between them so that a hybrid results, possessing genes from both parents. Such recombinants breed true thereafter. Recombinants may occur between (1) two active (infectious) viruses; (2) one active and one inactive virus; and (3) two inactive viruses.

When two different strains of the same virus (such as vaccinia or influenza), possessing distinctive markers (such as pock morphology or antigenic properties) are grown together, recombinants may be derived that possess the distinctive properties of both parents. Thus, if a human and an avian strain of influenza virus (whose hemagglutinin and neuraminidase antigens are different and easily identifiable) are grown together, a hybrid may be obtained with the hemagglutinin of one parent and the neuraminidase of the other. This has been demonstrated experimentally in vitro and in vivo. This may be one of the ways by which the pandemic strains of the influenza virus originate in nature.

When a cell is 'infected' with an active virus and a different but related inactivated virus, progeny possessing one or more genetic traits of the inactivated virus may be produced. This phenomenon is called *cross reactivation* or *marker rescue*. New antigenic variants of the influenza virus causing epidemics, often do not grow well in eggs as compared to established laboratory strains. When such an epidemic strain (for example strain A_2) is grown in eggs along with a standard strain

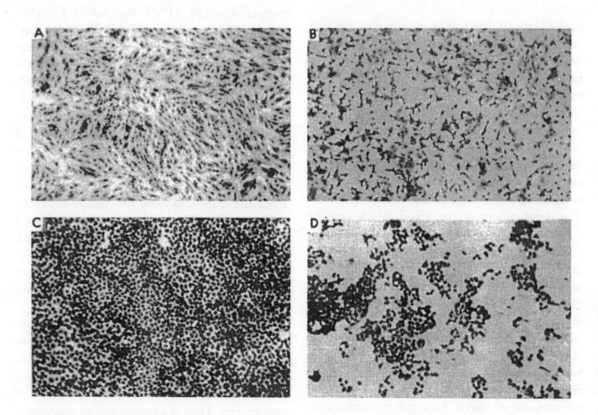

Fig. 48.5   A. Normal Vero cell monolayer.   B. Vero cell monolayer infected with Coxsackie B virus C. HeLa cell monolayer. D. HeLa cell monolayer infected with Coxsackie virus B3, stained after 48 hours. (Courtesy: Dr. J. Shanmugam, Sri Chitra Tirunal Medical Centre, Trivandrum)

(for example strain A_1) inactivated by UV irradiation, a progeny may be obtained which has the antigenic characters of A_2 but the growth characteristics of A_1. This finds application in the manufacture of the influenza virus vaccines.

When a cell is 'infected' with a large dose (high multiplicity) of a single virus inactivated by UV irradiation, live virus may be produced. The different virions that cause multiple infection of a cell may have suffered damage to different genes. Thus, from the total genetic pool it may be possible to obtain a full complement of undamaged genes. This explains how infectious progeny can be produced. This phenomenon is called *multiplicity*

reactivation. There is the potential danger of multiplicity reactivation taking place following the administration of UV irradiated vaccines. UV irradiation is therefore not acceptable as a method of producing inactivated virus vaccines.

Recombination may take place between the virus genome and host chromosome. No viral progeny is produced but the genetic recombination leads to changes in the host cell, such as malignant transformation.

As a general rule virus capsids enclose viral nucleic acids. Sometimes segments of host nucleic acid become encapsidated instead. For example, in a papovavirus capsid, a linear piece of host DNA roughly the same size as the papovavirus genome may be found. This is known as pseudovirion. As far as is known, each pseudovirion contains a different piece of host DNA. Generally, pseudovirions make up only a small fraction of the yield. When cells are infected with many virus particles (as in papovavirus), these progeny contain DNA molecules that consist of partly viral and partly host sequences.

Viral particles containing host DNA sequences are important because of their potential ability to transduce host genes from one cell to another. This could be exploited for correcting inborn errors of metabolism.

NONGENETIC INTERACTIONS

Phenotypic mixing: When two different viruses multiply in a cell, some 'mix up' may take place during assembly, so that the genome of one virus may be surrounded by a capsid belonging partly or entirely to the other virus. This is known as phenotypic mixing. This is not a stable variation. On subsequent passage, the capsid will be found to be of the original type only. In phenotypic mixing, when the nucleic acid of one virus is surrounded by the entire capsid of the other virus, it is known as *transcapsidation*. When phenotypic mixing occurs between two enveloped viruses, resulting in the sharing of peplomers between the two, mosaic envelopes result.

Genotypic mixing: or heterozygosis results from the incorporation of more than one complete genome into a single virus particle. There is no recombination between the different genomes so that the two kinds of viral progeny are formed on passage.

Complementation: Complementation is a functional interaction between the gene products (proteins specified by genes) of two viruses, one or both of which may be defective, resulting in the multiplication of one or both under conditions in which replication would not ordinarily occur. There is no genetic interaction and the progeny are like parental viruses. A number of different types of complementation may occur. When a rabbit is injected with a mixture of heat inactivated virulent myxomavirus and active avirulent fibroma virus it develops fatal myxomatosis. Both myxoma and fibroma are poxviruses. Heat inactivated myxoma virus cannot initiate infection because a heat labile enzyme (DNA dependent RNA polymerase) is destroyed. When co-infected with active fibroma virus, it provides the necessary enzyme so that myxoma virus can cause infection.

Tests for complementation between different mutants of a virus provide information about the functional organisation of the viral genome. Such tests using ts mutants have been very useful in the genetic mapping of viruses.

Interference: The usual result of mixed or multiple infection of cells is interference in which infection of a cell by one virus inhibits simultaneous or subsequent infection by another virus. The most important mediator of interference is interferon, a soluble cellular product (described in Chapter 49). Interference may also be produced by destruction of cell receptors by an active or inactive virus, so that subsequent viral attachment is not possible. Such viral attachment interference is seen with myxoviruses and enteroviruses for which cell receptors are important for the initiation of infection. Another type of interference is 'autointerference', in which a high multiplicity of infection inhibits production of infectious progeny.

Viral interference has been applied in the field in controlling poliomyelitis outbreaks by introducing into the population, the live attenuated poliovirus vaccine. The vaccine virus interferes with the spread of wild poliovirus and halts the outbreak. On the other hand, interference by pre-existing enteric viruses may pose a problem in live poliovirus vaccination.

Enhancement: Mixed infection of cells may sometimes lead to increased virus yield or greater CPE. This is known as 'enhancement'.

CLASSIFICATION AND NOMENCLATURE OF VIRUSES

Till about 1950 little was known of the basic properties of viruses. They were named haphazardly, based on the diseases they caused or on the place of their isolation. They were grouped according to assumed 'tropisms' or affinity to different systems or organs of the body. Thus human viruses were classified as dermotropic, that is those producing skin lesions (smallpox, chickenpox, measles), neurotropic, that is those affecting the nervous system (poliomyelitis, rabies), pneumotropic, that is those affecting the respiratory tract (influenza, common cold) and viscerotropic, that is those affecting visceral organs (yellow fever, hepatitis). Bawden (1941) made the pioneering suggestion that viral nomenclature and classification should be based on the properties of viruses and not upon host responses. From the early 1950s,

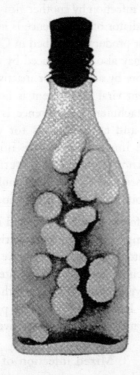

Fig. 48.6 Plaque formation in monkey kidney cells by poliovirus

viruses began to be classified into groups based on their physicochemical and structural features. Nomenclature and classification are now the official responsibility of the International Committee on Taxonomy of Viruses.

Viruses are classified into two main divisions depending on the type of nucleic acid they possess: riboviruses are those containing RNA and deoxyriboviruses are those containing DNA. Further classification is based on other properties such as the strandedness of nucleic acid, symmetry of nucleocapsid, presence of envelope, size and shape of virion and number of capsomers. Short descriptions of the major groups of viruses are given below.

DNA VIRUSES

Poxviridae family: These are large, brick shaped or ovoid viruses (300 × 240 × 100 nm), with complex structure, having a lipid containing an outer coat, one or two lateral bodies and a core carrying a single linear molecule of double stranded DNA. Multiplication and maturation take place in the cytoplasm. The family is divided into several genera.

Herpesviridae family: These are medium sized viruses containing linear double stranded DNA. The icosahedral nucleocapsid (100 nm) has 162 capsomers and is surrounded by a lipid containing envelope. Multiplication takes place in the nucleus and maturation by budding through the nuclear membrane. Only one genus, *Herpesvirus*, has been characterised, but several members of the family await classification.

Adenoviridae family: These are medium sized (70–90 nm) nonenveloped, icosahedral viruses with 252 capsomers. Members have been classified into two genera: Mastadenovirus (mammalian adenoviruses) and Aviadenovirus (adenoviruses of birds)

Papovaviridae family: These are small (40–55 nm) nonenveloped, double stranded DNA viruses with 72 capsomers. Two genera have been recognised. *Papillomavirus* and *Polyomavirus*.

Parvoviridae family: These are very small (18–26 nm) nonenveloped viruses with 31 capsomers. The genome consists of single stranded DNA.

Three genera have been described: *Parvovirus, Adenosatellovirus* and *Densovirus.*

Hepadnaviridae family: This consists of the human hepatitis type B virus and related viruses of animals and birds. (The name comes from *hepa* = liver, and *dna* for DNA core.) The virion is spherical, 42 nm in diameter, consisting of a 27 nm core surrounded by an envelope having virus-specific antigens.

RNA VIRUSES

Picornaviridae family: These are small (20–30 nm), nonenveloped, icosahedral viruses with single stranded RNA genome. Three genera are of medical importance:

Enterovirus, including polio, coxsackie, echo and several other related viruses.

Rhinovirus, including human, bovine and equine rhinoviruses.

Hepatovirus: Hepatitis A virus.

Orthomyxoviridae family: These are medium sized (80–120 nm) spherical or elongated enveloped viruses carrying hemagglutinin and neuraminidase peplomers. The genome consists of single stranded RNA in several (eight) pieces. Only one genus *Influenzavirus* has been recognised. Influenzavirus type C possesses several distinctive features and may have to be separated into a new genus.

Paramyxoviridae family: These are pleomorphic virions (150 nm) with lipid envelope, having surface projections. The genome is unsegmented single stranded linear RNA. Three genera have been recognised:

Paramyxovirus which consists of the Newcastle disease virus, mumps virus and parainfluenza viruses of humans, other mammals and birds.

Morbillivirus, containing measles, canine distemper, rinderpest and related viruses.

Pneumovirus, containing respiratory syncytial virus of humans and related viruses.

Togaviridae family: These are spherical viruses, 40–70 nm, with a lipoprotein envelope and single stranded RNA genome. Most members multiply in arthropods as well as in vertebrates. Three genera have been described

Alpha virus, consisting of viruses formerly classified as Group A arboviruses.

Rubivirus, consisting of the rubella virus Pestivirus, consisting of the mucosal disease virus, hog cholera virus and related viruses.

Flaviviridae family: Flaviviruses, formerly grouped under togaviridae, as Group B arboviruses, have been classified as a separate family because of differences in their molecular structure and replication strategy.

Bunyaviridae family: Spherical, enveloped virions, 90–100 nm. All are arthropod borne viruses. Five genera are established – the large genus *Bunyavirus* containing about 150 species–and four other genera – *Hantavirus, Nairovirus, Phlebovirus, Ukuvirus* – and many unassigned viruses.

Arenaviridae family: Spherical or pleomorphic viruses, 50–300 nm, containing a number of electron dense ribosome-like particles giving a sandy appearance (Hence the name; *arena,* meaning sand in Latin). Members are generally rodent parasites causing persistent infection in the natural host but capable of infecting human beings rarely, leading to severe hemorrhagic illness. Only one genus *Arenavirus* has been recognised. Species include lymphocytic chorio-meningitis virus, Lassa and members of the Tacaribe complex.

Rhabdoviridae family: Bullet shaped viruses 130–300 nm long and 70 nm wide, with lipoprotein envelope carrying peplomers. Two genera have been recognised:

Vesiculovirus, containing vesicular stomatitis virus, Chandipura virus (isolated from human in India) and related species.

Lyssavirus, containing the rabies virus and related viruses such as Lagos bat, Mokola, Duvenhage and others.

Other genera have been suggested to include rhabdoviruses of insects and plants.

Reoviridae family: Icosahedral, nonenveloped viruses, 60–80 nm in size with double layered capsids. Genome consists of double stranded RNA in 10–12 pieces. Three genera have been recognised.

Reovirus, containing reoviruses from humans, other mammals and birds.

Orbivirus, containing several species of arboviruses such as blue tongue virus, African horse sickness virus and Colorado tick fever virus.

Rotavirus including human rotaviruses, calf diarrhea virus and related agents. Other genera may have to be defined to include plant and insect viruses belonging to this family.

Coronaviridae family: Pleomorphic enveloped viruses around 100 nm, with unique club shaped peplomers projecting as a fringe from the surface, resembling the solar corona (hence the name). Only one genus *Coronavirus* has been recognised. Members include human corona viruses causing upper respiratory disease, SARS avian infectious bronchitis virus, calf neonatal diarrhea corona virus, murine hepatitis virus and related viruses

Retroviridae family: (Re = reverse, tr = transcriptase): These are RNA tumour viruses and related agents. Virions are icosahedral about 100 nm, with lipoprotein envelopes. The characteristic biochemical feature is the presence of RNA dependent DNA polymerase (reverse transcriptase) within the virus. Three subfamilies are recognised:

Oncovirinae, the RNA tumour virus group.

Spumivirinae, the foamy virus group (*spuma* = foam)

Lentivirinae, (*lenti* = slow) visna and maedi viruses of sheep belonging to the slow virus group.

Caliciviridae family: These are naked spherical particles (35–39 nm) with 32 cup-shaped depressions arranged in symmetry.

Filoviridae family: These are long, filamentous, enveloped viruses (80 nm diameter and upto 14,000 nm long) with helical nucleocapsid and ss RNA genome. This contains the *Marburg* and *Ebola* viruses causing human hemorrhagic fevers.

VIROIDS

The term 'viroid' was introduced by Diener (1971) to describe a new class of subviral agents characterised by the apparent absence of an extracellular dormant phase (virion) and by a genome much smaller than those of known viruses. The infective agent is a protein-free, low molecular weight RNA resistant to heat and organic solvents but sensitive to nucleases. First identified in the potato spindle tuber disease, viroids have been shown to cause some plant diseases also. It is possible that the causative agents of some animal and human diseases may turn out to belong to the class of viroids.

PRION

Yet another unconventional, virus-like agent has been named prion (1982). The causative agent of scrapie Kuru and Cruetzfeldt–Jacob disease has been shown to be a small particle (MW 50,000 and probably 4–6 nm diameter), without any detectable nucleic acid, resistant to heat (90 °C for three minutes), UV rays and nucleases, and sensitive to proteases. Prions are proteinaceous infectious particles. It has been suggested that they are may also be responsible for some other chronic neurological degenerative diseases of humans.

Further Reading

Belshe RB et al. 1991. *Textbook of Human Virology.* 2nd ed. St. Louis:Mosby Year Book.
Collier L et al. 1998. *Topley and Wilson's Microbiology and Microbial Infections.* 9th edn. vol I, Part I., London: Arnold.
Dimock N and L Primrose 1987. *Introduction to Modern Virology.* 3rd edn. Oxford: Blackwell.
Prusiner SB. 1984. Prions. *Adv Virus Res. 29*:1.
White DC and F Fenner 1986. *Medical Virology.* 3rd edn. New York: Academic Press.

Virus–Host Interactions: Viral Infections

Virus–host interactions may be considered at different levels – the cell, the individual and the community.

At the cellular level, viral infection may cause a broad spectrum of effects, ranging from no apparent cellular damage to rapid cell destruction. Some viruses, like poliovirus cause cell death (cytocidal effect) or even lysis (cytolysis). Others may cause cellular proliferation (as molluscum contagiosum) or malignant transformation (as oncogenic viruses). In some instances the virus and host cell enter into a peaceful coexistence, both replicating independently without any cellular injury, a condition known as 'steady state infection'. In tissue culture, viral infection may lead to readily observable cellular changes (cytopathic effects). These may not parallel the changes produced in the infected animal, as in the latter situation infection is influenced by the various defence mechanisms of the body.

Cellular injury may be due to a number of causes. Early or nonstructural viral proteins often cause a shutdown of host protein and DNA synthesis. Large amounts of viral macromolecules that accumulate in the infected cell may distort the cellular architecture and exert a toxic effect. The permeability of plasma membranes may be altered, releasing lysosomal enzymes and leading to autolysis.

Many viruses produce alterations in the cytoplasmic membrane of infected cells. Some (such as respiratory syncytial virus) cause fusion of adjacent cell membranes, leading to polykaryocytosis or syncytium formation. Virus coded antigens may appear on the surface of infected cells. These antigens may confer new properties on the cells. For example, viral hemagglutinin appears on the surface of cells infected with influenza virus and causes adsorption of erythrocytes to the cell surface (hemadsorption). Virus coded antigens also appear on the surface of cells transformed by oncogenic viruses.

Certain viruses such as measles, mumps, adenoviruses, cytomegalovirus and varicella virus cause damage to the chromosomes of host cells. Chromatid gaps and breaks in chromosome 17 occur frequently in cultured cells infected with adenovirus types 12 and 31.

The most characteristic histological feature in virus infected cells is the appearance of *inclusion bodies*. Inclusion bodies are structures with distinct size, shape, location and staining properties that can be demonstrated in virus infected cells under the light microscope. They may be situated in the cytoplasm (as with poxviruses), nucleus (herpesviruses) or both (measles virus). They are generally acidophilic and can be seen as pink structures when stained with Giemsa or eosin methylene blue stains. Some viruses (for example adenovirus) form basophilic inclusions. Demonstration of inclusion bodies helps in the diagnosis of some viral infections. The presence of intracytoplasmic eosinophilic inclusions (Negri bodies) in the brain cells of animals justifies the presumptive diagnosis of rabies. Vaccinia infected cells show rather smaller multiple inclusions known as Guarnieri bodies. Large inclusions (Bollinger bodies) are seen in fowlpox. Inclusion bodies in molluscum contagiosum (molluscum bodies) are very large (20–30μm) and can be readily seen under the low power microscope, intranuclear inclusion bodies were classified into two types by Cowdry (1934). Cowdry type A inclusions are of variable size and granular appearance (as with herpesvirus, yellow fever virus), while type B inclusions are more circumscribed and often multiple (as with adenovirus, poliovirus). Inclusion bodies may be crystalline aggregates of virions or made up of virus antigens present at the site of virus synthesis. Some inclusions represent degenerative changes produced by viral infection which confer altered staining properties on the cell.

PATHOGENESIS OF VIRAL INFECTION

Depending on the clinical outcome, viral infections can be classified as inapparent (subclinical) or apparent (clinical or overt) infections. The latter may be acute, subacute or chronic. Some virus infections are characterised by latency. Latent infections are of different types. Recurrent herpes simplex and herpes zoster are examples of latent infections in which clinical manifestations appear after prolonged periods of quiescence during which the viruses remain hidden in the nerve root ganglia. Another type of latent infection is persistent tolerant infection in which the virus is readily demonstrable in the tissues of the host but neither disease nor immune response develops. The host is immunologically tolerant to the virus as a result of congenital or neonatal infection. Disease sets in when the tolerance is interrupted. The classical example of persistent tolerant infection is lymphocytic choriomeningitis of mice. Another type of latent infection is seen in neurological diseases such as scrapie in sheep and kuru in human beings. This is called slowly progressive or slow infection as the incubation period is unusually long. Yet another class of latent infection is infection by oncogenic viruses. The human immunodeficiency virus leads to a special type of latency, with an initial asymptomatic period followed by progressive immune damage causing

secondary diseases, ending fatally after many years.

Viruses enter the body through the respiratory and alimentary tracts, skin, conjunctiva and the genital tract. Many viruses are transmitted vertically from parent to progeny.

The respiratory tract offers the most important portal of entry for viruses. A large number of viruses are able to infect the cells of this tract. Some of them multiply locally to initiate a silent local infection which is followed by lymphatic or hematogenous transport to other situations where more extensive multiplication takes place before systemic illness is manifested. Smallpox and chickenpox are examples of such systemic diseases in which the portal of entry is the respiratory tract. Other viruses such as influenza and rhinoviruses are restricted to the respiratory tract where they multiply and produce local disease. These are known as respiratory viruses.

The alimentary tract is the next most important route of entry for viruses. However, only some viruses are able to establish infection in the intestines. All enveloped viruses are destroyed by bile. Rhinoviruses are inactivated by gastric acidity. Only enteroviruses, adenoviruses, reoviruses, hepatitis viruses and the viruses causing gastroenteritis are able to set up intestinal infection. Some of these such as rotavirus remain confined to the gut causing local disease. Others such as poliovirus) after initial multiplication locally, are transported to other sites for further multiplication and subsequent spread to the target organs.

Of the viruses that enter through the skin, only a few produce local lesions. Papilloma, vaccinia, cowpox, molluscum contagiosum and orf are viruses that produce dermal lesions at the site of entry. Skin lesions of exanthematous viral diseases are secondary to systemic infection. Viruses enter the skin through abrasions (papillomavirus), insect bites (arboviruses), animal bites (rabies) or injections (type B hepatitis). Systemic spread occurs through lymphatics or blood. Rabies virus travels along the nerves to the spinal cord or brain.

The conjunctiva also may act as a portal of entry for viruses. This may lead to local disease (adenovirus) or to systemic spread (measles). Some viruses may enter through the genital tract or other sites of sexual contact (HIV).

Congenital infection may occur at any stage from the development of the ovum up to birth. In acute systemic infections, congenital infection usually leads to fetal death and abortion. Rubella and cytomegalovirus produce maldevelopment or severe neonatal disease. Vertical transmission is the natural mode of spread of many tumour viruses. The avian leukosis virus is transmitted in ovo and murine mammary tumour virus through breast milk.

SPREAD OF VIRUS IN THE BODY

The manner in which the infecting virus spreads from the point of entry, multiplies in sites of election and causes lesions in target tissues was first studied by Fenner (1948) using mousepox as the experimental model (Fig. 49.1). The mousepox virus enters the skin, where it multiplies initially and proceeds along the lymphatics to the local nodes. After multiplication in the lymph nodes, the virus enters the bloodstream (primary viremia) and is transported to the spleen and liver which act as the 'central foci' for viral multiplication. After extensive multiplication in the central foci, there occurs a massive spillover of the virus into the bloodstream (secondary viremia). This heralds the onset of clinical symptoms (the prodromal phase in eruptive fevers). The virus reaches the target organ (skin in eruptive fevers) through the bloodstream. Multiplication in the target sites produces the distinctive lesions. With minor modifications, this model holds good for most systemic virus diseases. The reasons for the difference in the foci of multiplication and target organs in the case of different viruses are obscure.

SIGNIFICANCE OF THE INCUBATION PERIOD

The incubation period represents the time taken for the virus to spread from the site of entry to the organs of viral multiplication and thence to the target organs for the production of lesions. Its duration is therefore influenced by the relation between the sites of entry, multiplication and lesion. Where the site of entry and site of lesion are the same, the incubation period is short—one to three days, as in respiratory viral infections and in gastroenteritis. In systemic diseases where the virus enters through the respiratory or alimentary tract and produces lesions in remote target sites, the incubation period is longer—10–20 days, as in chickenpox or poliomyelitis. There are, however, exceptions to this rule. In arbovirus diseases, as in yellow fever or dengue, the incubation period may be shorter (5–6 days), probably because the virus is introduced directly into the bloodstream by the insect vectors. The incubation period in type B hepatitis may be 2–6 months and in slow viral infections, many years. Papillomas and molluscum contagiosum have long incubation periods, probably because the viruses multiply slowly.

HOST RESPONSES TO VIRUS INFECTIONS

The outcome of a virus infection is influenced by the virulence of the infecting strain and the resistance offered by the host. Mechanisms of host resistance may be immunological or nonspecific. The latter includes various genetic and physiological factors such as interferon production, body temperature, nutrition and hormones.

Immunity in virus infections: Virions in general are good antigens and induce both humoral and cellular immune responses. The multiplication of a virus in the body during infection induces not only a quantitatively greater immune response but also liberates and makes available to the immune system the whole range of virus antigens, including

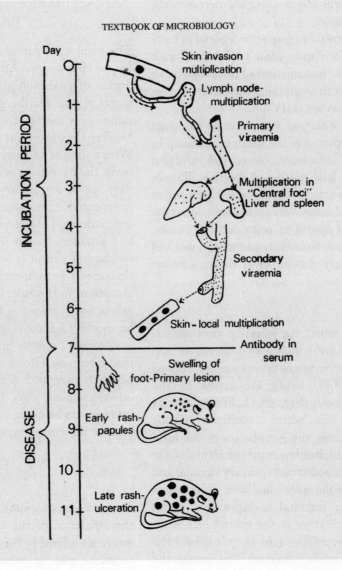

TEXTBOOK OF MICROBIOLOGY

Day

0 — Skin invasion
multiplication

Lymph node-
multiplication

1 —

Primary
viraemia

2 —

INCUBATION PERIOD

3 — Multiplication in
"Central foci"
Liver and spleen

4 —

Secondary
viraemia

5 —

6 — Skin - local multiplication

7 — Antibody in
serum

Swelling of
foot-Primary lesion

8 —

DISEASE

Early rash-
papules

9 —

10 —

Late rash-
ulceration

11 —

Fig. 49.1 Pathogenesis of mousepox—a model for acute exanthemata of humans (after Fenner)

surface and internal antigens as well as the nonstructural antigens such as early proteins.

In mediating humoral antiviral immunity, the important classes of antibodies are IgG, IgM and IgA. IgG and IgM play a major role in blood and tissue spaces, while IgA is more important on mucosal surfaces. Antibodies effect virus neutralisation by several mechanisms. They may

prevent adsorption of the virus to cell receptors, cause enhanced virus degradation or prevent release of the progeny virus from infected cells. Complement acts in conjunction with antibodies in causing surface damage to enveloped virions and in producing cytolysis of virus infected cells.

Not all antibodies are able to neutralise viral infectivity. Antibodies to internal antigens are non-neutralising. Antibodies to surface antigens vary in their neutralising ability. For instance, two types of surface antibodies appear following influenza infection—antihemagglutinin and antineuraminidase. The former can neutralise infectivity but the latter cannot. Antineuraminidase antibody can, however, inhibit the release of progenal virions from infected cells. Some antibodies can paradoxically enhance viral infectivity. Humoral antibodies may sometimes actually contribute to pathogenesis. Antibodies may cause complement dependent injury to cells or induce an immune complex type of tissue injury. The enhanced severity of respiratory syncytial viral infection in early infancy is believed to be due to the presence of passively acquired maternal antibodies. In older children who have no antibody, the virus causes a milder disease. The pathogenesis of some viral hemorrhagic fevers is immune thrombocytopenia. Most extrahepatic lesions in type B hepatitis are due to damage caused by immune complexes.

Cell mediated immunity is of critical importance in viral infections. The earliest indication of cell mediated immunity in viral infections was the demonstration of delayed hypersensitivity following vaccination in immune individuals. Similar skin reactivity is also seen in mumps. The normal resistance to virus infections shown by agammaglobulinemics is ascribed to their cell mediated immunity, though it may also be due to interferon or other nonimmune mechanisms. Individuals with deficient cellular immunity show a heightened susceptibility to infection by the herpes, pox and measles viruses. The administration of antilymphocyte serum induces fatal infection in mice injected with a sublethal dose of the ectromelia virus. Cell mediated immunity is considered to play a major role in recovery from viral infections in which viremia is not important and in which infected cells have viral specific antigens on their surface. In some virus infections cell mediated immunity may contribute to tissue damage, as in lymphocytic choriomeningitis in mice.

Some viral infections cause a suppression of the immune response. Measles infection induces a temporary depression of delayed hypersensitivity to tuberculin. Infection of adult mice with lymphocytic choriomeningitis or leukemia viruses inhibits antibody response to other antigens. HIV strikes at the centre of the immune system by infecting the CD4+ helper T cell.

In general, viral infections are followed by solid immunity to reinfection, which may often be lifelong. Apparent exceptions like the common cold and influenza are not due to lack of immunity but to reinfection being caused by antigenically different viruses. Live virus vaccines also induce more durable protection than bacterial vaccines.

Nonimmunological Responses

1. *Phagocytosis*: Polymorphonuclear leucocytes do not play any significant role in the defence against viral infections. In fact, more viral diseases are characterised by a polymorphonuclear leucopenia. On the other hand, macrophages phagocytose viruses and are important in clearing viruses from the bloodstream.

2. *Body temperature*: Fever may act as a natural defence mechanism against viral infections as most viruses are inhibited by temperatures above 39 °C. An exception is herpes simplex which is usually reactivated by fever to produce 'fever blisters'. *Herpes febrilis* is a frequent accompaniment of fevers caused by pneumococci, streptococci, influenza virus and malaria parasites, but for some unknown reason, is very rare in other fevers (typhoid, tuberculosis).

3. *Hormones*: Corticosteroid administration enhances most viral infections. Coxsackie virus B1 does not normally cause disease in adult mice but will induce a fatal infection in mice treated with cortisone. Normally mild infections such as varicella and vaccinia may be lethal in patients on cortisone. Injudicious use of steroids in the treatment of herpetic keratoconjunctivitis

may cause blindness. The particularly severe course of many viral infections in pregnancy may be related to the hormonal changes associated with pregnancy. The deleterious effect of cortisone may be due to its depression of the immune response and inhibition of interferon synthesis.

4. *Malnutrition*: Some viral infections, such as measles, produce a much higher incidence of complications and a higher case fatality rate in malnourished children than in well fed patients.

5. *Age*: Most viral infections are commoner and more dangerous at the two extremes of age. A notable exception was the influenza pandemic of 1918–1919 which caused the highest fatality in young adults.

6. *Interferon*: Isaacs and Lindenmann (1957) observed that chick chorioallantoic membrane fragments treated with live or inactivated influenza virus produced a diffusible antiviral substance which rendered cells resistant to viral infection. They gave the name interferon to this antiviral substance. It was subsequently found that interferon production is a natural defence mechanism possessed by vertebrate cells against viral infection.

Interferons are a family of host coded proteins produced by cells on induction by viral or nonviral inducers. Interferon by itself has no direct action on viruses but it acts on other cells of the same species, rendering them refractory to viral infection. On exposure to interferon, cells produce a protein (translation inhibiting protein, TIP) which selectively inhibits translation of viral mRNA, without affecting cellular mRNA. What has been called TIP is actually a mixture of at least three different enzymes (a protein kinase, an oligonucletide synthetase and an RNAase) which together block translation of viral mRNA into viral proteins. It has also been suggested that inhibition of viral transcription may also be responsible for the antiviral activity of interferon.

Interferons are species specific, in that interferon produced by one species can protect only cells of the same or related species against viral infections but not cells of unrelated species. Thus, the antiviral effect on human cells is shown by human interferon, and to some extent by monkey interferon but not by chick or mouse interferon. The activity is not virus-specific. Interferon induced by one virus (or even by nonviral inducers) can confer protection against infection by the same or unrelated viruses. However, viruses vary in their susceptibility to interferon. Viruses also vary in their capacity to induce interferon, cytocidal and virulent viruses being poor inducers and avirulent viruses being good inducers. RNA viruses are better inducers than DNA viruses. Examples of potent inducers are togaviruses, vesicular stomatitis virus, Sendai virus and NDV. Nucleic acids (for example double stranded RNA and some synthetic polymers (for example Poly I:C) are particularly efficient inducers. Interferon production is increased by increasing the temperature up to about 40 °C and is inhibited by steroids and increased oxygen tension. Interferon synthesis begins within about an hour of induction and reaches high levels in 6–12 hours. The promptness of interferon induction, much quicker than the antibody response, suggests that interferons may play a primary role in host defence against viral infections. Cellular transcription and protein synthesis are necessary for interferon production.

Based on antigenic characters, cell of origin and other properties, interferons have been classified into three types—alpha, beta and gamma. The abbreviation IFN designates interferon and species of origin is indicated as a prefix – for example, human interferon alpha is usually abbreviated as HuIFN-α.

Alpha interferon (IFN-α), formerly known as leucocyte interferon, is produced by leukocytes following induction by suitable viruses. It is a nonglycosylated protein. At least 16 antigenic subtypes have been identified.

Beta interferon (IFN-β), formerly known as 'fibroblast interferon, is produced by fibroblasts and epithelial cells following stimulation by viruses or polynucleotides. It is a glycoprotein.

Gamma interferon (IFN-γ), formerly known as immune interferon, is produced by T lymphocytes, on stimulation by antigens or mitogens. It is a glycoprotein. It is more concerned with immunomodulatory and antiproliferative functions than with antiviral defence. It also differs from alpha and beta interferons in having a separate cell receptor.

Interferons are inactivated by proteolytic enzymes but not by nucleases or lipases. They resist heating at 56–60 °C for 30–60 minutes and are stable over a wide range of pH (2–10), except gamma IFN, which is labile at pH 2. They have a molecular weight of about 17,000, are nondialysable and nonsedimentable (100,000 g). They are poorly antigenic, so no routine serological tests are available for their detection and estimation. Interferon assay is based on its biological activity, such as the ability to inhibit plaque formation by a sensitive virus. The potency of IFN is expressed as International Units (IU) per ml.

Many properties of interferon make it an ideal candidate for use in the prophylaxis and treatment of viral infections; it is nontoxic, nonantigenic, diffuses freely in the body and has a wide spectrum of antiviral activity. The major drawback initially was its species specificity – interferon produced by nonhuman cells was not clinically useful. This was overcome to some extent by producing interferon from buffy coat leucocytes from blood banks, with NDV or Sendai virus as the inducer. Now, human interferon is available in unlimited quantities following its commercial production by cloning in bacteria and yeast. Even so, its initial promise as an antiviral agent has not been fulfilled. Local application of high doses has shown some benefit against upper respiratory infections, herpetic keratitis and genital warts. Limited success has also been reported against generalised herpes infection in immunocompromised hosts, and against hepatitis B and C infections. Some encouraging results have

been reported in the use of interferon as an anticancer agent, particularly in lymphomas but there have been reports of toxic effects in cancer patients given high doses of interferon.

Although interferon was first recognised as an antiviral agent; it is now known to be a more general regulatory peptide belonging to the class of *cytokines*. The main biological effects of interferons are the following:

1. Antiviral effects: Induction of resistance to infections.
2. Antimicrobial effects: Resistance to intracellular infections, for example toxoplasma, chlamydia, malaria.
3. Cellular effects: Inhibition of cell growth and proliferation; and of DNA and protein synthesis; increased expression of MHC antigens on cell surfaces.
4. Immunoregulatory effects: Enhanced cytotoxic activity of NK, K and T cells; activation of macrophage cytocidal activity; modulation of antibody formation; activation of suppressor T cells; suppression of DTH.

LABORATORY DIAGNOSIS OF VIRAL DISEASES

Technical difficulties in virus isolation and identification, the length of time required for these procedures and the lack of specific therapy for viral infections have contributed to the sparse use of diagnostic virology till recently. The situation has changed in recent years. With the development of rapid techniques for the diagnosis of many virus infections and the availability of specific drugs against at least a few viruses, diagnostic virology is fast becoming a routine procedure.

The demonstration of viral infection in selected groups of persons (*screening*) is an important procedure in the prevention of some diseases (such as screening for HBV and HIV in blood donors). Etiological diagnosis of viral infections is useful in many ways. It is of vital important in some cases, as in rubella in pregnant women. It helps institution of early specific therapy as in herpetic encephalitis and lesions of the eye. It serves to define the etiology of vague syndromes such as upper respiratory infection or aseptic meningitis. It is essential for the detection and prediction of epidemics and the identification of antigenic variation in viruses. It is invaluable in the prompt control of outbreaks. It may lead to the discovery of new viral infections.

Successful diagnosis of viral infections depend as much on the awareness of the physician as on the capability of the virus laboratory. The appropriate specimens should be collected from patients, preserved and transported to the laboratory in the proper manner along with pertinent clinical and epidemiological information (Table 49.1).

In the laboratory, the following methods are commonly employed; microscopic demonstration of the virus or its inclusion body, demonstration of the virus antigen, isolation and identification of the virus, or detection of the specific antibody.

Table 49.1 Types of specimens to be sent for virus diagnosis

System	Specimens required[1]		
	For isolation	For direct examination[2]	For serology
Respiratory system nasopharyngeal	Throat swab, throat washings (EM) aspirates	Nasopharyngeal aspirate (IF)	Paired sera
Central nervous system	Feces, blood (for arbovirus isolation) CSF, (brain biopsy, throat swab, rectal swab)	Brain biopsy (IF & EM); CSF (EM & IF)	Paired sera
Cardiovascular system	Feces	Nil	Paired sera
Skin	Macular/papular scrapings, vesicular/pustular fluid, ulcer scrapings, crust, feces, throat swab	Vesicular/pustular fluid (EM&ID) Ulcer scrapings (EM), crusts, (EM & ID)	Paired sera
Eye	Conjunctival scrapings or swabs	Conjunctival scrapings, as smears on microscope slides (LM & IF)[3]	Paired sera
Liver	Blood (for yellow fever)	Serum (feces)	Serum
General; congenital infections	Throat swab (products of conception)	Nil	Single sera (mother & baby)
General; PUO	Heparinised blood (arbovirus and arenavirus infections) throat swabs, feces (fresh urine)	Nil	Paired sera

[1]Specimens within brackets are not appropriate for routine diagnosis but may be indicated in particular circumstances
[2]IF = Immunofluorescence; EM = Electron Microscopy; ID = Immunodiffusion; LM = Light Microscopy
[3]For diagnosis of rabies only.
(Adapted from WHO)

Microscopy: The demonstration of virus elementary bodies by examination of stained smears is now seldom employed. The detection of virus by electron microscopy is being used increasingly. In some diseases, it used to be the only diagnostic method (for example viral diarrhea). Demonstration of the inclusion body is a routine diagnostic method for rabies in dogs. The microscopic diagnosis of rabies has been rendered very sensitive by fluorescent antibody techniques. The use of direct and indirect fluorescent antibody techniques for the examination of material from lesions, as well as for the early demonstration of viral antigen in tissue cultures inoculated with specimens has enlarged the scope and greatly increased the speed of virus diagnosis.

Demonstration of virus antigen: In cases where virus antigen is abundant in the lesions, its demonstration by serological methods such as precipitation in gel or immunofluorescence offers a rapid method of diagnosis. Highly sensitive serological tests such as counterimmuno-electrophoresis, radioimmunoassay and enzyme linked immunosorbent assay have found wide application in diagnostic virology for the detection of viral antigens in clinical samples. Molecular methods such as probes and polymerase chain reaction provide rapid, sensitive and specific information about the presence of viruses in clinical samples. They are fast becoming routine diagnostic methods in the affluent countries, but in the poor nations, their availability is limited.

Isolation of virus: For virus isolation it is imperative that the specimen be collected properly and transported with least delay to the laboratory. As most viruses are heat labile, refrigeration is essential during transport. The methods used for isolation depend on the virus sought. In general, they consist of inoculation into animals, eggs or tissue culture, after the specimen is processed to remove bacterial contaminants. The isolates are identified by neutralisation or other suitable serological procedures. It has to be emphasised that the mere recovery of a virus from a patient does not justify the assumption that it is the causative agent of the patient's illness. Many viruses (For example adenoviruses, enteroviruses) are frequently found in normal individuals. The results of isolation should always be interpreted in the light of the clinical data. Demonstration of an immunological response to the virus isolate in the patient during the course of the disease reinforces the significance of the isolation.

Serological diagnosis: The demonstration of a rise in titre of antibodies to a virus during the course of a disease is strong evidence that it is the etiological agent. For this, it is essential to examine paired sera, the 'acute' sample collected early in the course of the disease and the 'convalescent' sample collected 10–14 days later. Examination of a single sample of serum for antibodies may not be meaningful except when IgM specific tests are done. The serological techniques employed would depend on the virus but those in general use are neutralisation, complement fixation, ELISA and hemagglutination inhibition tests.

Molecular diagnosis: The availability of molecular methods has transformed the diagnosis of viral diseases, enlarging the scope, sensitivity and specificity of such tests.

IMMUNOPROPHYLAXIS OF VIRAL DISEASES

Prolonged and effective immunity is a characteristic of most viral infections. Viral vaccines also confer solid protection and are, in general, more effective than bacterial vaccines. Viral vaccines may be live or killed (Table 49.2). Live vaccines are more effective than killed vaccines. The smallpox vaccine has been used as the sole tool for the global eradication of the disease. The early live vaccines were developed empirically from natural viruses (as Jenner's cowpox vaccine) or by attenuation by serial passage (as yellow fever vaccines). The basis of the latter technique was an unconscious selection of avirulent mutants. With the development of more

Table 49.2 Viral vaccines in common use

Disease	Type of vaccine	Mode of preparation
Poliomyelitis	Live	Avirulent strains grown in monkey kidney cell culture
	Killed	Virulent strains grown in monkey kidney cell culture, formalin-killed
Rabies	Killed (Semple type)	Fixed virus grown in sheep brain and inactivated by phenol or beta propiolactone
	Killed	Virus grown in cell culture and inactivated with beta propiolactone
Yellow fever	Live (17D)	Attenuated virus grown in chick embryos and lyophilised
Japanese encephalitis	Killed	Virus grown in mouse brain and inactivated by formalin
Varicella	Live	Attenuated virus grown in chick embryo fibroblast culture
Mumps	Live	Attenuated virus grown in human diploid cell culture
Influenza	Killed (subunit)	Virus disintegrated with sodium deoxycholate
	Live (attenuated)	Virus attenuated by serial passage in eggs
	Live (mutant)	ts mutants which are avirulent
	Live (recombinant)	Recombinants with surface antigens of new strains and growth characters of established strains
Measles	Live	Attenuated virus grown in tissue culture
Rubella	Live	Attenuated virus grown in tissue culture
Hepatitis B	Cloned subunit	HBsAg cloned in yeast

precise genetic techniques, live vaccines have been developed by plaque selection (Sabin vaccine for poliomyelitis) or from ts mutants or by recombination (as in influenza).

Killed vaccines have been prepared by inactivating viruses with heat, phenol, formalin or beta propiolactone. Ultraviolet irradiation is not satisfactory because of the risk of multiplicity reactivation. The reactogenicity of killed vaccines has been attempted to be reduced by the purification of the viruses. Adverse reactions may also be reduced by the use of 'subunit vaccines' in which the virus is split by detergents or other chemicals and only the relevant antigens incorporated in the vaccine. Vaccine production by cloning the desired antigen in bacteria or yeast is becoming increasingly common, as in hepatitis B.

Live vaccines have the following advantages: A single dose is usually sufficient. They can be administered by the route of natural infection so that local immunity is induced. They induce a wide spectrum of immunoglobulins to the whole range of viral antigens. They also induce cell mediated immunity. They provide more effective and more lasting immunity than killed vaccines. They can, in general, be prepared more economically and administered more conveniently, especially for mass immunisation. Some of them can be given as combined vaccines (measles–mumps–rubella vaccine).

They have the following disadvantages: There is a risk, however remote, of reversion to virulence. The vaccine may be contaminated with potentially dangerous viruses or other infectious agents. The virus may spread from the vaccines to contacts. While this is a serious danger in some situations, as when spread occurs to immunodeficient or other high risk contacts, in other cases, it may even be an advantage (as in poliomyelitis where the range of vaccination is extended by the natural spread of the vaccine virus among children and adults). Interference by pre-existing viruses may sometimes prevent a good immune response following live vaccination. Live vaccines are heat labile and they have to be kept under refrigeration. Some live vaccines may cause local and remote complications (as with smallpox vaccine).

Killed vaccines have the advantage of stability and safety. They can be given in combination as polyvalent vaccines. There is also no danger of the spread of the virus from the vaccine. The disadvantages are that multiple injections are needed and that local immunity and cell mediated immunity are not induced.

Passive immunisation with human gammaglobulin, convalescent serum or specific immune globulin gives temporary protection against many viral diseases such as measles, mumps and infectious hepatitis. These are indicated only when nonimmune individuals who are at special risk are exposed to infection. Combined active and passive immunisation is an established method for the prevention of rabies.

CHEMOPROPHYLAXIS AND CHEMOTHERAPY OF VIRUS DISEASES

The phenomenal success achieved by antibiotics and chemotherapeutic agents in the control of bacterial diseases is in marked contrast to the paucity of safe and effective drugs for viral diseases. As viruses are strict intracellular parasites that use the biosynthetic mechanisms of the host cell for replication, it was feared that it may not be possible to inhibit viral replication without damaging the host cell. However, there are several areas available for attack on viruses selectively. Viral infection may be checked at the level of attachment, transcription of viral nucleic acid, translation of viral mRNA, replication of viral nucleic acid and assembly and release of viral progeny. It may even be possible to target cell-free virions. A number of virus-specific enzymes have been identified which can be inhibited selectively, thereby preventing viral multiplication without affecting the host cells.

The first clinically useful antiviral drug came in 1960 when N-methyl isatin beta thiosemi-carbazone

(Methisazone, Marboran) was found to be effective against poxviruses. It was used successfully against eczema vaccinatum and for the prevention and treatment of smallpox. Shortly thereafter smallpox was eradicated and the drug went out of use.

In 1962, the antineoplastic drug idoxyuridine was found to be effective in herpetic eye infection. At about the same time, amantadine, a molecule with an unusual structure, synthesised at the Du Pont Chemical Company for use as a potential explosive proved ineffective for this purpose but was found to be active against influenza A virus. A landmark event was the discovery in the 1970s of acyclovir which was effective against herpesviruses and safe enough for parenteral administration. Serendipity as well as planned pursuit have led to the development of many antiviral agents, the need for which became urgent with the advent of the AIDS pandemic.

Available antiviral agents can be considered under the following categories:

Nucleoside analogues: *Deoxyuridines*: These analogues of thymidine block thymidine kinase and are effective against the herpes simplex virus. The first of these was *5-iodo-2-deoxyuridine* (*idoxyuridine, IDU*) used topically in herpetic keratitis. The related *5-trifluoromethyl-2-deoxyuridine* (*trifluridine, TFT*), being more soluble and less toxic has replaced IDU. *Bromovinyl deoxyuridine (BVDU)* is nontoxic and even more active, particularly against the varicella zoster virus.

Adenine arabinoside (*Vidarabine, ara-A*) has ribose substituted by arabinose in adenine. It was used topically in herpetic keratitis and parenterally against herpes simplex and varicella zoster infections. However, it has been replaced by acyclovir for the treatment of systemic infections. The related *cytosine arabinoside* (*cytarabine, ara-C*) is cytotoxic and immunosuppressive, and not used systemically.

Acyclovir (acylguanosine) is an analogue of guanine, acting against herpesviruses through thymidine kinase. Herpes viruses that code for their own thymidine kinase (HSV, V-Z) are far more susceptible than those which do not (CMV-EBV). The related drug *Ganciclovir* is more active against CMV.

The widely publicised drug *Azidothymidine* (Zidovudine, AZT) used against HIV infection is a thymidine analogue which blocks the synthesis of proviral DNA by inhibiting viral reverse transcriptase. AZT is used widely in HIV infection, but is toxic and costly.

A series of dideoxynucleosides (*Didanosine, Zalcitabine, Stavudine, Lamivudine*) have been synthesised and found to possess anti-HIV activity by blocking reverse transcriptase. The second group of drugs used in HIV infection is protease inhibitors (*Saquinavir, Ritonavir, Indinavir*).

Ribavirin (*Virazole*) is a synthetic nucleoside related to guanosine. It shows activity against many DNA and RNA viruses. Administered as an aerosol, it has been effective in the treatment of respiratory syncytial viral infection and also in influenza. Intravenous ribavirin has been reported to be effective against Lassa fever and other hemorrhagic fevers.

Other drugs: *Amantadine (Adamantanamine hydrochloride, Symmetrol)* blocks host cell penetration by influenza A virus but not B or C. A derivative *rimantadine* is less toxic and equally effective. A second line of drugs against influenza employs neuraminidase inhibition.

Enviroxine and related chemicals have shown activity against rhinoviruses.

Foscarnet (Trisodium phosphonoformate) specifically inhibits DNA polymerase of the herpes simplex virus and has some effect against hepatitis B and HIV also.

Suramin developed as an antiparasitic drug in 1916 was found to inhibit reverse transcriptase activity and so was one of the first drugs used against AIDS. Because of toxicity and inadequate efficacy its use was discontinued.

Interferons: The discovery of interferons, with activity against a wide range of viruses raised hopes of their application as antiviral drugs. However, most trials have been unsuccessful. Beneficial effect has been obtained in persistent infections such as hepatitis B and C, laryngeal papilloma and against CMV infections in transplant recipients. High doses of interferon lead to toxic effects.

In spite of intensive efforts, progress in the field of antiviral chemotherapy has not been satisfactory. Various factors contribute to this. Many compounds show antiviral activity in tissue culture but most of them prove to be ineffective or toxic in animal tests. The available drugs have a narrow range of activity. They are seldom able to eradicate the virus from the host so recurrence is common. Viruses develop resistance to the drugs and break through infection takes place even during treatment. The AIDS pandemic has been a catalyst in development of antiretroviral drugs. It is hoped that better understanding of the molecular and cellular biology of viruses and of virus–host interactions may lead to the development of more effective antiviral agents.

Further Reading

Collier L and J Oxford 2000. *Human Virology*. London: Oxford University Press.
Fields DN et al. 1996. *Virology*. 3rd edn. Philadelphia: Lippncott-Raven.
Harper DR. 1994. *Molecular Virology*. Oxford: Bios.
Zuckerman AJ et al.l 2000. *Clinical Virology*, 4th ed. Chichester:John Wiley.

Bacteriophages

Bacteriophages (commonly abbreviated as phages) are viruses that infect bacteria. Twort (1915) described a degenerative change in staphylococcal colonies isolated from calf lymph, which could be transmitted serially by application of culture filtrates from the original growth. d'Herelle (1917) observed that filtrates of feces cultures from dysentery patients induced transmissible lysis of a broth culture of a dysentery bacillus. He suggested that the lytic agent was a virus and gave it the name bacteriophage.

Phages occur widely in nature in close association with bacteria. They can be readily isolated from feces, sewage and other natural sources of mixed bacterial growth. Early hopes that phages could be used in the treatment of bacterial infections have not been fulfilled but these viruses have contributed much to microbiology. As phages could be grown easily on bacterial cultures, they provided the only convenient model for the study of virus–host interactions at the cellular and molecular levels

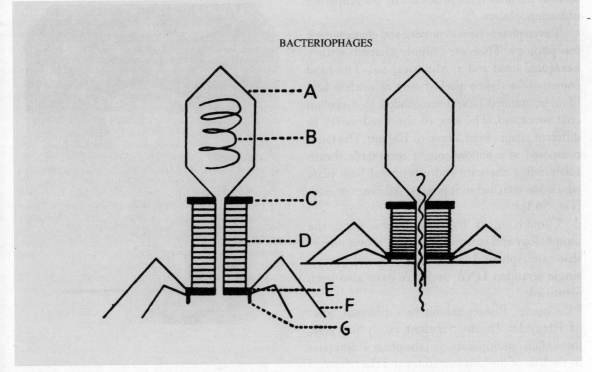

BACTERIOPHAGES

Fig.50.1 Morphology of bacteriophage. A. hexagonal head, B. DNA core, C. demarcation between head and tail, D. tail, E. base plate, F. tail fibres, G. prongs; Right, process of injection of phage DNA into host cell

before the development of cell culture techniques made similar studies with animal viruses possible. Phages play an important role in the transmission of genetic information between bacteria by the process of transduction. The presence of phage genome integrated with bacterial chromosomes confers on bacteria certain properties by a process known as *phage conversion*. Phages have been used as cloning vectors in genetic manipulations. The presence of high concentrations of phage particles, upto 10^8 per ml in some natural waters suggests that they may have a role in the control of bacterial populations in such environments. The specificity of the host range of phages is the basis of phage typing methods, by which bacteria can be identified and typed.

Morphology: Certain bacteriophages that infect *E. coli,* called the T even phages (T2, T4, T6), have been studied in great detail and traditionally serve as the prototypes in describing the properties of bacteriophages.

T even phages have a complex and characteristic morphology. They are tadpole shaped, with a hexagonal head and a cylindrical tail. The head consists of a tightly packed core of nucleic acid (double stranded DNA) surrounded by a protein coat or capsid. The size of the head varies in different phages from 28 nm to 100 nm. The tail is composed of a hollow core, a contractile sheath surrounding the core and a terminal base plate which has attached to it prongs, tail fibres or both (Fig. 50.1).

Though most bacteriophages have the morphology and structure described above, phages that are spherical or filamentous and possess single stranded DNA or RNA have also been identified.

Life cycle: Phages exhibit two different types of lifecycle. In the virulent or *lytic cycle,* intracellular multiplication of the phage culminates in the lysis of the host bacterium and the release of progeny virions. In the *temperate* or *lysogenic cycle* the phage DNA becomes integrated with the

bacterial genome, replicating synchronously with it, causing no harm to the host cell (Fig. 50.3).

Lytic cycle: Replication of a virulent phage can be considered in the following stages adsorption, penetration, synthesis of phage components, assembly, maturation and release of progeny phage particles.

Phage particles come into contact with bacterial cells by random collision. A phage attaches to the surface of a susceptible bacterium by its tail. Adsorption is a specific process and depends on the presence of complementary chemical groups on the receptor sites of the bacterial surface and on the terminal base plate of the phage. Under optimal conditions, adsorption is a very rapid process, being complete within minutes. Certain cofactors, such as cations, are necessary for adsorption. The

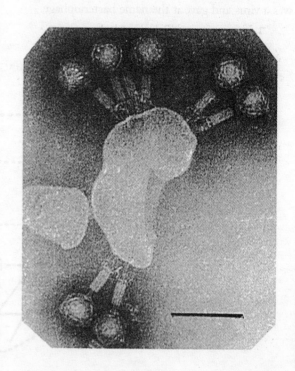

Fig. 50.2 Bacteriophages (x 200,000). Multiple infection of a bacterial cell (lysis from without) (Source: NICED)

TEXTBOOK OF MICROBIOLOGY

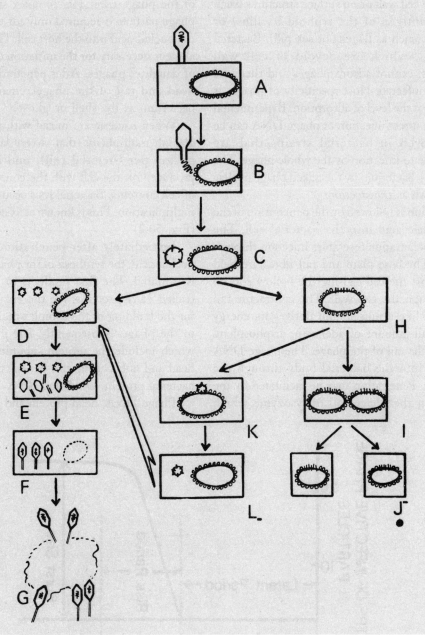

Fig. 50.3 Lytic and lysogenic life of bacteriophage. A. adsorption, B. injection of phage DNA, C. circularisation of phage DNA, D. replication of phage DNA, E. production of phage components, F. assenbly of phage, G. release of progeny phage, H. integration of phage DNA with host chromosome, I. binary fission of lysogenic bacterium, J. daughter bacteria carrying prophage, K. excision of prophage, L. same stage as C. (A to C injection; D to G lytic; H to J lysogenic cycle; K to L induction.)

bacterial receptor sites may be situated in different layers of the cell wall or on surface structures (such as the Vi antigen of the typhoid bacillus) or appendages (such as flagella or sex pili). Bacterial protoplasts, which are devoid of cell wall components, cannot adsorb phages and therefore will not be infected. Host specificity of phages is determined at the level of adsorption. Experimental infection by direct injection of phage DNA can be achieved even in bacterial strains that are insusceptible to infection by the whole phage. The infection of a bacterium by the naked phage nucleic acid is known as *transfection*.

Adsorption is followed by the penetration of the phage nucleic acid into the bacterial cell. The process of penetration resembles injection through a syringe. The base plate and tail fibres are held firmly against the cell causing the hollow core to pierce through the cell wall. The contractile tail sheath acts like a muscle and derives its energy from a small amount of adenosine triphosphate present on the tail of the phage. The phage DNA is injected into the bacterial body through the hollow core. Penetration may be facilitated by the presence on the phage tail of lysozyme which produces a hole on the bacterial wall for the entry of the phage core. The complex structure of the phage particle is required only for the injection of the nucleic acid into the host cell. The phage DNA alone is necessary for the initiation of the synthesis of daughter phages. After penetration, the empty head and tail of the phage remain outside the bacterium as the shell or 'ghost'.

When bacteria are mixed with phage particles at high multiplicity (that is very large number of phages per bacterial cell), multiple holes are produced on the cell with the consequent leakage of cell contents. Bacterial lysis occurs without viral multiplication. This is known as 'lysis from without' (Fig. 50.2).

Immediately after penetration of the phage nucleic acid, the synthesis of the phage components is initiated. The first products to be synthesised (called *early proteins*) are the enzymes necessary for the building of the complex molecules peculiar to the phage. Subsequently, *late proteins* appear, which include the protein subunits of the phage head and tail. During this period, the synthesis of bacterial protein, DNA and RNA ceases.

Phage DNA, head protein and tail protein are

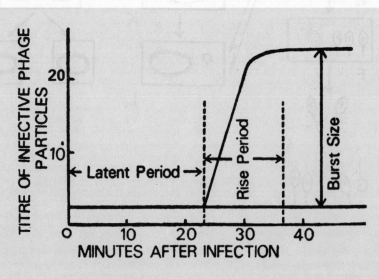

Fig. 50.4 One step growth curve of bacteriophage

synthesised separately in the bacterial cell. The DNA is condensed into a compact polyhedron and 'packaged' into the head and, finally, the tail structures are added. This assembly of the phage components into the mature infective phage particle is known as maturation.

Release of the mature progeny phages typically occurs by lysis of the bacterial cell. During the replication of the phage, the bacterial cell wall is weakened and it assumes a spherical shape. Phage enzymes act on the weakened cell wall causing it to burst or lyse resulting in the release of mature daughter phages.

The interval between the entry of the phage nucleic acid into the bacterial cell and the appearance of the first infectious intracellular phage particle is known as the *eclipse phase*. It represents the time required for the synthesis of the phage components and their assembly into mature phage particles. The interval between the infection of a bacterial cell and the first release of infectious phage particles is known as the *latent period*. Immediately following the latent period, the number of phage particles released increases for a few minutes till the maximum number of daughter phages is attained. This period, during which the number of infectious phages released rises, is known as the *rise period*. The average yield of progeny phages per infected bacterial cell is known as the *burst size*. This is estimated by experiments in which infection is established with one phage per bacterium and the release of infected phage particles is estimated serially over a period of time. The results of such an experiment plotted on a graph is known as the one-step growth curve (Fig. 50.4).

Lysogenic cycle: Unlike virulent phages which produce lysis of the host cell, temperate phages enter into a symbiotic relationship with their host cells without destroying them. Following entry into the host cell, the temperate phage nucleic acid becomes integrated with the bacterial chromosome. The integrated phage nucleic acid is known as the *prophage*. The prophage behaves like a segment of the host chromosome and replicates synchronously with it. This phenomenon is called *lysogeny* and a bacterium that carries a prophage within its genome is called a *lysogenic bacterium*. Lysogenisation does not upset the bacterial metabolism.

The prophage confers certain new properties on the lysogenic bacterium. This is known as *lysogenic conversion* or *phage conversion*. This is due to the synthesis of new proteins that are coded for by the prophage DNA. An example is toxin production by the diphtheria bacillus, which is determined by the presence in it of the prophage *beta*. The elimination of the prophage abolishes the toxigenicity of the bacillus.

During the multiplication of lysogenic bacteria, the prophage may become 'excised' from occasional cells. The excised prophage initiates lytic replication and the daughter phage particles are released, which infect other bacterial cells and render them lysogenic. This is known as spontaneous induction of prophage. While this is a rare event, all lysogenic bacteria in a population can be induced to shift to the lytic cycle by exposure to certain physical and chemical agents. Such inducing agents include UV rays, hydrogen peroxide and nitrogen mustard.

A lysogenic bacterium is resistant to reinfection by the same or related phages. This is known as *superinfection immunity*.

Bacteriophages may act as carriers of genes from one bacterium to another. This is known as *transduction*. Two types of transduction are recognised. In restricted transduction, only bacterial genes contiguous to the prophage are transmitted. For example, transduction by the prophage *lambda* in *E. coli* K12 transfers only the gal$^+$ gene (determining fermentation of galactose), which is the bacterial gene contiguous to the prophage. On the other hand, any bacterial gene may be transferred in generalised transduction. Transduction has been demonstrated in many genera of bacteria and constitutes one of the most important mechanisms of genetic exchange among bacteria in nature. Plasmid mediated drug resistance in staphylococci is an example of a medically important property that is transmitted by transduction.

Phage particles exhibit general stability of type and a low rate of heritable variation.

If a bacterium simultaneously adsorbs two related but slightly different DNA phage particles, both can infect and reproduce. On lysis, both types are released. When this occurs many of the progeny are observed to be recombinants.

PHAGE ASSAY

When a phage is applied on the lawn culture of a susceptible bacterium, areas of clearing occur after incubation. These zones of lysis are called *plaques*. The size, shape and nature of plaques are characteristic for different phages. Since under optimum conditions a single phage particle is capable of producing one plaque, plaque assay can be employed for titrating the number of viable phages in a preparation. As plaques are analogous to bacterial colonies, plaquing is also useful for the purification of phages.

PHAGE TYPING

The specificity of phage–bacterium interaction is made use of in the identification and typing of bacteria. Phages exhibit different degrees of host specificity. Some phages possess wide host ranges, covering many bacterial genera, while others have a narrow range limited to certain strains of bacteria only. With some phages serial passage in a strain of bacterium makes them specific for that strain and related strains (adaptation of host range).

Phages are available that lyse all members of a bacterial genus (for example genus-specific bacteriophage for *Salmonella*), all members of a species (for example specific bacteriophage for *B. anthracis*), and all members of a biotype or subspecies (for example Mukerjee's phage IV which lyses all strains of classical *V. cholerae* but not *V. cholerae* biotype E1 Tor). The most important application of phage typing is for intraspecies typing of bacteria, as in the phage typing of *S. typhi* and staphylococci. Adapted phages, active only against fresh isolates possessing the Vi antigen, are used for phage typing of typhoid bacilli. Staphylococcal phage typing is a pattern method, using a set of standard phages. A strain of Staphylococcus may be lysed by a number of phages and the phage type of a strain is designated by the numbers of the different phages that lyse it.

As lysis is influenced by the dose of infection, phage preparations used for typing should be standardised by titration. Titration is carried out by applying serial dilutions of the phage preparation on a lawn culture of a susceptible strain and observing the lysis after incubation. The highest dilution of the phage preparation that just produces confluent lysis is known as the routine test dose (RTD).

BACTERIOCINS

Gratia (1925) observed the production of a highly specific antibiotic substance by one strain of *E. coli* which was active against another strain of the same species. The name colicin was given to such substances produced by *E. coli* and other members of the family Enterobactericeae. With the recognition that colicin-like substances are produced by several other bacteria also, the generic name *bacteriocin* was proposed for the group of highly specific antibiotic-like substances produced by certain strains of bacteria which are active against other strains of the same or different species. Bacteriocins are given specific names based on the bacterial species of origin, for example colicins from *E .coli*, pyocins from *Ps. pyocyanea (aeruginosa)*, megacins from *B. megaterium* and diphthericins from *C. diphtheriae*.

Bacteriocins are proteins but some may have associated lipopolysaccharides derived from the cell walls of bacteria producing them. Bacteriocins and phages resemble each other in a number of respects. Both adsorb on the surface of susceptible bacterial cells on specific receptor sites some of which may be the same for phages and bacteriocins. Under

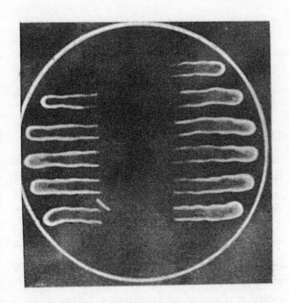

Fig. 50.5 Bacteriocin typing. Bacteriocin produced by the producer strain has inhibited the growth of test strains in the centre.

the electron microscope, some bacteriocins, especially pyocins, appear like the tail structures of phages. They may be considered products of defective phage genomes, able to code only for parts of phage particles.

The synthesis of bacteriocins is determined by the presence in bacteria of colicinogenic factors (Col factors). Col factors are episomes and can be transmitted from cell to cell by conjugation or transduction. Certain physical and chemical agents (UV rays, nitrogen mustard) induce colicin production by the cells harbouring Col factors.

A cell producing a bacteriocin is immune to it but may be sensitive to other bacteriocins. Bacteriocins have a very specific activity on bacteria, being capable of killing some but not all strains of a species. The specificity is made use of in typing certain species such as *Sh. sonnei*, *Proteus sp.*, *Ps. aeruginosa*. Bacteriocins kill susceptible cells without lysing them.

While phage typing schemes are generally based on the sensitivity of the test strains to the lytic action of phages, bacteriocin typing schemes depend on the ability of bacteriocins produced by the test strain to kill standard indicator strains of bacteria. The usual method of bacteriocin typing employs the plate diffusion technique. The test bacterium is inoculated as a broad streak on the centre of a culture medium, the bacterial growth is scraped off and the remaining cells killed by exposure to chloroform vapour. Standard indicator strains of bacteria are then streaked at right angles to the original inoculum. After incubation, the pattern of inhibition of the indicator strains represents the bacteriocin type of the test bacterium (Fig. 50.5).

Further Reading

Anderson TF. 1981. Reflections on phage genetics. *Ann Rev Genetics* 15:405

Day M. 1998. Bacteriocins and bacteriophages, In *Topley & Wilson's Microbiology and Microbial Infections*, Vol.2. London: Arnold.

Mathews CK et al (eds). 1983. *Bacteriophage T4*. Washington D.C: American Society for Microbiology.

Poxviruses

Poxviruses are the largest viruses that infect vertebrates, large enough to be seen under the light microscope. This group contains several viruses that infect human beings, animals, birds and insects. Based on genetic, antigenic and ecological criteria, the family *Poxviridae* has been classified into two subfamilies: *Chordopoxvirinae*, the poxviruses of vertebrates, and *Entomopoxvirinae*, the poxviruses of insects which do not infect vertebrates.

Chordopoxivirinae are classified into six genera or subgroups:

1. *Orthopoxvirus:* Mammalian poxviruses that tend to cause generalised infection with rash—variola, vaccinia, cowpox, monkeypox, rabbitpox, buffalopox, camelpox, mousepox.
2. *Parapoxvirus:* Viruses of ungulates that may occasionally infect human orf (contagious pustular dermatitis), paravaccinia (milker's nodes, bovine papular stomatitis).
3. *Capripoxvirus:* Viruses of goats and sheep—sheep-pox, goatpox, lumpy skin disease.
4. *Leporipox virus:* Viruses of leporids (rabbits, hares, squirrels)—myxoma and fibromas.
5. *Avipoxvirus:* Viruses of birds—fowlpox, turkeypox, pigeonpox, canarypox.
6. *Suipoxvirus:* Swinepox.

Poxviruses that have not been officially assigned to any genus include the virus of molluscum contagiosum, tanapox and the yaba monkey tumour.

Poxvirus diseases are characterised by skin lesions which may be localised or generalised. The most important of these was smallpox caused by the variola virus. Other poxviruses which can infect humans are vaccinia, cowpox, monkeypox, tanapox, molluscum contagiosum, paravaccinia and orf. Buffalopox and camelpox may occasionally infect humans causing lesions resembling vaccination.

VARIOLA AND VACCINIA

The variola virus is the causative agent of smallpox. For thousands of years, smallpox raged as a scourge of mankind, causing death and disfigurement. The global eradication of smallpox, achieved after 10 years of concerted campaigns under the auspices of the WHO, has been a most impressive medical achievement. Naturally occurring smallpox came to an end in 1977. On 8 May 1980, the WHO formally announced the global eradication of smallpox.

Smallpox used to occur in two distinct clinical varieties—the florid, highly fatal disease typically seen in Asia, and the mild, nonfatal disease (alastrim) typically seen in Latin America. The virus causing classical smallpox was called *variola major* and that causing alastrim *variola minor*. Variola major and minor were antigenically identical but they differed in certain biological characteristics. They were stable variants as the disease produced by each always bred true; alastrim did not lead to smallpox and vice versa.

The vaccinia virus was used as the smallpox vaccine. Jenner originally used the cowpox virus for vaccination against smallpox but during the several years in which the original vaccine virus was maintained by arm-to-arm passage in humans, it underwent some permanent changes so that it could be readily differentiated from fresh isolates of cowpox and smallpox viruses. Vaccinia virus is unique in that it is an 'artificial virus' and does not occur in nature as such. It has been studied in greater detail than variola, as it is safer to work with. Vaccinia virus is being employed as a vector for the development of recombinant vaccines. The vaccinia genome can accommodate about 25,000 foreign base pairs sufficient for introducing several genes. Many genes have been inserted, including those coding for the antigens of hepatitis B virus, HIV, rabies, and for pharmacologically important products such as neuropeptides. However the vaccinia virus is not suitable as a vector for human use due to its pathogenic effects.

Vaccinia and variola viruses are so similar in their properties that they can be considered together. Morphology: The virion is brick shaped. In vertical section it consists of a double layered membrane which surrounds a biconcave 'nucleoid' containing the DNA core. On either side of the nucleoid is a lens shaped structure called the lateral body (Fig. 51.1). The virion measures about 300 × 200 × 100 nm and so can be seen under the light microscope. Variola virus was first demonstrated microscopically by Buist in 1887. Paschen in 1906 developed a staining technique for the virus particles and demonstrated the elementary bodies (Paschen bodies) in smears from smallpox lesions.

Physical and chemical properties: Poxviruses are stable and if protected from sunlight may remain viable for months at room temperature. In the cold or when freeze dried, they survive for years. They are susceptible to ultraviolet light and other irradiations. They are resistant to 50% glycerol and 1% phenol but are readily inactivated by formalin and oxidising disinfectants. The virion consists essentially of DNA, protein and lipid. Though enveloped, the virus is not inactivated by ether. The virion contains a multiplicity of enzymes. The entire multiplication of the virus takes place in the cytoplasm of the infected cell.

Antigenic structure: All poxviruses share a common nucleoprotein (NP) antigen. By immunodiffusion some twenty different antigens

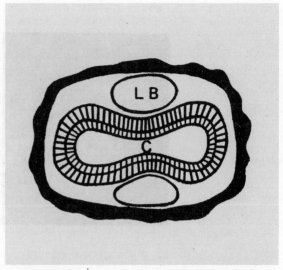

Fig.51.1 Structure of vaccinia virus. The nucleic acid is contained within a dumb-bell shaped core (C). Fitting into the concavities of the core are two lateral bodies (LB). The virion is enclosed within a protein shell which has an irregular surface.

have been identified. These include the LS antigen (a complex of two antigens, the heat labile L and the heat stable S antigens), agglutinogen, and hemagglutinin, which is responsible for the agglutination of erythrocytes of those fowls which are also agglutinated nonspecifically by tissue lipids. Cultivation and host range: The variola and vaccinia viruses can be differentiated by their growth characteristics and host range.

Chick embryo: Both viruses grow on the CAM of 11–13 day old chick embryo producing pocks in 48–72 hours. Variola pocks are small, shiny, white, convex, non-necrotic, non-hemorrhagic lesions. Vaccinia pocks are larger, irregular, flat, greyish, necrotic lesions, some of which are hemorrhagic (Fig. 51.2). The viruses may also be differentiated by their 'ceiling temperatures', the highest temperature above which pocks are not produced. The ceiling temperatures are 41.0 °C for vaccinia, 38 °C for variola major and 37.5 °C for variola minor.

Tissue culture: Variola and vaccinia viruses can be grown in tissue cultures of monkey kidney, HeLa

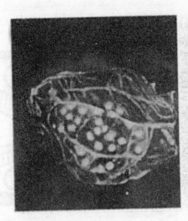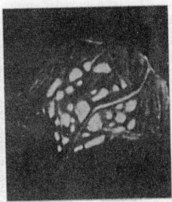

Fig. 51.2 Variola and vaccinia pocks on CAM. Left – variola, showing small, uniform pocks; right – vaccinia, showing large, irregular pocks

and chick embryo cells. Cytopathic effects are produced by vaccinia in 24–48 hours and more slowly by variola. Eosinophilic inclusion bodies – Guarnieri bodies – can be demonstrated in stained preparations. The inclusion bodies consist of aggregations of virus particles in a matrix. Vaccinia but not variola virus produces plaques in chick embryo tissue cultures.

Animals: The vaccinia virus can infect a wide range of animals experimentally. Monkeys, calves, sheep and rabbits can be infected by scarification leading to vesicular lesions. The variola virus produces similar lesions only in monkeys. Scarification of rabbit cornea with variola virus leads to keratitis and sections of the cornea will show typical Guarnieri bodies. Intranasal instillation of the variola virus in the monkey produces a self-limited attack of smallpox with generalised skin lesions.

SMALLPOX

Smallpox has been eradicated. The last natural case of variola major detected was Saiban Bibi, a Bangladeshi woman found with smallpox on the Karimganj railway platform in Assam on 24 May, 1975. The last case of variola minor occurred in Merca, Somalia, in October 1977. The coming generations are unlikely to witness the disease but its disappearance has been too recent for it to be ignored altogether. A brief account of smallpox is therefore being presented. (For more details about smallpox, the 3rd edition of this textbook may be consulted.)

Smallpox was an exclusively human infection, with no animal reservoir. There were no carriers as the virus was eliminated completely from the patient on recovery. The source of infection was a patient in the early phase of the disease, though infectivity extended from the appearance of buccal mucosal lesions (enanthems) to the disappearance of all the skin lesion (exanthems). Infection usually occurred only in close contacts. Virus entered the body by inhalation. After initial multiplication in the local lymphoid tissues, the virus reached the reticuloendothelial cells, where further multiplication took place, leading to a severe viremia with seeding of the mucosa and skin heralding the clinical disease. The incubation period was around 12 days.

The single crop of centrifugal exanthems passed through macular, papular, vesicular and pustular stages, before scabbing and healing by scar formation in 2–4 weeks. The exanthems varied in

Table 51.1 Comparison of properties of some orthopoxviruses

	Variola	Monkeypox	Vaccinia	Cowpox	Camelpox
Isolated from	Humans	Humans, Monkey, Anteater	Origin unknown	Humans, cow large felines	Camel
Pocks on CAM	Small, white	Small, pink	Large, white	Hemorrhagic	Small, white
Ceiling temperature on CAM (°C)	37.5–38.5	39	41	39.5	38.5
Growth on rabbit skin	-	++	+ or ++	+	+
Thymidine Kinase sensitivity	+	-	-	-	-
Pathogenicity for baby mice	Low	High	High	High	Low
Antigens Specific for {vaccinia	-	-	+	+	+
variola	+	-	+	?	+
monkeypox}	-	+	-	?	-
Polypeptide pattern	Character of variola	Character of monkeypox	Character of vaccinia	Character of cowpox	?

severity from the hemorrhagic, flat, ordinary or modified form, in descending order.

Smallpox could be diagnosed in the laboratory by detection of virus antigen or by isolation of the virus from the blood in the early phase (in severe cases only) or from the eruptive lesion (in all cases). On account of the distinctive morphology of the virion, rapid diagnosis was possible by electron microscopy, where the facility was available.

Empirical preventive measures against the disease had been in use in India and China for millennia. The practice of variolation spread from India to the West and in the 18th century became very popular in Europe, till it was replaced by vaccination introduced by Jenner in 1796. Smallpox vaccine was a live preparation of vaccinia virus propagated on the skin of calves. It was applied by scarification which caused a local pustular lesion, healing by scar formation. In spite of widespread and, in many places, compulsory vaccination, smallpox was not eliminated till a concerted programme of its global eradication was initiated by the WHO in 1967, with the cooperation of the member states. The disease was then present in 44 countries, with a global incidence of around 10 million cases annually. After ten years of intense effort, the disease was wiped out. Two factors which contributed to the success of the campaign were the use of freeze-dried vaccine (in place of the unreliable liquid vaccine used earlier) and the technique of vaccination by multiple puncture with the bifurcated needle, which was simple, effective and economical.

Though natural smallpox ceased in 1977, a small outbreak of variola major occurred in August, 1978, in Birmingham, following accidental spread of the virus from the virus laboratory in the medical school. It was promptly identified and controlled but the incident showed the hazard of keeping variola stocks in laboratories. Following a directive by the WHO, all such laboratory stocks of the virus have been destroyed. The last stocks of smallpox virus were held under high security in the Centers for Disease Control and Prevention , Atlanta, Georgia (USA) and the Centre for Research on Virology and Biotechnology, Koltsova (Russia).

They were to have been destroyed by June 30, 1999, but fears of the possible use of smallpox in bioterrorism led to an indefinite extension of the deadline.

When two years after the last case of smallpox, no further case could be detected anywhere in spite of active surveillance, the whole world was certified free of smallpox in October, 1979. Global eradication of smallpox was formally declared by the General Assembly of the WHO on 8 May, 1980. However, as a measure of protection against the remote danger of smallpox re-emerging, large stocks of smallpox vaccine are maintained by the WHO for rapid deployment, if needed.

OTHER POXVIRUS DISEASES

With the elimination of smallpox, it has become important to identify and characterise other orthopoxviruses which can infect human beings and cause disease resembling smallpox (Table 51.1).

Monkeypox: This virus was first isolated in 1958 from an outbreak of pox disease in a captive monkey colony in Copenhagen. Monkeys are only incidental; hosts being rodents. The first human case was reported in 1970 from Zaire. Human infection is common in Central and West Africa, with a fatality rate of 5–10%. The outbreak in America occured in 2003, in Wisconsin, USA, affecting 11 local persons and many prairie-dogs. The source of infection is said to be an imported African rodent, which had infected local human contacts and prairie-dogs.

The cases clinically resembled smallpox. However, person-to-person transmission appears to be rare. Serological studies have shown evidence of widespread natural infection in monkeys in Africa. The virus can be distinguished from variola.

Buffalopox was identified in cattle in India in 1934 and was considered an outbreak of vaccinia in them. Epizootics had occurred in buffaloes and lesions had been observed on the hands of persons in contact with infected animals. Two decades after eradication of smallpox and cessation of vaccination, buffalopox still occurs, proving it to be distinct from variola and vaccinia. Though it resembles them closely, it is possible to distinguish between them and in the laboratory. Smallpox vaccine does not seem to protect persons against occupational buffalopox.

Cowpox and milker's nodes: Both these infections are obtained from cows. Cowpox lesions are seen on the udder and teats of cows and may be transmitted to humans during milking. The lesions in humans usually appear on the hands or fingers and resemble primary vaccinia. The disease is associated with some fever and constitutional symptoms. Cowpox virus resembles variola and vaccinia antigenically but can be differentiated by the hemorrhagic lesions it produces on CAM and rabbit skin. Restriction endonuclease maps of vaccinia and cowpox genomes show distinct differences.

Cowpox infection has been observed only in Britain and Europe. There have been outbreaks of fatal cowpox infection in wild animals kept in zoos, including cheetahs and elephants. Natural infection has been observed in domestic cats. It has been suggested that the primary host of cowpox may not be cows but more likely wild rodents or cats.

Milker's node (paravaccinia) is a trivial occupational disease that humans get by milking infected cows. The lesions are small ulcerating nodules. The virus is unrelated to cowpox and does not grow in eggs. It can be grown in bovine kidney cultures. It resembles the orf virus morphologically.

Orf (contagious pustular dermatitis): Orf is a disease of sheep and goats transmitted to human beings by contact. In humans, the disease occurs as a single papulovesicular lesion with a central ulcer, usually on the hand, forearm or face. The virus is unrelated to the variola-vaccinia group and resembles paravaccinia virus morphologically.

Tanapox: This virus was isolated from epidemics of a febrile illness along the Tana river in Kenya in 1957–19. The patients had a single pock-like lesion on the upper part of the body. The virus is antigenically unrelated to other poxviruses and does not grow in eggs. It can be grown in human and monkey tissue cultures. Monkeys are the only animals susceptible. The virus is now active in Africa, particularly in Zaire. A similar virus has been isolated from outbreaks of disease in primate colonies in America.

Molluscum contagiosum: This disease, seen usually in children and young adults, is characterised by pink or pearly white wart-like nodules on the skin. Sections of the lesions show large (20–30 μm) eosinophilic hyaline inclusion bodies which displace the nuclei to the margin. These *molluscum bodies* are composed of large numbers of virus particles, embedded in a protein matrix. Humans are the only susceptible hosts. The virus cannot be grown in eggs, tissue cultures or animals.

The incidence of molluscum contagiosum as a sexually transmitted disease in young adults is increasing. When it occurs in the genital area, it may become inflamed and ulcerated and may simulate HSV infections.

Further Reading

Baxdy D. 1998. Poxviruses. In *Topley and Wilson's Microbiology and Infections*, 9th edn. vol.I London:Arnold.

Behbehani AM. 1983. The Smalpox Story: Life and death of an old disease. *Microbiol Rev* 47:455.

Fenner F *et al.* 1988. *Smallpox and its Eradication.* Geneva:WHO.

Frey SE and RB Belshe 2004. Poxivirus Zooroses. *New Engl J Med* 350:324

Jezek Z et al. 1986. Human Monkeypox. *J Infect Dis* 154:551.

Oriel JD. 1987. The increase in molluscum contagiosum. *BMJ* 294:74.

Zuckerman AJ. 1984. Paleontology of smallpox. *Lancet* 2:1454.

Herpesviruses

The herpesvirus family contains over a hundred species of enveloped DNA viruses that affect humans and animals. They are characterised by their ability to establish latent infections, enabling the virus to persist indefinitely within infected hosts and to undergo periodic reactivation.

The herpesvirus capsid is icosahedral, composed of 162 capsomers, and enclosing the core containing the linear double stranded DNA genome. The nucleocapsid is surrounded by the lipid envelope derived from the modified host cell nuclear membrane through which the naked virions bud during replication. The envelope carries surface spikes, about 8 nm long. Between the envelope and the capsid is an amorphous structure called the tegument, containing several proteins. The enveloped virion measures about 200 nm and the naked virion about 100 nm in diameter.

Herpesviruses replicate in the host cell nucleus. They form Cowdry type A intranuclear (Lipschutz) inclusion bodies. Like other enveloped viruses, herpesviruses are susceptible to fat solvents like alcohol, ether, chloroform and bile salts. They are heat labile and have to be stored at −70 °C.

The family Herpesviridae is divided into three subfamilies based on biological, physical and genetic properties:

Alphaherpesviruses, with a relatively short replicative cycle (12–18 hours), a variable host range and a tendency to cause latent infection in sensory ganglia. In culture they are rapidly cytopathic and infectious viruses may be released from cells, for example herpes simplex virus, varicella-zoster virus.

Betaherpesviruses, which replicate slowly (more than 24 hours), have a narrow host range, grow best in fibroblasts with a tendency to produce enlargement of infected cells (cytomegaly) and cause latent infection of salivary gland and other organs. In culture, the cytopathic effect is slow and the virus remains cell associated, for example cytomegalovirus.

Gammaherpesviruses, which have a narrow host range, replicate in lymphoblastoid cells, are specific for either B or T lymphocytes and frequently cause latent infection in lymphoid tissue, for example Epstein–Barr virus.

Eight different types of herpesviruses are known whose primary hosts are humas. They have been officially designated 'Human herpesvirus types 1–8' but their common names continue to be in general use, except for types 6,7 and 8 (Table 52.1).

The herpesvirus family has no common group antigen and the different herpesvirus species do not show any significant antigenic cross reaction, except between Herpes simplex types 1 and 2.

HERPES SIMPLEX

The herpes simplex virus (HSV) occurs naturally only in humas, but it can produce experimental infection in many laboratory animals. There are two types of the herpes simplex virus. HSV type 1 (Human herpes virus type 1 or HHV type 1) is usually isolated from lesions in and around the mouth and is transmitted by direct contact or droplet spread from cases or carriers. HSV type 2 (HHV type 2) is responsible for the majority of genital herpes infections and is commonly

Table 52.1 Classification of human herpesviruses

Species		Subfamily	Cytopathology	Site of latent infection
Official name	Common name			
Human herpesvirus type 1	Herpes simplex virus type 1	alpha	cytolytic	neurons
Human herpesvirus type 2	Herpes simplex virus type 2	alpha	cytolytic	neurons
Human herpesvirus type 3	Varicella zoster virus	alpha	cytolytic	neurons
Human herpesvirus type 4	Epstein–Barr virus	gamma	lymphoproliferative	lymphoid tissues
Human herpesvirus type 5	Cytomegalovirus	beta	cytomegalic	secretory glands Kidneys, other organs and tissues
Human herpesvirus type 6	Human B cell lymphotropic virus*	beta	lymphoproliferative	lymphoid tissues
Human herpesvirus type 7	R K virus*	beta	lymphoproliferative	lymphoid tissues
Human herpesvirus type 8		gamma		

* These names are no longer in use

transmitted venereally. Intracerebral inoculation in rabbits and mice leads to encephalitis, and corneal scarification produces keratoconjunctivitis in rabbits. The virus grows in a variety of primary and continuous cell cultures (monkey or rabbit kidney, human amnion, HeLa) producing cytopathic changes, well defined foci with heaped up cells and syncytial or giant cell formation. On chick embryo CAM, small (diameter less than 0.5 mm) white shiny non-necrotic pocks are produced (Fig. 52.2). The two types of the virus cross react serologically. They can be differentiated by the following features:

1) Antigenic differences can be made out using type specific monoclonal antibodies.
2) On chick embryo CAM type 2 strains form larger pocks resembling variola.
3) Types 2 strains replicate well in chick embryo fibroblast cells, while type 1 strains do so poorly.
4) The infectivity of type 2 is more temperature sensitive than that of type 1.

5) Type 2 strains are more neurovirulent in laboratory animals than type 1.
6) Type 2 strains are more resistant to antiviral agents like IUDR and cytarabine in culture.
7) Restriction endonuclease analysis of viral DNA enables differentiation between the two types as well as between strains within the same type.

Pathogenesis: Herpes simplex is one of the most common viral infections in humans, about 60–90 per cent of adults showing detectable antibody. Primary infection is usually acquired in early childhood, between two and five years of age. Humans are the only natural hosts and the sources of infection are saliva, skin lesions or respiratory secretions. Asymptomatic carriers form the more important source of infection, especially in genital infection with type 2 strains. Transmission occurs by close contact and may be venereal in genital herpes. The virus enters through defects in the skin or mucous membranes and multiplies locally, with cell-to-cell spread. The virus enters cutaneous nerve

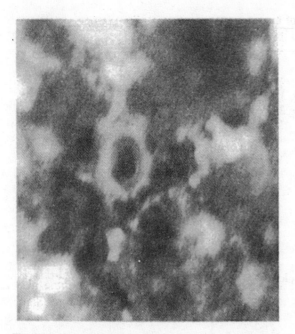

Fig. 52.1 Herpes simplex virus

fibres and is transported intra-axonally to the ganglia where it replicates. Centrifugal migration of the virus can take place from the ganglia to the skin and mucosa to cause cutaneous and mucosal lesions. The virus remains latent in the ganglia, particularly of the trigeminal (HSV type 1) and sacral (HSV type 2) nerves, to be reactivated periodically in some individuals causing recurrent oral and genital lesions. Antibodies may not prevent recurrences, but can reduce the severity of clinical disease. Cell mediated immunity is more important in resistance to and recovery from herpes simplex infections. Herpesvirus diseases are more frequent and severe in the HIV infected and other immunodeficient subjects.

The typical herpes lesions are thin walled, umbilicated vesicles, the roof of which breaks down, leaving tiny superficial ulcers. They heal without scarring. In general, primary infections, though self-limited, are more severe and widespread and associated with systemic manifestations. Recurrent infections are more localised.

As a general rule, HSV 1 produces 'above the waist' and HSV 2 'below the waist' lesions but the rule is not absolute. HSV 2 infection confers some protection against HSV 1, but not vice versa.

Clinical features: The clinical manifestations and course depend on the site of infection, age and immune status of the host, and the antigenic type of the virus.

Cutaneous infections: The most common site is the face—on the cheeks, chin, around the mouth or on the forehead. Lesions may also appear on the buttocks in infants as napkin rash.

The typical lesion is the 'fever blister' or herpes febrilis, caused by viral reactivation in febrile patients. In some sensitive persons, very minor stimuli, like common cold, exposure to sun or even mental strain or menses, may bring on such reactivation.

An occupational variety of cutaneous herpes is the herpetic whitlow seen in doctors, dentists and nurses. *Eczema herpeticum* is a generalised eruption caused by herpes infection in children suffering from eczema. Crops of vesicles appear on the affected

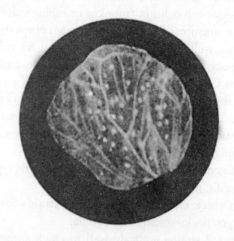

Fig. 52.2 Herpesvirus pocks on CAM: tiny, white, uniform pocks

area with widespread ulceration. A clinically indistinguishable picture is also produced by vaccinia virus infection, both designated *Kaposi's varicelliform eruption.*

Mucosal: The buccal mucosa is the site most commonly affected. Gingivostomatitis and pharyngitis are the most frequent conditions in primary infection and recurrent herpes labialis in recurrent infection. The vesicles may ulcerate and become secondarily infected.

Ophthalmic: HSV infection is the most common cause of corneal blindness in some developed countries. Acute keratoconjunctivitis may occur by itself or by extension from facial herpes. Follicular conjunctivitis with vesicle formation on the lids is another manifestation. The cornea may be involved, with typical branching dendritic ulcers. Debridement, topical antiviral drugs and interferon help in healing. Steroids are contraindicated as they lead to deep stromal involvement and healing may be delayed, with scarring and corneal blindness. Chorioretinitis and acute necrotising retinitis are uncommon but serious manifestations.

Nervous system: HSV encephalitis though rare, is the most common sporadic acute viral encephalitis in most parts of the world. HSV encephalitis has an acute onset, with fever and focal neurological symptoms. Brain biopsy was employed in diagnosis for instituting early specific therapy. This is now replaced by demonstration of HSV DNA in CSF by PCR, which is a very sensitive test in the acute stage. HSV meningitis is a self-limiting disease, usually resolving in about a week, without sequelae. The CSF shows lymphocytic pleocytosis and may yield the virus in culture.

HSV can cause sacral autonomic dysfunction and also rarely transverse myelitis or the Guillian–Barre syndrome. HSV has been implicated in the etiology of Bell's palsy.

Visceral: HSV esophagitis may cause dysphagia, substernal pain and weight loss. It may involve the respiratory tract causing tracheobronchitis and pneumonitis. HSV is an uncommon cause of hepatitis. Erythema multiforme may be seen in association with HSV infection. Disseminated HSV infection may occur in patients with immunodeficiency, malnutrition or burns.

Genital: In the 1970s genital herpes became the most rapidly increasing venereal disease, particularly in the USA. In men, the lesions occur mainly on the penis, or in the urethra causing urethritis. In women, the cervix, vagina, vulva and perineum are affected. When only the cervix is involved, the infection may be asymptomatic. The primary infection is usually more serious, accompanied by systemic features like fever and malaise. It is followed by several recurrent episodes which are milder. The vesiculo-ulcerative lesions may be very painful. Rectal and perineal lesions occur in homosexuals. Both types of HSV may cause genital lesions, though HSV 2 is responsible more frequently and causes many more recurrences.

There have been several reports of an association between HSV 2 and carcinoma of the cervix uteri but a causal relationship has not been established.

Congenital: Transplacental infection with HSV 1 or 2 can lead to congenital malformations, but this is rare. Infection may occur during birth, particularly if the mother has genital lesions due to HSV 2. In such cases, cesarian section may prevent infection. Postnatal infection is more commonly due to HSV 1. Neonatal herpes may be confined to the eyes, mouth or skin, but is more commonly a disseminated disease having multi-organ involvement, with or without encephalitis. The mortality rate is very high and survivors may have neurological impairment.

Laboratory diagnosis: The diagnosis of herpes virus infection may be made by microscopy, antigen or DNA detection, virus isolation or serology.

Microscopy: The Tzanck smear is a rapid, fairly sensitive and inexpensive diagnostic method. Smears are prepared from the lesions, preferably from the base of vesicles and stained with 1% aqueous solution of toluidine blue '0' for 15 seconds. Multinucleated giant cells with faceted nuclei and homogeneously stained 'ground glass' chromatin (Tzanck cells) constitute a positive smear. Intranuclear type A inclusion bodies may be seen in Giemsa stained smears. The virus particle may also be demonstrated under the electron microscope. It is not possible to differentiate between herpes simplex and varicella zoster by microscopy. The herpesvirus antigen may be demonstrated in smears or sections from lesions by the fluorescent antibody technique. The fluorescent antibody test on brain biopsy specimens provides reliable and speedy diagnosis in encephalitis. PCR based DNA detection has replaced brain biopsy.

Virus isolation: Inoculation in mice and on chick embryo CAM is insensitive and has been replaced by tissue culture for virus isolation. Primary human embryonic kidney, human amnion and many other cells are susceptible, but human diploid fibroblasts are preferred. Vesicle fluid, spinal fluid, saliva and swabs may be used. Typical cytopathic changes may appear as early as in 24–48 hours but cultures should be observed for two weeks before being declared negative. Drug susceptibility too can be tested in cell cultures.

Differentiation between HSV types 1 and 2 may be made by a variety of serological techniques, by nucleic acid hybridisation or by restriction endonuclease cleavage and electrophoretic analysis of viral DNA or viral protiens.

Serology: Serological methods are useful in the diagnosis of primary infections. Antibodies develop within a few days of infection and rise in titre of antibodies may be demonstrated by ELISA, neutralisation or complement fixation tests. In recurrent or reinfection herpes, there may be little change in the antibody titre.

Chemotherapy: Idoxyuridine used topically in eye and skin infections was one of the first clinically successful antiviral agents. The introduction of acyclovir and vidarabine enabled the effective management of deep and systemic infections. Early treatment with intravenous acyclovir has improved the outcome of encephalitis. Oral and topical use may help in less serious conditions. Valaciclovir and famciclovir are more effective oral agents. When resistance to these drugs develop, drugs like foscarnet which are independent of viral thymidine kinase action may be useful.

HERPESVIRUS SIMIAE: B VIRUS

This virus was isolated by Sabin and Wright (1934) from the brain of a laboratory worker who developed fatal ascending myelitis after being bitten by an apparently healthy monkey. It came to be known as the 'B' virus from the initials of this patient. Many similar cases have been reported since then. Herpesvirus simiae infects old world monkeys in the same manner that herpes simplex infects humans, the infection usually being asymptomatic. The typical lesions produced are vesicles on the buccal mucosa which ulcerate shedding the virus and infecting contacts. Though most human cases have followed monkey bites, the infection in some was acquired through the handling of monkey tissues.

Herpesvirus simiae is similar to herpes simplex virus in its properties. The two are antigenically related but the herpes simplex virus antibody does not protect against herpesvirus simiae infection. A formolised vaccine has been tried experimentally in laboratory workers at risk.

The disease in humans is usually fatal. The rare patients who survive have serious neurological sequelae. The official name for B virus is *Cercopithecine herpesvirus 1.*

VARICELLA ZOSTER

As early as 1889, Von Bokay had suggested that varicella (chickenpox) and herpes zoster are different manifestations of the same virus infection. Virological and epidemiological observations have proved this concept. The virus is therefore called varicella zoster virus (VZV). Chickenpox follows primary infection in a nonimmune individual, while herpes zoster is a reactivation of the latent virus when the immunity has fallen to ineffective levels.

Thus, chickenpox is 'caught' but not zoster. Contact with either zoster or chickenpox may lead only to chickenpox but not zoster.

VZV is similar to the herpes simplex virus in its morphology. It does not grow in experimental animals or chick embryos. The virus was first isolated by Weller in human embryonic tissue culture. It can be grown in cultures of human fibroblasts, human amnion or HeLa cells. The cytopathic effects are similar to, but less marked than those produced by the herpes simplex virus. In cultures the virus remains cell associated and does not appear free in the medium. By using highly specific antisera, it is possible to distinguish between herpes virus types 1, 2 and varicella zoster viruses. Only one antigenic type of VZV is known.

Varicella (chickenpox): Chickenpox is one of the mildest and most common of childhood infections. The disease may, however, occur at any age. Adult chickenpox, which is more serious, is rather common in some tropical areas.

The source of infection is a chickenpox or herpes zoster patient. Infectivity is maximum during the initial stages of the disease when the virus is present abundantly in the upper respiratory tract. The buccal lesions which appear in the early stage of the disease and the vesicular fluid are rich in virus content. Infectivity wanes as the disease progresses and the scabs are virtually noninfectious. There are no animal reservoirs of varicella.

The portal of entry of the virus is the respiratory tract or conjunctiva. After an incubation period of about two weeks (7–23 days) the lesions begin to appear. The patient is considered to be infectious during the two days before and five days after the onset of the lesions. In children, there is little prodromal illness and the disease is first noticed when skin lesions appear. Buccal lesions may not be noticed. The rash appears usually on the trunk. The evolution of the rash is so rapid that the various stages – macule, papule, vesicle, pustule and scab – cannot be readily followed in individual lesions. The rash is centripetal in distribution, affecting mainly the trunk and sparing the distal parts of the limbs, and is very superficial without involving the deeper layers of the skin, resembling a dew drop lying on the skin. The rash appears in crops during the first three or four days of the disease, so that lesions of varying age can be noticed on the same patient. It matures very quickly, beginning to crust within 48 hours.

When varicella occurs in the adult, systemic symptoms may be severe, the rash very profuse and the entire disease much more intense than in children. The rash may become hemorrhagic and occasionally bullous lesions appear. Pitted scars on the skin may remain after recovery. Varicella pneumonia is more common in adults, and often fatal in the elderly. Other complications like myocarditis, nephritis, acute cerebellar ataxia, meningitis and encephalitis may ensue. Secondary bacterial infections, usually due to staphylococci or streptococci, may occur. Rey syndrome may follow varicella in some cases with a history of administration of salicylates. But in most cases, chickenpox is an uneventful disease and recovery is the rule. One attack confers lasting immunity.

Chickenpox in pregnancy can be dangerous for both mother and baby. The disease tends to be more severe in pregnant women, with enhanced risk of complications like pneumonia. The baby may develop two types of complications, depending on the period of gestation when the woman develops chicken pox. If maternal varicella occurs during the first half of pregnancy, the fetal infection may usually be asymptomatic. Some infants may develop the *fetal varicella syndrome*, manifesting as cicatrising skin lesions, hypoplasia of limbs, chorioretinitis and CNS defects. Some babies may not exhibit any defects, but may carry latent VZV infection. When maternal varicella occurs near delivery, babies may develop *congenital (neonatal) varicella*, within two weeks of birth. If the mother's rash began a week or more before delivery, she would have developed antibodies which would have been passed, along with the virus, to the fetus transplacentally. Such a baby, though infected, usually escapes clinical disease. If the mother develops chicken pox less the a week (or within 2 days) of delivery, the baby would have received from the mother only the virus and not the antibody, so that it develops neonatal varicella. This is usually a serious disseminated disease, with high risk of pneumonia and encephalitis. As treatment for such conditions will have to be started early to be of any use, the babies are to be given VZV antiserum and chemotherapy immediately after birth.

Laboratory diagnosis: Diagnosis is usually clinical. Multinucleated giant cells and type A intranuclear inclusion bodies may be seen in smears prepared by scraping the base of the early vesicles (Tzanck smears) and stained with toluidine blue, Giemsa or Papanicolou stain. Electron microscopy of the vesicle fluid may demonstrate the virus with typical herpes morphology. Virus isolation can be attempted from the buccal or cutaneous lesions in the early stages by inoculating human amnion, human fibroblast, HeLa or Vero cells. The virus antigen can be detected in scrapings from skin lesions by immunofluorescence, and in vesicle fluid by counterimmunoelectrophoresis with zoster immune serum. ELISA and PCR techniques are also in use.

Prophylaxis and treatment: A live varicella vaccine was developed by Takahashi in Japan in 1974 by attenuating a strain of varicella virus (Oka strain, so named after the patient) by serial passage in tissue culture. Given subcutaneously, it induced good antibody response, but it was very labile and had to be stored frozen. A modified lyophilised form of the vaccine is now available, which can be stored between 2 °C and 8 °C It is recommended for children 1–12 years old as a single subcutaneous dose, and for those older as 2 doses 6–10 weeks apart. It is safe and effective. Occasionally children may develop a few vesicles which resolve quickly. It is not considered safe in pregnancy. Varicella zoster immunoglobulin (VZIG) prepared from patients convalescing from herpes zoster provides passive protection in immunocompromised children exposed to infection, but its availability is limited. It is not useful in treatment.

Specific treatment is indicated mainly in immunodeficient and elderly subjects and those with complications such as varicella pneumonia, encephalitis and disseminated zoster. Acyclovir and famciclovir are effective. Corticosteroids are contraindicated in varicella as they enhance the risk of pneumonia and disseminated disease.

HERPES ZOSTER (SHINGLES, ZONA)

The name is derived from *Herpein*, meaning to creep; *zoster*, meaning girdle.

While varicella is typically a disease of childhood, herpes zoster is one of old age, being common after the age of fifty years. The disease may, however, occur at any age and zoster has been reported very rarely even in the newborn.

Herpes zoster usually occurs in persons who had chickenpox several years earlier. The virus remaining latent in the sensory ganglia, may leak out at times but is usually held in check by the residual immunity. Years after the initial infection, when the immunity has waned, the virus may be reactivated, and triggered by some precipitating stimulus, travel along the sensory nerve to produce zoster lesions on the area of the skin or mucosa supplied by it. This reactivation is associated with inflammation of the nerve, which accounts for the neuritic pain that often precedes the skin lesions. The rash is typically unilateral and confined to the area supplied by a single sensory ganglion. The most common sites are the areas innervated by spinal cord segments D3 to L2 and the trigeminal nerve, particularly, its ophthalmic branch. The lesions are identical in nature to varicella lesions, except for their limited distribution. The rash heals in about two weeks. Pain and paresthesia at the affected area may persist for weeks or months. Other complications are lower motor neuron paralysis which sometimes ensues, meningoencephalitis and generalised zoster where the lesions are scattered widely, perhaps due to hematogenous dissemination of the virus. Herpes zoster ophthalmicus is a common and troublesome presentation. The Ramsay Hunt syndrome is a rare form of zoster affecting the facial nerve, with eruption on the tympanic membrane and the external auditory canal, and often a facial palsy. Chronic or recurrent zoster is often seen in the HIV infected.

Diagnosis is easily made clinically. Laboratory diagnosis and treatment are as for chickenpox.

Herpes zoster represents a mode of evolutionary adaptation by the VZ virus which is an obligate human parasite. In small communities, the susceptibles are completely eliminated by varicella infection in childhood. Therefore, the ability of the virus to remain latent and reappear as zoster years later confers on it a great survival advantage.

CYTOMEGALOVIRUSES

Cytomegaloviruses (CMV), formerly known as *salivary gland viruses*, are a group of ubiquitous herpesviruses of humans and animals. They are characterised by enlargement of infected cells and prominent intranuclear inclusions. Like other herpesviruses, they lead to prolonged latency in infected hosts. In the neonate and the immunodeficient, they cause severe disseminated disease, while in normal children and adults the infection is usually asymptomatic or self limited.

Large inclusion bearing cells had been reported from 1904 in the kidney, lung and liver of infants presumed to have died of congenital syphilis. They were mistaken for protozoa and had been called *Entamoeba mortinatalium*. Goodpasture and Talbot (1921) used the term 'cytomegalia' for this cell enlargement. From 1926, cytomegalia presumed to be due to viral infection was reported in the salivary glands of guinea pigs and children and the viral agent was called the 'salivary gland virus'. In 1956, the virus was isolated from human sources independently by Smith, Rowe and Weller. The name 'cytomegalovirus' was proposed for this group of viruses by Weller in 1960.

CMV are the largest viruses in the herpesvirus family, being 150–200 nm in size. The virus exhibits strict host specificity and infection, both in vivo and in vitro can be established only in the homologous species. Cytomegaloviruses have been identified in human beings, monkeys, guinea pigs and some other species. Human cytomegaloviruses can be grown in human fibroblast cultures. Epithelial cell cultures are not susceptible though epithelial cells are affected in vivo. Cultures have to be incubated for prolonged periods, upto 50 days, as the cytopathic effects are slow in appearance.

Human CMV is unrelated antigenically to other herpesviruses, and even to CMV of other species, except for simian CMV with which some antigenic cross reaction exists. Minor genetic and antigenic differences exist among human CMV isolates but they are of no clinical significance.

Clinical features: Cytomegalovirus disease is rare but infection with the virus is extremely common. As with herpes simplex the large majority of infections are inapparent, leading to prolonged latency, with occasional reactivation. Clinical disease may be caused by either intrauterine or postnatal infections.

Intrauterine infection leads to fetal death or cytomegalic inclusion disease of the newborn which is often fatal. This is a generalised infection associated with hepatosplenomegaly, jaundice, thrombocytopenic purpura and hemolytic anemia. The cytomegalic inclusion disease is probably the most important cause of microcephaly. Other manifestations include chorioretinitis and cerebral calcification resembling congenital toxoplasmosis. Survivors may show mental retardation.

Cytomegalic inclusion disease is seen almost exclusively in infants born to mothers developing primary CMV infection during pregnancy. Infants of mothers who have CMV reactivation during pregnancy tend to have chronic subclinical infection. Perinatal infection may be acquired from the infected mother through genital secretions or breast milk.

Primary infections in older children and adults are usually asymptomatic. However, a heterophile, antibody negative, infectious mononucleosis may be seen. This is more common following transfusion of CMV infected blood (post-transfusion mononucleosis).

In the immunocompromised host, CMV can cause severe and even fatal infections. This occurs in transplant recipients, cancer patients on chemotherapy, and more particularly in the HIV infected. CMV is an important pathogen in AIDS. In AIDS patients, the already weakened immune response is further damaged by the nonspecific CMI-inhibiting effect of CMV. One of the glycoproteins on the surface of CMV acts as a receptor for the *Fc* portion of immunoglobulin molecules. This leads to masking of the virus by attachment of irrelevant immunoglobulin molecules, preventing access to specific anti-CMV antibody.

Laboratory diagnosis: Diagnosis may be established by recovery of the virus from the urine, saliva or other body fluids by inoculating human fibroblast cultures. A simpler but less reliable technique is the demonstration of cytomegalic cells in the centrifuged deposits from urine or saliva.

Demonstration of antibody is useful in the diagnosis of primary infection but not in reactivation. Serological techniques in use include CF, IHA, IF and ELISA. Antibody detection may be necessary for screening blood or organ donors.

Epidemiology: CMV spreads slowly and probably requires close contact for transmission. It may spread through salivary or other secretions or by sexual contact. A special method of transmission is by blood transfusion or organ transplants. The virus has been detected in saliva, urine, cervical secretions, semen, blood and milk. Congenitally infected infants have viruria for upto 4–5 years. They are highly infectious in early infancy. About one per cent of neonates in the USA are infected with CMV. In the developing countries, the rate may be much higher. Upto 80 per cent of adults show CMV antibodies, indicating the high prevalence

of infection. Once infected, the person carries the virus for life.

Prevention and treatment: Prevention is indicated only in high risk cases such as organ transplants, immunodeficient persons and in premature infants. Screening of blood and organ donors and administration of CMV immunoglobulins have been employed in prevention. Acyclovir is useful in prophylaxis but not in treatment. Ganciclovir and foscarnet have been found effective and are used for the treatment of CMV disease in AIDS patients.

No vaccine is available. Experimentally, live attenuated vaccines (Towne 125 and AD 169 strains) and a purified CMV polypeptide vaccine have been found to be immunogenic but not effective in protecting immunodeficient subjects from CMV infection.

EPSTEIN–BARR VIRUS

In 1958, Burkitt described an unusual lymphoma among children in certain parts of Africa and suggested on epidemiological grounds that the tumour may be caused by a mosquito borne virus. This led to several attempts at isolating viruses from such tumours. A number of different viruses, apparently 'passenger viruses', were isolated from cultured lymphoma cells. One virus observed in the cultured lymphoma cells by Epstein, Barr and Achong in 1964 was a new type of herpesvirus, named the EB virus, specifically affecting cells of the B lymphocyte lineage. Only human and some subhuman primate B cells have receptors (CD 21 molecules) for the virus. EBV infected B cells are transformed so that they become capable of continuous growth in vitro.

Epidemiology: The Epstein–Barr (EB) virus is ubiquitous in all human populations. As with other herpesviruses, infection with the EB virus leads to latency, periodic reactivation and lifelong persistence. The EB virus antibodies are present in about 95 per cent of adults. In the overcrowded developing world, the EB virus infection occurs in infancy and childhood, when it is usually asymptomatic. In the affluent countries, primary infection is often delayed till adolescence and early adulthood, when it may lead to infectious mononucleosis.

The source of infection is usually the saliva of infected persons who shed the virus in oropharyngeal secretions for months following primary infection and intermittently thereafter. The EB virus is not highly contagious and droplets and aerosols are not efficient in transmitting infection. Intimate oral contact, as in kissing, appears to be the predominant mode of transmission. This accounts for infectious mononucleosis being called the 'kissing disease'. Infection may also follow blood or marrow transfusion but these are rare events.

EB virus infection may lead to the following clinical conditions:

1. Infectious mononucleosis.
2. EBV associated malignancies:
a. Burkitt's lymphoma.
b. Lymphomas in immunodeficient persons such as AIDS patients and transplant recipients.
c. Nasopharyngeal carcinoma in persons of Chinese origin.

Pathogenesis: The virus enters the pharyngeal epithelial cells through CR 2 (or CD 21) receptors, which are the same as for the C3d component of complement. It multiplies locally, invades the bloodstream and infects B lymphocytes in which two types of changes are produced. In most cases, the virus becomes latent inside the lymphocytes, which become transformed or 'immortalised' so that they become capable of indefinite growth in vitro. They are polyclonally activated to produce many kinds of immunoglobulins. The heterophile sheep erythrocyte agglutinin seen characteristically in infectious mononucleosis is an example of such polyclonal activation. A second type of effect, shown by a few infected B cells is lytic infection, with cell death and release of mature progeny virions.

The mononucleosis represents a polyclonal transformation of infected B lymphocytes. EB virus antigens are expressed on the surface of infected B cells. The atypical lymphocytes seen in blood smears in infectious mononucleosis are T lymphocytes undergoing blast transformation in response to such neoantigens.

Intermittent reactivation of the latent EB virus leads to clonal proliferation of infected B cells. In immunocompetent subjects, this is kept in check by activated T cells. In the immunodeficient, B cell clones may replicate unchecked, resulting in lymphomas. Hyperendemic malaria prevalent in Africa is believed to be responsible for the immune impairment in children with Burkitt's lymphoma. The frequency of lymphomas seen in many types of immunodeficiencies, most typically in AIDS, may have a similar pathogenesis. Nearly half the lymphomas seen in immunodeficient subjects contain EB virus DNA sequences.

Genetic and environmental factors are said to be important in the nasopharyngeal carcinoma seen in men of Chinese origin. EB virus DNA is regularly found in the tumour cells. These patients have high levels of EB virus antibodies. Genetic influence is best illustrated in the X-linked lymphoproliferative (XLP or Duncan) syndrome associated with extreme susceptibility to EB virus infection.

INFECTIOUS MONONUCLEOSIS (GLANDULAR FEVER)

This is an acute self-limited illness usually seen in nonimmune young adults following primary infection with the EB virus. The incubation period is 4–8 weeks. The disease is characterised by fever, sore throat, lymphadenopathy and the presence of abnormal lymphocytes in peripheral blood smears. A mild transient rash may be present. Some patients treated with ampicillin may develop a maculopapular rash due to immune complex reaction to the drug. There is often associated hepatitis which is usually subclinical and demonstrable only by liver function tests. A number of other complications have been recorded, including hematological, neurological, cardiac and pulmonary conditions and splenic rupture. In most cases, spontaneous resolution of the disease occurs in 2–4 weeks. In some it may be more prolonged and lead to a state of mental and physical fatigue in convalescence.

Laboratory diagnosis: Blood examination during the initial phase may show leucopenia due to a drop in the number of polymorphs. Later there is a prominent leucocytosis with the appearance of abnormal mononuclear cells characterised by deeply basophilic vacuolated cytoplasm and kidney shaped nuclei showing a lattice of fenestrated chromatin. These atypical mononuclear cells are not virus infected B lymphocytes but lymphoblasts derived from T cells reactive to the virus infection. The blood picture may sometimes resemble lymphocytic leukemia.

The standard diagnostic procedure is the Paul–Bunnel test. During infectious mononucleosis, heterophile antibodies agglutinate sheep erythrocytes. However, such antibodies may also occur after injections of sera and sometimes even in normal individuals. Infectious mononucleosis antibodies may be differentiated by absorption tests. Inactivated serum (56 °C for 30 minutes) in doubling dilutions is mixed with equal volumes of a 1% suspension of sheep erythrocytes. After incubation at 37 °C for four hours the tubes are examined for agglutination. An agglutination titre of 100 or above is suggestive of infectious mononucleosis. For confirmation, differential absorption of agglutinins with guineapig kidney

and ox red cells is necessary. The Forssman antibody induced by injection of horse serum is removed by treatment with guineapig kidney and ox red cells. Normally occurring agglutinins are removed by guineapig kidney, but not by ox red cells. Infectious mononucleosis antibody is removed by ox red cells but not guineapig kidney. This differential agglutination test has largely been replaced by a simple slide agglutination test employing sensitised horse erythrocytes, with the same sensitivity and specificity. The Paul–Bunnel antibody develops early during the course of infectious mononucleosis, and disappears within about two months.

Tests are also available for the demonstration of specific EB virus antibodies. Immuno-fluorescence and ELISA are commonly employed. The IgM antibody to VCA (virus capsid antigen) appears soon after primary infection and disappears in 1–2 weeks. It is a reliable indication of primary infection. The IgG anti-VCA antibody persists throughout life and indicates past or recent infection. The new appearance of antibody to the EB nuclear antigen (EBNA) is also a useful marker for primary infection.

Antibodies to early antigens (EA) are present in high titres in EB-associated lymphomas. However, these specific tests are of limited availability.

The infectious mononucleosis syndrome can follow infection by other agents such as cytomegalovirus and toxoplasmosis or as a reaction to noninfectious stimuli. However, the heterophile Paul–Bunnel test is positive only in disease caused by the EB virus.

Table 52.2 Differential absorption test for Paul–Bunnel antibody

	Result of absorption by	
	Guinea pig kidney	Ox red cells
Normal serum	Absorbed	Not absorbed
Antibody after serum therapy	Absorbed	Not absorbed
Infectious mononucleosis	Not absorbed	Absorbed

Human Herpes Virus Types 6,7,8

A herpesvirus, first iosolated in 1986 from the peripheral blood of patients with lympho-proliferative disease, was called the *human B-lymphotropic virus*. It has been renamed HHV-6. This is ubiquitos and spreads apparently through saliva in early infancy. Two variants recognised, A and B. Variant B is the cause of mild but common childhood illness `exanthem subitum' (roseola infantum or 'sixth disease'). In older age groups, it has been associated with infectious mononucleosis syndrome, focal encephalitis and, in the immunodeficient, with pneumonia and disseminated disease.

HHV 7 was isolated in 1990 from peripheral CD4 cells of a healthy person. Like HHV 6, HHV 7 also appears to be widely distributed and transmitted through saliva. It shares with HIV the same CD4 receptor on T cells and could therefore contribute to a further depletion of CD4 T cells in HIV infected persons. It has been said to cause some cases of exanthem subitum.

In 1994, DNA sequences presumed to represent a new herpesvirus were identified from tissues of Kaposi's sarcoma from AIDS patients. This has been named HHV 8. This has subsequently been identified also in Kaposi's sarcoma in persons not infected with HIV. It has been therefore referred to sometimes as *Kaposi's sarcoma-associated herpesvirus* (KSHV), but an etiological relationship is yet to be proved.

Further Reading

Corey L and P Spear 1986. Infections with Herpes Simplex viruses. *New Eng J Med 314*:686, 749.

Ho M. 1991. *Cytomegaloviruses: Biology and Infection*, 2nd edn. New York:Plenum Press.

Jaffe HW and PE Pellett 1999. Human herpesvirus 8 and Kaposi's sarcoma. *New Engl J Med 24*:340.

Kaplan JE. 1988. Herpesvirus simiae infection in monkey handlers. *J Infect Dis. 157*:1090.

Khanna R. et al. 1995. Immune regulation in Epstein–Barr virus disease. *Microbiol Rev 59*:387.

Levy JA. 1997. Three new human herpesviruses. *Lancet 349*:558.

Lusso P and RC Gallo 1994. Human herpes virus 6 in AIDS. *Lancet 343*:555.

Onorato IM et al. 1985. Epidemiology of cytomegalovirus infection. *Rev Infect Dis 7*:479.

Rickman AB et al. 1985. The Epstein–Barr virus as a model of virus-host interactions. *Brit Med Bull 41*:75.

Rowley AH et al. 1990. Rapid detection of Herpes simplex virus DNA. *Lancet 335*.

Strauss SE et al. 1993. Epstein–Barr virus infections. *Ann Int Med 118*:45.

Weller TH. 1983. Varicella and Herpes-Zoster: changing concepts. *New Eng J Med. 309*:1362, 1434.

Adenoviruses

Adenoviruses are a group of medium sized, nonenveloped, double stranded DNA viruses that share a common complement fixing antigen. They infect humans, animals and birds, showing strict host specificity.

In 1953, Rowe and associates grew surgically removed human adenoid tissue in plasma clot cultures and noticed that the epithelial outgrowths underwent spontaneous degeneration resembling viral cytopathic change. This was neutralised by human sera. A viral agent was shown to be responsible for this degeneration. This was the prototype of the group of viruses subsequently designated adenoviruses because they were originally isolated from the adenoids. Hilleman in 1954 isolated a related virus from the throat washings of military recruits with acute respiratory illness.

Over 50 serotypes of adenoviruses have been isolated from human sources. Most of the recent serotypes were recovered from AIDS patients. Adenovirus infections are common worldwide mostly in children. Many infections are asymptomatic. The virus may persist in the host for many months. Adenoviruses cause infections of the respiratory tract and eyes, and less often of the intestine and urinary tract.

In 1962 Huebner reported that adenovirus types 12 and 18 produced sarcoma when inoculated into baby hamsters. This led to the intense study of adenoviruses at the genetic and molecular levels. However, there is no evidence at all relating adenoviruses to natural malignancy in humans or animals.

Adenoviruses appear to have a spare capacity to carry DNA insert up to 7 kb and are being investigated as potential vectors in gene therapy.

Morphology: Adenoviruses are 70–75 nm in size. They have a characteristic morphology. The capsid is composed of 252 capsomers arranged as an icosahedron with 20 triangular facets and 12 vertices. Of the 252 capsomers, 240 have six neighbours and are called hexons, while the 12 capsomers at the vertices have five neighbours and are called pentons. Each penton unit consists of a penton base anchored in the capsid and a projection or fibre consisting of a rod like portion with a knob attached at the distal end. Thus, the virion has the appearance of a space vehicle.

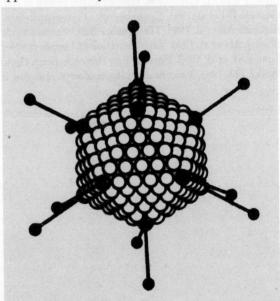

Fig. 53.1 Morphology of advenovirus

Table 53.1 Classification of human adenoviruses

Group (Subgenus)	Serotype (Species)	Hemagglutination		Oncogenic potential	
		Red cells	Pattern	Tumourogenicity in vivo	Transformation of cultured cells
A	12, 18, 31	Rat	±	High	+
B	3, 7, 11, 14, 16, 21, 34, 35	Monkey	+	Weak	+
C	1, 2, 5, 6	Rat	±	Nil	+
D	8–10, 13, 15, 17, 19, 20, 22–30, 32, 33, 36–39, 42–47		+	Nil	+
E	4	Rat	±	Nil	+
F	40, 41	Rat	±	NK	+

Note: + denotes complete and ± partial hemagglutination ; NK = not known

Resistance: Adnoviruses are relatively stable, remaining viable for about a week at 37 °C. They are readily inactivated at 50 °C. They resist ether and bile salts.

Growth and host range: Adenoviruses are host specific and so laboratory animals are not susceptible to adenoviruses infecting humans. Human adenoviruses grow only in tissue cultures of human origin, such as human embryonic kidney, HeLa or HEP-2. Cytopathic changes may take several days to develop and consist of cell rounding and aggregation into grape like clusters. Intranuclear inclusions may be seen in stained preparations.

Classification: The family Adenoviradae contains two genera: *Mastadenovirus,* the adenovirus of mammals and *Aviadenovirus,* that of birds. In addition to at least 47 serotypes of human origin, mastadenoviruses include simian, bovine, equine, ovine, canine, murine, porcine and cetacean serotypes. Aviadenoviruses have been isolated from fowls, gele and turkeys. They infect only the homologous species, with the exception of oncogenic human adenoviruses (for example types, 12, 18, 31) that cause sarcomas when injected into newborn hamsters.

All mammalian adenoviruses share a common complement fixing antigen. The group antigens are present mainly on hexons and can be detected by imunofluorescence or ELISA. Type-specific antigens are located on pentons and fibres. Serotypes are identified by the neutralisation test. Human adenoviruses are classified into six groups (also called subgroups or subgenera) based on properties such as hemagglutination, fibre length, DNA fragment analysis and oncogenic potential (Table 53.1).

Pathogenesis: Adenoviruses cause infections of the respiratory tract, eye, bladder and intestine. More than one type of virus may produce the same clinical syndrome and one type of virus may cause clinically different diseases (Table 53.2). The following syndromes have been recognised:

Pharyngitis: Adenoviruses are the major cause of nonbacterial pharyngitis and tonsillitis, presenting as febrile common cold. Types 1–7 are commonly responsible.

Pneumonia: Adenovirus types 3 and 7 are associated with pneumonia in adults resembling primary atypical pneumonia. In infants and young children types 7 may lead to more serious and even fatal pneumonia.

Acute respiratory diseases (ARD): This occurs usually as outbreaks in military recruits. Serotypes 4, 7 and 21 are the agents commonly isolated.

Pharyngoconjunctival fever: This syndrome of febrile pharyngitis and conjunctivitis

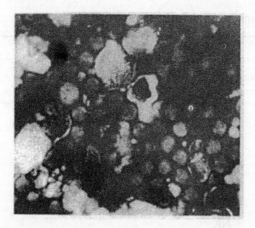

Fig. 53.2 Adenovirus in stools from a child with diarrhea. (x 200,000). Virus particles show characteristic hexagonal shape. Negative stain with 3 per cent ammonium molybdate, of fecal sediment (Courtesy: Prof. M Mathen, Christian Medical College, Vellore.)

seen in civilian population is usually associated with serotypes 3, 7 and 14.

Epidemic keratoconjunctivitis (EKC): This is a serious condition which may appear as an epidemics, usually caused by type 8 and less often by types 19 and 37.

Acute follicular conjunctivitis: This is a nonpurulent inflammation of the conjunctiva with enlargement of the submucous lymphoid follicles and of the preauricular lymph nodes. Types 3, 4 and 11 are commonly responsible. Adenoviral and chlamydial conjunctivitis are clinically similar.

Diarrhea: Adenoviruses can often be isolated from feces but their relation to intestinal disease has not been conclusively established. However, some fastidious adenoviruses, which can be demonstrated abundantly in feces by electron microscopy but fail to grow in conventional tissue cultures, can cause diarrheal disease in children (for example types 40, 41). They have been designated as enteric type adenoviruses. Special techniques of tissue culture (use of trypsinised monkey kidney cells or transformed human embryonic kidney cells) have been developed for their cultivation. They can also be identified by stool ELISA.

Acute hemorrhagic cystitis in children and *generalised exanthem* are two other syndromes which have been reported. Adenoviruses types 11 and 21 are responsible for the former.

Adenoviruses have been isolated from mesenteric lymph nodes in cases of *mesenteric adenitis* and *intussusception* in children.

Laboratory diagnosis: Diagnosis can be established by isolation of the virus from the throat, eye, urine or feces. The materials are inoculated in tissue cultures. Preliminary identification is possible by noting the cytopathic effects and by complement fixation tests with adenovirus antiserum. By hemagglutination with rat and monkey erythrocytes, the isolate can be classified into subgroups. Typing is done by neutralisation tests.

For serological diagnosis, rise in titre of antibodies should be demonstrated in paired sera. Examination of a single sample of serum is inconclusive as adenovirus antibodies are so common in the population.

Electron microscopy for fecal virus and immunofluorescence for viral antigen detection in

Table 53.2 Common syndromes associated with adenoviruses infection

Syndrome	Principal serotypes
Respiratory disease in children	1, 2, 5, 6
Sore throat, febrile cold, pneumonia	3, 4, 7, 14, 21
ARD in military recruits	4, 7, 21
Follicular (swimming pool) conjunctivitis	3, 7
Epidemic keratoconjunctivitis (shipyard eye)	8, 19, 37
Diarrhea	40, 41

nasopharyngeal and ocular infections are useful. **Prophylaxis:** Specific prevention is required only for the control of outbreaks in closed communities, as in military recruits. Killed and live vaccines have been used in them for prevention of ARD, with some success. No vaccine is available for general use.

ADENO-ASSOCIATED VIRUSES (AAV)

Electron microscopy of adenovirus preparations have revealed small icosahedral viral particles, 20–25 nm in diameter. They are unable to replicate independently as they lack enough DNA. They can multiply only in cells simultaneously infected with adenoviruses and are called adeno-associated viruses (AAV) or adenosatellite viruses. They have been classified as the genus *dependovirus* (referring to their dependence on adenoviruses) under the family Parvoviridae. They can be detected by electron microscopy and complement fixation or immunofluorescence with specific antisera. Types 1, 2 and 3 are of human origin and cause natural infection, while type 4 is of simian origin. Their pathogenic role is uncertain.

Further Reading

Baum SG. 1990. Adenoviruses. In G. Mandel et al. *Principles and Practice of Infectious Diseases* 3rd edn. New York: Wiley.

De Jong JC et al. 1983. Fastidious adenoviruses from human infant stool. *J Med Virol* 11:215.

Ginberg HS (ed). 1984. *The Adenoviruses.* New York: Plenum.

Keenlyside RA et al. 1983. Keratoconjunctivitis associated with adenovirus type 37. *J Infect Dis* 147:191.

Kemp MC et al. 1983. The changing etiology of epidemic keratoconjunctivitis. *J Infect Dis* 148:24.

Liu C. 1991. Adenoviruses. In *Textbook of Human Virology*, 2nd edn. Belshe:Mosby Year Books.

Picornaviruses

The family Picornaviridae comprises a large number of very small (*pico*, meaning small) RNA viruses. They are nonenveloped viruses, 27–30 nm in size, resistant to ether and other lipid solvents. Two groups of picornaviruses are of medical importance, the *enteroviruses* that parasitise the enteric tract and the *rhinoviruses* that infect the nasal mucosa. Two other picornavirus genera of veterinary importance are *aphthoviruses* causing the foot and mouth disease of cattle, and *cardioviruses* of mice, including the encephalomyocarditis virus.

ENTEROVIRUSES

Enteroviruses of medical importance include: Poliovirus types 1–3, Coxsackievirus A types 1–24, Coxsackievirus B types 1–6, Echovirus types 1–34 and Enterovirus types 68–71.

Paralytic disease of children (*infantile paralysis*) has been recognised from very early times. However, it was only towards the end of the nineteenth century that poliomyelitis (*polios* = grey; *myelitis* = inflammation of the spinal cord) was characterised as a separate clinical entity capable of causing infections in which paralytic cases are far outnumbered by silent inapparent infections. Landsteiner and Popper (1909) reported experimental transmission of the disease to monkeys by inoculation of spinal cord and fecal extract filtrates from fatal cases of poliomyelitis. The experimental study of the disease was restricted as monkeys were the only laboratory animals susceptible to the virus. Armstrong (1939) succeeded in adapting a poliovirus (type 2 Lansing strain) to cotton rats and mice but few strains could

be so adapted. Progress was also inhibited by the dogma then held that polioviruses were strictly neurotropic, multiplying only in the neural tissues. The demonstration by Enders, Weller and Robbins (1949) that polioviruses could grow in cultures of non-neural cells from human embryos, producing cytopathic effects, was a major breakthrough. The Nobel Prize was awarded to them in recognition of the seminal importance of this discovery in the development of virology as a whole.

A new type of virus was isolated by Dalldorf and Sickles (1948) from the feces of children with paralytic poliomyelitis, from whom type 1 poliovirus was also isolated. The virus caused paralysis on inoculation into suckling mice. This was called the coxsackie virus, as the patients came from the village of Coxsackie in New York. Many similar viruses have since been isolated from the feces and throats of patients with different diseases as well as from healthy individuals. They have been designated as coxsackie viruses, classified into groups A and B based on the pathological changes produced in suckling mice.

The introduction of tissue culture techniques in diagnostic virology led to the isolation of several cytopathogenic viruses from the feces of sick as well as healthy persons. They were called orphan viruses as they could not be associated with any particular clinical disease. They came to be known by the descriptive term 'enteric cytopathogenic human orphan (ECHO) viruses'. Several orphan viruses have also been isolated from animal feces.

The classification of enteroviruses as coxsackieviruses and echoviruses was not satisfactory. It was therefore decided that from 1969, any new enterovirus identified would not be classified into either of these groups but would be merely assigned enterovirus (EV) type numbers, starting with type 68 (because 67 types of enteroviruses had already been classified by then, consisting of three polio, 30 coxsackie and 34 echoviruses). Hence the next five new enterovirus types, became 68–72. Enterovirus 72 was the virus causing infectious hepatitis (Hepatitis type A), which has been reclassified as a separate genus *Hepatovirus*. Because of its special status, it is considered in the chapter on Hepatitis viruses.

Table 54.1 Enterovirus serotypes

Group	Serotype
Poliovirus	1–3
Coxsackie virus A	1–22, 24
Coxsackie virus B	1–6
Echovirus	1–9, 11–27, 29–31
Numbered } enterovirus	(EV) 68–71

Most enteroviruses are host specific, infecting only one or a few related species. There is no common group antigen for enteroviruses, though some of them show antigenic cross-reactions.

POLIOVIRUS

Morphology: The virion is a spherical particle, about 27 nm in diameter, composed of 60 subunits, each consisting of four *viral proteins* (VP1–VP4), arranged in icosahedral symmetry. VP1 which faces outside, carries the major antigenic site for combination with type specific neutralising antibodies. The genome is a single strand of positive sense RNA. It can be directly translated by host ribosomes to form a polyprotein which is cleaved into 11 different proteins.

The virus can be crystallised, and arrays of virus crystals can be seen in the cytoplasm of infected cells.

Resistance: Poliovirus is resistant to ether, chloroform, bile, proteolytic enzymes of the intestinal contents, and detergents. It is stable at pH 3. In feces, it can survive for months at 4 °C and years at –20 °C. Depending on conditions like temperature, moisture, pH and amount of virus, its survival in feces at room temperature may vary from one day to several weeks. It is readily inactivated by heat (55 °C for 30 minutes). Molar $MgCl_2$ protects the virus against heat inactivation. Milk or ice cream also provides such protection. Formaldehyde and oxidising disinfectants destroy the virus. Chlorination destroys the virus in water but organic matter delays inactivation. Phenolic disinfectants are not effective. Poliovirus does not survive lyophilisation well.

Antigenic properties: By neutralisation test, poliovirus strains have been classified into three types: 1, 2 and 3. The prototype strains are Brunhilde and Mahoney strains for type 1, Lansing and MEFI for type 2 and Leon and Saukett for type 3. Type 1 is the most common and causes most epidemics. Type 2 usually causes endemic infections. Type 3 strains have caused epidemics. Immunity is type specific.

By complement fixation, ELISA or precipitation tests, two antigens C and D (C = coreless or capsid; D = dense) can be recognised. The D antigen, also called the Native or N antigen, is associated with the whole virion and is type specific. The C antigen, also called the Heated or H antigen associated with the 'empty' noninfectious virus, is less specific and reacts with heterotypic sera. The D antigen is converted into the C antigen by heating the virus at 56 °C. Anti-D antibody is protective and therefore the potency of injectable poliovaccine can be measured in terms of D antigen units. Anti-C antibody does not neutralise virus infectivity.

Host range and cultivation: Natural infection occurs only in humans. Experimentally, monkeys may be infected by intracerebral or intraspinal inoculation. Chimpanzees and cynomolgus monkeys may also be infected orally. Some established strains have been adapted for growth in rodents and chick embryos but fresh isolates do not infect them.

The virus grows readily in tissue cultures of primate origin. Primary monkey kidney cultures are used for diagnostic cultures and vaccine production. The infected cells round up and become refractile and pyknotic. Eosinophilic intranuclear inclusion bodies may be demonstrated in stained preparations. Well-formed plaques develop in infected monolayers with agar overlay.

Pathogenesis: The virus is transmitted by the fecal–oral route through ingestion. Inhalation or entry through conjunctiva of droplets of respiratory secretions may also be possible modes of entry in close contacts of patients in the early stage of the disease. The virus multiplies initially in the epithelial cells of the alimentary canal and the lymphatic tissues, from the tonsils to the Peyer's patches. It then spreads to the regional lymph nodes and enters the blood stream (*minor* or *primary viremia*). After further multiplication in the reticuloendothelial system, the virus enters the bloodstream again (*major* or *secondary viremia)* and is carried to the spinal cord and brain. Direct neural transmission to the central nervous system may also occur under special circumstances, as in poliomyelitis following tonsillectomy.

In the central nervous system, the virus multiplies selectively in the neurons and destroys them. The earliest change is the degeneration of Nissl bodies (chromatolysis). Nuclear changes follow. When degeneration becomes irreversible, the necrotic cell lyses or is phagocytosed by leucocytes or macrophages. Lesions are mostly in the anterior horns of the spinal cord, causing flaccid paralysis, but the posterior horns and intermediate columns may also be involved to some extent. Pathological changes are usually more extensive than the distribution of paralysis. In some cases, encephalitis occurs primarily involving the brainstem but extending upto the motor and premotor areas of the cerebral cortex.

Clinical features: Following exposure to poliovirus, 90–95 per cent of susceptible individuals develop only *inapparent infection*, which causes

seroconversion alone. It is only in 5–10 per cent that any sort of clinical illness results. The incubation period is about 10 days on the average but may range from four days to four weeks. The earliest manifestations are associated with the phase of primary viremia and consist of fever, headache, sore throat and malaise lasting 1–5 days. This is called the *minor illness* and in many cases may be the only manifestation (*abortive poliomyelitis*). If the infection progresses, the minor illness is followed 3–4 days later by the major illness. The fever comes on again (biphasic fever), along with headache, stiff neck and other features of meningitis. This marks the stage of viral invasion of the central nervous system. Sometimes the disease does not progress beyond this stage of aseptic meningitis (*nonparalytic poliomyelitis*). In those proceeding to paralytic poliomyelitis, flaccid paralysis develops. Paralysis is focal in distribution initially but spreads over the next 3–4 days. Depending on the distribution of paralysis, cases are classified as spinal, bulbar or bulbospinal. Mortality ranges from 5–10 per cent and is mainly due to respiratory failure. Recovery of the paralysed muscles takes place in the next 4–8 weeks and is usually complete after six months, leaving behind varying degrees of residual paralysis.

Laboratory diagnosis: Virus isolation in tissue culture is the best method for specific diagnosis. Many specimens can be used, including blood, CSF, throat swab and feces. Virus can be isolated from blood during the phase of primary viremia, 3–5 days after infection, before neutralising antibodies appear. But this is of little practical importance. Unlike other enteroviruses, poliovirus can seldom be isolated from the CSF but can be obtained from the spinal cord and brain, postmortem. The virus can be isolated from the throat in the early stage of the disease. Virus isolation from feces is usually possible from over 80 per cent. of patients in the first week, 50 per cent. till 3 weeks and 25 per cent. till six weeks. As fecal excretion may be intermittent, best results are obtained by testing fecal samples collected on two separate days, as early in the illness as possible. Prolonged fecal excretion may be seen in the immunodeficient, but permanent carriers do not occur.

After appropriate processing to destroy bacteria (centrifugation, treatment with ether, addition of antibiotics), specimens are inoculated into tissue culture. Primary monkey kidney cells are usually employed, though any other human or simian cell culture may be used. The virus growth is indicated by typical cytopathic effects in 2–3 days. Identification is made by neutralisation tests with pooled and specific antisera. It must be remembered that the mere isolation of poliovirus from feces does not constitute a diagnosis of poliomyelitis as symptomless infections are so common. Virus isolation must be interpreted along with clinical and serological evidence.

Serodiagnosis is less often employed. Antibody rise can be demonstrated in paired sera by neutralisation or complement fixation tests. Antibodies appear soon after the onset of paralysis so that even the first sample of serum may contain appreciable amounts of antibody. Neutralising antibodies appear early and persist for life. In the CF test, antibodies to the C antigen appear first and disappear in a few months, while anti-D antibodies take some weeks to appear after infection but last for five years. The CF test is useful to identify exposure to poliovirus but not for type-specific diagnosis.

Immunity: Immunity in poliomyelitis is type specific. Humoral immunity provided by circulating and secretory antibody is responsible for protection against poliomyelitis. IgM antibody appears within a week of infection and lasts for about six months. IgG antibody persists for life. Neutralising antibody in blood generally protects against disease by the same serotype of the virus, but may not prevent infection of intestinal epithelial cells and virus shedding in feces. Secretory IgA in the gastrointestinal tract provides mucosal immunity preventing intestinal infection and virus shedding.

Breast milk containing IgA antibody protects infants from infection. Poliomyelitis tends to be more severe and virus shedding more prolonged in those with impaired humoral immune response. The virus also induces cell mediated immunity, but its importance appears to be uncertain as persons with defective cellular immunity are seen to respond normally to poliovirus infection.

Prophylaxis: Passive immunisation by the administration of human gammaglobulin is of little value.

Attempts at active immunisation with vaccines date from 1910, soon after the discovery of poliovirus. The early vaccines were crude suspensions of the spinal cord from infected monkeys, inactivated with formalin (Brodie and Park) or ricinoleate (Kolmer). They were not only ineffective but often even dangerous, leading to vaccination poliomyelitis. Polio vaccines therefore became unpopular. Brodie is believed to have taken his own life, distressed at the suffering caused by his vaccine. It was only after 1949, when tissue culture was used for growing the virus and the existence of three antigenic types of polioviruses was recognised, that fresh developments in vaccine preparation became possible. By 1953, Salk had developed a killed vaccine. Almost simultaneously, Koprowsky, Cox and Sabin independently developed live attenuated vaccines.

Salk's killed polio vaccine is a formalin inactivated preparation of the three types of poliovirus grown in monkey kidney tissue culture. Standard virulent strains are used. The three types of polioviruses are grown separately in monkey kidney cells. Viral pools of adequate titre are filtered to remove cell debris and clumps, and inactivated with formalin (1:4000) at 37 °C for 12–15 days. Stringent tests are carried out to ensure complete inactivation and freedom from extraneous agents. The three types are then pooled and after further tests for safety and potency, issued for use.

A nationwide controlled field trial conducted in 1954 in the USA confirmed the safety of the

Salk vaccine and showed that it gave 80–90 per cent protection against paralytic poliomyelitis. However, in 1955, an unfortunate incident occurred that led to doubts about the safety of the vaccine. Over 100 cases of paralytic poliomyelitis occurred in the vaccinees and their contacts following the use of an insufficiently inactivated vaccine. This 'Cutter incident' (so called after the manufacturer of the particular vaccine) was investigated in detail and led to the introduction of further safeguards. The vaccine, after these modifications, has been completely safe.

Killed vaccine is given by injection. It is therefore called inactivated or injectable poliovaccine (IPV). Three doses given 4–6 weeks apart constitute the primary vaccination, to be followed by a booster six months later. The first dose should be given to babies after the age of six months to ensure that immune response is not impaired by residual maternal antibodies. Immunity can be sustained by booster doses every 3–5 years thereafter. An enhanced potency IPV produced in human diploid cells induces better seroconversion following two subcutaneous doses, 4–8 weeks apart. A third dose may be given 6–12 months later.

Live polio vaccines were developed independently by Koprowsky, Cox and Sabin. All three vaccines were used initially, but now only Sabin's attenuated strains are employed. Sabin's vaccine strains were developed by plaque selection in monkey kidney tissue culture. Attenuated strains for live vaccine should possess the following criteria: (1) should not be neurovirulent as tested by intraspinal inoculation in monkeys; (2) should be able to set up intestinal infection following feeding and should induce an immune response; (3) should be stable and should not acquire neurovirulence after serial enteric passage; (4) should possess stable genetic characteristics (markers) by which they can be differentiated from the wild virulent strains.

Several markers have been described for differentiating the wild from the attenuated strains. The following markers were commonly used: (1) d marker: wild strains will grow well in low levels of bicarbonate but avirulent strains will not; (2) rct 40; wild strains grow well at 40 °C, while avirulent strains grow poorly; (3) MS: wild strains grow well in a stable cell line of monkey kidney, while avirulent strains grow poorly; and (4) McBride's intratypic antigenic marker shown by the rate of inactivation by specific antiserum. The above markers have been found to be not sufficiently discriminative. Molecular epidemiological methods give better results. These methods include the use of monoclonal antibodies specific for vaccine strains, oligonucleotide finger printing and nucleic acid sequencing.

Live polio vaccine is administered orally and is therefore known as the *oral polio vaccine* (OPV). It is prepared by growing the attenuated strains in monkey kidney cells. Very stringent precautions are taken to ensure freedom from extraneous agents like SV 40 and B virus. After tests for neurovirulence, genetic stability and potency, the vaccine is issued either in the monovalent or trivalent form, in pleasantly flavoured syrup. The use of molar $MgCl_2$ or sucrose stabilises the vaccine against heat inactivation, particularly under tropical conditions. The vaccine is usually given in the trivalent form. It can be given to young infants, as the maternal antibody has little effect on intestinal infection. Theoretically, a single dose should be sufficient to establish infection and immunity but in practice three doses are given at 4–8 week intervals, to ensure that all three types of the vaccine virus multiply in the intestine, overcoming interference among themselves and with other enteric viruses. It has been recommended that in the tropics the number of doses of vaccine be increased to five, in order to enhance seroconversion in the vaccinees.

OPV used in India is stated to contain Type 1 virus 10 lakh, Type 2 virus 2 lakh and Type 3 virus 3 lakh TC ID50 per dose (0.5 ml). The liquid vaccine is thermostabilised with $MgCl_2$ which acts only at a pH below 7.0. To maintain the pH, the vaccine has to be kept in airtight containers. The shelf life of the vaccine at 4–8 °C is four months and at −20 °C is two years. Improper storage conditions and 'cold chain' failure may be partly responsible for the apparent failure of OPV to control poliomyelitis in the developing countries.

There has been much controversy about the relative merits of killed and live vaccines. They may be considered under the following headings:

Safety: Both vaccines are safe. It has been suggested that the attenuated strains tend to acquire neurovirulence on serial enteric passage, as may happen following vaccination. A few cases of vaccine induced poliomyelitis have been reported but the incidence is so low that the risk is negligible. However it assumes importance where the disease has been eradicated by immunisation. About 5–10 cases of paralytic poliomyelitis are seen each year in the USA, all of which are caused by the vaccine strains, in vaccinees or their contacts. Well over a billion doses of OPV have been administered until now in different parts of the world. OPV is not safe in immunodeficient or immunosuppressed subjects but the killed vaccine does no harm.

Efficiency: A full course of killed vaccine induces a satisfactory immune response. One or two doses of OPV have produced 90–100 per cent seroconversion in children in the advanced countries. However, in the developing countries in the tropics, the response has not been so satisfactory. This is especially so with polio type 1, more than half the vaccinees in some series failing to show serological response after two or three doses. The reason for this disparity is not certain, though several possibilities have been suggested.

Interference by other enteroviruses so common in the tropics (experimentally, it has been shown that coxsackie B viruses may interfere with poliovirus, while coxsackie A may be synergistic); Frequent *diarrheal diseases* preventing colonisation by the vaccine virus; *Breast feeding* immediately before or after the vaccine is given. The vaccine virus may be neutralised by antibodies in the breast milk or by some other inhibitory agent in the intestinal secretions. An inhibitor of poliovirus has been identified in saliva. This can be countered by horse antiserum to human gammaglobulin. Because of the poor rate of seroconversion after oral immunisation in India and other tropical areas, primary immunisation with killed vaccines (given along with the triple antigen) has been proposed. This may be followed by live oral vaccines for achieving intestinal immunity.

Ease of administration: OPV is obviously preferable to killed vaccine given by injection. An advantage of the killed vaccine is that it can be administered along with the DPT vaccine as a quadruple vaccine.

Economy: Live vaccine is much more economical. This is an important aspect in mass vaccination campaigns in the developing countries.

Nature of immunity: This is perhaps the most important difference between the two. Killed vaccine induces only systemic antibody response. There is no intestinal immunity, so that even in the vaccinated, infection with a wild strain may lead to intestinal multiplication and dissemination of the virus. The individual alone is protected by the circulating antibodies. Live vaccine, on the other hand, also induces local immunity in the gut so that wild viruses are unable to multiply in the intestines and be shed. Hence, it protects the individual and the community.

Duration of immunity: Immunity following killed vaccine may need to be maintained by booster doses periodically, while immunity following live vaccine resembles natural active immunity in being more lasting.

Use in epidemics: Community-wide administration of OPV, ideally monovalent vaccine of the same type as that causing the epidemic, early during an epidemic of paralytic poliomyelitis can stop the epidemic. This has been successfully practised in different parts of the world.

Spread of vaccine virus in the community: The tendency of the vaccine virus to spread naturally in the community, especially among children, is a disadvantage in the advanced countries. Perhaps, it may even be beneficial and may help to extend the vaccine coverage in countries where wild virus is endemic. Ideally, however, it is desirable to vaccinate the whole community at one time so that natural dissemination is prevented. The strategy of administering the vaccine to all children in a region on the same day (*pulse immunisation*) has been found to be useful in the developing countries.

Eradication of poliomyelitis: By global immunisation with OPV it was considered possible to eradicate the disease. The World Health Organisation Assembly in 1988 had proposed global eradication of poliomyelitis by the year 2000. Poor progress in immunisation in many countries has been a set back to this objective.

Epidemiology: Poliomyelitis is an exclusively human disease and the only source of virus is humans, the patient or much more commonly the symptomless carrier. Patients shed the virus in feces for varying periods, about 50 per cent for three weeks and a small proportion for 3–4 months. No permanent carriers occur. However, the virus may persist in the environment (sewage) for upto six months. Virus shed in throat secretions during the early part of the disease may also be a source of infection for the contacts of patients.

Infection is, in general, asymptomatic. The ratio of subclinical to clinical infections has been stated as 100 or 1000 to 1. The outcome of infection is influenced by the virulence of the infecting strain, the dose of infection and the age of the individual, adults being more susceptible than children. The following factors may influence the incidence of paralysis: 1) Pregnancy carries an increased risk of paralysis, perhaps due to the associated hormonal changes. 2) Tonsillectomy during the incubation period may predispose to bulbar poliomyelitis. 3) Injections such as triple vaccine, especially alum-containing preparations, may lead to paralysis involving the inoculated limb. The mechanism is uncertain. The trauma may lead to virus entry into local nerve fibres, or the segment of spinal cord corresponding to the site may be more susceptible to viral damage due to reactive hyperemia. 4) Severe muscular exertion or trauma during the preparalytic stage increases the risk of paralysis.

Poliovirus type 1 is responsible for most epidemics of paralytic poliomyelitis. Type 3 also causes epidemics to a lesser extent. Type 2 usually causes inapparent infections in the western countries but in India paralysis due to type 2 is quite common. Immunity is type-specific but there is an significant amount of cross protection between types 1 and 2, between types 2 and 3 and little or none between types 1 and 3.

COXSACKIEVIRUS

The prototype strain was isolated by Dalldorf and Sickles (1948) from the village of Coxsackie in New York. Several related viruses have been isolated since then from different parts of the world. The characteristic feature of this group is its ability to infect suckling but not adult mice. Based on the pathological changes produced in suckling mice, coxsackieviruses are classified into two groups, A and B.

Properties of the virus: Coxsackieviruses are typical enteroviruses. Following inoculation in suckling mice, group A viruses produce a generalised myositis and flaccid paralysis leading to death within a week. Group B viruses produce a patchy focal myositis, spastic paralysis, necrosis of the brown fat and, often, pancreatitis, hepatitis, myocarditis and encephalitis. By neutralisation tests, Group A viruses are classified into 24 types and group B into six types. All types in group B share a common complement-fixing antigen. Coxsackie A 23 is the same as echo 9 and Coxsackie A24 the same as ECHO 34. Some coxsackieviruses (A 7, 20, 21, 24 and B 1, 3, 5, 6) agglutinate human or monkey erythrocytes.

Host range and growth: It is necessary to employ suckling mice for the isolation of coxsackieviruses. Inoculation is usually made by intracerebral, subcutaneous and intraperitoneal routes. Adult mice are not susceptible. Suckling hamsters can be infected experimentally.

All coxsackie B viruses grow well in monkey kidney tissue cultures, while in group A, only types 7 and 9 grow well. Group A 21 virus grows in HeLa cells.

Clinical features: Coxsackieviruses produce a variety of clinical syndromes in humans ranging from trivial to fatal infections. The following types have been recognised:

1. Herpangina (vesicular pharyngitis) is a common clinical manifestation of coxsackie group A infection in children. It is a severe febrile pharyngitis, with headache, vomiting and pain in the abdomen. The characteristic lesions are small vesicles, on the fauces and posterior pharyngeal wall, that break down to form ulcers.

2. Aseptic meningitis may be caused by most group A and all group B viruses. A maculopapular rash may be present. The disease may sometimes occur as epidemics. Type A 7 had caused outbreaks of paralytic disease in Russia, Scotland and elsewhere, the virus for a time having been erroneously referred to as Poliovirus type 4.

3. Hand-Foot-and-Mouth-Disease (HFMD) was identified in 1960 as an exanthematous fever affecting mainly young children, characterized by clusters of papulovesicular lesions on the skin and oral mucosa. It occurs as sporadic cases and as outbreaks. Coxsackie A-16, 9; B 1-3 were common causative agents initially. It was a benign illness resolving in 1-2 weeks. The situation changed drastically in the 1970's with enterovirus-71 becoming a causative agent, causing extensive epidemics with serious complications like aseptic meningitis, encephalitis, flaccid paralysis, pulmonary hemorrage, with many fatalities, particularily in East Asia from Taiwan to Singapore. HFMD in now an important emerging disease.

4. Minor respiratory infections resembling common cold may be caused by A 10, 21, 24 and B3.

5. Epidemic pleurodynia or Bornholm disease (so called because it was first described on the Danish island of Bornholm) is a febrile disease with stitch-like pain in the chest and abdomen, caused by group B viruses. The disease may occur sporadically or as epidemics.

6. Myocarditis and pericarditis in the newborn, associated with high fatality may be caused by group B viruses. The disease may sometimes occur in older children and adults also.

7. Juvenile diabetes has been claimed to be associated with coxsackie B4 infection but a causal role for this virus has not been established.

8. Orchitis due to coxsackievirus has also been reported.

9. Transplacental and neonatal transmission has been demonstrated with coxsackie B viruses resulting in a serious disseminated disease that may include hepatitis, meningoencephalitis and adrenocortical involvement.

10. Type B viruses have been associated with the condition called *postviral fatigue syndrome*, but neither the condition nor the association has been clearly defined.

Laboratory diagnosis : Virus isolation from the lesions or from feces may be made by inoculation into suckling mice. Identification is by studying the histopathology in infected mice and by neutralisation tests. Due to the existence of several antigenic types, serodiagnosis is not practicable.

Epidemiology: Like other enteroviruses, coxsackieviruses inhabit the alimentary canal primarily and are spread by the fecal–oral route. Coxsackie B virus epidemics tend to occur every 2–5 years. Young infants are most commonly affected. Vaccination is not practicable as there are several serotypes and immunity is type specific.

ECHOVIRUSES

When tissue cultures became routine procedures in diagnostic virology, several cytopathogenic viruses came to be isolated from the feces of sick as well as healthy individuals. These viruses were not pathogenic for laboratory animals. They were neutralised by pooled human gamma globulin. As they could not be associated with any particular clinical disease then, they were called orphans. They have been given the descriptive designation 'enteric cytopathogenic human orphan viruses' and are generally known by the sigla 'echoviruses'. Similar 'orphan' viruses have also been isolated from many animals.

Properties of the virus: Echoviruses resemble other enteroviruses in their properties. By neutralisation tests, they have been classified into 34 serotypes. Types 10 and 28 have been removed from the group, the former becoming a reovirus and the latter a rhinovirus.

Some echoviruses (types 3, 6, 7, 11, 12, 13, 19, 20, 21, 24, 29, 30 and 33) agglutinate human erythrocytes. Hemagglutination is followed by elution, rendering the cells inagglutinable by echo or coxsackieviruses but not by myxoviruses.

Growth and host range: All echoviruses grow well in human and simian kidney cultures producing cytopathic effects. Echoviruses infect only human beings naturally. They are not pathogenic to laboratory animals though occasional strains may produce paresis on inoculation into monkeys and newborn mice.

Clinical features: Though echoviruses were originally considered orphans they have since been shown to produce a variety of disease patterns. Most infections are asymptomatic. In general, the clinical features resemble those produced by coxsackieviruses. Fever with rash and aseptic meningitis, sometimes as epidemics, can be produced by several serotypes, predominantly by types 4, 6, 9, 16, 20, 28 and 30. Echoviruses perhaps constitute the most common cause of aseptic meningitis. Echoviruses have frequently been isolated from respiratory disease in children (types 1, 11, 19, 20 and 22) and gastroenteritis (type 18), but their etiological role has not been proved. Occasional cases of paralysis and hepatic necrosis have also been reported.

Laboratory diagnosis: Feces, throat swabs or CSF may be inoculated into monkey kidney tissue cultures and virus growth detected by cytopathic changes. The large number of serotypes makes identification by neutralisation tests laborious. This may be simplified by hemagglutination and the use of serum pools for neutralisation. Serological diagnosis is not practicable except in case of epidemics where the causative serotype has been identified.

Epidemiology: Like other enteroviruses, echoviruses inhabit the alimentary tract primarily and are spread by the fecal–oral route. Epidemics may occur, especially in summer. Vaccination has not been attempted.

NEW ENTEROVIRUS TYPES

Of the new enterovirus types, 68–71, type 68 was isolated from pharyngeal secretions of children with pneumonia and bronchitis. Type 69 is not associated with any human disease. Type 70 causes acute hemorrhagic conjunctivitis. EV-71, originally isolated from cases of meningitis and encephalitis, causes many other syndromes, including HFMD.

ACUTE HEMORRHAGIC CONJUNCTIVITIS

A pandemic of acute hemorrhagic conjunctivitis, apparently arising in West Africa in 1969 spread widely involving several parts of Africa, the Middle East, India, South East Asia, Japan, England and Europe. The incubation period for this virus is about 24 hours and the symptoms are sudden swelling, congestion, watering and pain in the eyes. Subconjunctival hemorrhage is a characteristic feature. There is transient corneal involvement but recovery is usually complete in 3–7 days. Radiculomyelopathy has been reported as a complication from India. Sometimes it leads to paralysis resembling poliomyelitis.

The causative agent was identified as enterovirus type 70. It grows only on cultured human cells (human embryonic kidney or HeLa) on primary

Table 54.2 Clinical syndromes commonly caused by enteroviruses

Syndrome	Poliovirus	Coxsackie A	Coxsackie B	ECHO	New entero-virus types
Paralysis	1, 2, 3	7	–		
Aseptic meningitis	1, 2, 3	7, 9, 23	1–6	Several(2, 3, 4, 6, 7, 9, 11, 14, 16, 17, 18, 19, 25, 33)	71
Encephalitis	1, 2, 3	9	3–6	6, 9, 17, 19	71
Fever with rash	–	9, 16, 23	–	4, 6, 9, 16	–
Hand, foot and mouth disease	–	5, 10, 16	–	–	71
Herpangina	–	1–6, 8, 10	–	–	–
Upper respiratory infection	–	21	–	11, 20	–
Pneumonitis, bronchiolitis	–	–	–	–	68
Bornholm disease	–	–	1.5	–	–
Myocarditis, pericarditis	–	–	1.5	–	–
Acute hemorrhagic conjunctivitis		24	–		70

isolation, but can be adapted to grow on monkey kidney cells. Coxsackievirus type A 24 also produces the same disease. Both these viruses show intratypic antigenic differences. Over the years the condition has recurred in different parts of the world.

RHINOVIRUSES

The common cold is probably the most common infectious disease of humans. Bacteria-free filtrates of nasal secretions from patients have been shown to transmit colds to human volunteers as early as in 1914. Dochez (1938) reported similar transmission of colds to chimpanzees. From 1946, a group of workers under Andrewes had been investigating the disease using human volunteers at the Common Cold Research Unit, Salisbury, UK. The common cold virus was isolated there by Tyrrell and his colleagues (1960) by inoculating specimens into monkey kidney tissue culture incubated on roller drums at 33 °C instead of 37 °C and using a medium containing a lower bicarbonate concentration than usual. A related virus had been described earlier independently by Price and by Pelon and colleagues (1956) and named JH and 2060, respectively. This was classified as echovirus type 28. These and several similar viruses from common cold cases reported thereafter by other workers were known as common cold viruses, Salisbury viruses or muriviruses, till the name *rhinovirus* was finally applied to this group ('rhino' referring to 'nose', the organ primarily affected).

Properties of the virus: Rhinoviruses resemble other picornaviruses in size and structure. They differ from enteroviruses in being more acid labile, but more heat stable. They are inactivated below pH 6, inactivation being complete at pH 3. They are relatively stable at 20–37 °C and may remain viable on fomites for days. Some serotypes survive for one hour at 50 °C.

By neutralisation tests, they have been classified into over 100 serotypes. Immunity is type specific.

Host range and growth: Apart from humans, rhinoviruses can produce experimental infection only in chimpanzees. Related rhinoviruses have been isolated from cattle and horses but their significance in human infection is not known.

Rhinoviruses can be grown in tissue cultures of human or simian origin with cytopathic changes, if good oxygenation (achieved by rolling), low pH (around 7) and low temperature (33 °C) are provided. Depending upon growth in tissue culture, rhinoviruses were classified into three groups, H, M and O. H strains grew only in human cells, while M strains grew equally well in human and monkey cells. O strains could be grown only in nasal or tracheal ciliated epithelium. This classification is no longer in use as the growth characteristics are not stable and can be changed by adaptation.

Pathogenesis: The virus attaches to receptors on nasal ciliated epthelial cells, enters and replicates within them, spreading to other cells. The cilia and cells are damaged and the epithelium is subjected to secondary bacterial infection. Local inflammation and cytokines may be responsible for the symptoms of common cold. Interferon production occurs early and specific antibody appears in nasal secretions. Both these may help in recovery. The antibody response, both nasal and systemic, varies in intensity and duration with different strains.

Laboratory diagnosis: Isolation of the virus may be obtained from nasal or throat swabs collected early in the infection, in human cell cultures, preferably MRC5 or W138 strains. Growth as evidenced by CPE may take two weeks to appear. Due to the large number of serotypes, serology is not feasible for diagnosis.

Epidemiology: The common cold is an infectious disease transmitted by droplets. Hand-to-hand contact, followed by self-inoculation of conjunctival or nasal mucosa appears to be an important mode of transmission. The incubation period is about two days, but may be up to seven days. The duration of virus shedding is not known, though it is unlikely to be prolonged. Contrary to popular belief, there appears to be no direct relation between inclement weather and the common cold. The multiplicity of serotypes makes vaccination impossible. Moreover, the common cold is a syndrome produced not only by rhinoviruses but also by a variety of other groups such as respiratory syncytial, corona, coxsackie, echo, adeno, influenza and parainfluenza viruses. Hope of specific control therefore lies in the development of antiviral chemotherapy.

Further Reading

Cochi SI et al. 1997. Global poliomyelitis eradication initiative. *J Infect Dis* 175:S 1.

Minor P. 1998. Picornaviruses. In *Topley & Wilson's Microbiology and Microbial Infections*, Vol. 1, 9th edn. London: Arnold.

Rotbart HA (ed). 1995. *Human Enterovirus infections*. Washington DC: ASM Press.

Sabin AB. 1985. Oral poliovirus vaccine: History of development. *J Infect Dis* 151:420.

Tyrrell DAJ. 1986. Common colds. *Intervirology* 25:177.

Yin-Murphy M. 1984. Acute hemorrhagic conjunctivitis. *Progr Med Virol* 29:23.

Orthomyxovirus

The name Myxovirus was used originally for a group of enveloped RNA viruses characterised by their ability to adsorb onto mucoprotein receptors on erythrocytes, causing hemagglutination. The name referred to the affinity of the viruses to mucins (from *myxa*, meaning mucus). Included in this group were influenza, mumps, Newcastle disease and parainfluenza viruses. The subsequent recognition of important differences between influenza viruses and the other viruses in this group led to their being reclassified into two separate families – *orthomyxoviridae* consisting of the influenza viruses and *paramyxoviridae* consisting of the Newcastle disease virus, mumpsvirus, parainfluenzaviruses, measles and respiratory syncytial viruses. Table 55.1 lists the important differences between orthomyxovirus and paramyxovirus.

INFLUENZA

Influenza is an acute infectious disease of the respiratory tract which occurs in sporadic, epidemic and pandemic forms. The name 'influenza' is said to have been given by Italians during the epidemic of 1743, which they ascribed to the malevolent influence of the heavenly bodies or of inclement weather. The modern history of the disease may be considered to date from the pandemic of 1889–1890, during which Pfeiffer isolated *Haemophilus influenzae* and claimed that it was the causative agent. The most severe pandemic occurred in 1918–1919, when it was shown that Pfeiffer's bacillus was not the primary cause of the disease, though it might act as a secondary invader. The isolation of the influenza virus in 1933 by Smith, Andrewes and Laidlaw was a milestone in the development of medical virology. They reproduced the disease in ferrets by intranasal inoculation with bacteria-free filtrates of nasopharyngeal secretions from patients. Burnet (1935) developed chick embryo techniques for the propagation of the virus.

A notable advance was the independent

Table 55.1 Distinguishing features of orthomyxovirus and paramyxovirus

Property	Orthomyxovirus	Paramyxovirus
Size of virion	80–120 nm	100–300 nm
Shape	Spherical; filaments in fresh isolates	Pleomorphic
Genome	Segmented; eight pieces of RNA	Single linear molecule of RNA
Diameter of nucleocapsid	9 nm	18 nm
Site of synthesis of ribonucleoprotein	Nucleus	Cytoplasm
Genetic reassortment	Common	Absent
RNA-dependent RNA synthesis	Required for multiplication	Not required
Effect of Actinomycin D	Inhibits multiplication	Does not inhibit
Antigenic stability	Variable	Stable
Hemolysin	Absent	Present

discovery by Hirst, and by McClelland and Hare (1941) that influenza viruses agglutinate fowl erythrocytes. The property of hemagglutination was found to be a common feature of many other viruses.

Francis and Magill (1940) independently isolated a serotype of influenza virus which was antigenically unrelated to the strains known till then. This was designated influenza virus type B, to distinguish it from the original serotype, which was named type A. Taylor (1949) isolated the third serotype of influenza virus, type C. The classification of influenza viruses into the three serotypes, A, B and C, is based on the antigenic nature of the 'internal' or ribonucleoprotein and the matrix (M) protein antigens.

Influenza occurs also in animals and birds in nature. Indeed, the avian influenza virus was demonstrated as early as in 1901, when Centanni and Avonuzzi showed that fowl plague was a viral disease. However, as fowl plague (avian influenza) is a septicemia, so different clinically from human influenza, the association between the two remained unknown till 1955, when Schaefer demonstrated that the fowl plague virus was antigenically related to type A influenza virus. Shope (1931) isolated the swine influenza virus. Not only did the swine disease resemble human influenza clinically but there was also epidemiological association between the two. It was widely held that the virus spread to swine from man at the time of the 1918 pandemic. Influenza viruses have also been isolated from horses, whales and seals.

Birds, particularly aquatic birds, appear to be the primary reservoir of influenza viruses and natural infection has been identified in several avian species. In birds it is usually an asymptomatic intestinal infection. The cloaca of healthy wild birds is the best source for isolation of avian influenza viruses. All isolates from nonhuman hosts belong to type A. Influenza virus types B and C appear to be exclusively human viruses and natural infection with them has not been identified in animals or birds. Ordinarily, nonhuman influenza viruses do not cause human infection. But they may play an important role in the emergence of pandemic influenza.

INFLUENZA VIRUSES

Morphology: The influenza virus is typically spherical, with a diameter of 80–120 nm but pleomorphism is common. Filamentous forms, upto several micrometres in length and readily visible under the dark ground microscope, are frequent in freshly isolated strains.

The virus core consists of ribonucleoprotein in helical symmetry. The negative sense single stranded RNA genome is segmented and exists as eight pieces. Also present is a viral RNA-dependent RNA polymerase which is essential for transcription of the viral RNA in infected host cells. The nucleocapsid is surrounded by an envelope, which has an inner membrane protein layer and an outer lipid layer. The membrane protein is also known as the matrix or 'M protein' composed of 2 components, M1 and M2. The protein part of the envelope is virus coded but the lipid layer is derived from the modified host cell membrane, during the process of replication by budding. Projecting from the envelope are two types of spikes (peplomers): *hemagglutinin* spikes which are triangular in cross section and the mushroom shaped *neuraminidase* peplomers which are less numerous (Fig. 55.1).

Resistance: The virus is inactivated by heating at 50 °C for 30 minutes. It remains viable at 0–4 °C for about a week. It can be preserved for years at −70 °C or by freeze drying. The virus survives slow drying and may remain viable on fomites such as blankets for about two weeks. Ether, formaldehyde, phenol, salts of heavy metals and many other chemical disinfectants destroy infectivity. Iodine is particularly effective.

Hemagglutinating, enzymic and complement-fixing activities of the virus are more stable than infectivity.

Hemagglutination: Hemagglutination is an important characteristic of influenza viruses. When mixed with a suspension of fowl erythrocytes, the virus is adsorbed onto the mucoprotein receptors on the cell surface. The virus links together adjacent cells producing hemagglutination. The hemagglutinin peplomers on the viral surface are responsible for this activity. Hemagglutination is followed after a time by the detachment of the virus from the cell surface, reversing the hemagglutination. This process is known as *elution* and is caused by the enzyme neuraminidase (sialidase) present on the viral surface. The enzyme acts on the cell receptor, destroying it by splitting off N-acetylneuraminic acid from it.

Virus particles which have eluted from red cells are still capable of agglutinating fresh red cells but red cells that have been acted on by the virus are not susceptible to agglutination by the same strain of the virus. Such red cells may, however, be agglutinated by other myxoviruses. The inability of these red cells to be reagglutinated by the same virus is due to the destruction of the specific cell receptors by the initial treatment with the virus. Myxoviruses can be arranged in a series in which the treatment of red cells with any one virus removes the receptors for that virus and the preceding viruses but not for the viruses later in the series. This is called the 'receptor gradient'. For myxoviruses in general, the gradient is mumps, Newcastle disease virus and influenza, in that order.

Neuraminidase is an isoenzyme and different serotypes of influenza virus possess enzymes that vary in their characteristics such as antigenic structure, temperature optima and heat stability. Neuraminidases are also present in bacteria and in the cells of higher organisms. Culture filtrates of *V. cholerae* are rich in neuraminidase activity and red cells pretreated with them are resistant to hemagglutination by influenza viruses. The culture filtrate was therefore called the receptor destroying enzyme (RDE) of *V. cholerae*.

Hemagglutination takes place within a wide range of temperature, from 0 °C to 37 °C. Influenza viruses vary in their ability to agglutinate red cells

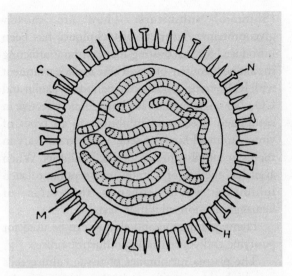

Fig. 55.1 Diagrammatic representation of influenza virus. H. haemagglutinin. N. neuraminidase. C. core containing eight strands of RNA. M. membrane protein.

of different species. In general, influenza virus types A and B agglutinate erythrocytes of fowl, human, guinea pig and some other species. Influenza virus type C agglutinates red cells of fowl only, at 4 °C.

Hemagglutination provides a convenient method for the detection and titration of the influenza virus in egg and other culture fluids. The highest dilution of the virus suspension that produces agglutination of a fixed quantity of cells is known as its hemagglutination (HA) titre. Hemagglutinin is more resistant to physical and chemical agents than infectivity. Therefore, hemagglutination can be used for the titration of the inactivated influenza virus also, as, for example, in the standardisation of killed influenza virus vaccines.

Hemagglutination inhibition (HI) offers a convenient method for the detection and quantitation of the antibody to the virus. A disadvantage of this serological technique is the frequent presence in sera of certain substances that cause nonspecific inhibition of hemagglutination. Different kinds of nonspecific inhibitors have been identified in sera and have been given names such as *alpha* (Francis), *beta* (Chu) and *gamma*

(Shimojo) inhibitors. They are mostly glycoproteins. A variety of techniques has been introduced for inactivating them without affecting the antibody content of sera. These include treatment with RDE, trypsin, potassium periodate, kaolin and CO_2. No single method has been found effective in completely destroying inhibitors to all types of viruses from all kinds of sera. Virus strains vary in their susceptibility to nonspecific inhibitors. When available, the use of a strain insusceptible to such inhibitors would enhance the value of hemagglutination inhibition tests.

Hemagglutination and elution can be used for purifying and concentrating influenza viruses.

The plasma membranes of tissue culture cells in which the virus is multiplying contain the hemagglutinin. Therefore, red cells are adsorbed onto the surface of such cells. This is the basis of *hemadsorption*, a technique by which the growth of the influenza virus in cell cultures can be identified.

Antigenic structure: The antigens of the influenza virus can be classified as the internal antigens and the surface antigens. The internal antigen is the ribonucleoprotein and is hence called the RNP antigen. Because it is found free in infected tissues and occurs in the supernatant when the virus containing fluid is centrifuged, it was also called the 'soluble' (S) antigen. The RNP antigen can be demonstrated by complement fixation and immunoprecipitation tests. It is type specific and based on its nature, influenza viruses are classified into types A, B and C. The RNP antigens of types A, B and C are distinct but all strains of any one type possess the same antigen. The RNP antigen is stable and does not exhibit any significant antigenic variation. Anti-RNP antibody develops after infection but not following killed vaccines.

Like the RNP antigen, the M protein antigen is also type-specific and distinct for A, B and C types of influenza viruses. The envelope lipid antigen is host-specific and is determined by the species in which virus replication takes place.

The term 'viral' or V antigen was formerly used to describe the surface antigen of the influenza virus. Antibodies to the V antigen were estimated by complement fixation. The V antigen is actually composed of at least two virus coded proteins, the hemagglutinin and the neuraminidase. The two proteins have been isolated and purified.

Hemagglutinin is a glycoprotein composed of two polypeptides, HA I and HA 2. It is responsible for hemagglutination and hemadsorption. It enables the virus to adsorb to mucoprotein receptors on red cells as well as on respiratory epithelial cells. Antihemagglutinin antibodies are produced following infection and immunisation. This antibody is protective by preventing adsorption of the virus to cells. The hemagglutinin is a strain specific antigen and is capable of great variation. Fifteen distinct HA subtypes, named H 1 to H 15 have been identified in avian influenza viruses, but only four of them have been found in human isolates so far.

Neuraminidase is a glycoprotein enzyme which destroys cell receptors by hydrolytic cleavage. The antineuraminidase antibody is formed following infection and immunisation. It is not as effective in protection as the antihemagglutinin antibody. It does not prevent the adsorption of virus onto cells but can inhibit the release and spread of progeny virions and may thus contribute to limiting the infection. It is a strain specific antigen and exhibits variation. Nine different subtypes have been identified (N 1–N 9).

Antigenic variation: A unique feature of the influenza virus is its ability to undergo antigenic variation. This is of great importance in the epidemiology of the disease. Antigenic variability is highest in influenza virus type A and less in type B, while it has not been demonstrated in type C.

The internal RNP antigen and M protein antigen are stable but both the surface antigens, hemagglutinin and neuraminidase, undergo independent antigenic variations, which may be of two types—*antigenic drift* or *antigenic shift*. The gradual sequential change in antigenic structure occurring regularly at frequent intervals is known as antigenic drift. Here, the new antigens, though different from the previous antigens, are yet related to them, so that they react with antisera to the predecessor virus strains, to varying degrees. Antigenic drift is due to mutation and selection, the process being influenced by the presence of antibodies to the predecessor strains in the host population. Antigenic drift accounts for the periodical epidemics of influenza.

Antigenic shift, on the other hand, is an abrupt, drastic, discontinuous variation in the antigenic structure, resulting in a novel virus strain unrelated antigenically to predecessor strains. Such changes may involve hemagglutinin, neuraminidase or both. Antibodies to predecessor viruses do not neutralise the new variants and can, therefore, spread widely in the population causing major epidemics or pandemics. The changes involved in antigenic shift are too extensive to be accounted for by mutation.

Antigenic classification: Influenza virus type A strains can be classified into subtypes based on variations in their surface antigens. Originally only variations in the hemagglutinin were studied, and subtyping depended only on antigenic shifts occurring in the hemagglutinin. The earliest human isolates (WS, PR8 and related strains) were designated A0. The related swine influenza virus isolated in 1931 was called Asw. In 1946, the hemagglutinin underwent a major change and the new strains (CAM, FMI and others) were named A1 or A′ (A prime). In 1957, new pandemic strains originated in Asia. These were called the A2 (Asian) strains. The next major change occurred in 1968 with the emergence of the A2 (Hong Kong) subtype. Within each of these subtypes, the strains have shown a gradual antigenic drift.

With the recognition that viral neuraminidase also undergoes independent antigenic variation, a new system of classification was proposed by the WHO in 1971, which took into account the nature of both the surface antigens. According to this, the hemagglutinins of A0, A1, A2 (Asian) and A2 (Hong Kong) were named H0, H1, H2 and H3, respectively. This classification was again modified by the WHO by grouping together Hsw, H0 and H1 under the designation H1. The neuraminidases of these viruses were of two subtypes – the subtype N1 occurring in A0 and A1 strains, and subtype N2 in A2 (Asian) and A2 (Hong Kong) strains. The complete designation of a strain will include the type, place of origin, serial number and year of isolation followed by the antigenic subtypes of the hemagglutinin and neuraminidase in parenthesis, for example A/Hong Kong/1/68(H3N2).

Influenza virus type B also exhibits antigenic variation but the changes have not been marked enough for the subtypes to be delineated. The type C virus does not undergo any significant antigenic variation.

P-Q-R variation: Influenza virus strains belonging to the same subtype – even strains isolated during the course of a single outbreak – may behave differently in neutralisation tests with antisera. Van der Veen and Mulder called this the *P-Q-R variation*. Strains in the P phase were neutralised by the homologous antiserum in high titres and by heterologous antiserum in low titres. Strains in the Q phase were neutralised poorly by either homologous or heterologous sera. R phase strains were neutralised by both homologous and heterologous sera in high titres. The P-Q-R variation appears to be due to the rearrangement of antigenic determinants on the surface of the virion. In the P phase, the dominant antigen is on the surface so that it reacts with the specific antibody with high avidity, while in the Q phase the dominant antigen is apparently buried under the surface and hence inaccessible to the antibody. The P-Q-R phases are interconvertible by passaging the virus in the presence of the appropriate antiserum.

O-D variation: Burnet and Bull (1943) observed that influenza virus type A underwent certain changes when serially passaged in eggs.

They called this the O-D variation. The fresh isolate was said to be in the 'Original' (O) phase and the passaged virus in the 'Derived' (D) phase. The O phase virus grew well in the amniotic cavity of chick embryos but only poorly or not at all in the allantoic cavity. It agglutinated mammalian erythrocytes (guineapig and human) to a high titre and fowl erythrocytes only weakly or not at all. Filamentous forms were common. It was infectious for humans. The D phase virus, on the other hand, grew equally well in the amniotic and allantoic cavities and agglutinated fowl erythrocytes as well as, or better than mammalian cells, showed no filamentous forms and was relatively avirulent for human beings. The O-D variation was considered a result of mutation.

Host range: The human influenza virus can cause experimental infection in a number of animal species. In most, the infection is asymptomatic, though virus shedding occurs from the respiratory tract for a few days. Intranasal inoculation in ferrets produces an acute respiratory disease. This was the manner in which the influenza virus was first isolated. Strains vary considerably in virulence to ferrets, some producing severe febrile disease and others only asymptomatic infection. The virus can be 'adapted' by serial intranasal passage in mice to produce fatal pulmonary infection. Neurotropic mutants have been isolated which regularly produce fatal encephalitis after intracerebral inoculation in mice.

The virus grows well in the amniotic cavity of chick embryos. After a few egg passages, the virus grows well in the allantoic cavity also, except for the type C virus which does not generally grow in the allantoic cavity. The influenza virus does not damage chick embryos, which may hatch out normally. Virus growth is detected by the appearance of hemagglutinin in the allantoic and amniotic fluids.

The virus grows in primary monkey kidney cell cultures, as well as in some continuous cell lines. Cytopathic effects are not prominent and virus growth is detected by hemadsorption or demonstration of hemagglutinin in the culture fluid.

When passaged serially in eggs, using as inocula undiluted infected allantoic fluid, the progeny virus will show high hemagglutinin titres, but low infectivity. This has been called the Von Magnus phenomenon and is due to the formation of incomplete virus particles lacking nucleic acid.

Pathogenesis: The route of entry is the respiratory tract. In experimental infection in volunteers, very small doses (approximately three viable particles) can initiate infection when given as aerosols. Larger doses are required when infection is by intranasal instillation. The viral neuraminidase facilitates infection by reducing the viscosity of the mucus film lining the respiratory tract and exposing the cell surface receptors for virus adsorption. The ciliated cells of the respiratory tract are the main sites of viral infection. These cells are damaged and shed, laying bare the basal cells in the trachea and bronchi. This renders the respiratory tract highly vulnerable to bacterial invasion. Viral pneumonia, seen only in the more severe cases, is associated with hyperemia and thickening of the alveolar walls, interstitial infiltration with leucocytes, capillary thrombosis and leucocytic exudation. In some cases, a hyaline membrane is formed, occupying the alveolar ducts and alveoli. In the late stages, there is infiltration with macrophages which engulf and remove desquamated alveolar cells.

The disease is ordinarily confined to the respiratory tract. Very rarely had the virus been isolated from the spleen, liver, kidneys and other organs during the 1957 pandemic.

Clinical features: The incubation period is 1–3 days. The disease varies in severity from a mild coryza to fulminating and rapidly fatal pneumonia. Most infections are subclinical. In the typical clinical disease, the onset is abrupt, with fever, headache and generalised myalgia. Respiratory symptoms are prominent and severe prostration is common. Abdominal pain and vomiting may occur, especially in type B infection in children, which may even present as an acute abdominal emergency. The uncomplicated disease resolves within about seven days.

The most important complication is pneumonia, which is mainly due to bacterial superinfection or, rarely, caused by the virus itself. Cardiac complications, such as congestive failure or myocarditis and neurological involvement, such as encephalitis, may occur rarely.

Influenza, particularly infection with type B, has been associated with Reye's syndrome. It especially affects young children and is characterised by acute degenerative changes in the brain, liver and kidneys. Type B infections may sometimes cause gastrointestinal symptoms (gastric flu).

Laboratory diagnosis: 1. *Demonstration of the virus antigen:* Rapid diagnosis of influenza may be made by demonstration of the virus antigen on the surface of the nasopharyngeal cells by immunofluorescence. Detection of the viral RNA by reverse transcriptase polymerase chain reaction is extremely sensitive, but is of limited availability.

2. *Isolation of the virus:* Virus isolation is obtained readily from patients during the first two or three days of the illness but less often in later stages. Throat garglings are collected using broth saline or other suitable buffered salt solution. If the specimen is not processed immediately, it should be stored at 4 °C, or if the delay is long, at –70 °C. The specimen should be treated with antibiotics to destroy bacteria. Isolation may be made in eggs or in monkey kidney cell culture.

The material is inoculated into the amniotic cavity of 11–13 day old eggs, using at least six eggs per specimen. After incubation at 35 °C for three days, the eggs are chilled and the amniotic and allantoic fluids harvested separately. The fluids are tested for hemagglutination using guineapig and fowl cells in parallel, at room temperature and at 4 °C. Some strains of the influenza virus type A agglutinate only guineapig cells on initial isolation. The type B virus agglutinates both cells, while type

C strains agglutinate only fowl cells at with antisera to types A, B and C. Subtype identification is made by hemagglutination inhibition test. Some of the recent type A strains can be isolated by direct allantoic inoculation of the clinical specimen into 9–11 day old eggs. However, type B and C viruses will be missed if only allantoic inoculation is used.

Inoculation into monkey kidney or other suitable continuous cell cultures, such as baboon kidney, is the preferred method where the facility is available. Inoculated cell cultures are incubated without serum, and in the presence of trypsin, which increases sensitivity of isolation. Incubation at 33 °C in roller drums is recommended. Virus growth can be identified by hemadsorption with human O group, fowl or guineapig erythrocytes. Rapid results can be obtained by demonstrating virus antigen in infected cell cultures by immunofluorescence.

3. *Serology:* Complement fixation and hemagglutination inhibition tests are employed for the serological diagnosis of influenza. It is essential to examine paired sera in parallel, to demonstrate rise in titre of antibodies.

Complement fixation tests with the RNP antigen of influenza virus types A, B and C are very useful as the antibodies are formed during infection only, and not following immunisation with inactivated vaccines. Complement fixation can also be done using V antigens for the demonstration of strain-specific antibodies. Because of its complexity, CF tests are now used only rarely.

Hemagglutination inhibition is a convenient and sensitive test for the serological diagnosis of influenza. However, it has some disadvantages. As the antihemaglutinin antibodies are subtype-specific, it is necessary to use as antigen the strain currently causing infection. The major drawback is the frequent presence in the sera of nonspecific inhibitors of hemagglutination. The sera, suitably treated for the removal of nonspecific inhibitors, are diluted serially in hemagglutination plates and the influenza virus suspension containing 4 HA units added to each cup. Fowl red cells are then added.

The highest dilution of serum that inhibits hemagglutination is its HI titre.

It is possible to estimate the neuraminidase antibody by enzyme neutralisation tests, but this is too cumbersome for routine use.

Radial immunodiffusion tests in agarose gel have been described for the identification of antibodies to the RNP antigen, hemagglutinin and neuraminidase. However, these are more useful as screening tests than for routine diagnosis.

Immunity: An attack of influenza confers protection effective for about one or two years. The apparent short duration of immunity is due to the antigenic variation that the virus undergoes frequently. Following infection and immunisation, circulating antibodies are formed against the various antigens of the virus. However, it is the local concentration of antihemagglutinin and, to a smaller extent, of antineuraminidase antibodies (mainly IgA) in the respiratory tract that is more relevant in protection.

When an individual experiences repeated infections with different antigenic variants of influenza virus type A, he responds by forming antibodies not only against each infecting strain but also against the strain that he first came into contact with. The dominant antibody response will be against the strain that caused the earliest infection. This phenomenon has been called the doctrine of 'original antigenic sin'.

Influenza virus infection induces cell mediated immunity also but its role in protection has not been clarified.

Epidemiology: Influenza occurs sporadically, as epidemics or in pandemic form. The source of infection is an infected individual. The virus is shed in the respiratory secretions shortly before the onset of illness and for 3–4 days thereafter. Subclinical infections are common. Influenza virus type C is endemic throughout the world and causes very mild or unapparent infections. Type B strains cause sporadic as well as epidemic influenza, while type A strains can cause pandemics as well. Sporadic influenza is of little public health importance as it is a mild self-limited condition. Epidemic influenza is important in temperate regions where it strikes during the winter months, causing considerable mortality in the aged and in those with cardiopulmonary diseases. In the tropics, epidemic influenza does not exhibit a winter prevalence, though it tends to occur frequently in the monsoon season.

What makes influenza an important and challenging disease is its propensity for causing pandemics. It is for this reason that worldwide surveillance is maintained on influenza, under the auspices of the WHO. Influenza pandemics have been recorded at irregular intervals from 1173. Pandemics of modern times date from 1889. The most severe pandemic in recorded history occurred in 1918–1919 ('Spanish flu'), during which over 200 million people were affected and more than 20 million perished. India suffered the most, with some 10 million deaths. An unusual feature of this pandemic was the very high rate of mortality among

Table 55.2 Classification and nomenclature of influenza virus A subtypes

Old designation	Current classification	1971 classification	Reference strains
A swine		HSW N1	A/Swine/Wisconsin/15/30
A0 ⎫	H1 N1	H0 N1	A/PR/8/34
A1 ⎭		H1 N1	A/FM/1/4
A2	H2 N2	H2 N2	A/Singapore/1/57
A2 (Hong Kong)	H3 N2	H3 N2	A/Hong Kong/1/68

young adults. The next pandemic occurred in 1957 when the 'Asian strain' H2N2 originated in China and spread throughout the world within a short period. However, the mortality rate was low though it caused widespread morbidity. The Hong Kong H3N2 strain appearing in 1968 also caused a pandemic but it was much less severe.

In 1977, epidemic influenza appeared in China and then in Russia (hence called the 'red flu' facetiously). The disease was mainly confined to the under-20 age group. The isolate was identified as H1N1 virus, antigenically very close to the strains prevalent from 1946 to 1957. This H1N1 virus has spread through most of the world, and with H3N2 virus, currently causes human influenza.

The reason why the virus is able to cause epidemics and pandemics is its ability to undergo antigenic variations. Antigenic drift, resulting from mutation and selection, is responsible for the epidemics. It has been shown experimentally that passaging the virus in the presence of antiserum leads to the appearance of such mutants. Pandemics are caused by a virus strain that has undergone antigenic shift. The variation in such instances is so marked and involves different polypeptides simultaneously that mutation cannot explain it. It is now held that pandemic strains originate from some animal or avian reservoir, either spreading to humans directly by host range mutation, or as a result of recombination between human and nonhuman strains. Hybrids can be produced by growing human and nonhuman strains together in eggs. Recombinants can also be obtained from experimental animals exposed to mixed infection. It has been shown by genetic studies that both the 1957 Asian virus and the 1968 Hong Kong virus were such recombinant hybrids.

The mere appearance of a new or hybrid strain may not lead to a pandemic. For this, the new strain should be capable of spreading rapidly among people. In fact there have been several instances when new hybrids have been detected, which failed to spread. The swine flu virus H1N1 caused a localised outbreak in a military camp in New Jersey, USA in 1976, leading to much anxiety and panic vaccination, but it did not spread. Though a few similar incidents have occurred since then, what raised a real threat of a new pandemic was the outbreak in Hong Kong of chicken flu in 1997 with a new strain of H5N1 influenza viurus, which caused 18 confirmed human cases with six deaths. However, all human cases were shown to have spread directly from chickens, without any transmission from person to person. Immediate containment measures and the slaughter of all (over 1.6 million) chickens in Hong Kong stopped the danger before the strain developed person to person transmissibility, which could have initiated a pandemic. This incident indicated the value of influenza surveillance and the potential danger from avian strains.

It is now known that wild aquatic birds carry the full repertoire of genes of all influenza strains, including old human pandemic strains, and that the viruses do not cause any disease in them or undergo any mutational changes. Birds shed the viruses abundantly in feces, which contaminate lakes and ponds. In cold climates as in Canada, the viruses persist in such waters for long periods and can readily be isolated from them. Domestic birds like ducks can get infected from wild birds and carry the infection to pigs, which may be an important link in the chain, as they are susceptible to infection by both human and avian influenza strains. Recombination may take place in pigs and such hybrid strains may lead to human infection with potential pandemic spread. The postulated role of ducks and pigs in the development of new hybrids explains why pandemic strains tend to originate in China where millions of birds, pigs and people live closely together. The reappearance of old strains, like the H1N1 in 1977 may have been from an avian reservoir of strains. Similarly, it is possible that an old pandemic strain present in wild birds may suddenly reappear. If this hypothesis is true, it would be prudent to keep wild and domestic birds separate, and also to keep pigs away from them. The practice of keeping several species of birds along with chickens in live bird markets is potentially dangerous.

A unique feature of influenza epidemiology was that once an antigenic variant emerged, it displaced completely the pre-existing strain. Thus when A1 (HINI) strains arose in 1946–47, they became the only viruses causing human disease, and the previous A0 (H0NI) strains disappeared completely. The A1 strains were displaced by Asian (H2N2) strains in 1957 and they, in turn, by the A2 Hong Kong (H3N2) strains in 1968. However, this rule has not been observed in recent years. Even after the re-emergence and wide dissemination of the HINI strain in 1977, the A2 Hong Kong H3N2 strains continue to be prevalent. The reason for this coexistence is not known.

There is considerable evidence to suggest that there occurs an orderly recycling of the virus subtypes at least with regard to their hemagglutinin (H) antigen. Seroepidemiological (seroarcheological) studies indicate that the severe pandemic of 1889 was caused by a virus with the antigenic structure H2N8 and that this was followed in 1900 by the subtype H3N8 which led to a moderate pandemic. In 1918 came the most severe of all pandemics, caused by the 'Swine type' H1N1 (formerly Hsw NI) virus. Mild epidemics occurred around 1933 and 1946 associated with minor variations in the H antigen (from Hsw to HO in 1933, HO to H1 in 1946). The next severe pandemic came in 1957 with the H2N2 (Asian) subtype. This was followed in 1968 by the H3N2 (Hong Kong) virus leading to a moderate pandemic. The year 1977 saw the reappearance of the H1N1 virus. Thus the sequence of variation in the H antigen has been H2→ H3→ H1→ H2→ H3→ H1 from 1889 to the present time (Table 55.3). From 1977, both H3N2 and H1N1 viruses have been circulating together. Table 55.3 lists the sequence of appearance of these various subtypes.

Table 55.3 Calendar of appearance of influenza A virus subtypes (from 1889)

(Data before 1933 based on 'Seroarcheology')

Date	Antigenic subtype	Remarks
1889–1900	H2 N8?	Pandemic and epidemics
1900–1910	H3 N8	Extensive epidemics
1918–1933	H1 N1 (former Hsw N1)	'Spanish flu'. The most severe pandemic recorded; Heavy mortality.
1933–1946	H1 N1 (former H0N1)	Discovery of influenza virus (WS strain–1933);Epidemics of 'A0' strains
1946–1957	H1 N1	Epidemics of ' A1' strains
1957–1968	H2 N2	Extensive pandemics of 'Asian flu' formerly called A2 (Asian) strain, low mortality.
1968 to the present time	H3 N2	Moderate pandemic of 'Hong Kong flu' formerly called A2 time (Hong Kong) strains, very low mortality.
1977 to the present time	H1 N1	Re-emergence of former A1 strains. First appeared in Russia and China ('Red flu'); Mild pandemic, very low mortality.

Prophylaxis: Influenza vaccines have been in use for many decades. The original vaccines consisted of the virus grown in the allantoic cavity of eggs, partially purified, and inactivated with formalin. Due to the presence of egg protein in it, this vaccine may cause reactions in allergic individuals. The whole virus vaccine induces fever and local pain. 'Subunit' vaccines have been introduced to minimise toxic reactions. The purified virus is disrupted by treatment with detergents so that the vaccine contains the immunogenic hemagglutinin and neuraminidase subunits.

The major difficulty in the immunoprophylaxis of influenza is the frequent change in the antigenic make-up of the virus. Vaccines cannot be made in bulk and stockpiled, as the appearance of a new variant will make the old vaccine obsolete. In cold countries, where it is necessary to protect old persons and other high risk individuals, the practice is to immunise them with a vaccine containing the latest strains of type A and B viruses.

The most important indication for immunoprophylaxis is when a pandemic is threatened by a new virus. Here, the time taken for the manufacture of the vaccine with the new variant is crucial, as the virus is likely to spread fast and infect whole populations before the vaccine becomes available. Moreover, most fresh isolates do not grow well in eggs till they are passaged serially. To overcome these hurdles, the recombinant vaccine has been introduced. A recombinant possesses the growth characters of old established strains and carries the surface antigens of the new variant. The recombinant will grow well in eggs, facilitating vaccine manufacture.

While killed vaccines induce the formation of circulating antibodies, they do not lead to any local protection in the respiratory tract. The level of antibodies on the respiratory mucosa is only a fraction of the serum level. It is in order to afford specific local immunisation that live vaccines have been employed. The earliest live vaccine was the virus attenuated by repeated egg passage. It was administered by intranasal instillation. However, it sometimes gave rise to clinical disease, especially in children. Another approach to live vaccine is the use of temperature sensitive mutants. Mutants can be readily isolated which are able to grow at the lower temperature of the nasopharyngeal mucosa (32–34 °C) but not in the lungs at 37 °C. Such ts mutants are avirulent. Recombinant live vaccines may be obtained by hybridisation between the ts mutants of established strains and a new antigenic variant.

Chemoprophylaxis has been reported to be successful with the antiviral drugs amantadine and rimantadine which block the viral M2 protein which functions as an ion channel. These act only with type A virus and not with type B, which lacks the M2 components.

Treatment: Amantadine and rimantadine are useful in the treatment of influenza. They reduce the average duration of the disease and cause symptomatic improvement, though virus shedding and antibody response are not affected. Resistance to these drugs develops rapidly.

Zanamivir and Oseltamivir, new drugs designed to block viral neuraminidase have been found effective in the treatment and prevention of influenza, when administered as a nasal spray.

Further Reading

Murphy BR and RG Webster 1996. *Orthomyxoviruses*. In Fields, BN et al (eds.) *Fields Virology*. New York: Raven Press.
Nicholson KG et al. 1998. *Textbook of Influenza*. London: Blackwell Science.
Richman DD et al. 1997. *Clinical Virology*, Churchill Livingstone.
Webster RG. 1992. Evolution and ecology of influenza A viruses. *Microbiol Rev.* 56:152.
Webster RG. 1998. Influenza, an emerging disease. *Emerging Infectious Diseases.* 4(1):436.

56 Paramyxoviruses

The family Paramyxoviridae contains important pathogens of infants and children, responsible for a major part of acute respiratory infections (respiratory syncytial virus and parainfluenza viruses) and also for two of the most contagious diseases of childhood (measles and mumps). Though much less common, infections may also occur in adults.

Paramyxoviruses resemble orthomyxoviruses in morphology but are larger and more pleomorphic. They are roughly spherical in shape and range in size from 100 to 300 nm, sometimes with long filaments and giant forms of upto 800 nm. The helical nucleocapsid is much wider than in orthomyxoviruses, with a diameter of 18 nm (except in *Pneumovirus* where it is 13 nm). The genome is a molecule of linear single stranded RNA. Unlike the orthomyxoviruses, in which the segmented nature of the genome facilitates genomic reassortments and antigenic variation so typical of influenza viruses, the paramyxoviruses with their unsegmented genome do not undergo genetic recombinations or antigenic variations. Hence all paramyxoviruses are antigenically stable.

The nucleocapsid is surrounded by a lipid envelope which has the matrix (M) protein at its base and two types of transmembrane glycoprotein spikes at the surface. The longer spike is the hemagglutinin (H), which may also possess neuraminidase (N) activity and is hence known as H or HN protein. It is responsible for adsorption of the virus to the host cell surface. The second spike is the F (fusion) protein, responsible for fusion of the viral envelope with the plasma membrane of the host cells, which is the essential early step for infection. It also brings about cell-to-cell fusion, causing large giant cells or syncytia, which are characteristic of paramyxovirus infections. The F protein also mediates the hemolytic activity of paramyxoviruses.

The family Paramyxoviridae is divided into four genera—*Rubulavirus Parainfluenzavirus, Morbillivirus* and *Pneumovirus* (Table 56.1).

RUBULAVIRUS

MUMPS VIRUS (GENUS RUBULAVIRUS)

Mumps is an acute infectious disease commonly affecting children and characterised by nonsuppurative enlargement of the parotid glands. As epidemic parotitis, it had been described by Hippocrates in the fifth century BC. The viral etiology of mumps was demonstrated by Johnson and Goodpasture (1934) by its experimental transmission to monkeys. Habel in 1945 cultivated the virus in embryonated eggs. In 1955, Henle and Deinhardt grew it in tissue culture.

Properties: The mumps virus is a typical paramyxovirus possessing both HN and F proteins. It agglutinates the erythrocytes of fowl, guineapig, humans and many other species. Hemagglutination is followed by hemolysis and elution at 37 °C. The virus can be grown in chick embryos – in the amniotic cavity for primary isolation and the allantoic cavity after adaptation. Eggs are inoculated at 6–8 days and incubated at 35 °C for five days before harvesting.

Cell cultures are better suited for isolation – primary monkey kidney being the preferred cell.

Table 56.1 Properties of Genera in the Family Paramyxoviridae

Property	Genus			
	Parainfluenzavirus	Mumps	Morbillivirus	Pneumovirus
Human viruses	Parainfluenza 1-4	Mumps	Measles	Respiratory syncytial virus
Diameter of nucleocapsid(nm)	18	18	18	13
Fusion (F) protein	+	+	+	+
Hemolysin	+	+	+	-
Hemagglutinin/Hemadsorption	+	+	+	-
Neuraminidase	+	+	-	-
Intracellular inclusions in cytoplasm (C)/ nucleus (N)	C	C	N, C	C

The cytopathic effect is slow and consists of syncytium formation and the presence of acidophilic cytoplasmic inclusions. Growth is best identified by hemadsorption.

The mumps virus is labile, being rapidly inactivated at room temperature or by exposure to formaldehyde, ether or ultraviolet light. It can be preserved at −70 °C or by lyophilisation.

The mumps virus is antigenically stable and only one serotype exists. Two complement fixing antigens can be recognised, as in influenza viruses—the soluble (S) antigen and the 'viral' (V) antigen.

Clinical features: Infection is acquired by inhalation, and probably also through the conjunctiva. The virus replicates in the upper respiratory tract and cervical lymph nodes and is disseminated through the bloodstream to various organs. The incubation period is long, about 12–25 days.

Parotid swelling is usually the first sign of illness though it may sometimes be preceded by prodromal malaise. Parotid swelling is unilateral to start with but may become bilateral. It is accompanied by fever, local pain and tenderness but the skin over the gland is not warm or erythematous. Parotitis is nonsuppurative and usually resolves within a week. However, involvement of the extraparotid sites may be more serious. Such involvement may sometimes occur even in the absence of parotitis.

Epididymo-orchitis is a complication seen in about a third of postpubertal male patients. The testis becomes swollen and acutely painful, with accompanying fever and chills. Orchitis is usually unilateral but when it is bilateral and followed by testicular atrophy, sterility or low sperm counts may result.

The central nervous system is involved in about 60 per cent of cases, as indicated by pleocytosis in the CSF but only about 10 per cent show symptoms of meningitis. Mumps has been reported to cause about 10–15 per cent of cases of 'aseptic meningitis'. Mumps meningitis and meningoencephalitis usually resolve without sequelae but deafness may sometimes result. Mumps meningitis may occasionally occur in the absence of parotitis, when diagnosis rests solely on laboratory evidence. The virus can be grown readily from the CSF in the early phase of meningitis.

Other less common complications are arthritis, oophoritis, nephritis, pancreatitis, thyroiditis and myocarditis.

Epidemiology: Mumps is endemic worldwide but has become less common in the advanced nations due to immunisation. It often occurs as epidemics in children 5–15 years of age, and also in young people living in groups such as in army camps. Household spread is common. Humans are the only natural hosts. The source of infection is a patient in the late incubation or early clinical stage of illness. No human carriers or animal reservoirs exist.

Infection is transmitted by direct contact, airborne droplets or fomites contaminated with saliva, and also possibly urine. The virus is detectable in the saliva for about a week before and a week or two after onset of parotitis. However, the peak infectivity is about a day or two before parotitis becomes evident, and subsides rapidly thereafter. The virus is also shed in the urine for upto two weeks after the clinical symptoms begin, though its role in the transmission of infection is not clear.

One attack of mumps confers lasting immunity so that second attacks do not occur.

Immunity: Infection leads to antibody response against both the internal (S) and surface (V) antigens. Antibodies to the S antigen appear early, within 3–7 days after the onset of symptoms, but disappear after about six months. Demonstration of antibody to the S antigen indicates current or recent infection. Antibodies to the V antigen take about a month to appear but persist for years. The antihemagglutinin antibody correlates well with immunity to infection. Even subclinical infections lead to HI antibody and resistance to infection. As antibodies are widespread in the population, passive immunity protects the newborns. Mumps is therefore very rare before six months of age.

Cell mediated immunity is developed following infection, but its significance is not known. Interferon also appears early in mumps infection.

Laboratory diagnosis: The typical case of mumps needs no laboratory confirmation but it may be essential in atypical infection and where meningitis or other systemic involvement is the sole manifestation. The diagnosis may be established by virus isolation and serological tests.

The virus may be isolated from the saliva, urine or CSF; from the saliva within 4–5 days, urine upto two weeks and CSF 8–9 days after the onset of illness. The specimens have to be inoculated soon after collection as the virus is labile. The prepared specimen is inoculated into monkey kidney cell cultures. Human amnion or HeLa cells are also suitable. Virus growth can be detected by hemadsorption and identified by hemadsorption inhibition using specific antiserum. Cytopathic changes are not reliable. Isolation may take 1–2 weeks. More rapid results can be obtained by immunofluorescence testing of infected cell cultures. This may become positive as early as 2–3 days after inoculation.

Isolation can also be made by inoculation into six to eight day old chick embryos by the amniotic route and testing the amniotic fluid after 5–6 days for hemagglutinins. The virus can be identified by hemagglutination inhibition using specific antisera. Egg inoculation is less sensitive than cell cultures for isolation.

Serological diagnosis depends on the demonstration of rise in titre of antibodies in paired serum samples. The CF and HI tests are commonly employed but cross reactions with parainfluenza viruses cause problems. IgM-ELISA is useful in this respect because cross reacting antibodies are IgG and do not interfere with IgM-ELISA.

A positive CF test for antibody to the S antigen in the acute phase serum is presumptive evidence of current infection.

Prophylaxis: An effective live virus vaccine is available against mumps. The Jeryl–Lynn strain of mumps virus, attenuated by passage in eggs and grown in chick embryo fibroblast culture is used as the vaccine. It is recommended for use only after one year of age as maternal antibodies may interfere with the multiplication of the vaccine virus if given earlier. Contraindications are pregnancy, immunodeficiency and hypersensitivity to neomycin or egg protein. The vaccine is given as a single subcutaneous injection, either alone or in combination with measles and rubella vaccines (MMR vaccine). It provides effective protection for at least ten years. The vaccine may not prevent the disease if given after exposure to the infection but there is no contraindication for its use in this situation. The mumps immunoglobulin is of no value either for postexposure prophylaxis or treatment.

PARAINFLUENZA VIRUSES

Four types of parainfluenza viruses have been identified (Table 56.2).

The first parainfluenza virus to be discovered was the Sendai virus in Japan in 1952. This has since been identified as a widespread natural parasite of mice, causing inapparent infections. Sendai virus antibodies were found prevalent in human sera throughout the world. This observation was explained when an antigenically identical virus was isolated in 1958 from children with acute respiratory infections, by the technique of hemadsorption in cell cultures. As a similar hemadsorption virus named HA-1 had been discovered earlier, this was designated HA-2. Both Sendai and HA-2 viruses are now classified as parainfluenza virus type 1— the Sendai virus representing the murine and HA-2 the human variety.

The Sendai virus is different from other parainfluenza viruses in growing readily in eggs, with the infected allantoic fluid showing high titres of hemagglutinin, resembling the influenza virus. So, for a time, it was called the 'hemagglutinating virus of Japan' (HVJ) and 'influenza virus type D'.

Parainfluenza virus type 2 was originally isolated in 1955 from children with acute laryngotracheobronchitis or 'croup'. It was therefore known as the 'croup associated' or CA virus. It grows in monkey kidney cell cultures producing a syncytial cytopathic effect. Antigenically similar viruses (simian viruses 5 and 41) cause natural infection in monkeys.

Parainfluenza virus type 3 was first detected in 1958 from children with respiratory infection, by hemadsorption in cell cultures and was named hemadsorption virus type 1 (HA-1). A related virus (SF-4) causes a respiratory illness in cattle known as 'shipping fever'.

Parainfluenza virus type 4 was isolated in 1960 from children with mild respiratory infection. Two antigenic subtypes, A and B, of this virus, have been recognised.

Clinical features: Parainfluenza viruses are responsible for about 10 per cent of respiratory infections in children needing hospitalisation. The most serious clinical disease caused is croup, which is most frequently due to types 1 and 2. Type 3 causes lower respiratory disease, including bronchitis, bronchiolitis and pneumonia. Type 4 causes minor respiratory illnesses. In adults, parainfluenza viruses cause milder respiratory infection in which sore throat and hoarseness of voice are common. Rarely they cause parotitis.

Parainfluenza viral infection is confined to the respiratory tract, unlike mumps which is a systemic disease, with the virus disseminating through the blood and multiplying in various organs and tissues.

Epidemiology: These are ubiquitous viruses. Parainfluenza virus type 3 infection is often experienced in the first year of life with about 50 per cent of infants being seropositive by 12 months of age. Type 1 and 2 viruses cause disease mainly in preschool children. Type 3 infection is more endemic than types 1 and 2 which tend to occur as epidemics.

First infections are more serious than reinfections, which are not infrequent. With type 4 virus, even first infections are very mild.

Infected children shed the virus in respiratory secretions for about a week. Spread is by airborne virus or through fingers. Nosocomial spread is not uncommon. No vaccine is available.

Laboratory diagnosis: Isolation of the viruses is the best method of diagnosis. Throat and nasal swabs are inoculated in primary monkey kidney cell cultures, or continuous monkey kidney cell lines (LLC–MK2) with trypsin. Cytopathic changes are not readily apparent, except with type 2 virus. Isolation may take ten days or more. Virus growth is detected by hemadsorption. Typing is by immunofluorescence, hemadsorption inhibition, or

Table 56.2 Parainfluenza virus types

Nomenclature of human types		Related animal viruses
Current	Former	
Parainfluenza type 1	Hemadsorption type 2(HA-2)	Sendai (mouse)
Parainfluenza type 2	Croup associated (CA)	Simian viruses 5, 41 (monkey)
Parainfluenza type 3	Hemadsorption type 1 (HA-1)	Shipping fever (cattle)
Parainfluenza type 4 {4A 4B		

hemagglutination inhibition.

Serological diagnosis is hampered by wide antigenic cross reactions. Paired sera can be tested by neutralisation, ELISA, HI or CF for rise in titre of antibodies.

NEWCASTLE DISEASE VIRUS (NDV)

The Newcastle disease virus (avian paramyxovirus type 1) is a natural pathogen of poultry in which it causes explosive outbreaks of pneumoencephalitis or 'influenza' with high mortality. In India it is known as the Ranikhet virus. Control measures consist of vaccination, and slaughter of infected birds.

Human infection with NDV is confined to a self-limited conjunctivitis in poultry workers and others in contact with infected birds.

Other types of avian paramyxoviruses cause inapparent infection in many species of birds.

GENUS PNEUMOVIRUS

RESPIRATORY SYNCYTIAL VIRUS (RSV)

RSV was first isolated in 1956 from chimpanzees with coryza and was called the 'chimpanzee coryza agent' (CCA). A year later, the virus was obtained from children with lower respiratory tract infection. Because it caused cell fusion and the formation of multinucleated syncytia in cell cultures, it was named respiratory syncytial virus (RSV). It is now recognised as the most important cause of lower respiratory tract infection in infants, particularly in the first few months of life.

RSV is pleomorphic and ranges in size from 150–300 nm. The viral envelope has two glycoproteins—the G protein by which the virus attaches to cell surfaces, and the fusion (F) protein which brings about fusion between viral and host cell membranes. The F protein is also responsible for cell-to-cell fusion, which leads to the characteristic syncytial cytopathic changes in RSV infection.

RSV differs from other paramyxoviruses in not possessing hemagglutinin activity. It also does not have neuraminidase or hemolytic properties. Another difference is that its nucleocapsid diameter (13 nm) is less than that of other paramyxoviruses (18 nm).

RSV does not grow in eggs but can be propagated on heteroploid human cell cultures, such as HeLa and Hep-2. It is highly labile and is inactivated rapidly at room temperature. It can be preserved by lyophilisation. It is antigenically stable and only one antigenic type exists. However, studies using monoclonal antibodies have identified two subtypes called A and B.

Clinical features: Most RSV infections are symptomatic. The virus can hardly ever be found in healthy persons.

Infection causes a broad range of respiratory illnesses. In infants, the disease may begin as febrile rhinorrhea, with cough and wheezing, progressing in 25–40 per cent to lower respiratory involvement, including tracheobronchitis, bronchiolitis and pneumonia. In about one per cent, the illness is serious enough to require hospitalisation. RSV is considered to be responsible for about half the cases of bronchiolitis, and a quarter of all pneumonias occurring in the first few months of life. Most patients recover in 1–2 weeks but those with immunodeficiency or cardiac defects may have protracted illness and high death rates.

RSV is an important cause of otitis media in young children. A relation between RSV and the sudden death syndrome in infants has been proposed but not proven.

In adults RSV infection may present as a febrile common cold. It can cause pneumonia in the elderly.

Epidemiology: RSV is global in distribution. It causes annual epidemics in the temperate regions during winter and in the tropics during rainy seasons. Outbreaks are common in children's wards, nurseries and day care centres. Infection is most common in children six weeks to six months of age, with the peak at 2–3 months. The newborns are believed to be protected by high levels of maternal antibody.

The virus is transmitted by close contact, and through contaminated fingers and fomites. Coarse droplets of respiratory secretions discharged during coughing and sneezing are more efficient in spreading the virus than fine aerosols. The incubation period is 4–6 days. Virus shedding may persist for 1–3 weeks, though children with defective cell mediated immunity may continue to shed the virus for months.

Reinfection with the virus is not uncommon but the disease so produced is milder than in primary infection. The role of the antibody in protection against the infection is not clear. Secretory IgA is considered more important than circulating IgG in protection. Cell mediated immunity appears more important than humoral antibodies in recovery from infection. RSV does not induce high levels of interferon production.

Laboratory diagnosis: RSV can be isolated from nasopharyngeal swabs or nasal washings. Samples should be inoculated in cell cultures (HeLa or HEP-2) immediately after collection. Freezing of clinical samples may destroy the virus. In cultured cells, RSV causes characteristic giant cell and syncytial formation but cytopathic effects take about 10 days to appear. Earlier detection of viral growth in cells is possible by immunofluorescence tests. Rapid diagnosis of RSV infection can be made by the immunofluorescence test on smears of nasopharyngeal swabs.

Serological diagnosis is by demonstration of rising antibody titres in paired serum samples by ELISA, CF, neutralisation or immunofluorescence tests.

Prophylaxis: No effective vaccine is available. Attempts at immunisation by formalinised vaccines had to be given up as the vaccinees developed more serious illness than the controls on subsequent exposure to the infection.

Treatment: Management of RSV infection is primarily by supportive care. Administration of ribovirin by continuous aerosol has been found beneficial in hospitalised patients, decreasing the duration of illness and of virus shedding.

GENUS MORBILLIVIRUS

MEASLES (RUBEOLA)

Measles is an ancient disease but for a long time no clear distinction was made between measles and other exanthematous diseases, including smallpox. It was only in 1629 that measles came to be considered a separate entity. Thomas Sydenham in 1690 gave the first clear and accurate description of measles in the English language.

In 1846 an outbreak of measles occurred in the remote Faroe Islands, affecting 75 per cent of the islanders. The classic study of this epidemic by Peter Panum, a Danish medical student, laid the basis of our scientific knowledge about measles.

The viral etiology of measles was established by Goldberger and Anderson in 1911 by transmitting the disease to monkeys through the inoculation of filtrates of blood and nasopharyngeal secretions from patients. The virus was isolated in monkey and human kidney cells by Enders and Peebles in 1954.

Measles virus: The virus has the general

morphology of paramyxoviruses (Fig. 56.2) It is a roughly spherical but often pleomorphic particle, 120–250 nm in diameter. The tightly coiled helical nucleocapsid is surrounded by the lipoprotein envelope carrying on its surface hemagglutinin (H) spikes. The envelope also has the F protein which mediates cell fusion and hemolytic activities. The measles virus agglutinates monkey erythrocytes but there is no elution as the virus does not possess neuraminidase activity.

The measles virus grows well on human or monkey kidney and human amnion cultures which are the preferred cells for primary isolation. Isolates can be adapted for growth on continuous cell lines (HeLa, Vero) and in the amniotic sac of hen's eggs. Cytopathic effects consist of multinucleate syncytium formation, with numerous acidophilic nuclear and cytoplasmic inclusions. Multinucleate giant cells (Warthin–Finkeldey cells) are also found in the lymphoid tissues of patients.

The virus is labile and readily inactivated by heat, ultraviolet light, ether and formaldehyde. It can be stabilised by molar $MgSO_4$, so that it resists heating at 50 °C for one hour.

The measles virus is antigenically uniform. It shares antigens with the viruses of canine distemper and bovine rinderpest.

Clinical features: It takes about 9–11 days from the time of exposure to infection for the first signs of clinical disease to appear. These consist of prodromal malaise, fever, conjunctival injection, cough and nasal discharge. After 3–4 days of prodromal illness, the rash appears. A day or two before the rash begins, Koplik's spots develop on the buccal mucosa and occasionally on the conjunctiva and intestinal mucosa. The prodromal illness subsides within a day or two of the appearance of the rash. The red maculopapular rash of measles typically appears on the forehead first and spreads downwards, to disappear in the same sequence 3–6 days later, leaving behind a brownish discolouration and finely granular desquamation.

Most patients recover uneventfully but quite a

few develop complications which may be due to the virus (croup, bronchitis) or to secondary bacterial infection (pneumonia, otitis media). Rarely, the virus may cause a fatal giant cell pneumonia, particularly in children with immunodeficiencies or severe malnutrition. Complications are more common and serious in the developing countries.

The most serious complication is meningoencephalitis. Many survivors have neurological sequelae. A rare late complication is subacute sclerosing panencephalitis (SSPE).

Protracted diarrhea is often seen as a complication in children in the poor nations. The virus may be recovered from the stools of patients with measles enteritis.

There occurs a suppression of delayed hypersensitivity after measles infection, which may last for weeks or a few months. Mantoux and other allergic skin tests may be negative during this period. Underlying tuberculosis may become worse following an attack of measles. Recovery from measles may also be associated with an improvement of allergic eczema or asthma, Hodgkin's disease or lipoid nephrosis.

Measles induces labour in some pregnant

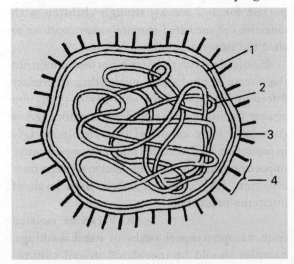

Fig.56.1 Measles virus. 1. Membrane (M) protein 2. Nucleocapsid 3. Lipoprotein membrane. 4. Spikes-hemagglutinin.

women, resulting in spontaneous abortion or premature delivery. The virus may cross the placenta and infect the fetus during maternal measles but there is no evidence of teratogeny. Thrombocytopenia may develop, leading to purpura and bleeding from the mouth, intestines and genitourinary tract.

Pathogenesis: The virus enters the body through the respiratory tract or the conjunctiva and multiplies locally and in the adjoining lymph nodes. The virus spreads to the reticuloendothelial system through the blood. After multiplication there, a secondary viremia transports the virus to the epithelial surfaces including the skin, mouth, respiratory tract and conjunctiva.

The pathognomonic Koplik's spots, which are small bluish white ulcerations on the buccal mucosa opposite the lower molars contain giant cells, cytoplasmic and intranuclear inclusions and virion components, indicating local viral replication. Evidence of viral replication can also be seen in the vascular endothelial cells at the sites of the skin rash. The rash represents an immune reaction between T lymphocytes and cells in which viral replication is taking place.

During the prodromal phase, which lasts for 2–4 days, the virus can be isolated from the blood, washed leucocytes, tears and respiratory secretions. It can be recovered from the urine uptil four days after the appearance of the skin rash.

Laboratory diagnosis: In a typical case of measles, the diagnosis is self-evident. In atypical cases, and for differentiation from rubella, laboratory tests are useful.

A simple diagnostic test, which can be used even before the rash appears, is the demonstration of multinucleated giant cells in Giemsa stained smears of nasal secretions. The measles virus antigen can be detected in these cells by immunofluorescence.

The virus can be isolated from the nose, throat, conjunctiva and blood during the prodromal phase and upto about two days after the appearance of the rash. The virus may be obtained from the urine for a few more days. Primary human or monkey kidney and amnion cells are most useful. Cytopathic changes may take upto a week to develop, but earlier diagnosis of viral growth is possible by immunofluorescence.

Serological diagnosis: Specific neutralisation, hemagglutination inhibition and complement fixing antibodies develop early. A fourfold rise in titre is looked for using sera collected during the acute phase and 10–21 days later. Demonstration of measles-specific IgM in a single specimen of serum drawn between one and two weeks after the onset of the rash is confirmatory. False negatives may occur if the serum is taken earlier than one week before or later than two weeks after the onset of the rash.

Demonstration of high titre measles antibody in the CSF is diagnostic of SSPE.

Epidemiology: Measles is endemic throughout the world and produces epidemics every 2–3 years. Epidemics are usually seen in late winter and early spring, with a peak in April. The disease has maximum incidence in children 1–5 years of age. It is uncommon in the first six months of life due to the presence of maternal antibody. One attack confers solid immunity.

People are the only natural hosts of measles. Monkeys are often found infected but they seem to acquire the infection from humans. Patients are infectious from three days before to the onset of symptoms until the rash desquamates. Infectivity is maximum at the prodrome and diminishes rapidly with the onset of the rash. Spread is by direct contact with respiratory secretions and aerosols created by coughing and sneezing. The virus enters the body through the respiratory tract and conjunctiva. In the nonimmune, infection almost always results in clinical disease.

In remote islands, the population may be highly susceptible to measles. When the virus is introduced into such communities, it may induce epidemics with high mortality. A classical example was observed in the Faroe Islands where measles appeared in 1846 after an absence of some 60 years. The epidemic spared only the very old persons who had been alive during the previous epidemic. When Greenland had its first exposure to the measles virus in 1951, the epidemic affected nearly all of the indigenous population.

Prophylaxis: Normal human gammaglobulin given within six days of exposure can prevent or modify the disease, depending on the dose. This is valuable in children with immunodeficiency, pregnant women and others at special risk.

A safe and effective live attenuated measles vaccine is available. The original live vaccines used the Edmonston strain developed by multiple passage through human kidney, amnion and chick embryo cultures. Due to its high risk of causing febrile rash (vaccination measles), further attenuation became necessary. The Schwartz and Moraten strains so developed were safe but effective only in children older than 15 months. In the tropics, measles is common and serious in children below 12 months. Therefore the Edmonston–Zagreb strain, attenuated by passage in human diploid cells, is preferred as the vaccine strain because it is able to produce seroconversion even in infants 4–6 months old. The recommended age for measles vaccination in the developing countries is now nine months, while in the advanced nations it remains 15 months.

The vaccine is given either by itself, or in combination as the MMR vaccine. A single subcutaneous injection of the measles vaccine provides protection beginning in about 12 days and lasting for over 20 years. Contraindications are immuno-deficiency, untreated tuberculosis and pregnancy.

A live attenuated vaccine has been developed which can be given by intranasal aerosol in young babies and gives good protection irrespective of the presence of maternal antibodies.

Efforts are being made to eradicate measles by vaccination. Considerable progress has been achieved in the USA and some other countries.

Further Reading

Bellini WJ et al. 1998. Paramyxoviruses. In Collins, L. et al (eds). *Topley & Wilson's Microbiology and Microbial Infections.* 9th edn, Vol.1. London: Arnold.

Chanock RM et al. 1992. Serious respiratory tract disease caused by RSV. *Pediatrics* 90:137.

Heilman CA. 1990. Respiratory syncytial and parainfluenza viruses. *J Infect Dis* 161:402.

Arboviruses

Arboviruses (arthropod-borne viruses) are viruses of vertebrates biologically transmitted by hematophagous insect vectors. They multiply in bloodsucking insects and are transmitted by bite to vertebrate hosts. Insect viruses and viruses of vertebrates that are sometimes mechanically transmitted by insects do not come into this category. Inclusion in this group is based on ecological and epidemiological considerations and hence it contains members that are dissimilar in other properties. With better understanding of the physical and chemical properties of individual viruses, they are reassigned to more defined taxonomical groups. Though taxonomically unacceptable, the name 'arbovirus' is a useful biological concept.

A similar ecological group is that of the rodentborne (robo) viruses which are maintained in nature by direct transmission between rodents, and sometimes infecting other species, including humans, by direct contact without the agency of arthropod vectors. Roboviruses, like arboviruses, belong to different taxonomical families, some of them in common with arboviruses.

Arboviruses are worldwide in distribution but are far more numerous in the tropical than in the temperate zones. Over 500 viruses have been listed in the *International Catalogue of Arboviruses* published in 1985. Most of them cause silent infections in rodents and other wild mammals but about 100 of them can infect humans. In India, over 40 arboviruses have been detected, of which more than 10 are known to produce human disease.

Arboviruses have been named according to the disease caused (Yellow fever), the place of isolation of the virus (Kyasanur Forest Disease) or the local name for the disease (Chikungunya). They are classified according to their physical and chemical features into taxonomical families. Arboviruses have been placed in Toga-, Flavi-, Bunya-, Reo- and Rhabdovirus families (Table 57.1). Within each family, they are classified into genera, and antigenic groups, based on serological relationships. Some viruses are ungrouped.

Arboviruses have a very wide host range including many species of animals and birds. The ability to multiply in arthropods is their special characteristic. The most important arbovirus vectors are mosquitoes, followed by ticks. *Phlebotomus, Culicoides* and *Cimicidae* are less common vectors.

In the laboratory, mice are commonly used for growing arboviruses, intracerebral inoculation in suckling mice being the most sensitive method for their isolation. They can be grown in the yolk sac or chorioallantoic membrane of chick embryo, in tissue cultures of primary cells like chick embryo fibroblasts or continuous cell lines like vero or HeLa, and in cultures of appropriate insect tissues.

Most arboviruses agglutinate the red cells of goose or day-old chicks. Hemagglutination is influenced by pH and temperature, the optimal requirements varying with different viruses. Spontaneous elution does not occur. Hemagglutination is inhibited specifically by antibody, and nonspecifically by lipoprotein inhibitors in serum, brain and other tissues.

In general, arboviruses are labile, being readily inactivated at room temperature and by bile salts,

Table 57.1 Taxonomy of some important arboviruses

Family	Genus	Important species
Togaviridae	Alphavirus	Chikungunya, O'nyong-nyong, Mayaro, Semliki Forest Sindbis, Ross River, Eastern, Western and Venezuelan equine encephalitis viruses
Flaviviridae	Flavivirus	Japanese encephalitis, Murray Valley encephalitis, WestNile, Ilheus, St. Louis encephalitis, Yellow Fever, Dengue types 1, 2, 3, 4, Russian Spring Summer encephalitis complex, Louping ill, Powassan, Kyasanur Forest Disease. Omsk hemorrhagic fever
Bunyaviridae	Bunyavirus	California encephalitis, Oropouche, Turlock
	Phlebovirus	Sandfly fever viruses, Rift valley fever virus
	Nairovirus	Crimean Congo hemorrhagic fever viruses, Nairobi sheep disease virus, Ganjam virus
	Hantavirus	Hantan, Seoul, Puumala, Prospect Hill, Sin Nombre viruses
Reoviridae	Orbivirus	Colorado tick fever, African horse sickness, Blue tongue viruses
Rhabdoviridae	Vesiculovirus	Vesicular stomatitis virus, Chandipura virus

ether and other lipid solvents. Infectivity may be retained at −70 °C or by lyophilisation.

Antigenic structure: Three antigens are important in serological studies – hemagglutinins, complement fixing and neutralising antigens – all integral parts of the virus particle. Considerable antigenic cross reactions occur among arboviruses. The plaque reduction neutralisation test (PRNT) shows the greatest specificity.

Pathogenesis: The virus enters the body through the bite of the insect vector. After multiplication in the reticuloendothelial system, viremia of varying duration ensues and, in some cases, the virus is transported to the target organs, such as the central nervous system in encephalitides, the liver in yellow fever and the capillary endothelium in hemorrhagic fevers.

Arboviruses cause the following clinical syndromes: fever with or without rash and arthralgia; encephalitis; hemorrhagic fever; and the characteristic systemic disease, yellow fever (Table 57.2). All infections occur with varying degrees of severity, subclinical infections being very common. Arboviruses also cause a number of veterinary diseases such as Eastern, Western and Venezuelan equine encephalitis in horses in America, Rift Valley fever in sheep and cattle in Africa, Blue tongue in asses in India, Africa and America, Ganjam disease of sheep in India and African horse sickness in horses and mules in Africa and Asia.

Laboratory diagnosis: Diagnosis may be established by virus isolation or serology. As all arbovirus infections are viremic, blood collected during the acute phase of the disease may yield the virus. Isolation may also be made from the CSF in some encephalitic cases but the best specimen for virus isolation is the brain. Specimens are inoculated intracerebrally into suckling mice. The animals develop fatal encephalitis, though serial blind passages may be necessary in some cases. Some viruses may also be isolated in tissue cultures or, less readily, in eggs. Isolates are identified by hemagglutination inhibition, complement fixation, gel precipitation, immunofluorescence, immunochromatography, ELISA or neutralisation with appropriate antisera. Virus isolation from insect vectors and reservoir animal or avian species also aids in the identification of arbovirus activity in the area.

Diagnosis may also be made serologically by demonstrating rise in antibody titre in paired serum samples by hemagglutination inhibition, complement fixation or neutralisation tests. Serological diagnosis is often complicated due to the antigenic cross-reaction between related viruses. This is especially so in the sera of persons who had prior infection or immunisation with other arboviruses because of the broad antigenic reactivity in such cases.

Epidemiology: Arbovirus infections are zoonoses, being maintained in nature in animals, with a few possible exceptions such as dengue and O'nyong-nyong. The epidemiology of arbovirus infections is linked with the ecology of their arthropod vectors and vertebrate hosts. Most arboviruses exist in nature in animal or avian species in which infection is asymptomatic. Infection is maintained in these species by a silent cycle involving mosquitoes or other arthropods naturally feeding on these species. The vector arthropod gets infected by biting a viremic vertebrate. The vector, in turn, becomes infective only after an incubation period during which the virus multiplies in its body to a sufficiently high titre (extrinsic incubation period). Human disease results only when the virus is accidentally transferred to humans either directly by the vector or through the intermediary of animal reservoirs. A second epidemiological pattern is seen in diseases like dengue where no nonhuman vertebrate host has been identified. Here, the virus is maintained in a cycle composed of humans and the domestic mosquito. In certain tick-borne infections, the virus may be maintained for considerable periods by transovarial transmission in ticks before it finds a vertebrate host.

Although the large majority of arbovirus infections are caused by vector arthropod bites, a few may also follow ingestion of infected cow's or goat's milk, inhalation of aerosols containing the virus or contact with infected secretions or blood.

Control: Control measures are indicated only in those infections that lead to epidemics or epizootics. These consist essentially of vector control and immunisation. While vaccination is very effective in yellow fever, it has not been of equal value in the control of other arbovirus diseases. Administration of hyperimmune serum has been shown to be effective in some cases experimentally but this has little clinical application.

TOGAVIRUSES

Togaviruses are spherical enveloped viruses with a diameter of 50–70 nm. The genome is a molecule of single stranded RNA. The virus replicates in the host cell cytoplasm and is released by budding through host cell membranes. The name Togavirus is derived from 'toga', meaning the Roman mantle or cloak, and refers to the viral envelope.

The family Togaviridae contains, besides the arboviruses belonging to the genus *Alphavirus*, the rubella virus (genus *Rubivirus*) and others, which are not arthropodborne and differ in their epidemiology and other features. They are not therefore considered in this chapter. The genus *Alphavirus* was formerly classified as 'Group A arboviruses' which explains the name *Alphavirus* (from *Alpha*, the first letter of the Greek alphabet, corresponding to the letter A).

ALPHAVIRUS

The genus *Alphavirus* contains some 32 species, of which at least 13 are known to infect humans. All of them are mosquitoborne. They exhibit cross reaction in hemagglutination inhibition and to a

Table 57.2 Arboviruses associated with different clinical syndromes

Virus	Genus	Distribution	Vector	Reservoir
FEVER WITH OR WITHOUT RASH AND ARTHRALGIA				
Chikungunya	Alphavirus	Africa, Asia	Mosquito	Not known (? Monkeys)
O' nyong-nyong	Alphavirus	Africa	Mosquito	Not known
Ross River	Alphavirus	Australia	Mosquito	Small animals
Sindbis	Alphavirus	Africa, Asia	Mosquito	Birds, mammals
Mayaro	Alphavirus	South America	Mosquito	Monkeys, marsupials
Dengue, types 1-4	Flavivirus	Widespread, especially Asia Pacific, Caribbean	Mosquito	Not known (? Monkeys)
West Nile	Flavivirus	Asia, Africa, USA	Mosquito	Birds
Sandfly fever	Bunyavirus	Mediterranean, Asia, Tropical America	Sandfly	not known (? Small mammals)
Rift Valley fever	Bunyavirus	Africa	Mosquito	Sheep, cattle
Oropouche	Bunyavirus	South America	Mosquito	Not known
Colorado tick fever	Orbivirus	USA	Tick	Rodents
ENCEPHALITIS				
Eastern equine encephalitis	Alphavirus	Americas	Mosquito	Birds
Western equine encephalitis	Alphavirus	Americas	Mosquito	Reptiles(? Birds)
Venezuelan equine	Alphavirus	Americas	Mosquito	Rodents
St. Louis encephalitis	Flavivirus	Americas	Mosquito	Birds
West Nile	Flavivirus	Africa, Europe, USA, West Asia	Mosquito	Birds
Japanese encephalitis	Flavivirus	East & South East Asia	Mosquito	Birds
Murray Valley encephalitis	Flavivirus	Australia	Mosquito	Birds
RSSE complex	Flavivirus	East Europe, USSR	Tick	Rodents, other mammals, birds, ticks
Louping ill	Flavivirus	Britain	Tick	Sheep
Powassan	Flavivirus	North America	Tick	Rodents
California	Bunyavirus	North America	Mosquito	Rodents
HEMORRHAGIC FEVER				
Chikungunya	Alphavirus	Africa, Asia	Mosquito	Not known (? Monkeys)
Dengue types 1-4	Flavivirus	Tropics	Mosquito	Not known (? Monkeys)
Yellow fever	Flavivirus	Africa, South America	Mosquito	Monkeys, man
Kyasanur Forest Disease	Flavivirus	USSR	Tick	Rodents(? Ticks)
Omsk hemorrhagic fever	Flavivirus	USSR	Tick	Small mammals
Crimean Congo hemorrhagic fever	Flavivirus	USSR, Central Asia Africa	Tick	Small mammals

lesser extent in complement fixation tests. The neutralisation test is more specific. They produce epidemics of encephalitis in America and dengue-like fever in the tropics.

Encephalitis viruses: Three members of this group, Eastern, Western and Venezuelan equine encephalitis viruses, cause encephalitis in horses and humans. Eastern equine encephalitis (EEE) occurs along eastern Canada, USA and the Caribbean, causing sporadic cases and small epidemics. Western equine encephalitis (WEE) is more widely distributed in America and causes large epidemics. Venezuelan equine encephalitis (VEE), prevalent in Central and South America, usually causes an influenza-like illness, with encephalitis in a small proportion of cases. Several species of *Culex* and *Anopheles* mosquitoes are the vectors, and wild birds the reservoirs. Formalinised vaccines have been developed for EEE and WEE and a live attenuated vaccine for VEE.

Viruses Causing Febrile Illness

1. *Chikungunya virus:* This virus was first isolated from human patients and *Aedes aegypti* mosquitoes from Tanzania in 1952. The name 'chikungunya' is derived from the native word for the disease in which the patient lies 'doubled up' due to severe joint pains. Epidemics of chikungunya have occurred in many African countries. In 1958, the virus caused a large epidemic of hemorrhagic fever in Thailand. The virus first appeared in India in 1963, when along with dengue, it caused very extensive epidemics in Calcutta, Madras and other areas. Chikungunya outbreaks occurred at irregular intervals along the east coast of India and in Maharashtra till 1973. Since then the virus has been quiescent.

The disease presents as a sudden onset of fever, crippling joint pains, lymphadenopathy and conjunctivitis. A maculopapular rash is common and some show hemorrhagic manifestations. Hemorrhagic lesions were common in Calcutta

when the disease first appeared there in 1963 but have been extremely rare afterwards. The fever is typically biphasic with a period of remission after 1–6 days of fever. The vector is *Aedes aegypti*. No animal reservoir has been identified. Antibody to the virus has been demonstrated in horses, cattle and other domestic animals but its significance is not known. No vaccine is available.

2. *O'nyong-nyong virus:* This virus was first isolated in Uganda. This is confined to Africa, is closely related to the chikungunya virus antigenically and causes a similar disease. This is transmitted by the Anopheles species. The Mayaro virus causes a similar disease in the West Indies and South America.

3. *Semliki Forest virus:* This virus was, first isolated in 1942 in Uganda from Aedes mosquitoes has not been associated with clinical illness in humans though neutralising antibodies to the virus have been demonstrated in Africans. The Sindbis virus, originally isolated from Culex mosquitoes in the Sindbis district of Egypt in 1952, has subsequently been recovered from other parts of Africa, India, Philippines and Australia. In Africa, it is known to be associated with febrile illness in human beings. In India, antibodies have been detected in human sera but no association has been established with human disease. The closely related Ross River virus has been associated with epidemic polyarthritis in Australia.

FLAVIVIRUSES

The family Flaviviridae contains only one genus, *Flavivirus*. They are somewhat smaller than alphaviruses, being 40 nm in diameter. The name *Flavivirus* refers to the type species, the Yellow fever virus (*Flavus*, L = yellow).

There are over 60 arthropod-borne flaviviruses. Representative members of this group are distributed in all parts of the world, covering all the zoogeographic regions. They may be considered under two sections, the mosquito-borne and the tick-borne viruses.

MOSQUITOBORNE GROUP

Encephalitis viruses: Five members of this group cause encephalitis, each of them limited to a geographic zone:

1. *St. Louis encephalitis virus:* This is prevalent in North and Central America and is the most important mosquitoborne disease in the USA. It has caused several large epidemics in recent years, the clinical picture ranging from mild febrile illness to frank encephalitis and the case fatality ranging from 2–20 per cent. Wild birds act as the reservoir and *Culex tarsalis* as the vector.

2. *Ilheus virus:* This occurs in South and Central America, maintained in forests by a cycle involving mosquitoes, wild birds and monkeys. Human infection is largely subclinical or leads to febrile illness. Encephalitis is rare.

3. *West Nile virus:* This virus, originally isolated in 1937 from the West Nile province of Uganda, has since been reported from many African countries, Israel, Cyprus, France and India. It causes a dengue-like illness in humans and encephalitis in horses. It is endemic in Egypt, affecting mainly children. In Israel it has caused epidemics. The virus is maintained in nature in wild birds by Culex mosquitoes. In India, the virus has been isolated from Culex mosquitoes and from febrile as well as encephalitic patients, from Rajasthan to Karnataka.

In 1999, West Nile fever unexpectedly appeared in New York, entering the western hemisphere for the first time. It caused a mosquito-borne epidemic of fever, encephalitis and muscle weakness, with a case fatality exceeding 10 per cent. There was also a simultaneous spread among birds, with crows being most affected. Since then the virus has spread over much of the USA becoming a major public health problem.

4. *Murray Valley encephalitis virus:* This is confined to Australia and New Guinea. The virus was isolated during an epidemic of encephalitis in the Murray River Valley in 1951. Perhaps the same virus had been isolated earlier during the epidemics of encephalitis in 1917–1918, when it went by the name of Australian 'X' disease. The virus is believed to occur normally in an enzootic cycle involving wild birds and mosquitoes, and to break out only occasionally into epidemics. *Culex annulirostris* is the vector.

5. *Japanese encephalitis:* This virus occurs along the Orient, from Korea and Japan in the north to India and Malaysia in the south. The disease has been recognised in Japan since 1871 and was named Japanese 'B' encephalitis to distinguish it from 'encephalitis A' (encephalitis lethargica, von Economo's disease) which was then prevalent. The virus was first isolated in Japan during an epidemic in 1935. Several large epidemics have occurred since then. Epidemics show a seasonal incidence (summer–autumn) in the temperate regions, though this is not evident in the tropical areas. *Culex tritaeniorhynchus*, a rural mosquito that breeds in rice fields, is the principal vector.

Japanese encephalitis virus causes the most serious clinical disease among the five viruses of this group. The disease typically has an abrupt onset with fever, headache and vomiting. After 1–6 days, signs of encephalitis set in with nuchal rigidity, convulsions, altered sensorium and coma. The fever is high and continuous. There is neutrophil leucocytosis in the peripheral blood and pleocytosis with normal or raised sugar and a slightly raised protein in the CSF. The mortality rate in some epidemics has been upto 50 per cent. Convalescence may take many weeks. Residual neurological damage may persist in upto 50 per cent of survivors. The large majority of infections are, however, asymptomatic and it has been estimated that 500–1000 inapparent infections occur for every case of clinical disease.

In India, Japanese encephalitis was first recognised in 1955 when the virus was isolated from mosquitoes of the *Culex vishnui* complex from Vellore during an outbreak of encephalitis in Tamil Nadu. The virus continued to be active in Tamil Nadu and Andhra in subsequent years also, causing illness mainly in children, indicating the endemic nature of the virus. Most of the cases occurred between October and November.

Japanese encephalitis remained confined to the southeastern parts of India till 1973, when it caused a large outbreak of encephalitis in West Bengal. The epidemic affected adults also, with mortality rates approaching 50 per cent, suggesting that the virus was freshly introduced into the area. Cases occurred mainly between June and October. From 1976, there have been periodical outbreaks of the disease in various parts of India—Dibrugarh (Assam) in the east, Gorakhpur (Uttar Pradesh) and Haryana in the north and Goa and Maharashtra in the west. In the south, outbreaks have occurred in Kolar in Karnataka, various areas in Andhra Pradesh, Tirunelveli and South Arcot in Tamil Nadu, in Pondicherry and lately in Kerala. In addition, sporadic cases have been reported from different parts of the country, excepting the northwestern states. Japanese encephalitis has become a major public health problem of national importance in India (Fig. 57.1).

The natural cycle of the virus has been worked out in detail in Japan. Herons act as reservoir hosts and pigs as amplifier hosts. Human infection is a tangential 'dead-end' event and occurs when the infected mosquitoes reach high density. The natural cycle in India also may be similar. Natural infection has been demonstrated in Ardeid birds (herons and egrets), as well as bird-to-bird transmission through *Culex tritaeniorhynchus*. Other birds such as ducks, pigeons and sparrows may also be involved. Vertebrate hosts may include cattle and buffaloes, besides pigs. The major vector *Culex tritaeniorhynchus* has a predilection for cattle and bites them in preference to humans or pigs, but as cattle do not develop viremia, they do not contribute to spread of the virus. The high cattle– pig ratio in India has been suggested as a factor limiting human infection.

Preventive measures include mosquito control and locating piggeries away from human dwellings. A formalin inactivated mouse brain vaccine using the Nakayama strain has been employed successfully for human immunisation in Japan and, in a small scale, in India also. Two doses at two weeks' interval followed by a booster 6–12 months later constitute a full course. Immunity produced by the vaccine is shortlived. A live attenuated vaccine has been developed in China from JE strain SA 14-14-2, passed through weanling mice. The vaccine is produced in primary baby hamster kidney cells. Administered in two doses, one year apart, the vaccine has been reportedly effective in preventing clinical disease.

Vaccination of pigs has been proposed in view of their importance as amplifier hosts. During major epidemics, slaughter of pigs have been employed as a measure of containment. A million pigs were reportedly slaughtered in Malaysia in 1999 to stop an epidemic of encephalitis.

Yellow fever: Yellow fever was recognised as a clinical entity as early as in the seventeenth century and was familiar to pirates as the 'Yellow Jack'. It is a native of Africa and was transported thence along the trade routes to Europe and America. The most serious epidemics occurred in the Western Hemisphere—Central America and the Caribbean, and even as far north as New York. Since the early twentieth century, the disease has been largely confined to certain areas of Africa and South and Central America.

Carlos Finlay in Cuba in 1881 suggested that yellow fever was spread by *Aedes aegypti* mosquitoes. In 1900, the US Army Yellow Fever Commission, under Walter Reed, confirmed this observation and demonstrated that Aedes mosquitoes were infected by feeding on human patients during the early viremic phase of the disease

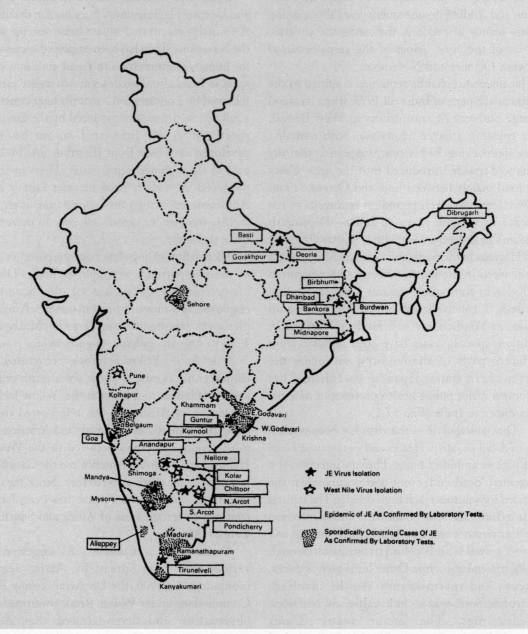

Fig. 57.1 Distribution of Japanese encephalitis in India (Courtesy: National Institute of Virology, Pune)

and became infective after an extrinsic incubation period of 12 days. This led to the prompt eradication of the disease from Cuba and the Panama Canal area by controlling the Aedes aegypti mosquitoes. There were even hopes of ultimate total eradication of the disease but these had to be abandoned when in 1932 outbreaks of yellow fever occurred in Brazil in areas devoid of *Aedes aegypti*. It was then recognised that the virus survives in another cycle – the forest or sylvatic cycle – involving forest animals and mosquitoes.

The yellow fever virus was first isolated in 1927 by inoculating rhesus monkeys with the blood of an African patient named Asibi. The virus was shown by Theiler (1930) to grow well following intracerebral inoculation in mice. The infected mouse brain was used as a vaccine in former French West Africa (Dakar vaccine) though this was encephalitogenic. It was later replaced by a non-neurotropic (17D) vaccine.

After an incubation period of 3–6 days, the disease starts as a fever of acute onset with chills, headache, nausea and vomiting. The pulse is usually slow despite a high temperature. Jaundice, albuminuria, and hemorrhagic manifestations develop and the patient may die of hepatic or renal failure. Most cases are less severe, especially in the endemic areas, and may present as undifferentiated fever without jaundice.

Histologically, the liver shows cloudy and fatty degeneration and necrosis which is typically midzonal. The necrosed cells coalesce and become hyalinised leading to the formation of characteristic eosinophilic masses known as Councilman bodies. Acidophilic intranuclear inclusion bodies (Torres bodies) may be seen in the infected liver cells in the early stages. The histological picture of the liver is specific enough to be diagnostic, and this was the basis of early surveys undertaken to detect areas of yellow fever activity. A special instrument (viscerotome) was employed for the collection of liver tissue from fatal cases for histological diagnosis.

The epidemiology of yellow fever was clarified only after the recognition that the disease occurs in two distinct patterns. In the urban cycle, humans at both as the natural reservoir and as the definitive case, the virus being transmitted by the domestic *Aedes aegypti* mosquito. In the forest or sylvatic cycle, wild monkeys act as the reservoirs and forest mosquitoes (*Haemagogus spegazzinii* in South America and *Aedes africanus* and *A. simpsoni* in Africa) as the vectors. Human cases occur only when humans trespass into the forest or when the monkeys raid villages near the forest.

The control of urban yellow fever can be achieved by eradicating the vector mosquito, as was shown in Cuba and Panama early this century by Gorgas but this is obviously impracticable with the sylvatic disease. Two very effective vaccines have been developed for human use. The French neurotropic vaccine (Dakar) produced from infected mouse brain was thermostable and administered by scarification and hence convenient for use under tropical field conditions. However, the vaccine carries a high risk of producing encephalitis in the vaccinees, especially in children. A safe and equally effective vaccine, the 17D vaccine was developed by Theiler in 1937 by passaging the Asibi strain serially in mouse embryo and whole chick embryo tissues and then in chick embryo tissue from which the central nervous tissue has been removed. The 17D vaccine is thermolabile and is administered by subcutaneous inoculation. Vaccination which is mandatory for travel to or from endemic areas is valid for 10 years beginning 10 days after vaccination. In India, the 17D vaccine is manufactured at the Central Research Institute, Kasauli.

Yellow fever is largely confined to Central and South America and Africa. Yellow fever does not exist in India and it is important to us for this paradoxical reason. India offers a receptive area with a large population of *Aedes aegypti* and nonimmune humans. Strict vigilance is enforced on vaccination and quarantine for travel from endemic areas. This, no doubt, has checked the entry of the virus into India through legitimate passengers. It is likely that stray virus introduced may have been kept out, due to the prevalence in the local *Aedes aegypti* of Dengue virus, and of antibodies to a wide range of arboviruses in the local population. Another reason could have been that in Africa, yellow fever was mainly in the west, and in India, Aedes mosquitoes were along the east coast, so that even stray importations of virus by sea may not have found suitable vectors. This is no longer valid as yellow fever has in recent years have caused epidemics in East Africa, and Aedes mosquitoes have spread all along the west coast of India. If ever yellow fever gets established in India, the consequences could be catastrophic.

Dengue: Dengue virus is widely distributed throughout the tropics and subtropics. (The name 'dengue' is derived from the Swahili *Ki denga pepo*, meaning a sudden seizure by a demon. The term 'break-bone fever' was coined during the Philadelphia epidemic in 1780). Dengue fever is clinically similar to the illness caused by chikungunya and O'nyong-nyong viruses. Four types of dengue virus exist: DEN 1 first isolated from Hawai in 1944, DEN 2 from New Guinea in 1944 and DEN 3 and 4 from the Philippines in 1956. Immunity is type specific so that it is possible for a person to have four separate episodes of dengue fever. Dengue has been increasing worldwide over the last few decades and today ranks as the most important vectorborne disease, with about 2.5 billion people in 200 countries at risk.

Dengue presents clinically after an incubation period of 3–14 days, as fever of sudden onset with headache, retrobulbar pain, conjunctival injection, pain in the back and limbs (break-bone fever), lymphadenopathy and maculopapular rash. The fever is typically biphasic (saddle back) and lasts for 5–7 days. Dengue may also occur in more serious forms, with hemorrhagic manifestations (dengue Hemorrhagic fever) or with shock (dengue shock syndrome). These complications, first recognised

in Thailand, have since occurred in many countries in Southeast Asia and the Western Pacific. They are more common in previously healthy children in the indigenous populations of endemic areas. They may be a hypersensitivity or enchancement response to sequential dengue virus infection in persons sensitised by prior exposure to other serotypes of the virus.

Dengue virus is transmitted from person to person by *Aedes aegypti* mosquitoes. The extrinsic incubation period is 8–10 days. No vertebrate hosts other than humans have been identified.

Dengue was initially confined to the east coast of India and has caused epidemics, sometimes along with the chikungunya virus, as in 1963 when extensive outbreaks affected Calcutta and Madras. Subsequently it has spread westwards and in the 1990s Surat and Delhi had major epidemics with deaths due to DHF and DSS. All four types of dengue virus are present in this country. Occasionally, more than one type of the virus has been isolated from the same patient.

Demonstration of circulating IgM antibody provides early diagnosis, as it appears within two to five days of the onset of illness and persists for one to three months. IgM ELISA test offers reliable diagnosis. A strip immunochromatographic test for IgM is available for rapid diagnosis.

Control of dengue is limited to vector control as no vaccine is currently available.

TICKBORNE GROUP

These viruses produce two clinical syndromes, encephalitis and hemorrhagic fevers.

Tickborne encephalitis viruses: A number of viruses belonging to the Russian Spring Summer Encephalitis (RSSE) complex cause encephalitis along a wide area of the northern landmass from Scotland to Siberia. The names given to the disease vary from one area to another depending on the variations in the prominent clinical features. Thus, in Scotland, it is called 'louping ill' as the disease occurs primarily in sheep in which it causes a curious 'leaping' gait. Human cases that result from contact with these sheep are mild and present as aseptic meningitis. It is called Central European Encephalitis, biphasic meningoencephalitis and RSSE, in Central Europe, Eastern Europe and USSR, respectively. RSSE is the most serious form, with high rates of fatality and permanent paralytic sequelae in some survivors. Infection is transmitted by the bite of Ixodid ticks. The virus is transmitted transovarially in ticks so that they can act as vectors as well as reservoir hosts. Wild rodents and migrating birds are other reservoirs. Biphasic meningoencephalitis may be transmitted to human beings by drinking the milk of infected goats. The control of infection by the RSSE complex depends on the avoidance of tick bites. A formalin inactivated RSSE vaccine has been found useful.

Another tickborne virus, the Powassan virus causes encephalitis in Canada and Northern USA.

Tickborne hemorrhagic fevers:

1. *Kyasanur Forest Disease (KFD)*: This is a hemorrhagic fever found in Karnataka state (India). In 1957, several dead monkeys were noticed in the Kyasanur forest in Shimoga district in Karnataka along with a severe prostrating illness in some of the villagers in the area. A similar illness had also been observed in the locality a year earlier. A new arbovirus antigenically related to the RSSE complex, was isolated by investigators from the National Institute of Virology (then Virus Research Centre), Pune, from the patients and dead monkeys. It was named the KFD virus after the name of the place from where the first isolations were made.

KFD has a sudden onset with fever, headache, conjunctivitis, myalgia and severe prostration. Some cases develop hemorrhages into the skin, mucosa and viscera. The case fatality rate is about five per cent. For many years after its discovery in 1957, the epizootic and epidemic activity of KFD remained confined to the areas contiguous to its original focus in Sagar, Sorab and

Shikarpur taluks of Shimoga district. Between 1972 and 1975, a few other smouldering foci developed in the adjacent areas in North Kanara. Though the disease had not been observed anywhere else, the virus appeared to be more widely distributed, as antibodies had been demonstrated in humans and animals in the Kutch and Saurashtra peninsula and in some other scattered places in India.

The situation changed suddenly in 1982 with the appearance of an epizootic and epidemic in Belthangadi taluk in South Kanara. This followed the clear felling of part of an evergreen reserve forest in the area in September 1982. The outbreak, known locally as 'monkey fever', started with dead monkeys being observed in October. The first human case was seen late in December. During the next five months, 1142 human cases were recorded with 104 deaths. The outbreak subsided with the onset of the monsoon in June but reappeared the following December. The ecological disturbance caused by clear felling of the virgin forest is believed to have activated a silent enzootic focus of the virus (Fig. 57.2). Forest birds and small mammals are believed to be the reservoir hosts. Infection is transmitted by the bite of ticks, the principal vector being *Haemaphysalis spinigera*. As infection in monkeys leads to fatal disease, they are unlikely to be the primary reservoirs but only amplifer hosts. Haemaphysalis ticks may act as the reservoir to some extent as transovarial transmission of the virus has been demonstrated in them.

Though KFD is related antigenically to the RSSE complex, the RSSE vaccine has not been found to confer any protection against the disease. A killed KFD virus vaccine was used in a small field trial and appeared to provide some degree of protection.

2. *Omsk hemorrhagic fever.* This occurs in Russia and Romania. It is clinically similar to KFD and is caused by a related virus. Dermacentor ticks are the vectors.

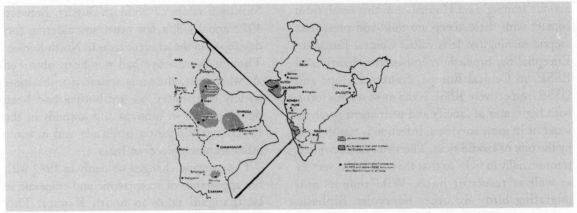

Fig. 57.2 Distribution of Kyasanur Forest Disease (Courtesy: National Institute of Virology, Pune)

BUNYAVIRUSES

This family containing over 300 species is the largest group of arboviruses. The virus is about 100 nm in diameter and has a complex structure, with a triple segmented genome of single stranded RNA.

Most bunyaviruses are mosquitoborne. Some are transmitted by sandflies (for example, Phlebotomus fever) or ticks (Crimean Congo hemorrhagic fever). Some are established pathogens, causing natural diseases, and even epidemics and epizootics, while many have been isolated only from insect vectors and have not been associated with any human or animal disease. Bunyaviruses are so named from the type species Bunyamwera virus isolated from mosquitoes in Uganda in 1946.

The family Bunyaviridae contains four genera of medical importance—Bunyavirus, Phlebovirus, Nairovirus and Hantavirus. A number of viruses are yet ungrouped.

Genus Bunyavirus: The genus contains over 150 species, of which only a few cause human infections. The clinical disease caused is encephalitis, aseptic meningitis and fever. The California encephalitis group of viruses are endemic in the USA. Large epidemics of fever with aseptic meningitis have been caused by Oropouche virus (member of the Simbu group) in Brazil. The midge *Culicoides paraensia* is the major vector for the Oropouche virus.

Genus Phlebovirus: The major members of this genus are the sandfly fever and Rift Valley fever viruses.

Phlebotomus fever or sandfly fever, also known as Pappataci fever and three-day fever, is a self-limited, nonfatal fever transmitted by the bite of the sandfly *Phlebotomus papatasii*. It occurs along the Mediterranean Coast and Central Asia, extending as far east as Pakistan and North West India. Cases have also been reported from South and Central America. Twenty antigenic types of the virus exist, of which only five cause human disease —Naples, Sicilian, Punta Toro, Chagres, Candiru. The virus has been isolated from sandflies and patients in India. No vertebrate host other than humans has been identified. There is evidence for vertical transmission of the virus in sandflies.

Rift Valley fever is a mosquitoborne virus causing enzootic hepatitis in sheep and other domestic animals in Africa. It is named after Rift Valley, Kenya, where it was first recognised. Human infection causes a disease resembling influenza. In 1977–80, Rift Valley fever caused extensive epidemics, with many deaths in Egypt and an outbreak of hemorrhagic fever with many deaths in 1997–98 in Kenya. In 2000, it spread outside Africa for the first time, causing epidemics in Yemen and Saudi Arabia with hundreds of deaths.

Genus Nairovirus: The genus is named after

the type species Nairobi Sheep Disease Virus. Members of the Crimean Congo hemorrhagic group are the major human pathogens in this genus. The Crimean hemorrhagic fever virus, first isolated in Crimea in 1945, was subsequently found to be identical with the Congo fever virus isolated in 1956 in Congo (Zaire), hence the name Crimean Congo Hemorrhagic Fever (CCHF). The disease is endemic in Eastern Europe, Central Asia and many parts of Africa. Cattle, sheep, goats and other domesticated animals act as natural reservoirs. It is transmitted by Hyalomma ticks. During the acute phase of the disease, the blood of the patients is highly infectious and direct transmission may occur through contact. A related virus, Hazara, has been isolated in Pakistan. It is also widespread in Iran, Iraq and the UAE. Antibodies to the CCHF group of viruses have been detected in human and animal sera from India.

Nairobi sheep disease is an acute, hemorrhagic gastroenteritis caused by a Nairovirus in sheep and goats in East Africa. It is transmitted by Rhipicephalus ticks. The virus produces a mild febrile illness in shepherds tending infected flocks.

The Ganjam virus, isolated from ticks collected from sheep and goats in Orissa, India, is closely related to the Nairobi sheep disease virus. The Ganjam virus has also been isolated from human sources. Accidental infection in laboratory workers has caused mild febrile illness.

Genus Hantavirus: This virus causes hemorrhagic fever with renal syndrome (HFRS), also known as endemic or epidemic nephrosonephritis, Manchurian epidemic hemorrhagic fever, nephropathia epidemica, rodent-borne nephropathy and other names. This condition first attracted attention in the early 1950s when a large number of US soldiers serving in Korea got the infection but it has been prevalent in Scandinavia, Russia and China for centuries.

The disease occurs in two forms—the milder epidemic nephritis (EN) common in Scandinavia and the more serious epidemic hemorrhagic fever (EHF) in the far east. The clinical picture resembles typhoid, leptospirosis and scrub typhus.

The genus contains at least four species—Hantaan virus causing the severe HFRS in the Far East, North Asia and Russia, Seoul virus causing a milder type of disease and probably present worldwide, Puumala virus responsible for nephropathia epidemica in Northern and Eastern Europe, and Prospect Hill virus isolated from voles in the USA, which has not been associated with human illness.

Hantavirus species are natural pathogens of rodents—field mice (Apodemus agrarius) being the major host for Hantaan, rats (Rattus rattus and R. norvegicus) for Seoul, and voles for Puumala and Prospect Hill viruses. Viremia is present in infected rodents and the virus is shed in urine, feces and saliva in high titres. Transmission from rodent to rodent and rodent to humans is primarily respiratory, by inhalation of the virus contained in dried excreta. Domestic rats appear to be the source of infection in urban cases of HFRS. Though there are reports of the role of mites in the transmission of the infection, this is not confirmed. In the absence of proved arthropod transmission, HFRS should be considered a robovirus and not strictly an arbovirus infection.

Demonstration of IgM antibody by ELISA or of rising titres of immune adherence hemagglutinating antibodies in paired sera are used for laboratory diagnosis.

A new syndrome, the Hantavirus pulmonary syndrome was identified in south western USA in 1993. After a prodrome of fever, malaise, myalgia and gastrointestinal symptoms, lasting for 3–4 days, patients develop pulmonary involvement with early radiological picture of pulmonary edema, but few physical findings. In severe cases, tachypnea, tachycardia, hypotension and hypoxia lead to death. The disease is caused by a newly identified hantavirus, the Sin Nombre (meaning nameless) virus, which is associated with the deer mouse and other rodents of the sigmodontine subfamily. No arthropod has been linked with transmission of the virus. Infection appears to be caused by inhalation of the virus aerosols in dried rodent feces. Related viruses cause a similar syndrome in many parts of South America.

REOVIRIDAE

The genus *Orbivirus* of the family Reoviridae contains arthropod borne viruses which infect animals and humans that differ from other arboviruses in having double stranded RNA genomes.

The Colorado tick fever virus, an orbivirus, causes a self-limited mild fever without rash. It is spread by the wood tick *Dermacentor andersoni* and the distribution of the disease in Western USA is limited to the habitat of the tick, which acts both as the vector and reservoir. Natural infection occurs in rodents.

The African horse sickness virus, transmitted by *Culicoides*, has for long been known to cause disease among equines in Africa. In 1959–60 it spread eastwards in epizootic waves to Iran, Afghanistan, Pakistan and India. It caused extensive disease among army horses and mules in India.

Palyam, Kasba and Vellore viruses belonging to the orbivirus group have been isolated from mosquitoes in India but their pathogenic significance is not known.

RHABDOVIRIDAE

Chandipura virus, belonging to the *Vesiculovirus* genus of Rhabdoviridae, was isolated in 1967 from the blood of patients during an epidemic of dengue–chikungunya fever in Nagpur. The virus appears to multiply in sandflies and Aedes mosquitoes. Antibodies are common in human sera from different parts of India, as well as in animal sera. The pathogenic significance of this virus has not been established.

UNGROUPED ARBOVIRUSES

A number of arboviruses isolated from insects, animals, birds and human beings have not yet been assigned to any taxonomic group. Examples of ungrouped arboviruses isolated from India are the following:

Wanowri Virus: This was isolated from Hyalomma ticks in India and from the brain of a young girl who died after a two-day fever in Sri Lanka. The virus is also present Iran and Egypt.

Bhanja virus: This was isolated from haemophysalis ticks from goats in Ganjam, Orissa. It virus is present in goats in West Africa and South East Europe. Human infections with disease and death have been reported from Yugoslavia. Laboratory infections also have been recorded.

Further Reading

Banerjee K. 1996. Emerging viral infections with special reference to India. *Ind J Med Res* 103:177.
Fields BN et al (eds). 1996. *Fields' Virology*, 3ʳᵈ edn, Philadelphia: Lippincott-Raven.
Gibbons RV and DW Vaughan 2002. Dengue: an escalating problem. *Br Med J* 324:1563.
Gubler DJ and JT Roehrig 1998. Arboviruses. In *Topley & Wilson's Microbiology and Microbial Infections*, 9ᵗʰ edn. London:Arnold.
Hennessy S et al. 1996. Effectivenes of a live JE vaccine. *Lancet* 347:1583.
Khan AS et al. 1996. Hantavirus pulmonary syndrome. *Lancet* 347:739.

Rhabdoviruses

Bullet shaped, enveloped viruses with single stranded RNA genome are classified as rhabdoviruses (from *rhabdos*, meaning rod). The family Rhabdoviridae contains viruses that infect mammals, reptiles, birds, fishes, insects and plants. Some members multiply in vertebrates and arthropods. Rhabdoviruses infecting mammals belong to two genera, *Vesiculovirus* containing vesicular stomatitis virus and related viruses, and *Lyssavirus* containing rabies virus and related viruses. The name lyssavirus is derived from *lyssa*, meaning rage, a synonym for rabies.

RABIES VIRUS

Morphology: The rabies virus is bullet-shaped,

180 x 75 nm, with one end rounded or conical and the other planar or concave. The lipoprotein envelope carries knob like spikes, composed of glycoprotein G. Spikes do not cover the planar end of the virion. Spikes may be released from the envelope by treatment with lipid solvents or detergents. Beneath the envelope is the membrane or matrix (M) protein layer which may be invaginated at the planar end. The membrane may project outwards from the planar end of some virions forming a bleb. The core of the virion consists of helically arranged ribonucleoprotein. The genome is unsegmented linear negative sense RNA. Also present in the nucleocapsid are RNA dependent RNA transcriptase and some structural proteins.

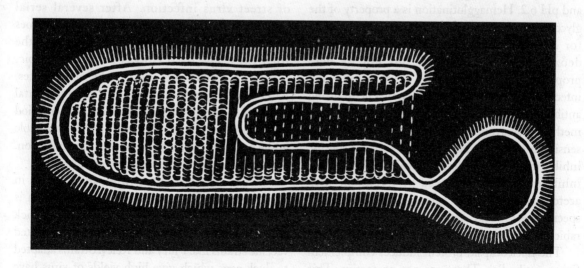

Fig. 58.1 Rabies virus: Bullet shaped virion, showing tightly wound helix of ribonucleoprotein in the core, and bilayered membranous envelope carrying glycoprotein spikes.

Resistance: The virus is sensitive to ethanol, iodine preparations, quaternary ammonium compounds, soap, detergents and lipid solvents such as ether, chloroform and acetone. It is inactivated by phenol, formalin, beta propiolactone, ultraviolet irradiation and sunlight. Thermal inactivation occurs in one hour at 50 °C and five minutes at 60 °C. It dies at room temperature but can survive for weeks when stabilised by 50% glycerol. It survives at 4 °C for weeks. It can be preserved at −70 °C or by lyophilisation. For storage in dry ice, the virus has to be sealed in vials as it is inactivated on exposure to CO_2.

Antigenic properties: The surface spikes are composed of glycoprotein G, which is important in pathogenesis, virulence and immunity. It mediates the binding of the virus to acetyl choline receptors in neural tissues, induces hemagglutination-inhibiting (HI) and neutraling (protective) antibodies and stimulates cytotoxic T cell immunity. It is a serotype specific antigen. The purified glycoprotein may therefore provide a safe and effective subunit vaccine.

Rabies virus possesses hemagglutinating activity, optimally seen with goose erythrocytes at 0–4 °C and pH 6.2. Hemagglutination is a property of the glycoprotein spikes. It is inactivated by heat (56 °C for 30–60 minutes), ether, trypsin, pronase, deoxycholate or Tween 80 but not by beta propiolactone. HI antibodies develop following infection or immunisation and parallel neutralising antibodies. HI tests would therefore provide a useful method of assaying immunity to rabies but the low sensitivity of the test and the presence of nonspecific inhibitors in all sera limit its value. Nonspecific inhibitors can be destroyed by treatment with acetone or kaolin. The hemagglutinin antigen is species specific and distinct from the antigens on rabies related viruses.

The nucleocapsid protein induces complement fixing antibodies. These are not protective. This antigen is group specific and cross-reactions are seen with some rabies related viruses. Antiserum prepared against the nucleocapsid antigen is used in diagnostic immunofluorescence tests. Other antigens identified include two membrane proteins, glycolipid and RNA dependent RNA polymerase.

HOST RANGE AND GROWTH CHARACTERISTICS

Animals: All mammals are susceptible to rabies infection, though differences in susceptibility exist between species. Cattle, cats and foxes are highly susceptible, whereas skunks, opossums and fowl are relatively resistant. Humans and dogs occupy an intermediate position. Pups are more susceptible than adult dogs. Experimental infection can be produced in any laboratory animal but mice are the animals of choice. They can be infected by any route. After intracerebral inoculation, they develop encephalitis and die within 5–30 days.

The rabies virus isolated from natural human or animal infection is termed the *street virus.* Following inoculation by any route, it can cause fatal encephalitis in laboratory animals after a long and variable incubation period of about 1–12 weeks. Intracytoplasmic inclusion bodies (Negri bodies) can be demonstrated in the brain of animals dying of street virus infection. After several serial intracerebral passages in rabbits, the virus undergoes certain changes and becomes what is called the *fixed virus.* The fixed virus is more neurotropic, though it is much less infective by other routes. After intracerebral inoculation, it produces fatal encephalitis after a short and fixed incubation period of 6–7 days. Negri bodies are usually not demonstrable in the brain of animals dying of fixed virus infection. The fixed virus is used for vaccine production.

Chick embryos: The rabies virus can be grown in chick embryos. The usual mode of inoculation is into the yolk sac. Serial propagation in chick embryos has led to the development of attenuated vaccine strains like Flury and Kelev. Strains adapted to duck eggs which give high yields of virus have been used for the preparation of inactivated vaccines.

Tissue culture: The rabies virus can grow in several primary and continuous cell cultures such as chick embryo fibroblast, porcine or hamster kidney but cytopathic effects are not apparent and the yield of virus is low. The fixed virus strains adapted for growth in human diploid cell, chick embryo and vero cell cultures are used for the production of vaccines.

RABIES

Rabies has been recognised from very ancient times as a disease transmitted to humans and animals by the bite of 'mad dogs'. The name 'rabies' comes from the Latin word *rabidus*, meaning mad, derived from the Sanskrit root *rabhas*, for frenzy. Reference to rabies occurs in the Mesopotamian laws of Eshnunna (Circa 2200 BC). The disease was traditionally associated with the appearance of the Dog Star Sirius in the 'dog days' of summer when dogs were considered to be prone to spells of 'madness'. The disease in human beings is called *hydrophobia* because the patient exhibits fear of water, being incapable of drinking though subject to intolerable thirst. Rabies in animals is not called hydrophobia because they do not have this peculiar feature.

The causative agent of rabies had, for centuries, been associated with the saliva of rabid dogs but it was only in 1804 that Zinke adduced proof by transmitting the disease to normal dogs by the inoculation of saliva from rabid dogs. In 1821, Magendie and Breschet infected dogs with saliva from a human patient, proving the identity of the agent causing human and animal rabies. In a series of studies dating from 1881, Pasteur established that the rabies virus was present in the brain of infected animals. By serial intracerebral passage in rabbits, he obtained the fixed virus and demonstrated that dogs could be rendered immune by a series of injections of fixed virus of graded infectivity. This vaccine was prepared by drying for various periods pieces of spinal cord from rabbits infected with the fixed virus. In July 1885, Joseph Meister, a nine-year-old boy, severely bitten by a rabid dog and in grave risk of developing rabies, was given a course of 13 inoculations of the infected cord vaccine by Pasteur. The boy survived. This dramatic event was a milestone in the development of medicine.

Pathogenesis: Human infection is usually caused by the bite of rabid dogs or other animals. The virus present in the saliva of the animal is deposited in the wound. If untreated, about half of such cases may develop rabies. Rarely, infection can also occur following non-bite exposures such as licks or aerosols or transplantation of cornea or other virus infected tissues. Humans appear to possess a high degree of natural resistance to rabies. The extent of inapparent or abortive infection with rabies virus in humans is not known but the finding, in a survey, of rabies antibodies in six per cent of veterinarians without any history of antirabic vaccination suggests that it does occur.

The virus appears to multiply in the muscles, connective tissue or nerves at the site of deposition for 48–72 hours. It penetrates the nerve endings and travels in the axoplasm towards the spinal cord and brain. The movement of the virus in the axons is passive, at a speed of about 3 mm per hour. The infection spreads centripetally from the axon to the neuronal bodies, and progressively up the spinal cord through the synapses of the neurons. The virus ascends rapidly to the brain where it multiplies and spreads centrifugally along the nerve trunks to various parts of the body including the salivary glands. It multiplies in the salivary glands and is shed in the saliva. The presence of the virus in the saliva and the irritability and aggression brought on by the encephalitis ensure the transmission and survival of the virus in nature. The virus ultimately reaches virtually every tissue in the body, though the centrifugal dissemination may be interrupted at any stage by death. The virus is almost invariably present in the cornea and the facial skin of patients because of their proximity to the brain. This provides a method for the antemortem diagnosis of human rabies. The virus may also be shed in milk and urine. Viremia is not clinically significant though it has been demonstrated under experimental conditions.

In humans the incubation period is usually from 1–3 months, though it may be as short as 7 days or as long as three years. The incubation period is usually short in persons bitten on the face or head, and long in those bitten on the legs. This may be related to the distance the virus has to travel to reach the brain. The incubation period is generally shorter in children than in adults.

The course of the disease in humans can be classified into four stages—prodrome, acute encephalitic phase, coma and death. The onset is marked by prodromal symptoms such as fever, headache, malaise, fatigue and anorexia. An early symptom is often a neuritic type of pain or paresthesia and fasciculation at the site of virus entry. Apprehension, anxiety, agitation, irritability, nervousness, insomnia or depression characterise the prodromal phase, which usually lasts 2–4 days. Excessive libido, priapism and spontaneous ejaculation may occur rarely.

The acute neurological phase usually begins with hyperactivity, which is characteristically intermittent, with bouts of bizarre behaviour, agitation or seizures appearing between apparently normal periods. Such hyperactivity may be spontaneous or precipitated by external stimuli. The pathognomonic feature is difficulty in drinking, together with intense thirst. Patients may be able to swallow dry solids but not liquids. Attempts to drink bring on such painful spasms of the pharynx and larynx producing choking or gagging that patients develop a dread of even the sight or sound of water (hydrophobia). Generalised convulsions follow. Death usually occurs within 1–6 days due to respiratory arrest during convulsions.

Some patients progress to paralysis. In rare cases, hyperactivity may not be prominent and paralytic features dominate from the beginning. Such paralytic disease is more common in Latin America and Trinidad after exposure to vampire bat rabies,

and in those who have received postexposure vaccination. Patients who survive the stage of acute neurological involvement lapse into coma, which may last for hours or days. Death is due to respiratory arrest or other complications.

Some persons exposed to real or imaginary risk of rabies develop a psychological disorder which has been called lyssaphobia or hydrophobiophobia. Patients present with anxiety, irritability and exaggerated hydrophobia. They are afebrile. Sedation and reassurance are generally all that are called for.

In dogs, the incubation period is usually 3–6 weeks but it may range from 10 days to a year. The initial signs are an alert, troubled air and a change in disposition with restlessness, snapping at imaginary objects, licking or gnawing at the site of the bite. After 2–3 days of this prodromal stage, the disease develops into either the *furious* or *dumb* type of rabies. In *furious rabies,* which is much more common, the dog runs amok, biting without provocation and indiscriminately. The lower jaw droops and saliva drools from the mouth. Paralysis, convulsions and death follow. The second type, *dumb rabies*, is the paralytic form in which the animal lies huddled, unable to feed. The dog may not bite but attempts to feed it are dangerous. The dumb form is as infectious as the furious type. About 60 per cent of rabid dogs shed the virus in saliva. Rabid dogs usually die in 3–5 days.

There have been reports of persons developing rabies after being bitten by apparently healthy dogs. However, in countries like India where stray dogs are so common, it is not always easy to exclude the possibility of such patients having been bitten earlier by other animals. The presence and prevalence of rabies virus carrier state in dogs has been a matter of controversy and concern. If at all, this is a very rare event. The possibility of carrier dogs has not so far altered the recommendations for postexposure treatment.

Rabies in cats is similar to canine rabies. Feline rabies is an important source of human infection in countries like the USA, where rabies in domestic dogs is rare. In cattle and horses, rabies manifests as irritability, restlessness and unusual aggressiveness but it is a dead end as they hardly ever bite humans or other animals. In wild animals, the chief characteristic of rabies is the loss of fear of man and other animals. Unprovoked attacks by jackals or other wild animals should be taken as indication of rabies.

Histopathological changes in the brain are minor compared to the clinical evidence of severe neurological damage and the fatal outcome. Vascular congestion, perivascular infiltration and cerebral edema, with some neuronal destruction, are the usual findings. Demyelination in the white matter is common. In the spinal cord, the posterior horns are more severely involved. Some degree of leptomeningitis is common. The greater localisation of the virus in the limbic system, with relative sparing of the neocortex, correlates with the alertness, aggressiveness and loss of natural timidity seen in clinical rabies. The characteristic histopathological feature in rabies is the intracytoplasmic inclusion body (Negri body) in the neurons, most abundant in the cerebellum and hippocampus. Negri bodies are composed of a finely fibrillar matrix and rabies virus particles.

Laboratory Diagnosis

Human rabies: Laboratory diagnosis of human rabies till recently was of little practical importance as death was considered inevitable and no serious attempt at treatment was made, other than heavy sedation. If a patient survived, he was considered not to have had rabies! But now that survival from established rabies has been demonstrated in rare instances, it is necessary to be able to make laboratory distinction between rabies and other forms of encephalitis, particularly that following antirabic vaccination.

The method most commonly used for diagnosis is the demonstration of rabies virus antigens by immunofluorescence. The specimens tested are corneal smears and skin biopsy (from face or neck) or saliva antemortem, and brain postmortem. Direct immunofluorescence is done using antirabies serum tagged with fluorescein isothiocyanate. The use of monoclonal antibody instead of crude antiserum makes the test more specific.

Diagnosis may be made postmortem by the demonstration of Negri bodies in the brain, but they may be absent in about 20 per cent of cases.

Isolation of the virus by intracerebral inoculation in mice can be attempted from the brain, CSF, saliva and urine. Chances of isolation are greater early in the disease. A few days after onset, neutralising antibodies appear and the virus can then be isolated only occasionally. The inoculated mice are examined for signs of illness, and their brains are examined at death or at 28 days postinoculation for Negri bodies, or by immunofluorescence.

A more rapid and sensitive method is isolation of the virus in tissue culture cell lines (WI 38, BHK 21, CER). CPE is minimal and so virus isolation is identified by immunofluorescence. A positive IF test can be obtained as early as 2–4 days after inoculation. The identity of the isolate can be established by the neutralisation test with specific antirabies antibody.

High titre antibodies are present in the CSF in rabies but not after immunisation. Their demonstration can therefore be used for diagnosis.

Detection of rabies virus RNA by reverse transcription PCR is a sensitive method, if facilities are available.

Animal rabies: Laboratory diagnosis of rabies in dogs and other biting animals is of great importance in assessing the risk of infection and deciding postexposure treatment. The whole carcass or the severed head of the animal suspected to have died of rabies may be sent to the laboratory. Alternatively, the brain may be removed carefully and two portions, one in 50% glycerol saline and the other in Zenker's fixative, sent for biological test and microscopy, respectively. The portion of brain sent should include the hippocampus and cerebellum as Negri bodies are most abundant there. The following tests are done in the laboratory:

1. *Demonstration of rabies virus antigen by immunofluorescence:* In experienced hands, this is more sensitive than the visualisation of Negri bodies, and quite as sensitive as the 'biological' (mouse inoculation) test, with the advantage of immediate results. Examination of salivary glands by immunofluorescence is useful. It may indicate whether the animal was shedding the virus in the saliva.

2. *Demonstration of inclusion bodies:* This is still the method most commonly used as facilities for immunofluorescence and biological tests are not available in many laboratories. Impression smears of the brain are stained by Seller's technique (basic fuchsin and methylene blue in methanol), which has the advantage that fixation and staining are done simultaneously. Negri bodies are seen as intracytoplasmic, round or oval, purplish pink structures with characteristic basophilic inner granules. Negri bodies vary in size from 3–27 μm (Fig. 58.2). Other types of inclusion bodies may sometimes be seen in the brain in diseases such as canine distemper but the presence of inner structures in the Negri bodies makes differentiation easy. If impression smears are negative, the tissue should be sectioned and stained by Giemsa or Mann's method. Failure to find Negri bodies does not exclude the diagnosis of rabies.

3. *Isolation of the rabies virus (biological test):* This is done as described above, for human rabies diagnosis.

Prophylaxis: Specific prophylaxis is ideally given before exposure to infection. In animals, this is imperative but human pre-exposure immunisation was only employed in persons at high risk, such as veterinarians and dog handlers because neural vaccines carry some risk of serious complications. The introduction of cell culture vaccines, which are free from serious complications, has made pre-exposure immunisation in humans safe and feasible.

Specific prophylaxis is generally employed after exposure to infection and is therefore called antirabic treatment. This consists of local treatment, antirabic vaccines and hyperimmune serum.

Local treatment: Animal bites deposit the virus in the wounds. Prompt cauterisation of the wounds therefore helps to destroy the virus. The wound should be immediately scrubbed well with soap and water. This is a very important step in the prevention of rabies as soap destroys the virus effectively. After washing the soap away completely, the wound is treated with quaternary ammonium compounds (such as cetavlon), tincture or aqueous solution of iodine, or alcohol (40–70 per cent). In severe wounds, antirabic serum may be applied topically and infiltrated around the wound. It is advisable to postpone suturing the wound. Antitetanus measures and antibiotics to prevent sepsis may be used as necessary.

Antirabic vaccines: Antirabic vaccines fall into two main categories: neural and non-neural. The former are associated with serious risk of neurological complications and have been replaced by the latter.

Neural vaccines: These are suspensions of nervous tissues of animals infected with the fixed rabies virus. The earliest was Pasteur's cord vaccine prepared by drying over caustic potash, for varying periods, pieces of infected rabbit spinal cord. This was replaced by infected brain vaccines, of which there have been several preparations.

1. *Semple vaccine:* This vaccine developed by Semple (1911) at the Central Research Institute, Kasauli (India), had been the most widely used vaccine for over half a century. It is a 5% suspension of sheep brain infected with fixed virus and inactivated with phenol at 37 °C, leaving no residual live virus.

2. *Beta propiolactone (BPL) vaccine:* This is a modification of the Semple vaccine, in which beta propiolactone is used as the inactivating agent instead of phenol. It is believed to be more antigenic, so that smaller doses are considered adequate. The major antirabic vaccine producing

laboratories in India manufacture BPL vaccine.

3. *Infant brain vaccines:* The encephalitogenic factor in brain tissue is a basic protein associated with myelin. It is scanty or absent in the nonmyelinated neural tissue of newborn animals. So vaccines were developed using infant mouse, rat or rabbit brain. Occasional cases of neurological reactions have occurred following infant brain vaccines also. Infant brain vaccine is impractical in India due to the very large quantities required.

Neural vaccines are unsatisfactory for many reasons. They are poor immunogens as they contain mostly nucleocapsid antigen, with only small quantities of glycoprotein G, which is the sole protective antigen. They may contain infectious agents which may not be inactivated during vaccine preparation and storage. They are encephalitogenic. Neural vaccines have been abandoned in the developed countries. The only reason for their continued production and use in a few developing countries is that they are cheap.

NON-NEURAL VACCINES

1. *Egg vaccines:* (a) *Duck egg vaccine* prepared from a fixed virus adapted for growth in duck eggs and inactivated with beta propiolactone was used, but was discontinued because of its poor immunogenicity. A purified, more potent duck egg vaccine was developed, but was supplanted by tissue culture vaccines which became available then. (b) Live attenuated chick embryo vaccines: two types of vaccines were developed with the Flury strain–the Low Egg Passage (LEP) vaccine at 40–50 egg passage level for immunisation of dogs and the High Egg Passage (HEP) vaccine at 180 passage level for cattle and cats. these are not in use now.

2. *Tissue culture vaccines:* The first cell culture vaccine was the human diploid cell (HDC) vaccine developed by Koprowsky, Wiktor and Plotkin. It is a purified and concentrated preparation of fixed rabies virus (Pitman–Moore

strain) grown on human diploid cells (WI 38 or MRC 5) and inactivated with beta propiolactone or tri-n-butyl phosphate. It is highly antigenic and free from serious side effects. Its only disadvantage is its high cost.

Other equally effective and more economical vaccines have been developed. These include: *primary cell culture* vaccines grown on chick embryo, hamster kidney and dog kidney cells and *continuous cell culture* vaccines grown on *Vero cell line* derived from the kidneys of vervet monkey or African green monkey (*Cercopithecus aethiops*).

In India the following cell culture vaccines are available: Human diploid cell (HDC) vaccine *Purified chick embryo cell (PCEC) vaccine* and *Purified vero cell (PVC) vaccine.* All three of them are equally safe and effective.

3. *Subunit vaccine:* The glycoprotein subunit on the virus surface, which is the protective antigen, has been cloned and recombinant vaccines produced. They are still in the experimental stage.

VACCINATION SCHEDULES

Antirabic vaccine should be administered when a person has been bitten, scratched or licked by an animal which is rabid or cannot be apprehended. When the biting animal can be observed, it should not be destroyed but should be kept for ten days. The observation period of ten days is recommended because the virus may be present in the saliva 3–4 days before onset of symptoms and the animal usually dies within 5–6 days of developing the disease. If the animal remains healthy after this period, there is no risk of rabies and vaccination, if already started, may be discontinued. This, of course, does not take into account the rare possibility of the carrier state in dogs.

In cases where the vaccine is started with the biting animal kept under observation, an alternative recommendation is to stop treatment after five days. The animal is observed for a further five days, vaccine being started again if the animal becomes ill or dies during the period.

Neural vaccines: The dosage of the vaccine depends on the degree of risk to which the patient has been exposed. Accordingly, patients are classified as follows:

Class I: Patients in whom the risk is estimated to be slight. These include:

a. Licks, including direct contact with saliva on definitely remembered fresh cuts or abrasions on all parts of the body except the head, face, neck or fingers.

b. Licks on intact mucous membrane or conjunctiva.

c. Bites or scratches which have raised the epidermis but have not drawn blood, on all parts of the body except the head, face, neck or fingers.

d. Consumption of unboiled milk or handling raw flesh of rabid animals.

Class II: Persons who are estimated to be at moderate risk. These include:

a. Licks on definitely remembered fresh cuts or abrasions on the fingers.

b. All bites or scratches on the fingers which are not lacerated, not more than half a centimetre long and have not penetrated the true skin.

c. Bites or scratches on all parts of the body except the head, face, neck or fingers which have drawn blood but excluding bites which have five teeth marks or more, or in which extensive laceration has occurred.

Class III: Persons in whom the risk is estimated to be great. These include:

a. Licks on definitely remembered fresh cuts or abrasions on head, face or neck.

b. All bites or scratches on the head, face or neck.

c. All bites or scratches on the fingers which are lacerated, more than half centimetre. long or have penetrated the true skin.

d. All bites penetrating the true skin and drawing blood, when there are five teeth marks or more.

e. All bites on any part of the body causing extensive laceration.

f. All jackal and wolf bites.

g. Any Class II patient who has not received treatment within 14 days of exposure.

The recommended schedule of vaccination for the different classes is as follows:

	Semple vaccine	BPL vaccine
Class I	2 ml x 7 days	2 ml x 7 days
Class II	5 ml x 14 days	3 ml x 10 days
Class III	10 ml x 14 days	5 ml x 10 days

The above schedule for the BPL vaccine is recommended by the Pasteur Institute, Coonoor. The Central Research Institute, Kasauli, recommends a slightly different dosage for its vaccine. *(The manufacturer's instructions should be followed in every case).*

The immunity following vaccination with neural vaccines is expected to last for six months only and any exposure later should receive fresh treatment. The vaccine is administered subcutaneously on the anterior abdominal wall.

Antirabic vaccine may cause certain adverse reactions. These range from minor local reactions to serious neuroparalytic complications. The latter may be of the neuritic type, the dorsilumbar type, the Landry type of ascending paralysis or encephalomyelitis. The etiology of neurological complication is believed to be immune response to the injected brain tissue resulting in organ specific immunological damage as in experimental allergic encephalomyelitis. These complications usually occur within 1–4 weeks of commencement of vaccination. The incidence of complications varies with different vaccines, one in 2000 to one in 12,000. When such complications are noticed during the course of vaccination, further vaccination should be withheld and the patient started on corticosteroids. If further vaccination is considered imperative, non-neural vaccine should be used. Severe exertion and the use of alcohol during vaccination have been said to increase the risk of neurological reactions.

Cell culture vaccines: All three cell culture vaccines available in India (HDC, PCEC and PVC)

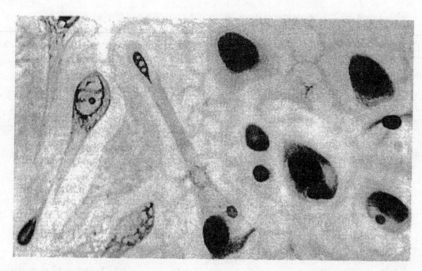

Fig. 58.2 Negri bodies: Ovoid inclusions in the cytoplasm of neurons in rabid dog brain

have the same dosage schedule, which is the same for both adults and children.

Pre-exposure prophylaxis requires three doses of the vaccine injected on day 0, 7, 21 or 0, 28 and 56. A booster dose is recommended after one year and then one every five years.

Postexposure prophylaxis requires five or six doses, on days 0, 3, 7, 14, 30 and optionally 90. This course is expected to give protection for at least five years, during which period any further exposure may need only one or two booster doses (on days 0, 3) depending on the degree of risk. After five years, it is advisable to give a full five injection course if exposed to infection.

The vaccine is to be given IM or SC in the deltoid region, or in children on the anterolateral aspect of the thigh. Gluteal injections are to be avoided as they are found to be less immunogenic.

It has been shown that a dose of 0.1 ml administered intradermally is as effective as a 0.5–1.0 ml dose SC or IM and that immunisation may thus be made more economical. However, this is not recommended as a routine practice, as intradermal injection is technically difficult, and it will be ineffective if this dose is given subcutaneously by mistake.

Passive immunisation: Antirabic serum is manufactured by hyper immunisation of horses. Crude equine antirabies serum is not to be used as it is liable to induce anaphylactic reactions. Purified equine rabies immune globulin (ERIG) is much safer, though not completely free from risk. Human rabies immune globulin (HRIG) is free from the danger of sensitisation but should be ensured free from HIV and hepatitis viruses. HRIG is much costlier than ERIG.

Passive immunisation is an important adjunct to vaccination and should be invariably employed whenever the exposure is considered of high risk. The recommended dose of HRIG is 20 IU/kg body weight, half the volume infiltrated at the site of the wound and the other half injected in the gluteal region. Passive immunisation should be given before or simultaneously with the first injection of the vaccine, but not after it. In persons receiving the serum and vaccine, a booster dose of cell culture vaccine on day 90 may be given.

Recommendations for postexposure prophylaxis, as endorsed by the WHO in 1988, are shown in

'*Vaccine failures*' (persons developing rabies even after a full course of immunisation) are not uncommon with neural vaccines, while they are

Table 58.1 Recommendation for postexposure prophylaxis (WHO)

Category of risk	Type of exposure	Recommended prophylaxis
I	Touching or feeding of animals; licks on intact skin	None (if history is reliable).
II	Nibbling of uncovered skin; minor scratches or abrasions without bleeding; licks on broken skin	Start vaccine. May be discontinued if animal is well after 10 days
III	Transdermal bites or scratches – contamination of mucous membrane with saliva	Rabies immune globulin vaccine to be started. May be discontinued if animal is well after 10 days

extremely rare when immediate local treatment has been followed by rabies immunoglobulin and a full course of a cell culture vaccine. In view of the safety of the cell culture vaccine, it would be advisable to recommend the vaccine even when there is the slightest risk of exposure to rabies.

Vaccine for animals: Antirabies immunisation in animals is to be done as pre-exposure prophylaxis. Postexposure treatment is not generally of much use. Neural vaccines are not satisfactory as they are not adequately immunogenic, need multiple doses and have to be repeated every six months. Concentrated cell culture vaccines containing inactivated virus are now available, which give good protection after a single IM injection. Injections are given at 12 weeks of age and repeated at 1–3 year intervals. Rabies vaccines may be given separately or as combined vaccine for immunisation against other common veterinary infections also.

Treatment: Until recently, rabies was considered to be invariably fatal and no serious attempt at treatment was made, apart from sedation. It has now been demonstrated that complete recovery can occur from established rabies, with intensive supportive care and management of complications. No specific antirabies agent is available.

Epidemiology: Human rabies is a dead end. Direct person-to-person transmission of rabies has not been recorded, though the virus is present in the saliva of patients. Therefore, there is no danger in examining or nursing hydrophobia patients provided suitable precautions are taken. An unusual mode of transmission of rabies has occurred in some recipients of corneal grafts. The donors had died of unsuspected rabies and the infection was transmitted through the cornea.

Rabies virus is present in terrestrial animals in all parts of the world except Australasia and Antartica, and some islands like Britain. Two epidemiological types of rabies exist, – Urban, transmitted by domestic animals like dogs and cats; and sylvatic, involving animals in the wild, such as jackals, wolves, foxes, mongooses, skunks and bats. Most cases of human rabies follow dog bites but in endemic areas almost any animal can transmit rabies. In India, antirabic treatment is to be considered following the bite of any animal except rats. Where urban or domestic rabies has been controlled, as in the USA, the majority of infections are due to bites by wild animals.

The primary source of the rabies virus in nature seems to be in the mustelids and viverrids, the ermine in the northern coniferous forests, the skunk, mink and weasel in North America, the mottled pole cat in the USSR, the civet and pole cat in Africa and the mongoose in Asia. Rabies virus has been isolated repeatedly from the brain and salivary glands of apparently healthy wild rodents. The virus survives in this reservoir population by achieving a state of latency with occasional activation such that only a small proportion of them will be shedding the virus at any one time. From the reservoir species, wild vectors such as foxes, wolves and jackals acquire the infection and occasionally epizootics occur in these species. Carnivorous animals may acquire the infection by eating carcasses containing the virus. From these species the disease spreads to dogs and other domestic animals.

A smouldering epizootic of rabies in the red fox in Europe had spread westwards steadily from Poland to France during the last few decades. Vaccine baits (chicken head or other meat containing live attenuated rabies virus) have been used to immunise the red fox in an attempt to check the epizootic in the forests of Europe.

Another natural cycle of rabies concerns bats. A fatal paralytic disease of cattle and humans was noticed in Central and South America and the West Indies early in the twentieth Century. This was identified as rabies only years later. The disease was shown to be transmitted by vampire bats that sweep down on their prey at night. Vampire bat rabies had taken a heavy toll of cattle. Vampire bats may

shed the rabies virus as symptomless carriers over a period of several months.

Rabies also occurs in insectivorous and frugivorous bats. Infection in insectivorous bats is symptomatic, while frugivorous bats become asymptomatic carriers. While in canines rabies is neurotropic, in bats the virus is primarily adapted to the respiratory tract. Humans may be infected by aerosols if they enter caves where infected bats colonise. Pneumotropic rabies virus strains have been obtained from bats. Bat rabies is largely confined to the Americas. A few strains of the rabies virus have been isolated from bats in Europe but their epidemiological significance is not known.

Rabies is endemic in India. It has been estimated that more than 30,000 people die of rabies in India every year and more than 700,000 receive antirabies vaccine. Human rabies can be checked by control of rabies in domestic animals, by registration, licensing and vaccination of pets and destruction of stray animals. With the dog population in India estimated as over 16 million, the problem is immense. However, rabies can be eliminated only if the wild vectors such as jackals and foxes, and the reservoir mustelids and viverrids are controlled. Rabies has been eliminated from islands like Britain and Japan by rigid quarantine. Australia which has

Table 58.2 Lyssavirus sero/genotypes

Genotype/ Serotype	Virus	Isolated from	Distribution
1	Rabies	Warm blooded animals	Worldwide with few exceptions
2	Lagos bat/ Natal bat	Bat/cat	Nigeria/Central and SouthAfrica
3	Mokola	Shrew/cat/dog/human	Nigeria/other African countries
4	Duvenhage	Human/bat	South Africa
5	European bat lyssavirus: Type I	Bat/human	Europe
6	European bat lyssavirus: Type II	Bat/human	Europe
7	Australian bat lyssavirus:	Bat/human	Australia

no native mustelid or viverrid population has no rabies. Eradication of rabies from countries like India with abundant wildlife may not be practicable.

RABIES RELATED VIRUSES

The genus Lyssavirus consists of the rabies virus and other serologically related viruses. Lyssaviruses have been classified into seven serotypes.

1. Rabies virus is classified as Lyssavirus serotype 1
2. The Lagos bat virus, classified as Lyssavirus serotype 2, was isolated in 1956 from the pooled brains of frugivorous bats from Lagos Island, Nigeria. It causes a rabies-like illness following intracerebral inoculation. Negri bodies are found in infected monkey brain but not in mice or dogs.
3. The Mokola virus, first isolated in 1968 from shrews captured near Ibadan, Nigeria, has later been found in many wild and domestic animals in Africa. It was also recovered from two children with central nervous system disease, one of whom died. A case of laboratory infection with the virus occurred in a person possessing high titres of antibody to the rabies virus. It is classified as Lyssavirus serotype 3.
4. The Duvenhage virus was reported in 1971 from the brain of a man who died in South Africa of clinical rabies after being bitten by a bat. It is classified as Lyssavirus serotype 4.
5. 6. Rabies-like viruses isolated from European bats have been classified into two groups: European bat lyssavirus types 1 and 2. They can infect humans, as was found in the UK in 2002, when a wildlife worker fell ill with 'rabies' and died. This was the first 'rabies' death in the UK in a century.
7. Australia was considered free of rabies and related viruses till 1996, when a lyssavirus was isolated from a frugivorous bat. Since then a number of similar isolates have been obtained from different types of bats in Australia. Fatal infections have occurred in persons having contact with bats. The virus antibody is widely prevalent among Australian bats which appear to be carriers. The virus, named *Australian bat lyssavirus* is closely related to, but distinct from the rabies virus. Antirabic vaccine and serum appear to protect against experimental infection.

The relevance of rabies related viruses in human disease is not clear, though some of them have caused illness and death in humans. They are considered to represent a biological bridge between the rabies virus and other rhabdoviruses.

Further Reading

Baer GM. 1991. *The Natural History of Rabies*, Boston: CRC Press.
Fishbein BD and LE Robinson 1993. Rabies, *New Engl J Med* 329:1632.
Rupprecht CE et al. 1994. Lyssaviruses. *Current Topics in Microbiol Immunol* 187.
Smith JS et al. 1990. Unexplained rabies in three immigrants in the United States. *New Eng J Med 324:1990.*
Smith JS. 1996. *New aspects of rabies. Clin Microbiol Rev* 9:166.
WHO. 1992. *Expert Committee on Rabies*, 8th Report. Technical Series No. 824, Geneva.

Hepatitis Viruses

The term 'viral hepatitis' refers to a primary infection of the liver by any one of a heterogeneous group of 'hepatitis viruses', which currently consists of types A, B, C, D, E and G. (The designation 'type F' had been proposed for a putative virus believed to cause transfusion-associated hepatitis, distinct from type A to E. But it proved to be a mutant (HBx) of type B virus and not a separate entity. Type F was therefore deleted from the list of hepatitis viruses.)

Hepatitis viruses are taxonomically unrelated. Except for type B which is a DNA virus all the others are RNA viruses. The features common to them are their hepatotropism and ability to cause a similar icteric illness, ranging in severity from the unapparent to the fulminant fatal forms.

As all types of hepatitis viruses cause a clinically indistinguishable acute illness, their differentiation is based on their serological and molecular markers. Hepatitis may occur incidentally during many other viral infections, such as with yellow fever, Lassa fever, Marburg, EB, cytomegalo, herpes simplex, varicella zoster, measles, rubella or coxsackie viruses. These are not included in the category of viral hepatitis.

By epidemiological and clinical criteria, two types of viral hepatitis had been recognised for long. One type occurred sporadically or as epidemics, affecting mainly children and young adults, and transmitted by the fecal–oral route. This was called *infective* or *infectious hepatitis,* later termed type A hepatitis. A second type of viral hepatitis, transmitted mainly by inoculation was originally observed in persons receiving serum inoculation or blood transfusion. This had been given various names such as *homologous serum jaundice, serum hepatitis* (because of its association with human or homologous antisera so commonly used for prophylaxis or therapy early in the twentieth century) and *transfusion hepatitis.* It was later called *type B hepatitis.*

For a time it was believed that all viral hepatitis was caused by either of the two hepatitis viruses, type A accounting for all infectious hepatitis and type B for all post-transfusion or serum hepatitis. However, with the development of techniques for identifying type A and type B viruses, it became apparent that in many cases of infectious and post-transfusion hepatitis no evidence could be found of infection with either type A or B viruses. It therefore became evident that the clinical syndrome of type A or B hepatitis could also be caused by one or more other uncharacterised viruses. The term *non-A non-B hepatitis* was applied to this group. Soon a type C virus was identified as causing many transfusion-associated hepatitis cases. A defective virus which depends on the helper functions of type B virus was called delta or type D hepatitis viruses. Yet another type of hepatitis transmitted by the fecal-oral route, prevalent mostly in the developing nations was found to be caused by hepatitis E virus. The sixth member of the group, hepatitis G virus can also cause hepatitis, but its role has not yet been adequately understood.

TYPE A HEPATITIS

Type A hepatitis (infectious hepatitis) is a subacute disease of global distribution, affecting mainly children and young adults.

Clinical features: The large majority of infections are asymptomatic. Overt illness is seen in only about 5 per cent of those infected. The incubation period is 2–6 weeks. The clinical disease consists of two stages: the prodromal or preicteric and the icteric stages. The onset may be acute or insidious, with fever, malaise, anorexia, nausea, vomiting and liver tenderness. These usually subside with the onset of jaundice. Recovery is slow, over a period of 4–6 weeks. Very rarely a rapidly fatal fulminant hepatitis may occur. The disease is milder in children, in whom many infections may be anicteric. Mortality is low (0.1–1 per cent), with most of the deaths occurring in adults.

Hepatitis A virus (HAV): In 1973, Feinstone and coworkers, using immunoelectron microscopy (IEM) demonstrated this virus in the feces of experimentally infected human volunteers. Chimpanzees and marmosets can be infected experimentally. HAV can be grown in some human and simian cell cultures and is the only human hepatitis virus which can be cultivated in vitro. It has also been cloned.

HAV is a 27 nm nonenveloped RNA virus belonging to the picornavirus family. It was originally designated as 'enterovirus 72'. Because of its unique features. HAV is now recognised as the prototype of a new genus *Hepatovirus*. Only one serotype of the virus is known.

HAV is resistant to inactivation by heat at 60 °C for one hour, ether and acid at pH3, but is inactivated by boiling for one minute, 1:4000 formaldehyde at 37 °C for 72 hours, and chlorine 1 ppm for 30 minutes. It is not affected by anionic detergents. It survives prolonged storage at a temperature of 4 °C or below.

Epidemiology: Natural infection with HAV is seen only in humans. Though primates such as chimpanzees have been shown to acquire the infection from humans and transmit it to human contacts, there is no evidence of any extrahuman source of the virus in nature.

HAV transmission is by the fecal–oral route. Infection is by ingestion. The virus multiplies in the intestinal epithelium and reaches the liver by hematogenous spread. It is shed in feces during the late incubation period and prodromal phase of the illness. Once jaundice develops, it is rarely detectable in feces. Chronic carriers are not seen. Virus persistence in nature depends on continuing inapparent infections.

A brief viremia occurs during the preicteric phase, but ceases with the onset of jaundice. Chronic viremia does not occur. Parenteral transmission is therefore very rare. Infection has been reported in recipients of some clotting factor concentrates. Transplacental infection has not been documented. HAV may be present occasionally in the saliva and urine of patients, but this is not considered relevant in its spread.

Type A hepatitis occurs sporadically or as outbreaks, which may be caused by contaminated food, water or milk. Shellfish has been known to be responsible for outbreaks. Domestic or institutional spread of infection among children is common. Overcrowding and poor sanitation favour its spread.

The epidemiology of type A hepatitis resembles that of poliomyelitis. In the developing countries, infection is acquired in childhood and by the age of ten, 90 per cent of the population possess antibody to the virus and are immune. In India, type A hepatitis is the most common cause of acute hepatitis in children, but is much less frequent in adults. In affluent countries, and even in those developing countries with improved personal hygiene and sanitation, its incidence has been declining, with an upward shift in the age group affected. In the temperate regions, the disease shows an autumn-winter predilection, but in the tropics no seasonal distribution is evident. In India, the disease tends to be associated with heavy rainfall.

Laboratory diagnosis: Etiological diagnosis of type A hepatitis may be made by demonstration of the virus or its antibody. The virus can be visualised by IEM in fecal extracts during the late incubation period and the preicteric phase, but seldom later. HAV tests are not widely available or useful in practice. Diagnosis is usually by detection of antibody. IgM anti-HAV antibody appears during the late incubation period, reaches peak levels in 2–3 weeks and disappears after 3–4 months. IgG antibody appears at about the same time, peaks in 3–4 months and persists much longer, perhaps for life (Fig. 59.1). Demonstration of IgM antibody in serum indicates current or recent infection, while IgG antibody denotes recent or remote infection and immunity. ELISA kits for detection of IgM and IgG antibodies are available.

Prophylaxis: General prophylaxis consists of improved sanitary practices and prevention of fecal contamination of food and water.

Specific passive prophylaxis by pooled normal human immunoglobulin (16% solution in a dose of 0.2–0.12 ml/kg body weight) IM, before exposure or in early incubation period, can prevent or attenuate clinical illness, while not necessarily preventing infection and virus excretion.

A safe and effective formalin inactivated, alum conjugaged vaccine containing HAV grown in human diploid cell culture is available. A full course consists of two intramuscular injections of the vaccine. Protection begins 4 weeks after injection and lasts for 10 to 20 years.

Natural infection with HAV, clinical or subclinical, leads to lifelong immunity. There is no cross immunity between HAV and any of the other hepatitis viruses.

Treatment is symptomatic. No specific antiviral drug is available.

TYPE B HEPATITIS

Type B hepatitis is the most widespread and the most important type of viral hepatitis. More than a

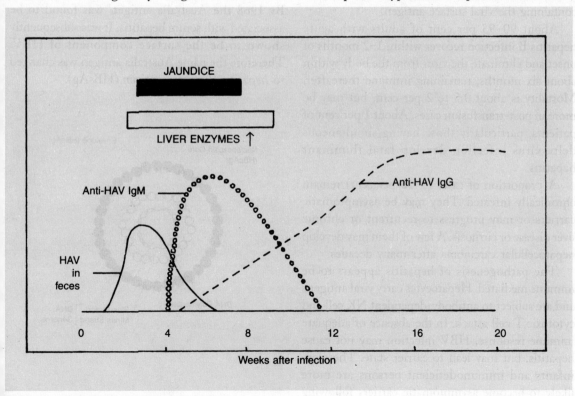

Fig. 59.1 Typical course of hepatitis type A

third of the world's population is estimated to be have been infected by hepatitis B virus (HBV). About a quarter of them become HBV carriers. A quarter of these develop serious liver disease, including chronic hepatitis, cirrhosis and primary hepatic cancer. As there is an effective vaccine against HBV, hepatocellular carcinoma becomes the only human cancer which is vaccine-preventable. The WHO estimates that HBV infection causes more than a million deaths a year worldwide.

Clinical features: The incubation period is long, about 1–6 months. The clinical picture of hepatitis B is similar to that of type A, but it tends to be more severe and protracted. The onset is insidious and fever is not prominent. Extrahepatic complications like arthralgia, urticaria and rarely polyarteritis or glomerulonephritis may occur. These are ascribed to circulating immune complexes containing the viral surface antigen.

About 90–95 per cent of adults with acute hepatitis B infection recover within 1–2 months of onset and eliminate the virus from the body within about six months, remaining immune thereafter. Mortality is about 0.5 to 2 per cent, but may be more in post-transfusion cases. About 1 per cent of patients, particularly those having simultaneous delta virus infection develop fatal fluminant hepatitis.

A proportion of cases (1–10 per cent) remain chronically infected. They may be asymptomatic carriers or may progress to recurrent or chronic liver disease or cirrhosis. A few of them may develop hepatocellular carcinoma after many decades.

The pathogenesis of hepatitis appears to be immune mediated. Hepatocytes carry viral antigens and are subject to antibody-dependent NK cell and cytotoxic T cell attack. In the absence of adequate immune response, HBV infection may not cause hepatitis, but may lead to carrier state. Therefore infants and immunodeficient persons are more likely to become asymptomatic carriers following infection.

Hepatitis B virus (HBV): HBV is a 42 nm DNA virus with an outer envelope and an inner core, 27 nm in diameter, enclosing the viral genome and a DNA polymerase (Fig 59.2). Because of its unique features. HBV is assigned to a separate family *Hepadnaviridae* (hepatotropic DNA viruses), which consists of two genera, *Orthohepadnavirus* containing HBV as well as the woodchuck and ground squirrel hepatitis viruses, and *Avihepadnavirus* containing the Pekin duck and grey heron hepatitis viruses. HBV is *Hepadnavirus* type 1.

The discovery of HBV was serendipitous. In 1965, Blumberg, studying human serum lipoprotein allotypes, observed in the serum of an Australian aborigine, a new antigen which gave a clearly defined line of precipitation with sera from two hemophiliacs who had received multiple blood transfusions. This was named the *Australia antigen*. By 1968 the 'Australia antigen' was found to be associated with serum hepatitis. It was subsequently shown to be the surface component of HBV. Therefore the name Australia antigen was changed to *hepatitis B surface antigen* (HBsAg).

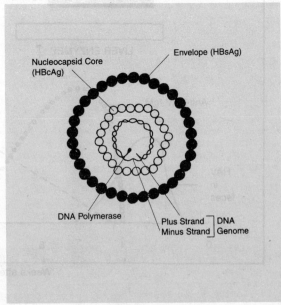

Fig. 59.2 Hepatitis B virus structure

Under the electron microscope, sera from type B hepatitis patients show three types of particles (Figs. 59.3, 59.4). The most abundant form is a spherical particle, 22 nm in diameter. The second type of particle is filamentous or tubular with a diameter of 22 nm and of varying length. These two particles are antigenically identical and are surface components of HBV (HBsAg) which are produced in great excess. The third type of particle, far fewer in number, is a double walled spherical structure, 42 nm in diameter. This particle is the complete hepatitis B virus. It was first described by Dane in 1970 and so is known as the *Dane particle*.

The envelope proteins expressed on the surface of the virion and the surplus 22 nm diameter spherical and filamentous particles constitute the hepatitis B surface antigen. HBsAg consists of two major polypeptides, one of which is glycosylated.

HBsAg exhibits antigenic diversity. It contains two different antigenic components – the common group reactive antigen *a*, and two pairs of type specific antigens *d-y* and *w-r*, only one member of each pair being present at a time. HBsAg can thus be divided into four major antigenic subtypes: *adw, adr, ayw* and *ayr*. The subtypes do not seem to be important in immunity because of the dominant antigen *a* shared by all. The subtypes breed true, and the index case and contacts in an outbreaks have the same subtype. They show a distinct geographical distribution. Subtype *ayw* is common from West Asia through the Middle East, to Western and Northern India; *adw* is common in Europe, Australia and the Americas; *adr* is prevalent in South and East India and the Far East; *ayr* is very rare. A number of other surface antigenic reactivities (*a, x, f, t, j, n, g*) have been reported, but not adequately studied.

Mild detergent treatment disrupts the viral envelope and exposes the core or nucleocapsid. The antigen expressed on the core is called the *hepatitis B core antigen* (HBcAg). A third antigen called the *hepatitis B e antigen* (HBeAg) is a soluble nonparticulate nucleocapsid protein. HBcAg and

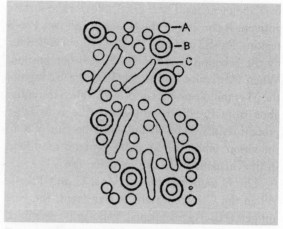

Fig. 59.3 Different types of particles seen in serum of patient with type B hepatitis : A. Spherical 22 nm particle. B. Double shelled 42 nm particle (Dane particle). C. Tubular 22 nm particle.

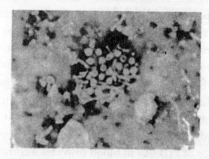

Fig. 59.4 Electron micrograph of HBV–Pooled plasma (114,000) (Courtesy: National Institute of Virology, Pune)

HBeAg, though immunologically distinct, are coded for by the same gene.

The nucleocapsid encloses the viral genome consisting of two linear strands of DNA held in a circular configuration. One of the strands (the plus strand) is incomplete, so that the DNA appears partially double stranded and partially single stranded. Associated with the *plus* strand is a viral *DNA polymerase*, which has both DNA-dependent DNA polymerase and RNA-dependent reverse transcriptase functions. This polymerase can repair the gap in the plus strand and render the genome fully double stranded (Fig. 59.5).

The genome has a compact structure with four

overlapping genes. The S gene codes for the surface antigen. It consists of the S region and two Pre-S regions, Pre-S2 and Pre-S1. The protein coded for by the S region is called the S or major protein. When translation begins from the Pre-S2 region, the M or middle protein is formed. When the entire gene from Pre-S1 is translated, the L or large protein results. The L protein is present only in the virion, while the M and S proteins are found in the circulating HBsAg particles also.

The C gene has two regions, C and Pre-C. When the C region alone is translated, the core antigen (HBcAg) is formed. HBcAg is assembled as the nucleocapsid core particles. It is not secreted and does not circulate in blood, but can be demonstrated in hepatocytes by immuno-fluorescence. Antibodies to HBc, both IgM and IgG appear in blood. IgG antibody to HBcAg persists in blood long after all other serological markers have disappeared and so provides a useful marker of prior infection with HBV. If translation begins from the Pre-C region, the resulting protein is HBeAg, a nonparticulate soluble antigen possessing a signal protein which enables it to be secreted. It is therefore present in circulation. The presence of HBeAg in blood provides a convenient and readily detectable marker of HBV replication and high infectivity.

The P gene is the largest and codes for the DNA polymerase enzyme. The X gene codes for a small nonparticulate protein (HBxAg), which has transactivating effects on both viral and some cellular genes. This leads to enhanced replication of HBV, as well as of some other viruses, such as the human immunodeficiency virus. HBxAg and its antibody are present in patients with severe chronic hepatitis and hepatocellular carcinoma.

A few cases of infection by mutant viruses have been identified. Two types of mutations have been studied. One type, initially identified in Mediterranean countries, presents as severe chronic hepatitis, caused by pre-core mutants unable to synthesise HBeAg. Those infected with precore

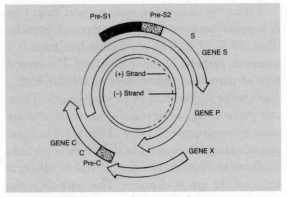

Fig. 59.5 HBV genes and gene products

Genes	Regions	Gene products	
S	S	Major protein (S)	
	S+ Pre-S2	Middleprotein(M)	} HBsAg
	S+Pre-S1&S2	Large protein (L)	
C	C	HbcAg	
	C+Pre-C	HbeAg	
P		DNA polymerase	
X		HBxAg	

mutants may be positive for anti-HBe and anti-HBc. The second group of so-called 'escape mutants' have been seen in some infants born to HBeAg positive mothers, and in liver transplant recipients who had received combined immunisation with anti-HBV immunoglobulin and vaccine. They show mutation in the common *a* determinant of HBsAg, preventing them from being neutralised by anti-HBsAg antibody. If such mutants become more common, they may pose problems in hepatitis B prophylaxis.

HBV replicates within hepatocytes. Viral DNA exists in the hepatocyte nucleus in the free extrachromosomal state or integrated with the cell chromosome. Replication resembles that seen in retroviruses, in that DNA is synthesised from an RNA template by reverse transcription.

HBV DNA and protein have also been identified in extrahepatic sites such as bone marrow, spleen, lymph nodes and circulating lymphocytes, but apparently no damage is produced in these locations. The significance of this extrahepatic presence is not understood.

HBV does not grow in any conventional culture system. However, limited production of the virus and its proteins can be obtained from several cell lines transfected with HBV DNA. HBV proteins have been cloned in bacteria and yeast. The chimpanzee is susceptible to experimental infection and can be used as a laboratory model.

HBV is a relatively heat stable virus. It remains viable at room temperature for long periods. Heat at 60 °C for 10 hours reduces infectivity by hundred-to thousandfold. It is susceptible to chemical agents. Exposure to hypochlorite (10,000 ppm available chlorine) or 2% glutaraldehyde inactivates infectivity, though HBsAg may not be destroyed by such treatment.

Epidemiology: Hepatitis B occurs throughout the world. There is no seasonal distribution. The infection is usually sporadic, though occasional outbreaks have occurred in hospitals, orphanages and institutions for the mentally handicapped.

The prevalence of hepatitis carriers varies widely in different countries, in relation to their living standards. The overpopulated under developed regions have *high endemicity* (carrier rate more than 8 per cent as in equatorial Africa, South East Asia, China, parts of South America); *low endemicity* in the developed countries (carrier rate less than 2 per cent in Western Europe, North America, Australia) and *intermediate endemicity* in other areas (carrier rate 2 to 7 per cent, as in Eastern Europe, the Middle East, South Asia and parts of South America). India falls in the intermediate group, with higher carrier rates in the southern part of the country and lower rates in the northern part.

The rich and the poor countries also differ in the age and modes of infection. In the former, infection occurs mostly in adolescents and young adults through contaminated syringes and needles, typically among drug addicts, and through sex, particularly by homosexual intercourse. In the poor countries, infection occurs usually at younger ages, either perinatally from mother to baby, or horizontally among children. Perinatal and horizontal infection in infants and neonates generally leads to asymptomatic infection, with circulating HBeAg and HBV DNA, without any rise in transaminase levels. This is due to their inability to mount an immune response against the virus. Such cases become chronic carriers, with an enhanced risk of developing hepatocellular carcinoma in later life.

Natural infection occurs only in humans. There is no animal reservoir. The virus is maintained in the large pool of carriers whose blood contains circulating virus for long periods, in some even lifelong. A carrier is a person with detectable HBsAg in blood for more than 6 months. Following infection, about 5–10 per cent of adults, 30 per cent of children and 90 per cent of neonates become carriers. The carrier state is more common among males. There are over 350 million carriers now worldwide. Of them, about 45 million are in India, which has the second largest carrier pool, next only to China.

Carriers are of two categories, the highly infectious *super carriers* and the *simple carriers*. The former have high titre HBsAg, along with HBeAg, DNA polymerase and HBV in circulation, and generally elevated transaminases. Some of them have enormous antigenemia and viremia, upto 10^{13} HBsAg particles equal to 500 µg of protein, and 10^8 HBV per ml of blood. About a quarter of the carriers in India are HBeAg positive. Simple carriers have low infectivity and low titre HBsAg in blood, with negative HBeAg, HBV and DNA polymerase. Many super carriers in time become simple carriers.

HBV is a bloodborne virus and the infection is transmitted by parenteral, sexual and perinatal modes. Blood of carriers, and less often of patients, is the most important source of infection. The virus may also be present in other body fluids and excretions, such as saliva, breast milk, semen, vaginal secretions, urine, bile and feces. Of these, semen and saliva are known to transmit the infection; others may also do so, though much less efficiently than blood. Feces are not known to be infectious.

Transfusion of carrier blood, once the most widely known mode of infection has largely been eliminated wherever donor screening is strictly enforced. Therapeutic and prophylactic preparations from pooled human blood and serum have led to hepatitis, but this risk is now minimal, with screening of donors and production techniques ensuring virus inactivation. However, HBsAg screening is not a totally failsafe method as infection has occurred even with HBsAg negative, anti-HBc positive blood, which may have had undetectable amounts of virus.

Many other therapeutic, diagnostic, prophylactic and even nonmedical procedures are now the main modes of infection. HBV is very highly infectious, far more that HIV. Any object or procedure than can convey minute traces of infected blood or other material, as little as 0.00001 ml, can be infectious. These include shared syringes, needles and other sharp items or endoscopes, personal articles such as razors, nail clippers or combs, and practices such as acupuncture, tattooing, ritual circumcision, ear or nose piercing, and field camps for surgery or disease detection by blood testing where separate sterile articles may not be available. Professionals using sharp articles like barbers, dentists and doctors may unwittingly transmit the virus if great care is not taken.

Infection by direct contact with open skin lesions such as pyoderma, eczema, cuts and scratches is very common among young children in developing countries, as also through household transmission where opportunities exist for contact with blood or saliva among members.

HBV has been said to survive in mosquitoes and bed bugs for about 2 weeks after blood meal, but no virus multiplication occurs. They do not appear to transmit the infection.

Congenital or vertical transmission is quite common from carrier mothers. The risk to babies is high if the mother is HBeAg positive (60–90 per cent) and low if negative (5–15 per cent). True congenital infection (in utero, transplacental) is rare. Infection is usually acquired during birth by contact of maternal blood with the skin and mucosa of the fetus, or in the immedicate postnatal period. Infection by ingestion has been reported, but its efficiency is very low. However it is safer if carrier mothers do not breast feed when proper nutrition of their babies can be otherwise ensured. HBV infected neonates generally do not suffer from any clinical illness, but remain carriers for life and some of them may develop hepatocellular carcinoma after many decades.

Sexual transmission of HBV occurs everywhere, but is more important in the developed countries, particularly in the promiscuous homosexual. The risk of transmission by heterosexual and homosexual contact increases with the number of partners and the duration of such relationships. HBV infection has occurred after artificial insemination. Semen donor screening is therefore obligatory.

Certain groups and occupations carry a high risk of infection. These include medical and paramedical personnel, staff of blood banks, dialysis units, medical laboratories and mental health institutions, barbers and sex workers. Dentists and doctors have been responsible for small outbreaks. In non-endemic countries like Britain, HBV carriers are barred from invasive medical practice. Carriers are also not permitted to be medical students.

The only safe and effective measure for prevention is universal active immunisation. Its success has been demonstrated in some highly endemic areas like Taiwan where the carrier rate fell from 18 per cent in 1986 to 8 per cent in 1993 following immunisation. In 1992, the World Health Assembly recommended the integration of hepatitis B vaccine into the national immunisation programmes of all nations by 1997. More than 80 countries have conformed. India is one of the few countries yet to initiate this measure mainly because of the high cost of imported vaccine. Now that the vaccine is manufactured in India, and is available at lower cost, it should be possible to include this in the national immunisation schedule.

Laboratory diagnosis: Specific diagnosis of hepatitis B rests on the serological demonstration of the viral markers. It is therefore necessary to understand the sequence of their appearance in blood (Fig. 59.6).

HBsAg is the first marker to appear in blood after infection, being detectable even before elevation of transaminases and onset of clinical illness. It remains in circulation throughout the icteric or symptomatic course of the disease. In the typical case, it disappears within about 2 months of the start of clinical disease, but may sometimes last for 6 months and even beyond. When it is no longer detectable, its antibody, anti-HBs appears and remains for very long periods. Anti-HBs is the protective antibody.

HBcAg is not demonstrable in circulation because it is enclosed within the HBsAg coat, but its antibody, anti-HBc appears in serum a week or two after the appearance of HBsAg. It is therefore the earliest antibody marker to be seen in blood, long before anti-HBe or anti-HBs. As anti-HBc remains lifelong, it serves as a useful indicator of prior infection with HBV, even after all the other viral markers become undetectable. Initially, anti-HBc is predominantly IgM, but after about 6 months, it is mainly IgG. Selective tests for IgM or IgG anti-HBc therefore enable distinction between recent or remote infection respectively.

HBeAg appears in blood concurrently with HBsAg, or soon afterwards. Circulating HBeAg is an indicator of active intrahepatic viral replication, and the presence in blood of DNA polymerase, HBV DNA and virions, reflecting high infectivity. The disappearance of HBeAg coincides with the fall of transminase levels in blood. It is followed by the appearance of anti-HBe.

For the diagnosis of HBV infection, detection of HBsAg in blood is all that ordinarlly necessary. The simultaneous presence of IgM anti-HBc

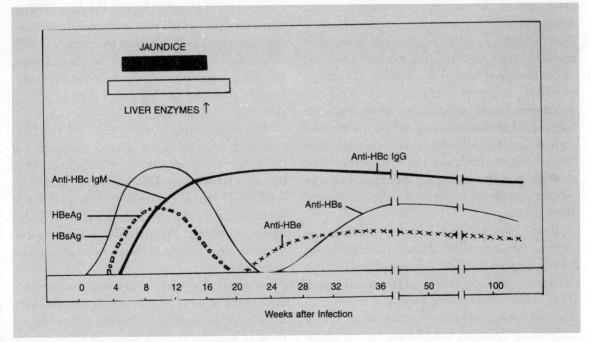

Fig. 59.6 Typical course of acute hepatitis type B

indicates recent infection and the presence of IgG anti-HBc remote infection. Occasionally, when the level of HBsAg is too low to be detectable, diagnosis has to be made by testing for IgM anti-HBc.

HBeAg provides information about relative infectivity. Its presence denotes high infectivity and its absence, along with the presence of anti-HBe, indicates low infectivity. As it is invariably present during acute hepatitis, its testing is indicated only in chronic infection and carriers.

The presence of anti-HBs without any other serological virus marker indicates immunity following vaccination. Table 59.1 shows the interpretation of various serological patterns in hepatitis B.

Like HBeAg, HBV DNA is also an indicator of viral replication and infectivity. Molecular methods such as DNA:DNA hybridisation and PCR, at present used for HBV DNA testing are highly sensitive and quantitative. HBV DNA level in serum reflects the degree of viral replication in the liver and so helps to assess the progress of patients with chronic hepatitis under antiviral chemotherapy.

Prophylaxis: General prophylaxis consists in avoiding risky practices like promiscuous sex, injectable drug abuse and direct or indirect contact with blood, semen or other body fluids of patients and carriers. Health education, use of the disposable syringes and needles, screening of blood, semen and organ donors, have all helped to an extent, but these alone cannot eliminate the risk altogether, particularly in the developing countries. The only certain method appears to be universal immunisation.

Both passive and active methods of immunisation are available. Hyperimmune hepatitis B immune globulin (HBIG) prepared from human volunteers with high titre anti-HBs, administered IM in a dose of 300–500 i.u. soon after exposure to infection constitutes passive immunisation. It may not prevent infection, but protects against illness and the carrier state.

Active immunisation is more effective. The first vaccine introduced in 1982, was prepared from pooled plasma of healthy human carriers with high level antigenemia. The 22 nm HBsAg particles separated by ultracentrifugation were treated with proteinase, urea and formaldehyde and used as the vaccine. This was immunogenic, but became unacceptable because its source was human plasma, limited in availability and not totally free from possible risk of unknown pathogens. It continues to be used in some countries because it is cheaper.

The currently preferred vaccine is genetically engineered by cloning the S gene of HBV in baker's yeast. It consists of nonglycosylated HBsAg particles alone. It is given with alum adjuvant, IM into the deltoid or, in infants into the anterolateral aspect of the thigh. Gluteal injection is not recommended as it may result in poor immune response. Three doses given at 0, 1 and 6 months constitute the full course. Seroconversion occurs in about 90 per cent of the vaccinees. A special vaccine containing all antigenic components of HBsAg (Pre-S1, Pre-S2 and S) has been developed, which gives greater seroconversion. Serconversion can be checked by testing for anti-HBs which is usually detectable for about 5 years. Clinical protection is believed to last much longer. Booster doses are needed only for those at high risk.

For nonimmune persons exposed to HBV, combined immunisation is recommended. For babies born to carrier mothers, a single injection of 0.5 ml of HBIG given IM immediately after birth, is followed by the full course of vaccine at a different anatomical site, the first dose being given within 12 hours of birth. When HBIG is not available, the vaccine given alone has been reported to provide protection.

Treatment: No specific antiviral treatment is available for acute HBV infection. Interferon alpha, alone or in combination with other antiviral agents such as lamivudine and famcyclovir, has been beneficial in some cases of chronic hepatitis. There is no effective treatment for the carrier state, though spontaneous resolution takes place in some of them.

TYPE C HEPATITIS

Attempts to identify the group of 'non-A non-B' viruses by experimental infection in chimpanzees led to the discovery of hepatitis C virus (HCV). It is now the commonest cause of post-transfusion hepatitis in the developed countries.

Clinical features: The incubation period is long, 15–160 days, with a mean of 50 days. The acute illness is usually mild or anicteric. Overt jaundice is seen in about 5 per cent of patients only. The important part in type C hepatitis is the chronic illness. About 50 to 80 per cent of patients progress to chronic hepatitis, with some developing cirrhosis and hepatocellular carcinoma.

Epidemiology: HCV infection is seen only in humans. The source of infection is the large number of carriers, estimated to be about 200 million worldwide. In general the epidemiology resembles that of hepatitis B.

Infection is mainly by blood transfusion and other modes of contact with infected blood or blood products. Injectable drug abusers, transplant recipients and immunocompromised persons are at high risk. Sexual transmission is probably less important. Vertical transmission from mother to baby may take place.

The infection occurs throughout the world, with carrier rates varying from 1–20 per cent. HCV infection is prevalent in India too, with an estimated 12.5 million cases. A quarter of all chronic hepatitis cases in India is believed to be due to HCV infection.

Hepatitis C virus (HCV): The virus has not been grown in culture, but has been cloned in *Escherichia coli*. HCV is a 50–60 nm virus with a linear single stranded RNA genome, enclosed within a core and surrounded by an envelope, carrying glycoprotein spikes. HCV resembles flaviviruses in structure and organisation, and has been classified as a new genus *Hepacivirus* in the family Flaviviridae.

The virus shows considerable genetic and antigenic diversity. At least six different genotypes and many subtypes have been identified, indicating high mutability. Some genotypes are seen worldwide, while others are localised. Because of this diversity there is little heterologous or even homologous postinfection immunity in hepatitis C.

Laboratory diagnosis: The standard method of diagnosis is antibody detection by ELISA. The

Table 59.1 Interpretation of commom serological patterns in HBV infection

Virus/Antibody Markers					Interpretation
HBsAg	HBeAg	anti-HBc	anti-HBs	anti-HBe	
+	+	IgM	-	-	Acute HBV infection; highly infectious
+	+	IgG	-	-	Late/chronic HBV infection or carrier state; highly infectious
+	-	IgG	-	+/-	Late/chronic HBV infection or carrier state; low infectivity
-	+/-	IgM	-	+/-	Seen rarely in early acute HBV infection; infectious
-	-	IgG	+/-	+/-	Remote HBV infection; infectivity nil or very low
-	-	-	+	-	Immunity following HBV vaccine

antigens used are various structural and non-structural proteins cloned in *E. coli*. There have been three successive generations of such antigens, introduced to improve sensitivity and specificity of serological diagnosis. Even the third generation ELISA currently in use, employing NS-5 region protein and synthetic peptides becomes positive only months after the infection and shows nonspecific reactions. Confirmation by immunoblot assay is therefore recommended. In HCV infection antibodies appear irregularly and late, limiting their diagnostic utility.

Identification of HCV RNA in blood provides more sensitive and specific results within a few days of exposure to HCV. Molecular methods like PCR and branched DNA assay are employed for the purpose.

Prophylaxis: Only general prophylaxis, such as blood screening, is possible. No specific active or passive immunising agent is available.

Treatment: Prolonged treatment with interferon alpha, either alone or in combination with antiviral agents like ribavirin has been reported to be useful in some cases.

TYPE D (DELTA) HEPATITIS

In 1977, Rizzetto and colleagues in Italy identified a new viral antigen in the liver cell nuclei of patients infected with hepatitis B virus. This has been shown to be due to the hepatotropic virus Delta or Hepatitis D Virus (HDV). Delta is a defective RNA virus dependent on the helper function of HBV for its replication and expression. Therefore, it has no independent existence and can survive and replicate only as long as HBV infection persists in the host.

HDV is a spherical, 36 nm particle with an outer coat composed of the hepatitis B surface antigen surrounding the circular single stranded RNA genome. Though it resembles some plant viruses, such as viroids or satellite viruses, it has been proposed to be classified in a new genus *Deltavirus*, because of its special features.

Its mode of transmission is the same as for HBV. Two types of infection are recognised, *coinfection* and *superinfection*. In coinfection, delta and HBV are transmitted together at the same time. In superinfection, delta infection occurs in a person already harbouring HBV. Coinfection clinically presents as acute hepatitis B, ranging from mild to fulminant disease. Superinfection usually leads to more serious and chronic illness, with deterioration of the underlying HBV infection. No association has been noted between HDV and hepatocellular carcinoma.

Delta antigen is primarily expressed in liver cell nuclei, where it can be demonstrated by immunofluorescence. It is only occasionally present in serum. Anti-delta antibodies appear in serum and can be identified by ELISA. The IgM antibody appears 2–3 weeks after infection and is soon replaced by the IgG antibody in acute delta infection. However, in chronic infection, the IgM antibody persists for years. Delta RNA sequences have been cloned and DNA probes have been developed for the rapid identification of delta particles in circulation. The woodchuck has been found to be a suitable experimental model for the study of HDV infection.

HDV is distributed worldwide but is more common in certain endemic areas. In the Mediterranean countries, where it is endemic, infection is spread commonly by nonpercutaneous routes, especialy by close personal contact. In the nonendemic areas, such as Northern Europe and North America, infection is more often through blood and blood products and is commonly seen in drug addicts and hemophiliacs. Introduction of HDV into nonendemic areas where HBV infection is common may lead to outbreaks of severe hepatitis with high mortality.

No specific prophylaxis exists, but immunisation with the HBV vaccine is effective as HDV cannot infect persons immune to HBV. Screening of blood donors for HBsAg automatically limits blood borne HDV infection.

TYPE E HEPATITIS

(Enterically transmitted NANB or Epidemic NANB hepatitis)

Hepatitis viruses A and B account for less than half the cases of acute hepatitis in many developing countries. The bulk of NANB hepatitis in these areas is transmitted enterically through fecal pollution of drinking water (hence the name *enterically transmitted* NANB or E-NANB). It often appears as epidemics (hence also called *epidemic* NANB). The largest such epidemic occurred in Delhi during the winter of 1955–56, affecting over 30,000 persons within six weeks. Several outbreaks and sporadic infections have been reported from many parts of the Indian subcontinent, Central and South Asia, North Africa and Central America. This hepatitis was not seen in Western countries except when imported from endemic areas, but recently occasional cases have been reported from Europe. The disease is now called Type E hepatitis and its causative agent hepatitis E virus (HEV). In India, HEV is responsible for the majority of epidemic and sporadic hepatitis in adults.

Type E hepatitis was previously mistaken for hepatitis A because of clinical and epidemiological similarities. It was recognised as a separate entity because of the absence of serological and virological evidence of HAV infection in these cases. The source of infection is fecal contamination of drinking water and the environment. Secondary attack rate among household contacts is very low in type E hepatitis, 2–3 per cent as against 10–20 per cent in HAV infection.

The incubation period ranges from 2 to 9 weeks with an average of six weeks. Most cases occur in the young to middle aged adults (15–40 years old). The disease is generally mild and self limited, with a low case fatality of about one per cent. A unique feature is the clinical severity and high case fatality rate of 20–40 per cent in pregnant women, especially in the last trimester of pregnancy.

HEV is a spherical nonenveloped virus, 32–34 nm in diameter, with a single stranded RNA genome. The surface of the virion shows indentation and spikes. The virus is very labile. In morphology and physical characteristics, it resembles Caliciviruses such as the Norwalk virus. It has been provisionally classified in the genus *Hepesvirus* under the family Caliciviridae. HEV can be demonstrated by IEM in the bile and feces of patients in the incubation period or acute phase of illness. Carrier state has not been observed. Experimental infection can be transmitted to many species of primates. It has been reported to be prevalent in animal reservoirs such as pigs. In vitro cultivation has not been successful so far. The viral genome has been cloned. Comparison of virus strains from different areas indicates that only one serotype of the virus exists. ELISA kits are available for IgG and IgM anti bodies, using recombinant and synthetic peptide antigens.

HEPATITIS G VIRUS

Two flavivirus-like isolates were obtained in 1995 from Tamarin monkeys inoculated with blood from a young surgeon (GB) with acute hepatitis. A similar virus was isolated from another human specimen the same year. These isolates were called GB viruses A, B and C respectively.

In 1996, an isolate closely resembling GBV-C was obtained from a patient with chronic hepatitis. This has been called hepatitis G virus (HGV). It has not been grown, but its RNA genome has been cloned. HGV RNA has been found in patients with acute, chronic and fulminant hepatitis, hemophiliacs, patients with multiple transfusions and hemodialysis, intravenous drug addicts and blood donors. HGV appears to be a blood borne virus resembling HCV. Its role in hepatitis is yet to be clarified.

Table 59.2 Viral hepatitis types: comparative features

	A	B	C	D	E
Virus	HAV, 27nm RNA, Picornavirus (Hepatovirus)	HBV, 47nm DNA (Hepadnavirus)	HCV, 30-60nm RNA, Flavivirus (hepacivirus)	HDV, 35-37nm Defective RNA Deltavirus	HEV,32-34nm RNA Herpesvirus
Modes of infection	Fecal-oral	Percutaneous Vertical, Sexual	Percutaneous	Percutaneous	Fecal-Oral
Age Affected	Children	Any age	Adults	Any age	Young adults
Incubation Period(days)	15-45	30-180	15-160	30-180	15-60
Onset	Acute	Insidious	Insidious	Insidious	Acute
Illness	Mild	Occasionally severe	Moderate	Occasionally severe	Mild, except in pregnancy
Carrier state	Nil	Common	Present	Nil(only with HBV)	Nil
Oncogenicity	Nil	Present specially after neonatal infection	Present	Nil	Nil
Prevalence	Worldwide	Worldwide	Probably worldwide	Endemic areas (Mediterranean,N.Europe, Central and N. America)	Only developing countries(India, Asia Africa, Central, America)
Specific prophylaxis	Ig and Vaccine	Ig and vaccine	Nil	HBV vaccine	Nil

Further Reading

Alter HJ. 1997. Acute non A-E hepatitis in the USA and the role of hepatitis G virus infection, *New Engl J Med* 336:741.

British Medical Bulletin. 1990. *Hepatitis* 2:46

Brown JL. 1995. Hepatitis C. *J Infect* 30:95.

Collier L (ed). 1998. Hepatitis A and E *Topley & Wilson's Microbiology and Microbial Infections* 9th edn. London:Arnold.

Dienstag JL and KJ Isselbacher 1998. In Acute Viral Hepatitis. *Harrison's Principles of Internal Medicine* 14th edn. New York: Mc-Graw Hill.

Hollinger FB and TJ Liary 2002. Hepatitis B virus. In Field's Virology, Vol 2. 4th ed. Philadelphia: Williams and Wilkins.

Hoofnagle JH. 1989. Type D (Delta) Hepatitis. *J Amer Med Assoc* 261:1321.

Krawczynski K. 1993. Hepatitis E. *Hepatology* 17:932

Lenor SM and DL Thomas 1997. Vaccines to prevent viral hepatitis. *New Engl J Med* 336:196.

Maillard ME and JR Gollan 2003. Suppressing Hepatitis B. *New Eng J Med* 348: 848.

Sarin SK and AK Singal (eds). 1996. *Hepatitis B in India*. New Delhi: CBS Publishers.

Van Damme P et al. 1997. Integration of hepatitis B vaccination into national immunization programmes. *BMJ* 314:1033.

Miscellaneous Viruses

PAPOVAVIRUSES

The term 'Papova' is a sigla indicating the names of viruses included in this group: *papilloma* virus of human beings and rabbits, *polyoma* virus of mice and *vacuolating virus* of monkeys. The family Papovaviridae has two genera – *Polyomavirus* which contains the simian vacuolating virus (SV 40) and polyomaviruses, and *Papillomavirus* containing human and animal papilloma viruses.

They are small, nonenveloped, icosahedral DNA tumour viruses. Most of the naturally occurring papovavirus tumours are benign, but some such as rabbit papilloma are potentially malignant. Polyoma and the vacuolating virus SV 40 produce malignant tumours when inoculated into newborn mice or hamsters. These viruses have been widely employed in the study of viral oncogenesis.

Polyoma virus often causes latent infection in laboratory mice. However, when inoculated into newborn mice, it produces a wide variety of malignant tumours. Hence the name *polyoma*.

The simian vacuolating virus (SV 40) was isolated from uninoculated rhesus and cynomolgus monkey kidney tissue cultures. The virus did not produce any cytopathic effects in the original cultures but when fluid from such cultures was inoculated into kidney cell cultures from other simian species (African green or grivet monkey), cytopathic effects occurred, consisting of prominent cytoplasmic vacuolation. SV 40 is oncogenic in newborn hamsters. Its only medical importance is that because of its oncogenic potential, live viral vaccines should be manufactured only in monkey kidney tissue cultures tested and found free from SV 40 infection.

Papillomaviruses are species specific and infect squamous epithelia and mucous membranes, inducing different types of warts or papillomata in their hosts. Human papillomavirus (HPV) infects only humans and grows only in organ cultures of human skin. Over 70 types of HPV have been recognised based on genetic homology. There is correlation between the virus type and the type of lesion produced. Common warts (verruca vulgaris) usually found on the hands and feet of children and adolescents are mostly caused by types 1, 2, 3 and 4. Condyloma acuminatum or genital wart which is a more moist, soft, pedunculated wart found on the external genitalia is usually due to types 6 and 11. This may be transmitted venereally and may occasionally turn malignant. There is a close association between specific HPV types and genital malignancies in both sexes. HPV types 6 and 11 are associated with intraepithelial neoplasia, while HPV 16 and 18 are etiologically related to more severe invasive malignancies such as uterine cervical cancer. Cofactors appear to be important in the induction of HPV associated malignancies.

Human papovaviruses have been isolated from a number of patients with impaired immunity. The JC virus was isolated in 1971 from the brain of a patient with Hodgkin's disease and progressive multifocal leukoencephalopathy (PML). Isolation of similar strains from PML cases has been reported from the USA, UK and France. The JC virus grows only in human fetal glial cell cultures. It is oncogenic, producing malignant gliomas following intracerebral inoculation in newborn hamsters.

Another human papovavirus is the BK virus,

isolated in 1971 from the urine of a patient with kidney transplant. Several similar isolates have been reported from other kidney transplant patients. The BK virus differs from the JC virus in being able to grow in a wide range of primary and continuous cell cultures. It is less oncogenic. Both JC and BK viruses agglutinate guinea pig and chicken erythrocytes.

Antibodies to JC and BK viruses are present widely in human sera, being found in about 75 per cent of adults. It is believed that primary infection with these papovaviruses occurs commonly in childhood. The brain and renal tract are two sites where virus multiplication has been demonstrated. The infection is ordinarily asymptomatic but the virus may remain latent. If the immune system is impaired in later life following disease or transplantation, the virus may be reactivated, leading to PML or renal disease.

PARVOVIRUS

Parvoviruses are very small (about 20 nm) viruses with a single stranded DNA genome. They are host specific, each species being affected by a genetically and antigenically stable parvovirus. Some veterinary parvoviruses, such as the feline and canine parvoviruses are important enough to warrant routine immunization. At present only one medically important human parvovirus has been recognised, *Parvovirus B19*, originally discovered in the blood of symptomless blood donors.

Parvovirus B19 is present world wide. Infection is commonly acquired in childhood and is often asymptomatic. It usually presents as a respiratory infection, with an erythematous maculopapular rash and arthralgia. In its full blown form (erythema infectiosum), it starts with prominent erythema of the cheeks (slapped cheek disease), spreading to the trunk and limbs, followed by lymphadenopathy and arthralgia. It occurs usually in children, 5–10 years old and has been called the fifth disease, as it was the fifth in the old list of six exanthematous fevers of children.

Parvovirus B19 induces *aplastic crisis* in children with chronic hemolytic anemias, as in sickle cell disease. In the immunodeficient, it may cause persistent anemia. Parvovirus B19 infection during the second or third trimester of pregnancy may result in nonimmune fetal hydrops.

Transmission appears to be respiratory, though it may also be through blood. Infection leads to viremia and virus replication in the throat, followed by antibody response. Diagnosis may be made by detection of virus in the blood in early cases, and of antibody later.

RUBELLA

Rubella or German measles is a mild exanthematous fever characterised by transient macular rash and lymphadenopathy. In itself, the disease is trivial but rubella in the pregnant woman may lead to congenital malformations in the baby. The teratogenic property of rubella was discovered by an Australian ophthalmologist Gregg, who in 1941 observed a sudden increase in congenital cataract in infants and related it to maternal rubella. Observations from different countries soon confirmed that maternal rubella induces congenital malformations of different kinds, the commonest being the triad of cataract, deafness and cardiac defects. Further progress had to wait till rubella virus was isolated in tissue culture in 1962.

Properties: Rubella virus is a pleomorphic, roughly spherical particle, 50–70 nm in diameter, with single stranded RNA genome and surrounded by an envelope carrying hemagglutinin peplomers. It agglutinates goose, pigeon, day-old chick and human erythrocytes at 4 °C. Structurally and in many other features, it resembles togaviruses. *Rubella virus* has been classified in the family Togaviridae as the only member of the genus *Rubivirus*.

The virus is inactivated by ether, chloroform, formaldehyde, beta propiolactone and desoxycholate. It is destroyed by heating at 56 °C, but survives for several years at −60 °C.

Cultivation and host range: The virus can be grown in many primary cell cultures and continuous cell lines, such as rabbit kidney (RK 13), baby hamster kidney (BHK 21) and Vero, but cytopathic changes develop only in a few cell lines such as RK 13. In others, virus growth can be identified by interference, using a challenge virus such as ECHO 11.

Experimental infection can be produced in human volunteers and monkeys. A suitable experimental model for the teratogenic effects of rubella is the pregnant rabbit, in which the virus infects the fetus transplacentally, leading to congenital malformations.

Clinical features: After an incubation period of 2–3 weeks a generalised rash develops, first on the face and then spreading to the neck, trunk and extremities sparing the palms and soles. The rash is generally discrete and ordinarily disappears by the third day. There is nontender enlargement of posterior cervical glands. Koplik spots, seen in measles, are absent. The disease occurs principally in children but may affect all ages. The common complications are arthralgia and arthritis, commoner in women and with increasing age. Based on the results of in vitro studies, rubella infection is presumed to cause chromosomal breakages and inhibition of mitoses in infected embryonic cells.

Infection is acquired by inhalation. The virus can be recovered from the throat for about seven days before the rash. Viremia has been demonstrated as early as the seventh day before the rash and ceases shortly after the appearance of the rash. The virus can also be demonstrated in feces and urine. Patients with subclinical infection are infectious and also develop viremia. Infection of the fetus is by the bloodstream.

Fetal damage caused by maternal rubella is related to the stage of pregnancy. If rubella occurs in very early pregnancy, the fetus may die. Congenital malformations are commonest during the first trimester with a reported risk of up to 90 per cent. Later, the damage caused may be more subtle, in the form of communication defects or developmental retardation and may not be apparent till the child grows older. The commonest malformations caused by rubella are cardiac defects, cataract and deafness, which constitute the *classical congenital rubella syndrome*. Multiple defects are common. Several other features have been recognised in babies with congenital rubella, including hepatosplenomegaly, thrombocytopenic purpura, myocarditis and bone lesions, constituting the *'expanded rubella syndrome'*.

The rubella virus is present in all excretions of congenitally infected infants. About a third of them continue to shed the virus for six months, and a few for a year or more. The virus may persist in tissues such as cataractous lenses for several years. Infected babies constitute an important source of infection to the staff in nurseries.

Laboratory diagnosis: Routine diagnosis of rubella is not called for but laboratory confirmation becomes important when rubella is suspected in pregnant women. Diagnosis can be established by virus isolation or serology. The virus may be isolated from blood during the early stage or more successfully from throat swabs in rabbit kidney or vero cells. The virus grows better if cultures are incubated at a lower temperature, 33–35 °C. Rubella virus isolation is not commonly employed for diagnosis because of the difficulties and delay involved. Serological diagnosis is the method in routine use. ELISA for IgM and IgG antibodies gives valuable information. IgM antibody alone, without IgG means current acute infection. IgG antibody alone, without IgM means past infection or vaccination and denotes immunity.

In congenital rubella, the virus may be isolated from a variety of sources such as urine, throat swabs, leucocytes, bone marrow or cerebrospinal fluid. Serological diagnosis is made by demonstrating IgM antibodies. These indicate immune response in the fetus as against IgG antibodies which may be passively transferred from the mother.

Prophylaxis: Rubella infection confers lasting immunity as there is only one antigenic type of the virus. Reinfections have however been reported.

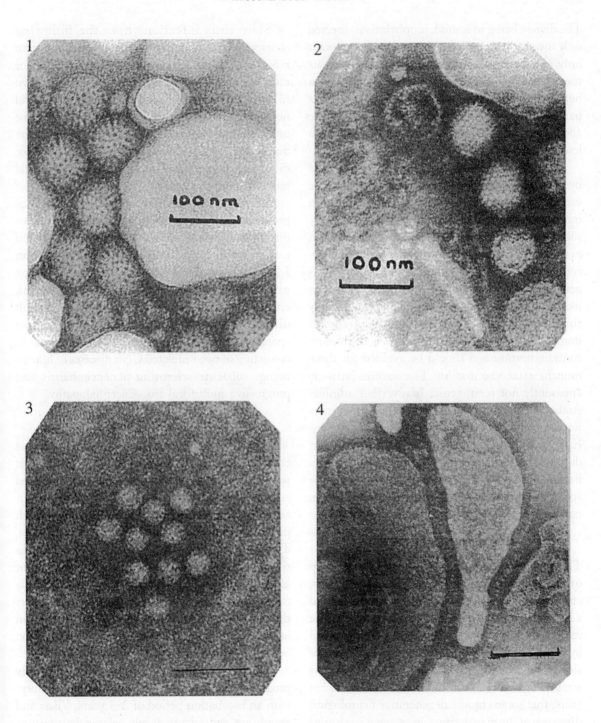

Fig. 60.1 Electron micrographs of viruses associated with diarrhea (x 200,000)   1. Rotavirus;   2. Adenovirus;
3. Small round structured virus (Norwalk-like calciviruses); 4. Coronavirus

The disease being so is mild, prophylaxis is directed only towards its teratogenic hazard and so relevant only in women of childbearing age. An obvious method of protection is to acquire the infection before puberty. This was achieved by 'rubella parties', formerly practised in Australia, where adolescent girls voluntarily exposed themselves to known rubella cases.

Live attenuated vaccines have been developed by serial passage of the virus in tissue culture. The vaccine in use now is the RA 27/3 strain grown in human diploid cell culture and administered by subcutaneous injection. The vaccine may be given as such or in combination with measles and mumps components as the MMR vaccine. The vaccine is generally well tolerated, though minor reactions like lymphadenopathy, rash and arthralgia may sometime occur. It should not be given to immunodeficient subjects. Pregnancy is an absolute contraindication and should be avoided for three months after vaccination. The vaccine virus is apparently not teratogenic. Inadvertent administration of the vaccine to a pregnant women may not therefore lead to congenital defects in the baby.

Epidemiology: Rubella is worldwide in distribution. Serological surveys in different countries have shown that 80–90 per cent are immune by the age of 15 years. About 10–20 per cent of mothers are nonimmune and therefore vulnerable.

SLOW VIRUS DISEASES

The term 'slow virus disease' is applied to a group of infections in animals and human beings, characterised by a very long incubation period and a slow but relentless course, terminating fatally. The concept of 'slow infection' was originally proposed by Sigurdsson (1954), a veterinary pathologist for slowly progressing infections of sheep, such as scrapie, visna and maedi. The recognition in recent years, that some chronic degenerative neurological diseases of human beings may have a similar pathogenesis, has led to considerable interest in this concept.

Slow virus infections have the following characteristics: (1) incubation periods ranging from months to years; (2) course of illness lasting for months or years, with remissions and exacerbations; (3) predilection for involvement of the central nervous system; (4) absence of immune response or an immune response that does not arrest the disease, but may actually contribute to pathogenesis; (5) a genetic predisposition; and (6) invariable fatal termination.

Slow virus diseases may be classified into three groups: *Group A* consisting of slowly progressive infections of sheep, caused by serologically related nononcogenic retroviruses called lentiviruses (from Latin. *lentus*, meaning slow), *Group B* comprising prion diseases of the CNS, scrapie, mink encephalopathy, Kuru and Creutzfeldt–Jakob disease, collectively known as the subacute spongiform viral encephalopathies and *Group C* consisting of two unrelated CNS diseases of human beings subacute sclerosing panencephalitis and progressive multifocal leucoencephalopathy.

GROUP A

Visna, a demyelinating disease of sheep was originally recognised in Iceland in 1935 where it was eradicated in 1951 by slaughter of all affected animals. The disease has an incubation period of about two years. It has an insidious onset with pareses, progressing to total paralysis and death. The virus can be grown in sheep choroid plexus tissue cultures, from the CSF, blood and saliva of affected animals. High levels of neutralising antibody can be detected in circulation, but they do not protect the host. Instead, the CNS lesions may represent an immune disease, due to an antigen–antibody reaction on the surface of infected glial cells.

Maedi (progressive pneumonia) is a slowly progressive fatal hemorrhagic pneumonia of sheep, with an incubation period of 2–3 years. Visna and maedi are caused by closely related lentiviruses which may be variant strains of a single virus. Human immunodeficiency virus, the causative agent of AIDS, also belongs to this group of lentiviruses. AIDS shows many features of a slow virus disease.

GROUP B (Prion Diseases)

The subacute spongiform viral encephalopathies are chronic progressive degenerative diseases of the CNS. The pathology consists of progressive vacuolation in the dendritic and axonal processes of the neurons and extensive astroglial hypertrophy and proliferation, culminating in a spongiform degeneration in the grey matter. There is no sign of any inflammatory or immune response.

The infectious agents are unique in being protein in nature, devoid of DNA and RNA, and unusually resistant to physical and chemical agents such as heat, irradiation and formalin. They can be transmitted to experimental animals by parenteral and oral challenge. Prusiner gave the name *prion* to these proteinaceous infectious agents. Stanley B. Prusiner was awarded the Nobel prize for Medicine in 1997 for his pioneering work on prions.

The pathogenic mechanism appears to be proliferation of an abnormal prion protein (PrP^{sc}) which is derived from the normal prion protein PrP^c. The accumulation of PrP^{sc} in the central nervous system as diffuse deposits and in the form of plaques disrupts the architecture and function of the brain, causing disease.

Prion diseases of animals: *Scrapie* is the prototype prion disease. It has been known as a natural disease of sheep for two centuries. Transmission occurs vertically, from ewe to lamb, and less often by contact. The incubation period is about two years. The affected animals are irritable and develop intense pruritus, scraping themselves against trees and rocks, hence the name scrapie. Emaciation and paralysis set in, leading to death. The disease can be transmitted to sheep, mice and many other experimental animals by injection of suspensions of brain and spinal cord from affected animals. Different breeds of sheep exhibit marked genetic differences in susceptibility to infection. No immune response has been demonstrated in natural

or experimental scrapie. Immunosuppression and interferon do not affect the course of the disease. The causative agent has been maintained in brain tissue explant cultures through several serial passages.

Mink encephalopathy is a scrapie-like disease of mink. It is believed to have spread to mink by feeding them on scrapie infected sheep meat.

Bovine spongiform encephalopathy (BSE, 'mad cow disease') has been enzootic in Britain from 1986. The infection is presumed to have spread to cattle by the practice of feeding them with abattoir waste and offal which may have contained scrapie infected meat.

Human prion diseases: These include *Creutzfeldt–Jakob disease (CJD)*, Gerstmann–Straussler–Scheinker (GSS) syndrome, Kuru and fatal familial insomnia.

CJD is a subacute presenile encephalopathy, with progressive incoordination and dementia, ending fatally in about a year. The disease was known as both sporadic and inherited forms. Iatrogenic CJD has occurred after corneal transplant and injection of pituitary growth hormone, presumably from the donors having had the infection.

The appearance of a new variant of CJD affecting younger persons (below 45 years) in Britain in 1996 raised fears of infection through eating BSE infected beef. This aroused a panic reaction about export of British beef, and many thousands of British cattle had to be slaughtered before the anxiety was allayed.

Kuru (meaning tremor) was identified in 1957 as a mysterious disease seen only in the Fore tribe inhabiting the eastern highlands of New Guinea. The disease had an incubation period is 5–10 years and led to progressive cerebellar ataxia and tremors, ending fatally in 3–6 months. The infection is believed to have been introduced through cannibalism and maintained by the tribal custom of eating the dead bodies of relatives after ritual nonsterilising cooking. Following the abolition of cannibalism in New Guinea the disease has disappeared. Carlton Gajdusek was awarded the

Nobel prize for Medicine in 1976 for his important contributions on Kuru.

GROUP C

Subacute sclerosing panencephalitis (SSPE) is a very rare delayed sequel to infection with measles virus. The disease sets in many years after the initial infection and is characterised by progressive deterioration of mental and motor functions. Death occurs 1–3 years after onset of symptoms. Brain cells from patients show serological and electron microscopic evidence of measles virus infection. The virus cannot be isolated in routine cultures, but only by co-cultivation of infected brain cells with susceptible cells of nonneural origin. Measles virus strains isolated from SSPE are defective. Patients show very high levels of measles virus antibody in serum. Antibody is regularly found in CSF and is pathognomonic. CMI to measles virus is absent in SSPE.

It has been reported that SSPE may also develop as a very rare late complication of live measles virus vaccination. A similar picture has also been described as a rare complication of rubella infection.

Progressive multifocal leucoencephalopathy (PML) is a rare subacute demyelinating disease seen in elderly persons whose immune process is impaired as a result of malignancy or immunosuppression. There is progressive deterioration of motor functions, vision and speech. Death occurs in 3–4 months. A papovavirus has been demonstrated by electron microscopy and cultured from brain biopsies of patients.

VIRAL HEMORRHAGIC FEVERS

Haemorrhagic manifestations are sometimes seen in many viral fevers. However, the term haemorrhagic viral fevers is not applied to them, but only to a group of diseases, apparently zoonotic in nature, with typical hemorrhage features caused by viruses belonging to two families: Arenavirus and Filovirus. They have localised distribution, in South America and Africa. They usually cause asymptomatic infection in the local population but at times they erupt in sudden outbreaks killing many and causing terror.

ARENAVIRUSES

A group of enveloped viruses with negative sense single stranded RNA genome, causing chronic unapparent infection in rodents has been classified as *arenaviruses*. Electron microscopy of thin sections shows characteristic electron-dense granules resembling grains of sand within virus particles. Hence the name *arena* (L), meaning sand. These particles are cellular ribosomes picked up by the virus presumably during maturation by budding from host cells. Arenaviruses are spherical or pleomorphic particles, ranging in size from 80 to 300 nm.

The prototype is lymphocytic choriomeningitis (LCM) virus which is a natural parasite of mice. Humans probably acquire the infection from the excreta of rodents. Most human infections are asymptomatic but some may develop an influenza-like illness or meningitis. LCM has been reported to account for 5–10 per cent of sporadic viral meningitis in human beings.

Many colonies of laboratory mice are carriers of LCM virus. Chronically infected animals shed the virus in urine and feces and act as a source of infection to contacts. Infection is transmitted vertically and virtually every tissue and organ of congenitally infected mice are involved. Such infection is asymptomatic in spite of large loads of the virus in the body. Disease may supervene spontaneously after several months or can be precipitated by transfer of lymphocytes from uninfected or immunised mice. The disease which results is a fatal involvement of the CNS or chronic glomerulonephritis due to deposition of immune complexes. When the virus is injected into LCM free adult mice, an acute fatal infection occurs. Natural infection in carrier mice serves as a model for persistent tolerant infections.

Arenaviruses have assumed considerable medical importance after the recognition that some members of the family cause hemorrhagic fevers in humans (Argentinian and Bolivian hemorrhagic fevers and Lassa fever).

South American hemorrhagic fevers: Two related viruses, the Junin and Machupo viruses, cause the Argentinian and Bolivian hemorrhagic fevers respectively. They belong to the Tacaribe group of arenaviruses. Rodents act as reservoirs and transmission is believed to occur through rodent excreta.

Lassa fever: This is the most highly publicised of viral hemorrhagic fevers and is caused by another arenavirus. It was first noticed in 1969 in an American Mission station in Lassa, Nigeria. Many outbreaks have subsequently occurred in widely separated foci in West Africa. The case fatality rate has been 35–70 per cent in hospitalised patients. Natural reservoir is the multimammate rat. Rodent excreta probably act as the source of infection. The incubation period is 3–16 days. The virus is present in the throat, urine and blood of patients. Person-to-person transmission may occur by droplet infection. Nosocomial infection has occurred frequently. Ribavirin has proved useful in treatment.

Filoviruses: These are long threadlike viruses, hence the name (*filum* means thread). They range in size from 80 to 800–1000 nm. Marburg and Ebolaviruses causing hemorrhagic fever belong to the genus *Filovirus*.

Marburg virus: Marburg disease is a hemorrhagic fever that occurred simultaneously in laboratory workers in Marburg, Frankfurt (Germany) and Belgrade (Yugoslavia) in 1967. The infection arose from tissues of African green monkeys to which the laboratory workers had been exposed. The monkeys had been imported from Uganda. Person-to-person transmission occurred. The primary cases had a fatality rate of 30 per cent but the secondary cases were nonfatal.

The Marburg virus was isolated in guinea pigs and tissue culture from the blood and tissues of these patients. The virus appears to persist in the body and has been isolated after 80 days of onset of illness from semen and the anterior chamber of the eye. A case of sexual transmission has been recorded.

No further Marburg virus infection was seen except for three cases identified in South Africa in 1975 and two in Kenya in 1980.

Ebola virus: In 1976, several cases of a similar hemorrhagic fever occurred in the equatorial provinces of Sudan and Zaire, with high fatality. The causative virus was morphologically identical to the Marburg virus but antigenically distinct. It has been called Ebola virus after the Ebola river, beside which the first cases were noticed. In 1979 Ebola re-emerged in Sudan, with serial person-to-person spread. In 1995 a large outbreak, with heavy fatality in Kikwit, Zaire. Three distinct strains of Ebola virus have been recognised. These are the Zaire strain (EBO-Z) with a case fatality rate of up to 90 per cent, the Sudan strain (EBO-S) with a case fatality rate of up to 50 per cent, and the mild Reston strain (EBO-R) isolated from quarantined monkeys, imported from the Philippines and held at Reston, Virginia, USA.

The reservoir of Ebola virus and its natural history still remain unclear, despite frequent outbreaks with high fatality.

CORONAVIRUSES

A group of spherical or pleomorphic enveloped RNA viruses, carrying petal or club shaped peplomers on their surface has been classified as coronaviruses. The name refers to the fringe of surface projections surrounding the virus, resembling the solar corona. The group originally contained veterinary pathogens such as avian infectious bronchitis virus, mouse hepatitis virus and transmissible gastroenteritis virus of swine. Human coronaviruses were first isolated from cases of common cold by inoculating organ cultures of human embryonic trachea with nasopharyngeal washings. Inhibition of ciliary motility indicates virus growth. Though many strains grow only on organ cultures, some grow on monolayers of diploid human embryonic fibroblasts, with minimal cytopathic effects. Many serotypes of human coronaviruses have been recognised. Inoculation in human volunteers induces common cold after an incubation period of 2–5 days. The resulting immunity is poor and reinfections can occur even with the same serotype. They appear to be the second most common cause of common cold, particularly in winter, next only to rhinoviruses.

SEVERE ACUTE RESPIRATORY SYNDROME (SARS)

In November 2002, Guangdong province in South China experienced an outbreak of an unusual respiratory infection, with many deaths. The world outside knew about it only in February 2003, when a physician from Guangdong visited Hong Kong, fell ill and died there, after infecting twelve persons who had stayed in the same hotel. They in turn, went to their separate countries to fall ill and initiate outbreaks there.

In February in Hanoi, Vietnam, a private hospital sought the help of a WHO local office about an unusual case of pneumonia. Dr Carlo Urbani, the nearest WHO infectious disease specialist volunteered. As a former President of *Medesins sans Frontieres*, he had ample experience in tackling epidemics. Sensing the danger he immediately arranged for isolation and quarantine, but by then outbreaks had begun in many countries: Canada, USA, Ireland and some European

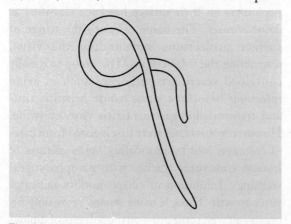

Fig. 60.2: Ebola virus (long thin filamentous form)

countries, Hong Kong, China, Taiwan and most countries in South East Asia. The new disease was named *severe acute respiratory syndrome* (SARS). By July, when the pandemic was controlled, it had affected over 30 countries, with many thousand cases and over 800 deaths. India escaped the SARS epidemic; though a few suspect cases were detected and quarantined.

In an unprecedented concerted international study using a wide array of tests to identify the causative agent, a coronavirus was found in the respiratory secretions of patients, identified by electron microscopy, and confirmed by growth in Vero cell culture, animal inoculation, cloning, sequencing and histology. Molecular and serological tests for rapid diagnosis were developed. This appears to be a new virus distinct from other coronaviruses, which had been classified into three types: Mammalian viruses in types 1 and 2 and avian viruses in type 3. The new SARS virus becomes coronavirus type 4. That it is a new virus is indicated by the absence of an antibody to it in human and animal sera collected in previous years. It may be a recombinant of some animal and human virus. The virus has been isolated from Chinese wild civets and raccoon dogs, but not from pigs, dogs, cattle or poultry.

SARS spreads by inhalation of the virus present in droplets or aerosols of respiratory secretions of patients. Fecal aerosols also may be infectious. The incubation period is under 10 days. The disease starts as fever with cough or other respiratory symptoms. Diarrhea is sometimes seen. The chest radiograph shows pneumonic changes. Death is due to respiratory failure. Reverse transcription PCR has been used for early diagnosis, while demonstration of rise in titre of antibodies by ELISA or indirect immunofluorescent test in paired serum samples are useful later. No specific therapy or prophylaxis has been identified. The virus is highly mutable and so vaccine prophylaxis may not be easy. Control has been achieved by strict isolation and quarantine.

It has been suggested that the causative agent isolated be designated 'Urbani SARS associated coronavirus' in memory of Dr Carlo Urbani who identified the new epidemic, initiated early steps for its control and died of it within a month!

REOVIRIDAE

The family Reoviridae derives its name from the prototype virus which was known as the Respiratory Enteric Orphan virus, because it could be isolated frequently from the respiratory and enteric tracts, but was not associated with any disease. Members of this family are double shelled icosahedral viruses, 55–57 nm in diameter. The genome consists of double stranded RNA in 10–12 pieces, a feature unique among animal viruses. They are nonenveloped and resistant to lipid solvents. The family contains three genera—*Reovirus, Orbivirus* and *Rotavirus.*

REOVIRUS

The genus Reovirus contains three mammalian serotypes (Reovirus types 1, 2 and 3) which possess a common complement-fixing antigen but can be differentiated by neutralisation tests. Reoviruses agglutinate human erythrocytes. Hemagglutination is type specific and is neutralised by the specific antibody. Reoviruses have not been proved to cause any human disease.

ORBIVIRUS

These have a double shell in which the outer layer is fuzzy and indistinct. The inner layer has 32 ring shaped capsomers. The name orbivirus is derived from *orbi*, in Latin, meaning ring. Orbiviruses multiply in insects and vertebrates thus qualifying as arboviruses. They are responsible for veterinary diseases such as African horse sickness and blue tongue. The only known orbivirus infection of human beings is Colorado tick fever.

ROTAVIRUS

These double walled viruses present a characteristic appearance under the electron microscope,

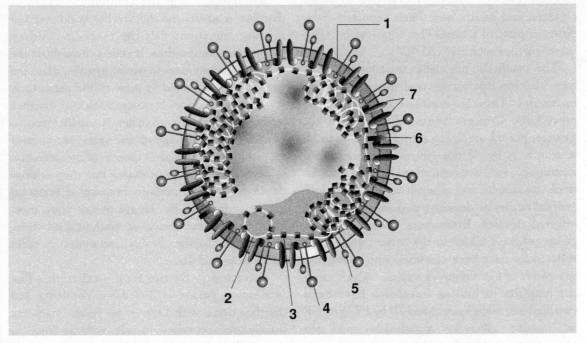

Fig. 60.3 : SARS - associated coronavirus (diagrammatic representation) 1. Envelope; 2. RNA; 3. Nucleocapsid nucleoprotein; 4. spike glycoprotein; 5. Hemagglutinin-acetyl esterase glycoprotein; 6. small envelope glycoprotein; 7. membrane glycoprotein.

resembling little wheels with short spokes radiating from a wide hub to a clearly defined outer rim. The name is derived from *rota*, in Latin, meaning wheel. Both 'complete' and 'incomplete' particles are seen. The complete or 'double shelled' virus measures about 70 nm in diameter and has a smooth surface. The incomplete or 'single shelled' virus is smaller, about 60 nm, with a rough surface and is rotavirus that has lost the outer shell. 'Empty' particles without the RNA core are also seen.

Bishop and colleagues (1973) in Melbourne identified rotaviruses in ultrathin sections of duodenal mucosal biopsies from acute infantile gastroenteritis cases, by electron microscopy, using negative staining techniques. The virus was also present in the feces. These observations have been confirmed and rotaviruses are now recognised as the most common cause of diarrheal disease in infants and children.

Outbreaks of rotavirus diarrhea in older children and adults have been reported from different parts of China. This rotavirus is called 'adult diarrhea rotavirus' (ADRV).

The methods originally used for diagnosis were electron microscopy and immunoelectron microscopy. These are expensive and complicated procedures. Concentrations of more than 10^6 particles per ml are necessary for the virus to be seen in feces by electron microscopy. Serological techniques for demonstration of the virus in stools are simpler and as sensitive. IgM and IgG antibodies can be demonstrated in the blood of infected children. Rotaviruses share a common group antigen situated in the inner capsid layer. Rotaviruses have been classified into antigenic groups (A to G). Group A strains, which cause the majority of human infections have been classified into *subgroups* (I and II) by ELISA, CF or immune adherence agglutination, and into many *serotypes* (1, 2, 3 etc) by neutralisation tests. ADRV strains belong to group B. By polyacrylamide gel electrophoresis, rotavirus strains can be classified into several electrophoretypes, based on the patterns of migration of the viral RNA.

Rotaviruses are a class of viruses causing diarrhea in the young of many animals and some birds. The human rotavirus is related to the viruses of epidemic diarrhea of infant mice (EDIM), Nebraska calf diarrhea and the simian virus SA11. All rotaviruses share common antigens. Though the viruses are in general species specific, interspecies infection can be induced experimentally. Human rotavirus infection has been transferred to piglets, calves and monkeys. It is not known whether human infection can be caused by animal rotaviruses.

Human rotavirus does not grow readily in cell cultures but some strains have been adapted for serial growth in tissue cultures. Rotavirus growth is facilitated by trypsin treatment and rolling of tissue cultures. As calf and simian viruses grow readily in cell cultures, they have been used as antigens for serological studies.

Rotaviruses are the commonest cause of diarrhea in infants and children the world over and account for about half the cases of children hospitalised for diarrhea. It occurs throughout the year but predominates in winter months, when the virus may be detected in most of the patients. It sometimes produces large epidemics of diarrhea in winter. Rotavirus diarrhea is usually seen in children below the age of five years, but is most frequent between 6 and 24 months of age. Infection is not infrequent in neonates but they seldom develop diarrhea, perhaps because of maternal passive immunitiy. By the age of five years, most children have had clinical or subclinical infection, so rotavirus diarrhea is very uncommon in older children and adults.

Infection is by the fecal–oral route. The incubation period is 2–3 days. Vomiting and diarrhea occur with little or no fever. Stools are usually greenish yellow or pale, with no blood or mucus. The disease is self-limited and recovery occurs within 5–10 days. Mortality is low. Rehydration is all the treatment needed.

Rotavirus vaccines have been developed, but are not in use now.

OTHER VIRUSES CAUSING DIARRHEA

Besides rotaviruses, the following viruses are known or suspected to cause diarrheal disease:

Norwalk virus: A 27 nm virus was shown to be responsible for an epidemic of gastroenteritis affecting school children and teachers in Norwalk, Ohio, in 1972. The virus induced diarrhea in human volunteers. Serological surveys have shown that infection with Norwalk virus is widespread in many countries. Extensive epidemics of Norwalk virus diarrhea associated with consumption of raw oysters have been reported from Australia and America. It appears to be an important cause of diarrhea in adults and children.

The virus can be demonstrated in feces by electron microscopy. Antibody to the virus can be detected by immune electron microscopy and radioimmunoassay. It has not yet been propagated in cell cultures. Little is known about the properties of the virus. It has been included in the family *Caliciviridae* consisting of small round RNA viruses, 22–30 nm in size, many of which have been reported from diarrheal feces. The name calicivirus is derived from the presence of 32 cup shaped depressions on the virus surface (from *calyx*, meaning cup).

Adenovirus: Several outbreaks of diarrhea in children have been associated with the presence of large numbers of adenoviruses in feces. These adenoviruses can be only grown with difficulty in tissue culture. They have been designated types 40 and 41. Adenovirus associated diarrhoea has been seen more often in summer months.

Astrovirus: These star shaped, 28 nm isometric particles have been associated with some epidemics of diarrhea in children. Similar viruses have also been identified in lamb and calf diarrhea.

Coronavirus: These are well established causes of acute diarrhea in calves, piglets and dogs. They have been observed in human feces also but their relation to diarrhea is uncertain.

Hendra and Nipah viruses: Two new zoonotic viruses, closely related but distinct are Hendra (1994) and Nipah (1999) viruses named after the place they were first isolated in, in Australia and Malaysia respectively. They have been classified under the family Paramyxoviridae. They are prevalent in Australia and in Malaysia, Indonesia, Philippines and the Pacific Islands.

Their natural hosts are fruit bats in which they cause silent infection. Symptomatic infection occurs in horses, pigs and many other domesticated wild animals. Human infection is usually subclinical, but may be a flulike fever which may lead to fatal encephalitis, sometimes as outbreaks. Hendra virus outbreaks have been minor, but nipah virus has caused large outbreaks with case fatality rates of up to 50 per cent in persons in contact with pigs. Large scale slaughter of pigs had been undertaken in order to stop outbreaks.

Further Reading

Burke B and U Desselberger 1996. Rotavirus pathogenesis. *Lancet* 218:299.

Carter MJ and WD Cubitt 1995. Norwalk and related viruses. *Curr Opin Infect Dis* 8:403.

Fields BN et al. 1996. Virology, 3rd edn. Philadelphia:Lippincott-Raven.

Johnson KM et al. 1989. Clinical virology of Lassa fever. *J Infect Dis* 155:456.

Kapikian AZ. 1994. Viral infections of the gastrointestinal tract. New York: Marcel-Dekker.

Lee HW and G Van der Groen 1989. Hemorrhagic fever with renal syndrome. *Progr Med Virol* 36:62.

Holmes KV. 2003. SARS. *New Eng J Med* 348:1948.

Prusiner SB. 1998. Prions of humans and animals. In *Topley and Wilson's Microbiology and Microbial Infections*, 9th edn. London: Arnold.

Richmond JK and DJ Baglole 2003. Lassa Fever. *Br Med J* 327:1271.

Wenzel RA and MB Edmond 2003. Managing SARS. *New Eng J Med* 348:1947.

Oncogenic Viruses

The association of viruses with malignancy dates from the observation by Ellerman and Bang (1908) that the mode of transmission in leukemia in fowls resembled that of an infectious disease. Rous (1911) showed that a solid malignant tumour, fowl sarcoma, was caused by a virus, a discovery for which he was awarded the Nobel prize belatedly in 1966. Viruses causing tumours in animals were first demonstrated by Shope, who isolated the rabbit fibroma virus in 1932 and the papilloma virus in 1933. Though these are benign tumours, papillomas may turn malignant. Bittner (1936) proposed that breast cancer in mice could be caused by a virus transmitted from mother to offspring through breast milk. During the 1950s many viruses were identified which induced leukemia in rodents. Considerable interest was aroused by the discovery by Stewart and Eddy (1957) of the polyoma virus which could produce a wide variety of neoplasms when injected into newborn rodents. Injection of certain types of human adenovirus into newborn hamsters was shown by Trentin (1962) to cause sarcomas.

Burkitt (1963) identified a peculiar geographical distribution of lymphoma in African children and suspected that it may be caused by a virus transmitted by an insect. The Epstein–Barr virus isolated from Burkitt's lymphoma has been identified as the etiological agent. Many viruses have been isolated from human cancer or demonstrated electronmicroscopically in affected cells and tissues but most of them were merely 'passenger' viruses present in the lesions and not the causative agents. However, it is now

Table 61.1 Properties of cells transformed by viruses

I	Altered cell morphology: Fibroblasts become shorter, parallel orientation is lost,chromosomal aberrations appear
II	Altered cell metabolism;Increased growth rate, increased production of organic acids and acid mucopolysaccharides
III	Altered growth characteristics: Loss of contact inhibition, formation of heaped-up growth (microtumours), capacity to divide indefinitely in serial culture, capacity to grow in suspension or in semisolid agar
IV	Antigenic alterations: Appearance of new virus specified antigens (T antigen–TSTA) Loss of surface antigens, cells become agglutinable by lectins
V	Capacity to induce tumours in susceptible animals

acknowledged that virus infections account for 10 to 20 per cent of human malignancies. These include hepatocellular carcinoma caused by Hepatitis B or C viruses, uterine cervical cancer by certain types of papilloma viruses, anaplastic nasopharyngeal carcinomas by EB virus and adult cutaneous T cell lymphoma/leukemia by HTLV-1.

Viruses that produce tumours in their natural hosts or in experimental animals, or induce malignant transformation of cells on culture, are known as oncogenic viruses. Transformation represents the various changes that accompany the conversion of a normal cell into the malignant cell

Table 61.2 List of oncogenic viruses

RNA VIRUSES

I. Retroviruses
1. Avian leukosis viruses
2. Murine leukosis viruses
3. Murine mammary tumour virus
4. Leukosis-sarcoma virus of various animals
5. Human T cell leukemia viruses

DNA VIRUSES

I. Papovavirus
1. Papillomaviruses of human beings, rabbits and other animals
2. Polyomavirus
3. Simian virus 40
4. BK and JV viruses

II. Poxvirus
1. Molluscum contagiosum
2. Yaba virus
3. Shope fibroma

III. Adenovirus
Many human and nonhuman types

IV. Herpesvirus
1. Marek's disease virus
2. Lucke's frog tumourvirus
3. Herpes virus pan, papio, ateles and saimiri
4. Epstein–Barr virus
5. Herpes simplex virus types 1 and 2
6. Cytomegalovirus

V. Hepatitis B and C viruses

(Table 61.1). Transformation from normal to malignant cell is a multistep process and may be partial or complete. For example, some viral agents can 'immortalise' infected cells, so that they become capable of continuous multiplication in culture, without possessing other features of malignancy. Transformation is recognised primarily by a change in morphology of cultured cells. Transformed cells are altered in shape and lose the property of 'contact inhibition' so that, instead of growing as monolayer, they grow piled up, one over another, forming 'microtumours'. Foci of transformation can easily be made out and are used in the assay of oncogenic viruses, such as the Rous sarcoma virus.

About a quarter of the 600 or so animal viruses possess oncogenic potential (Table 61.2). The viruses associated with cancers in human beings are shown in Table 61.3. Both RNA and DNA viruses are oncogenic. While all oncogenic RNA viruses (formerly called oncornaviruses) belong to a single family (retrovirus), oncogenic viruses occur among all major groups of DNA viruses, except parvovirus. Retroviruses are responsible for naturally occurring leukemia and sarcoma in several species of animals. Among DNA viruses, some herpesviruses and hepadnaviruses cause malignant tumours in their natural hosts.

ONCOGENIC DNA VIRUSES

PAPOVAVIRUSES

Papilloma viruses cause benign tumours in their natural hosts but some of them (e.g., condyloma acuminatum in humans, rabbit papilloma) may turn malignant. The association between human papilloma virus (HPV) infection and cancer of cervix uteri, particularly HPV types 16 and 18 has been established. The continuous cell line HeLa, derived many decades ago from a cervical carcinoma and used widely in various laboratories, has been found to contain HPV-18 DNA. In general, infectious virus particles cannot be demonstrated in tumours induced by DNA viruses but papilloma in the wild cotton tail rabbit is an exception. Rabbit papilloma virus, or DNA extracted from it, can produce papilloma in rabbits following subcutaneous injection.

The polyoma virus causes natural latent infection in laboratory and domestic mice. However, when injected into infant mice or other rodents, it induces a wide variety of histologically diverse tumours. The virus can be cultivated in mouse embryo fibroblasts or baby hamster kidney cells, in which it induces transformation. The polyoma virus produces a hemagglutinin.

The papovaviruses BK and JC, which cause widespread asymptomatic human infection, can induce tumours in immunodeficient subjects.

Simian virus 40 (SV 40) was discovered in

Table 61.3 Viruses associated with human cancer

Virus Family	Virus	Types of cancer
Papovaviridae	Human papilloma virus	Cervical, vulvar, penile cancers
		Squamous cell carcinoma
Herpesviridae	E-B Virus	Nasopharyngeal carcinoma
		African Burkitt's lymphoma
	HSV type 2	B cell lymphoma, Cervical carcinoma
Hepadnaviridae	Hepatitis B virus	Hepatocellular carcinoma
Flaviviridae	Hepatitis C virus	
Retroviridaee	HTL virus	Adult T cell leukemia

apparently normal monkey kidney cultures used for the production of the polio vaccine. It causes an inapparent infection in rhesus and cynomolgus monkeys and does not cause cytopathic effects in cell cultures from such monkeys. However, when fluid from such cultures is inoculated into renal cell cultures derived from African green monkeys, cytopathic change with prominent cytoplasmic vacuolation results. Injection into newborn hamsters produces tumours. Transformation is induced in cultured cells from several species, including human cells. Millions of doses of polio vaccine prepared in monkey kidney cultures that may have harboured SV 40 virus had been used before the virus was discovered. These individuals have been followed up for over 25 years and no SV 40-related tumours have been reported. There was considerable apprehension when the oncogenic effect of SV 40 was discovered. However, there is no evidence that the injection of vaccine containing SV 40 has induced cancer in humans.

POXVIRUS

Three members of the poxvirus group induce benign tumours, rabbit fibroma, molluscum contagiosum and Yaba virus. The last causes naturally occurring benign histiocytomas in monkeys. It is apparently transmitted by insects. Similar tumours can be induced experimentally in many species of primates, including human beings. The tumours regress spontaneously in a few weeks. Nonprimates are unsusceptible.

ADENOVIRUS

Though some types (12, 19, 21) of human adenovirus may produce sarcomas in newborn rodents after experimental inoculation, they do not appear to have any association with human cancer.

HERPESVIRUS

Many herpesviruses have been associated with natural cancers in animals and humans.

a. Marek's disease: This is a fatal contagious neurolymphomatosis of chickens. No infectious virus particle can be isolated from the lesions or seen under the electron microscope. However, sick birds shed large quantities of virus from their feather follicles. The virus is a typical herpesvirus. Marek's disease can be induced in young chicken by the injection of the virus. The virus grows well in chick embryo fibroblasts producing cytopathic changes but no evidence of transformation. Marek's disease can be prevented by a live avirulent vaccine. This is the first instance of a malignant disease being controlled by a viral vaccine.

b. Lucke's tumour of frogs: A herpesvirus is considered to be the etiological agent of a renal adenocarcinoma in frogs.

c. Herpesvirus saimiri: This virus was isolated from a culture of Squirrel monkey kidney cells. It causes fatal lymphoma or reticulum cell sarcoma when injected into owl, monkeys or rabbits. Herpesvirus saimiri infection has been suggested as a primate model for the study of interactions between the EB virus and human beings.

d. Epstein–Barr virus: A herpesvirus, called the Epstein–Barr virus, is found regularly in cultured lymphocytes from Burkitt's lymphoma patients. In the body, the tumour cells contain no virus but cell lines established from them contain 5–20 per cent of cells that produce the virus. The virus multiplies only in human lymphoid cell lines. Serological surveys show that infection with the virus is worldwide. Infection is usually asymptomatic. In young adults without pre-existing antibodies, EB virus infection induces infectious mononucleosis. Lymphoma is believed to occur when the infection takes place in children whose immune systems are compromised, as for instance, by chronic malaria. EB virus associated lymphomas have been reported in transplant recipients. EBV has also been linked to nasopharyngeal carcinoma in the Chinese male population in southeast Asia and East Africa.

e. Herpes simplex and cancer cervix: An association has been proposed between herpes simplex type 2 infection and cancer of the uterine cervix, though not proved. It has also been suggested that herpes simplex type 1 infection may be associated with cancer of the lip. Herpesvirus type 8 has been linked to Kaposi's sarcoma.

f. Cytomegalovirus infection has been associated with carcinoma of the prostate and Kaposi sarcoma.

Hepatitis B Virus

HBV has been claimed to be directly or indirectly involved in the etiology of hepatocellular carcinoma. Studies in many countries have demonstrated an excess prevalence of markers of HBV infection in patients with primary hepatocellular carcinoma as compared with matched controls or with the general population. Hepatitis C virus infection has also been reported to lead to hepatocellular carcinoma.

ONCOGENIC RNA VIRUSES

Retrovirus

Retroviruses are enveloped, spherical viruses that are released by budding through the host cell membrane. They are approximately 100 nm in size. The genome consists of two identical, linear, single stranded RNA molecules. The icosahedral nucleocapsid core encloses the helical ribonucleoprotein and is surrounded by an envelope composed of glycoprotein and lipid.

The characteristic feature of retroviruses is the presence within the virion of the unusual enzyme RNA dependent DNA polymerase or reverse transcriptase (hence the name *retro*, meaning reverse). Unlike the classical transcription of genetic information from DNA to RNA, the reverse transcriptase enzyme prepares a DNA copy of the retroviral RNA genome—initially an RNA:DNA hybrid and then its double stranded DNA form. The double stranded DNA form of retroviral genome, called the *provirus*, is integrated into the DNA of the infected host cell. It is from the provirus that all retrovirus proteins are translated. Infection with oncogenic retroviruses does not lead to cytolysis or death of infected cells but the provirus remains integrated with the host cell DNA for the rest of the life of the cell.

While all oncogenic RNA viruses belong to the family *Retroviridae*, all retroviruses are not oncogenic. The family *Retroviridae* is classified into three subfamilies.

1. *Oncovirinae* comprising all oncogenic RNA viruses (formerly called oncornavirus).
2. *Spumavirinae* containing the nononcogenic 'foamy viruses' (*spuma* = foam) causing asymptomatic infection in several animal species, and presenting as contaminants of primary cell cultures in which they induce foamy degeneration.
3. *Lentivirinae* including the viruses causing 'slow infections' (*lentus* = slow) in animals (see chapter 60), as well as the human and related animal immunodeficiency viruses (see chapter 62).

Retroviruses are widely distributed, being found in nearly all vertebrates, including animals, birds and reptiles. Based on the host range and types of disease caused, oncogenic retroviruses can be considered under the following groups:

1. The Avian Leukosis Complex: A group of antigenically related viruses which induce avian leukosis (lymphomatosis, myeloblastosis and erythroblastosis viruses) or sarcoma in fowls (Rous sarcoma virus, RSV).

2. Murine Leukosis Viruses: This group consists of several strains of murine leukemia and sarcoma viruses, named after the investigators who first described them (e.g. Gross, Friend, Moloney, Rauscher).

3. Mammary tumour virus of mice: This virus occurs in certain strains of mice having a high natural incidence of breast cancer. It used to be known as the 'milk factor' or 'Bittner virus'. It multiplies in the mammary gland and is transmitted from mother to offspring through breast milk. Mice can be infected by oral, subcutaneous or intraperitoneal routes. Mammary cancer occurs only in susceptible strains of mice, after a latent period of 6–12 months.

4. Leukosis-sarcoma viruses of other animals: A number of viruses have been isolated from leukosis and sarcomas in various species of animals – cat, hamster, rat, guinea pig and monkey.

5. Human T cell leukemia (lymphotropic) viruses: (HTLV): Retroviruses named human T cell leukemia viruses were isolated in 1980 from cell cultures from adult patients with cutaneous T cell lymphoma (mycosis fungoides) and leukemia (Sezary syndrome) in the USA. Similar viruses have been isolated from patients with adult T cell leukemia in Japan and the Caribbean. HTLV type I is present worldwide but the disease is limited to endemic areas. Besides adult T cell leukemia, HTLV-I has also been associated with tropical spastic paraparesis, a demyelinating disease. The virus preferentially infects T4 (CD4) cells. Infected T cells express large

quantities of interleukin-2 receptors. The closely related HTLV-II is also associated with T cell malignancy. HTLV infection is known to be spread through blood transfusion and other methods of transfer of leucocytes.

Host specificity: Retroviruses usually infect only one host species, the specificity being conditioned mainly by the presence of viral receptors on the host cell surface. Depending on their ability to grow in cells from different species, retroviruses have been classified into (1) ecotropic (multiplying in cells of native host species only); (2) amphotropic (multiplying in cells of native and foreign species); and (3) xenotropic (multiplying only in cells of foreign species but not of native host species).

Virus transmission: Two types of retrovirus transmission occur. Exogenous retroviruses are spread horizontally. Most oncogenic retroviruses are exogenous. Endogenous retroviruses are transmitted vertically from parent to offspring, by the provirus integrated with the germ line cell genome. The endogenous retrovirus provirus behaves like a cellular gene and is subject to

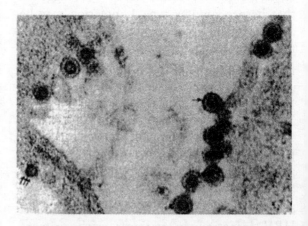

Fig. 61.1 Mouse mammary cancer. Section stained with uranyl acetate and lead nitrate, showing mature budding B type virus (arrow) and intracellular immature A type virus (triple arrow). (x 150,000) (Courtesy: Cancer Research Institute, Mumbai.)

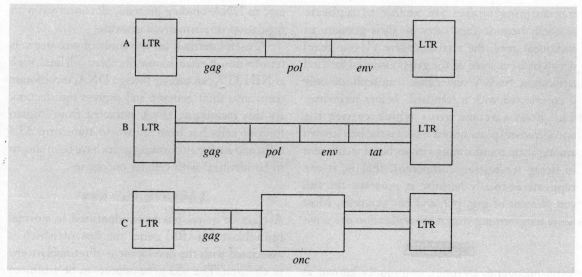

Fig. 61.2 Provirus genomic structure of different types of retroviruses
A. Basic retrovirus genome–e.g. Avian leukemia viruses, slow transforming viruses
B. Transregulating retroviruses–e.g. HTLV, HIV
C. Acute transforming retrovirus; oncogene replacing part of basic genome. Replication defective.

regulatory control by the host cell. Endogenous retroviruses are usually silent and do not transform cells or cause any disease. They can be detected either by 'activation' after exposure to radiation or chemicals, or by nucleic acid hybridisation techniques.

Resistance: Retroviruses are labile, being inactivated at 56 °C in 30 minutes, by mild acids, ether and formalin. They are stable at –30 °C.

Antigens: Two types of antigens are present— the type specific glycoprotein antigens on the envelope, and the group specific nucleoprotein antigens in the virion core. Cross-reactions do not occur between surface antigens of retroviruses from different host species.

Genomic structure: Retroviruses have a relatively simple genomic structure (Fig. 61.2).

The provirus of a standard retrovirus (such as a nondefective avian or murine leukemia virus) consists of three genes required for viral replication – gag, pol, and env in that order from the 5' to 3' end. The gag gene codes for the nucleocapsid core proteins which are group specific antigens (hence the name gag); the pol gene encodes the RNA dependent DNA polymerase; and the env gene encodes the envelope glycoproteins. Long terminal repeat (LTR) sequences are present at either end of the provirus and linked directly to the host DNA. The LTRs exert regulatory control on the provirus gene functions.

Some retroviruses (transregulating viruses) such as HTLV or HIV carry a fourth gene, tex or tat, after the env gene. This is a transactivating gene that regulates the function of viral genes.

The standard oncogenic retroviruses, such as chronic leukemia viruses, are slow transforming viruses, i.e., they have a low oncogenic potential and induce malignant change, generally only of blood cells, after a long latent period. They do not transform cultured cells. They are capable of replicating normally. In contrast, the acute transforming viruses are highly oncogenic and cause malignancy after a short latent period of weeks or months. They can cause different types of malignancies – sarcoma, carcinoma, leukemia – and also transform cells in culture. However, most acute transforming viruses are unable to replicate normally because they carry on their genome an additional gene, the viral oncogene (*V-onc* gene) which replaces some of the genes essential for viral replication. Such V-onc viruses can replicate only if co-infected with a standard helper retrovirus. The Rous sarcoma virus which carries the oncogenic *src* (pronounced 'Sark') is the best known among acute transforming viruses but it is different in being *replication competent,* that is, it can replicate normally because it posseses the full complement of *gag, pol,* and *env* genomes. Most acute transforming viruses are *replication defective.*

ONCOGENES

Viral oncogenes (V-onc), commonly known as 'cancer genes' are genes which encode proteins triggering transformation of normal cells into cancer cells. Oncogenes are not essential for the replication of the virus and mutants lacking them occur, which replicate normally without being oncogenic.

Genes closely resembling viral oncogenes are found in normal as well as cancer cells. Oncogenes isolated from cancer cells are called cellular oncogenes (C-onc). Similar genes found in normal cells are called proto-oncogenes. They are not of viral origin. On the contrary viral oncogenes appear to be of host cell origin. Cellular oncogenes contain introns characteristic of eukaryotic genes, whereas viral oncogenes do not. Apparently viral oncogenes originated at some distant past from proto-oncogenes by recombination between retroviral and cellular genes.

Proto-oncogenes are widespread in vertebrates and metazoa—from human beings to fruitflies. They are well conserved in their genomes, suggesting that they serve some essential functions in normal cells. They have been found to code for proteins involved in regulating cell growth and differentiation. The presumed functions of many oncogenes have been identified. For example, the oncogene src is related to tryrosine-specific protein kinases, sis to a platelet derived growth factor, and myc to DNA-binding proteins, all concerned with regulation of normal cell growth.

A useful method for the study of oncogenes is transfection. Certain mouse fibroblast cell lines, such as NIH 3T3, can take up foreign DNA, incorporate them into their genome and express *transfection.* By this technique, DNA extracted from human tumour cells has been shown to transform 3T3 cells, and such transforming genes have been shown to be identical with cellular oncogenes.

ANTI-ONCOGENES

A class of genes has been identified in normal retinoblastoma (Rb) gene, the loss of which is associated with the development of retinoblastoma in children. The p53 gene appears to be a tumour suppressor gene with a wide range of effects. Specific chromosomal deletions, recognised in association with certain types of human cancers may reflect the loss of tumour suppressor genes.

MECHANISMS OF VIRAL ONCOGENESIS

While it is known that oncogenic viruses are able to transform cells in culture and induce tumours in animals, under natural or experimental conditions, the exact mechanisms of viral oncogenesis are not well understood. Malignancy is a stable heritable change and, as such, should be the result of a modification of the host cell genome.

In the case of oncogenic DNA viruses, the viral DNA (or a portion of it) is integrated with the host cell genome. The viral DNA being incomplete or 'defective', no infectious virus is produced. However, under its influence, the host cell undergoes malignant transformation. A virus transformed cancer cell is in many ways analogous to a bacterium lysogenised by a defective phage. In both cases, the cell is not destroyed and no virus is produced. Acquisition of new characteristics by the transformed cell resembles lysogenic conversion in bacteria.

In general, retroviruses induce tumours by two mechanisms—either by introducing into the

Table 61.4 Some oncogenes* and their chromosomal location in humans

Viraloncogene	Origin	Natural tumour	Human gene	Chromosomal location in human beings
V-src	chicken	Sarcoma	C-src	20
V-ras	rat	Sarcoma	C-ras	11
V-myc	chicken	Leukemia	C-myc	8
V-fes	cat	Sarcoma	C-fes	15
V-sis	monkey	Sarcoma	C-sis	22
V-mos	mouse	Sarcoma	C-mos	8

* Oncogenes are given three letter codes from the animal or tumour from which they are derived, preceded by either V- or C-, for viral or cellular genes respectively;

src = sarcoma of chicken, ras = rat sarcoma, sis = simian sarcoma,

cellular genome a new transforming gene (oncogene) or by inducing or altering the expression of a pre-existing cellular gene. Several molecular mechanisms have been suggested for the conversion of benign proto-oncogenes to cancer genes. The genes may get overexpressed and the overproduced gene product may lead to abnormal growth. Recombination between retroviral and cellular genes, promoter insertion, chromosomal translocation, gene amplification and mutation are some of the genetic processes relevant in this connection.

Further Reading

Bishop JM. 1989. The molecular genetics of cancer. *Science* 235:305.

Friend, SH *et al.* 1988. Oncogenes and tumour suppressor genes. *New Engl J Med* 318:618.

Neil MS and JA Wyke 1998. Viral oncogenicity. In *Topley and Wilson's Microbiology and Microbial Infections*, 9th edn. Vol.I. London:Arnold.

Varmus H. 1988. Retroviruses. *Science* 240:1427.

Weinberg RA. 1988. Finding the antioncogene. *Scient Amer* 259:44.

Weinberg RA. 1989. Oncogenes, antioncogenes and the molecular basis of carcinogenesis. *Cancer Res* 49:3713.

Human Immunodeficiency Virus: AIDS

The emergence and pandemic spread of the *acquired immunodeficiency syndrome* (AIDS) have posed the greatest challenge to public health in modern times. After the sudden appearance of syphilis in Europe five hundred years ago, rarely has any new disease had as great an impact on medicine, science and society and caused as much panic among the public and governments globally as has AIDS. The full consequences of this phenomenon may not be evident for several years because of the silent spread and slow evolution of this infection.

The first indication of this new syndrome came in the summer of 1981, with reports from New York and Los Angeles (USA), of a sudden unexplained outbreak of two very rare diseases – Kaposi's sarcoma and *Pneumocystis carinii* pneumonia in young adults who were homosexuals or addicted to injected narcotics. They appeared to have lost their immune competence, rendering them vulnerable to overwhelming and fatal infections with relatively avirulent micro organisms, as well as to lymphoid and other malignancies. This condition was given the name *acquired immune deficiency syndrome* (AIDS).

In 1983 Luc Montagnier and colleagues from the Pasteur Institute, Paris isolated a retrovirus from a West African patient with persistent generalised lymphadenopathy, which is a manifestation of AIDS, and called it *lymphadenopathy associated virus* (LAV). It produced lytic infection in fresh peripheral blood lymphocytes but could not be established in permanent cell lines. In 1984, Robert Gallo and colleagues from the National Institutes of Health, USA, reported isolation of a retrovirus

from AIDS patients and called it *human T cell lymphotropic virus*-III or HTLV-III. Retroviruses HLTV-I and II had already been described earlier in association with human T cell leukemia. HTLV-III could be grown in continuous culture in T cell leukemia cell line, yielding sufficient antigen for serological tests. Other similar isolates were reported from AIDS cases under different names. Serological analysis and molecular cloning established the common identity of these viruses in spite of varying degrees of antigenic differences between them. To resolve this nomenclatural confusion, the International Committee on Virus Nomenclature in 1986 decided on the generic name human immunodeficiency virus (HIV) for these viruses.

In 1985, serological tests (ELISA) became available for detection of anti-HIV antibodies. This made possible a more realistic estimation of the extent of HIV infection. Till then, the infection could be recognised only when patients developed the characteristic clinical features such as opportunistic infections or malignancies. These end-stage cases represented only the tip of the iceberg. Serological screening of high risk groups, blood donors and others revealed a very large and expanding reservoir of HIV in patients and carriers in different parts of the world.

The rate of infection has been steadily mounting. The developing world has to carry the brunt of the disease burden. According to the status paper from UNAIDS/WHO in November 2003, there are 40 million HIV-infected persons currently worldwide. Of these 5 million were newly infected

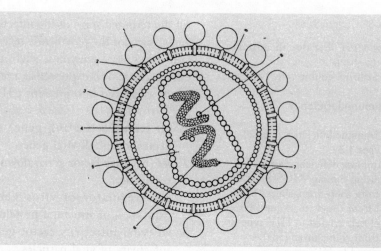

Fig. 62.1 Structure of HIV (diagrammatic representation) 1. Envelope glycoprotein spike (gp 120), 2.Transmembrance pedicle glycoprotein (gp41), 3. Outer icosahedral shell of nucleocapsid (p18), 4. Cone shaped core of nucleocapsid (p24), 5. Inner core, 6. Viral proteins associated with RNA, 7. Viral RNA, 8. Reverse transcriptase, 9. Envelope lipid bilayer.

in 2003. Three million patients died of AIDS in 2003.

HUMAN IMMUNODEFICIENCY VIRUS (HIV)

HIV, the etiological agent of AIDS, belongs to the lentivirus subgroup of the family Retroviridae. The lentivirus subgroup includes the causative agents of the slow virus diseases visna/maedi in sheep and infectious anaemia in goats and horses. Besides HIV, the related animal immunodeficiency viruses also are assigned to this group (Table 62.1).

STRUCTURE

HIV is a spherical enveloped virus, about 90–120 nm in size (Fig. 62.1). The nucleocapsid has an outer icosahedral shell and an inner coneshaped core, enclosing the ribonucleoproteins. The genome is diploid, composed of two identical single stranded, positive sense RNA copies. In association with viral RNA is the reverse transcriptase enzyme, which is a characteristic feature of retroviruses. When the virus infects a cell, the viral RNA is transcribed by the enzyme, first into single stranded DNA and then to double stranded DNA (provirus)

which is integrated into the host cell chromosome. The provirus can remain latent for long periods, though it influences host cell functions. At times, in response to viral promoters, the provirus initiates viral replication by directing synthesis of viral RNA and other components

During viral replication, when the naked virus buds out through the host cell surface membrane, it acquires a lipoprotein envelope, which consists of lipid derived from the host cell membrane and glycoproteins which are virus coded. The major virus coded envelope proteins are the projecting knoblike spikes on the surface and the anchoring transmembrane pedicles. The spikes, constitute the major surface component of the virus which binds to the CD4 receptors on susceptible host cells. Transmembrane pedicles cause cell fusion.

VIRAL GENES AND ANTIGENS

The genome of HIV contains the three structural genes (*gag, pol* and *env*) characteristic of all retroviruses, as well as other nonstructural and regulatory genes specific for the virus (Fig. 62.2). The products of these genes, both structural and

Table 62.1 Lentiviruses

A. Causing 'slow virus' diseases in animals
1. Visna/Maedi in sheep
   2. Caprine arthritis/equine infectious anemia
B. Causing immunodeficiency
I. In primates:
   1. Human Immunodeficiency Viruses (HIV) types 1,2
   2. Simian Immunodeficiency viruses (SIV) causing Simian AIDS(SAIDS):
   a. isolated from sooty mangabeys (SIV-SM) and from rhesus macaque (SIV-MAC) closely related to HIV type 2
   b. isolated from chimpanzee (cpz) – closely related to HIV type 1
II. In nonprimates
   1. Feline T lymphotropic virus (FTLV) causing Feline AIDS (FAIDS)

nonstructural, act as antigens (Table 62.2). Sera of infected persons contain antibodies to them. Detection of these antigens and antibodies is useful in the diagnosis and prognosis of HIV infections.

A. Genes coding for structural proteins:
(1) The *gag* gene determines the core and shell of the virus. It is expressed as a precursor protein, p55. (The proteins and glycoproteins are indicated by their mass expressed in kilodaltons. There are minor differences in the designations used by different authors – e.g., p18 is referred to by some as p17). This precursor protein is cleaved into three proteins, p15, p18 and p24, which make up the viral core and shell. The major core antigen is p24 which can be detected in serum during the early stages of HIV infection before antibodies appear. Late in the course of infection, the decline of free anti-p24 antibody and reappearance of p24 antigen in circulation point to exacerbation of the illness.
(2) The *env* determines the synthesis of envelope glycoprotein gp160, which is cleaved into the two envelope components – gp120 which forms the surface spikes and gp41 which is the transmembrane anchoring protein. The spike glycoprotein gp120 is the major envelope antigen, and antibodies to gp120 are present in circulation

till the terminal stage of the infection. (3) The *pol* gene codes for the polymerase reverse transcriptase and other viral enzymes, such as protease and endonuclease. It is expressed as a precursor protein, which is cleaved into proteins p31, p51 and p66.

B. Nonstructural and regulatory genes:
1. *tat* (trans activating gene) enhancing the expression of all viral genes.
2. *nef* (negative factor gene) down regulating viral replication.
   rev (regulator of virus gene) enhancing expression of structural proteins.
3. *vif* (viral infectivity factor gene) influencing infectivity of viral particles.
4. *vpu* (only in HIV-1) and vpx (only in HIV-2) enhancing maturation and release of progeny virus from cells. (Detection of the type-specific sequences *vpu* and *vpx* is useful in distinguishing between infection by HIV-1 and 2).
5. *vpr* stimulating promoter region of the virus.
6. LTR (long terminal repeat) sequences, one at either end, containing sequences giving promoter, enhancer and integration signals.

ANTIGENIC VARIATION AND DIVERSITY OF HIV

HIV is a highly mutable virus, unlike HTLV. It exhibits frequent antigenic variations as well as differences in other features such as nucleotide sequences, cell tropism, growth characteristics and cytopathology. Not only are there differences between isolates of HIV from different places or persons but also between sequential isolates from the same person, and even between those obtained from different sites of the same person at the same time. This great variability of HIV is believed to be due to the error prone nature of reverse transcription.

Antigenic variation is most frequent in respect of the envelope proteins but is also seen with other antigens. Based on molecular and antigenic differences, two types of HIV have been recognised. The original isolates of HIV and the related strains prevalent all over the world belong to HIV type 1. HIV strains, first isolated from West Africa in 1986, which react with HIV type 1 antiserum very weakly or not at all have been termed HIV type 2. The envelope antigens of the two types are different, though their core polypeptides show some cross reactivity. HIV-2 has only 40 per cent genetic identity with HIV-1. It is more closely related to simian immunodeficiency virus than to HIV-1. It is much less virulent than HIV-1. It is largely confined to West Africa, though isolations have been reported from some other areas, including western and southern India.

HIV-1 strains have been classified into at least ten subtypes based on sequence analysis of their *gag* and *env* genes. These subtypes are designated as A to J and constitute Group M (for 'major'), which cause the large majority of HIV-1 infections worldwide. A few HIV-1 strains isolated from West Africa (Cameroon, Gabon) do not fall within the Group M and have been designated Group O (for 'outlier'). Some later isolates of HIV-1 from Cameroon, distinct from M and O groups have been called Group N (for new).

HIV-1 subtypes show a geographical distribution, though this is often blurred by viral trafficking. All known HIV virus groups and subtypes are present in Cameroon, West Africa, which may perhaps be the site of origin of the virus. Subtype A is the most prevalent, being found worldwide, while B is the most common in the Americas and Europe. The common subtypes in Africa are A, C and D, while in Asia the common subtypes are E, C and B. Subtype E is the commonest in Thailand. In India and China, subtype C is the most prevalent.

Antigenic differences between HIV strains may be important in serodiagnosis. Infection by HIV-1 or 2 may not be identified unless the corresponding type is represented in the test antigen. Even with HIV-1 strains, the differences between the subgroups are significant enough so that Group O strains may be missed if the test antigen contains

Group M only. Even subtype differences may cause discrepancies so it may be advantageous to use antigens containing the prevalent subtypes in different countries.

The subtypes seem to vary in frequency of transmissibility by different routes. The subtypes common in Asia and Africa (C and E) are more readily transmitted by heterosexual contact than the American strains (subtype B) which are preferentially spread through blood – by injection and homosexual contact (homosexual transmission is considered to be bloodborne as the virus is likely to enter directly into the blood through minor mucusal tears).

Differences in growth characteristics are sometimes observed between HIV isolates from asymptomatic carriers and from AIDS patients. The former grow slowly and infect only the peripheral blood lymphocytes, while the latter grow faster and yield high titres in established cell lines of lymphoid and monocytoid origin. Strain variations may account for differences in clinical course of HIV infected persons.

Resistance: HIV is thermolabile, being inactivated in 10 minutes at 60 °C and in seconds at 100 °C. At room temperature (20–25 °C), in dried blood it may survive for upto seven days. A. At autopsy, HIV has been isolated from various tissues upto 16 days after death. It withstands lyophilisation. The virus in lyophilised blood products can be inactivated by heating at 68 °C for 72 hours and in liquid plasma at 60 °C for 10 hours.

Table 62.2 Major antigens of HIV

A.	Envelope antigens:
	1. Spike antigen – gp120
	(Principal envelope antigen)
	2. Transmembrane pedicle protein –gp 41
B.	Shell antigen
	1. Nucleocapsid protein – p18
C.	Core antigens:
	1. Principal core antigen – p24
	2. Other core antigens – p15, p55
D.	Polymerase antigens – p31, p51, p66

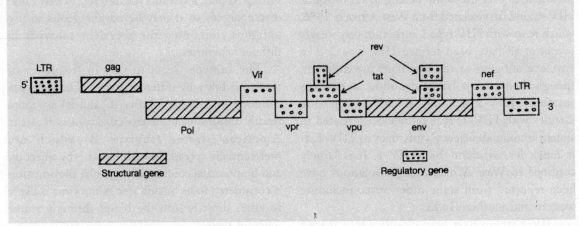

Fig. 62.2 HIV genome—diagrammatic representation

HIV is inactivated in 10 minutes by treatment with 50% ethanol, 35% isopropanol, 0.5% lysol, 0.5% paraformaldehyde, 0.3% hydrogen peroxide, 1% nonidet p40, or 10% household bleach. It is also inactivated at the extremes of pH (pH 1 and 13). Bleaching powder or household bleach are effective for surface decontamination. The standard recommendation is a hypochlorite solution at a concentration of 0.5% available chlorine (5 g/l; 5000 ppm). For treatment of contaminated medical instruments, a 2% solution of glutaraldehyde is useful.

Pathogenesis: Infection is transmitted when the virus enters the blood or tissues of a person and comes into contact with a suitable host cell, principally the CD4 lymphocyte. Infection is likely to result more often following the introduction of HIV infected cells (as in blood transfusion or sexual contact) than of cell free virus (as in injection of blood products).

The receptor for the virus is the CD4 antigen and therefore the virus may infect any cell bearing the CD4 antigen on the surface. This is primarily the CD4+ (helper/inducer) T lymphocyte. Some other immune cells also possess the CD4 antigen on the surface and so are susceptible to infection. Thus about 5–10 per cent of B lymphocytes and

10–20 per cent of monocytes and macrophages, including specialised macrophages such as alveolar macrophages in the lungs and Langerhans cells in the dermis are susceptible. Glial cells and microglia in the central nervous system are also susceptible. Follicular dendritic cells from tonsils can be infected by HIV without the involvement of CD4.

Specific binding of the virus to CD4 receptor is by the envelope glycoprotein gp120. However, for infection to take place, cell fusion is essential. This is brought about by the transmembrane gp41. Binding to CD4 receptor is not by itself enough for cell fusion and virus entry. This requires participation of a coreceptor molecule, which has been identified as CXCR 4 for T cell-tropic HIV strains and CCR 5 for macrophage-tropic strains.

After fusion of the virus with the host cell membrane, the HIV genome is uncoated and internalised into the cell. Viral reverse transcriptase mediates transcription of its RNA into double stranded DNA, which is integrated into the genome of the infected cell through the action of the viral enzyme integrase, causing a latent infection. From time to time, lytic infection is initiated releasing progeny virions which infect other cells. The long and variable incubation period of HIV infection is because of the latency. In an infected individual,

HIV can be isolated from the blood, lymphocytes, cell-free plasma, semen, cervical secretions, saliva, tears, urine and breast milk.

The primary pathogenic mechanism in HIV infection is the damage caused to the CD4+ T lymphocyte. The T4 cells decrease in numbers and the T4:T8 (helper: suppressor) cell ratio is reversed. Viral infection can suppress the function of infected cells without causing structural damage. Infected T4 cells do not appear to release normal amounts of interleukin-2, gamma interferon and other lymphokines. This has a marked damping effect on cell mediated immune response.

Though the major damage is to cellular immunity, humoral mechanisms also are affected. Helper T cell activity is essential for optimal B cell function, particularly in responding to thymus dependent antigens. AIDS patients are unable to respond to new antigens. An important feature in HIV infection is the polyclonal activation of B lymphocytes leading to hypergammaglobulinemia. All classes of immunoglobulins are involved but levels of IgG and IgA are particularly raised. In infants and children, IgM levels also are elevated. The hypergammaglobulinemia is more a hindrance than a help because it is composed mainly of 'useless immunoglobulin' to irrelevant antigens and also autoantibodies. This may also be responsible for allergic reactions due to immune complexes (type 3 hypersensitivity).

Monocyte-macrophage function is also affected apparently due to lack of secretion of activating factors by the T4 lymphocytes. As a result, chemotaxis, antigen presentation and intracellular killing by monocytes/macrophages are diminished. The activity of NK cells and cytotoxic T lymphocytes is also affected. The principal immunological abnormalities seen in HIV infection are listed in Table 62.3.

Clinical manifestations in HIV infections are due not primarily to viral cytopathology but are secondary to the failure of immune responses. This renders the patient susceptible to opportunistic infections and malignancies. An exception to this may be the dementia and other degenerative neurological lesions seen in AIDS. These may be due to the direct effect of HIV on the central nervous system.

ACQUIRED IMMUNE DEFICIENCY SYNDROME (AIDS)

CLINICAL FEATURES OF HIV INFECTION

AIDS is only the last stage in the wide spectrum of clinical features in HIV infection. The Centers for Disease Control (USA) have classified the clinical course of HIV infection under various groups (Table 62.4).

The natural evolution of HIV infection can be considered in the following stages:

1. Acute HIV infection: Within 3–6 weeks of infection with HIV, about 50 per cent of persons experience low grade fever, malaise, headache, lymphadenopathy, sometimes with rash and arthropathy resembling glandular fever. Rarely, there may be acute encephalopathy. Spontaneous resolution occurs within weeks. Tests for HIV antibodies are usually negative at the onset of the illness but become positive during its course. Hence this syndrome has been called 'seroconversion illness', though in many of those infected , 'acute retroviral syndrome' or seroconversion occurs without any apparent illness. HIV antigenemia (p24 antigen) can be demonstrated at the beginning of this phase. The pathogenesis of seroconversion illness is believed to be due to immune complexes as well as to the direct effects of viral multiplication.

2. Asymptomatic or latent infection: All persons infected with HIV, whether or not they experience seroconversion illness, pass through a phase of symptomless infection (clinical latency) which may last up to several years. They show positive HIV antibody tests during this phase and are infectious. The infection progresses in course of time through various stages, CD4 lymphocytopenia, minor opportunistic infections,

persistent generalised lymphadenopathy, AIDS-related complex (ARC), ultimately terminating in full blown AIDS, with its characteristic infections and malignancies. The median time between primary HIV infection and development of AIDS has been stated as approximately 10 years. About 5–10 per cent of the infected appear to escape clinical AIDS for 15 years or more. They have been termed 'long term survivors' or 'long term nonprogressors'. The mechanisms for such prolonged survival are not clear, though many viral and host determinants may be responsible.

This period of clinical latency however does not mean microbiological latency as virus multiplication goes on throughout. The host mounts an immune response against the virus, both humoral and cellular, which can only limit the virus load, but not clear it completely. A chronic persistent infection with varying degrees of viral multiplication is the result. The CD4+ T cell count decreases steadily, from over 1000 per microlitre to about 500 or less by the stage of acute infection. When the count falls to 200 or less, clinical AIDS usually sets in. For this reason the case definition by CDC includes all HIV infected cases with CD4+ T cell counts of 200 or less, irrespective of their clinical condition.

3. Persistent generalised lymphadenopathy (PGL):

This has been defined as the presence of enlarged lymph nodes, at least 1cm, in diameter, in two or more noncontiguous extrainguinal sites, that persist for at least three months, in the absence of any current illness or medication that may cause lymphadenopathy. This by itself is benign but the cases may progress to ARC or AIDS.

4. AIDS related complex (ARC):

This group includes patients with considerable immunodeficiency, suffering from various constitutional symptoms or minor opportunistic infections. The typical constitutional symptoms are fatigue, unexplained fever, persistent diarrhea and marked weight loss of more than 10 per cent of body weight. The common opportunistic infections are oral candidiasis, herpes zoster, hairy cell leucoplakia, salmonellosis or tuberculosis. Generalised lymphadenopathy and splenomegaly are usually present. ARC patients are usually severely ill and many of them progress to AIDS in a few months.

5. AIDS:

This is the end-stage disease representing the irreversible breakdown of immune defence mechanisms, leaving the patient prey to progressive opportunistic infections and malignancies.

The clinical severity of AIDS varies with the type of infection or malignancy present. In early AIDS, many patients are ill only during episodes of infection, which may respond to treatment. Between episodes they may be relatively well and able to resume normal life. Patients with Kaposi's

Table 62.3 Immunological abnormalities in HIV infection

I. Features that characterise AIDS
  1. Lymphopenia.
  2. Selective T cell deficiency-Reduction in number of T4 (CD4) cells, Inversion of T4:T8 ratio.
  3. Decreased delayed hypersensitivity on skin testing.
  4. Hypergammaglobulinemia - predominantly IgG and IgA; and IgM also in children.
  5. Polyclonal activation of B cells and increased spontaneous secretion of Ig.
II. Other consistently observed features:
  1. Decreased in vitro lymphocyte proliferative response to mitogens and antigens.
  2. Decreased cytotoxic responses by T cells and NK cells.
  3. Decreased antibody response to new antigens.
  4. Altered monocyte/macrophage function.
  5. Elevated levels of immune complexes in serum.

sarcoma are less ill than those with other malignancies. The illness progresses inexorably and death ensues in months or years. According to the system most affected, patients present with various complaints, some of which are as follows:

a. The commonest presentation is with increasing dry cough, dyspnea and fever. In the USA and other Western countries, the characteristic pathogen initially was *P. carinii* but now *M. tuberculosis* or an atypical mycobacterium such as *M. avium intracellulare* is more often responsible. In developing countries, the most important pathogen is *M. tuberculosis,* with many strains being multidrug resistant. In fact the poor nations are facing a double epidemic, jointly with HIV and drug resistant tuberculosis. Pneumonia may be viral (CMV) or fungal (cryptococcus, histoplasma). Recurrent pneumonia is considered to be indicative of AIDS.

b. *Gastrointestinal system:* The mouth is often involved in AIDS, with thrush, herpetic stomatitis, gingivitis, hairy leukoplakia or Kaposi's sarcoma. Dysphagia may be due to esophageal candidiasis. A characteristic intestinal pathogen in AIDS is cryptosporidium. Salmonellae, mycobacteria, isospora, CMV or adenoviruses also frequently cause intestinal infections. Systemic strongyloidosis may occur. Chronic colitis is common in male homosexuals ('gay bowel syndrome'), from which ameba, giardia and a host of diarrheagenic bacteria have been reported.

c. *Central nervous system:* The typical CNS opportunistic infections are toxoplasmosis and cryptococcosis. Infections are also seen with CMV, herpes simplex, papovaviruses, mycobacteria, aspergillus and candida. Lymphomas of the central nervous system are common.

d. *Malignancies:* Kaposi's sarcoma was the characteristic lesion seen in male homosexuals. It is an indolent multifocal nonmetastasising mucosal or cutaneous tumour, probably of endothelial origin. The other tumours commonly seen are lymphomas, both the Hodgkin and non-Hodgkin types.

e. *Cutaneous:* Besides Kaposi's sarcoma, herpes lesions, candidiasis, xeroderma, seborrheic dermatitis, prurigo, folliculitis, impetigo and molluscum contagiosum are the common cutaneous lesions.

6. **Dementia:** HIV may cause direct cytopathogenic damage in the central nervous system. It can cross the blood-brain barrier and cause encephalo-

---

Table 62.4 Summary of classification system for HIV infection (Centers for Disease Control, USA)

Group I	Acute HIV syndrome
Group II	Asymptomatic infection
Group III	Persistent generalised lymphadenopathy
Group IV	Other diseases
Subgroup A	Constitutional disease – ARC
Subgroup B	Neurologic diseases
Subgroup C	Secondary infectious diseases
Subgroup C1	Specified infectious diseases listed in the CDC surveillance definition for AIDS, such as *P. carinii* pneumonia, cryptosporidiosis, toxoplasmosis, generalised strongyloidiasis, cryptococcosis CMV or herpes diseases.
Category C2	Other specified secondary diseases, such as oral hairy leukoplakia, salmonella bacteremia, nocardiosis, tuberculosis, thrush
Subgroup D	Secondary cancers, such as Kaposi's sarcoma, lymphomas
Subgroup E	Other conditions

pathy leading to loss of higher functions, progressing to dementia.

7. Pediatric AIDS: About a third to half the number of babies born to infected mothers are infected with HIV. Virus transmission may occur to the fetus in pregnancy as early as the first trimester, but infection is more common perinatally. Many of the infected children may not survive for a year. Children may also acquire the infection from blood transfusion or blood products.

There are many differences between adult and pediatric AIDS. Children develop humoral immunodeficiency early, leading to recurrent bacterial infections. Failure to thrive, chronic diarrhea, lymphadenopathy, tuberculosis and opportunistic bacterial infections are common manifestations in pediatric AIDS. Lymphocytic interstital pneumonia is seen mostly in children, while Kaposi sarcoma, toxoplasmosis and cryptococcosis are less common than in adults.

Laboratory Diagnosis

Laboratory procedures for the diagnosis of HIV infection include tests for immunodeficiency as well as specific tests for HIV.

A. Immunological tests: The following parameters help to establish the immunodeficiency in HIV infection.

1. Total leucocyte and lymphocyte count to demonstrate leucopenia and a lymphocyte count usually below 2000/mm^3.
2. T cell subset assays. Absolute CD4+ T cell count will be usually less than 200/mm^3. T4:T8 cell ratio is reversed.
3. Platelet count will show thrombocytopenia.
4. Raised IgG and IgA levels.
5. Diminished CMI as indicated by skin tests.
6. Lymph node biopsy showing profound abnormalities.

B. Specific tests for HIV infection: These include demonstration of HIV, its antigens or other components and antibodies and isolation of the virus.

1. *Antigen detection:* Following a single massive infection, as by blood transfusion, the virus antigens may be detectable in blood after about two weeks. The major core antigen p24 is the earliest virus marker to appear in blood and is the one tested for. IgM antibodies appear in about 4–6 weeks, to be followed by IgG antibodies (Fig. 62.3; Table 62.6).

If the infecting dose is small, as following a needle-stick injury, the process may be considerably delayed. The appearance of p24 antigenemia and viremia, followed by IgM antibody response coincides with the acute or seroconversion illness. Afterwards, free p24 antigen disappears from circulation and remains absent during the long asymptomatic phase, to reappear only when severe clinical disease sets in. However antibody-bound p24 antigen continues to be demonstrable, after dissociation. The p24 antigen capture assay (ELISA) which uses anti-p24 antibody as the solid phase can be used for this. The test is positive in about 30 per cent of HIV infected persons. With prior dissociation of the antigen–antibody complex, the positive rate increases to about 50 per cent. In the first few weeks after infection and in the terminal phase, the test is uniformly positive. The test is most useful in persons recently exposed to risk of infection, in whom antibody test is negative. It is currently used for screening blood donors in the USA, along with HIV ELISA.

2. *Virus isolation:* Once infected with HIV, a person remains infected for life. The virus is present in circulation and body fluids, within lymphocytes or cell-free. Virus titres parallel p24 titres, being high soon after infection, low and antibody-bound during the asymptomatic period, and again high towards the end. An infected person may therefore be infectious throughout, the infectivity being highest in the early phase and again when the person becomes terminally ill. The virus is present in many parts of the body and can be isolated from the peripheral

lymphocytes. The technique of isolation is by co-cultivation of the patient's lymphocytes with uninfected lymphocytes in the presence of interleukin-2. Viral replication can be detected by the demonstration of reverse transcriptase activity as well as antigens, in the system. However, viral isolation is not suitable as a routine diagnostic test. The test will be positive only in a proportion of persons infected with HIV. Because of the risk involved, virus isolation is to be attempted only in laboratories with adequate containment facilities.

3. *Polymerase chain reaction:* As the most sensitive and specific test, PCR has become the gold standard for diagnosis in all stages of HIV infection. Two forms of PCR have been used, DNA PCR and RNA PCR. In the DNA PCR, peripheral lymphocytes from the subject are lysed and the proviral DNA amplified using primer pairs from relatively constant regions of HIV genome, generally from *gag* and LTR regions. The amplified DNA is characterised by nucleic acid hybridisation. The test is highly sensitive and specific when done with proper controls and can detect HIV proviral DNA at a frequency of one copy per 10,000 cells. A related test, HIV RNA PCR can be used for diagnosis as well as for monitoring the level of viremia. The PCR tests are complex and costly and are indicated only when other methods cannot give a definitive result.

4. *Antibody detection:* Demonstration of antibodies is the simplest and most widely employed technique for the diagnosis of HIV infection. However, it needs to be emphasised that it may take 2–8 weeks to months for antibodies to appear after infection, and during part of this period, the individual may be highly infectious. This seronegative infective stage is known as the *window period.* For this reason, antibody screening is not totally dependable for spotting infectious persons, for example, from among blood donors. Infection

can be detected during the window period by p24 assay. Many instances of HIV transmission by blood transfusion from seronegative donors have been documented. Following sexual exposure to HIV, antibodies may take 2 months to appear, if infection has taken place. Therefore antibody testing will have to be done after 2–6 months to ascertain whether infection has occurred or not, after a single sexual exposure.

Once antibodies appear they increase in titre and broaden in spectrum for the next several months. IgM antibodies disappear in 8–10 weeks while IgG antibodies remain throughout. When immunodeficiency becomes severe following clinical AIDS, some components of anti-HIV antibody, for example, anti-p24 may disappear.

Serological tests for anti-HIV antibodies are of two types—screening and confirmatory tests. Screening tests possess high sensitivity, have a broadly reactive spectrum, are simple to perform and can be automated for handling large numbers of samples at a time. They are not highly specific and may give a few false positive results. All sera positive on screening tests are to be rechecked before the sample is declared positive. The most widely used screening test is ELISA.

a. *ELISA tests:* Direct solid phase antiglobulin ELISA is the method most commonly used. The antigen is obtained from HIV grown in continuous T lymphocyte cell line or by recombinant techniques and should represent all groups and subtypes of HIV-1 and HIV-2. The antigen is coated on microtitre wells or other suitable solid surface. The test serum is added, and if the antibody is present, it binds to the antigen. After washing away the unbound serum, antihuman immunoglobulin linked to a suitable enzyme is added, followed by a colour-forming substrate. If the test serum contains anti-HIV antibody, a photometrically detectable colour is formed which can be read by special ELISA readers.

ELISA is simple and relatively inexpensive but

Table 62.5 Opportunistic infections and malignancies typically associated with HIV infection

I.   Parasitic
    1. Pneumocystis carinii pneumonia
    2. Toxoplasmosis
    3. Cryptosporidiosis
    4. Isosporiasis
    5. Generalised strongyloidiasis
II.   Mycotic
    1. Candidiasis
    2. Cryptococcosis
    3. Aspergillosis
    4. Histoplasmosis
III. Bacterial
    1. Mycobacterial infections-
       Tuberculosis and nontuberculous
       infections
    2. Salmonellosis
    3. Campylobacter infection
    4. Nocardia and actinomycetes
    5. Legionellosis
IV. Viral
    1. CMV
    2. Herpes simplex
V.   Malignancies
    1. Kaposi sarcoma
    2. Lymphomas – Hodgkin and non-
       Hodgkin types

false positive reactions are not uncommon, particularly with sera containing rheumatoid factor, antilymphocyte or other autoantibodies. Sera stored for long periods contain nonspecific 'sticky' immunoglobulins. False positive results can also occur in hepatic disease.

Modifications of ELISA in which the antibody in test serum either competes with enzyme conjugated anti-HIV antibody, or is captured by antihuman immunoglobulin onto solid phase are more specific. Capture ELISA specific for IgM antibody is also available. Immunometric assays are highly sensitive and specific.

While ELISA is ideal for screening several serum samples at a time, it is inconvenient for testing single samples quickly. A number of 'rapid tests' have been introduced for this purpose, such as cylinder or cassette ELISA,

immunochromatographic, coated particle agglutination, immunoperoxidase or dip stick tests.

Tests using finger-prick blood, saliva and urine have also been developed.

b. *Western blot test:* The confirmatory test commonly employed is the *Western blot test.* In this test, HIV proteins separated according to their electrophoretic mobility (and molecular weight) by polyacrylamide gel electrophoresis are blotted onto strips of nitrocellulose paper. These strips are reacted with test sera and then with enzyme conjugated antihuman globulin. A suitable substrate is then added, which produces a prominent colour band where the specific antibody has reacted with the separated viral protein. The position of the band on the strip indicates the antigen with which the antibody has reacted. In a positive serum, bands will be seen with multiple proteins, typically with p24 (*gag* gene, core protein), p31 (*pol* gene, reverse transcriptase) and gp41, gp120 or gp160 (*env* gene, surface antigens). A positive reaction with proteins representing the three genes *gag, pol, env* is conclusive evidence of HIV infection. The test may be considered positive even if it shows bands against at least two of the following gene products: p24, gp41, gp120/160. However, interpretation becomes difficult when bands that appear do not satisfy these criteria. This may happen in early infection but may also be nonspecific. Western blot is a very useful confirmatory test but the interpretation remains subjective and demands considerable experience. Indeterminate results are not uncommon. In such cases the the Western blot may be repeated alater. If no definitive result can be given even then, it may be necessary to have p24 assay done.

A positive result in any one screening test may not be accepted without confirmation. It was the practice to use for confirmation the Western blot test which was considered the 'gold standard'. However, as the test is costly, the practice now

Table 62.6 Evolution of serological markers during HIV infection

State of infection	Markers			
	p24 Ag (free)	Anti HIV IgG	Anti HIV IgM	Western blot patttern
Early infection	–	–	–	
Acute (seroconversion) illness	+ → –	– → +	+	Partial: p24 and/or gp120
Carrier asymptomatic	–	+	–	Full pattern
PGL	+	+	–	Loss of p24/p55
AIDS	+			Absence of p24: loss of other reactivities

is to perform either two different types of ELISA or an ELISA with any of the rapid tests. A serum positive in both tests is considered positive. When in doubt, retesting after 1 or 2 months may be useful.

Apart from diagnosing HIV infection, the laboratory would be called upon to identify the opportunistic infections that are a feature of AIDS. Routine microbiological methods would suffice for this. However, serological diagnosis of infections may not always be reliable in AIDS as antibody formation may be affected by the immune deficiency.

Applications of Serological Tests

Serological tests for HIV infection are employed in the following situations:

1. **Screening:** Screening is defined as the systematic application of HIV testing, whether voluntary or mandatory, to entire populations or selected target groups. Screening of entire populations neither feasible nor practicable. However, screening of a target population is valuable. As iatrogenic transfer of HIV is an important mode of spread of the infection to unsuspecting recipients, it should be mandatory that all donors of blood, blood products, semen, cells, tissues and organs be screened. As antibody tests are negative during the early stage of HIV infection when the individual is infectious, screening

may not detect all dangerous donors but can still eliminate a large majority of them. Screening for p24 antigen can detect those in the window period also. A person found positive for HIV antigen or antibody should never donate blood or other biological materials. As the infection can be transmitted from mother to baby before, during or after birth, antenatal screening is useful. Some countries have laws requiring screening of incoming foreigners.

2. **Seroepidemiology:** Antibody surveys have been most useful in identifying the geographical extent of HIV infection and in other epidemiological studies such as spread of the infection from identified sources.

3. **Diagnosis:** Serology is almost always positive in persons with clinical features of AIDS. It may, however, be negative in acute illness and sometimes in the very late cases where the immune system is nonreactive. Routine serology may also be negative when the infection is with a different AIDS virus. For example, HIV-2 infections are likely to be missed if antibody testing is done with the HIV-1 antigen alone. Test antigens should be updated when new virus types or subtypes are identified, and should be able to detect antibody against all prevalent types of HIV.

Antibody testing may also help to check whether infection has taken place following an exposure, such as sexual contact, blood transfusion or needle-stick injury. Serology after two months and, if

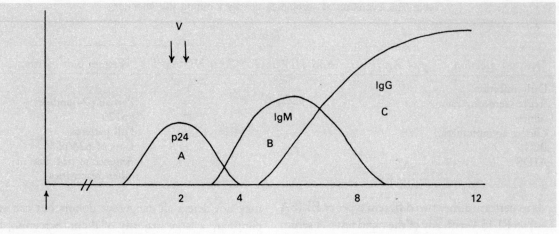

Fig. 62.3 Sequence of appearance of p24 antigen and antibodies after a massive HIV infection (as by blood transfusion).

↑ exposure ; A = p24 antigen; B = IgM antibody; C = IgG antibody; 2, 4, 8, 12 = weeks after exposure.

↓ V ↓ = virus readily isoloated from blood.

negative, after six months would be sufficient. If serology is negative six months after exposure, infection is unlikely to have occurred.

4. Prognosis: In a person infected with HIV, loss of detectable anti-p24 antibody indicates clinical deterioration. This is also associated with HIV antigenemia and increased virus titre in circulation.

LABORATORY MONITORING OF HIV INFECTION

Some laboratory tests are important in monitoring the course of HIV infection. The most important of these is CD4+ T cell count which reflects the current immunological competence of the patient. HIV positive persons should have frequent CD+ T cell counts. When the count falls below 500, it is an indication of disease progression and the need for antiretroviral therapy. Counts below 200 denote risk of serious infections.

Direct measurement of HIV RNA becomes necessary, particularly in the course of treatment. This is done usually by two methods, the reverse transcriptase PCR (RT-PCR) assay and the branched DNA (bDNA) assay.

Beta-2-microglobulin and Neopterin are two substances which have a predictive value on the progression of HIV disease. They can be measured in serum or urine. Their concentrations are low in asymptomatic infection and rise with advancing disease.

EPIDEMIOLOGY AND PREVENTION

AIDS is a new disease which came to light only in 1981 when it caused outbreaks in the USA. However, in retrospect, the virus appears to have been seeded in the United States at least in the mid-1970s and a few unrecognised cases of AIDS had occurred in New York in 1978. The origin of the virus has been the subject of much controversy, reminiscent of the situation five hundred years ago when syphilis was first recognised. It had been suggested that the virus may have originated in Africa, perhaps from a simian immunodeficiency virus and spread to the USA, probably through Haiti. In the permissive American society of the 1970s, the virus spread widely among male homosexuals and drug addicts, finally to come out into the open as outbreaks in 1981. The virus may have spread to Europe from America, as well as directly from the former African colonies of the European nations.

Conclusive evidence has now been obtained from molecular studies, including genetic typing of mitochondrial DNA from human and chimpanzee viruses. It shows that the progenitor of HIV-1 entered the human population from chimpanzees of the subspecies *Pan troglodytes troglodytes* living in equatorial west Africa (Cameroon, Gabon, equatorial Guinea), where the virus is considered, on other evidence, to have emerged in humans. HIVs are believed to have been present in monkeys for over 100,000 years. Transmission to chimpanzees is a far more recent phenomenon and may have happened through their killing and eating monkeys. Human infection could have come from chimpanzees who were hunted by them and killed for meat. The cpz SIV may have taken root in humans by becoming HIV through mutation or recombination.

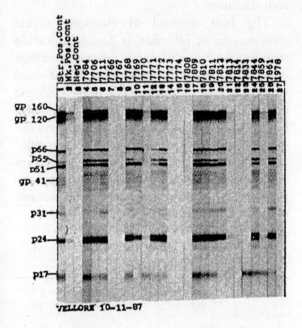

Fig. 62.4 Western blot test for HIV antibody. Nitro-cellulose strips containing separated HIV proteins are reacted with test (nos. 4 to 27) and control strong positive, weak positive and negative (nos. 1 to 3) sera. Antibody bound specifically to HIV proteins is visualised by using goat antihuman immunoglobulin-biotin conjugate and 4-chloro 1-naphthol substrate. A serum is considered positive if it shows antibody binding to at least 2 gene products of the 3 major HIV genes, namely *gag* (p 17, p 24, p 55), *env* (gp 41, gp 120, gp 160) and *pol* (p 31, p 51 and p 66). Examples of typical results are sera nos. 4, 5, 6 for positive, 7, 8 for negative and 11, 21 for weak positive reactions. [*Courtesy:* Prof T. Jacob John, Department of Virology and Immunology, CMC Hospital, Vellore.]

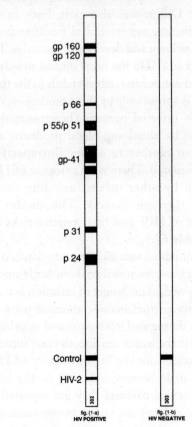

Fig. 62.5 HIV—Western blot test strips (positive and negative)

The three groups of HIV-1 (M, O, N) may represent independent transmissions from chimpanzees to humans. The source of HIV-2 has already been established as SIV from the sooty mangabey monkey *Cercocebus atys*.

The virus has spread virtually all over the world, though the prevalence rates in different countries vary widely. Initially North America, Brazil, Western Europe, Australia, Central and West Africa had high prevalence, while Eastern Europe and Asia, were only sparsely affected. However this soon changed. By vigorous measures and active public participation, the developed countries have succeeded in reducing spread of the infection. But in many countries of Africa and Asia, the infection has spread unhindered reaching epidemic proportions. Differences also exist, both in the modes of infection and in clinical manifestations, between the affluent and developing countries. The epidemiology of AIDS has been studied mostly in the developed nations and only sketchily in the third world. HIV is spread only by three modes—sexual contact with infected persons (heterosexual or homosexual); by blood and blood products; and from infected mother to babies (intrapartum, perinatal, postnatal). There is no evidence of HIV transmission by other means including casual contact or through insects. The modes of transmission of HIV and their relative risks are shown in Table 62.7.

HIV is primarily a sexually transmitted infection. In the USA it was transmitted predominantly among male homosexuals. The danger of infection is more for the passive partner because mucosal tears are very frequent during anal intercourse and virus laden lymphocytes in the semen can directly enter through these. One reason for the high incidence of HIV infection in male homosexuals may be the large numbers of sexual partners they are reported to have. In the affluent countries, homosexual and bisexual men are infected far more often than the heterosexuals. For this reason, infection was found predominantly in men and only occasionally in women. However, the situation is very different in Africa and Asia where men and women are equally affected. In some places, more women are found infected due to the high rate of infection in prostitutes. Transmission in the developing countries is almost always heterosexual and can take place in both directions.

The best method of checking sexual transmission of infection is health education regarding the danger of promiscuity and other high risk activities. Some changes in life style and sexual attitudes have already taken place in the USA and the incidence in homosexuals has come down. Persons indulging in high risk sexual practices and spouses of infected persons should be counselled regarding 'safer sex' methods. The use of condoms offers considerable, though not complete, protection. The risk of HIV transmission increases with multiple partners.

Table 62.7 Common modes of transmission of HIV and their relative risk

	Types of exposure	Approximate chance of infection per exposure
I	Sexual intercourse: anal, vaginal, oral	0.1–1.0%
II	Blood and blood products, Factor VII etc Blood transfusion	>90%
III	Tissue and organ donation: semen, cornea, bone marrow, kidney etc	50–90%
IV	Injections and injuries: shared needles by drug addicts Injections with unsterile syringes and needles Needle-stick and other injuries in health staff ? Surgical wounds	0.5–1.0%
V	Mother to baby: Transplacental At birth After birth Breast milk	30%

The second mode of transmission is through blood and blood products. Before the danger of HIV transmission was recognised, many persons had received blood and blood products containing the infectious virus. Screening of blood donors is now mandatory. Even screening may not completely eliminate the danger as the early infectious case may be missed but the risk is reduced considerably. This can be remedied by p24 antigen screening. In the advanced countries, any person who has indulged in high risk practices is advised not to donate blood. This restriction also applies to the donation of semen, cornea, bone marrow, kidney and other organ as infection can be transmitted through any of these. However, such restraints may not be effective in the developing countries, where professional donors constitute a real hazard. Manufacturing processes of blood products have now been modified to eliminate the infectious virus.

Contaminated needles can transmit the infection. This is particularly relevant in drug addicts who share syringes and needles. This mode of infection was believed to be important only in the affluent nations, and not in the poor countries. However, the identification of the wide prevalence of injectable drug addiction and HIV infection among young people in the northeastern states of India proved this belief to be mistaken.

The use of unsterile syringes and needles by qualified and unqualified health workers makes iatrogenic infection likely. Even in large hospitals, sterilisation and asepsis are often unsatisfactory. In immunisation and family planning camps, the same syringes and instruments may be used for many persons. The use of disposable syringes, needles and other equipments should be obligatory.

The danger of needle-stick injury is present in medical and paramedical personnel, though the chances of infection are much less than with hepatitis B virus. The risk of infection following needle-stick injury or injury with sharp instruments used on seropositive patients has been estimated to be about one per cent. The risk to medical and nursing personnel appears to be minimal provided they take adequate precautions. However, considering the unsatisfactory asepsis and hygiene in many hospitals in the poor countries, the risk may be real. Medical and paramedical staff need to be educated on caring for patients infected with HIV. Guidelines have been laid down for hospitals regarding the management of AIDS patients.

Transmission of infection from mother to baby can take place before, during or after birth. As infection occurs in about half such babies, infected women should be informed of the danger and advised against pregnancy. HIV may be present in breast milk and may be transmitted through breast feeding.

Normal social and domestic contact does not transmit the infection. Shaking hands, hugging, putting cheeks together or dry kissing are safe. There has been no confirmed case of transmission through saliva, though the virus may be present in the saliva of infected persons. A salivary protein called secretory leucocyte protease inhibitor has anti-HIV activity. Sharing rooms, bathrooms, and cooking and eating facilities are not considered dangerous. There is no evidence that mosquitoes, bed bugs or other blood-sucking insects can transmit the virus. Infection is not transmitted through air, food, water or fomites.

AIDS in the developing countries differs from the disease in the western countries clinically too. In Africa, the major manifestation is pronounced wasting so that it has been called the 'slim disease'. The high prevalence of tuberculosis and parasitic infections complicate the clinical picture.

HIV infection was detected rather late in India, the first cases having been found in female sex workers in Madras (Chennai) in 1986 and the first AIDS patient the same year from Bombay (Mumbai). Since then in every high risk group, the rate of infection has been mounting. HIV infection has spread throughout the country, though information is available from some parts only. By the end of 2003, India is believed to have about

5 million HIV-infected people, the second largest such population after South Africa.

Prophylaxis: The prevention of AIDS rests at present on general measures such as health education, identification of sources and elimination of high risk activities. No specific vaccine is available. The high mutability, diverse antigenic types and subtypes, long latency and persistence in infected cells as provirus pose serious problems in the development of vaccines. An ideal vaccine should not only prevent infection but also have therapeutic application in asymptomatic seropositives.

The lack of a suitable experimental animal is a severe constraint. Chimpanzees, monkeys and rabbits can be infected but they do not develop the disease. Infection with the simian immunodeficiency virus is a convenient model. Several possible strategies have been explored for vaccine production. These include immunisation with (a) modified whole virus; (b) subunits, based on envelope glycoproteins expressed in animal cells, bacteria, viruses – or as synthetic epitopes on adjuvant carriers; and (c) target cell protection by anti-CD4 antibody or genetically engineered CD4. A number of candidate vaccines are being tested in clinical trials in humans.

Treatment: Approaches to the treatment of AIDS include: (1) the treatment and prophylaxis of infections and tumours; (2) general management; (3) immunorestorative measures; and (4) specific anti-HIV agents.

Prompt diagnosis and appropriate treatment of opportunistic infections and tumours in the early stage of AIDS can be very useful and the patient may be able to resume normal life in between episodes of illness. General management of the patient requires the understanding and cooperation of the health staff in the hospital and of relatives at home. Groundless fears about imaginary risks have to be allayed and reassurance given that the patient can be kept at home or treated in the hospital without danger to contacts, if proper precautions are taken.

Steps at immunorestorative therapy such as administration of interleukin-2, thymic factors, leucocyte transfusion and bone marrow transplantation have not been very helpful.

Specific treatment with antiretroviral drugs is the mainstay in the management of HIV infection. A number of effective drugs have become available in recent years. These include nucleoside analogues like Zidovudine (Azidothmidine, AZT), Didanosine, Zalcitabine, Lamivudine and protease inhibitors like Saquinavir, Ritonavir, Indinavir, which have been used as monotherapy or in various combinations. Adverse reactions and high cost restrict their wide use in poor countries.

Further Reading

Broder SC and TC Merigan (ed). 1993. *Textbook of AIDS Medicine*. London: Williams and Wilkins.

Fauci AS and HC Lane 1998. HIV Disease. In *Harrison's Principles of Internal Medicine*, 14th edn. Vol. 2. New York: McGraw-Hill.

Centers for Disease Control and Prevention, 1993. Revised classification system for HIV infection. Morbidity Mortality Weekly Report. 41 (RR-17).

Normal Microbial Flora of the Human Body

Human beings like other animals, harbour a wide array of microorganisms both on and in their bodies. The normal microbial flora are more or less constant for each species and are broadly divided into residents and transients. The former constitute a constant population which cannot be completely removed permanently, while the latter vary from time to time and are temporary. The *residents* prevent permanent colonisation of the body by other organisms. A knowledge of the normal flora of the body is essential to an understanding of the interaction of human beings and their pathogen laden environment. The normal microbial flora play an important role in body economy. They can (1) become pathogenic when host defences falter, (2) prevent or interfere with colonisation/invasion of the body by pathogens, (3) raise the overall immune status of the host against pathogens having related or shared antigens, and (4) cause confusion in diagnosis due to their ubiquitous presence in the body and their resemblance to some of the pathogens. Members of the normal flora form part and parcel of the host and include saprophytes, commensals, facultative pathogens and true pathogens.

The microflora of the intestinal tract synthesise vitamin K and several B vitamins which supply on occasion the body's needs. The antibiotic substances produced by some, for example, colicins, have a harmful effect on pathogens. The endotoxins liberated by them may help the defence mechanism of the body by triggering the alternative complement pathway, as long as they are not produced in excessive amounts.

On the contrary, the opportunistic pathogens among them cause disease when the body's defence mechanisms fail. Their abnormal multiplication can cause diseases such as enteritis and endotoxic shock. Penicillinase producing organisms can aggravate infection by interfering with therapy. Certain streptococci of the mouth cause dental caries.

In environments laden with pathogens for example, hospitals, a shift in the normal flora of the individuals there can cause an increase in carriage of antibiotic resistant staphylococci. It has also been shown that such people can be recolonised with penicillin sensitive staphylococci of strain 502 A which are harmless and thus overcome the damage done. When large numbers of people congregate from different parts of the country as in army camps, the new recruits experience increased colonisation rates of *Neisseria meningitidis* and Group A Streptococcus and viruses such as rhinoviruses and adenoviruses sometimes resulting in epidemics.

NORMAL FLORA OF THE SKIN

The human skin is constantly and continuously bombarded by organisms present in the environment. It is also contaminated by one's own secretions and excretions, the extent depending on the individual's personal hygiene. The flora depend on the area of the body, the clothing one wears, one's occupation and environment. Transient microflora tend to occur more frequently on the skin.

Cultures from the skin have frequently demonstrated diphtheroids (including propionibacteria); staphylococci (aerobic and anaerobic); Gram positive aerobic spore bearing bacilli; *Str. viridans; Str. faecalis;* Gram negative bacilli such as *E. coli,* Proteus, and other intestinal organisms; mimieae; mycobacteria (non-pathogenic); *Candida albicans;* cryptococci and *Pityrosporum ovale.*

Often the skin of the face, neck, hands and buttocks carries pathogenic hemolytic streptococci and staphylococci. Penicillin resistant staphylococci are seen in individuals working in hospitals.

Hair frequently harbours *Staph. aureus* and forms a reservoir for cross infection.

NORMAL FLORA OF THE CONJUNCTIVA

The conjunctiva is relatively free from organisms due to the flushing action of tears. The predominant organisms of the eye are diphtheroids (*Corynebacterium xerosis*), Moraxella species, staphylococci and nonhemolytic streptococci.

NORMAL FLORA OF THE NOSE, NASOPHARYNX AND ACCESSORY SINUSES

The floor of the nose harbours corynebacteria, staphylococci and streptococci. *Haemophilus* species and *Moraxella lacunata* may also be seen.

The nasopharynx of the infant is sterile at birth but, within 2–3 days after birth, acquires the common commensal flora and the pathogenic flora carried by the mother and the attendants. The nasopharynx can be considered the natural habitat of the common pathogenic bacteria which cause infections of the nose, throat, bronchi and lungs. Certain Gram negative organisms from the intestinal tract such as *Pseudomonas aeruginosa, E.coli,* paracolons and Proteus are also occasionally found in normal persons. After penicillin therapy, they may be the predominant flora.

NORMAL FLORA OF THE MOUTH AND UPPER RESPIRATORY TRACT

The mouth contains a plethora of organisms – pigmented and nonpigmented micrococci, some of which are aerobic, Gram positive aerobic spore bearing bacilli, coliforms, Proteus and lactobacilli. The gum pockets between the teeth, and the crypts of the tonsils have a wide spectrum of anaerobic flora—anaerobic micrococci, microaerophilic and anaerobic streptococci, vibrios, fusiform bacilli, corynebacterium species, actinomyces, leptothrix, mycoplasma, neisseria, and bacteroides are all found in varying extents. Among fungi, Candida and geotrichum have been reported.

The mouth of the infant is not sterile at birth. It generally contains the same types of organisms in about the same relative numbers as those present in the mother's vagina, that is a mixture of micrococci, streptococci, coliform bacilli and Doderlien's bacilli. These organisms diminish in number during the first 2–5 days after birth and are replaced by the types of bacteria present in the mouth of the mother and nurse.

Within 12 hours after birth alpha hemolytic streptococci are found in the upper respiratory tract and become the dominant organisms of the oropharynx and remain so for life. In the pharynx and trachea, flora similar to that of the mouth establish themselves. Few bacteria are found in normal bronchi. Smaller bronchi and alveoli are normally sterile.

NORMAL FLORA OF THE INTESTINAL TRACT

In 80–90 per cent newborn infants, the meconium is sterile but in 10–20 per cent a few organisms, probably acquired during labour, may be present. In all cases, within 4–24 hours of birth an intestinal flora is established partly from below and partly by invasion from above. In breast fed children the intestine contains lactobacilli (*L. bifidus* constituting 99 per cent of total organisms in the feces), enterococci, colon bacilli and staphylococci. In artificially fed (bottle fed) children *L. acidophilus* and colon bacilli and in part by enterococci, Gram positive aerobic and anaerobic bacilli. With the change of food to the adult pattern, the flora change. Diet has a marked influence on the relative composition of the intestinal and fecal flora.

In the normal adult, the microorganisms on the surface of the esophageal wall are those swallowed with saliva and food. Because of the low pH of the stomach, it is virtually sterile except soon after eating. In patients with carcinoma of the stomach or achlorhydria or pyloric obstruction, there is proliferation of Gram positive cocci and bacilli.

The number of bacteria increases progressively beyond the duodenum to the colon, being comparatively low in the small intestine. In the adult duodenum there are 10^3-10^6 bacteria per gram, in the jejunum and proximal ileum 10^5-10^8 bacteria per gram, and in the lower ileum and cecum 10^8-10^{10} bacteria per gram of contents. In the duodenum and upper ileum, lactobacilli and enterococci predominate but in the lower ileum and cecum the flora resemble the fecal flora. There are about 10^{11} bacteria per gram of contents in the colon and rectum, constituting 10–20 per cent of the fecal mass. In the adult normal colon, the resident bacterial flora are mostly (96–99 per cent) anaerobes – anaerobic streptococci, anaerobic lactobacilli, clostridia, and bacteroides and about 1–4 per cent aerobes—enterococci, coliforms, and small numbers of Proteus, Pseudomonas, lactobacilli, mycoplasma, Candida and others.

Normal Flora of the Genitourinary Tract

Mycobacterium smegmatis, a harmless commensal, is found in the smegma of the genitalia of both men and women. This may, by its presence in the voided specimens of urine, cause confusion. From apparently normal men, aerobic and anaerobic bacteria can be cultured from a high proportion, including lactobacilli, *Gard. vaginalis*, *alpha hemolytic streptococci* and *Bacteroides species*. *Chlam. trachomatis* and *Ureaplasma urealyticum* may also be present. The female urethra is either sterile or contains a few Gram positive cocci.

The vulva of the newborn child is sterile but after 24 hours it acquires a varied flora of nonpathogenic organisms from the skin, vagina and intestines. The nature of the flora in the vagina depends on the pH of its secretions and its enzyme content. In the first 24 hours it is invaded by micrococci, enterococci and diphtheroids. In 2–3 days, the maternal estrin induces glycogen deposition in the vaginal epithelium. This facilitates the growth of a lactobacillus (Doderlien's bacillus) which produces acid from glycogen, and the flora for a few weeks is similar to that of the adult. After the passively transferred estrin has been eliminated in the urine, the glycogen disappears, along with Doderlien's bacillus and the pH of the vagina becomes alkaline. This brings about a change in the flora to micrococci, alpha and nonhemolytic streptococci, coliforms and diphtheroids. At puberty, the glycogen reappears and the pH changes to acid due to the metabolic activity of Doderlien's bacilli, *E.coli* and yeasts. This change probably helps in the prevention of colonisation by possible harmful micro organisms. During pregnancy there is an increase in *Staphylococcus epidermidis*, Doderlien's bacilli and yeasts. Occasionally other members of the intestinal flora may be present. After menopause, the flora resembles that found before puberty. The normal vaginal flora often includes anaerobic cocci and bacilli, listeria, anaerobic streptococci, mimeae, mycoplasma, *Gardnerella vaginalis*, neisseriae and spirochetes.

Bacteria in the Blood and Tissues

The commensals from the normal flora of the mouth, nasopharynx and intestinal tract may get into the blood and tissues. They are usually quickly eliminated by the normal defence mechanisms of the body. Occasional isolation of diphtheroids or nonhemolytic streptococci from normal and abnormal lymph nodes may be those which escaped elimination. Unless the organisms of doubtful pathogenicity are isolated more than once in serial blood cultures, they have little significance.

Further Reading

Hentges DJ. 1983. *Human Intestinal Microflora in Health and Disease* New York: Academic Press.
Moukowiak PA. 1982. The normal microbial flora. *New Eng J Med* 307:83.
Murray PR. 1998. Human Microbiota. In *Topley & Wilson's Microbiology and Microbial Infections*, 9th edn, Vol. 2. London: Arnold.
Noble WC. 1981. *Microbiology of Human Skin*. London: Lloyd-Luke.
Skinner FA and JG Carr (ed). 1974. *The Normal Microbial Flora of Man*. London: Academic Press.

Bacteriology of Water, Milk and Air

BACTERIOLOGY OF WATER

Drinking water has to be visually acceptable, being clear and colourless, and without disagreeable taste or odour. It should also be safe, being free from chemical toxins and pathogenic micro organisms. Many major human diseases, for example, typhoid fever, cholera and other diarrheal diseases, poliomyelitis and viral hepatitis A and E are waterborne. These pathogens reach water sources through fecal or sewage pollution. It is essential to prevent such contamination, treat the water suitably to remove or destroy microorganisms, and also to ensure the safety of such protected water supplies by regular bacteriological surveillance.

Natural water sources, even when unpolluted, frequently contain some saprophytic bacteria, such as the *Pseudomonas, Serratia, Flavobacterium, Chromobacterium, Acinetobacter* and *Alcaligenes* species. Soil bacteria, such as aerobic spore forming bacilli, and those found on decaying vegetation, such as the Enterobacter species, may also be washed into natural waters during the rains. These are harmless. Only pathogens introduced into water by excremental or sewage pollution pose a risk to human health.

BACTERIOLOGICAL EXAMINATION OF WATER

Bacteriological analysis of water supplies should be a regular periodical procedure and not a random exercise. Guidelines have been laid for the frequency of such analysis, ranging from daily to monthly samplings, depending on the size of the populations served.

Drinking water should be free of any pathogenic microorganisms. Ideally, therefore, tests should be aimed at detecting these. However, they are generally present in such low concentrations that they escape detection. The practice, therefore, is to test for fecal pollution, assuming that it points to the possibility of the presence of enteric pathogens also. The primary test employed as an indicator of fecal pollution of water is the presence of coliform bacteria because they are invariably present in the feces of human beings and other warm blooded animals in large numbers and can be easily detected in water, even in high dilutions. Though coliform bacteria are not exclusively of fecal origin, they serve as presumptive evidence, to be confirmed by the detection of thermotolerant E. coli, which provides definite proof of fecal pollution.

Other bacteria are also sometimes used as indicators of fecal pollution. These include 'fecal streptococci' (resistant to 45 °C, 40% bile, potassium tellurite and sodium azide concentrations inhibitory to coliforms) and *Clostridium perfringens*.

Guidelines have been laid down for the collection of water samples for bacteriological tests. Sodium thiosulphate should be added to samples of chlorinated water to inactivate residual chlorine which may lower bacterial counts by continued activity. Samples should be sent to the laboratory and tested without delay.

The following tests are generally done for routine bacteriological analysis of water:

1. Plate count: This consists of counting the numbers of colonies formed in pourplate cultures of the water samples, on nutrient agar incubated

aerobically, in parallel, at 37 °C for 1–2 days and at 22 °C for 3 days. Those that grow at 37 °C are those most likely to be associated with organic material of human or animal origin, whereas those growing at a lower temperature are mainly saprophytes that normally inhabit water or are derived from soil and vegetables.

The agar count at 22 °C gives an indication of the amount of decomposing organic matter in the water available for bacterial nutrition. Though most bacteria growing at 22 °C are nonpathogenic to human beings, on general grounds, the greater the amount of organic matter present, the more likely is the water to be contaminated with parasitic and potentially pathogenic organisms. The agar count at 37 °C is a more important index of dangerous pollution. A rise in colony count is the usual signal of some defect in filter beds demanding immediate attention.

2. Detection of coliform bacteria and E. coli

a) Presumptive coliform count – Multiple tube technique: The test is called presumptive because the reaction observed may occasionally be due to the presence of some other organisms and the presumption that the reaction is due to coliform organisms has to be confirmed.

An estimate of the number of coliform organisms is usually made by adding varying quantities of water (0.1–50 ml) to bile salt lactose peptone water (with an indicator for acidity) and incubating at appropriate temperatures. Acid and gas formation indicate the growth of coliform bacilli. Thus it is possible to state the smallest quantity of water containing a coliform bacillus and

to express the degree of contamination with this group of organisms.

The following range is put up:

One 50 ml quantity of water added to 50 ml double strength medium.

Five 10 ml quantities each to 10 ml double strength medium.

Five 1 ml quantities each to 5 ml single strength medium.

Five 0.1 ml quantities each to 5 ml single strength medium.

MacConkey's fluid medium (modified) is used. The range of quantities depends on the likely strength of contamination. For highly contaminated waters, smaller volumes are tested. The bottles are incubated at 37 °C and examined after 18–24 hours. The 'presumptive positives' are read off and the remaining negative bottles are reincubated for another 24 hours. Any further positives are added to the previous figures. The probable number of coliforms per 100 ml are read off from the probability tables of McCrady. This is known as the 'presumptive coliform count' or the most probable number of coliforms (MPN).

b) Differential coliform test: The Eijkman test is usually employed to find out whether the coliform bacilli detected in the presumptive test are E. coli. After the usual presumptive test, subcultures are made from all the bottles showing acid and gas to fresh tubes of single strength MacConkey's medium already warmed to 37 °C. They are incubated at 44 °C and examined after 24 hours. Incubation at 44 °C should be carried out in thermostatically controlled water baths that do not deviate more than 0.5 °C from 44 °C. Those showing gas in

Table 64.1 Classification of drinking water according to bacteriological tests

	Presumptive coliform count per 100 ml	E. coli count per 100 ml
Class I Excellent	0	0
Class II Satisfactory	1-3	0
Class III Suspicious	4-10	0
Class IV Unsatisfactory	More than 10	0.1 or more

Durham's tubes contain *E. coli*. From the number of positive tubes obtained, results are read off the probability tables. Further confirmation of the presence of *E. coli* can be obtained by testing for indole production and citrate utilisation.

c) Membrane filtration method: A measured volume of water is filtered through a millipore filter. All the bacteria present are retained on its surface. It is placed on suitable media face upwards and incubated at the appropriate temperature, and the colonies that develop on the surface of the membrane are counted. After 18 hours of incubation the presumptive coliform counts and *E. coli* counts can be directly made.

3. Detection of fecal streptococci: Subcultures are made from all the positive bottles in the presumptive coliform test into tubes containing 5 ml of glucose azide broth. The presence of *Str. faecalis* is indicated by the production of acid in the medium within 18 hours at 45 °C. The positive tubes should be plated onto MacConkey's agar for confirmation.

Millipore membrane technique can also be adopted for this purpose.

4. Examination for Cl. perfringens: This is tested by incubating varying quantities of the water in litmus milk medium (anaerobically) at 37 °C for five days and looking for stormy fermentation.

5. Tests for pathogenic bacteria: Under special circumstances, specific pathogens such as typhoid bacilli or cholera vibrios may have to be looked for in water. This used to be done by adding the water samples to tenfold concentrated liquid media, incubating and subculturing onto appropriate solid media. A simpler and more sensitive method is to filter the water sample through membrane filters and incubate the filters on appropriate solid media.

VIRUSES IN WATER

Methods are available for the isolation of enteroviruses and other cytopathogenic viruses from water but they do not form part of routine testing. As a general rule, it is assumed that the viruses in water are destroyed by chlorination, when the concentration of free residual chlorine is at least 0.5 mg per litre, for a minimum contact period of 30 minutes at pH below 8 and a turbidity of 1 nephalometric turbidity unit or less.

PROTOZOA IN WATER

Entamoeba histolytica, Giardia species and *Balantidium coli* can contaminate drinking water. However, there is no good indicator for protozoal contamination of water. Coliform counts are not reliable as indicators of protozoal contamination of chlorinated water as they are more resistant to chlorine than are coliforms.

BACTERIOLOGY OF MILK

TYPES OF BACTERIA IN MILK

These can be classified as below:

1. Acid forming bacteria: The commonest are lactic streptococci including *Str. lactis* and *Str. faecalis*. Lactobacilli are also found. These ferment lactose in the milk, producing acids, mainly lactic acids, which lead to the formation of a smooth gelatinous curd.

2. Alkali forming bacteria: These consist of alkaligenes spp, some aerobic spore bearers and Achromobacter. These render the milk alkaline.

3. Gas-forming bacteria: Coliform bacilli are the commonest. Others are *Cl. perfringens* and *Cl. butyricum*. Acid and gas are produced. A smooth gelatinous curd riddled with gas bubbles is formed. Coliform bacilli are responsible for the ropiness in milk.

4. Proteolytic bacteria: Spore-bearing aerobes such as *B. subtilis* and *B. cereus, Proteus vulgaris,* staphylococci and micrococci come under this category.

5. Inert bacteria: Bacteria which produce no visible change in milk are called inert. These include some cocci of the udder, members of the Achromobacter group and most of the pathogenic organisms in the milk.

6. Human milk: Breast milk contains small numbers of *Staph. epidermidis, Str. mitis, Gaffkya tetragena* and *Staph. aureus*. A few other species may also be found in some samples.

MILKBORNE DISEASES

Infections of animals that can be transmitted to human beings: The most important diseases are tuberculosis, brucellosis, streptococcal and staphylococcal infections, salmonellosis and Q fever. Diseases of less importance include cowpox and milker's nodes which are usually transmitted during milking rather than through ingestion of milk. Foot and mouth disease, anthrax and leptospirosis have been transmitted on rare occasions. Tickborne encephalitis virus may be transmitted through goat milk. Milkborne infectious hepatitis has been reported.

Occasionally, milk may be contaminated with *Streptobacillus moniliformis* from the nasal secretion of rats and with *Campylobacter jejuni* from animal feces. *Yersinia enterocolitica* is not uncommon in milk and may give rise to gastroenteritis if present in large numbers.

The organisms that cause all the diseases mentioned above are destroyed by adequate pasteurisation.

2. Infections primary to humans that can be transmitted through milk

a) *Enteric infections:* These are caused by consumption of milk which has been mixed with water contaminated by human excreta. A less common source are the human carriers of enteric infections employed in the dairies. The diseases caused are typhoid and paratyphoid fevers, shigellosis, cholera (rarely) and diarrhea due to *E. coli.*

b) *Streptococcal infections:* Cows may have udder or teat infections and the organisms get into the milk. Milk handlers may be carriers and may contaminate the milk.

c) *Staphylococcal food poisoning:* Milk from cows suffering from staphylococcal mastitis is contaminated with the organism. If the milk is consumed after being allowed to remain at temperatures favourable for its multiplication the enterotoxin is produced, which causes food poisoning. Many such outbreaks have been reported.

d) *Diphtheria:* Milk contaminated either from a human carrier or more usually through diphtheritic lesions on the teats, when consumed unpasteurised, causes disease.

e) *Tuberculosis:* Milk contaminated by excretions from persons suffering from tuberculosis, when consumed, leads to the disease.

Bacteriological examination: The routine bacteriological examination of milk consists of the following:

1. Viable count: This is estimated by doing plate counts with serial dilutions of the milk sample. Raw milk always contains bacteria, varying in number from about 500 to several million per ml.

2. Test for coliform bacilli: This is tested by inoculating varying dilutions of milk into MacConkey's fluid medium and noting the production of acid and gas after incubation. Contamination with coliforms comes mainly from dust, dirty utensils and dairy workers.

3. Methylene blue reduction test: This is a simple substitute for the viable count. It depends on the reduction of methylene blue by bacteria in milk when incubated at 37 °C in complete darkness. The rate of reduction is related to the degree of bacterial contamination. Raw milk is considered satisfactory if it fails to reduce the dye in 30 minutes under standard conditions.

The Resazurin test is similar but the dye resazurin, on reduction, passes through a series of colour changes – from blue to pink to colourless – the shade of colour after incubation with milk for a particular period of time, depending on the degree of contamination. Generally the 10-minute resazurin test is done, in which the shade of colour is noted after incubation with the milk for ten minutes.

4. Phosphatase test: This is a check on the pasteurisation of milk. The enzyme phosphatase normally present in milk is inactivated if pasteurisation has been carried out properly. Residual phosphatase activity indicates that pasteurisation has not been adequate.

5. Turbidity test: This is a check on the 'sterilisation' of milk. If milk has been boiled or heated to the temperature prescribed for 'sterilisation', all heat coagulable proteins are precipitated. If ammonium sulphate is then added to the milk, filtered and boiled for five minutes, no turbidity results. This test can distinguish between pasteurised and 'sterilised' milk.

6. Examination for specific pathogens
a. Tubercle bacillus: The milk is centrifuged at 3000 rpm for 30 minutes and the sediment inoculated into two guineapigs. The animals are observed for a period of three months for tuberculosis. Tubercle bacilli may also be isolated in culture. Microscopic examination for tubercle bacilli is unsatisfactory.

b) Brucella: Isolation of brucella may be attempted by inoculating cream heavily on serum dextrose agar or by injecting centrifuged deposit of the milk sample intramuscularly into guineapigs. The animals are sacrificed after six weeks and the serum tested for agglutinins and the spleen inoculated in culture media. Brucellosis in animals can be detected also by demonstrating the antibodies in milk, by the milk-ring or the whey agglutination tests.

The tests adopted for the routine examination of milk should reveal the degree of bacterial contamination and thereby indicate whether the milk is produced and handled in a hygienically satisfactory manner. The plate count gives a rough and direct assessment of the viable bacteria in the milk. It is easily explainable to the producer and gives a fair idea of the improvement or deterioration in the conditions of production. The coliform test is a useful indicator of fecal contamination, and also of contamination by dust or unclean utensils. Phosphatase test, if positive after proper pasteurisation of milk, shows contamination after pasteurisation. The dye test is a rough and quick test to determine the quality of the milk as its arrives from the producer.

BACTERIOLOGY OF AIR

In the course of a day, a person inhales over 15 cubic meters of air. Hence the bacterial content of the air one breathes is important, particularly when it contains pathogens. The bacterial content of air depends on the location, i.e., whether it is outdoor air or indoor air.

The bacterial content of outdoor air depends on many factors such as the density of human and animal populations, the nature of the soil, the amount of vegetation, the atmospheric conditions such as humidity, temperature and wind conditions, rainfall and sunlight. Most of the bacteria are nonpathogenic and even the rare pathogen that may contaminate the air is seldom able to survive the adverse conditions of the outdoor air to cause disease.

Spores and fragments of moulds are more numerous than bacteria. Bacteria in the upper air consist largely of aerobic spore-bearing bacilli and to a much less extent *Achromobacter, Sarcina* and *Micrococcus.* They are mainly derived from soil and surface dust and may be carried horizontally and vertically for miles. Infective materials are seldom carried for more than short distances and their capacity to cause infection is impaired, except in rare cases such as the foot and mouth disease virus. Pathogenic bacteria do not multiply in air.

In the case of indoor air, the bacteria may be distributed through gross droplets and droplet nuclei from nose and mouth and through dust particles. Dust consists of particles of varying sizes originating from animal, vegetable or mineral sources. The ultimate source of common pathogenic organisms is dust derived from human beings. Nasal secretions via the ala nasi and upper lip get carried by the hands to the skin, clothing and bedding from where they get detached as dust. Organisms may also get directly detached from the skin of different parts of the body including the perineum and septic wounds. Intestinal organisms, through dried particles of feces from napkins of infants, also get disseminated. The heavy particles fall to the ground, while those 1 mm or less in diameter mostly remain suspended in air. Hemolytic streptococci from patients or carriers, tubercle bacilli and diphtheria bacilli and staphylococci are found in ward dust where such patients are treated. Under favourable conditions, they may remain alive for many weeks. Bed clothes are an abundant source of bacteria laden dust. Desquamated epithelial cells from the body get liberated into the environment through physical activity. The stream of air enveloping the body also serves as a source of organisms in the dust.

During coughing, sneezing and talking, varying numbers of droplets are expelled from the body, ranging in size from less than 1 mm to 15 mm. Depending on their sizes, they travel or remain suspended in air or fall to the ground and in the process get evaporated, the smaller the size, the faster the evaporation. On evaporation, they get converted to very minute particles called 'droplet nuclei' and their fate depends on the air currents in the atmosphere. The viability of the bacteria in droplet nuclei depends on numerous factors and is unpredictable. Experiments show that the proportion of dust particles and droplet nuclei reaching the lung depend on their sizes. All particles over 5 mm are retained in the nose, most of 1 mm reach the lung and are retained in the alveoli but below 1 mm the proportion retained in the lung diminishes.

Infective or potentially infective droplets may also be liberated in the form of aerosols by various laboratory procedures, dental manipulations and in the flushing of water closets.

MEASUREMENT OF AIR CONTAMINATION

Sedimentation method: Open plates of culture media are exposed for specific periods, e.g., half to one hour, the plates are incubated at 37 °C for 24 hours and the number of colonies counted. When pathogenic staphylococci and streptococci are looked for, blood agar plates are used. This method gives an idea of the relative numbers and species of micro organisms present in air and is specially used for testing the air in surgical theatres and hospital wards.

Slit sampler: Since the plate exposure method has many limitations, a more elaborate method, the slit sampler, has been introduced. In this, a known volume of air is directed onto a plate through a slit 0.25 mm wide, the plate being mechanically rotated so that the organisms are evenly distributed over it.

BACTERIOLOGICAL EXAMINATION OF ENVIRONMENTAL DUST

Sweep plate: Personal clothing, bed clothes and domestic furnishing material such as curtains may contain bacteria laden dust. When a Petri dish containing a suitable culture medium is removed from its lid and rubbed over the surface of the fabric, with the medium facing the fabric, dust settles on the medium. Colonies can be identified and counted after incubation.

Dust sampling: Moistened cottonwool swabs may be used for collecting dust from the floor, wall, furniture and other surfaces. The swabs are placed in broth and anaerobic media such as Robertson's cooked meat and incubated. After subculturing on plates, the isolates can be identified. This is routinely employed for assessing the level of asepsis in surgical theatres, particularly for the detection of spores of tetanus bacilli and other clostridia in theatre dust.

Further Reading

Linton AH and HM Dick (eds). 1990. Bacteria in the Environment. In *Topley & Wilson's Principles of Bacteriology, Virology and Immunity,* Vol. I General Bacteriology and Immunity. Section B. 211–291. London: Edward Arnold.

World Health Organization, Geneva: *Guidelines for Drinking Water Quality.*
   Vol. I. Recommendations (1983)
   Vol II. Health Criteria (1984)
   Vol. III. Drinking water quality control in small community supplies (1985).

Medical Mycology

Fungi had been recognised as causative agents of human disease earlier than bacteria. Fungi causing favus (*Trichophyton schonleinii*) and thrush (*Candida albicans*) had been described as early as in 1839. In spite of the earlier beginnings, the study of pathogenic fungi has received only scant attention in comparison with the study of the other pathogens. This is probably due to the relatively benign nature of the common mycotic diseases and because the techniques employed in mycology are more those of botanists than of bacteriologists. Fungus infections, however, are extremely common and some of them are serious and even fatal. With the control of most bacterial infections in the developed countries, fungus infections have assumed greater importance. For instance, it has been stated that in the USA fungus infections cause as many fatalities today as whooping cough, diphtheria, scarlet fever, typhoid, dysentery and malaria put together. Most fungi are soil saprophytes, and human infections are mainly opportunistic. Modern advances in treatment, such as antibiotics, steroids and immunosuppressive agents have led to an increase in opportunistic fungus infections.

Fungi are eukaryotic protista that differ from bacteria and other prokaryotes in many ways. They possess rigid cell walls containing chitin, mannan and other polysaccharides. The cytoplasmic membrane contains sterols. They possess true nuclei with nuclear membrane and paired chromosomes. They divide asexually, sexually or by both processes. They may be unicellular or multicellular. The cells show various degrees of specialisation.

The simplest type of fungus is the unicellular budding yeast. Elongation of the cell produces a tubular, thread like structure called *hypha*. A tangled mass of hyphae constitutes the *mycelium*. Fungi which form mycelia are called moulds or filamentous fungi. Hyphae may be septate or nonseptate. The septa, when present, have holes through which free flow of cytoplasmic material can take place. In a growing colony of filamentous fungus, the mycelium can be divided into the vegetative mycelium which grows into the medium and the aerial mycelium which projects from the surface.

Depending on cell morphology, fungi can be divided into four classes: yeasts, yeast like fungi, moulds and dimorphic fungi.

Yeasts are unicellular fungi which occur as spherical or ellipsoidal cells and reproduce by simple budding. On culture, they form smooth, creamy colonies. The only pathogenic yeast is *Cryptococcus neoformans*.

Yeast-like fungi grow partly as yeast and partly as elongated cells resembling hyphae. The latter form a *pseudomycelium*. *Candida albicans* is a pathogenic yeast-like fungus.

Moulds or filamentous fungi form true mycelia and reproduce by the formation of different types of spores. Dermatophytes are examples of pathogenic moulds.

Dimorphic fungi can occur as filaments or as yeasts, depending on the conditions of growth. In host tissues or cultures at 37 °C they occur as yeasts, while in the soil and in cultures at 22 °C they appear as moulds. Most fungi causing systemic infections are dimorphic fungi.

The systematic classification of fungi, based on their sexual spore formation, recognises four classes. *Phycomycetes* are lower fungi which have nonseptate hyphae and form endogenous asexual spores, called *sporangiospores*, contained within swollen sac-like structures called sporangia. Phycomycetes also produce sexual spores known as *oospores* in some fungi and *zygospores* in some others. The other three classes (the higher fungi) have septate hyphae and form exogenous asexual spores called '*conidia*'. The *ascomycetes* form sexual spores (*ascospores*) within a sac or ascus. Ascomycetes include both yeasts and filamentous fungi. The *basidiomycetes* form sexual spores (*basidiospores*) on a 'basidium' or base. The fourth class, *Fungi imperfecti* (also called deuteromycetes or hyphomycetes), is a provisional group consisting of fungi whose sexual phases have not been identified. Most fungi of medical importance belong to this group.

The laboratory diagnosis of fungus infections is made by microscopic examination of materials from the lesions and by morphological studies of fungus isolates. Tissue specimens, such as skin scrapings, are generally examined as wet mounts after treatment with 10% potassium hydroxide. The alkali digests cells and other tissue materials, enabling the fungus elements to be seen clearly. Small bits of fungus colonies may be teased onto a slide and mounted in lactophenol cotton blue for microscopic study. Slide culture provides a useful technique for the study of fungus morphology. The periodic acid Schiff (PAS) and methanamine silver stains are valuable methods for the demonstration of fungal elements in tissue sections.

The commonest culture media used in mycology are Sabouraud's glucose agar (pH 5.4), Czapek-Dox medium and Cornmeal agar. The addition of antibiotics prevents bacterial contamination. Cycloheximide (actidione) incorporated in the medium inhibits many contaminant moulds. Cultures are routinely incubated in parallel at room temperature (22 °C) for weeks and at 37 °C for days. Identification is based on the morphology of the fungus and of its colony. Biochemical and serological tests, which form the mainstay of bacterial identification, are seldom employed in mycology. Diagnostic mycology rests largely on a detailed study of the morphological evolution of the isolate and has therefore been termed an 'exercise in contemplative observation'.

Growth characteristics useful for identification are the rapidity of growth, colour and morphology of the colony on the obverse and pigmentation on the reverse. The morphology of hyphae, spores and other structures is studied in teased mounts or slide cultures. Hyphal diameter, presence or absence of septa and of special structures are of diagnostic importance. Special hyphal structures frequently found are spring-like helical coils (spiral hyphae), localised swellings formed by tightly twisted hyphae resembling tennis racquets (racquet hyphae) and numerous short branches appearing at the ends of hyphae (favic chandelier) (Fig. 65.1). The morphology of asexual spores or conidia is of

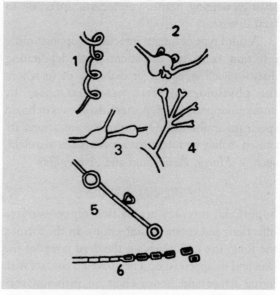

Fig.65.1 Mycelial forms and asexual spores of fungi. 1. spiral hypha, 2. nodular organ, 3. racquet mycelium, 4. favi chandelier, 5. chlamydo-spores along hypha, 6. arthrospores.

diagnostic importance. They may be small, single celled 'microconidia' or large, single or multicelled 'macroconidia'. The type of spore formation is distinctive for different fungi. *Blastospores* are formed by budding, as in yeasts. *Arthrospores* are formed along the mycelium by segmentation and condensation of hyphae. *Chlamydospores* are thick walled resting spores formed by rounding up and thickening of hyphal segments.

MYCOSES
(FUNGUS INFECTIONS)

Human fungus infections are broadly of two types – superficial and deep seated (systemic). Superficial infections are by far commoner and comprise the various types of tinea or ringworm affecting the skin, hair and nails. These are mild though chronic diseases. Fungi causing superficial mycoses are specialised saprophytes, with the capacity to digest keratin. Systemic mycoses are caused by fungi that are mostly soil saprophytes. Infection is accidental. Systemic mycoses occur in varying degress of severity, ranging from asymptomatic infection to fatal disease.

A third type of fungus infection is opportunistic infection, occurring in patients with debilitating diseases such as cancer or diabetes, or in whom the physiological state has been upset by immunosuppressive drugs, steroids, X-rays or broad spectrum antibiotics. Opportunistic infections are caused mainly by fungi that are normally avirulent, such as *Mucor, Penicillium* and *Aspergillus*.

SUPERFICIAL MYCOSES

Superficial mycoses are of two types—surface infections and cutaneous infections. In the former, the fungi live exclusively on the dead layers of the skin and its appendages. They have no contact with living tissue and hence elicit no inflammatory response. The only changes produced are cosmetic effects. *Tinea (Pityriasis) versicolor, Tinea nigra* and *Piedra* fall into this group. The most important cutaneous infection is *dermatophytosis* caused by a group of related fungi called the dermatophytes. Infection is generally confined to the cornified layer of the skin and its appendages but a variety of inflammatory and allergic responses are induced in the host by the presence of the fungi and their metabolic products. Another type of cutaneous infection is caused by *Candida albicans*. Though Candida infection is mostly confined to the skin and mucosa, it can also cause systemic disease rarely, involving any organ. Candida infection, therefore, represents a bridge connecting superficial and deep mycoses.

PITYRIASIS VERSICOLOR

Pityriasis versicolor (Tinea versicolor) is a chronic, usually asymptomatic, involvement of the stratum corneum, characterised by discrete or confluent macular areas of discolouration or depigmentation of the skin. The areas involved are mainly the chest, abdomen, upper limbs and back. The causative agent is a lipophilic, yeast-like fungus *Pityrosporum orbiculare (Malassezia furfur)*. The disease is worldwide in distribution but is particularly prevalent in the tropics. It occurs mainly in young adults. Diagnosis is established by examination of skin scrapings, which show an abundance of yeast-like cells and short, branched filaments (Fig. 65.2). The fungus can be grown on Sabouraud's agar, covered with a layer of olive oil. The fungus may be demonstrated on the normal skin also and the disease may be considered an opportunisitic infection.

TINEA NIGRA

Tinea nigra is a localised infection of the stratum corneum, particularly of the palms, producing black or brownish macular lesions. It is found mainly in the tropics and is caused by *Cladosporium Wernickii* (now designated as *Hortaea Wernickii*). Skin scrapings show brownish, branched, septate hyphae and budding cells. Colonies on Sabouraud's medium are grey or black in colour.

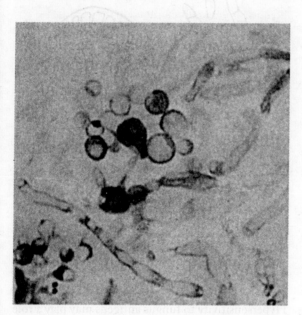

Fig.65.2 *Pityrosporum orbiculare* in stratum corneum. Clusters of small, round, budding yeast cells are interspersed among septate branching hyphae. Skin scraping, KOH preparation.

PIEDRA

Piedra is a fungus infection of the hair, characterised by the appearance of firm, irregular nodules along the hair shaft. The nodules are composed of fungus elements cemented together on the hair. Two varieties of piedra are recognised – black piedra caused by *Piedraia hortae* and white piedra caused by *Trichosporon beigelii.*

DERMATOPHYTOSES

Dermatophytes are a group of closely related filamentous fungi that infect only superficial keratinised tissues – the skin, hair and nails. They cause a variety of clinical conditions, collectively known as dermatophytoses, popularly called tinea or ringworm. The term dermatomycosis, sometimes used as a synonym, would also include skin lesions produced by other fungi such as *Candida albicans* and also the cutaneous manifestations of systemic mycoses.

Dermatophytes have been classified into three genera—*Trichophyton, Microsporum* and *Epidermophyton.* About 40 species of

Table 65.1 Some characteristics of common dermatophytes

Species	Colony	Morphology
T. rubrum	Velvety, red pigment on reverse	Few, long, pencil shaped macroconidia
T. mentagrophytes	White to tan, cottony or powdery. Pigment variable	Clusters of microconidia. Cigar shaped macroconidia with terminal rat-tail filaments
T. tonsurans	Cream or yellow, with central furrows	Abundant microconidia. Thick walled, irregular macroconidia
T. schoenleinii	Smooth, waxy, brownish	Hyphal swellings, chlamydospores, favic chandelier
T. violaceum	Very slow growing. Waxy, violet to purple pigment	Distorted hyphae, Conidia rare
M. audouinii	Velvety, brownish, slow growing	Thick walled chlamydospores, conidia rare and irregular
M. canis	Cottony, orange pigment on reverse	Abundant, thick walled, spindle shaped macroconidia with upto 15 septa
M. gypseum	Powdery, buff coloured	Abundant, thin walled macroconidia with 4-6 septa
E. floccosum	Yellowish green, powdery	Club-shaped macroconidia in clusters

dermatophytes are known to cause infection in humans and animals.

In lesions, dermatophytes appear as hyphae and arthrospores. In cultures on Sabouraud's agar, they form characteristic colonies consisting of septate hyphae and two types of asexual spores, microconidia and macroconidia. Sexual spores of some species have been identified recently. Differentiation into the three genera is based mainly on the nature of macroconidia (Fig. 65.3).

Trichophyton: Colonies may be powdery, velvety or waxy, with pigmentation characteristic of different species. Microconidia are abundant and are arranged in clusters along the hyphae or borne on conidiophores. Macroconidia are relatively scanty. They are generally elongated, with blunt ends (Fig. 65.4). Macroconidia have distinctive shapes in different species and are of importance in species identification. Some species possess special hyphal characters, such as spiral hyphae, racquet mycelium and favic chandeliers. Trichophytons infect skin, hair and nails. *T. rubrum* is the most common species infecting human beings. It often causes chronic, treatment resistant lesions.

Microsporum: Colonies are cottonlike, velvety or powdery, with white to brown pigmentation. Microconidia are relatively scanty and are not distinctive. Macroconidia are the predominant spore form. They are large, multicellular, spindle shaped structures, borne singly on the ends of hyphae. Microsporum species infect the hair and skin but usually not the nails.

Epidermophyton: Colonies are powdery and greenish yellow in colour. Microconidia are absent. Macroconidia are multicellular, pear shaped and typically arranged clusters. Epidermophyton attacks the skin and nails but not the hair. The genus contains only one species, *E. floccosum*.

Pathogenicity: Dermatophytes grow only on the keratinised layers of the skin and its appendages and do not ordinarily penetrate the living tissues. The mechanisms of pathogenesis in dermatophytosis are not clear. Fungal products may

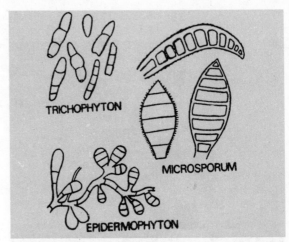

Fig.65.3 Macroconidia of dermatophytes. Cylindrical in Trichophyton, fusiform in Microsporum, and club shaped in Epidermophyton.

be responsible for inciting local inflammation. Hypersensitivity to fungus antigens may play a role in pathogenesis and is probably responsible for the sterile vesicular lesions sometimes seen in sites distant from the ringworm. These lesions are called *dermatophytids* (or the 'id' reaction). Hypersensitivity can be demonstrated by skin testing with the fungus antigen, trichophytin.

Clinically, ringworm can be classified depending on the site involved. Tinea corporis (Tinea glabrosa) is ringworm of the smooth or nonhairy skin of the body. A special type is Tinea imbricata which is found in the tropics and is characterised by extensive concentric rings of papulosquamous scaly patches, Tinea cruris is involvement of the groin and the perineum. Tinea barbae or barber's itch is involvement of the bearded areas of the face and neck. Tinea pedis or athletes' foot is ringworm of the foot and Tinea capitis ringworm of the scalp. 'Favus' is a chronic type of ringworm in which dense crusts (scutula) develop in the hair follicles, which lead to alopecia and scarring. Scalp infection sometimes produces severe boggy lesions with marked inflammatory reaction called 'kerion'. Table 65.2 lists the clinical types of dermatophytoses and their common causative agents.

Laboratory diagnosis: The routine method of diagnosis is by the examination of KOH mounts. Scrapings are taken from the edges of ringworm lesions. The specimen is mixed with a drop of 10% KOH on a slide, and after placing a coverslip, the preparation is gently heated to bring about 'clearing'. Microscopy reveals branched septate hyphae (Fig. 65.5). Selection of infected hair for examination is facilitated by exposure to UV light (Wood's lamp). Infected hair will be fluorescent. Two types of hair infection may be distinguished in wet mounts, 'ectothrix' in which arthrospores are seen as a sheath surrounding the hair and 'endothrix' in which the spores are inside the hair shaft (Fig. 65.6). Demonstration of the fungus in nails may be difficult and may be possible only after clearing with KOH for a day or two.

Species identification is possible only by culture examination. Specimens are inoculated on Sabouraud's medium (with antibiotics and cycloheximide) and incubated at room temperature.

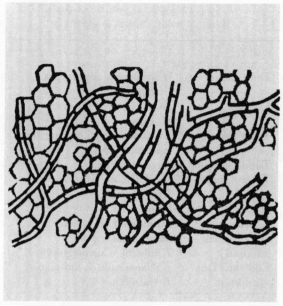

Fig.65.5 Dermatophyte hyphae in skin scraping, KOH mount. Partly digested epithelial cells form the background.

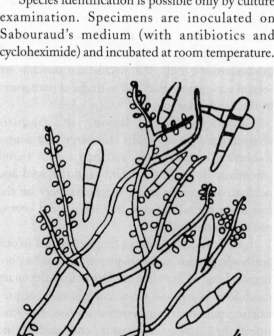

Fig. 65.4 Trichophyton rubrum: culture mount showing microconidia along sides of hyphae, and long cylindrical macroconida.

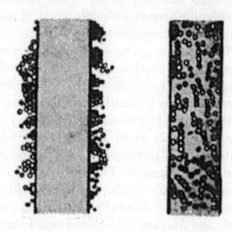

Fig. 65.6 Ectothrix and endothrix types of hair infection. 1. ectothrix type with fungal arthrospores surrounding hair 2. endothrix type showing arthrospores inside hair shaft.

Table 65.2 Clinical types of dermatophytoses and their common causative agents

Disease	Common causative agents
Tinea capitis	Microsporum any species, Trichophyton most species
Favus	T. schoenleinii, T. violaceum, M. gypseum
Tinea barbae	T. rubrum, T.mentagrophytes, T. verrucosum
Tinea imbricata	T. concentricum
Tinea corporis	T. rubrum and any other dermatophyte
T.cruris	E.floccosum, T. rubrum
T. pedis	T. rubrum, E. floccosum
Ectothrix hair infection	Microsporum species, T. rubrum, T.mentagrophytes
Endothrix hair infection	T. schoenleinii, T. tonsurans, T. violaceum

Growth is slow and colonies may appear only in 1–3 weeks.

Epidemiology: Dermatophytosis occurs throughout the world but certain types of disease and some species of fungi show geographically restricted distribution. Social and cultural patterns also influence dermatophytoses. Tinea pedis, so common in the temperate climates where all wear shoes is rare in the tropics where most walk barefoot. Many factors, such as age, hormones and intercurrent diseases, affect the susceptibility to dermatophytosis.

Depending on their natural habitat, dermatophytes may be classfied as anthropophilic, zoophilic and geophilic species. Human beings are the main or only hosts for anthropophilic dermatophytes. T. rubrum, E. floccosum and M. audouinii are examples. They cause mild but chronic lesions. Zoophilic species are natural parasites of animals. Examples are T. verrucosum in cattle and M. canis in dogs and cats. Human infections with zoophilic dermatophytes cause severe inflammation but are more readily curable. Geophilic species, which occur naturally in soil, are relatively less pathogenic for human beings. Examples are M. gypseum and T. ajelloi.

Treatment: Topical antifungal agents are usually effective. T. rubrum infections may be resistant to treatment. Oral griseofulvin is the drug of choice.

CANDIDOSIS

Candidosis (candidiasis, moniliasis) is an infection of the skin, mucosa, and rarely of the internal organs, caused by a yeastlike—fungus Candida albicans, and occasionally by other Candida species.

Candida albicans is an ovoid or spherical budding cell, which produces pseudomycelia both in culture and in tissues (Fig. 65.7). Candida species are normal inhabitants of the skin and mucosa. Candidosis is an opportunistic endogenous infection, the commonest predisposing factor being diabetes.

Cutaneous candidosis may be intertriginous or paronychial. The former is an erythematous, scaling or moist lesion with sharply demarcated borders, where papular lesions are most prominent. The sites affected are those where the skin is macerated by perspiration—groin, perineum, axillae and inframammary folds. Paronychia and onychia are seen in occupations that lead to frequent immersion of the hands in water.

Common mucosal lesions are vaginitis characterised by an acidic discharge and found frequently in pregnancy, and oral thrush found commonly in bottle fed infants and the aged and deblitated. Creamy white patches appear on the tongue or buccal mucosa, that leave a red oozing surface on removal.

Intestinal candidosis is a frequent sequel to oral antibiotic therapy and may present as diarrhea not responding to treatment. Bronchopulmonary candidosis is seen as a rare complication of pre-existing pulmonary or systemic disease. Systemic infections, such as septicemia, endocarditis and meningitis may occur as terminal complications in severe generalised diseases such as leukemia and in persons on prolonged immunosuppression. Candida granuloma and chronic mucocutaneous candidiasis are serious manifestations seen in immunodeficiencies.

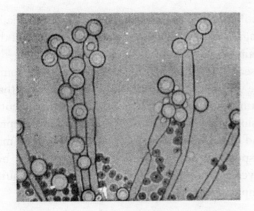

Fig. 65.7a Yeasts and chlamydospores of *Candida albicans*

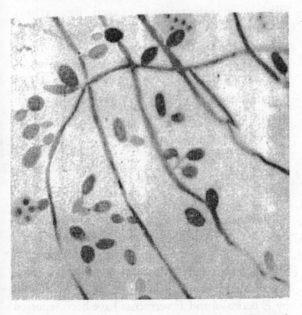

Fig. 65.7b *Candida albicans* in a stained specimen of sputum. The presence of hyphal elements in addition to yeast forms indicates colonisation of tissue by the organism.

Diagnosis can be established by microscopy and culture. Wet films or Gram stained smears from lesions or exudates show budding Gram positive cells. As Candida can be seen on normal skin or mucosa as well, only its abundant presence is of significance. Demonstration of mycelial forms indicates colonisation and tissue invasion and is,

therefore, of greater significance. Cultures can be obtained readily on Sabouraud's and on ordinary bacteriological culture media. Colonies are creamy white, smooth and with a yeasty odour. *Candida albicans* can be identified from other Candida species (*C. stellatoidae, C. tropicalis, C. pseudotropicalis, C. krusei, C. guilliermondii, C. parapsilosis, C. viswanathii*) by growth characteristics and sugar assimilation and fermentation tests. *C. albicans* alone forms chlamydospores on corn meal agar cultures at 20 °C. A rapid method of identifying *C. albicans* is based on its ability to form germ tubes within two hours when incubated in human serum at 37 °C (Reynolds-Braude phenomenon).

Agglutinins appear in the sera of patients but as they are frequent in normal persons also, they are not helpful in diagnosis. Delayed hypersensitivity to Candida is so universal that skin testing with Candida extracts is used as an indicator of the functional integrity of cell mediated immunity.

Management of candidosis is mainly by removing the predisposing causes. All Candida strains are sensitive to Nystatin but as it is poorly absorbed from the gut, it is not useful in systemic diseases. Amphotericin B, 5-fluorocytosine and clotrimazole may be used for disseminated candidosis.

DEEP MYCOSES

Deep mycotic infections may be classified as those that affect mainly or exclusively the subcutaneous tissues (subcutaneous or intermediate mycosis) and those that involve the internal organs (deep seated or systemic mycoses).

Subcutaneous mycoses:
1. Mycotic mycetoma
2. Chromoblastomycosis
3. Sporotrichosis
4. Rhinosporidiosis
5. Subcutaneous phycomycosis

Systemic mycoses:
1. Cryptococcosis

2. Blastomycosis
3. Paracoccidioidomycosis
4. Coccidioidomycosis
5. Histoplasmosis

MYCETOMA

Mycetomas are chronic, slowly progressive infections of the subcutaneous tissue, usually of the foot and rarely of the other parts of the body. The disease was originally reported by Gill (1842) from Madurai, south India, and Carter (1860) established its fungal etiology. It is therefore commonly known as Maduramycosis or Madura foot. However, this condition had been referred to in the Atharva Veda as *Padavalmika* (foot anthill). It is seen mainly in the tropics, though occasional cases have been reported from the temperate countries. Its incidence varies markedly from one place to another; for instance, in India, it is quite common in Tamil Nadu but rare in Kerala.

Mycetomas may be caused by a number of actinomycetes and filamentous fungi. A similar condition called 'botryomycosis' is caused by *Staphylococcus aureus* and some other bacteria. Etiological diagnosis, therefore, is of importance in treatment.

The causative agent is believed to enter through minor trauma. The disease usually begins as a small subcutaneous swelling of the foot, which enlarges, burrowing into the deeper tissues and tracking to the surface as multiple sinuses discharging viscid, seropurulent fluid containing granules. These 'granules' or 'grains' are microcolonies of the etiological agents and their demonstration is of diagnostic value. The colour and consistency of the grains vary with the different agents causing the disease (Table 65.3). In actinomycotic mycetoma, the grains will be composed of very thin (less than 1μm in diameter) filaments, while in mycotic lesions, they will be broader and often show septae and chlamydospores. Actinomycotic lesions may respond to sulphonamides and antibiotics but mycotic lesions are resistant and may require amputation.

CHROMOMYCOSIS

The term chromomycosis includes a group of clinical manifestations caused by various dematiaceous (pigmented) fungi.

1. **Chromoblastomycosis:** The most common form of chromomycosis is known as chromoblastomycosis or verrucous dermatitis. The lesions consist of warty cutaneous nodules which resemble the florets of cauliflower. The disease is usually confined to the subcutaneous tissue of the feet and lower legs.

The etiological agents are soil inhabiting fungi of the family Dematiaceae. They enter the skin by traumatic implantation. The lesion develops slowly around the site of implantation. The most common fungi responsible are the Fonsecaea (Hormodendrum) species – *F. pedrosoi, F. compactum, F. dermatitidis; Phialophora* species *P. verrucosa* and the Cladosporium species – *C. carrionii.* Infections caused by *F. pedrosoi* and *P. verrucosa* have been reported to disseminate to other areas, especially the brain.

Table 65.3 Colour of grains in mycetomas of various etiology

White to yellow	Brown to black	Red
Nocardia asteroides	Madurella mycetomi	Actinomadura pelletierii
Nocardia brasiliensis	Madurella grisea	
Actinomadura madurae	Phialophora jeanselmei	
Streptomyces somaliensis		
Allescheria boydii		

Histologically, the lesions show the presence of the fungus as round or irregular, dark brown, yeastlike bodies with septae, called *sclerotic cells* (Fig. 65.8). Diagnosis can be established by demonstration of these sclerotic bodies in KOH mounts or in sections, and by culture on Sabouraud's agar.

The disease is mainly tropical and is more common among barefoot agricultural workers and woodcutters.

Amphotericin B, thiobendazole and 5-fluorocytocine have been found useful in treatment.

2. Other infections caused by dematiaceous fungi (Phaeohyphomycosis): This group includes localised or systemic infections caused by certain species *Phialophora, Cladosporium* or other dematiaceous soil fungi, showing brown filaments in the affected tissues. The sites of lesions may be cutaneous, subcutaneous, deeper tissues, or organs like the brain or lung. The tissue reactions and morphology of the fungus in lesions differ from those seen in chromoblastomycosis. Sclerotic cells or granules are not found. The fungi appear in lesions as distorted hyphal strands. Phaeohyphomycosis is generally seen in debilitated or immunodeficient hosts. Some of the clinical types are:

1. Brain abscess caused by *Cladosporium bantianum*, and
2. Subcutaneous or intramuscular lesions with abscesses or cysts containing masses of brown hyphae (formerly known as *phaeosporotrichose*) caused by *Phialophora jeanselmei, P. spinifera, P. dermatitidis* or *P. richardsiae*.

SPOROTRICHOSIS

Sporotrichosis is caused by the fungus *Sporothrix (Sporotrichum) schenckii* and is characterised by the development on the skin, in subcutaneous tissues and in lymph nodes, of nodules which soften and break down to form indolent ulcers. The fungus is a saprophyte found widely on plants, thorns and timber. Infection is acquired through thorn pricks or other minor injuries. Rare instances of transmission from patients and infected horses and rats have been recorded. The disease is worldwide, though most cases occur in the USA.

The fungus spreads from the primary site through lymphatics but seldom extends beyond the regional lymph nodes. Most cases occur in the upper limb. In infected tissues, the fungus is seen as cigar shaped yeast cells, without mycelia. Sometimes 'asteroid bodies' are seen in the lesion, composed of a central fungus cell with eosinophilicmaterial radiating from it.

Diagnosis is made by culture as frequently the fungus may not be demonstrable in pus or tissues. *S. schenckii* is a dimorphic fungus occurring in the yeast phase in tissues and in cultures at 37 °C, and in the mycelial phase in nature and in cultures at room temperature. The septate hyphae are very thin (1–2 μm diameter) and carry flower-like clusters of small conidia borne on delicate sterigmata (Fig. 65.9). Rats are highly susceptible and can be infected by intraperitoneal or intratesticular inoculation.

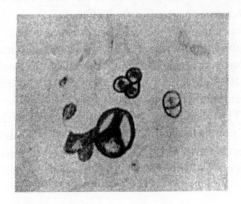

Fig. 65.8 Chromoblastomycosis: KOH mount of lesion showing large septate 'sclerotic bodies'

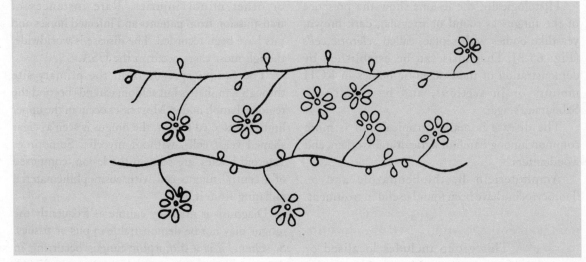

Fig.65.9 *Sporothrix (Sporotrichum) schenkii*: culture mount showing fine branching hyphae and pear shaped conidia borne in rosette like clusters at tips of lateral branches and singly along sides of hyphae.

RHINOSPORIDIOSIS

Rhinosporidiosis is a chronic granulomatous disease characterised by the development of friable polyps, usually confined to the nose, mouth or eye but rarely seen on the genitalia or other mucous membranes. Though the disease was first identified in Argentina, the large majority of cases come from India and Sri Lanka. While the disease is generally confined to mucous membranes, hematogenous dissemination has been recorded very rarely.

Histologically the lesion is composed of large numbers of fungal spherules embedded in a stroma of connective tissue and capillaries. The spherules are 10–200 μm in diameter and contain thousands of endospores (Fig 65.10).

The causative fungus *Rhinosporidium seeberi* has not been cultivated in media. The mode of infection is not known though infection is believed to originate from stagnant water or aquatic life.

SUBCUTANEOUS PHYCOMYCOSIS

In this condition, originally reported from Indonesia and subsequently identified in many Asian and African countries, a painless subcutaneous nodule develops which enlarges to involve a whole limb or large areas of the body. The causative agent is *Basidiobolus haptosporus*, a saprophytic phycomycete found in decaying vegetation and in the intestines of many reptiles and amphibians. It has been suggested that the infection may be acquired by insect bites.

CRYPTOCOCCOSIS

Cryptococcosis (torulosis) is a subacute or chronic infection caused by the yeast *Cryptococcus neoformans*. It is a round or ovoid budding cell, 4–20 μm in diameter, with a prominent polysaccharide capsule (Fig. 65.11). It is a soil saprophyte and is particularly abundant in the feces of pigeons and other birds.

Infection is usually acquired by inhalation but may sometimes be through the skin or mucosa. Most infections are asymptomatic. Pulmonary cryptococcosis may lead to a mild pneumonitis. As no calcification occurs, healed pulmonary lesions are not evident radiologically. Dissemination of infection leads to visceral, cutaneous and meningeal disease. Visceral forms simulate tuberculosis and

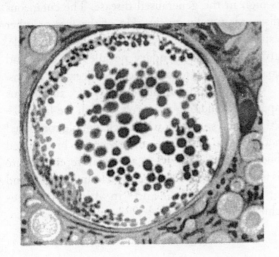

Fig.65.10 Rhinosporidium. Mature sporangium (centrally located) in the stroma of a lesion.

cancer clinically. Bones and joints may be involved. Cutaneous cryptococcosis varies from small ulcers to large granulomas. Cryptococcal meningitis is the most serious type of infection and can resemble tuberculous or other chronic types of meningitis. Its onset is insidious and the course slow and progressive. It is often seen in AIDS.

Diagnosis is established by demonstration of capsulated, budding yeast cells in the lesions and by culture. The capsules stand out in India ink preparations. The fungus grows readily on Sabouraud's agar forming smooth, mucoid, cream coloured colonies. The ability to grow at 37 °C and hydrolyse urea differentiates *C. neoformans* from nonpathogenic cryptococci. Pathogenicity can be demonstrated by intracerebral or intraperitoneal inoculation into mice, which develop a fatal infection. Capsulated budding yeast cells can be demonstrated in the brain of infected mice.

Two perfect stages of the fungus have been discovered. They belong to the class Basidiomycetes and have been termed *Filobasidiella neoformans* and *F. basilispora.*

Four serological types of cryptococcal capsular polysaccharide – A, B, C and D – have been identified. Demonstration of the capsular antigen by precipitation can sometimes be valuable in diagnosing some cases of cryptococcal meningitis, when the CSF is negative by smear and culture. Amphotericin B, 5-fluorocytosine, clotrimazole and miconazole are useful in the treatment of the disease.

Cryptococcosis is worldwide in distribution. As it was originally reported from Europe, it used to be known as 'European blastomycosis'. Several cases of cryptococcosis have been identified in India, this being the only deep mycosis common in this

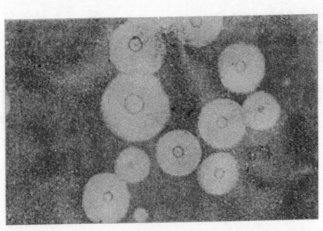

Fig. 65.11 *Cryptococcus neoformans*: Indian ink preparation of spinal fluid showing yeast cells surrounded by a large capsule

country. *C. neoformans* can produce disease in animals, particularly mastitis in cattle. The role of animal cryptococcosis in causing human disease is not known.

BLASTOMYCOSIS

This is a chronic infection caused by the dimorphic fungus *Blastomyces dermatitidis*, characterised by the formation of suppurative and granulomatous lesions in any part of the body but with a marked predilection for the lungs and skin. As the infection is largely confined to the North American continent, it is known as the 'North American blastomycosis'. A number of cases have, however, been reported from Africa lately. The fungus has also been isolated in Delhi from the bronchial aspirates of a patient and from the lungs of insectivorous bats.

Soil is considered to be the source of infection, which is acquired by inhalation. Primary infection of the lung may resemble tuberculosis or histoplasmosis. It may be asymptomatic or may lead to focal or diffuse consolidation, miliary lesions or abscess formation. The fungus may spread from the lungs through the bloodstream and form multiple abscesses in various parts of the body. Case fatality is high in the generalised disease. The cutaneous disease is usually on the skin of the face or other exposed parts of the body. The initial lesion is a papule, around which secondary nodules develop and coalesce, leading to large, elevated ulcerative lesions.

In tissue and in cultures at 37 °C, the fungus appears as budding yeast cells, which are large (7–20 μm) and spherical, with thick, double contoured walls. Each cell carries only a single broadbased bud (Fig 65.12). At room temperature, the culture is filamentous with septate hyphae and many round or oval conidia, and in older cultures chlamydospores also.

PARACOCCIDIOIDOMYCOSIS

This is a chronic granulomatous disease of the skin, mucosa, lymph nodes and internal organs caused by *Paracoccidioides brasiliensis*. As the disease is confined to South America, it is called 'South American blastomycosis'. Ulcerative granulomas of the buccal and nasal mucosa are a prominent feature of the disease.

The yeast phase is found in tissues and in cultures at 37 °C. It consists of large, round or oval cells with multiple budding (Fig. 65.12). The mycelial phase develops at room temperature.

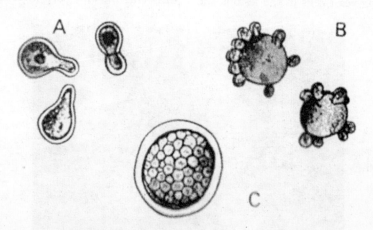

Fig. 65.12 A. *Blastomyces dermatitis* yeast phase showing spherical or oval double walled cells with single broad based buds; B. *Paracoccidioides brasiliensis* yeast phase showing spherical thick walled cells with multiple buds; C. *Coccidioides immitis* tissue phase showing spherule with numerous endospores.

COCCIDIOIDOMYCOSIS

Coccidioidomycosis is an infection caused by the dimorphic fungus *Coccidioides immitis*. The infection may be inapparent, benign, severe or even fatal. The disease is endemic in the dry, arid regions of southwestern USA, where the fungus is present in the soil and in rodents.

Infection is acquired by inhalation of dust containing arthrospores of the fungus. In most cases, the respiratory infection is asymptomatic and leads only to immunisation, which can be demonstrated by a positive skin test with 'coccidioidin' (analogous to the tuberculin test). Many persons develop a self-limited influenza-like fever (known as 'valley fever' or 'desert rheumatism'). Less than one per cent of infected persons develop chronic progressive disseminated disease (coccidioidal granuloma) which is highly fatal. It resembles clinically and histologically disseminated tuberculosis.

The fungus is dimorphic, occurring in the tissue as a yeast and in culture (both at 37 °C and at room temperature) as the mycelial form. The tissue form is a spherule, 15–75 μm in diameter, with a thick doubly refractile wall and filled with endospores (Fig. 65.12). The mycelial phase consists of hyphae which fragment into arthrospores which are highly infectious. Cultures should be handled with particular care as they may cause laboratory infection.

HISTOPLASMOSIS

Histoplasmosis is an intracellular infection of the reticuloendothelial system caused by the dimorphic fungus *Histoplasma capsulatum*. The disease was originally described by Darling (1905) who believed the causative agent to be a protozoon related to *Leishmania donovani*.

The disease is worldwide in distribution but is most common in the USA where it is endemic in many central and eastern states. In endemic areas the fungus is present in the soil, rotting trees and is particularly abundant in bird feces. Infection is acquired by inhalation. The large majority of infections are asymptomatic and, as in tuberculosis,

heal, leaving behind an area of miliary calcification. It was the investigation of tuberculin negative individuals with pulmonary calcification that made evident the frequency of asymptomatic infection with the fungus. Some infected persons develop pulmonary disease which resembles tuberculosis. Disseminated histoplasmosis develops only in a small minority of infected individuals. The reticuloendothelial system is involved with resultant lymphadenopathy, hepatosplenomegaly, fever, anemia and a high rate of fatality. Granulomatous and ulcerative lesions may develop on the skin and mucosa.

In tissues, the fungus is present inside phagocytic cells in the yeast phase—oval, budding cells measuring 2–4 μm. The yeast phase is also formed in blood agar cultures at 37 °C. On Sabouraud's agar at room temperature, white cottony mycelial growth appears, with large (8–20 μm) thick walled, spherical spores with tubercles or fingerlike projections (Fig.65.13). The appearance of the tuberculate spores is diagnostic.

Diagnosis may be made by microscopical examination of stained smears of blood, bone marrow, scrapings from lesions or biopsies of lymph nodes, and by the culture of the fungus from these materials. Antibodies are formed during the infection. They decline if the infection is inactive but increase in titre in progressive disease. Latex agglutination, complement fixation and precipitation tests are useful in diagnosis. Delayed hypersensitivity is developed following infection. It can be demonstrated by skin testing with 'histoplasmin', which is analogous to the tuberculin test for tuberculosis.

'African histoplasmosis' involves mainly the skin, subcutaneous tissues and bones. The lungs are not commonly affected and disseminated disease is infrequent. The causative agent has been named *Histoplasma duboisii* and it differs from *H. capsulatum* in forming much larger yeast-like cells (7–15 μm). In the mycelial form, the two species are indistinguishable.

Amphotericin B has been found useful in therapy.

OPPORTUNISTIC SYSTEMIC MYCOSES

Some saprophytic fungi which are ubiquitous in the environment are important in medical mycology for two reasons. Firstly, they are common laboratory contaminants on culture media—*Aspergillus, Penicillium, Mucor* and *Rhizopus* species grow on virtually anything. Secondly, they can produce serious and even fatal infection in persons who are otherwise debilitated. Aspergillosis and mucormycosis are important opportunistic systemic mycoses.

ASPERGILLOSIS

Aspergilli and Penicillia constitute the commonest moulds seen on damp bread or almost any other organic matter. Of the 300 odd species of aspergilli, *A. fumigatus* is highly pathogenic for birds, and occasionally causes invasive disease in human beings. A few other species may also cause opportunistic human disease. The commonest human disease caused by aspergilli is otomycosis.

Systemic aspergillosis occurs as the following clinical types:

1. Pulmonary aspergillosis
   a. Aspergillus asthma
   b. Bronchopulmonary aspergillosis
   c. Colonising aspergillosis (Aspergilloma)

2. Disseminated aspergillosis

Aspergillus asthma occurs in atopic individuals following sensitisation to inhaled aspergillus spores. In bronchopulmonary aspergillosis, the fungus grows within the lumen of the bronchioles, which may be occluded by fungus plugs. The fungus can be demonstrated in sputum. The condition is made worse by the development of hypersensitivity to the fungus. Colonising aspergillosis usually develops in pre-existing pulmonary cavities, such as in tuberculosis or cystic disease. The fungus grows into large 'balls' (aspergilloma). Surgical removal becomes necessary as the disease commonly causes massive hemoptysis. In invasive aspergillosis, the fungus actively invades the lung tissue. Disseminated aspergillosis involving the brain, kidney and other organs is a fatal complication sometimes seen in

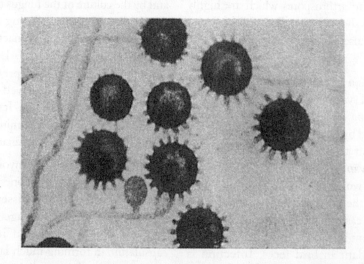

Fig. 65.13 Histoplasma capsulatum

debilitated patients on prolonged treatment with antibiotics, steroids and cytotoxic drugs.

Diagnosis may be made by microscopic examination and by culture. The fungus grows rapidly on culture media. Identification of Aspergillus is easy, based on growth characteristics and morphology. Aspergilli have septate hyphae. Asexual conidia are arranged in chains, carried on elongated cells called 'sterigmata', borne on the expanded ends (vesicles) of conidiophores (Fig. 65.14).

As aspergilli are such common contaminants, their demonstration in exudates and isolation in cultures have to be interpreted with care.

PENICILLIOSIS

Penicillium species have been very rarely incriminated in opportunistic human infections *P. marneffei* has been reported to be an important opportunist pathogen in the HIV infected. Members of this genus can be identified by the brushlike arrangement of conidia (Fig. 65.14).

MUCORMYCOSIS

Mucormycosis is an invasive disease caused by phycomycetes, mainly by species of *Rhizopus*, *Mucor* and *Absidia*. It used to be a rare terminal complication of uncontrolled diabetes and other chronic debilitating diseases. The incidence of the disease has increased considerably as a result of the widespread use of antibiotics, steroids and antimetabolites. The fungi are normally avirulent and are able to invade tissues only when general resistance is extremely low.

The primary infection is usually in the upper respiratory tract or nose, where the spores germinate and the mycelia invade the adjacent tissues—the orbit, sinuses and the brain. Primary infection may also occur in the lung, the fungi invading the arteries to cause thrombosis and infarction. The disease is fatal.

Diagnosis is usually made during histological examination of autopsy material, by the presence of broad, nonseptate mycelia in tissues. The fungi can be grown easily on Sabouraud's medium without cycloheximide. Mucor shows branched sporangiophores arising randomly along aerial mycelium. Rhizoids are absent. Rhizopus has rhizoids, and sporangiophores arise in groups directly above the rhizoids (Fig. 65.14).

OTOMYCOSIS

Otomycosis is a fungal infection of the external ear. It is a very common disease and is usually caused by species of aspergilli (*A. niger, A. fumigatus*) and penicillia. The symptoms are itching, pain and deafness. Secondary bacterial infection, commonly due to Pseudomonas and Proteus, causes suppuration. Diagnosis can be made by demonstration of the fungi in scrapings and by culture.

OCULOMYCOSIS

Mycotic keratitis usually follows corneal trauma. Fungal spores colonise the injured tissue and initiate an inflammatory reaction, leading to hypopyon ulcer and endophthalmitis. If not recognised and treated early, enucleation may become necessary. The widespread use of corticosteriods in ophthalmology has resulted in an increased incidence of keratomycosis.

Many saprophytic fungi can cause ocular infection, *Aspergillus species, Fusarium* and *Candida albicans* being most often responsible. Diagnosis may be made by examination of deep scrapings. Superficial swabs may not show the fungus. Local application of amphotericin B, Nystatin and Pimaricin (Natamycin) may be useful.

MYCOTIC POISONING

Many fungi form poisonous substances. Mycotic poisoning is of two types – mycetism in which a fungus which is eaten for itself causes toxic effects and mycotoxicosis in which fungal toxins contaminate some article of food.

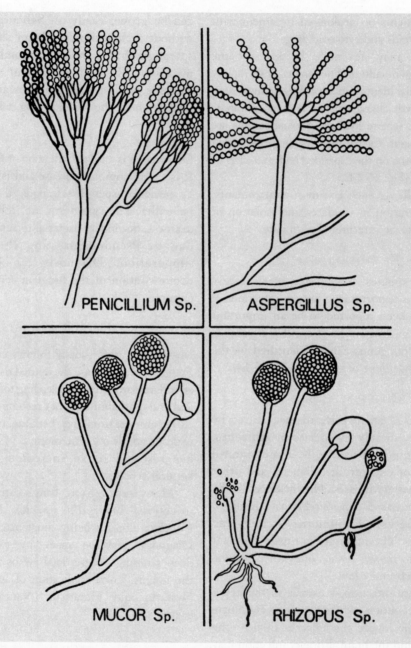

Fig. 65.14 Common contaminant fungi, culture mounts. *Penicillium* showing the 'penicillus' or brush, consisting of chains of spores extending from the ends of short branches of conidiophores. *Aspergillus* showing unbranched nonseptate conidiophores, terminating in a globose vesicle bearing phialids from which arise chains of conidia. *Mucor* showing nonseptate mycelium without rhizoids (rootlike structures). Sporangiophores, which may be branched, terminate in large globose sporangia containing numerous spores. *Rhizopus* showing nonseptate mycelium with rhizoids. Unbranched sporangiophores arise opposite rhizoids.

Mycetism has been known from ancient times, several varieties of poisonous mushrooms having been identified as inedible. Mycetism may cause gastrointestinal disease, dermatitis or death. The hallucinogenic agents (d-lysergic acid, psilocybin) produced by the *Psilocybe* species and other fungi have attracted much attention in recent years.

The best known mycotoxin is 'aflatoxin' produced by *Aspergillus flavus*. It is frequently present in mouldy foods, particularly in groundnuts, corn and peas. It is highly toxic to animals and birds, and probably to human beings as well. It can cause hepatomas in ducklings and rats, and its possible carcinogenic effect in human beings has caused great concern. There have been several reports of aflatoxicosis from India, involving human beings and animals.

Ergotoxicosis (ergotism) is due to the toxic alkaloids produced by the fungus *Claviceps purpurea*, while growing on the fruiting heads of rye.

Further Reading

Evans EGV et al (eds). 1989. *Medical Mycology*, Oxford: Oxford University Press.
Kibbler CC et al. 1996. *Principles and Practice of Clinical Mycology*. Chichester: Wiley.
Kwon-Chung KJ and JE Bennett 1992. *Medical Mycology*. Philadelphia: Lea and Febiger.
Richardson MD and DW Warnock 1993. *Fungal Infection*. Oxford: Blackwell.
Rippon JW. 1988. *Medical Mycology*. Philadelphia: WB Saunders.

Laboratory Control of Antimicrobial Therapy

ANTIBIOTIC SENSITIVITY TESTS

Apart from rare exceptions like *Strep. pyogenes,* pathogenic bacteria exhibit very great strain variations in susceptibility to antibiotics and chemotherapeutic agents. This is particularly marked in the case of *Staph. aureus* and Gram negative bacilli. Therefore, it is essential to determine the susceptibility of isolates of pathogenic bacteria to antibiotics that are likely to be used in treatment. Antibiotic sensitivity tests are of two types, diffusion tests and dilution tests.

Diffusion test: Here the drug is allowed to diffuse through a solid medium so that a gradient is established, the concentration being highest near the site of application of the drug and decreasing with distance. The test bacterium is seeded on the medium and its sensitivity to the drug determined from the inhibition of its growth. Several methods have been used for the application of the drug. It may be added to ditches or holes cut in the medium or to hollow cylinders (Heatly cups) placed on it. The method most commonly employed is to use filter paper discs, impregnated with antibiotics.

The *disc diffusion* method uses filter paper discs, 6.0 mm in diameter, charged with appropriate concentrations of the drugs. The discs are stored dry in the cold. They may be prepared in the laboratory or purchased commercially. A suitable dilution of a broth culture or a broth suspension of the test bacterium is flooded on the surface of a solid medium (Mueller–Hinton agar or nutrient agar). The plate is tilted to ensure uniform spreading and the excess broth pipetted off. Inoculation may also be performed by spreading with swabs. After

drying the plate (37 °C for 30 mins), antibiotic discs (four or five per 10 cm plate) are applied with sterile forceps. After overnight incubation, the degree of sensitivity is determined by measuring the zones of inhibition of growth around the discs. Growth will be inhibited around discs containing antibiotics to which the bacterium is susceptible but not around those to which it is resistant.

The diameter of the zone of inhibition is influenced by a variety of factors, such as diffusibility of the drug, the disc concentration, the nature and composition of the medium, its thickness, presence of inhibitory or stimulatory substances, pH and time of incubation. It is, therefore, necessary to standardise all the variables. It is also necessary to check the potency of the discs periodically using as control a standard bacterium of known sensitivity, such as *Staph. aureus* Oxford strain (NCTC 6571).

There are several recommendations regarding the antibiotic concentrations to be used in discs. The Kirby–Bauer and the ICS methods are in common use. Table 66.1 shows the disc concentrations and the critical zone sizes for antibiotics in common use.

A suitable method for routine use in diagnostic laboratories is the technique originally described by Stokes. This incorporates built-in controls against many variables and therefore provides dependable results. A standard sensitive strain of bacterium is inoculated in the middle third of the culture plate. The standard strains used are *Staph. aureus* ATCC 25923, *E. coli* ATCC 25922 or *Ps.aeruginosa* ATCC 27853, depending on the bacterium to be tested. The test bacterium is inoculated over the upper and lower thirds of the plate. Antibiotics discs are applied between the standard and test inocula, so that zones of inhibition formed around each disc are composed of standard and test bacteria. Comparison of the zones of inhibition between the standard and test bacteria indicates the sensitivity of the latter.

The results are reported as 'sensitive', 'moderately sensitive' or 'resistant' to the different drugs. Antibiotics for sensitivity tests should be chosen with discrimination. Only those clinically relevant should be tested. Thus chloramphenicol need not be tested against urinary pathogens as the drug is excreted in urine mostly in the inactive form. Nitrofurantoin needs be tested only against urinary pathogens. Sensitivity tests on methenamine mandelate are not relevant as the drug is active only in vivo. Some drugs, such as sulphonamides and trimethoprim, are inhibited by certain substances present in most culture media. These substances may be neutralised by the addition of lysed horse blood.

It is important that sensitivity tests be done only with known or presumed pathogens. If sensitivity tests are done with commensal or contaminated bacteria and reported, the clinician may be misled.

The disc diffusion test, as described above, is done after the pathogenic bacteria are isolated from clinical specimens. When results are required in a hurry, the 'primary disc diffusion test' may be performed. Here, the swab or other clinical specimen is directly inoculated uniformly on the surface of a plate and discs applied. The results of the primary test should be verified by testing the isolates subsequently.

A recent modification of the agar diffusion sensitivity test employing a quantitative diffusion gradient is known as the Epsilometer or E-test. It uses an absorbent strip with a known gradient of drug concentrations along its length. When the strip is placed on the agar plate seeded with the test bacterium, antibiotic diffuse into the medium. The MIC is obtained by noting the lowest concentration of the gradient which inhibits the bacterial growth.

Dilution test: Here, serial dilutions of the drug are prepared and inoculated with the test bacterium. This is too laborious for routine use. Dilution tests are generally employed when the therapeutic dose is to be regulated accurately as in the treatment of bacterial endocarditis, for tests on slow growing bacteria such as tubercle bacilli, and when small degrees of resistance are to be demonstrated. Dilution tests may be done by the tube dilution or agar dilution methods.

In the tube dilution method, serial dilutions of the drug in broth are taken in tubes and a standardised suspension of the test bacterium

Table 66.1 Disc concentrations and interpretation of disc diffusion test

Drug	Disc conc.	Inhibition zone diameter in nm		
		Resistant	Intermediate	Sensitive
Ampicillin	10 µg	<20	21–29	<30
Chloramphenicol	30 µg	<12	13–17	<18
Colistin	10 µg	<8	9–10	<11
Erythromycin	15 µg	<13	14–17	<18
Kanamycin	30 µg	<13	14–17	<18
Methicillin	5 µg	<9	10–13	<14
Penicillin	10 units	<20	21–29	<30
Streptomycin	10 µg	<12	13–16	<17
Sulphonamides	300 µg	<14	15–19	<20

inoculated. After overnight incubation, the 'minimum inhibitory concentration' (MIC) is read by noting the lowest concentration of the drug that inhibits growth. The 'minimum bactericidal concentration' (MBC) is the lowest concentration of the drug that kills the bacterium. It can be estimated by subculturing from the broth tubes that show no growth on to suitable solid media.

The 'agar dilution' method is more convenient when several strains are to be tested at the same time. Here, serial dilutions of the drug are prepared in agar and poured into plates. The advantage is that many strains can be inoculated on each plate containing an antibiotic dilution. Automated versions of sensitivity tests are available and are in use in large laboratories.

Antibiotic assays in body fluids: These are required to verify whether adequate drug concentrations are achieved in blood and other body fluids, and to guard against excessive blood levels of potentially toxic drugs. The assays are generally done by making serial dilutions of the specimen and inoculating standard suspensions of bacteria of known MIC. Assays can also be done by the agar diffusion method. This depends on the direct relationship between antibiotic concentration and the diameter of the zone of inhibition with a standard sensitive strain of bacterium.

Further Reading

Lonian V. 1986. *Antibiotics in laboratory Medicine*. Baltimore: Williams and Wilkins.

Murray P et al (eds). 1995. *Manual of Clinical Microbiology*. Washington: ASM Press.

Williams RJ and DI Heymann 1998. Containment of antibiotic resistance. *Science* 279:1153

Immunoprophylaxis

An important contribution of microbiology to medicine has been immunisation, which is one of the most effective methods of controlling infectious diseases. By systematic active immunisation, many developed countries have virtually eliminated 'vaccine preventable diseases' (VPD) such as diphtheria, pertussis, tetanus, measles, mumps, rubella and poliomyelitis. The global eradication of smallpox, of course, has been the crowning glory of immunisation.

Immunoprophylaxis may be in the form of (1) routine immunisation, which forms part of basic health care; or (2) immunisation of individuals or selected groups exposed to risk of specific infections.

ROUTINE IMMUNISATION

Routine immunisation schedules have been developed for different countries, and modified from time to time, based on the prevalence of infectious diseases, their public health importance, availability of suitable vaccines, their cost benefit factors, and logistics. In India, the Expanded Programme on Immunisation (EPI) and the Universal Immunisation Programme (UIP) have been able to afford protection for much of the target population against VPDs.

The National Immunisation Schedule in force in India is shown in Table 67.1.

In India, EPI and UIP have led to a significant decline in the recorded incidence of VPDs, as well as of infant and child mortality. For example, it has been reported that in 1992 alone, 1.7 million lives of children under five years were saved, as compared to the mortality figures in 1984, the year before UIP was started.

Table 67.1 National Immunisation Schedule (INDIA)

Age		Vaccine
At birth[1]	......	BCG, OPV-O
6 weeks	......	BCG[2], DPT-1, OPV-1
10 weeks	......	DPT-2, OPV-2
14 weeks	......	DPT-3, OPV-3
9 months	......	Measles
16–24 months	......	DPT, OPV
5–6 years (school entry)	......	DT[3]
10 years	......	TT[4]
16 years	......	TT[4]
For pregnant women[5]		TT-1 or booster
One month after TT-1		TT-2

Note: 1. For institutional births only. OPV-0 is additional, and not to be counted for the primary course of 3 doses starting at 6 weeks.
2. Only for infants not given BCG at birth.
3. A second dose of DT to be given to children with no documentary evidence or history of primary DPT immunisation.
4. A second dose of TT to be given after one month to those with no record or history of prior DPT, DT or TT immunisation.
5. For prevention of tetanus in the neonate primarily, but also in the mother

Immunisation with three doses of OPV has not been consistently effective in India and other developing countries, with high rates of seroconversion failures. This is sought to be met through the strategy of 'mop up' rounds by giving OPV to all the children in an area on the same day, expecting natural spread of the vaccine virus among the children to reinforce immunisation. These rounds are preferably held during October to April, as the polio season in India is from May to October, with a peak in July–August.

Different countries employ different immunisation schedules depending on their priorities.

INDIVIDUAL IMMUNISATION

Vaccines offered under national programmes are limited by economic considerations and so some important vaccines may be omitted because they are costly. These may be supplemented by individual initiative, whenever possible.

Hepatitis B vaccine: Many developing countries, including India, have high endemicity for this virus. Perinatal transmission and acquisition of the virus infection in the first five years of life are common in such areas, in contrast to low endemic areas where infection is usually acquired in adolescence or adulthood from sexual or household contacts, contaminated needles, blood or blood products or occupational exposure. Besides the morbidity and mortality due to acute and chronic virus infection, chronic carriage which may be very prolonged is itself a serious public health problem. It has also become an economic problem as carriers are denied entry or employment in many foreign countries. Inclusion of the hepatitis B vaccine in routine childhood immunisation will therefore be beneficial. The fact that a quarter to half the adult dose of the vaccine is adequate for children brings down the cost. Till it becomes part of the national immunisation schedule, it would be desirable to have the vaccine administered to as many children and adults as possible by individual immunisation or through voluntary agencies. The recent reduction in cost of the vaccine as a result of indigenous manufacture, has made mass vaccination more feasible.

MMR vaccine: The composite measles-mumps-rubella vaccine is employed in the affluent countries but in the developing countries only the measles vaccine is given at nine months, the earliest age when it is likely to be immunogenic in the presence of maternal antibodies in the baby. Whenever possible, a dose of MMR vaccine may be beneficial at 16–24 months or later, not only to reinforce immunity against measles but also to protect against mumps and rubella.

Varicella vaccine: Chickenpox is very mild disease in children, but in adults it can be serious and even fatal. In most parts of the world, chickenpox is very rare in adults, but in some areas in the tropics it is not uncommon. The age of incidence of varicella is reported to be rising. Varicella vaccine had been used for many years in immunocompromised children. Recently, with the development of a more stable and effective vaccine, its scope has been extended for general use for prevention of varicella and herpes zoster. The live attenuated vaccine is recommeded as a single subcutaneous dose in children 9 months to 12 years of age, and as 2 doses at an interval of at least 6 weeks, in those older. Pregnancy is a contraindication.

Typhoid vaccine: Typhoid fever continues to be a major public health problem in the developing countries. Immunisation against typhoid is a real need, particularly in view of the spread of drug resistant typhoid strains. The original typhoid vaccine is not widely used because of its uncertain benefit and frequent adverse reactions. Two recent typhoid vaccines, the live oral Gal-E mutant vaccine and the injectable purified Vi polysaccharide vaccine may be acceptable because they offer prolonged protection and are free from reactions. They are recommended for immunisation of those five years old or above and so may be employed at school entry.

Immunoprophylaxis of individual diseases has been described in the respective chapters.

Further Reading

Ellis RW and G Douglas 1994. *New vaccine technologies. J Amer Med Assoc* 271:929

Galazka AM et al. 1984. Indications and contraindications for vaccines. *Bull Wld Hlth Org* 62:357.

Guidebook on immunization. 2001. Mumbai: Indian Academy of Pediatrics.

Mackett M and JD Williamson 1995. *Human vaccines and vaccination* Oxford:Bios Scientific.

Peter G 1992. Childhood immunisations. *New Eng J Med* 327:1794.

Plotkin SA and EA Mortimer 1988. *Vaccines.* Philadelphia: Saunders.

Wilson GS. 1967. *Hazards of immunisation.* London: Athlone Press.

Hospital Infection

Hospitals have always acted as a source of infection to patients admitted to them. Suppuration and gangrene were common postoperative consequences in hospitals old time. Even before the microbial etiology of infections was established, Semmelweiss was able to control puerperal sepsis in hospital by simple hand washing, and Lister overcame surgical infections with phenol sprays. The concept of asepsis and its application in hospital practice reduced their incidence, but hospital infections still cause considerable morbidity and mortality. The incidence of hospital infection has been reported to be 2–12 per cent in the advanced countries; it is much higher in the crowded hospitals in the developing countries. Even when hospitalisation does not lead to obvious infection, it causes a change in the patient's microbial flora, the normal flora being gradually replaced by the drug resistant microorganisms typical of the hospital environment.

The terms *hospital infection, hospital-acquired infection* or *nosocomial infection* (from *nosocomeion*, meaning hospital) are applied to infections developing in hospitalised patients, not present or in incubation at the time of their admission. Such infections may become evident during their stay in hospital or, sometimes, only after their discharge. Hospital infections are typically exogenous, the source being any part of the hospital ecosystem, including people, objects, food, water and air in the hospital. Such infections may be iatrogenic in that they may be induced by some diagnostic or therapeutic intervention in the hospital. They may be opportunistic in that microorganisms of low virulence may cause disease

in hospitalised patients whose immune mechanisms are impaired. However, it must be understood that nosocomial infections are not synonymous with iatrogenic or opportunistic infections, as the latter may occur outside hospitals also.

Several factors contribute to the occurrence and severity of hospital infections: (1) Many patients in hospitals have impaired defence mechanisms due to their disease or the therapy administered. They are, therefore, highly susceptible to infection. (2) The hospital environment is heavily laden with a wide variety of pathogens. Patients shed them from their bodies; hospital personnel spread them through their hands and clothes. Bedding, linen and utensils act as fomites. Equipment may be contaminated. Pathogens are present in the hospital dust and air, and sometimes even in antiseptic lotions and ointments. Contamination of hospital food or water may cause outbreaks of infections. (3) Major invasive procedures, diagnostic or therapeutic, are carried out only in hospitals. The slightest lapse in asepsis during these procedures can lead to infection. (4) Hospital infections are generally more serious and refractory to treatment as the infecting agents are resistant to most antibiotics in common use. (5) Hospital infections are in a sense diseases of medical progress. Advances in treatment of cancer, organ transplantation, implanted prostheses and other sophisticated medical technologies enhance the risk of infection to patients.

MICROBIOLOGY OF HOSPITAL INFECTIONS

Almost any pathogen can, on occasion, cause

hospital infection but those that are able to survive in the hospital environment for long periods and develop resistance to antibiotics and disinfectants are particularly important in this respect. *Strep. pyogenes* was, perhaps, the most important cause of hospital infection formerly but is hardly ever encountered now as it is highly susceptible to antibiotics. *Staph. aureus* strains, resistant to multiple antibiotics and belonging to phage type 80/81, spread globally in the 1950s and 1960s, colonising hospitals and causing nosocomial infection with such frequency that they came to be called 'hospital staphylococci'. The original phage types have since been replaced by others belonging to group III but staphylococci continue to be very common agents in hospital infection. *Staph. epidermidis* and Group D streptococci also are sometimes responsible for hospital infections.

In recent decades, the enteric Gram negative bacilli—*E. coli, Klebsiella, Enterobacter, Proteus* and *Serratia*—have become the most important group of hospital pathogens, particularly following the dissemination among them of R factors conferring multiple drug resistance. During the late 1970s multidrug resistant salmonellae, particularly *S. typhimurium*, became a prominent hospital pathogen.

Ps. aeruginosa and other *Pseudomonas* species have always been important causes of hospital infection because of their intrinsic resistance to most antibiotics and ability to survive and even multiply at low temperatures and in disinfectant solutions. They may also carry drug resistant plasmids.

Tetanus spores can survive in dust for a very long time and may sometimes contaminate cotton, suture materials, plaster of paris and other items used in hospitals. Hospital tetanus is usually a result of faulty sterilisation techniques or other lapses in asepsis.

HIV and hepatitis B and C viruses are the important infections transmitted through blood and blood products. Screening of donors and ensuring the absence of viable viruses in blood products have checked this risk to a large extent. However, HIV infection escapes detection during the window period. Screening for HCV antibody as practised now is not very satisfactory. In view of the inherent risk of transmission of known and unknown pathogens, it is safer to limit blood transfusion to the absolute minimum and employ autologous transfusion instead, wherever possible. The use of shared syringes and needles also carries the risk of transmission of these viruses.

Viral diarrhea and chickenpox are other viral infections that spread in hospitals. Cytomegalovirus, herpesvirus, influenza, enteroviruses and arenaviruses may also cause hospital infection.

The range of hospital pathogens also includes yeasts (*Candida albicans*), moulds, (*Aspergillus, Mucor*) and protozoa (*Entamoeba histolytica, Plasmodia, Pneumocystis carinii, Toxoplasma gondii*).

COMMON TYPES OF HOSPITAL INFECTIONS

1. Wound infection: This may range in severity from delayed wound healing or stitch abscess caused by *Staph. epidermidis* or other resident skin flora, to severe spreading infections due to exogenous pathogens. Several factors influence the occurrence of postoperative wound infections, such as the site and duration of surgery, health of the patient and skill of the operator. Most wound infections manifest within a week of surgery. *Strep. pyogenes* and clostridial infections appear within a day or two, while staphylococcal infections typically take four or five days and Gram negative bacillary infections six or seven days to appear. Routine preoperative antibiotics do not prevent wound infections, though they may sometimes be delayed. In special cases where antibiotic cover is indicated, it should be given parenterally immediately before, during and immediately following surgery.

Nonsurgical sites of wound infections include infection 'cut-downs', umbilical stumps, ulcers and burns. *Ps. aeruginosa* is the most important cause of infection in burns.

Tetanus as a result of hospital infections is now rare but should be kept in mind and toxoid administered to nonimmune patients before elective surgery. Many cases of neonatal tetanus have occurred due to the use of contaminated umbilical cord ties.

2. Urinary tract infections: Even with adequate precautions, catheterisation in hospitals leads to urinary infections in about two per cent; with indwelling catheters, the rate goes upto 50 per cent or more. *E. coli, Proteus, Ps. aeuruginosa* and other Gram negative bacilli are the causative agents. Mixed infection is common. Infection can be prevented by strict asepsis during catheterisation. Indwelling catheters are to be used only when unavoidable, and then only with proper closed drainage.

3. Respiratory infections: Aspiration in unconscious patients and pulmonary ventilation or instrumentation may lead to nosocomial pneumonia, particularly in those with pre-existing cardiopulmonary disease. Multidrug resistant *Staph. aureus* and Gram negative bacilli are the common pathogens. Antibiotic treatment is unsatisfactory. Postural drainage is useful in the prevention and management of such cases.

4. Bacteremia and septicemia: These may be consequences of infections at any site but are commonly caused by infected intravenous cannulae. The longer the cannulae are kept in situ, the greater the risk of infection. 'Cut-downs' on the leg veins in infants or children with diarrhea generally get left in place for long periods, the site being bathed in diarrheal stools. Phlebitis sets in with consequent bacteremia. Many a child admitted with diarrhea thus dies of septicemia. Gram negative bacilli are the common pathogens. 'Cut-downs' are safer on the arms than on legs. Intravenous rehydration in diarrhea should be restricted to emergencies and should be replaced by oral fluids as early as possible. Infection can be prevented by proper skin toilet before 'cut-down' and the use of stainless steel needles instead of plastic cannulae.

Staph. epidermidis bacteremia is seen commonly in patients with artificial heart valves. Bacteremia in those with valvular defects may lead to endocarditis.

DIAGNOSIS AND CONTROL OF HOSPITAL INFECTION

Hospital infection may occur sporadically or as outbreaks. Etiological diagnosis is by the routine bacteriological methods of smear, culture, identification and sensitivity testing. When an outbreak occurs, the source should be identified and eliminated. This requires the sampling of possible sources of infection such as hospital personnel, inanimate objects, water, air or food. Typing of isolate – phage, bacteriocin, antibiogram or biotyping – from cases and sites may indicate a causal connection. Obvious examples of sources of hospital outbreaks are nasal carriage of staphylococci by surgeons or pseudomonas growing in hand lotions. Carriers should be suitably treated.

Sterilisation techniques have to be tested. The cause of infection may be a defective autoclave or improper techniques such as boiling infusion sets in ward sterilisers. A careful analysis of the pattern of infection may often reveal the source but sometimes it eludes the most diligent search.

It must be emphasised that control of hospital infection should be not merely a spasmodic exercise to be employed when an outbreak occurs but rather a permanent ongoing activity in any large hospital. Every major hospital should have 'infection control teams' consisting of microbiologists, medical and nursing staff and hospital administrators. Besides investigating and controlling outbreaks, their functions include formulating appropriate guidelines for admission, nursing and treatment of infectious patients, surveillance on sterilisation and disinfectant practices, determining antibiotic policies and immunisation schedules, and educating patients and hospital personnel on infection control. Such measures help in reducing the incidence of hospital infections, even if they do not eliminate them altogether.

Unfortunately, in many hospitals, infection control is attempted by resorting to more and more of antibiotics. This is not only futile but may even be positively harmful by encouraging selective colonisation by multiresistant pathogens. In the final analysis, prevention of hospital infection rests on a proper understanding of aseptic practices and meticulous attention to hygienic principles. Sir William Osler's aphorism that 'soap, water and commonsense are the best disinfectants' applies even today in the context of hospital infection.

BIOMEDICAL WASTE MANAGEMENT

Biomedical or hospital waste means any waste generated during health care, research, testing or related procedures on human beings or animals conducted in hospitals, clinics, laboratories or similar establishments. This is far more dangerous and offensive than domestic waste. It contains infectious or other hazardous materials that may injure, infect or otherwise harm patients, their visitors, hospital personnel and the public at large in several ways. Biomedical waste if kept untreated would ferment, attract flies and other insects, birds and animals, making the place filthy and unhygienic. It contains 'sharps' such as needles or broken glass that can cause injury and infection. Discarded waste attracts ragpickers who may repack disposables or drugs and sell them. The waste may contain harmful chemicals and radioactive materials. Liquid wastes can spread, seep into soil and contaminate wells and tanks polluting them. Unless carefully managed, biomedical waste can be serious pollutants of soil, water and air.

With public opinion rising against environmental pollution, governments across the world are forced to bring legal restraints in this area. The Goverment of India has promulgated the Medical Waste (Management and Handling) Rules, 1998 under which the persons who are in charge of medical and other institutions where such wastes are generated (called 'occupiers') are held legally responsible for maintaining the conditions prescribed in the rules, which have come into effect from 1 January 2003. The occupiers have to obtain due authorisation from the prescribed authority after setting up the required waste management facilities.

QUANTITY AND TYPES OF BIOMEDICAL WASTE

The amount of waste generated in hospitals under Indian conditions has been estimated as 1 to 2 kg per bed per day. This is composed of different types of infectious waste, not all of which is infections. On an average about 85 per cent is harmless and 15 per cent hazardous.

Harmless waste is paper, cardboard, cartons, flowers and ordinary office, or kitchen waste akin to domestic waste.

Infections waste is any waste likely to carry and transmit any type of pathogenic microbes. This includes human or animal tissues or organs removed at biopsy, surgery or autopsy, placenta and other peoducts of conception, any pathological fluid or diacharges, dressing, swabs and other soiled items, laboratory samples sent for microbiology, pathology and biochemical tests, all microbial cultures, used syringe needles, used scalped blades and other sharps.

Noninfectious hazardous waste may be *chemical* (toxic, corrosive, inflammable, reactive and otherwise injurious), *radioactive* (handling and management of which are under the direction of the Bhabha Atomic Research Centre), and *pharmacological* (surplus or time expired drugs) .

Waste management: A primary prerequisite for effective waste management is a clean and tidy environment. Waste tends to accumulate in dirty surrounding. The hospital and its premises should be kept in a clean and hygienic condition. This requires frequent soap and water washing, mopping and good housekeeping.

The objectives of biowaste management are to prevent harm resulting from waste, minimise its volume, retrive reusable materials, and ensure safe and economical disposal. The different steps in waste management are reduction, reuse, segregation, storage, transportation and treatment ('treatment' here means all procedures and processes intended to reduce the bulk of the waste and make it noninfections and harmless).

Reduction in volume can be achieved by proper planning and using reusable items wherever safely possible. Segregation means the separation of waste at the point of generation into the various types with respect to its category and mode of mixed together with harmless ones like paper or packing materials, the whole of it becomes contaminated and will have to be autoclaved, instead of only the originally infected items. The segregated waste is to be put into different coloured containers, as prescribed in the Rules for necessary treatment.

WASTE TREATMENT

Several methods of waste treatment are available and the choice of methods is based on the item of waste and the facilities available. The place of final disposal may be in the premises or away from crowded areas if possible. Some of the methods are indicated below.

Chemical disinfection: This is a very useful method for many items, particularly in small places like clinics. It is also an important preliminary process before final treatment with some materials. For example, contaminated materials like sputum or pus are to be disinfected before being buried or autoclaved.

Deep burial: Where large areas of uninhabited land are available this is convenient. Materials after chemical disinfection are put in deep trenches, covered with lime and filled with soil. This is a safe method for disposal of sharps also.

Incineration: This is a safe method of treating large solid infectious waste, particularly anatomy waste and amputated limbs, animals carcasses and the like. The incinerator subjects them to very high heat, converting them to ash, which would be only about a tenth of orginal volume. However, it is expensive and is generally used only by very large establishments.

Autoclaving: This is widely used in laboratories and clinics for treating infections waste before disposal.

Microwave: This is another useful method of sterilization of small volume waste at the point of generation. This cannot be used for animal or human body parts, metal items or toxic or radioactive material.

Liquid waste: Pathological, chemical and toxic liquid waste should be appropriately treated with disinfectants or reagents and neutralised before flushing into the sewer.

Proper disposal of hospital waste is part of hospital infection prevention measures. Apart from its being a mandatory legal requirement, strict adherence to the Biomedical Waste Management Rules promulgated by the Goverment of India is a duty that should be done to protect the health and well-being, not only of the patients and staff of the hospitals, but also of the public at large, for the first rule in Medicine, as well as in Nursing is 'Primum non nocere'—Do no harm.

Further Reading

Ayliffe GA et al. 1992. Control of Hospital Infection. London: Chapman and Hall.
Bennett JV and PS Brachman 1996. Hospital Infections. 4th edn. Boston: Little Brown.
Lowbury EJ et al. 1985. Control of Hospital Infection: A Practical Handbook, 2nd edn. London: Chapman and Hall.

INDEX